PEARSON

Campbell Biology
Concepts and Connections
With Additional Readings

Second Custom Edition for Tacoma Community College

Taken from:

Campbell Biology: Concepts & Connections, Eighth Edition
by Jane B. Reece, Martha R. Taylor, Eric J. Simon, Jean L. Dickey and Kelly Hogan

Get Ready for A&P, Third Edition
by Lori K. Garrett

Biology of Cancer
by Randall W. Phillis and Steve Goodwin

Stem Cells and Cloning, Second Edition
by Kelly A. Hogan

Understanding the Human Genome Project, Second Edition
by Michael A. Palladino

Genetic Testimony: A Guide to Forensic DNA Profiling
by Charlotte A. Spencer

Cover Art: Courtesy of Photodisc/Getty Images.

Taken from:

Campbell Biology: Concepts & Connections, Eighth Edition
by Jane B. Reece, Martha R. Taylor, Eric J. Simon, Jean L. Dickey, and Kelly Hogan
Copyright © 2015, 2012, 2009 by Pearson Education, Inc.
Upper Saddle River, New Jersey 07458

Get Ready for A&P, Third Edition
by Lori K. Garrett
Copyright © 2013, 2010, 2008 by Pearson Education, Inc.
Upper Saddle River, New Jersey 07458

Biology of Cancer
by Randall W. Phillis and Steve Goodwin
Copyright © 2003 by Pearson Education, Inc.
Upper Saddle River, New Jersey 07458

Stem Cells and Cloning, Second Edition
by Kelly A. Hogan
Copyright © 2009 by Pearson Education, Inc.
Upper Saddle River, New Jersey 07458

Understanding the Human Genome Project, Second Edition
by Michael A. Palladino
Copyright © 2006 by Pearson Education, Inc.
Upper Saddle River, New Jersey 07458

Genetic Testimony: A Guide to Forensic DNA Profiling
by Charlotte A. Spencer
Copyright © 2004 by Pearson Education, Inc.
Upper Saddle River, New Jersey 07458

This special edition published in cooperation with Pearson Learning Solutions.

All trademarks, service marks, registered trademarks, and registered service marks are the property of their respective owners and are used herein for identification purposes only.

Pearson Learning Solutions, 501 Boylston Street, Suite 900, Boston, MA 02116
A Pearson Education Company
www.pearsoned.com

Printed in the United States of America

1 2 3 4 5 6 7 8 9 10 VOCR 17 16 15 14

000200010271923819

NB

ISBN 10: 1-269-95981-6
ISBN 13: 978-1-269-95981-0

About the Authors

Jane B. Reece has worked in biology publishing since 1978, when she joined the editorial staff of Benjamin Cummings. Her education includes an A.B. in biology from Harvard University, an M.S. in microbiology from Rutgers University, and a Ph.D. in bacteriology from the University of California, Berkeley. At UC Berkeley, and later as a postdoctoral fellow in genetics at Stanford University, her research focused on genetic recombination in bacteria. Dr. Reece taught biology at Middlesex County College (New Jersey) and Queensborough Community College (New York). During her 12 years as an editor at Benjamin Cummings, she played a major role in a number of successful textbooks. She is coauthor of *Campbell Biology*, Tenth Edition, *Campbell Biology in Focus*, *Campbell Essential Biology*, and *Campbell Essential Biology with Physiology*, Fourth Edition.

Martha R. Taylor has been teaching biology for more than 35 years. She earned her B.A. in biology from Gettysburg College and her M.S. and Ph.D. in science education from Cornell University. At Cornell, she has served as assistant director of the Office of Instructional Support and has taught introductory biology for both majors and nonmajors. Most recently, she was a lecturer in the Learning Strategies Center, teaching supplemental biology courses. Her experience working with students in classrooms, in laboratories, and with tutorials has increased her commitment to helping students create their own knowledge of and appreciation for biology. She has been the author of the *Student Study Guide* for all ten editions of *Campbell Biology*.

Eric J. Simon is a professor in the Department of Biology and Health Science at New England College (Henniker, New Hampshire). He teaches introductory biology to science majors and nonscience majors, as well as upper-level courses in tropical marine biology and careers in science. Dr. Simon received a B.A. in biology and computer science and an M.A. in biology from Wesleyan University, and a Ph.D. in biochemistry from Harvard University. His research focuses on innovative ways to use technology to improve teaching and learning in the science classroom, particularly for nonscience majors. Dr. Simon is the lead author of the introductory nonmajors biology textbooks *Campbell Essential Biology*, Fifth Edition, and *Campbell Essential Biology with Physiology*, Fourth Edition, and the author of the introductory biology textbook *Biology: The Core*.

Jean L. Dickey is Professor Emerita of Biological Sciences at Clemson University (Clemson, South Carolina). After receiving her B.S. in biology from Kent State University, she went on to earn a Ph.D. in ecology and evolution from Purdue University. In 1984, Dr. Dickey joined the faculty at Clemson, where she devoted her career to teaching biology to nonscience majors in a variety of courses. In addition to creating content-based instructional materials, she developed many activities to engage lecture and laboratory students in discussion, critical thinking, and writing, and implemented an investigative laboratory curriculum in general biology. Dr. Dickey is author of *Laboratory Investigations for Biology*, Second Edition, and coauthor of *Campbell Essential Biology*, Fifth Edition, and *Campbell Essential Biology with Physiology*, Fourth Edition.

Kelly Hogan is a faculty member in the Department of Biology at the University of North Carolina at Chapel Hill, teaching introductory biology and introductory genetics to science majors. Dr. Hogan teaches hundreds of students at a time, using active-learning methods that incorporate technology such as cell phones as clickers, online homework, and peer evaluation tools. Dr. Hogan received her B.S. in biology at the College of New Jersey and her Ph.D. in pathology at the University of North Carolina, Chapel Hill. Her research interests relate to how large classes can be more inclusive through evidence-based teaching methods and technology. She provides faculty development to other instructors through peer-coaching, workshops, and mentoring. Dr. Hogan is the author of *Stem Cells and Cloning*, Second Edition, and is lead moderator of the *Instructor Exchange*, a site within MasteringBiology® for instructors to exchange classroom materials and ideas.

Neil A. Campbell (1946–2004) combined the inquiring nature of a research scientist with the soul of a caring teacher. Over his 30 years of teaching introductory biology to both science majors and nonscience majors, many thousands of students had the opportunity to learn from him and be stimulated by his enthusiasm for the study of life. While he is greatly missed by his many friends in the biology community, his coauthors remain inspired by his visionary dedication to education and are committed to searching for ever better ways to engage students in the wonders of biology.

Make important connections between biological concepts and your life

NEW! Each chapter opens with a **high-interest question** to spark your interest in the topic. Questions are revisited later in the chapter, in either a Scientific Thinking or Evolution Connection module.

CHAPTER

12 DNA Technology and Genomics

Papaya fruit, shown in the photograph below, are sweet and loaded with vitamin C. They are borne on a rapidly growing treelike plant (*Carica papaya*) that grows only in tropical climates. In Hawaii, papaya is both a dietary staple and a valuable export crop.

Although thriving today, Hawaii's papaya industry seemed doomed just a few decades ago. A deadly pathogen called the papaya ringspot virus (PRV) had spread throughout the islands and appeared poised to completely eradicate the papaya plant population. But scientists from the University of Hawaii were able to rescue the industry by creating new, genetically engineered PRV-resistant strains of papaya. Today, the papaya industry is once again vibrant—and the vast majority of Hawaii's papayas are genetically modified organisms (GMOs).

However, not everyone is happy about the circumstances surrounding the recovery of the Hawaiian papaya industry. Although genetically modified papayas are approved for consumption in the United States (as are many other GMO fruits and vegetables), some critics have raised safety concerns—for the people who eat them and for the environment. On three occasions over a three-year

? *Are genetically modified organisms safe?*

span, thousands of papaya ... down under the cover of da... GMO crops. Although few ... should we in fact be concer... question continues to foste...

In addition to GMOs i... in many other ways: Gene... dustrial products, DNA p... ence, new technologies p... and DNA can even be us... chapter, we'll discuss eac... specific techniques used... legal, and ethical issues ...

230

MasteringBiology®

◁ ABC News Videos and Current Events articles from The *New York Times* connect what you learn in biology class to fascinating stories in the news.

BIG IDEAS

Gene Cloning
(12.1–12.5)

A variety of laboratory techniques can be used to copy and combine DNA molecules.

Genetically Modified Organisms
(12.6–12.10)

Transgenic cells, plants, and animals are used in agriculture and medicine.

DNA Profiling
(12.11–12.16)

Genetic markers can be used to definitively match a DNA sample to an individual.

Genomics
(12.17–12.21)

The study of complete DNA sets helps us learn about evolutionary history.

sland of Hawaii were hacked ably as a protest against such criminal behavior, afety of GMO crops? This ebate and disagreement. technologies affect our lives o produce medical and in- ged the field of forensic sci- ata for biological research, historical questions. In this tions. We'll also consider the lied, and some of the social, the new technologies.

◁ **Big Ideas** help you connect the overarching concepts that are explored in the chapter.

CONNECTION

▽ **Connection** modules in every chapter relate biology to your life and the world outside the classroom.

16.5 Biofilms are complex associations of microbes

CONNECTION

In many natural environments, prokaryotes attach to surfaces in highly organized colonies called **biofilms**. A biofilm may consist of one or several species of prokaryotes, and it may include protists and fungi as well. Biofilms can form on almost any support, including rocks, soil, organic material (including living tissue), metal, and plastic. You have a biofilm on your teeth—dental plaque is a biofilm that can cause tooth decay. Biofilms can even form without a solid foundation, for example, on the surface of stagnant water.

Biofilm formation begins when prokaryotes secrete signaling molecules that attract nearby cells into a cluster. Once the cluster becomes sufficiently large, the cells produce a gooey coating that glues them to the support and to each other, making the biofilm extremely difficult to dislodge. For example, if you don't scrub your shower, you could find a biofilm growing around the drain—running water alone is not strong enough to wash it away. As the biofilm gets larger and more complex, it becomes a "city" of microbes. Communicating by chemical signals, members of the community coordinate the division of labor, defense against invaders, and other activities. Channels in the biofilm allow nutrients to reach cells in the interior and allow wastes to leave, and a variety of environments develop within it.

Biofilms are common among bacteria that cause disease in humans. For instance, ear infections and urinary tract infections are often the result of biofilm-forming bacteria. Cystic fibrosis patients are vulnerable to pneumonia caused by bacteria that form a biofilm in their lungs. Biofilms of harmful

bacteria can also form on implanted medical devices such as catheters, replacement joints, or pacemakers. The complexity of biofilms makes these infections especially difficult to defeat. Antibiotics may not be able to penetrate beyond the outer layer of cells, leaving much of the community intact. For example, some biofilm bacteria produce an enzyme that breaks down penicillin faster than it can diffuse inward.

Biofilms that form in the environment can be difficult to eradicate, too. A variety of industries spend billions of dollars every year trying to get rid of biofilms that clog and corrode pipes, gum up filters and drains, and coat the hulls of ships (Figure 16.5). Biofilms in water distribution pipes may survive chlorination, the most common method of ensuring that drinking water does not contain any harmful microorganisms. For example, biofilms of *Vibrio cholera*, the bacterium that causes cholera, found in water pipes were capable of withstanding levels of chlorine 10 to 20 times higher than the concentrations routinely used to chlorinate drinking water.

▲ Figure 16.5 A biofilm fouling the insides of a pipe

? Why are biofilms difficult to eradicate?

The biofilm sticks to each other, the outer layer of cells may prevent antimicrobial substances from penetrating into the interior of the biofilm.

EVOLUTION CONNECTION

◁ **Evolution Connection** modules present concrete examples of the evidence for evolution within each chapter, providing you with a coherent theme for the study of life.

10.19 Emerging viruses threaten human health

EVOLUTION CONNECTION

Emerging viruses are ones that seem to burst on to the scene, becoming apparent to the medical community quite suddenly. There are many familiar examples, such as the 2009 H1N1 influenza virus (discussed in the chapter introduction). Another example is **HIV** (human immunodeficiency virus), the virus that causes **AIDS** (acquired immunodeficiency syndrome). HIV appeared in New York and California in the early 1980s, seemingly out of nowhere. Yet another example is the deadly Ebola virus, recognized initially in 1976 in central Africa; it is one of several emerging viruses that cause hemorrhagic fever, an often fatal syndrome characterized by fever, vomiting, massive bleeding, and circulatory system collapse. A number of other dangerous newly recognized viruses cause encephalitis, inflammation of the brain. One example is the

Why are viral diseases such a constant threat?

West Nile virus, which appeared in North America in 1999 and has since spread to all 48 contiguous U.S. states. West Nile virus is spread primarily by mosquitoes, which carry the virus in blood sucked from one victim and can transfer it to another victim. West Nile virus cases surged in 2012, especially in Texas. Severe acute respiratory syndrome (SARS) first appeared in China in 2002. Within eight months, about 8,000 and 10% died. Researchers quickly

▼ Figure 10.19 A Hong Kong health-care worker prepares to cull a chicken to help prevent the spread of the avian flu virus (shown in the inset)

Colorized TEM 146,000X

To the Student: How to use this book and MasteringBiology®

Stay focused on the key concepts

Central concepts summarize the key topic of each module, helping you stay focused as you study.

Checkpoint questions at the end of each module help you stay on track.

NEW and revised art provides clear visuals to help you understand key topics. Selected figures include numbered steps that are keyed to explanations in the text.

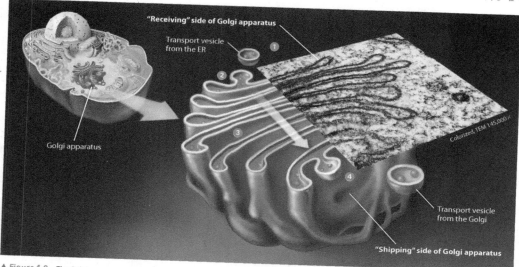

4.9 The Golgi apparatus modifies, sorts, and ships cell products

After leaving the ER, many transport vesicles travel to the **Golgi apparatus**. Using a light microscope and a staining technique he developed, Italian scientist Camillo Golgi discovered this membranous organelle in 1898. The electron microscope confirmed his discovery more than 50 years later, revealing a stack of flattened sacs, looking much like a pile of pita bread. A cell may contain many, even hundreds, of these stacks. The number of Golgi stacks correlates with how active the cell is in secreting proteins—a multistep process that, as you have just seen, is initiated in the rough ER.

The Golgi apparatus serves as a molecular warehouse and processing station for products manufactured by the ER. You can follow these activities in Figure 4.9. Note that the flattened Golgi sacs are not connected, as are ER sacs. ❶ One side of a Golgi stack serves as a receiving dock for transport vesicles produced by the ER. ❷ A vesicle fuses with a Golgi sac, adding its membrane and contents to the "receiving" side. ❸ Products of the ER are modified as a Golgi sac progresses through the stack. ❹ The "shipping" side of the Golgi

functions as a depot, dispatching its products in vesicles that bud off and travel to other sites.

How might ER products be processed during their transit through the Golgi? Various Golgi enzymes modify the carbohydrate portions of the glycoproteins made in the ER, removing some sugars and substituting others. Molecular identification tags, such as phosphate groups, may be added that help the Golgi sort molecules into different batches for different destinations.

Finished secretory products, packaged in transport vesicles, move to the plasma membrane for export from the cell. Alternatively, finished products may become part of the plasma membrane itself or part of another organelle, such as a lysosome, which we discuss next.

? What is the relationship of the Golgi apparatus to the ER in a protein-secreting cell?

The Golgi receives transport vesicles budded from the ER that contain proteins synthesized by bound ribosomes. The Golgi finishes processing the proteins and dispatches transport vesicles to the plasma membrane, where the proteins are secreted.

"Receiving" side of Golgi apparatus

Transport vesicle from the ER ❶

Golgi apparatus ❷

❸

Colorized, TEM 145,000×

❹

Transport vesicle from the Golgi

"Shipping" side of Golgi apparatus

▲ Figure 4.9 The Golgi apparatus receiving, processing, and shipping products

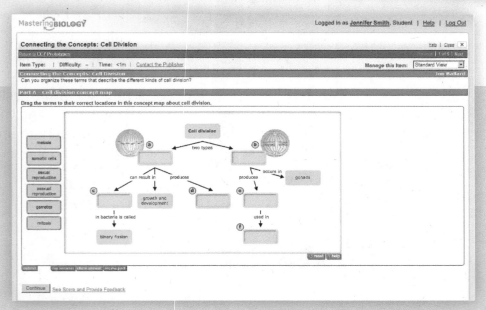

MasteringBiology®
◁ **Connecting the Concepts** activities link one biological concept to another.

Learn how to to think like a scientist

▷ **New Scientific Thinking** modules explore how scientists use the processes of science for discovery. Each module concludes with a question that challenges you to think like a scientist.

SCIENTIFIC THINKING

▷ **New Scientific Thinking** topics include:

▸ Module 2.15 — Scientists study the effects of rising atmospheric CO_2 on coral reef ecosystems

▸ Module 8.10 — Tailoring treatment to each patient may improve cancer therapy

▸ Module 25.3 — Coordinated waves of movement in huddles help penguins thermoregulate

▸ Module 26.3 — A widely used weed killer demasculinizes male frogs

▸ Module 29.2 — The model for magnetic sensory reception is incomplete

---

SCIENTIFIC THINKING

12.9 Genetically modified organisms raise health concerns

As soon as scientists realized the power of DNA technology, they began to worry about potential dangers. Early concerns focused on the possibility that recombinant DNA technology might create new pathogens. To guard against rogue microbes, scientists developed a set of guidelines including strict laboratory safety and containment procedures, the genetic crippling of transgenic organisms to ensure that they cannot survive outside the laboratory, and a prohibition on certain dangerous experiments. Today, most public concern centers on GMOs used for food.

Are genetically modified organisms safe?

Human Safety Genetically modified organisms are used in crop production because they are more nutritious or because they are cheaper to produce. But do these advantages come at a cost to the health of people consuming GMOs? When investigating complex questions like this one, scientists often use multiple experimental methods. A 2012 animal study involved 104 pigs that were divided into two groups: The first was fed a diet containing 39% GMO corn and the other a closely related non-GMO corn. The health of the pigs was measured over the short term (31 days), the medium term (110 days), and the normal generational life span. The researchers reported no significant differences between the two groups and no traces of foreign DNA in the slaughtered pigs.

Although pigs are a good model organism for human digestion, critics argue that human data are required to draw conclusions about the safety of dietary GMOs for people. The results of one human study, conducted jointly by Chinese and ... were published in 2012. Sixty-eight Chi... (ages 6–8) were fed Golden Rice, spinach ...eta-carotene), or a capsule containing ...ver 21 days, blood samples were drawn ...h vitamin A the body produced from ...e data show that the beta-carotene in ... the capsules was converted to vitamin ...nilar efficiency, while the beta-carotene ...ificantly less vitamin A (Figure 12.9). ...hers to conclude that GMO rice can ... preventing vitamin A deficiency. ...findings, this study caused an uproar. ...lled the study an unethical "scandal," ...scientists had used Chinese schoolchil-...jects. The project leaders countered ...n and consent had been obtained in ...ited States. The controversy highlights ...n conducting research on human ...ies are of limited value, but human ...al. To date, no study has documented ...from GMO foods, and there is gen-...scientists that the GMO foods on the ...er, it is not yet possible to measure the ...y) of GMOs on human health.

...Advocates of a cautious approach ... that transgenic plants might pass

...ology and Genomics

their new genes to related species in nearby wild areas, disturbing the composition of the natural ecosystem. Critics of GMO crops can point to several studies that do indeed show unintended gene transfer from engineered crops to nearby wild relatives. But GMO advocates counter that no lasting or detrimental effects from such transfers have been demonstrated, and that some GMOs (such as bacteria engineered to break down oil spills) can actively help the environment.

Labeling Although the majority of several staple crops grown in the United States—including corn and soybeans—are genetically modified, products made from GMOs are not required to be labeled in any way. Chances are you ate a food containing GMOs today, but the lack of labeling means you probably can't say for certain. Labeling of foods containing more than trace amounts of GMOs is required in Europe, Japan, Australia, China, Russia, and other countries. Labeling advocates point out that the information would allow consumers to decide for themselves whether they wish to be exposed to GMO foods. Some biotechnology advocates, however, respond that similar demands were not made when "transgenic" crop plants produced by traditional breeding techniques were put on the market. For example, triticale (a crop used primarily in animal feed but also in some human foods) was created decades ago by combining the genomes of wheat and rye—two plants that do not interbreed in nature. Triticale is now sold worldwide without any special labeling.

Scientists and the public need to weigh the possible benefits versus risks on a case-by-case basis. The best scenario would be to proceed with caution, basing our decisions on sound scientific information rather than on either irrational fear or blind optimism.

? Why might crop plants engineered to be resistant to weed killer pose a danger to the environment?

The genes for herbicide resistance could transfer to closely related weeds, which could themselves then become resistant.

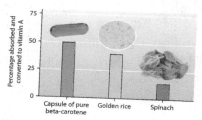

▲ Figure 12.9 Vitamin A production after consumption of different sources of beta-carotene

Data from G. Tang et al, Beta-carotene in Golden Rice is as good as beta-carotene in oil at providing vitamin A to children, *American Journal of Clinical Nutrition* 96(3): 658–64 (2012).

Scientific Thinking | Signed in as Libby Reiser, Instructor | Help | Close

What Roles Do Diet and the Microbial... | Scientific Thinking: What Roles Do Diet and the Microbial Community in the In...

Item Type: Coaching Activities | Difficulty: — | Time: — | Contact the Publisher | Manage this Item: Standard View ▾

Scientific Thinking: What Roles Do Diet and the Microbial Community in the Intestines Play in Obesity?

Fast foods, cookies and ice cream, sodas and energy drinks–Americans eat a lot of processed foods high in fats and simple sugars. Not surprisingly, this type of diet can lead to weight gain and is one of the main culprits in the obesity epidemic in this country. But, is there more to this story?

The foods you eat serve as food for the community of microorganisms that inhabit your digestive tract. Those microbes have their own food "preferences," metabolizing different types of food molecules and releasing their byproducts, which your body then absorbs.

Scientists have hypothesized that a high-fat, high sugar diet actually alters the composition of the microbial community that inhabits the beginning of the large intestine, which contributes to obesity. Because of the difficulties of carrying out experiments on humans, scientists have used mice as an animal model in which to test this hypothesis.

Part A - Designing a controlled experiment

In one experiment, scientists raised mice in germ-free conditions (who therefore lacked intestinal microbes). The mice were fed a low-fat diet rich in the complex plant polysaccharides often called fiber.

When the mice were 12 weeks old, the scientists transplanted the microbial community from the intestine of a single "donor" mouse into all of the germ-free mice. Then they divided the mice randomly into two groups and fed each group a different diet.

- Group 1 (the control group) continued to eat a low-fat, low-fiber diet.

- Group 2 (the experimental group) ate a high-fat, high-sugar diet

---

MasteringBiology®

◁ **NEW! Scientific Thinking activities** teach you how to practice important scientific skills like understanding variables and making predictions. Specific wrong-answer feedback coaches you to the correct response.

To the Student: How to use this book and MasteringBiology®

Maximize your learning and success

▷ **New Visualizing the Concept** modules walk you through challenging concepts and complex processes.

▷ The brief narrative works together with the artwork to help you visualize and understand the topic.

Hints embedded within the module emulate the guidance that you might receive during instructor office hours or in a tutoring session. These hints provide additional information to deepen your understanding of the topic.

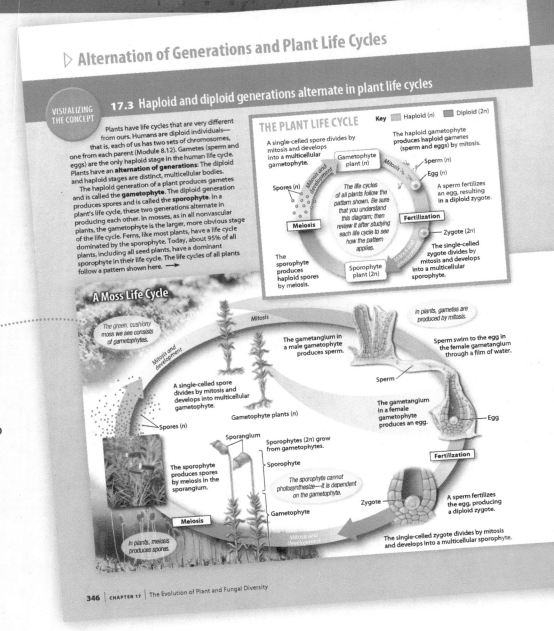

▷ **Alternation of Generations and Plant Life Cycles**

VISUALIZING THE CONCEPT

17.3 Haploid and diploid generations alternate in plant life cycles

Plants have life cycles that are very different from ours. Humans are diploid individuals—that is, each of us has two sets of chromosomes, one from each parent (Module 8.12). Gametes (sperm and eggs) are the only haploid stage in the human life cycle. Plants have an **alternation of generations**: The diploid and haploid stages are distinct, multicellular bodies.

The haploid generation of a plant produces gametes and is called the **gametophyte**. The diploid generation produces spores and is called the **sporophyte**. In a plant's life cycle, these two generations alternate in producing each other. In mosses, as in all nonvascular plants, the gametophyte is the larger, more obvious stage of the life cycle. Ferns, like most plants, have a life cycle dominated by the sporophyte. Today, about 95% of all plants, including all seed plants, have a dominant sporophyte in their life cycle. The life cycles of all plants follow a pattern shown here.

THE PLANT LIFE CYCLE   Key ▢ Haploid (n) ▮ Diploid (2n)

A single-celled spore divides by mitosis and develops into a multicellular gametophyte.

The haploid gametophyte produces haploid gametes (sperm and eggs) by mitosis.

Gametophyte plant (n)

Spores (n)

The life cycles of all plants follow the pattern shown. Be sure that you understand this diagram; then review it after studying each life cycle to see how the pattern applies.

Meiosis

Fertilization

Sperm (n)

Egg (n)

A sperm fertilizes an egg, resulting in a diploid zygote.

Zygote (2n)

The sporophyte produces haploid spores by meiosis.

Sporophyte plant (2n)

The single-celled zygote divides by mitosis and develops into a multicellular sporophyte.

A Moss Life Cycle

The green, cushiony moss we see consists of gametophytes.

Mitosis

In plants, gametes are produced by mitosis.

The gametangium in a male gametophyte produces sperm.

Sperm swim to the egg in the female gametangium through a film of water.

Sperm

A single-celled spore divides by mitosis and develops into multicellular gametophyte.

Gametophyte plants (n)

The gametangium in a female gametophyte produces an egg.

Egg

Spores (n)

Sporangium

Sporophytes (2n) grow from gametophytes.

Sporophyte

The sporophyte produces spores by meiosis in the sporangium.

The sporophyte cannot photosynthesize—it is dependent on the gametophyte.

Gametophyte

Zygote

Fertilization

A sperm fertilizes the egg, producing a diploid zygote.

Meiosis

In plants, meiosis produces spores.

The single-celled zygote divides by mitosis and develops into a multicellular sporophyte.

346 | CHAPTER 17 | The Evolution of Plant and Fungal Diversity

MasteringBiology®

▷ **NEW! Visualizing the Concept Activities** include interactive videos that were created and narrated by the authors of the text.

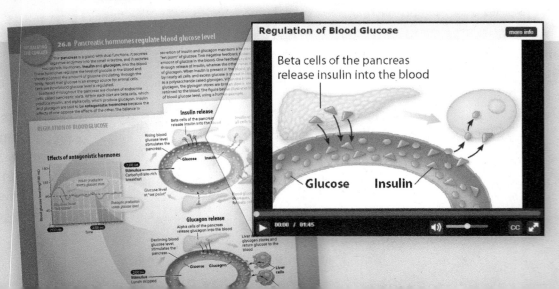

Regulation of Blood Glucose   more info

Beta cells of the pancreas release insulin into the blood

Glucose   Insulin

▶ 00:00 / 01:45   🔊 ————●——   CC ⛶

viii

fe Cycle

Gametophyte plant (*n*)

Mitosis

single-celled spore divides by
itosis and develops into a
ulticellular gametophyte.

The male
gametangium
produces sperm.

Sperm

Sperm swim to the
egg in the female
gametangium
through a film
of water.

Underside
of gametophyte:
actual size 0.5 cm
across

The female
gametangium
produces
an egg.

Egg

*Mitosis and
development*

res

The sporophyte
produces spores by
meiosis in sporangia.

Although eggs and sperm
are usually produced in separate
locations on the same gametophyte,
a variety of mechanisms promote
cross-fertilization between
gametophytes.

Fertilization

Meiosis

Mature
sporophyte

Zygote

The new
sporophyte
grows from the
gametophyte.

*Mitosis and
development*

Clusters of sporangia
on this fern look like
brown dots.

The single-celled zygote divides
by mitosis and develops into a
multicellular sporophyte.

The tiny gametophyte soon
disintegrates, and the sporophyte
grows independently.

The ferns we see
are sporophytes.

? What is the major difference between the moss and fern life cycles?

In mosses the dominant plant body is the gametophyte. In
ferns the sporophyte is dominant and independent of the gametophyte.

Alternation of Generations and Plant Life Cycles **347**

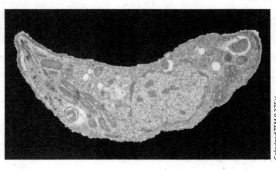

Colorized TEM 9,375×

▲ **Figure 4.1C**   Transmission electron micrograph of *Toxoplasma*
(This parasite of cats can be transmitted to humans, causing the disease
toxoplasmosis.)

Try This   Describe a major difference between the *Paramecium* in Figure 4.1B and the protist
in this figure. (*Hint:* Compare the notations along the right sides of the micrographs.)

△ **New! Try This** activities help you actively
engage with the figures and develop
positive study habits.

MasteringBiology®

◁ **New Dynamic Study Modules** enable
you to study effectively on your own and
more quickly learn the information. These
modules can be accessed on smartphones,
tablets, and computers.

Resources save you hours of time preparing for class

▷ **NEW! Learning Catalytics™** is a "bring your own device" student engagement, assessment, and classroom intelligence system. This technology has grown out of twenty years of cutting-edge research, innovation, and implementation of interactive teaching and peer instruction.

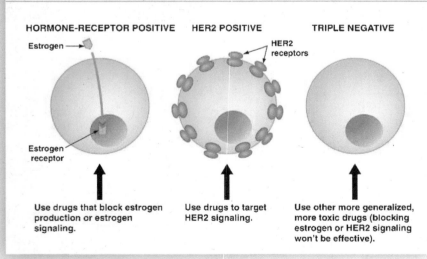

Three classes of breast cancer tumors lead to more personalized therapy

HORMONE-RECEPTOR POSITIVE

Estrogen

Estrogen receptor

Use drugs that block estrogen production or estrogen signaling.

HER2 POSITIVE

HER2 receptors

Use drugs to target HER2 signaling.

TRIPLE NEGATIVE

Use other more generalized, more toxic drugs (blocking estrogen or HER2 signaling won't be effective).

Connect your lectures to current topics

◁ **Campbell Current Topics PowerPoint** slides help you prepare a high-impact lecture developed around current issues. Topics include cancer, global climate change, athletic cheating, nutrition, and more.

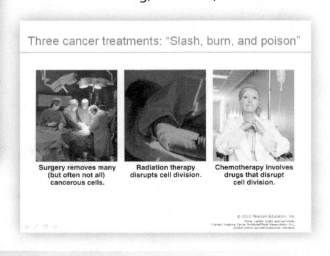

Three cancer treatments: "Slash, burn, and poison"

Surgery removes many (but often not all) cancerous cells.

Radiation therapy disrupts cell division.

Chemotherapy involves drugs that disrupt cell division.

MasteringBiology®

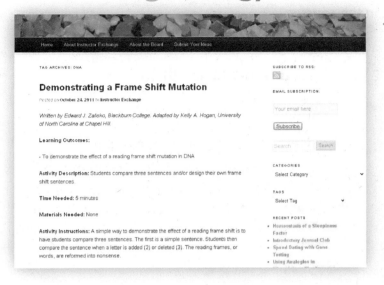

◁ **Instructor Exchange,** moderated by co-author Kelly Hogan, offers a library of active learning strategies contributed by instructors from across the country.

▽ **BioFlix activities** offer students 3-D animations to help them visualize and learn challenging topics.

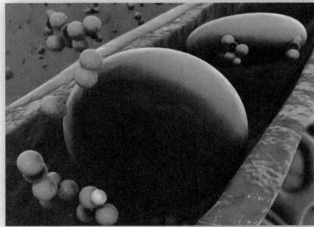

Assign tutorials to help students prepare for class

▽ **Video Tutor Sessions and MP3 Tutor Sessions,** hosted by co-author Eric Simon, provide on-the-go tutorials focused on key concepts and vocabulary.

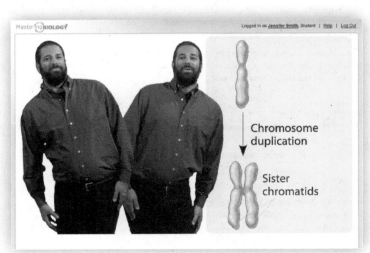

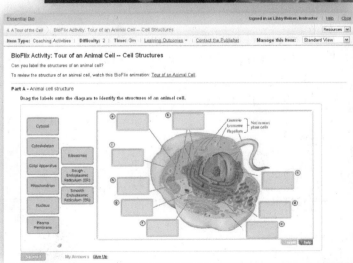

MasteringBiology® is an online assessment and tutorial system designed to help you teach more efficiently. It offers a variety of interactive activities to engage students and help them to succeed in the course.

Access students' results with easy-to-interpret student performance data

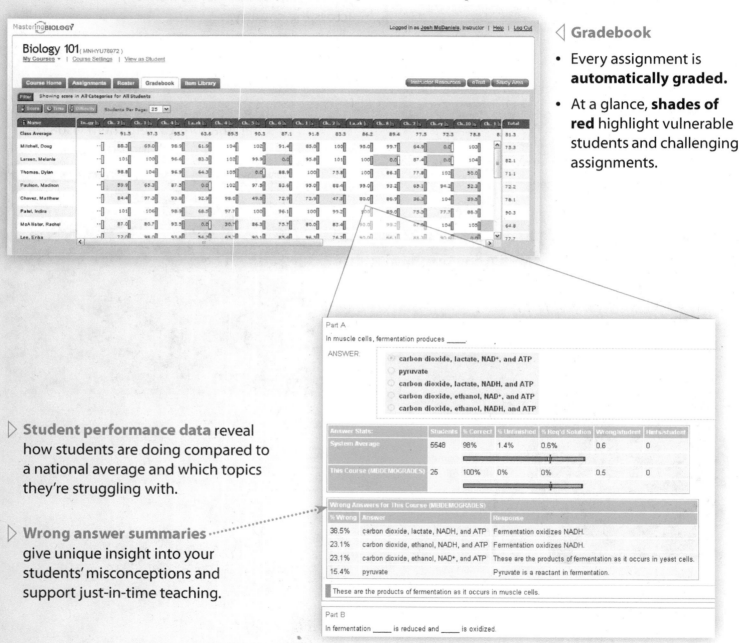

◁ **Gradebook**

- Every assignment is **automatically graded.**

- At a glance, **shades of red** highlight vulnerable students and challenging assignments.

▷ **Student performance data** reveal how students are doing compared to a national average and which topics they're struggling with.

▷ **Wrong answer summaries** give unique insight into your students' misconceptions and support just-in-time teaching.

Gain insight into student progress at a glance

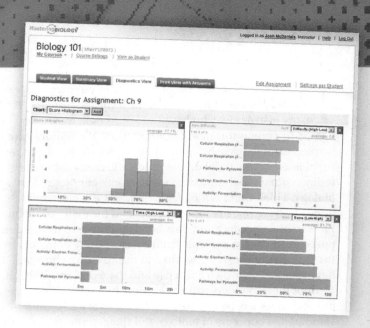

▷ **Get daily diagnostics.**

Gradebook Diagnostics provide unique insight into class performance. With a single click, see a summary of how your students are struggling or progressing.

MasteringBiology® is easy for you and your students to use

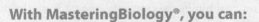

◁ **The Mastering platform** is the most effective and widely used online tutorial, homework, and assessment system for the sciences.

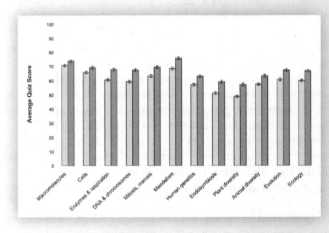

△ **Efficacy studies**

Go to the **"Proven Results"** tab at www.masteringbiology.com to see efficacy studies.

With MasteringBiology®, you can:

- **Assign** publisher-created pre-built assignments to get started quickly.
- **Easily edit** any of our questions or answers to match the precise language you use.
- **Import your own questions** and begin compiling meaningful data on student performance.
- **Easily export grades** to Microsoft®Excel or other course-management systems.

Preface

Inspired by the thousands of students in our own classes over the years and by enthusiastic feedback from the many instructors who have used our book, we are delighted to present this new, Eighth Edition. We authors have worked together closely to ensure that both the book and the supplementary material online reflect the changing needs of today's courses and students, as well as current progress in biology. Titled *Campbell Biology: Concepts & Connections* to honor Neil Campbell's founding role and his many contributions to biology education, this book continues to have a dual purpose: to engage students from a wide variety of majors in the wonders of the living world and to show them how biology relates to their own existence and the world they inhabit. Most of these students will not become biologists themselves, but their lives will be touched by biology every day. Understanding the concepts of biology and their connections to our lives is more important than ever. Whether we're concerned with our own health or the health of our planet, a familiarity with biology is essential. This basic knowledge and an appreciation for how science works have become elements of good citizenship in an era when informed evaluations of health issues, environmental problems, and applications of new technology are critical.

Concepts and Connections

Concepts   Biology is a vast subject that gets bigger every year, but an introductory biology course is still only one or two semesters long. This book was the first introductory biology textbook to use concept modules to help students recognize and focus on the main ideas of each chapter. The heading of each module is a carefully crafted statement of a key concept. For example, "A nerve signal begins as a change in the membrane potential" announces a key concept about the generation of an action potential (Module 28.4). Such a concept heading serves as a focal point, and the module's text and illustrations converge on that concept with explanation and, often, analogies. The module text walks the student through the illustrations, just as an instructor might do in class. And in teaching a sequential process, such as the one diagrammed in Figure 28.4, we number the steps in the text to correspond to numbered steps in the figure. The synergy between a module's narrative and graphic components transforms the concept heading into an idea with meaning to the student. The checkpoint question at the end of each module encourages students to test their understanding as they proceed through a chapter. Finally, in the Chapter Review, all the key concept statements are listed and briefly summarized under the overarching section titles, explicitly reminding students of what they've learned.

Connections   Students are more motivated to study biology when they can connect it to their own lives and interests—for example, when they are able to relate science to health issues, economic problems, environmental quality, ethical controversies, and social responsibility. In this edition, blue Connection icons mark the numerous application modules that go beyond the core biological concepts. For example, the new Connection Module 26.12 describes the potential role oxytocin plays in human–dog bonding. In addition, our Evolution Connection modules, identified by green icons, connect the content of each chapter to the grand unifying theme of evolution, without which the study of life has no coherence. Explicit connections are also made between the chapter introduction and either the Evolution Connection module or the new Scientific Thinking module in each chapter; new high-interest questions introduce each chapter, drawing students into the topic and encouraging a curiosity to explore the question further when it appears again later in the chapter.

New to This Edition

New Scientific Thinking Modules   In this edition we placed greater emphasis on the process of scientific inquiry through the addition to each chapter of a new type of module called Scientific Thinking, which is called out with a purple icon. These modules cover recent scientific research as well as underscore the spirit of inquiry in historical discoveries. All Scientific Thinking modules strive to demonstrate to students what scientists do. Each of these modules identifies key attributes of scientific inquiry, from the forming and testing of hypotheses to the analysis of data to the evaluation and communication of scientific results among scientists and with society as a whole. For example, the new Module 2.15 describes how scientists use both controlled experiments and observational field studies to document the effects of rising atmospheric CO_2 on coral reef ecosystems. Module 13.3 describes the scientific search for the common ancestor of whales, using different lines of inquiry from early fossil clues, molecular comparisons, and a series of transitional fossils that link whales to cloven-hoofed mammals, animals that live on land. And to prepare students for the renewed focus in the book on how biological concepts emerge from the process of science, we have significantly revised the introduction in Chapter 1, Biology: Exploring Life. These changes will better equip students to think like scientists and emphasize the connections between discovery and the concepts explored throughout the course.

New Visualizing the Concept Modules   Also new to this edition are modules that raise our hallmark art–text integration to a new level. These Visualizing the Concept modules take challenging concepts or processes and walk students through them in a highly visual manner, using engaging, attractive art; clear and concise labels; and instructor "hints" called out in light blue bubbles. These short hints emulate the one-on-one coaching an instructor might provide to a students during office hours and help students make key connections within the figure. Examples of this new feature include Module 9.8, which demonstrates to students the process of reading and analyzing a family pedigree; Module 17.3, which introduces the concept of plant life cycles through a combination of photographs and detailed life cycle art displayed across an impressive two-page layout; and Module 26.8, which walks students through the concept of homeostatic controls in blood glucose levels.

New "Try This" Tips   One theme of the revision for the Eighth Edition is to help all students learn positive study habits they can take with them throughout their college careers and, in particular, to encourage them to be active in their reading and studying. To foster good study habits, several figures in each chapter feature a new "Try This" study tip. These action-oriented statements or questions direct students to study a figure more closely and explain, interpret, or extend what the figure presents. For example, in Figure 3.13B, students are asked to "Point out the bonds and functional groups that make the R groups of these three amino acids either hydrophobic or hydrophilic." Figure 6.10B is a new figure illustrating the molecular rotary motor ATP synthase, and the accompanying Try This tip asks students to "Identify the power source that runs this motor. Explain where this 'power' comes from." Figure 36.7, on the effect of predation on the life history traits of guppies, offers the following Try This tip: "Use the figure to explain how the hypothesis was tested."

Improvements to End-of-Chapter Section   The Testing Your Knowledge questions are now arranged to reflect Bloom's Taxonomy of cognitive domains. Questions and activities are grouped into Level 1: Knowledge/Comprehension, Level 2: Application/Analysis, and Level 3: Synthesis/Evaluation. In addition, a new Scientific Thinking question has been added to each chapter that connects to and extends the topic of the Scientific Thinking module. Throughout the Chapter Review, new questions have been added that will help students better engage with the chapter topic and practice higher-level problem solving.

New Design and Improved Art   The fresh new design used throughout the chapters and the extensive reconceptualization of many figures make the book even more appealing and accessible to visual learners. The cellular art in Chapter 4, A Tour of the Cell, for example, has been completely reimagined for more depth perspective and richer color. The new big-picture diagrams of the animal and plant cells are vibrant and better demonstrate the spatial relationships among the cellular structures with an almost three-dimensional style. The illustrations of cellular organelles elsewhere in Chapter 4 include electron micrographs overlaid on diagrams to emphasize the connection between the realistic micrograph depiction and the artwork. Figure 4.9, for example, shows a micrograph of an actual Golgi apparatus paired with an illustration; an accompanying orientation diagram—a hallmark of *Concepts and Connections*—continues to act as a roadmap that reminds students of how an organelle fits within the overall cell structure. Finally, throughout the book we have

introduced new molecular art; for example, see Figure 10.11B for a new representation of a molecule of tRNA binding to an enzyme molecule.

The Latest Science   Biology is a dynamic field of study, and we take pride in our book's currency and scientific accuracy. For this edition, as in previous editions, we have integrated the results of the latest scientific research throughout the book. We have done this carefully and thoughtfully, recognizing that research advances can lead to new ways of looking at biological topics; such changes in perspective can necessitate organizational changes in our textbook to better reflect the current state of a field. You will find a unit-by-unit account of new content and organizational improvements in the "New Content" section on pp. xvii–xviii following this Preface.

New MasteringBiology®   A specially developed version of MasteringBiology, the most widely used online tutorial and assessment program for biology, continues to accompany *Campbell Biology: Concepts & Connections*. In addition to 170 author-created activities that help students learn vocabulary, extend the book's emphasis on visual learning, demonstrate the connections among key concepts (helping students grasp the big ideas), and coach students on how to interpret data, the Eighth Edition features two additional new activity types. New Scientific Thinking activities encourage students to practice the basic science skills explored in the in-text Scientific Thinking feature, allowing students to try out thinking like a scientist and allowing instructors to assess this understanding; new Visualizing the Concept activities take students on an animated and narrated tour of select Visualizing the Concept modules from the text, offering students the chance to review key concepts in a digital learning modality. MasteringBiology® for *Campbell Biology: Concepts & Connections,* Eighth Edition, will help students to see strong connections through their print textbook, and the additional practice available online allows instructors to capture powerful data on student performance, thereby making the most of class time.

This Book's Flexibility

Although a biology textbook's table of contents is by design linear, biology itself is more like a web of related concepts without a single starting point or prescribed path. Courses can navigate this network by starting with molecules, with ecology, or somewhere in between, and courses can omit topics. *Campbell Biology: Concepts & Connections* is uniquely suited to offer flexibility and thus serve a variety of courses. The seven units of the book are largely self-contained, and in a number of the units, chapters can be assigned in a different order without much loss of coherence. The use of numbered modules makes it easy to skip topics or reorder the presentation of material.

■ ■ ■

For many students, introductory biology is the only science course that they will take during their college years. Long after today's students have forgotten most of the specific content of their biology course, they will be left with general impressions and attitudes about science and scientists. We hope that this new edition of *Campbell Biology: Concepts & Connections* helps make those impressions positive and supports instructors' goals for sharing the fun of biology. In our continuing efforts to improve the book and its supporting materials, we benefit tremendously from instructor and student feedback, not only in formal reviews but also via informal communication. Please let us know how we are doing and how we can improve the next edition of the book.

Jane Reece, janereece@cal.berkeley.edu

Martha Taylor (Chapter 1 and Unit I), mrt2@cornell.edu

Eric Simon (Units II and VI and Chapters 21 and 27), esimon@nec.edu

Jean Dickey (Units III, IV, and VII and Chapters 22, 23, and 30), dickeyj@clemson.edu

Kelly Hogan (Chapters 20, 24–26, 28, and 29), leek@email.unc.edu

New Content

Below are some important highlights of new content and organizational improvements in *Campbell Biology: Concepts & Connections*, Eighth Edition.

Chapter 1, Biology: Exploring Life   The snowy owl, our cover organism for the Eighth Edition, is featured in the chapter introduction. The discussion of the evolutionary adaptations of these owls to life on the arctic tundra links to a new Scientific Thinking module on testing the hypothesis that camouflage coloration protects some animals from predation. An expanded module on evolution as the core theme of biology now includes a phylogenetic tree of elephants to enhance the discussion of the unity and diversity of life.

Unit I, The Life of the Cell   Throughout the Eighth Edition, the themes introduced in new chapter introductions are expanded and further explored in either Scientific Thinking or Evolution Connection modules. For instance, in this unit, Chapter 5, The Working Cell, begins with the question "How can water flow through a membrane?" and an essay that describes the role these water channels play in kidney function; the essay is illustrated with a computer model of aquaporins spanning a membrane. Module 5.7, a Scientific Thinking module, then details the serendipitous discovery of aquaporins and presents data from a study that helped identify their function. Chapter 7, Photosynthesis: Using Light to Make Food, begins with the question "Will global climate change make you itch?" and uses the example of proliferation of poison ivy to introduce this chapter on photosynthesis. Then, Module 7.13, another Scientific Thinking module, explores various ways that scientists test the effects of rising atmospheric CO_2 levels on plant growth and presents results from a study on poison ivy growth. The Scientific Thinking question at the end of the chapter continues this theme, with data from a study on pollen production by ragweed under varying CO_2 concentrations, beginning with the question "Will global climate change make you sneeze as well as itch?" This unit also has three of the new Visualizing the Concept modules: Module 3.14: A protein's functional shape results from four levels of structure; Module 5.1: Membranes are fluid mosaics of lipids and proteins with many functions; and Module 7.9: The light reactions take place within the thylakoid membranes. These modules use both new and highly revised art to guide students through these challenging topics in a visual, highly intuitive manner. Chapter 6, How Cells Harvest Chemical Energy, now includes a new figure and expanded explanation of the amazing molecular motor, ATP synthase. The art program in Chapter 4, A Tour of the Cell, has been completely reimagined and revised. The beautiful new diagrams of animal and plant cells and their component parts are designed to help students appreciate the complexities of cell structure and explore the relationship between structure and function.

Unit II, Cellular Reproduction and Genetics   The purpose of this unit is to help students understand the relationship between DNA, chromosomes, and organisms and to help them see that genetics is not purely hypothetical but connects in many important and interesting ways to their lives, human society, and other life on Earth. In preparing this edition, we worked to clarify difficult concepts, enhancing text and illustrations and providing timely new applications of genetic principles. The content is reinforced with updated discussions of relevant topics, such as personalized cancer therapy, the H1N1 and H5N1 influenza viruses, umbilical cord blood banking, and the science and controversy surrounding genetically modified foods. This edition includes discussion of many recent advances in the field. Some new topics concern our basic understanding of genetics and the cell cycle, such as how sister chromatids are physically attached during meiosis, how chemical modifications such as methylation and acetylation affect inheritance, and the roles of activators and enhancers in controlling gene expression. Other topics include recent advances in our understanding of genetics, such as the analysis of recent human evolution of high-altitude-dwelling Sherpas, expanded roles for microRNAs in the control of genetic information, and our improved understanding of the cellular basis of health problems in cloned animals. In some cases, sections within chapters have been reorganized to present a more logical flow of materials. Examples of new organization include the discussion of human karyotypes and the diagnosis of chromosomal abnormalities (Modules 8.18–8.20) and the processes of reproductive and therapeutic cloning (Modules 11.12–11.14). Material throughout the unit has been updated to reflect recent data, such as the latest cancer statistics and results from whole-genome sequencing.

Unit III, Concepts of Evolution   This unit presents the basic principles of evolution and natural selection, the overwhelming evidence that supports these theories, and their relevance to all of biology—and to the lives of students. A new chapter introduction in Chapter 13, How Populations Evolve, highlights the role that evolution plays in thwarting human attempts to eradicate disease. The chapter has been reorganized so that the opening module on Darwin's development of the theory of evolution is followed immediately by evidence for evolution, including a Scientific Thinking module on fossils of transitional forms. Another new module (13.4) assembles evidence from homologies, including an example of "pseudogenes." New material in this unit also supports our goal of directly addressing student misconceptions about evolution. For example, a new chapter introduction and Scientific Thinking module in Chapter 14, The Origin of Species, tackle the question "Can we observe speciation occurring?" and a new chapter introduction in Chapter 15, Tracing Evolutionary History, poses the question (answered in Module 15.12) "How do brand-new structures arise by evolution?"

Unit IV, The Evolution of Biological Diversity   The diversity unit surveys all life on Earth in less than a hundred pages! Consequently, descriptions and illustrations of the unifying characteristics of each major group of organisms, along with a small sample of its diversity, make up the bulk of the content. Two recurring elements are interwoven with these descriptions: evolutionary history and examples of relevance to our everyday lives and society at large. For the Eighth Edition, we have improved and updated those two elements. For example, Chapter 16, Microbial Life: Prokaryotes and Protists, opens with a new introduction on human microbiota and the question "Are antibiotics making us fat?" The related Scientific Thinking module (16.11) updates the story of Marshall's discovery of the role of *Helicobacter pylori* in ulcers with a new hypothesis about a possible connection between *H. pylori* and obesity. A new chapter introduction and Scientific Thinking module in Chapter 17, The Evolution of Plant and Fungal Diversity, highlight the interdependence of plants and fungi. The alternation of generations and the life cycle in mosses and ferns are presented in an attractive two-page Visualizing the Concept module (17.3), while details of the pine life cycle have been replaced with a new Module 17.5 that emphasizes pollen and seeds as key adaptations for terrestrial life. The animal diversity chapters (18, The Evolution of Invertebrate Diversity; and 19, The Evolution of Vertebrate Diversity) also have new opening essays. A Visualizing the Concept module (18.3) beautifully illustrates features of the animal body plan. A new Module 18.16 calls attention to the value of invertebrate diversity. Chapter 19 includes a Visualizing the Concept module (19.9) on primate diversity and also updates the story of hominin evolution, including the recently described *Australopithecus sediba*.

Unit V, Animals: Form and Function   This unit combines a comparative approach with an exploration of human anatomy and physiology. Many chapters begin with an overview of a general problem that animals face and a comparative discussion of how different animals address this problem, all framed within an evolutionary context. For example, the introduction to Chapter 20, Unifying Concepts of Animal Structure and Function, begins with the question "Does evolution lead to the perfect animal form?" Module 20.1 is a new Evolution Connection that discusses the long, looped laryngeal nerve in vertebrates (using the giraffe as an example) to illustrate that a structure in an ancestral organism can become adapted to function in a descendant organism without being "perfected," thereby combating common student misconceptions about evolution. The main portion of every chapter is devoted to detailed presentations of human body systems, frequently illuminated by discussion of the health consequences of disorders in those systems. For example, Chapter 28, Nervous Systems, includes new material describing a genetic risk for developing Alzheimer's disease, the long-term consequences of traumatic brain injury, and how some antidepressants may not be as effective at combating depression as once thought. In many areas, content has been updated to reflect

newer issues in biology. The chapter introduction and new Scientific Thinking module in Chapter 26, Hormones and the Endocrine System, discuss the consequences of endocrine disruptors in the environment. The Scientific Thinking module in Chapter 23 describes large clinical trials investigating the hypothesis that heart attacks are caused by the body's inflammatory response. Chapter 27, Reproduction and Embryonic Development, has a new chapter introduction on viral STDs, improved figures presenting embryonic development, as well as a Visualizing the Concept module on human pregnancy. Improvements to this unit also include a significant revision to the presentation of nutrition in Modules 21.14 to 21.21 and a reorganization of text and art in Modules 25.6 and 25.7 to guide students through the anatomy and physiology of the kidneys.

Unit VI, Plants: Form and Function   To help students gain an appreciation of the importance of plants, this unit presents the anatomy and physiology of angiosperms with frequent connections to the importance of plants to society. New Connections in this edition include an increased discussion of the importance of agriculture to human civilization (including presentation of genomic data investigating this question) in Chapter 31, issues surrounding organic farming (including presentation of data on the nutritional value of organic versus conventionally grown produce) in Chapter 32, an expanded discussion of phytoestrogens, as well as a new discussion on the production of seedless vegetables in Chapter 33. Throughout the unit, the text has been revised with the goal of making the material more engaging and accessible to students. For example, the difficult topic of transpiration is now presented in an entirely new, visual style within a Visualizing the Concept module (Module 32.3), and streamlined and simplified discussions were written for such topics as the auxin hormones and phytochromes. All of these changes are meant to make the point that human society is inexorably connected to the health of plants.

Unit VII, Ecology   In this unit, students learn the fundamental principles of ecology and how these principles apply to environmental problems. Along with a new introduction in each chapter, the Eighth Edition features many new photos and two Visualizing the Concept modules (35.7 and 37.9)—one focuses on whether animal movement is a response to stimuli or requires spatial learning and the other explores the interconnection of food chains and food webs. Scientific Thinking modules sample the variety of approaches to studying ecology, including the classic field study that led to the concept of keystone species (37.11); the "natural experiment" of returning gray wolves to the Yellowstone ecosystem (38.11); and the combination of historical records, long-term experimentation, and modern technology to investigate the snowshoe hare–lynx population cycle (36.6). The pioneering work of Rachel Carson (34.2) and Jane Goodall (35.22) is also described in Scientific Thinking modules. Modules that present data on human population (36.3, 36.9–36.11), declining biodiversity (38.1), and global climate change (38.3, 38.4) have all been updated.

Acknowledgments

This Eighth Edition of *Campbell Biology: Concepts & Connections* is a result of the combined efforts of many talented and hardworking people, and the authors wish to extend heartfelt thanks to all those who contributed to this and previous editions. Our work on this edition was shaped by input from the biologists acknowledged in the reviewer list on pages xx–xxii, who shared with us their experiences teaching introductory biology and provided specific suggestions for improving the book. Feedback from the authors of this edition's supplements and the unsolicited comments and suggestions we received from many biologists and biology students were also extremely helpful. In addition, this book has benefited in countless ways from the stimulating contacts we have had with the coauthors of *Campbell Biology*, Tenth Edition.

We wish to offer special thanks to the students and faculty at our teaching institutions. Marty Taylor thanks her students at Cornell University for their valuable feedback on the book. Eric Simon thanks his colleagues and friends at New England College, especially within the collegium of Natural Sciences and Mathematics, for their continued support and assistance. Jean Dickey thanks her colleagues at Clemson University for their expertise and support. And Kelly Hogan thanks her students for their enthusiasm and thanks her colleagues at the University of North Carolina, Chapel Hill, for their continued support.

We thank Paul Corey, president, Science, Business, and Technology, Pearson Higher Education. In addition, the superb publishing team for this edition was headed up by acquisitions editor Alison Rodal, with the invaluable support of editor-in-chief Beth Wilbur. We cannot thank them enough for their unstinting efforts on behalf of the book and for their commitment to excellence in biology education. We are fortunate to have had once again the contributions of executive director of development Deborah Gale and executive editorial manager Ginnie Simione Jutson. We are similarly grateful to the members of the editorial development team—Debbie Hardin, who also served as the day-to-day editorial project manager, and Susan Teahan—for their steadfast commitment to quality. We thank them for their thoroughness, hard work, and good humor; the book is far better than it would have been without their efforts. Thanks also to senior supplements project editor Susan Berge for her oversight of the supplements program and to editorial assistants Rachel Brickner, Katherine Harrison-Adcock, and Libby Reiser for the efficient and enthusiastic support they provided.

This book and all the other components of the teaching package are both attractive and pedagogically effective in large part because of the hard work and creativity of the production professionals on our team. We wish to thank managing editor Mike Early and production project manager Lori Newman. We also acknowledge copyeditor Joanna Dinsmore, proofreader Pete Shanks, and indexer Lynn Armstrong. We again thank senior photo editor Donna Kalal and photo researcher Kristin Piljay for their contributions, as well as project manager for text permissions Alison Bruckner. S4Carlisle Publishing Services was responsible for composition, headed by senior project editor Emily Bush, with help from paging specialist Donna Healy; and Precision Graphics, headed by project manager Amanda Bickel, was responsible for rendering new and revised illustrations. We also thank manufacturing buyer Jeffrey Sargent.

We thank Gary Hespenheide for creating a beautiful and functional interior design and a stunning cover, and we are again indebted to design manager Marilyn Perry for her oversight and design leadership. The new Visualizing the Concept modules benefited from her vision, as well as from the early input of art editor Elisheva Marcus and the continuing contributions of artist Andrew Recher of Precision Graphics. Art editor Kelly Murphy envisioned the beautiful new cell art throughout the book.

The value of *Campbell Biology: Concepts & Connections* as a learning tool is greatly enhanced by the hard work and creativity of the authors of the supplements that accompany this book: Ed Zalisko (*Instructor's Guide* and *PowerPoint® Lecture Presentations*); Jean DeSaix, Tanya Smutka, Kristen Miller, and Justin Shaffer (*Test Bank*); Dana Kurpius (*Active Reading Guide*); Robert Iwan and Amaya Garcia (*Reading Quizzes* and media correlations); and Shannon Datwyler (*Clicker Questions* and *Quiz Shows*). In addition to senior supplements project editor Susan Berge, the editorial and production staff for the supplements program included supplements production project manager Jane Brundage, *PowerPoint® Lecture Presentations* editor Joanna Dinsmore, and project manager Sylvia Rebert of Progressive Publishing Alternatives. And the superlative MasteringBiology® program for this book would not exist without Lauren Fogel, Stacy Treco, Tania Mlawer, Katie Foley, Sarah Jensen, Juliana Tringali, Daniel Ross, Dario Wong, Taylor Merck, Caroline Power, and David Kokorowski and his team. And a special thanks to Sarah Young-Dualan for her thoughtful work on the Visualizing the Concepts interactive videos.

For their important roles in marketing the book, we are very grateful to senior marketing manager Amee Mosley, executive marketing manager Lauren Harp, and vice president of marketing Christy Lesko. We also appreciate the work of the executive marketing manager for MasteringBiology®, Scott Dustan. The members of the Pearson Science sales team have continued to help us connect with biology instructors and their teaching needs, and we thank them.

Finally, we are deeply grateful to our families and friends for their support, encouragement, and patience throughout this project. Our special thanks to Paul, Dan, Maria, Armelle, and Sean (J.B.R.); Josie, Jason, Marnie, Alice, Jack, David, Paul, Ava, and Daniel (M.R.T.); Amanda, Reed, Forest, and dear friends Jamey, Nick, Jim, and Bethany (E.J.S.); Jessie and Katherine (J.L.D.); and Tracey, Vivian, Carolyn, Brian, Jake, and Lexi (K.H.)

Jane Reece, Martha Taylor, Eric Simon, Jean Dickey, and Kelly Hogan

Reviewers

Visualizing the Concept Review Panel, Eighth Edition

Erica Kipp, *Pace University*
David Loring, *Johnson County Community College*
Sheryl Love, *Temple University*
Sukanya Subramanian, *Collin County Community College*
Jennifer J. Yeh, *San Francisco, California*

Reviewers of the Eighth Edition

Steven Armstrong, *Tarrant County College*
Michael Battaglia, *Greenville Technical College*
Lisa Bonneau, *Metropolitan Community College*
Stephen T. Brown, *Los Angeles Mission College*
Nancy Buschhaus, *University of Tennessee at Martin*
Glenn Cohen, *Troy University*
Nora Espinoza, *Clemson University*
Karen E. Francl, *Radford University*
Jennifer Greenwood, *University of Tennessee at Martin*
Joel Hagen, *Radford University*
Chris Haynes, *Shelton State Community College*
Duane A. Hinton, *Washburn University*
Amy Hollingsworth, *The University of Akron*
Erica Kipp, *Pace University*
Cindy Klevickis, *James Madison University*
Dubear Kroening, *University of Wisconsin, Fox Valley*
Dana Kurpius, *Elgin Community College*
Dale Lambert, *Tarrant County College*
David Loring, *Johnson County Community College*
Mark Meade, *Jacksonville State University*
John Mersfelder, *Sinclair Community College*
Andrew Miller, *Thomas University*
Zia Nisani, *Antelope Valley College*
Camellia M. Okpodu, *Norfolk State University*
James Rayburn, *Jacksonville State University*
Ashley Rhodes, *Kansas State University*
Lori B. Robinson, *Georgia College & State University*
Ursula Roese, *University of New England*
Doreen J. Schroeder, *University of St. Thomas*
Justin Shaffer, *North Carolina A&T State University*
Marilyn Shopper, *Johnson County Community College*
Ayesha Siddiqui, *Schoolcraft College*
Ashley Spring, *Brevard Community College*
Thaxton Springfield, *St. Petersburg College*
Linda Brooke Stabler, *University of Central Oklahoma*
Patrick Stokley, *East Central Community College*
Lori Tolley-Jordan, *Jacksonville State University*
Jimmy Triplett, *Jacksonville State University*
Lisa Weasel, *Portland State University*
Martin Zahn, *Thomas Nelson Community College*

Reviewers of Previous Editions

Michael Abbott, *Westminster College*
Tanveer Abidi, *Kean University*
Daryl Adams, *Mankato State University*
Dawn Adrian Adams, *Baylor University*
Olushola Adeyeye, *Duquesne University*
Shylaja Akkaraju, *Bronx Community College*
Felix Akojie, *Paducah Community College*
Dan Alex, *Chabot College*
John Aliff, *Georgia Perimeter College*
Sylvester Allred, *Northern Arizona University*
Jane Aloi-Horlings, *Saddleback College*
Loren Ammerman, *University of Texas at Arlington*
Dennis Anderson, *Oklahoma City Community College*
Marjay Anderson, *Howard University*
Bert Atsma, *Union County College*
Yael Avissar, *Rhode Island College*
Gail Baker, *LaGuardia Community College*
Caroline Ballard, *Rock Valley College*
Andrei Barkovskii, *Georgia College and State University*
Mark Barnby, *Ohlone College*
Chris Barnhart, *University of San Diego*
Stephen Barnhart, *Santa Rosa Junior College*
William Barstow, *University of Georgia*
Kirk A. Bartholomew, *Central Connecticut State University*
Michael Battaglia, *Greenville Technical College*
Gail Baughman, *Mira Costa College*
Jane Beiswenger, *University of Wyoming*
Tania Beliz, *College of San Mateo*
Lisa Bellows, *North Central Texas College*
Ernest Benfield, *Virginia Polytechnic Institute*
Rudi Berkelhamer, *University of California, Irvine*
Harry Bernheim, *Tufts University*
Richard Bliss, *Yuba College*
Lawrence Blumer, *Morehouse College*
Dennis Bogyo, *Valdosta State University*
Lisa K. Bonneau, *Metropolitan Community College, Blue River*
Mehdi Borhan, *Johnson County Community College*
Kathleen Bossy, *Bryant College*
William Bowen, *University of Arkansas at Little Rock*
Robert Boyd, *Auburn University*
Bradford Boyer, *State University of New York, Suffolk County Community College*
Paul Boyer, *University of Wisconsin*
William Bradshaw, *Brigham Young University*
Agnello Braganza, *Chabot College*
James Bray, *Blackburn College*
Peggy Brickman, *University of Georgia*
Chris Brinegar, *San Jose State University*
Chad Brommer, *Emory University*
Charles Brown, *Santa Rosa Junior College*
Carole Browne, *Wake Forest University*
Becky Brown-Watson, *Santa Rosa Junior College*
Delia Brownson, *University of Texas at Austin and Austin Community College*
Michael Bucher, *College of San Mateo*
Virginia Buckner, *Johnson County Community College*
Joseph C. Bundy, Jr., *University of North Carolina at Greensboro*
Ray Burton, *Germanna Community College*
Warren Buss, *University of Northern Colorado*
Linda Butler, *University of Texas at Austin*
Jerry Button, *Portland Community College*
Carolee Caffrey, *University of California, Los Angeles*
George Cain, *University of Iowa*
Beth Campbell, *Itawamba Community College*
John Campbell, *Northern Oklahoma College*
John Capeheart, *University of Houston, Downtown*
James Cappuccino, *Rockland Community College*
M. Carabelli, *Broward Community College*
Jocelyn Cash, *Central Piedmont Community College*
Cathryn Cates, *Tyler Junior College*
Russell Centanni, *Boise State University*
David Chambers, *Northeastern University*
Ruth Chesnut, *Eastern Illinois University*
Vic Chow, *San Francisco City College*
Van Christman, *Ricks College*
Craig Clifford, *Northeastern State University, Tahlequah*
Richard Cobb, *South Maine Community College*
Mary Colavito, *Santa Monica College*
Jennifer Cooper, *Itawamba Community College*
Bob Cowling, *Ouachita Technical College*
Don Cox, *Miami University*
Robert Creek, *Western Kentucky University*
Hillary Cressey, *George Mason University*
Norma Criley, *Illinois Wesleyan University*
Jessica Crowe, *South Georgia College*
Mitch Cruzan, *Portland State University*
Judy Daniels, *Monroe Community College*
Michael Davis, *Central Connecticut State University*
Pat Davis, *East Central Community College*
Lewis Deaton, *University of Louisiana*
Lawrence DeFilippi, *Lurleen B. Wallace College*
James Dekloe, *Solano Community College*
Veronique Delesalle, *Gettysburg College*
Loren Denney, *Southwest Missouri State University*
Jean DeSaix, *University of North Carolina at Chapel Hill*
Mary Dettman, *Seminole Community College of Florida*
Kathleen Diamond, *College of San Mateo*
Alfred Diboll, *Macon College*
Jean Dickey, *Clemson University*
Stephen Dina, *St. Louis University*
Robert P. Donaldson, *George Washington University*
Gary Donnermeyer, *Iowa Central Community College*
Charles Duggins, *University of South Carolina*
Susan Dunford, *University of Cincinnati*
Lee Edwards, *Greenville Technical College*
Betty Eidemiller, *Lamar University*
Jamin Eisenbach, *Eastern Michigan University*
Norman Ellstrand, *University of California, Riverside*
Thomas Emmel, *University of Florida*
Cindy Erwin, *City College of San Francisco*
Gerald Esch, *Wake Forest University*
David Essar, *Winona State University*

Cory Etchberger, *Longview Community College*
Nancy Eyster-Smith, *Bentley College*
William Ezell, *University of North Carolina at Pembroke*
Laurie Faber, *Grand Rapids Community College*
Terence Farrell, *Stetson University*
Shannon Kuchel Fehlberg, *Colorado Christian University*
Jerry Feldman, *University of California, Santa Cruz*
Eugene Fenster, *Longview Community College*
Dino Fiabane, *Community College of Philadelphia*
Kathleen Fisher, *San Diego State University*
Edward Fliss, *St. Louis Community College, Florissant Valley*
Linda Flora, *Montgomery County Community College*
Dennis Forsythe, *The Citadel Military College of South Carolina*
Robert Frankis, *College of Charleston*
James French, *Rutgers University*
Bernard Frye, *University of Texas at Arlington*
Anne Galbraith, *University of Wisconsin*
Robert Galbraith, *Crafton Hills College*
Rosa Gambier, *State University of New York, Suffolk County Community College*
George Garcia, *University of Texas at Austin*
Linda Gardner, *San Diego Mesa College*
Sandi Gardner, *Triton College*
Gail Gasparich, *Towson University*
Janet Gaston, *Troy University*
Shelley Gaudia, *Lane Community College*
Douglas Gayou, *University of Missouri at Columbia*
Robert Gendron, *Indiana University of Pennsylvania*
Bagie George, *Georgia Gwinnett College*
Rebecca German, *University of Cincinnati*
Grant Gerrish, *University of Hawaii*
Julie Gibbs, *College of DuPage*
Frank Gilliam, *Marshall University*
Patricia Glas, *The Citadel Military College of South Carolina*
David Glenn-Lewin, *Wichita State University*
Robert Grammer, *Belmont University*
Laura Grayson-Roselli, *Burlington County College*
Peggy Green, *Broward Community College*
Miriam L. Greenberg, *Wayne State University*
Sylvia Greer, *City University of New York*
Eileen Gregory, *Rollins College*
Dana Griffin, *University of Florida*
Richard Groover, *J. Sargeant Reynolds Community College*
Peggy Guthrie, *University of Central Oklahoma*
Maggie Haag, *University of Alberta*
Richard Haas, *California State University, Fresno*
Martin Hahn, *William Paterson College*
Leah Haimo, *University of California, Riverside*
James Hampton, *Salt Lake Community College*
Blanche Haning, *North Carolina State University*
Richard Hanke, *Rose State College*
Laszlo Hanzely, *Northern Illinois University*
David Harbster, *Paradise Valley Community College*
Sig Harden, *Troy University Montgomery*
Reba Harrell, *Hinds Community College*
Jim Harris, *Utah Valley Community College*
Mary Harris, *Louisiana State University*
Chris Haynes, *Shelton State Community College*

Janet Haynes, *Long Island University*
Jean Helgeson, *Collin County Community College*
Ira Herskowitz, *University of California, San Francisco*
Paul Hertz, *Barnard College*
Margaret Hicks, *David Lipscomb University*
Jean Higgins-Fonda, *Prince George's Community College*
Phyllis Hirsch, *East Los Angeles College*
William Hixon, *St. Ambrose University*
Carl Hoagstrom, *Ohio Northern University*
Kim Hodgson, *Longwood College*
Jon Hoekstra, *Gainesville State College*
Kelly Hogan, *University of North Carolina at Chapel Hill*
John Holt, *Michigan State University*
Laura Hoopes, *Occidental College*
Lauren Howard, *Norwich University*
Robert Howe, *Suffolk University*
Michael Hudecki, *State University of New York, Buffalo*
George Hudock, *Indiana University*
Kris Hueftle, *Pensacola Junior College*
Barbara Hunnicutt, *Seminole Community College*
Brenda Hunzinger, *Lake Land College*
Catherine Hurlbut, *Florida Community College*
Charles Ide, *Tulane University*
Mark Ikeda, *San Bernardino Valley College*
Georgia Ineichen, *Hinds Community College*
Robert Iwan, *Inver Hills Community College*
Mark E. Jackson, *Central Connecticut State University*
Charles Jacobs, *Henry Ford Community College*
Fred James, *Presbyterian College*
Ursula Jander, *Washburn University*
Alan Jaworski, *University of Georgia*
R. Jensen, *Saint Mary's College*
Robert Johnson, *Pierce College, Lakewood Campus*
Roishene Johnson, *Bossier Parish Community College*
Russell Johnson, *Ricks College*
John C. Jones, *Calhoun Community College*
Florence Juillerat, *Indiana University at Indianapolis*
Tracy Kahn, *University of California, Riverside*
Hinrich Kaiser, *Victor Valley College*
Klaus Kalthoff, *University of Texas at Austin*
Tom Kantz, *California State University, Sacramento*
Jennifer Katcher, *Pima Community College*
Judy Kaufman, *Monroe Community College*
Marlene Kayne, *The College of New Jersey*
Mahlon Kelly, *University of Virginia*
Kenneth Kerrick, *University of Pittsburgh at Johnstown*
Joyce Kille-Marino, *College of Charleston*
Joanne Kilpatrick, *Auburn University, Montgomery*
Stephen Kilpatrick, *University of Pittsburgh at Johnstown*
Lee Kirkpatrick, *Glendale Community College*
Peter Kish, *Southwestern Oklahoma State University*
Cindy Klevickis, *James Madison University*
Robert Koch, *California State University, Fullerton*
Eliot Krause, *Seton Hall University*
Dubear Kroening, *University of Wisconsin, Fox Valley*
Kevin Krown, *San Diego State University*

Margaret Maile Lam, *Kapiolani Community College*
MaryLynne LaMantia, *Golden West College*
Mary Rose Lamb, *University of Puget Sound*
Dale Lambert, *Tarrant County College, Northeast*
Thomas Lammers, *University of Wisconsin, Oshkosh*
Carmine Lanciani, *University of Florida*
Vic Landrum, *Washburn University*
Deborah Langsam, *University of North Carolina at Charlotte*
Geneen Lannom, *University of Central Oklahoma*
Brenda Latham, *Merced College*
Liz Lawrence, *Miles Community College*
Steven Lebsack, *Linn-Benton Community College*
Karen Lee, *University of Pittsburgh at Johnstown*
Tom Lehman, *Morgan Community College*
William Lemon, *Southwestern Oregon Community College*
Laurie M. Len, *El Camino College*
Peggy Lepley, *Cincinnati State University*
Richard Liebaert, *Linn-Benton Community College*
Kevin Lien, *Portland Community College*
Harvey Liftin, *Broward Community College*
Ivo Lindauer, *University of Northern Colorado*
William Lindsay, *Monterey Peninsula College*
Kirsten Lindstrom, *Santa Rosa Junior College*
Melanie Loo, *California State University, Sacramento*
David Loring, *Johnson County Community College*
Eric Lovely, *Arkansas Tech University*
Paul Lurquin, *Washington State University*
James Mack, *Monmouth University*
David Magrane, *Morehead State University*
Joan Maloof, *Salisbury State University*
Joseph Marshall, *West Virginia University*
Presley Martin, *Drexel University*
William McComas, *University of Iowa*
Steven McCullagh, *Kennesaw State College*
Mitchell McGinnis, *North Seattle Community College*
James McGivern, *Gannon University*
Colleen McNamara, *Albuquerque TVI Community College*
Caroline McNutt, *Schoolcraft College*
Scott Meissner, *Cornell University*
Joseph Mendelson, *Utah State University*
Timothy Metz, *Campbell University*
Iain Miller, *University of Cincinnati*
Robert Miller, *University of Dubuque*
V. Christine Minor, *Clemson University*
Brad Mogen, *University of Wisconsin, River Falls*
James Moné, *Millersville University*
Jamie Moon, *University of North Florida*
Juan Morata, *Miami Dade College*
Richard Mortensen, *Albion College*
Henry Mulcahy, *Suffolk University*
Christopher Murphy, *James Madison University*
Kathryn Nette, *Cuyamaca College*
James Newcomb, *New England College*
Zia Nisani, *Antelope Valley College*
James Nivison, *Mid Michigan Community College*
Peter Nordloh, *Southeastern Community College*
Stephen Novak, *Boise State University*
Bette Nybakken, *Hartnell College*
Michael O'Donnell, *Trinity College*
Steven Oliver, *Worcester State College*
Karen Olmstead, *University of South Dakota*

Steven O'Neal, *Southwestern Oklahoma State University*
Lowell Orr, *Kent State University*
William Outlaw, *Florida State University*
Phillip Pack, *Woodbury University*
Kevin Padian, *University of California, Berkeley*
Kay Pauling, *Foothill College*
Mark Paulissen, *Northeastern State University, Tahlequah*
Debra Pearce, *Northern Kentucky University*
David Pearson, *Bucknell University*
Patricia Pearson, *Western Kentucky University*
Kathleen Pelkki, *Saginaw Valley State University*
Andrew Penniman, *Georgia Perimeter College*
John Peters, *College of Charleston*
Gary Peterson, *South Dakota State University*
Margaret Peterson, *Concordia Lutheran College*
Russell L. Peterson, *Indiana University of Pennsylvania*
Paula Piehl, *Potomac State College*
Ben Pierce, *Baylor University*
Jack Plaggemeyer, *Little Big Horn College*
Barbara Pleasants, *Iowa State University*
Kathryn Podwall, *Nassau Community College*
Judith Pottmeyer, *Columbia Basin College*
Donald Potts, *University of California, Santa Cruz*
Nirmala Prabhu, *Edison Community College*
Elena Pravosudova, *University of Nevada, Reno*
James Pru, *Belleville Area College*
Rongsun Pu, *Kean University*
Charles Pumpuni, *Northern Virginia Community College*
Kimberly Puvalowski, *Old Bridge High School*
Rebecca Pyles, *East Tennessee State University*
Shanmugavel Rajendran, *Baltimore City Community College*
Bob Ratterman, *Jamestown Community College*
Jill Raymond, *Rock Valley College*
Michael Read, *Germanna Community College*
Brian Reeder, *Morehead State University*
Bruce Reid, *Kean College*
David Reid, *Blackburn College*
Stephen Reinbold, *Longview Community College*
Erin Rempala, *San Diego Mesa College*
Michael Renfroe, *James Madison University*
Tim Revell, *Mt. San Antonio College*
Douglas Reynolds, *Central Washington University*
Fred Rhoades, *Western Washington University*
John Rinehart, *Eastern Oregon University*
Laura Ritt, *Burlington County College*
Lynn Rivers, *Henry Ford Community College*
Bruce Robart, *University of Pittsburgh at Johnstown*
Jennifer Roberts, *Lewis University*
Laurel Roberts, *University of Pittsburgh*
Luis A. Rodriguez, *San Antonio Colleges*
Duane Rohlfing, *University of South Carolina*
Jeanette Rollinger, *College of the Sequoias*

Steven Roof, *Fairmont State College*
Jim Rosowski, *University of Nebraska*
Stephen Rothstein, *University of California, Santa Barbara*
Donald Roush, *University of North Alabama*
Lynette Rushton, *South Puget Sound Community College*
Connie Rye, *East Mississippi Community College*
Linda Sabatino, *State University of New York, Suffolk County Community College*
Douglas Schamel, *University of Alaska, Fairbanks*
Douglas Schelhaas, *University of Mary*
Beverly Schieltz, *Wright State University*
Fred Schindler, *Indian Hills Community College*
Robert Schoch, *Boston University*
Brian Scholtens, *College of Charleston*
John Richard Schrock, *Emporia State University*
Julie Schroer, *Bismarck State College*
Fayla Schwartz, *Everett Community College*
Judy Shea, *Kutztown University of Pennsylvania*
Daniela Shebitz, *Kean University*
Thomas Shellberg, *Henry Ford Community College*
Cara Shillington, *Eastern Michigan University*
Lisa Shimeld, *Crafton Hills College*
Brian Shmaefsky, *Kingwood College*
Mark Shotwell, *Slippery Rock University*
Jane Shoup, *Purdue University*
Michele Shuster, *New Mexico State University*
Linda Simpson, *University of North Carolina at Charlotte*
Gary Smith, *Tarrant County Junior College*
Marc Smith, *Sinclair Community College*
Michael Smith, *Western Kentucky University*
Phil Snider, *University of Houston*
Sam C. Sochet, *Thomas Edison Career and Technical Education High School*
Gary Sojka, *Bucknell University*
Ralph Sorensen, *Gettysburg College*
Ruth Sporer, *Rutgers University*
Linda Brooke Stabler, *University of Central Oklahoma*
David Stanton, *Saginaw Valley State University*
Amanda Starnes, *Emory University*
John Stolz, *Duquesne University*
Ross Strayer, *Washtenaw Community College*
Donald Streuble, *Idaho State University*
Megan Stringer, *Jones County Junior College*
Mark Sugalski, *New England College*
Gerald Summers, *University of Missouri*
Marshall Sundberg, *Louisiana State University*
Christopher Tabit, *University of West Georgia*
David Tauck, *Santa Clara University*
Hilda Taylor, *Acadia University*
Franklin Te, *Miami Dade College*
Gene Thomas, *Solano Community College*
Kenneth Thomas, *Northern Essex Community College*

Kathy Thompson, *Louisiana State University*
Laura Thurlow, *Jackson Community College*
Anne Tokazewski, *Burlington County College*
John Tolli, *Southwestern College*
Bruce Tomlinson, *State University of New York, Fredonia*
Nancy Tress, *University of Pittsburgh at Titusville*
Donald Trisel, *Fairmont State College*
Kimberly Turk, *Mitchell Community College*
Virginia Turner, *Harper College*
Mike Tveten, *Pima College*
Michael Twaddle, *University of Toledo*
Rani Vajravelu, *University of Central Florida*
Leslie VanderMolen, *Humboldt State University*
Cinnamon VanPutte, *Southwestern Illinois College*
Sarah VanVickle-Chavez, *Washington University*
John Vaughan, *Georgetown College*
Martin Vaughan, *Indiana University*
Mark Venable, *Appalachian State University*
Ann Vernon, *St. Charles County Community College*
Rukmani Viswanath, *Laredo Community College*
Frederick W. Vogt, *Elgin Community College*
Mary Beth Voltura, *State University of New York, Cortland*
Jerry Waldvogel, *Clemson University*
Robert Wallace, *Ripon College*
Dennis Walsh, *MassBay Community College*
Patricia Walsh, *University of Delaware*
Lisa Weasel, *Portland State University*
James Wee, *Loyola University*
Harrington Wells, *University of Tulsa*
Jennifer Wiatrowski, *Pasco-Hernando Community College*
Larry Williams, *University of Houston*
Ray S. Williams, *Appalachian State University*
Lura Williamson, *University of New Orleans*
Sandra Winicur, *Indiana University, South Bend*
Robert R. Wise, *University of Wisconsin Oshkosh*
Mary E. Wisgirda, *San Jacinto College*
Mary Jo Witz, *Monroe Community College*
Neil Woffinden, *University of Pittsburgh at Johnstown*
Michael Womack, *Macon State University*
Patrick Woolley, *East Central College*
Maury Wrightson, *Germanna Community College*
Tumen Wuliji, *University of Nevada, Reno*
Mark Wygoda, *McNeese State University*
Tony Yates, *Seminole State College*
William Yurkiewicz, *Millersville University of Pennsylvania*
Gregory Zagursky, *Radford University*
Martin Zahn, *Thomas Nelson Community College*
Edward J. Zalisko, *Blackburn College*
David Zeigler, *University of North Carolina at Pembroke*
Uko Zylstra, *Calvin College*

Detailed Contents

Taken from: *Campbell Biology: Concepts & Connections*, Eighth Edition
by Jane B. Reece, Martha R. Taylor, Eric J. Simon, Jean L. Dickey, and Kelly Hogan

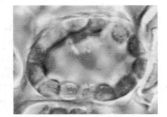

UNIT II

Cellular Reproduction and Genetics 123

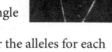
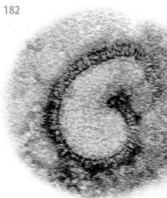

UNIT III

Concepts of Evolution 253

13 How Populations Evolve 254

14 The Origin of Species 276

15 Tracing Evolutionary History 292

UNIT IV

The Evolution of Biological Diversity   317

16   Microbial Life: *Prokaryotes and Protists*   318

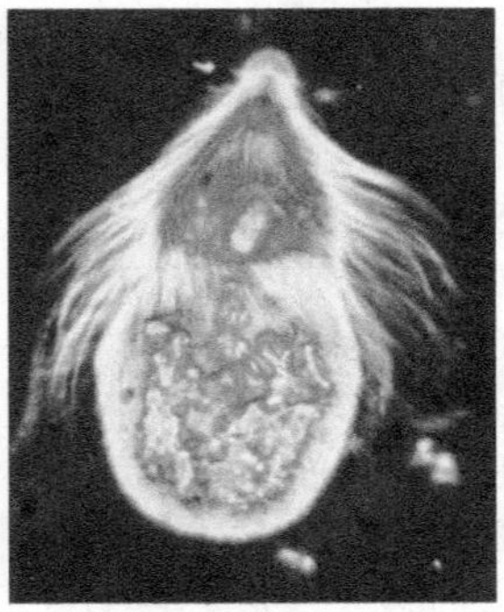

Taken from: *Get Ready for A&P*, Third Edition by Lori K. Garrett

17   Study Skills: *The Proper Care and Feeding of a Human Brain*   341

18 Chemistry: *The Science of Stuff*   365

19 Cell Biology: *Life's Little Factories*   391

Taken from: *Genetic Testimony: A Guide to Forensic DNA Profiling*, by Charlotte A. Spencer

23   Genetic Testimony: *A Guide to Forensic DNA Profiling*   491

Biology: *Exploring Life*

Snowy owls (*Bubo scandiacus*), such as the one on the cover of this textbook and pictured below, are strikingly beautiful owls with bright orange eyes and wingspans as wide as five feet. These swift and silent predators exhibit remarkable adaptations for life in their frozen, barren habitat. The layers of fine feathers on their face, body, legs, and even their feet provide insulation in subzero weather. They breed on the Arctic tundra, nesting on open ground. The female broods the eggs and young, while the male provides a steady supply of food. His keen vision and acute hearing help him locate small mammals such as voles and lemmings, which he then snatches in mid-flight with his sharp talons.

? *Why do so many animals match their surroundings?*

The majority of owl species are nocturnal. But during the endless days of arctic summers, snowy owls hunt in daylight. Projecting upper eyelids help shield their eyes from bright sun. As with all owls, the overlapping fields of vision of their forward-facing eyes provide superior depth perception. These large eyes cannot move, so an owl must turn its whole head to follow a moving object. This is not a problem for an owl, as you can see in the photo below, because adaptations of its neck

vertebrae enable it to rotate its head a full 270 degrees. Imagine being able to look over your left shoulder by turning your head to the right!

You may think of owls in general in shades of brown, nesting in tree cavities and blending in with their surroundings. And with snowy owls, you may think of Harry Potter's white-feathered companion. In real life, these owls also blend in with their wintry habitat. Later in this chapter, you will read about an experiment that tests the hypothesis that camouflage coloration protects animals from predators.

The amazing adaptations of snowy owls are the result of evolution, the process that has transformed life from its earliest beginnings to the astounding array of organisms living today. In this chapter, we begin our exploration of biology—the scientific study of life.

BIG IDEAS

Themes in the Study of Biology
(1.1–1.4)
Common themes help to organize the study of life.

▽

Evolution, the Core Theme of Biology
(1.5–1.7)
Evolution accounts for the unity and diversity of life and the evolutionary adaptations of organisms to their environment.

▽

The Process of Science
(1.8–1.9)
In studying nature, scientists make observations, form hypotheses, and test predictions.

▽

Biology and Everyday Life
(1.10–1.11)
Learning about biology helps us understand many issues involving science, technology, and society.

▷ Themes in the Study of Biology

1.1 All forms of life share common properties

Defining **biology** as the scientific study of life raises the obvious question: What is *life*? Even a small child realizes that a bug or a flower is alive, whereas a rock or a car is not. But the phenomenon we call life defies a simple, one-sentence definition. We recognize life mainly by what living things do. **Figure 1.1** highlights seven of the properties and processes that we associate with life.

1. *Order.* This sunflower illustrates the ordered structure that typifies life. Living cells make up this complex organization.

2. *Reproduction.* Organisms reproduce their own kind. Here a baby African elephant walks beneath its mother.

3. *Growth and development.* Inherited information in the form of DNA controls the pattern of growth and development of all organisms, including this hatching crocodile.

4. *Energy processing.* This caterpillar will use the chemical energy stored in the plant it is eating to power its own activities and chemical reactions.

5. *Regulation.* Many types of mechanisms regulate an organism's internal environment, keeping it within limits that sustain life. Pictured here is a lizard "sunbathing"—which helps raise its body temperature on cool mornings.

6. *Response to the environment.* All organisms respond to environmental stimuli. This Venus flytrap closed its trap rapidly in response to the stimulus of a damselfly landing on it.

7. *Evolutionary adaptation.* A snowy owl's sharp talons facilitate prey capture and its feathered feet keep it warm in its cold habitat. Such adaptations evolve over many generations as individuals with traits best suited to their environment have greater reproductive success and pass their traits to offspring.

Figure 1.1 reminds us that the living world is wondrously varied. How do biologists make sense of this diversity and complexity, and how can you? Indeed, biology is a subject of enormous scope that gets bigger all the time. One of the ways to help you organize this information is to connect what you learn to a set of themes that you will encounter throughout your study of life. The next few modules introduce several important themes: novel properties emerging at each level of biological organization, the correlation of structure and function, and the exchange of matter and energy as organisms interact with the environment. We then focus on the core theme of biology—evolution, the theme that makes sense of both the unity and diversity of life.

Let's begin our journey with a tour through the levels of the biological hierarchy.

? **How would you define life?**

● Life can be defined by a set of common properties such as those described in this module.

(1) Order　　**(2) Reproduction**　　**(3) Growth and development**　　**(4) Energy processing**

(5) Regulation　　**(6) Response to the environment**　　**(7) Evolutionary adaptation**

▲ Figure 1.1　Some important properties of life

1.2 In life's hierarchy of organization, new properties emerge at each level

As **Figure 1.2** illustrates, the study of life extends from the global scale of the biosphere to the microscopic level of molecules. At the upper left we take a distant view of the **biosphere**, all of the environments on Earth that support life.

These include most regions of land, bodies of water, and the lower atmosphere. A closer look at one of these environments brings us to the level of an **ecosystem**, which consists of all the organisms living in a particular area, as well as the physical components with which the organisms interact, such as air, soil, water, and sunlight.

The entire array of organisms in an ecosystem is called a **community**. In this community, we find alligators and snakes, herons and egrets, myriad insects, trees and other plants, fungi, and enormous numbers of microorganisms. Each unique form of life is called a species.

A **population** includes all the individuals of a particular species living in an area. Next in the hierarchy is the **organism**, an individual living thing, such as an alligator.

Within a complex organism, life's hierarchy continues to unfold. An **organ system**, such as the circulatory system or nervous system, consists of several organs that cooperate in a specific function. For instance, the organs of the nervous system are the brain, the spinal cord, and the nerves. An alligator's nervous system controls all its actions.

An **organ** is made up of several different **tissues**, each in turn made up of a group of similar cells that perform a specific function. A **cell** is the fundamental unit of life. In the nerve cell shown here, you can see several organelles, such as the nucleus. An **organelle** is a membrane-enclosed structure that performs a specific function within a cell.

Finally, we reach the level of molecules in the hierarchy. A **molecule** is a cluster of small chemical units called atoms held together by chemical bonds. Our example in Figure 1.2 is a computer graphic of a section of DNA (deoxyribonucleic acid)—the molecule of inheritance.

Now let's work our way in the opposite direction in Figure 1.2, moving up life's hierarchy from molecules to the biosphere. At each higher level, there are novel properties that arise, properties that were not present at the preceding level. For example, life emerges at the level of the cell—a test tube full of organelles is not alive. Such **emergent properties** represent an important theme of biology. The familiar saying that "the whole is greater than the sum of its parts" captures this idea. The emergent properties of each level result from the specific arrangement and interactions of its parts.

? **Which of these levels of biological organization includes all others in the list: cell, molecule, organ, tissue?**

Organ

Biosphere

Florida

Ecosystem
Florida Everglades

Community
All organisms in this wetland ecosystem

Population
All alligators living in the wetlands

Organism
an American alligator

Organ system
Nervous system

Nerve   Spinal cord

Brain

Organ
Brain

Tissue
Nervous tissue

Cell
Nerve cell

Nucleus

Organelle
Nucleus

Molecule
DNA

Atom

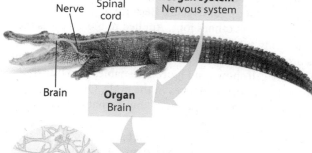
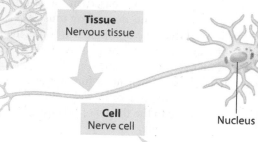
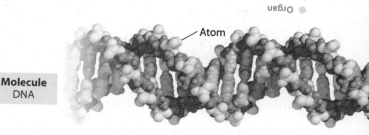

▲ **Figure 1.2** Life's hierarchy of organization

1.3 Cells are the structural and functional units of life

The cell has a special place in the hierarchy of biological organization. It is the level at which the properties of life emerge—the lowest level of structure that can perform all activities required for life. A cell can regulate its internal environment, take in and use energy, respond to its environment, and build and maintain its complex organization. The ability of cells to give rise to new cells is the basis for all reproduction and also for the growth and repair of multicellular organisms.

All organisms are composed of cells. They occur singly as a great variety of unicellular (single-celled) organisms, such as amoebas and most bacteria. And cells are the subunits that make up multicellular organisms, such as owls and trees. Your body consists of trillions of cells of many different kinds.

All cells share certain characteristics. For example, every cell is enclosed by a membrane that regulates the passage of materials between the cell and its surroundings. And every cell uses DNA as its genetic information. However, we can distinguish between two main forms of cells. **Prokaryotic cells** were the first to evolve and were Earth's sole inhabitants for more than 1.5 billion years. Fossil evidence indicates that **eukaryotic cells** evolved from prokaryotic ancestral cells about 1.8 billion years ago.

Figure 1.3 shows these two types of cells as artificially colored photographs taken with an electron microscope. A prokaryotic cell is much simpler and usually much smaller than a eukaryotic cell. The cells of the microorganisms we call bacteria are prokaryotic. Plants, animals, fungi, and protists (mostly unicellular organisms) are all composed of eukaryotic cells. As you can see in Figure 1.3, a eukaryotic cell is subdivided by membranes into various functional compartments, or organelles. These include a nucleus, which houses the cell's DNA.

The properties of life emerge from the ordered arrangement and interactions of the structures of a cell. Such a combination of components forms a more complex organization that we can call a *system*. Systems and their emergent properties are not unique to life. Consider a box of bicycle parts. When all of the individual parts are properly assembled, the result is a mechanical system you can use for exercise or transportation.

The emergent properties of life, however, are particularly challenging to study because of the unrivaled complexity of biological systems. Biologists today often use an approach called **systems biology**—the study of a biological system and the modeling of its dynamic behavior by analyzing the interactions among its parts. Biological systems can range from the functioning of the biosphere to the molecular machinery of an organelle.

Cells illustrate another theme of biology: the correlation of structure and function. Experience shows you that form

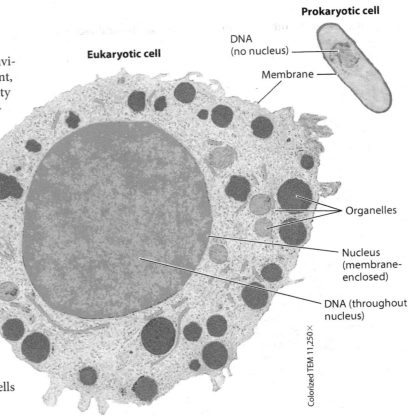

Prokaryotic cell

DNA (no nucleus)

Membrane

Eukaryotic cell

Organelles

Nucleus (membrane-enclosed)

DNA (throughout nucleus)

Colorized TEM 11,250×

▲ **Figure 1.3** Contrasting the size and complexity of prokaryotic and eukaryotic cells (shown here approximately 11,250 times their real size)

generally fits function. A screwdriver tightens or loosens screws, a hammer pounds nails. Because of their form, these tools can't do each other's jobs. Applied to biology, this theme of form fitting function is a guide to the structure of life at all its organizational levels. For example, the long extension of the nerve cell shown in Figure 1.2 enables it to transmit impulses across long distances in the body. Often, analyzing a biological structure gives us clues about what it does and how it works.

The activities of organisms are all based on cells. For example, your every thought is based on the actions of nerve cells, and your movements depend on muscle cells. Even a global process such as the cycling of carbon is the result of cellular activities, including the photosynthesis of plant cells and the cellular respiration of nearly all cells, a process that uses oxygen to break down sugar for energy and releases carbon dioxide. In the next module, we explore these processes and how they relate to the theme of organisms interacting with their environments.

? **Why are cells considered the basic units of life?**

● They are the lowest level in the hierarchy of biological organization at which the properties of life emerge.

1.4 Organisms interact with their environment, exchanging matter and energy

An organism interacts with its environment, and that environment includes other organisms as well as physical factors. Figure 1.4 is a simplified diagram of such interactions taking place in a forest in Canada. Plants are the producers that provide the food for a typical ecosystem. A tree, for example, absorbs water (H_2O) and minerals from the soil through its roots, and its leaves take in carbon dioxide (CO_2) from the air. In photosynthesis, a tree's leaves use energy from sunlight to convert CO_2 and H_2O to sugar and oxygen (O_2). The leaves release O_2 to the air, and the roots help form soil by breaking up rocks. Thus, both organism and environment are affected by the interactions between them.

The consumers of a ecosystem eat plants and other animals. The moose in Figure 1.4 eats the grasses and tender shoots and leaves of trees in a forest ecosystem in Canada. To release the energy in food, animals (as well as plants and most other organisms) take in O_2 from the air and release CO_2. An animal's wastes return other chemicals to the environment.

Another vital part of the ecosystem includes the small animals, fungi, and bacteria in the soil that decompose wastes and the remains of dead organisms. These decomposers act as recyclers, changing complex matter into simpler chemicals that plants can absorb and use.

The dynamics of ecosystems include two major processes—the recycling of chemicals and the flow of energy. These processes are illustrated in Figure 1.4. The most basic chemicals necessary for life—carbon dioxide, oxygen, water, and various minerals—cycle within an ecosystem from the air and soil to plants, to animals and decomposers, and back to the air and soil (shown with blue arrows in the figure).

By contrast, an ecosystem gains and loses energy constantly. Energy flows into the ecosystem when plants and other photosynthesizers absorb light energy from the sun (yellow arrow) and convert it to the chemical energy of sugars and other complex molecules. Chemical energy (orange arrow) is then passed through a series of consumers and, eventually, to decomposers, powering each organism in turn. In the process of these energy conversions between and within organisms, some energy is converted to heat, which is then lost from the system (red arrow). In contrast to chemicals, which recycle within an ecosystem, energy flows through an ecosystem, entering as light and exiting as heat.

In this first section, we have touched on several themes of biology, from emergent properties in the biological hierarchy of organization, to cells as the structural and functional units of life, to the exchange of matter and energy as organisms interact with their environment. In the next section, we begin our exploration of evolution, the core theme of biology.

> **?** Explain how the photosynthesis of plants functions in both the cycling of chemicals and the flow of energy in an ecosystem.

● Photosynthesis uses light energy to convert carbon dioxide and water to energy-rich food, making it the pathway by which both chemicals and energy become available to most organisms.

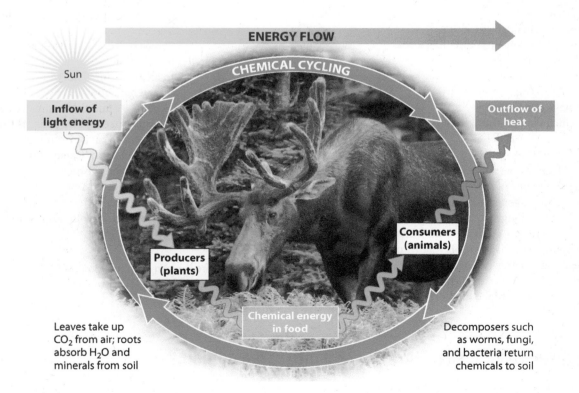

▲ Figure 1.4   The cycling of chemicals and flow of energy in an ecosystem

1.5 The unity of life is based on DNA and a common genetic code

All cells have DNA, and the continuity of life depends on this universal genetic material. DNA is the chemical substance of **genes**, the units of inheritance that transmit information from parents to offspring. Genes, which are grouped into very long DNA molecules called chromosomes, also control all the activities of a cell.

How does the molecular structure of DNA account for its ability to encode and transmit information? Each DNA molecule is made up of two long chains, called strands, coiled together into a double helix. The strands are made up of four kinds of chemical building blocks. Figure 1.5 (left side) illustrates these four building blocks, called nucleotides, with different colors and letter abbreviations of their names. The right side of the figure shows a short section of a DNA double helix.

Each time a cell divides, its DNA is first replicated, or copied—the double helix unzips and new complementary strands assemble along the separated strands. Thus, each new cell inherits a complete set of DNA, identical to that of the parent cell. You began as a single cell stocked with DNA inherited from your two parents. The replication of that DNA during each round of cell division transmitted copies of the DNA to what eventually became the trillions of cells of your body.

The way DNA encodes a cell's information is analogous to the way we arrange letters of the alphabet into precise sequences with specific meanings. The word *rat*, for example, conjures up an image of a rodent; *tar* and *art*, which contain the same letters, mean very different things. We can think of the four building blocks as the alphabet of inheritance. Specific sequential arrangements of these four chemical letters encode precise information in genes, which are typically hundreds or thousands of "letters" long.

The DNA of genes provides the blueprints for making proteins, and proteins serve as the tools that actually build and maintain the cell and carry out its activities. A bacterial gene may direct the cell to "Make a yellow pigment." A particular human gene may mean "Make the hormone insulin." All

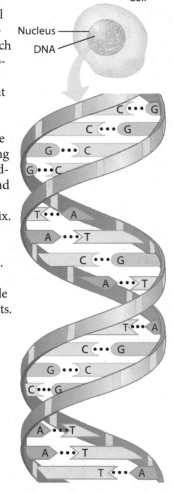

▲ Figure 1.5   The four building blocks of DNA (left); part of a DNA double helix (right)

forms of life use essentially the same genetic code to translate the information stored in DNA into proteins. This makes it possible to engineer cells to produce proteins normally found only in some other organism. Thus, bacteria can be used to produce insulin for the treatment of diabetes by inserting a gene for human insulin into bacterial cells.

The diversity of life arises from differences in DNA sequences—in other words, from variations on the common theme of storing genetic information in DNA. Bacteria and humans are different because they have different genes. But both sets of instructions are written in the same language.

The entire "library" of genetic instructions that an organism inherits is called its **genome**. A typical human cell has two similar sets of chromosomes, and each set contains about 3 billion nucleotide pairs. In recent years, scientists have determined the entire sequence of nucleotides in the human genome, as well as the genomes of thousands of other species. More species continue to be added to the list of species whose genomes have been sequenced as the rate at which sequencing can be done has accelerated rapidly in recent years. To deal with the resulting deluge of data, scientists are applying a systems biology approach at the molecular level. In an emerging field known as genomics, researchers now study whole sets of genes in a species and then compare genes across multiple species. The benefits from such an approach range from identifying genes that may be implicated in human cancers to revealing the evolutionary relationships among diverse organisms based on similarities in their genomes. Genomics affirms the unity of life based on the universal genetic material—DNA.

In the next module, we see how biologists attempt to organize the diversity of life.

? **What are the two main functions of DNA?**

● DNA is the genetic material that is passed from parents to offspring, and it codes for proteins that control the activity of cells.

1.6 The diversity of life can be arranged into three domains

We can think of biology's enormous scope as having two dimensions. The "vertical" dimension, which we examined in Module 1.2, is the size scale that stretches from molecules to

the biosphere. But biology also has a "horizontal" dimension, spanning across the great diversity of organisms existing now and over the long history of life on Earth.

Diversity is a hallmark of life. Biologists have so far identified and named about 1.8 million species. Estimates of the total number of species range from 10 million to more than 100 million.

There seems to be a human tendency to group things, such as owls or butterflies, although we recognize that each group includes many different species. And then we cluster groups into broader categories, such as birds and insects. Taxonomy, the branch of biology that names and classifies species, arranges species into a hierarchy of broader and broader groups: genus, family, order, class, phylum, and kingdom.

Historically, biologists divided all of life into five kingdoms. But new methods for assessing evolutionary relationships, such as comparisons of DNA sequences, have led to an ongoing reevaluation of the number and boundaries of kingdoms. Although the debate on such divisions continues, there is consensus among biologists that life can be organized into three higher levels called **domains**. Figure 1.6 shows representatives of domains Bacteria, Archaea, and Eukarya.

Domains **Bacteria** and **Archaea** both consist of prokaryotes, organisms with prokaryotic cells. Bacteria are the most diverse and widespread prokaryotes. Many of the prokaryotes known as archaea live in Earth's extreme environments, such as salty lakes and boiling hot springs. Each rod-shaped or round structure in the photos of the prokaryotes in Figure 1.6 is a single cell. These photos were made with an electron microscope, and the number along the side indicates the magnification of the image.

All the eukaryotes, organisms with eukaryotic cells, are grouped in domain **Eukarya**. Protists are a diverse collection of mostly single-celled organisms. Pictured in Figure 1.6 is an assortment of protists in a drop of pond water. Biologists are currently assessing how to group the protists to reflect their evolutionary relationships.

The three remaining groups within Eukarya are distinguished partly by their modes of nutrition. Kingdom Plantae consists of plants, which produce their own food by photosynthesis. The plant pictured in Figure 1.6 is a tropical bromeliad, a plant native to the Americas.

Kingdom Fungi, represented by the mushrooms in Figure 1.6, is a diverse group whose members mostly decompose the remains of dead organisms and organic wastes and absorb the nutrients into their cells.

Animals obtain food by eating other organisms. The sloth in Figure 1.6 resides in South American rain forests. There are actually members of two other groups in the sloth photo. The sloth is clinging to a tree (kingdom Plantae), and the greenish tinge in its hair is a luxuriant growth of photosynthetic prokaryotes (domain Bacteria). This photograph exemplifies a theme reflected in our book's title: connections between living things. The sloth depends on trees for food and

Bacteria — Domain Bacteria
Colorized SEM 7,500×

Archaea — Domain Archaea
Colorized SEM 10,000×

Domain Eukarya

Protists (multiple kingdoms)
LM 340×

Kingdom Plantae

Kingdom Fungi

Kingdom Animalia

▲ Figure 1.6   The three domains of life

shelter; the tree uses nutrients from the decomposition of the sloth's feces; the prokaryotes gain access to the sunlight necessary for photosynthesis by living on the sloth; and the sloth is camouflaged from predators by its green coat.

The diversity of life and its interconnectedness are evident almost everywhere. Earlier we looked at life's unity in its shared properties and common genetic code. In the next module, we explore how evolution explains both the unity and the diversity of life.

? **To which of the three domains of life do we belong?**

● Eukarya

1.7 Evolution explains the unity and diversity of life

Evolution can be defined as the process of change that has transformed life on Earth from its earliest beginnings to the diversity of organisms living today. The fossil record documents the fact that life has been evolving on Earth for billions of years, and patterns of ancestry can be traced through this record. For example, the mammoth being excavated in **Figure 1.7A** is clearly related to present-day elephants. We can explain the shared traits of mammoths and elephants with the premise that they descended from a common ancestor in the distant past. Their differences reflect the evolutionary changes that occurred within their separate lineages during the history of their existence on Earth. Thus, evolution accounts for life's dual nature of kinship and diversity.

▲ **Figure 1.7A** Excavation of 26,000-year-old fossilized mammoth bones from a site in South Dakota

This evolutionary view of life came into sharp focus in November 1859, when Charles Darwin (**Figure 1.7B**) published one of the most important and influential books ever written. Entitled *On the Origin of Species by Means of Natural Selection*, Darwin's book was an immediate bestseller and soon made his name synonymous with the concept of evolution.

As a young man, Darwin made key observations that greatly influenced his thinking. During a five-year, around-the-world voyage, he collected and documented plants and animals in widely varying locations—from the isolated Galápagos Islands off the coast of Ecuador to the heights of the Andes mountains to the jungles of Brazil. He was particularly struck by the adaptations of these varied organisms that fit them to their diverse habitats. After returning to England, Darwin spent more than two decades continuing his observations, performing experiments, corresponding with other scientists, and refining his thinking before he finally published his work.

The first of two main points that Darwin presented in *The Origin of Species* was that species living today arose from a successor of ancestors that differed from them. Darwin called this process "descent with modification." It was an insightful

▲ **Figure 1.7B** Charles Darwin in 1859

phrase, because it captured both the unity of life (descent from a common ancestor) and the diversity of life (modifications that evolved as species diverged from their ancestors). **Figure 1.7C** illustrates this unity and diversity among birds. These three birds all have a common "bird" body plan of wings, beak, feet, and feathers, but these features are highly specialized for each bird's unique lifestyle.

Darwin's second point was to propose a mechanism for evolution, which he called **natural selection**. Darwin started with two observations, from which he drew two inferences.

OBSERVATION #1: Individual variation. Individuals in a population vary in their traits, many of which are inherited from parents to offspring.

OBSERVATION #2: Overproduction of offspring. All species can produce far more offspring than the environment can support. Competition for resources is thus inevitable, and many of these offspring fail to survive and reproduce.

INFERENCE #1: Unequal reproductive success. Individuals with heritable traits best suited to the local environment are more likely to survive and reproduce than are less well-suited individuals.

INFERENCE #2: Accumulation of favorable traits over time. As a result of this unequal reproductive success over many generations, a higher and higher proportion of individuals in the population will have the advantageous traits.

▲ **Figure 1.7C** Unity and diversity among birds

Try This For each bird, describe some adaptations that fit it to its environment and way of life.

① Population with varied inherited traits.

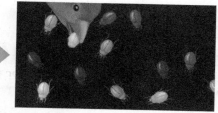

② Elimination of individuals with certain traits and reproduction of survivors.

③ Increasing frequency of traits that enhance survival and reproductive success.

▲ **Figure 1.7D** An example of natural selection in action

Try This Describe what might happen if some of these beetles colonized a sand dune habitat.

Figure 1.7D uses a simple example to show how natural selection works. ① An imaginary beetle population has colonized an area where the soil has been blackened by a recent brush fire. Initially, the population varies extensively in the inherited coloration of individuals, from very light gray to charcoal. ② A bird eats the beetles it sees most easily, the light-colored ones. This selective predation reduces the number of light-colored beetles and favors the survival and reproductive success of the darker beetles, which pass on the genes for dark coloration to their offspring. ③ After several generations, the population is quite different from the original one. As a result of natural selection, the frequency of the darker-colored beetles in the population has increased.

Darwin realized that numerous small changes in populations as a result of natural selection could eventually lead to major alterations of species. He proposed that new species could evolve as a result of the gradual accumulation of changes over long periods of time. This could occur, for example, if one population fragmented into subpopulations isolated in different environments. In these separate arenas of natural selection, one species could gradually divide into multiple species as isolated populations adapted over many generations to different sets of environmental factors.

The fossil record provides evidence of such diversification of species from ancestral species. **Figure 1.7E** traces an evolutionary tree of elephants and some of their relatives. (Biologists' diagrams of evolutionary relationships generally take the form of branching trees, usually turned sideways and read from left to right.) You can see that the three living species of elephants are very similar because they shared a recent common ancestor (dating to about 3 million years ago, which is relatively recent in an evolutionary timeframe). Notice that all the other close relatives of elephants are extinct—their branches do not extend to the present. (The mammoth being excavated in Figure 1.7A belonged to the genus *Mammuthus*, whose members became extinct less than 10,000 years ago.) If we were to trace this family tree back to about 60 million years ago, however, you would find a common ancestor that connects elephants to their closest living relatives—the manatees and hyraxes. The fossil record, along with other evidence such as comparisons of DNA, allows scientists to trace the evolutionary history of life back through time.

All of life is connected, and the basis for this kinship is evolution—the core theme that makes sense of everything we

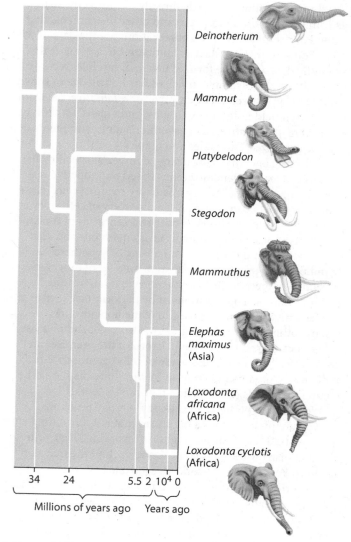

▲ **Figure 1.7E** An evolutionary tree of elephants

Try This Use this tree to determine when mastodons (in the genus *Mammut*) last shared a common ancestor with African elephants.

know and learn about life. In the next module, we introduce scientific inquiry, the process we use to study the natural world.

? **Explain the cause and effect of unequal reproductive success.**

● Those individuals with heritable traits best suited to the local environment produce the greatest number of offspring. Over many generations, the frequency of those adaptive traits increases in the population.

1.8 In studying nature, scientists make observations and form and test hypotheses

Science is a way of knowing—an approach to understanding the natural world. It stems from our curiosity about ourselves and the world around us. At the heart of science is the process of inquiry, the search for information and explanations of natural phenomena. Scientific inquiry usually involves making observations, forming hypotheses, and testing them.

Observations may be made directly or indirectly, such as with the help of microscopes and other instruments that extend our senses. Recorded observations are the data of science. You may think of data as numbers, but a great deal of scientific data are in the form of detailed, carefully recorded observations. For example, much of our knowledge of snowy owl behavior is based on descriptive, or *qualitative*, data, documented in field notes, photographs, and videos. Other types of data are *quantitative*, such as numerical measurements that may be organized into tables and graphs.

Collecting and analyzing a large number of specific observations can lead to generalizations based on inductive reasoning. For example, "All organisms are made of cells" is an inductive conclusion based on the discovery of cells in every biological specimen observed over two centuries of time.

Observations often prompt us to ask questions and seek answers through the forming and testing of hypotheses. A **hypothesis** is a proposed explanation for a set of observations. A good hypothesis leads to predictions that can be tested by making additional observations or by performing experiments.

Deductive reasoning is used to come up with ways to test hypotheses. Here, the logic flows from general premises to the specific results we should expect if the premises are correct. *If* all organisms are made of cells (premise 1), *and* humans are organisms (premise 2), *then* humans should be composed of cells (a prediction that can be tested).

We all use hypotheses in solving everyday problems. Let's say you are preparing for a big storm that is approaching your area and find that your flashlight isn't working. That your flashlight isn't working is an observation, and the question is obvious: Why doesn't it work? Reasonable hypotheses are that the batteries are dead or the bulb is burned out. Each of these hypotheses leads to predictions you can test with experiments. For example, the dead-battery hypothesis predicts that replacing the batteries with new ones will fix the problem. **Figure 1.8** diagrams the results of testing these hypotheses.

An important point about scientific inquiry is that we can never *prove* that a hypothesis is true. As shown in Figure 1.8, the burned-out bulb hypothesis is the more likely explanation in our hypothetical scenario. But perhaps the old bulb was simply loose and the new bulb was inserted correctly. We could test this hypothesis by trying another experiment—carefully reinstalling the original bulb. If the flashlight still doesn't work, the burned-out bulb hypothesis is supported by another line of evidence. Testing a hypothesis in various ways provides additional support for a hypothesis and increases our confidence in it.

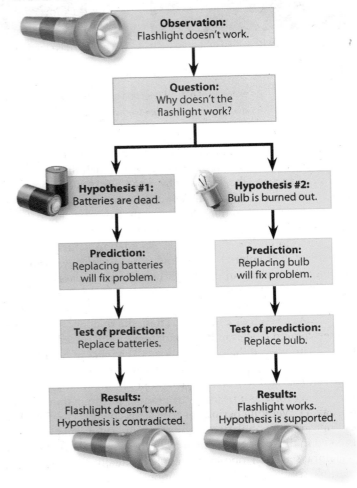

▲ **Figure 1.8** An everyday example of forming and testing hypotheses

A scientific **theory** is much broader in scope than a hypothesis and is supported by a large and usually growing body of evidence. For example, the theory of evolution explains a great diversity of observations and is supported by multiple lines of evidence. In addition, the theory of evolution has not been contradicted by any scientific data.

Another important aspect of science is that it is necessarily repetitive: In testing a hypothesis, researchers may make observations that call for rejecting the hypothesis or at least revising and further testing it. This process allows biologists to circle closer and closer to their best estimation of how nature works. As in all quests, science includes elements of challenge, adventure, and luck, along with careful planning, reasoning, creativity, cooperation, competition, and persistence.

Science is a social activity, with most scientists working in teams, which often include graduate and undergraduate students. Scientists share information through peer-reviewed publications, seminars, meetings, and personal communication. Scientists build on what has been learned from earlier research and often check each other's claims by attempting to confirm observations or repeat experiments.

To help you better understand what scientists do, we include a Scientific Thinking module in each chapter. These discussions will encompass several broad activities of science: the forming and testing of hypotheses using various research methods; the analysis and evaluation of data; the use of tools and technologies that have built and continue to expand scientific knowledge; and the communication of the results of scientific studies and the evaluation of their implications for society as a whole.

? What is the main criterion for a scientific hypothesis?

● It must generate predictions that can be tested.

1.9 Hypotheses can be tested using controlled field studies

SCIENTIFIC THINKING

You have undoubtedly observed that many animals match their environment: white snowy owls in their arctic habitat, toads the color of dead leaves, flounders that blend in with the sandy sea floor. From these observations, you might hypothesize that such color patterns have evolved as adaptations that protect animals from predation. Can scientists test this camouflage hypothesis? Let's consider an experiment with two populations of mice that belong to the same species (*Peromyscus polionotus*) but live in different environments.

The beach mouse lives along the Florida seashore, a habitat of white sand dunes with sparse clumps of beach grass. The inland mouse lives on darker soil farther inland. As you can see in **Figure 1.9**, there is a striking match between mouse coloration and habitat. In 2010, biologist Hopi Hoekstra of Harvard University and a group of her students headed to Florida to test the camouflage hypothesis. They reasoned that *if* camouflage coloration protects mice from predators, *then* mice with coloration that did not match their habitat would be preyed on more heavily than the native mice that were well-matched to their environment.

The researchers built 250 plastic models of mice and painted them to resemble either beach or inland mice. Equal numbers of models were placed randomly in both habitats. The models resembling the native mice in each habitat were

TABLE 1.9 | RESULTS FROM CAMOUFLAGE EXPERIMENT

| Habitat | Number of Attacks | | |
	On Camouflaged Models	On Non-camouflaged Models	% Attacks on Non-camouflaged Models
Beach (light habitat)	2	5	71%
Inland (dark habitat)	5	16	76%

Data from S. N. Vignieri et al., The selective advantage of crypsis in mice, *Evolution* 64: 2153–2158 (2010).

the control group, and the mice with the non-native coloration were the experimental group. Signs of predation were recorded for three days. Judging by the bite marks and surrounding tracks, the researchers determined the predators were likely foxes, coyotes, owls, herons, and hawks.

As you can see by the results presented in **Table 1.9**, the noncamouflaged models had a much higher percentage of predation attacks in both the beach and inland habitats. The data thus fit the key prediction of the camouflage hypothesis.

Why do so many animals match their surroundings?

This study is an example of a **controlled experiment**, one that is designed to compare an experimental group (the noncamouflaged mice models) with a control group (the camouflaged models that matched the mice native in each area). Ideally, in a controlled experiment the two groups differ only in the one factor the experiment is designed to test—in this case, coat color and its effect on the success of predators. The experimental design left coloration as the only factor that could account for the higher predation rate on the noncamouflaged mice in both the beach and the inland habitats. This study is also an example of a field study, one not done in a laboratory but out in nature. Researchers tested their hypothesis using the natural habitat of the mice and their predators.

Beach population Beach mice living on sparsely vegetated sand dunes along the coast have light tan, dappled coats.

Inland population Members of the same species living about 30 km inland are darker in color.

? These two populations of mice belong to the same species, yet they have very different coloration. How does natural selection explain these differences?

▲ **Figure 1.9** Beach mouse and inland mouse with their native habitat

● Camouflaged mice are more likely to survive and reproduce, passing their protective coloration to their offspring.

1.10 Evolution is connected to our everyday lives

EVOLUTION CONNECTION

To emphasize evolution as the core theme of biology, we include an Evolution Connection module in each chapter in this text. But how is evolution connected to your everyday life?

You just learned that natural selection is the primary mechanism of evolution, in which the environment "selects" for adaptive traits when organisms with such traits are better able to survive and reproduce. Through the selective breeding of plants and animals, humans are also an agent of evolution. As a result of **artificial selection**, our crops, livestock, and pets bear little resemblance to their wild ancestors. Humans have been modifying species for millennia, and recent advances in biotechnology have increased our capabilities. Plant biologists using genomics can identify beneficial genes in relatives of our crop plants, enabling the breeding or genetic engineering of enhanced crops. Genes from totally unrelated species have also been inserted into plants. For example, genes for such traits as drought or flood tolerance, improved growth, and increased nutrition have been engineered into rice plants (Figure 1.10).

But humans also affect evolution unintentionally. The impact of habitat loss and global climate change can be seen in the loss of species. Indeed, scientists estimate that the current rate of extinction is 100 to 1,000 times the typical rate seen in the fossil record. Our actions are also driving evolutionary changes in species. For example, our widespread use of antibiotics and pesticides has led to the evolution of antibiotic resistance in bacteria and pesticide resistance in insects.

How can evolutionary theory help address such worldwide problems? Understanding evolution can help us develop strategies for conservation efforts and prompt us to be more judicious in our use of antibiotics and pesticides. It can also help us create flu vaccines and HIV drugs by tracking the rapid evolution of these viruses. Identifying shared genes and studying their actions in closely related organisms may produce new knowledge about cancer or other diseases and lead to new medical treatments. New sources of drugs may be found by tracing the evolutionary history of medicinal plants and identifying beneficial compounds in their relatives. Our understanding of evolution can yield many beneficial results.

▲ **Figure 1.10**   Researcher working with transgenic rice

? **How might an understanding of evolution contribute to the development of new drugs?**

● As one example, we can test the actions of potential drugs in organisms that share our genes and similar cellular processes.

1.11 Biology, technology, and society are connected in important ways

CONNECTION

Many of the current issues facing society are related to biology, and they often involve our expanding technology. What are the differences between science and technology? The goal of science is to understand natural phenomena. In contrast, the goal of **technology** is to apply scientific knowledge for some specific purpose. Scientists usually speak of "discoveries," whereas engineers more often speak of "inventions." These two fields, however, are interdependent. Scientists use new technology in their research, and scientific discoveries often lead to the development of new technologies.

The potent combination of science and technology can have dramatic effects on society. For example, the discovery of the structure of DNA by Watson and Crick 60 years ago and subsequent advances in DNA science led to the technologies of DNA manipulation that today are transforming applied fields such as medicine, agriculture, and forensics.

Technology has improved our standard of living in many ways, but not without consequences. Technology has helped Earth's population to grow tenfold in the past three centuries and more than double to 7 billion in just the past 40 years. Global climate change, toxic wastes, deforestation, and nuclear accidents are just some of the repercussions of more and more people wielding more and more technology. Science can help identify problems and provide insight into how to slow down or prevent further damage. But solutions to these problems have as much to do with politics, economics, and cultural values as with science and technology. Every citizen has a responsibility to develop a reasonable amount of scientific literacy to be able to participate in the debates regarding science and technology. The crucial science-technology-society relationship is a theme we will return to throughout this text.

We hope this book will help you develop an appreciation for biology and help you apply your new knowledge to evaluating issues ranging from your personal health to the well-being of the whole world.

? **How do science and technology interact?**

● New scientific discoveries may lead to new technologies; new technologies may increase the ability of scientists to discover new knowledge.

For practice quizzes, BioFlix animations, MP3 tutorials, video tutors, and more study tools designed for this textbook, go to

MasteringBiology®

Reviewing the Concepts

Themes in the Study of Biology (1.1–1.4)

1.1 All forms of life share common properties. Biology is the scientific study of life. Properties of life include order, reproduction, growth and development, energy processing, regulation, response to the environment, and evolutionary adaptation.

1.2 In life's hierarchy of organization, new properties emerge at each level. Biological organization unfolds as follows: biosphere > ecosystem > community > population > organism > organ system > organ > tissue > cell > organelle > molecule. Emergent properties result from the interactions among component parts.

1.3 Cells are the structural and functional units of life. Eukaryotic cells contain membrane-enclosed organelles, including a nucleus. Prokaryotic cells lack such organelles. Structure is related to function at all levels of organization. Systems biology models the complex behavior of biological systems.

1.4 Organisms interact with their environment, exchanging matter and energy. Ecosystems are characterized by the cycling of chemicals from the atmosphere and soil through producers, consumers, decomposers, and back to the environment. Energy flows one way through an ecosystem—entering as sunlight, converted to chemical energy by producers, passed on to consumers, and exiting as heat.

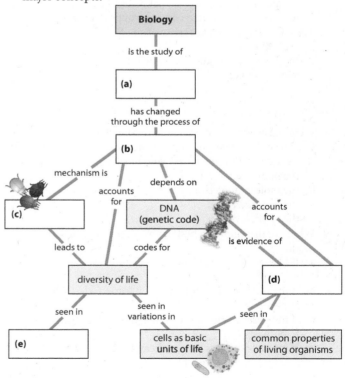

Evolution, the Core Theme of Biology (1.5–1.7)

1.5 The unity of life is based on DNA and a common genetic code. DNA is responsible for heredity and for programming the activities of a cell. A species' genes are coded in the sequences of the four building blocks making up DNA's double helix. Genomics is the analysis and comparison of genomes.

1.6 The diversity of life can be arranged into three domains. Taxonomists name species and classify them into a system of broader groups. Domains Bacteria and Archaea consist of prokaryotes. The eukaryotic domain, Eukarya, includes various protists and the kingdoms Fungi, Plantae, and Animalia.

1.7 Evolution explains the unity and diversity of life. Darwin synthesized the theory of evolution by natural selection.

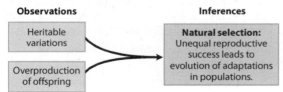

Observations	Inferences
Heritable variations	**Natural selection:** Unequal reproductive success leads to evolution of adaptations in populations.
Overproduction of offspring	

The Process of Science (1.8–1.9)

1.8 In studying nature, scientists make observations and form and test hypotheses. Scientists use inductive reasoning to draw general conclusions from many observations. They form hypotheses and use deductive reasoning to make predictions, which can be tested with experiments or additional observations. Data may be qualitative or quantitative. A scientific theory is broad in scope and is supported by a large body of evidence.

1.9 Hypotheses can be tested using controlled field studies. Researchers found that mice models that did not match their habitat had higher predation rates than camouflaged models. In a controlled experiment, the use of control and experimental groups can demonstrate the effect of a single variable.

Biology and Everyday Life (1.10–1.11)

1.10 Evolution is connected to our everyday lives. Evolutionary theory is useful in medicine, agriculture, forensics, and conservation. Human-caused environmental changes are powerful selective forces that affect the evolution of many species.

1.11 Biology, technology, and society are connected in important ways. Technological advances stem from scientific research, and research benefits from new technologies.

Connecting the Concepts

1. Complete the following map organizing some of biology's major concepts.

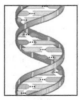

Testing Your Knowledge

Level 1: Knowledge/Comprehension

2. All the organisms on your campus make up
   a. an ecosystem.
   b. a community.
   c. a population.
   d. the domain Eukarya.

3. Single-celled amoebas and bacteria are grouped into different domains because
   a. amoebas eat bacteria.
   b. bacteria are not made of cells.
   c. bacterial cells lack a membrane-enclosed nucleus.
   d. amoebas are motile; bacteria are not.

4. Which of the following statements best distinguishes hypotheses from theories in science?
   a. Theories are hypotheses that have been proved.
   b. Hypotheses usually are narrow in scope; theories have broad explanatory power.
   c. Hypotheses are tentative guesses; theories are correct answers to questions about nature.
   d. Hypotheses and theories are different terms for essentially the same thing in science.

5. Which of the following best demonstrates the unity among all living organisms?
   a. descent with modification
   b. DNA and a common genetic code
   c. emergent properties
   d. natural selection

6. A controlled experiment is one that
   a. proceeds slowly enough that a scientist can make careful records of the results.
   b. keeps all variables constant.
   c. is repeated many times to make sure the results are accurate.
   d. tests experimental and control groups in parallel.

7. The core idea that makes sense of all of biology is
   a. evolution.
   b. the correlation of function with structure.
   c. systems biology.
   d. the process of science.

Level 2: Application/Analysis

8. A biologist studying interactions among the protists in an ecosystem could *not* be working at which level in life's hierarchy? (*Choose carefully and explain your answer.*)
   a. the population level
   b. the molecular level
   c. the organism level
   d. the organ level

9. Which of the following best describes the logic of scientific inquiry?
   a. If I generate a testable hypothesis, tests and observations will support it.
   b. If my prediction is correct, it will lead to a testable hypothesis.
   c. If my observations are accurate, they will support my hypothesis.
   d. If my hypothesis is correct, I can expect certain test results.

10. In an ecosystem, how is the movement of energy similar to that of chemicals, and how is it different?

11. Explain the role of heritable variations in Darwin's theory of natural selection.

12. Describe the process of scientific inquiry and explain why it is not a rigid method.

13. Contrast technology with science. Give an example of each to illustrate the difference.

14. Biology can be described as having both a vertical scale and a horizontal scale. Explain what that means.

Level 3: Synthesis/Evaluation

15. Explain what is meant by this statement: Natural selection is an editing mechanism rather than a creative process.

16. The graph below shows the results of an experiment in which mice learned to run through a maze.

   a. State the hypothesis and prediction that you think this experiment tested.
   b. Which was the control group and which the experimental? Why was a control group needed?
   c. List some variables that must have been controlled so as not to affect the results.
   d. Do the data support the hypothesis? Explain.

17. **SCIENTIFIC THINKING** Suppose that in an experiment similar to the camouflage experiment described in Module 1.9, a researcher observed and recorded more total predator attacks on dark-model mice in the inland habitat than on dark models in the beach habitat. From comparing these two pieces of data, the researcher concluded that the camouflage hypothesis is false. Do you think this conclusion is justified? Why or why not?

18. The fruits of wild species of tomato are tiny compared to the giant beefsteak tomatoes available today. This difference in fruit size is almost entirely due to the larger number of cells in the domesticated fruits. Plant biologists have recently discovered genes that are responsible for controlling cell division in tomatoes. Why would such a discovery be important to producers of other kinds of fruits and vegetables? To the study of human development and disease? To our basic understanding of biology?

19. The news media and popular magazines frequently report stories that are connected to biology. In the next 24 hours, record the ones you hear or read about in three different sources and briefly describe the biological connections in each story.

Answers to all questions can be found in Appendix 4.

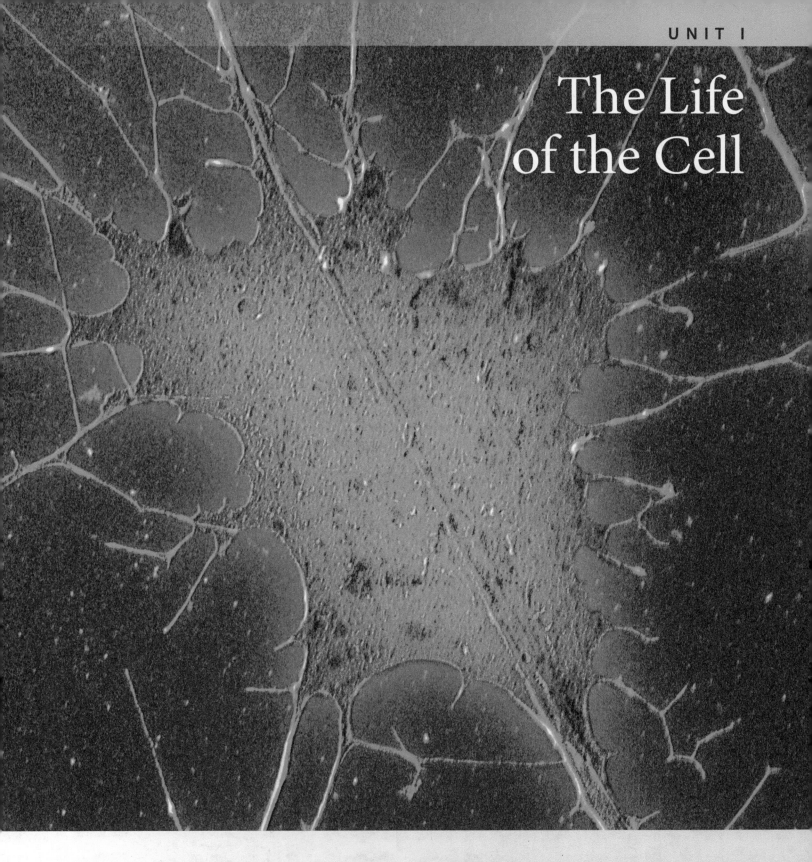

The Life of the Cell

The Chemical Basis of Life

Coral reefs are among the most diverse ecosystems on Earth. They are formed from the gradual buildup of the calcium carbonate skeletons of small coral animals. As you can see in the photo below, these structurally diverse habitats provide havens for a huge diversity of fish and other marine organisms. But in recent years, something in the air is threatening coral reefs. How might a chemical compound in the air harm such a vibrant ecosystem? The answer is chemistry. When carbon dioxide dissolves in water, it reacts with water to form an acid, which then makes the water more acidic. Later in the chapter we will see how scientists are exploring the effects of this ocean acidification on coral reefs.

? *Will rising atmospheric CO_2 harm coral reefs?*

Why do we begin our study of biology with a chapter on chemistry? Well, chemistry is the basis of life—it explains how elements combine into the compounds that make up your body and the bodies of all other living organisms and how chemical reactions underlie the functions of all cells.

Life and its chemistry are tied to water. Life began in water and evolved there for 3 billion years before spreading onto land. And all life, even land-dwelling life, is still dependent on water. Your

cells are about 75% water, and that is where the chemical reactions of your body take place. What properties of the simple water molecule make it so indispensable to life on Earth? You'll find out in this chapter.

This chapter will also make connections to one of the main themes in biology—the organization of life into a hierarchy of structural levels, with new properties emerging at each successive level (see Chapter 1). You will see that emergent properties are apparent even at the lowest levels of biological organization—the ordering of atoms into molecules and the interactions of those molecules. Thus we begin our study of biology with some basic concepts of chemistry that will apply throughout our study of life.

BIG IDEAS

Elements, Atoms, and Compounds
(2.1–2.4)
Living organisms are made of atoms of certain elements, mostly combined into compounds.

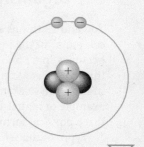

Chemical Bonds
(2.5–2.9)
The structure of an atom determines what types of bonds it can form with other atoms.

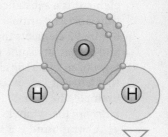

Water's Life-Supporting Properties
(2.10–2.16)
The unique properties of water derive from the polarity and hydrogen bonding of water molecules.

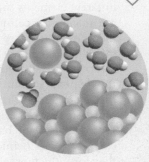

2.1 Organisms are composed of elements, in combinations called compounds

You and all things around you are made of matter—the physical "stuff" of the universe. **Matter** is defined as anything that occupies space and has mass. (In everyday language, we can think of mass as an object's weight.) Matter is found on Earth in three physical states: solid, liquid, and gas. Water is a rare example of matter that exists in the natural environment in all three physical forms: as ice, liquid water, and water vapor.

Types of matter as diverse as water, rocks, air, and biology students are all composed of chemical elements. An **element** is a substance that cannot be broken down to other substances by ordinary chemical means. Today, chemists recognize 92 elements that occur in nature; gold, copper, carbon, and oxygen are some examples. Chemists have also made a few dozen synthetic elements. Each element has a symbol, the first letter or two of its English, Latin, or German name. For example, the symbol for sodium, Na, is from the Latin word *natrium*; the symbol O comes from the English word *oxygen*.

A **compound** is a substance consisting of two or more different elements combined in a fixed ratio. Compounds are much more common than pure elements. In fact, few elements exist in a pure state in nature.

Many compounds consist of only two elements; for instance, table salt (sodium chloride, NaCl) has equal parts of the elements sodium (Na) and chlorine (Cl). Pure sodium is a metal and pure chlorine is a poisonous gas. Chemically combined, however, they form an edible compound (**Figure 2.1**). Hydrogen (H) and oxygen (O) are elements that typically exist as gases. Chemically combined in a ratio of 2:1, however, they form the most abundant compound on the surface of Earth—water (H_2O). These are simple examples of organized matter having emergent properties: A compound has characteristics different from those of its elements.

Most of the compounds in living organisms contain at least three or four elements. Sugar, for example, is formed of carbon (C), hydrogen, and oxygen. Proteins are compounds containing carbon, hydrogen, oxygen, nitrogen (N), and a small amount of sulfur (S). Different arrangements of the atoms of these elements give rise to the unique properties of each compound.

How many of the 92 natural elements are essential for life? The requirements are similar among organisms, but there is some variation. For example, humans need 25 elements, but plants need only 17. Four elements—oxygen, carbon, hydrogen, and nitrogen—make up about 96% of all living matter. These elements are the main ingredients of biological molecules. As you can see in **Table 2.1**, which lists the 25 elements found in humans, calcium (Ca), phosphorus ⓟ, potassium (K), sulfur, sodium, chlorine, and magnesium (Mg) account for most of the remaining 4% of your body. These elements are involved in such important functions as bone formation

TABLE 2.1 | ELEMENTS IN THE HUMAN BODY

Element	Symbol	Percentage of Body Weight (Including Water)	
Oxygen	O	65.0	
Carbon	C	18.5	96.3%
Hydrogen	H	9.5	
Nitrogen	N	3.3	
Calcium	Ca	1.5	
Phosphorus	P	1.0	
Potassium	K	0.4	
Sulfur	S	0.3	3.7%
Sodium	Na	0.2	
Chlorine	Cl	0.2	
Magnesium	Mg	0.1	

Trace elements, less than 0.01% of human body weight: Boron (B), chromium (Cr), cobalt (Co), copper (Cu), fluorine (F), iodine (I), iron (Fe), manganese (Mn), molybdenum (Mo), selenium (Se), silicon (Si), tin (Sn), vanadium (V), zinc (Zn)

(calcium and phosphorus) and nerve signaling (potassium, sodium, calcium, and chlorine).

The **trace elements** listed at the bottom of the table are essential for humans, but only in minute quantities. Some trace elements, such as iron (Fe), are needed by all forms of life. Iron makes up only about 0.004% of your body weight but is vital for energy processing and for transporting oxygen in your blood. Other trace elements are required only by certain species. For example, iodine is an essential element only for vertebrates—animal with backbones, which, of course, includes you. We explore the importance of trace elements to your health next.

? Explain how table salt illustrates the theme of emergent properties.

The elements that make up the edible crystals of table salt, sodium and chlorine, are in pure form a metal and a poisonous gas.

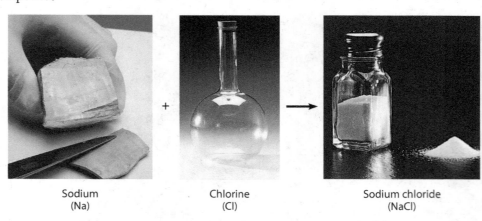

Sodium (Na)   +   Chlorine (Cl)   →   Sodium chloride (NaCl)

▲ **Figure 2.1** The emergent properties of the edible compound sodium chloride

2.2 Trace elements are common additives to food and water

CONNECTION

Trace elements are required in very small quantities, but, in some cases, even those small requirements are difficult to fulfill.

Iodine is an essential ingredient of a hormone produced by the thyroid gland, which is located in your neck. You need to ingest only a tiny speck of iodine each day, about 0.15 milligram (mg). An iodine deficiency in the diet causes the thyroid gland to grow to abnormal size, a condition called goiter (Figure 2.2A). The most serious effects of iodine deficiency take place during fetal development and childhood, leading to miscarriages, poor growth, and mental impairment. A global strategy to eliminate iodine deficiency involves universal iodization of all salt used for human and animal consumption. Unfortunately, about 30% of global households still do not have access to iodized salt, and an estimated 2 billion people are still at risk of iodine deficiency. Seafood, kelp, dairy products, and dark, leafy greens are good natural sources. Thus, deficiencies are often found in inland regions, especially in areas where the soil is lacking in iodine. Although most common in developing nations, iodine deficiencies may also result from excessive consumption of highly processed foods (which often use non-iodized salt) and low-salt diets intended to lower the risk of cardiovascular disease.

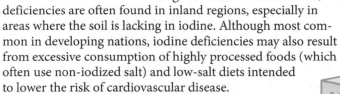

▲ Figure 2.2A   Goiter, a symptom of iodine deficiency, in a Burmese woman

Iodine is just one example of a trace element added to food or water to improve health. For more than 60 years, the American Dental Association has supported fluoridation of community drinking water as a public health measure. Fluoride is a form of fluorine (F), an element in Earth's crust that is found in small amounts in all water sources. In many communities, fluoride is added during the municipal water treatment process to raise levels to a concentration that can reduce tooth decay. If you mostly drink bottled water, however, your fluoride intake may be reduced, although some bottled water now contains added fluoride. Fluoride is also frequently added to dental products, such as toothpaste and mouthwash (Figure 2.2B).

Chemicals are added to food to help preserve it, make it more nutritious, or simply make it look better. Read the nutrition facts label from the side of the cereal box in Figure 2.2C to see a familiar example of how foods are fortified with mineral elements. Iron, for example, is commonly added to foods. (You can actually see that iron has been added to a fortified cereal by crushing the cereal and then stirring a magnet through it.) Also note that the nutrition facts label lists numerous vitamins that are added to improve the nutritional value of the cereal. For instance, the cereal in this example supplies 10%

◀ Figure 2.2B
Mouthwash and toothpaste with added fluoride

of the recommended daily value for vitamin A. Vitamins consist of more than one element and are examples of compounds.

In the next module, we explore the chemical properties of elements and how the structure of an atom—the smallest unit of an element—determines those properties.

? In addition to iron, what other trace elements are found in the cereal in Figure 2.2C? Does one serving provide the total daily amount needed of these elements?

● Zinc and copper: one serving provides 100% of the zinc but only 4% of the copper needed in a day.

▲ Figure 2.2C   Nutrition facts from a fortified cereal

Nutrition Facts

Serving Size ¾ cup (30g)
Servings Per Container about 17

Amount Per Serving	Whole Grain Cereal	with ½ cup skim milk
Calories	100	140
Calories from Fat	5	10
		% Daily Value**
Total Fat 0.5g*	1%	1%
Saturated Fat 0g	0%	0%
Trans Fat 0g		
Polyunsaturated Fat 0g		
Monounsaturated Fat 0g		
Cholesterol 0mg	0%	1%
Sodium 135mg	6%	9%
Potassium 125mg	4%	10%
Total Carbohydrate 23g	8%	10%
Dietary Fiber 3g	10%	10%
Sugars 5g		
Other Carbohydrate 15g		
Protein 2g		
Vitamin A	10%	15%
Vitamin C	100%	100%
Calcium	100%	110%
Iron	100%	100%
Vitamin D	10%	25%
Vitamin E	100%	100%
Thiamin	100%	100%
Riboflavin	100%	110%
Niacin	100%	100%
Vitamin B$_6$	100%	100%
Folic Acid	100%	100%
Vitamin B$_{12}$	100%	110%
Pantothenic Acid	100%	100%
Phosphorus	8%	20%
Magnesium	6%	10%
Zinc	100%	100%
Copper	4%	4%

* Amount in cereal. A serving of cereal plus skim milk provides 1g total fat, less than 5mg cholesterol, 260mg sodium, 290mg potassium, 29g total carbohydrate (11g sugars) and 7g protein.

** Percent Daily Values are based on a 2,000 calorie diet. Your daily values may be higher or lower depending on your calorie needs:

		Calories	2,000	2,500
Total Fat	Less than		65g	80g
Sat Fat	Less than		20g	25g
Cholesterol	Less than		300mg	300mg
Sodium	Less than		2,400mg	2,400mg
Potassium			3,500mg	3,500mg
Total Carbohydrate			300g	375g
Dietary Fiber			25g	30g

2.3 Atoms consist of protons, neutrons, and electrons

Each element has its own type of atom, which is different from the atoms of other elements. An **atom**, named from a Greek word meaning "indivisible," is the smallest unit of matter that still retains the properties of an element. Atoms are so small that it would take about a million of them to stretch across the period printed at the end of this sentence.

Subatomic Particles   Physicists have split the atom into more than a hundred types of subatomic particles. However, only three kinds of particles are relevant here. A **proton** is a subatomic particle with a single positive electrical charge (+). An **electron** is a subatomic particle with a single negative charge (−). A **neutron**, as its name implies, is electrically neutral (has no charge).

Figure 2.3 shows two very simple models of an atom of the element helium (He), the "lighter-than-air" gas that makes balloons rise. Notice that two protons (+) and two neutrons (●) are tightly packed in the atom's central core, or **nucleus**. Two electrons (−) form a sort of cloud of negative charge around the nucleus. The attraction between the negatively charged electrons and the positively charged protons holds the electrons near the nucleus. The left-hand model shows the two electrons on a circle around the nucleus. The right-hand model, slightly more realistic, shows a spherical cloud of negative charge created by the two rapidly moving electrons. Neither model is drawn to scale. In real atoms, the electrons are very much smaller than the protons and neutrons, and the electron cloud is very much bigger compared to the nucleus. Imagine that this atom was the size of a baseball stadium: The nucleus would be the size of a pea in center field, and the electrons would be like two tiny gnats buzzing around the stadium.

Atomic Number and Mass Number   So what makes the atoms of different elements different? All atoms of a particular element have the same unique number of protons. This number is the element's **atomic number**. Thus, an atom of helium, with 2 protons, has an atomic number of 2. Unless otherwise indicated, an atom has an equal number of protons and electrons, and thus its net electrical charge is 0 (zero).

What other numbers are associated with an atom? An atom's **mass number** is the sum of the number of protons and neutrons in its nucleus. For helium, the mass number is 4. The mass of a proton and the mass of a neutron are almost identical and are expressed in a unit of measurement called the dalton. Protons and neutrons each have masses close to 1 dalton. An electron has only about 1/2,000 the mass of a proton, so it contributes very little to an atom's mass. Thus, an atom's **atomic mass** (or weight) is approximately equal to its mass number—the sum of its protons and neutrons—in daltons.

Isotopes   All atoms of an element have the same atomic number, but some atoms of that element may differ in mass number. The different **isotopes** of an element have the same number of protons and behave identically in chemical reactions, but they have different numbers of neutrons. Table 2.3 shows the numbers of subatomic particles in the three isotopes of carbon. Note that carbon's atomic number is 6—all of its atoms have 6 protons. Carbon-12 (named for its mass number), with 6 neutrons, accounts for about 99% of naturally occurring carbon. Most of the remaining 1% consists of carbon-13, with a mass number of 13 and thus 7 neutrons. A third isotope, carbon-14, with 8 neutrons, occurs in minute quantities. Of course, all three isotopes have 6 protons—otherwise, they would not be carbon.

Both carbon-12 and carbon-13 are stable isotopes, meaning that their nuclei remain intact more or less forever. The isotope carbon-14, on the other hand, is unstable, or radioactive. A **radioactive isotope** is one in which the nucleus decays spontaneously, giving off particles and energy. Radiation from decaying isotopes can damage cellular molecules and thus can pose serious risks to living organisms. But radioactive isotopes can be helpful, as in their use in dating fossils (see Module 15.5). They are also used in biological research and medicine, as we see next.

TABLE 2.3 | ISOTOPES OF CARBON

	Carbon-12		Carbon-13		Carbon-14	
Protons 6	}	Mass number 12	6 }	Mass number 13	6 }	Mass number 14
Neutrons 6			7		8	
Electrons 6			6		6	

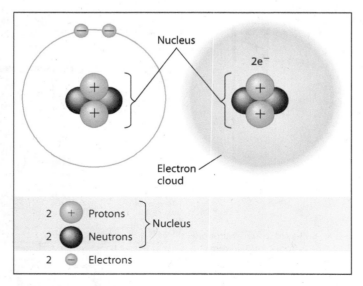

▲ **Figure 2.3**   Two models of a helium atom. (Note that these models are not to scale; they greatly overestimate the size of the nucleus in relation to the electron cloud.)

?   A nitrogen atom has 7 protons, and its most common isotope has 7 neutrons. A radioactive isotope of nitrogen has 9 neutrons. What is the atomic number and mass number of this radioactive nitrogen?

Atomic number = 7; mass number = 16

2.4 Radioactive isotopes can help or harm us

CONNECTION

Living cells cannot readily distinguish between isotopes of the same element. Consequently, organisms take up and use compounds containing radioactive isotopes in the usual way. Because radioactivity is easily detected and measured by instruments, radioactive isotopes are useful as tracers—biological spies, in effect—for monitoring the fate of atoms in living organisms.

Basic Research Biologists often use radioactive tracers to follow molecules as they undergo chemical changes in an organism. For example, researchers have used carbon dioxide (CO_2) containing the radioactive isotope carbon-14 to study photosynthesis. Using sunlight to power the conversion, plants take in CO_2 from the air and use it to make sugar molecules. Radioactively labeled CO_2 has enabled researchers to trace the sequence of molecules made by plants in the chemical route from CO_2 to sugar.

Medical Diagnosis and Treatment Radioactive isotopes may also be used to tag chemicals that accumulate in specific areas of the body, such as phosphorus in bones. After injection of such a tracer, a special camera produces an image of where the radiation collects. In most diagnostic uses, the patient receives only a tiny amount of an isotope.

Sometimes radioactive isotopes are used for treatment. As you learned in Module 2.2, the body uses iodine to make a thyroid hormone. Because radioactive iodine accumulates in the thyroid, it can be used to kill cancer cells there.

Substances that the body metabolizes, such as glucose or oxygen, may also be labeled with a radioactive isotope. **Figure 2.4A** shows a patient being examined by a PET (positron-emission tomography) scanner, which can produce three-dimensional images of areas of the body with high metabolic activity. PET is useful for diagnosing certain heart disorders and cancers and for basic research on the brain.

The early detection of Alzheimer's disease may be a new use for such techniques. This devastating illness gradually destroys a person's memory and ability to think. As the disease progresses, the brain becomes riddled with deposits (plaques) of a protein called beta-amyloid. Researchers have identified

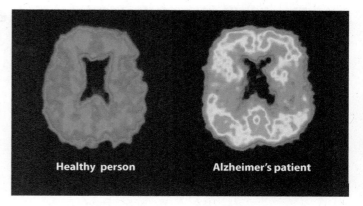

▲ **Figure 2.4B** PET images of brains of a healthy person (left) and a person with Alzheimer's disease (right). Red and yellow colors indicate high levels of PIB bound to beta-amyloid plaques.

a protein molecule called PIB that binds to beta-amyloid. PIB contains a radioactive isotope that can be detected on a PET scan. **Figure 2.4B** shows PET images of the brains of a healthy person (left) and a person with Alzheimer's (right) injected with PIB. Notice that the brain of the Alzheimer's patient has high levels of PIB (red and yellow areas), whereas the unaffected person's brain has lower levels (blue). New therapies are focused on limiting the production of beta-amyloid or clearing it from the brain. A diagnostic test using PIB would allow researchers to monitor the effectiveness of new drugs in people living with the disease.

Dangers Although radioactive isotopes have many beneficial uses, uncontrolled exposure to them can harm living organisms by damaging molecules, especially DNA. The particles and energy thrown off by radioactive atoms can break chemical bonds and also cause abnormal bonds to form. The explosion of a nuclear reactor in Chernobyl, Ukraine, in 1986 released large amounts of radioactive isotopes into the environment, which drifted over large areas of Russia, Belarus, and Europe. A few dozen people died from acute radiation poisoning, and more than 100,000 people were evacuated from the immediate area. Increased rates of thyroid cancer in children exposed to the radiation have been reported. Likewise, scientists will carefully monitor the long-term health consequences of the 2011 post-tsunami Fukushima nuclear disaster in Japan.

Natural sources of radiation can also pose a threat. Radon, a radioactive gas, may be a cause of lung cancer. Radon can contaminate buildings in regions where underlying rocks naturally contain uranium, a radioactive element. Homeowners can buy a radon detector or hire a company to test their home to ensure that radon levels are safe. If levels are found to be unsafe, technology exists to remove radon from homes.

? **Why are radioactive isotopes useful as tracers in research on the chemistry of life?**

Organisms incorporate radioactive isotopes of an element into their molecules, and researchers can use special scanning devices to detect the presence of these isotopes in biological pathways or locations in the body.

▲ **Figure 2.4A** Technician monitoring the output of a PET scanner

▷ Chemical Bonds

2.5 The distribution of electrons determines an atom's chemical properties

To understand how atoms interact with each other, we need to explore atomic structure further. Of the three subatomic particles—protons, neutrons, and electrons—only electrons are directly involved in the chemical activity of an atom.

If you glance back to the model of the helium atom in Figure 2.3, you see that its 2 electrons are shown together on a

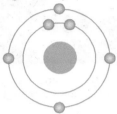

▲ Figure 2.5A An electron distribution model of carbon

circle around the nucleus. But where should the electrons be shown in an atom with more than 2 electrons— say, in carbon, whose atomic number is 6? As you see in Figure 2.5A, 2 electrons are still shown on an inner circle, but the next 4 are placed on a larger outside circle. It turns out that electrons can be located in different **electron shells**, each with a characteristic distance from the nucleus.

Depending on an element's atomic number, an atom may have one, two, or more electron shells.

Figure 2.5B is an abbreviated version of the periodic table of the elements (see Appendix 2 for the complete table). The figure shows the distribution of electrons for the first 18 elements, arranged in rows according to the number of electron shells (one, two, or three). Within each shell, electrons travel in different *orbitals*, which are discrete volumes of space in which electrons are most likely to be found. Each orbital can hold a maximum of 2 electrons. The first electron shell has only one orbital and can hold only 2 electrons. Thus, hydrogen and helium are the only elements in the first row. For the second and third rows, the outer shell has four orbitals and can hold up to 8 electrons (four pairs).

It is the number of electrons present in the outermost shell, called the valence shell, that determines the chemical properties of an atom. Atoms whose outer shells are not full tend to interact with other atoms in ways that enable them to complete or fill their valence shells.

Look at the electron shells of the atoms of the four elements that are the main components of biological molecules (highlighted in green in Figure 2.5B). Because their outer shells are incomplete, all these atoms react readily with other atoms. The hydrogen atom has only 1 electron in its single electron shell, which can accommodate 2 electrons. Atoms of carbon, nitrogen, and oxygen also have unpaired electrons and incomplete shells. In contrast, the helium atom has a first-level shell that is full with 2 electrons. Neon and argon also have full outer shells. As a result, these elements are chemically inert (unreactive).

How do chemical interactions between atoms enable them to fill their outer electron shells? When two atoms with incomplete outer shells react, each atom will share, donate, or receive electrons, so that both partners end up with completed outer shells. These interactions usually result in atoms staying close together, held by attractions known as **chemical bonds**. In the next two modules, we look at two important types of chemical bonds.

> **?** How many electrons and electron shells does a sodium atom have? How many electrons are in its valence shell?

11 electrons; 3 electron shells; 1 electron in the outer shell

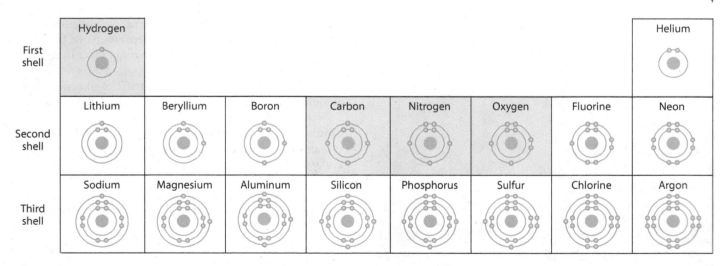

▲ Figure 2.5B The electron distribution diagrams of the first 18 elements in the periodic table

Try This As you read from left to right across each row, describe how the number of electrons changes. Note that the electrons don't pair up until all orbitals have at least one electron.

2.6 Covalent bonds join atoms into molecules through electron sharing

In a **covalent bond**, two atoms, each with an unpaired electron in its outer shell, actually *share* a pair of electrons. Sharing one or more pairs of electrons enables atoms to complete their outer shells. Atoms held together by covalent bonds form a **molecule**. For example, a covalent bond connects two hydrogen atoms in a molecule of the gas H_2, and a covalent bond connects each of two hydrogen atoms to an oxygen atom in a molecule of water (H_2O).

How many covalent bonds can an atom form? It depends on the number of additional electrons needed to fill its valence shell. This number is called the valence, or bonding capacity, of an atom. Look back at the electron distribution diagrams in Figure 2.5B and see if you can determine how many covalent bonds hydrogen, oxygen, nitrogen, and carbon can form.

Figure 2.6 shows how molecules can be represented in several different ways. Let's see what we can learn from this figure. As you will notice in the electron distribution diagram, the hydrogen atoms in H_2 are held together by a pair of shared electrons. But two atoms can share more than just one pair of electrons. In an oxygen molecule (O_2), for example, the two oxygen atoms share two pairs of electrons, forming a double bond. A double bond is indicated in a structural formula by a pair of lines.

H_2 and O_2 are molecules composed of only one element. Methane (CH_4) and water (H_2O) are compounds. Methane is a major component of natural gas. As shown in Figure 2.6, it takes four hydrogen atoms to satisfy carbon's valence of 4.

Atoms in a molecule are in a constant tug-of-war for the shared electrons of their covalent bonds. An atom's attraction for shared electrons is called its **electronegativity**. The more electronegative an atom, the more strongly it pulls shared electrons toward its nucleus. In molecules of only one element, such as H_2 and O_2, the two identical atoms exert an equal pull on the electrons. The bonds in such molecules are said to be **nonpolar covalent bonds** because the electrons are shared equally between the atoms. Compounds such as methane also have nonpolar bonds, because the atoms of carbon and hydrogen are not substantially different in electronegativity.

Water, on the other hand, is composed of atoms with quite different electronegativities. Oxygen is one of the most electronegative of the elements. As indicated by the arrows in the blowup of a water molecule in Figure 2.6, oxygen attracts the shared electrons in H_2O much more strongly than does hydrogen, so that the electrons spend more time near the oxygen atom than near the hydrogen atoms. This unequal sharing of electrons produces a **polar covalent bond**. In a polar covalent bond, the pulling of shared, negatively charged electrons closer to the more electronegative atom makes that atom partially negative and the other atom partially positive. Thus, in H_2O, the oxygen atom actually has a slight negative charge and each hydrogen atom a slight positive charge.

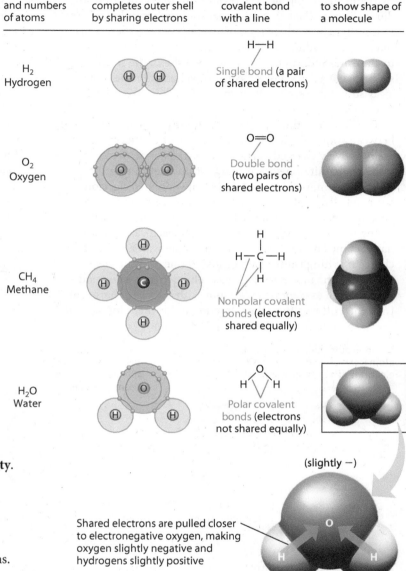

Molecular Formula: tells types and numbers of atoms	Electron Distribution Diagram: shows how each atom completes outer shell by sharing electrons	Structural Formula: represents each covalent bond with a line	Space-Filling Model: uses color-coded balls to show shape of a molecule
H_2 Hydrogen		H—H Single bond (a pair of shared electrons)	
O_2 Oxygen		O=O Double bond (two pairs of shared electrons)	
CH_4 Methane		H—C—H with H above and below Nonpolar covalent bonds (electrons shared equally)	
H_2O Water		H—O—H Polar covalent bonds (electrons not shared equally)	

(slightly −)

Shared electrons are pulled closer to electronegative oxygen, making oxygen slightly negative and hydrogens slightly positive

(slightly +) (slightly +)

Polar covalent bonds in a water molecule (Polarity refers to a separation of charges—think of the positive and negative poles or ends of a battery.)

▲ **Figure 2.6** Alternative ways to represent four common molecules

In some cases, two atoms are so unequal in their attraction for electrons that the more electronegative atom strips an electron completely away from its partner, as we see next.

? **What is chemically nonsensical about this structure?**

● Each C has only three bonds instead of the four required by its valence.

2.7 Ionic bonds are attractions between ions of opposite charge

Table salt is an example of how the transfer of electrons can bond atoms together. **Figure 2.7A** shows how a sodium atom (Na) and a chlorine atom (Cl) can form the compound sodium chloride (NaCl). Notice that sodium has only 1 electron in its outer shell, whereas chlorine has 7. When these atoms interact, the sodium atom transfers its single outer electron to chlorine. Sodium now has only two shells, the second shell having a full set of 8 electrons. When chlorine strips away sodium's electron, its own outer shell is now full with 8 electrons.

But how does this electron transfer result in an ionic bond between sodium and chlorine? Remember that electrons are negatively charged particles. The transfer of an electron moves one unit of negative charge from one atom to the other. Sodium, with 11 protons but now only 10 electrons, has a net electrical charge of 1+. Chlorine, having gained an extra electron, now has 18 electrons but only 17 protons, giving it a net electrical charge of 1−. In each case, an atom has become an **ion**—an atom or molecule with an electrical charge resulting from a gain or loss of one or more electrons. (Note that the names of negatively charged ions often end in −*ide*, such as *chloride*.) Two ions with opposite charges attract each other. When the attraction holds them together, it

is called an **ionic bond**. The resulting compound, in this case NaCl, is electrically neutral.

Sodium chloride is a familiar type of **salt**, a synonym for an ionic compound. Salts often exist as crystals in nature. **Figure 2.7B** shows the ions Na⁺ and Cl⁻ in a crystal of sodium chloride. An NaCl crystal can be of any size (there is no fixed number of ions), but sodium and chloride ions are always present in a 1:1 ratio. The ratio of ions can differ in the various kinds of salts.

The environment affects the strength of ionic bonds. In a dry salt crystal, the bonds are so strong that it takes a hammer and chisel to break enough of them to crack the crystal. If the same salt crystal is placed in water, however, the ionic bonds break when the ions interact with water molecules and the salt dissolves, as we'll discuss in Module 2.13. Most drugs are manufactured as salts because they are quite stable when dry but can dissolve easily in water.

> **?** Explain what holds together the ions in a crystal of table salt (NaCl).
>
> ● Opposite charges attract. The positively charged sodium ions (Na⁺) and the negatively charged chloride ions (Cl⁻) are held together by ionic bonds, attractions between oppositely charged ions.

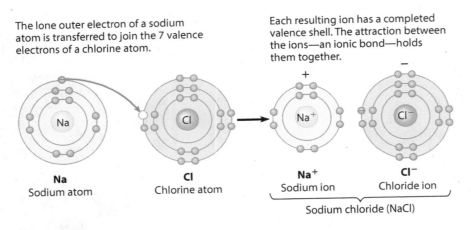

The lone outer electron of a sodium atom is transferred to join the 7 valence electrons of a chlorine atom.

Each resulting ion has a completed valence shell. The attraction between the ions—an ionic bond—holds them together.

Na Sodium atom   **Cl** Chlorine atom   **Na⁺** Sodium ion   **Cl⁻** Chloride ion

Sodium chloride (NaCl)

▲ **Figure 2.7A**   Formation of an ionic bond, producing sodium chloride

Cl⁻
Na⁺

▲ **Figure 2.7B**   A crystal of sodium chloride

2.8 Hydrogen bonds are weak bonds important in the chemistry of life

In living organisms, most of the strong chemical bonds are covalent, linking atoms to form a cell's molecules. But crucial to the functioning of a cell are weaker bonds within and between molecules, such as the ionic bonds we just discussed. One of the most important types of weak bonds is the **hydrogen bond**, which is best illustrated with water molecules.

As you saw in Figure 2.6, the hydrogen atoms of a water molecule are attached to oxygen by polar covalent bonds. Because of these polar bonds and the wide V shape of the

molecule, water is a **polar molecule**—that is, it has an unequal distribution of charges. It is slightly negative at the oxygen end of the molecule (the point of the V) and slightly positive at each of the two hydrogen ends. This partial positive charge allows each hydrogen to be attracted to—in a sense, to "flirt" with—a nearby atom (often an oxygen or nitrogen) that has a partial negative charge.

Figure 2.8, on the next page, illustrates how these weak bonds form between water molecules. They are called

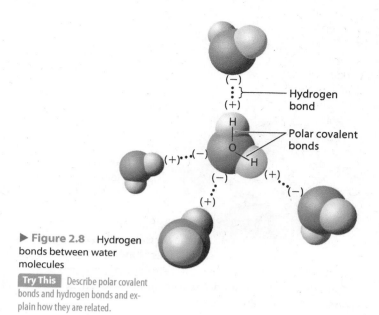

▶ **Figure 2.8** Hydrogen bonds between water molecules

Try This Describe polar covalent bonds and hydrogen bonds and explain how they are related.

Hydrogen bond

Polar covalent bonds

hydrogen bonds because the positively charged atom in this type of attraction is always a hydrogen atom. As Figure 2.8 shows, each hydrogen atom of a water molecule can form a hydrogen bond (depicted by dotted lines) with a nearby partially negative oxygen atom of another water molecule. And the negative (oxygen) pole of a water molecule can form hydrogen bonds to two hydrogen atoms. Thus, each water molecule can hydrogen-bond to as many as four partners.

You will learn later how hydrogen bonds help to create a protein's shape (and thus its function) and hold the two strands of a DNA molecule together (see Chapter 3). Later in this chapter, we explore how water's polarity and hydrogen bonds give it unique, life-supporting properties. But first we discuss how the making and breaking of bonds change the composition of matter.

? **What enables neighboring water molecules to hydrogen-bond to one another?**

● The molecules are polar, with each positive end (hydrogen end) of one molecule attracted to the negative end (oxygen end) of another molecule.

2.9 Chemical reactions make and break chemical bonds

Your cells are constantly rearranging molecules in **chemical reactions**—breaking existing chemical bonds and forming new ones. A simple example of a chemical reaction is the reaction between hydrogen gas and oxygen gas that forms water (this is an explosive reaction, which, fortunately, does not occur in your cells):

$$2\ H_2 + O_2 \rightarrow 2\ H_2O$$

In this case, two molecules of hydrogen ($2\ H_2$) react with one molecule of oxygen (O_2) to produce two molecules of water ($2\ H_2O$). The arrow in the equation indicates the conversion of the starting materials, called the **reactants**, to the **product**, the material resulting from the chemical reaction. Notice that the same *numbers* of hydrogen and oxygen atoms appear on the left and right sides of the arrow, although they are grouped differently. Chemical reactions do not create or destroy matter; they only rearrange it in various ways. As shown in **Figure 2.9**, the covalent bonds (represented here as white "sticks" between atoms) holding hydrogen atoms together in H_2 and holding oxygen atoms together in O_2 are broken, and new bonds are formed to yield the H_2O product molecules.

Organisms cannot make water from H_2 and O_2, but they do carry out a great number of chemical reactions that rearrange matter in significant ways. Let's examine a chemical reaction that is essential to life on Earth: photosynthesis. The raw materials of photosynthesis are carbon dioxide (CO_2), which is taken from the air, and water (H_2O), which plants absorb from the soil. Within green plant cells, sunlight powers the conversion of these reactants to the sugar product glucose ($C_6H_{12}O_6$) and oxygen (O_2), a by-product that the plant releases into the air. The following chemical shorthand summarizes the process:

$$6\ CO_2 + 6\ H_2O \rightarrow C_6H_{12}O_6 + 6\ O_2$$

Although photosynthesis is actually a sequence of many chemical reactions, we see that we end up with the same number and kinds of atoms we started with. Matter has simply been rearranged, with an input of energy provided by sunlight.

Your body routinely carries out thousands of chemical reactions. These reactions take place in the watery environment of your cells. We look at the life-supporting properties of water next.

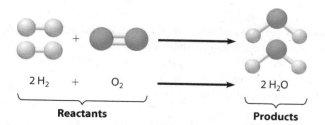

2 H₂   +   O₂   →   2 H₂O

Reactants   **Products**

▲ **Figure 2.9** Breaking and making of bonds in a chemical reaction

? **Fill in the blanks with the correct numbers in the following chemical process:**

$$C_6H_{12}O_6 + \_\_O_2 \rightarrow \_\_CO_2 + \_\_H_2O$$

What process do you think this reaction represents? (*Hint:* Think about how your cells use these reactants to produce energy.)

● $C_6H_{12}O_6 + 6\ O_2 \rightarrow 6\ CO_2 + 6\ H_2O$; the breakdown of sugar in the presence of oxygen to carbon dioxide and water, with the release of energy that the cell can use

▷ Water's Life-Supporting Properties

2.10 Hydrogen bonds make liquid water cohesive

We can trace water's life-supporting properties to the structure and interactions of its molecules—their polarity and resulting hydrogen bonding between molecules (review Figure 2.8).

Hydrogen bonds between molecules of liquid water last for only a few trillionths of a second, yet at any instant, many molecules are hydrogen-bonded to others. This tendency of molecules of the same kind to stick together, called **cohesion**, is much stronger for water than for most other liquids. The cohesion of water is important in the living world. Trees, for example, depend on cohesion to help transport water and nutrients from their roots to their leaves. The evaporation of water from a leaf exerts a pulling force on water within the veins of the leaf. Because of cohesion, the force is relayed all the way down to the roots. **Adhesion**, the clinging of one substance to another, also plays a role. The adhesion of water to the cell walls of a plant's thin veins helps counter the downward pull of gravity.

Related to cohesion is **surface tension**, a measure of how difficult it is to stretch or break the surface of a liquid. Hydrogen

▼ Figure 2.10 Surface tension allowing a water strider to walk on water

bonds give water unusually high surface tension, making it behave as though it were coated with an invisible film. You can observe the surface tension of water by slightly overfilling a glass; the water will stand above the rim. The water strider in Figure 2.10 takes advantage of the high surface tension of water to "stride" across ponds without breaking the surface.

? After a hard workout, you may notice "beads" of sweat on your face. Can you explain what holds the sweat in droplet form?

● The cohesion of water molecules and its high surface tension hold water in droplets. The adhesion of water to your skin helps hold the beads in place.

2.11 Water's hydrogen bonds moderate temperature

Thermal energy is the energy associated with the random movement of atoms and molecules. Thermal energy in transfer from a warmer to a cooler body of matter is defined as **heat**. **Temperature** measures the intensity of heat—that is, the *average* speed of molecules in a body of matter. If you have ever burned your finger on a metal pot while waiting for the water in it to boil, you know that water heats up much more slowly than metal. In fact, because of hydrogen bonding, water has a stronger resistance to temperature change than most other substances.

Heat must be absorbed to break hydrogen bonds, and heat is released when hydrogen bonds form. To raise the temperature of water, hydrogen bonds between water molecules must be broken before the molecules can move faster. Thus, water absorbs a large amount of heat (much of it used to disrupt hydrogen bonds) while warming up only a few degrees. Conversely, when water cools, water molecules slow down and more hydrogen bonds form, releasing a considerable amount of heat.

Earth's giant water supply moderates temperatures, helping to keep temperatures within limits that permit life. Oceans, lakes, and rivers store a huge amount of heat from the sun during warm periods. Heat given off from gradually cooling

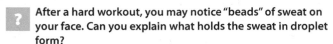

▲ Figure 2.11 Sweating as a mechanism of evaporative cooling

water warms the air. That's why coastal areas generally have milder climates than inland regions. Water's resistance to temperature change also stabilizes ocean temperatures, creating a favorable environment for marine life. Because water accounts for approximately 66% of your body weight, it also helps moderate your temperature.

When a substance evaporates (changes physical state from a liquid to a gas), the surface of the liquid that remains behind cools down. This **evaporative cooling** occurs because the molecules with the greatest energy (the "hottest" ones) leave. It's as if the 10 fastest runners on the track team left school, lowering the average speed of the remaining team. Evaporative cooling helps prevent some land-dwelling organisms from overheating. Evaporation from a plant's leaves keeps them from becoming too warm in the sun, just as sweating helps dissipate our excess body heat (Figure 2.11). On a much larger scale, the evaporation of surface waters cools tropical seas.

? Explain the popular adage "It's not the heat, it's the humidity."

● High humidity hampers cooling by slowing the evaporation of sweat.

2.12 Ice floats because it is less dense than liquid water

Water exists on Earth in three forms: gas (water vapor), liquid, and solid. Unlike most substances, water is less dense as a solid than as a liquid. As you might guess, this unusual property is due to hydrogen bonds.

As water freezes, each molecule forms stable hydrogen bonds with its neighbors, holding them at "arm's length" and creating a three-dimensional crystal. In **Figure 2.12**, compare the spaciously arranged molecules in the ice crystal with the more tightly packed molecules in the liquid water. The ice crystal has fewer molecules than an equal volume of liquid water. Therefore, ice is less dense and floats on top of liquid water.

If ice sank, then eventually ponds, lakes, and even oceans would freeze solid. Instead, when a body of water cools, the floating ice insulates the water below from colder air above. This "blanket" of ice prevents the water from freezing and allows fish and other aquatic forms of life to survive under the frozen surface.

In the Arctic, this frozen surface serves as the winter hunting ground for polar bears (Figure 2.12). The shrinking of this ice cover as a result of global climate change may doom these bears.

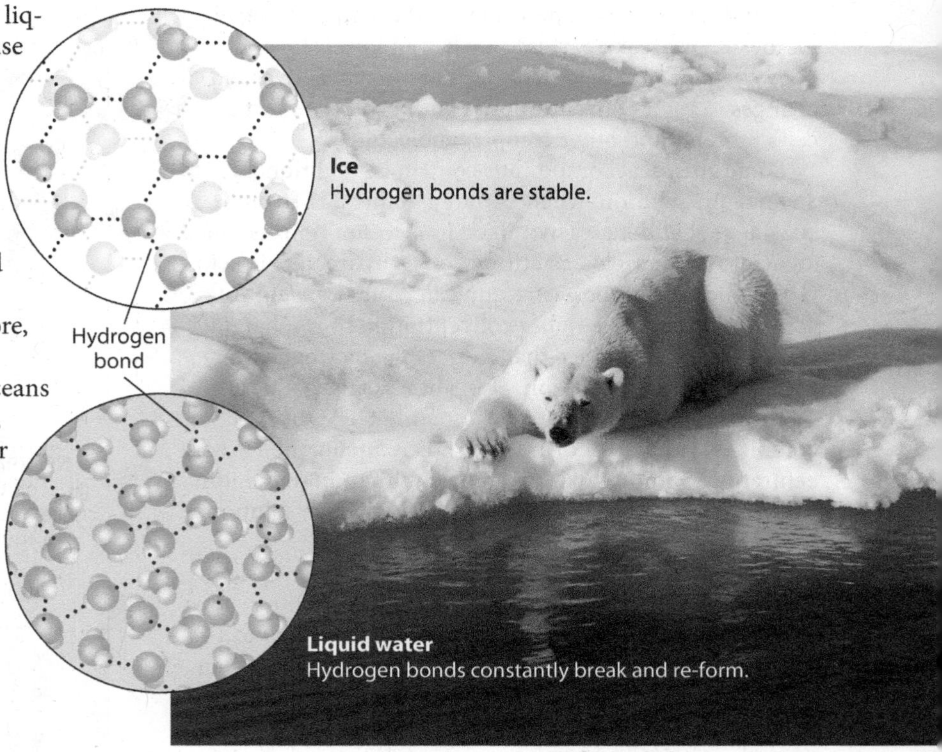

? **Explain how freezing water can crack boulders.**

● Water in the crevices of a boulder expands as it freezes because the water molecules become spaced farther apart in forming ice crystals, which can crack the rock.

Ice
Hydrogen bonds are stable.

Hydrogen bond

Liquid water
Hydrogen bonds constantly break and re-form.

▲ **Figure 2.12** Hydrogen bonds between water molecules in ice and water

2.13 Water is the solvent of life

If you add a teaspoon of table salt to a glass of water, the salt will eventually dissolve, forming a solution. A **solution** is a liquid consisting of a uniform mixture of two or more substances. The dissolving agent (in our example, water) is the **solvent**, and a substance that is dissolved (in this case, salt) is a **solute**. An **aqueous solution** (from the Latin *aqua*, water) is one in which water is the solvent.

Water's versatility as a solvent results from the polarity of its molecules. **Figure 2.13** shows how a teaspoon of salt dissolves in water. At the surface of each grain, or crystal, the sodium and chloride ions are exposed to water. These ions and the water molecules are attracted to each other due to their opposite charges. The oxygen ends of the water molecules have a partial negative charge and cling to the positive sodium ions (Na⁺). The hydrogen ends of the water molecules, with their partial positive charge,

Positive hydrogen ends of water molecules attracted to negative chloride ion

Negative oxygen ends of water molecules attracted to positive sodium ion

Salt crystal

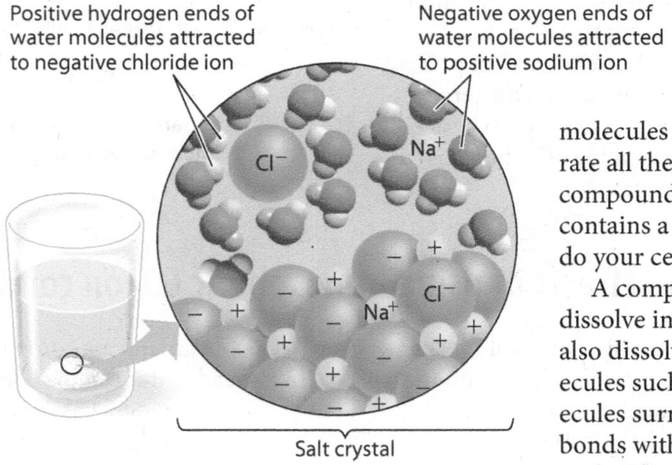

▲ **Figure 2.13** A crystal of salt (NaCl) dissolving in water

are attracted to the negative chloride ions (Cl⁻). Working inward from the surface of each salt crystal, water molecules eventually surround and separate all the ions. Water dissolves other ionic compounds as well. Seawater, for instance, contains a great variety of dissolved ions, as do your cells.

A compound doesn't need to be ionic to dissolve in water. A spoonful of sugar will also dissolve in a glass of water. Polar molecules such as sugar dissolve as water molecules surround them and form hydrogen bonds with their polar regions. Even large molecules, such as proteins, can dissolve if they have ionic or polar regions on their surface. As the solvent inside all cells, in blood, and in plant sap, water dissolves an enormous variety of solutes necessary for life.

? **Why are blood and most other biological fluids classified as aqueous solutions?**

● The solvent in these fluids is water.

2.14 The chemistry of life is sensitive to acidic and basic conditions

In liquid water, a small percentage of the water molecules dissociate or break apart into hydrogen ions (H^+) and hydroxide ions (OH^-). These ions are very reactive, and changes in their concentrations can drastically affect a cell's proteins and other complex molecules.

Some chemical compounds contribute additional H^+ to an aqueous solution, whereas others remove H^+ from it. A substance that donates hydrogen ions to solutions is called an **acid**. An example of a strong acid is hydrochloric acid (HCl), the acid in the gastric juice in your stomach. An acidic solution has a higher concentration of H^+ than OH^-.

A **base** is a substance that reduces the hydrogen ion concentration of a solution. Some bases, such as sodium hydroxide (NaOH), do this by donating OH^-; the OH^- combines with H^+ to form H_2O, thus reducing the H^+ concentration. Sodium hydroxide is a common ingredient in oven cleaners. Other bases accept H^+ ions from solution, resulting in a higher OH^- concentration.

We use the **pH scale** to describe how acidic or basic a solution is (pH stands for potential of hydrogen). As shown in Figure 2.14, the scale ranges from 0 (most acidic) to 14 (most basic). Each pH unit represents a 10-fold change in the concentration of H^+ in a solution. For example, lemon juice at pH 2 has 10 times more H^+ than an equal amount of a cola at pH 3 and 100 times more H^+ than tomato juice at pH 4.

Pure water and aqueous solutions that are neither acidic nor basic are said to be neutral; they have a pH of 7, and the concentrations of H^+ and OH^- are equal. The pH inside most cells is close to 7.

The pH of human blood plasma (the fluid portion of the blood) is very close to 7.4. A person cannot survive for more than a few minutes if the blood pH drops to 7.0 or rises to 7.8. How can your body maintain a relatively constant pH in your cells and blood? Biological fluids contain **buffers**, substances that minimize changes in pH. They do so by accepting H^+ when it is in excess and donating H^+ when it is depleted.

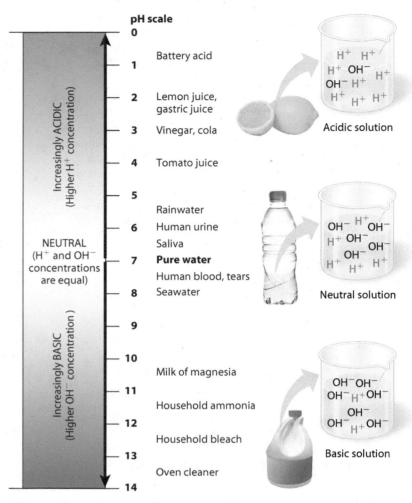

▲ **Figure 2.14**   The pH scale, which reflects the relative concentrations of H^+ and OH^-

? Compared to a basic solution at pH 9, the same volume of an acidic solution at pH 4 has _____ times more H^+.

100,000

2.15 Scientists study the effects of rising atmospheric CO_2 on coral reef ecosystems

SCIENTIFIC THINKING

Carbon dioxide is the main product of fossil fuel combustion, and its steadily increasing release into the atmosphere is linked to global climate change. About 25% of this CO_2 is absorbed by the oceans—and this naturally occurring remedy to excess CO_2 would seem to be a good thing. However, as CO_2 levels on the planet continue to rise, the increasing absorption of CO_2 is expected to change ocean chemistry and harm marine life and ecosystems.

In **ocean acidification**, CO_2 dissolving in seawater lowers the pH of the ocean. Recent studies estimate that the pH of the oceans is 0.1 pH unit lower now than at any time in the past

Will rising atmospheric CO_2 harm coral reefs?

420,000 years and may drop from the current level of 8.1 to 7.8 by the end of this century. How will this affect marine organisms?

Several studies investigating the impact of a lower pH on coral reef ecosystems have looked at the process called calcification, in which coral animals combine calcium and carbonate ions to form their calcium carbonate skeletons. As seawater acidifies, the extra hydrogen ions (H^+) combine with carbonate ions (CO_3^{2-}) to form bicarbonate ions (HCO_3^-). This reaction reduces the carbonate ion concentration available to corals and other shell-building animals. Scientists predict that ocean acidification will cause the carbonate ion concentration to decrease by 40% by the year 2100.

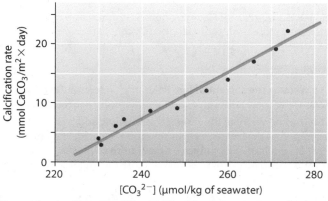

Calcification rate (mmol CaCO$_3$/m^2 × day) vs [CO$_3{}^{2-}$] (μmol/kg of seawater)

Source: Adaptation of figure 5 from "Effect of Calcium Carbonate Saturation State on the Calcification Rate of an Experimental Coral Reef" by C. Langdon, et al., from *Global Biogeochemical Cycles*, June 2000, Volume 14(2). Copyright © 2000 by American Geophysical Union. Reprinted with permission of Wiley Inc.

▲ **Figure 2.15A** The effect of carbonate ion concentration on calcification rate in an artificial coral reef system. (The independent variable shown on the *x* axis is the concentration of carbonate ions, which the researchers manipulated. The dependent variable—the calcification rate, shown on the *y* axis—is what was measured in the experiment and was predicted to "depend on" or respond to the experimental treatment.)

In a controlled experiment, scientists looked at the effect of decreasing carbonate ion concentration on the rate of calcium deposition by reef organisms. The Biosphere 2 aquarium in Arizona contains a large coral reef system that behaves like a natural reef. Researchers measured how the calcification rate changed with differing amounts of dissolved carbonate ions. Figure 2.15A presents the results of one set of experiments, in which pH, temperature, and concentration of calcium ions were held constant while the carbonate ion concentration of the seawater was varied. As you can see from the graph, the lower the concentration of carbonate ions, the lower the rate of calcification, and the slower the growth of coral animals.

Controlled studies such as this one have provided evidence that ocean acidification and the resulting reduction in carbonate ion concentration will negatively affect coral reefs. But

Rising CO$_2$ bubbles lower the pH of the water

▲ **Figure 2.15B** A "champagne" reef with bubbles of CO$_2$ rising from a volcanic seep

scientists have also looked to natural habitats to study how ocean acidification affects coral reef ecosystems. A 2011 study looked at three volcanic seeps in Papua New Guinea. As you can see in **Figure 2.15B**, bubbles of CO$_2$ released from underwater volcanoes around such "champagne reefs" lower the pH of the water. Researchers surveyed three study sites in which the pH naturally varied from 8.1 to 7.8. They found reductions in coral diversity and the recruitment of juvenile coral as the pH of the sites declined, both of which undermine the resiliency of a reef community. Researchers also found a shift to less structurally complex and slower growing corals. The structural complexity of coral reef ecosystems makes them havens for a great diversity of organisms.

Scientists often synthesize their conclusions using multiple lines of evidence. The results from both controlled experimental studies and observational field studies of sites where pH naturally varies have dire implications for the health of coral reefs and the diversity of organisms they support.

 What is the relationship between fossil fuel consumption and coral reefs?

● Some of the increased CO$_2$ released by burning fossil fuels dissolves in and lowers the pH of the oceans. A lower pH reduces levels of carbonate ions, which then lowers the rate of calcification by coral animals. A lower pH also changes the composition and resiliency of coral reefs.

2.16 The search for extraterrestrial life centers on the search for water

EVOLUTION CONNECTION

When astrobiologists search for signs of extraterrestrial life on distant planets, they look for evidence of water. Why? As we've seen in this chapter, the emergent properties of water support life on Earth in many ways. Is it possible that some form of life has evolved on other planets that have water in their environment? Scientists with the National Aeronautics and Space Administration (NASA) are looking into this possibility.

Like Earth, Mars has an ice cap at both poles, and scientists have found signs that water may exist elsewhere on the planet. In 2008, the robotic spacecraft *Phoenix* landed on Mars and sent back images showing that ice is present just under Mars's surface. Then, in 2011, high-resolution images sent to Earth from the Mars Reconnaissance Orbiter showed

evidence for liquid water beneath the surface. Distinctive streaks form along steep slopes during the Mars spring and summer, which then vanish during the winter. Careful study of these images over time has led scientists to conclude that these streaks are most likely seasonal streams of flowing water resulting when subsurface ice melts during the warm season. This exciting finding has reinvigorated the search for signs of life, past or present, on Mars and other planets. If any life-forms or fossils are found, their study will shed light on the process of evolution from an entirely new perspective.

 Why is the presence of water important in the search for extraterrestrial life?

● Water plays important roles in life as we know it, from moderating temperatures on the planet to functioning as the solvent of life.

CHAPTER **2** REVIEW

For practice quizzes, BioFlix animations, MP3 tutorials, video tutors, and more study tools designed for this textbook, go to

MasteringBiology®

Reviewing the Concepts

Elements, Atoms, and Compounds (2.1–2.4)

2.1 Organisms are composed of elements, in combinations called compounds. Oxygen, carbon, hydrogen, and nitrogen make up about 96% of living matter.

2.2 Trace elements are common additives to food and water.

2.3 Atoms consist of protons, neutrons, and electrons.

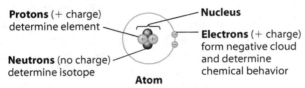

Protons (+ charge) determine element

Nucleus

Electrons (+ charge) form negative cloud and determine chemical behavior

Neutrons (no charge) determine isotope

Atom

2.4 Radioactive isotopes can help or harm us. Radioactive isotopes are valuable in basic research and medicine.

Chemical Bonds (2.5–2.9)

2.5 The distribution of electrons determines an atom's chemical properties. An atom whose outer electron shell is not full tends to interact with other atoms and share, gain, or lose electrons, resulting in attractions called chemical bonds.

2.6 Covalent bonds join atoms into molecules through electron sharing. In a nonpolar covalent bond, electrons are shared equally. In polar covalent bonds, such as those found in water, electrons are pulled closer to the more electronegative atom.

2.7 Ionic bonds are attractions between ions of opposite charge. Electron gain and loss create charged atoms, called ions.

2.8 Hydrogen bonds are weak bonds important in the chemistry of life. The slightly positively charged H atoms in one polar molecule may be attracted to the partial negative charge of an oxygen or nitrogen atom in a neighboring molecule.

2.9 Chemical reactions make and break chemical bonds. The composition of matter is changed as bonds are broken and formed to convert reactants to products.

Water's Life-Supporting Properties (2.10–2.16)

2.10 Hydrogen bonds make liquid water cohesive. Cohesion creates surface tension and allows water to move from plant roots to leaves.

2.11 Water's hydrogen bonds moderate temperature. Heat is absorbed when hydrogen bonds break and released when hydrogen bonds form. This helps keep temperatures relatively steady. As the most energetic water molecules evaporate, the surface of a substance cools.

2.12 Ice floats because it is less dense than liquid water. Floating ice protects lakes and oceans from freezing solid, which in turn protects aquatic life.

Liquid water: Hydrogen bonds constantly break and re-form

Ice: Stable hydrogen bonds hold molecules apart

2.13 Water is the solvent of life. Polar or charged solutes dissolve when water molecules surround them, forming aqueous solutions.

2.14 The chemistry of life is sensitive to acidic and basic conditions. A compound that releases H^+ in solution is an acid, and one that accepts H^+ is a base. The pH scale ranges from 0 (most acidic) to 14 (most basic). The pH of most cells is close to 7 (neutral) and is kept that way by buffers.

2.15 Scientists study the effects of rising atmospheric CO_2 on coral reef ecosystems. The acidification of the ocean threatens coral reefs and other marine organisms.

2.16 The search for extraterrestrial life centers on the search for water. The emergent properties of water support life on Earth and may contribute to the potential for life to have evolved on other planets.

Connecting the Concepts

1. Fill in the blanks in this concept map to help you tie together the key concepts concerning elements, atoms, and molecules.

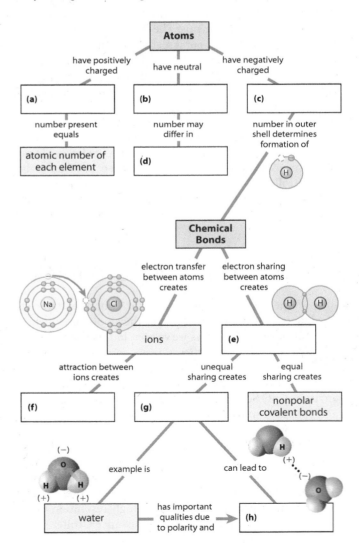

2. Create a concept map to organize your understanding of the life-supporting properties of water. A sample map is in the answer section, but the value of this exercise is in the thinking and integrating you must do to create your own map.

Testing Your Knowledge

Level 1: Knowledge/Comprehension

3. Changing the _____ would change it into an atom of a different element.
   a. number of electrons surrounding the nucleus of an atom
   b. number of protons in the nucleus of an atom
   c. electrical charge of an atom
   d. number of neutrons in the nucleus of an atom
4. A solution at pH 6 contains _____ H^+ than the same amount of a solution at pH 8.
   a. 20 times more
   b. 100 times more
   c. 2 times less
   d. 100 times less
5. Most of the unique properties of water result from the fact that water molecules
   a. are the most abundant molecules on Earth's surface.
   b. are held together by covalent bonds.
   c. are constantly in motion.
   d. are polar and form hydrogen bonds.
6. A can of cola consists mostly of sugar dissolved in water, with some carbon dioxide gas that makes it fizzy and makes the pH less than 7. In chemical terms, you could say that cola is an aqueous solution where water is the _____, sugar is a _____, and carbon dioxide makes the solution _____.
   a. solvent ... solute ... basic
   b. solute ... solvent ... basic
   c. solvent ... solute ... acidic
   d. solute ... solvent ... acidic

Level 2: Application/Analysis

7. The atomic number of sulfur (S) is 16. Sulfur combines with hydrogen by covalent bonding to form a compound, hydrogen sulfide. Based on the number of valence electrons in a sulfur atom, predict the molecular formula of the compound. (*Explain your answer.*)
   a. HS
   b. H_2S
   c. H_4S_2
   d. H_4S
8. In what way does the need for iodine or iron in your diet differ from your need for calcium or phosphorus?
9. Use carbon-12, the most common isotope of carbon, to define these terms: atomic number, mass number, valence. Which of these numbers is most related to the chemical behavior of an atom? Explain.
10. In terms of electron sharing between atoms, compare nonpolar covalent bonds, polar covalent bonds, and ions.

11. The diagram below shows the arrangement of electrons around the nucleus of a fluorine and a potassium atom. What kind of bond do you think would form between these two atoms?

Fluorine atom   Potassium atom

Level 3: Synthesis/Evaluation

12. Look back at the abbreviated periodic table of the elements in Figure 2.5B. If two elements are in the same row, what do they have in common? If two elements are in the same column, what do they have in common? Would you predict that elements in the same row or the same column will have similar chemical properties? Explain.
13. **SCIENTIFIC THINKING** A recent experimental study looked at the combined effects of ocean acidification (see Module 2.15) and increased ocean temperatures, both aspects of global climate change, on the growth of polyps, juvenile coral animals. Researchers reported the average polyp biomass (in μg/polyp) after 42 days of growth under four treatments: a control with pH and temperature maintained close to normal reef conditions, a pH lowered by 0.2 units, a temperature raised by 1°C, and a combined lower pH and higher temperature. The results showed that polyp biomass was reduced somewhat in both the low-pH and high-temperature treatments, but the combined treatment resulted in a reduction in growth by almost a third—a statistically significant result. Experiments often look at the effects of changing one variable at a time, while keeping all other variables constant. Explain why this experiment considered two variables—both a higher temperature and a lower pH—at the same time.
14. In agricultural areas, farmers pay close attention to the weather forecast. Right before a predicted overnight freeze, farmers spray water on crops to protect the plants. Use the properties of water to explain how this method works. Be sure to mention why hydrogen bonds are responsible for this phenomenon.
15. This chapter explains how the emergent properties of water contribute to the suitability of the environment for life. Until fairly recently, scientists assumed that other physical requirements for life included a moderate range of temperature, pH, and atmospheric pressure. That view has changed with the discovery of organisms known as extremophiles, which have been found flourishing in hot, acidic sulfur springs and around hydrothermal vents deep in the ocean. What does the existence of life in such environments say about the possibility of life on other planets?

Answers to all questions can be found in Appendix 4.

3

The Molecules of Cells

What does evolution have to do with drinking milk?

Is a big glass of milk a way to a healthy diet—or an upset stomach? Quite often, the answer is the latter. Most of the world's adult populations cannot easily digest milk-based foods. Such people suffer from lactose intolerance, the inability to properly break down lactose, the main sugar found in milk. Almost all infants are able to drink breast milk or other dairy products, benefiting from the proteins, fats, and sugars in this nutritious food. But as they grow older, many people find that drinking milk comes with a heavy dose of digestive discomfort.

The young man in the photograph below can enjoy drinking milk because his body continues to produce lactase—the enzyme that speeds the digestion of lactose into smaller sugars that his digestive system can absorb. In most human populations, the production of this enzyme begins to decline after the age of 2. In the United States, as many as 80% of African Americans and Native Americans and 90% of Asian Americans are lactase-deficient once they reach their teenage years. Americans of northern European descent make up one of the few groups in which lactase production continues

into adulthood. Why are some people lactose tolerant while others are not? As you'll find out later in this chapter, the answer has to do with evolution and the inheritance of a genetic mutation that occurred in the ancestors of certain groups.

In people who easily digest milk, lactose (a sugar) is broken down by lactase (a protein), which is coded for by a gene made of DNA (a nucleic acid). Such molecular interactions, repeated in countless variations, drive all biological processes. In this chapter, we explore the structure and function of sugars, proteins, fats, and nucleic acids—the biological molecules that are essential to life. We begin with a look at carbon, the versatile atom at the center of life's molecules.

Introduction to Organic Compounds
(3.1–3.3)

Carbon-containing compounds are the chemical building blocks of life.

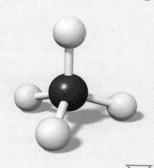

Carbohydrates
(3.4–3.7)

Carbohydrates serve as a cell's fuel and building material.

Lipids
(3.8–3.11)

Lipids are hydrophobic molecules with diverse functions.

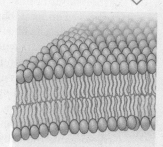

Proteins
(3.12–3.14)

Proteins are essential to the structures and functions of life.

Nucleic Acids
(3.15–3.17)

Nucleic acids store, transmit, and help express hereditary information.

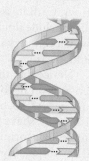

▷ Introduction to Organic Compounds

3.1 Life's molecular diversity is based on the properties of carbon

When it comes to making molecules, carbon usually takes center stage. Almost all the molecules a cell makes are composed of carbon atoms bonded to one another and to atoms of other elements. Carbon is unparalleled in its ability to form large and complex molecules, which build the structures and carry out the functions required for life. Carbon-based molecules are called **organic compounds**, and they usually contain hydrogen atoms in addition to carbon.

Why are carbon atoms the lead players in the chemistry of life? Remember that the number of electrons in the outermost shell determines an atom's chemical properties. A carbon atom has 4 electrons in a valence shell that holds 8. Carbon completes its outer shell by sharing electrons with other atoms in four covalent bonds (see Module 2.6).

Figure 3.1A presents a ball-and-stick model of methane (CH_4), one of the simplest organic molecules. It shows that carbon's four bonds (the white "sticks") angle out toward the corners of an imaginary tetrahedron (an object with four triangular sides, as illustrated in red to the right of the model). This shape occurs wherever a carbon atom participates in four single bonds. In molecules with more than one carbon, each carbon atom is a connecting point from which a molecule can branch in up to four directions. In addition, different shapes occur when carbon atoms form double bonds. Thanks to the geometry of carbon's single and double bonds, large organic molecules can have very elaborate shapes. And as you will see repeatedly, a molecule's shape usually determines its function.

Carbon chains form the backbone of most organic molecules. **Figure 3.1B** illustrates four ways in which such "carbon skeletons" (shaded in gray in the figure) can vary. They may differ in length and can be straight, branched, or arranged in rings. Carbon skeletons may also include double bonds, which can vary in number and location.

Notice that the two compounds on the bottom left of Figure 3.1B, butane and isobutane, have the same molecular formula, C_4H_{10}. They differ, however, in the arrangement of their carbon skeleton. The two molecules on the top right

The four single bonds of carbon point to the corners of a tetrahedron.

▲ **Figure 3.1A**   A model of methane (CH_4) and the tetrahedral shape of a molecule in which a carbon atom forms four single bonds to other atoms

also have the same numbers of atoms (C_4H_8), but they have different three-dimensional shapes because of the location of the double bond. Compounds with the same formula but different structural arrangements are called **isomers**. The different shapes of isomers result in unique properties and add greatly to the diversity of organic molecules.

Isomers can also result from the different spatial arrangements that can occur when four different partners are bonded to a carbon atom. This type of isomer is important in the pharmaceutical industry, because the two isomers of a drug may not be equally effective or may have different (and sometimes harmful) effects.

Methane (Figure 3.1A) and the compounds illustrated in Figure 3.1B are composed of only carbon and hydrogen—they are called **hydrocarbons**. The majority of naturally occurring hydrocarbons are found in crude oil and natural gas and provide most of the world's energy. Hydrocarbons are rare in living organisms, but hydrocarbon chains are found in regions of some molecules. For instance, fats contain hydrocarbon chains that provide fuel to your body.

In the next module, we see how attaching atoms other than just hydrogen to carbon skeletons produces a huge diversity of biological molecules.

? One isomer of methamphetamine is the addictive illegal drug known as "crank." The other is a medicine for sinus congestion. How can you explain the differing effects of the two isomers?

● Isomers have different structures, or shapes, and the shape of a molecule usually helps determine the way it functions in the body.

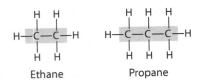

Ethane   Propane

Length: Carbon skeletons vary in length.

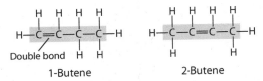

Double bond

1-Butene   2-Butene

Double bonds: Carbon skeletons may have double bonds, which can vary in location.

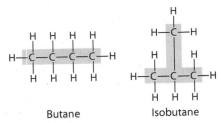

Butane   Isobutane

Branching: Carbon skeletons may be unbranched or branched.

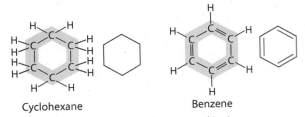

Cyclohexane   Benzene

Rings: Carbon skeletons may be arranged in rings. (In the abbreviated ring structures, each corner represents a carbon and its attached hydrogens.)

▲ **Figure 3.1B**   Four ways in which carbon skeletons can vary

3.2 A few chemical groups are key to the functioning of biological molecules

The unique properties of an organic compound depend not only on the size and shape of its carbon skeleton but also on the groups of atoms that are attached to that skeleton.

Figure 3.2 shows what a difference chemical groups can make. The hormones testosterone and estradiol (a type of estrogen) differ only in the groups of atoms highlighted here with colored boxes. These subtle differences affect the functioning of these molecules, helping to produce male and female features in lions, humans, and other vertebrates.

Table 3.2 illustrates six important chemical groups. The first five are called **functional groups**. They affect a molecule's function by participating in chemical reactions. These groups are polar, which tends to make compounds containing them **hydrophilic** (water-loving) and therefore soluble in water—a necessary condition for their roles in water-based life. The sixth group, a methyl group, is nonpolar and not reactive, but it affects molecular shape and thus function.

A **hydroxyl group** consists of a hydrogen atom bonded to an oxygen atom, which in turn is bonded to the carbon skeleton. Ethanol, shown in the table, and other organic compounds containing hydroxyl groups are called alcohols.

In a **carbonyl group**, a carbon atom is linked by a double bond to an oxygen atom. If the carbonyl group is at the end of a carbon skeleton, the compound is called an aldehyde; if it is within the chain, the compound is called a ketone. Simple sugars contain a carbonyl group and several hydroxyl groups.

A **carboxyl group** consists of a carbon double-bonded to an oxygen atom and also bonded to a hydroxyl group. The carboxyl group acts as an acid by contributing an H^+ to a solution (see Module 2.14) and thus becoming ionized. Compounds with carboxyl groups are called carboxylic acids.

An **amino group** has a nitrogen bonded to two hydrogens and the carbon skeleton. It acts as a base by picking up an H^+ from a solution. Organic compounds with an amino group are called amines. The building blocks of proteins—amino acids—contain an amino and a carboxyl group.

TABLE 3.2	IMPORTANT CHEMICAL GROUPS OF ORGANIC COMPOUNDS
Chemical Group	**Examples**
Hydroxyl group —OH	Alcohol
Carbonyl group C=O	Aldehyde / Ketone
Carboxyl group —COOH	Carboxylic acid / Ionized
Amino group —NH₂	Amine / Ionized
Phosphate group —OPO₃²⁻	Organic phosphate
Methyl group —CH₃	Methylated compound

A **phosphate group** consists of a phosphorus atom bonded to four oxygen atoms. It is usually ionized and attached to the carbon skeleton by one of its oxygen atoms. Compounds with phosphate groups are called organic phosphates and are often involved in energy transfers, as is the energy-rich compound ATP, shown in the table.

A **methyl group** consists of a carbon bonded to three hydrogen atoms. The methylated compound in the table—a component of DNA—affects the expression of genes.

You will meet these chemical groups again as you learn about the four major classes of organic molecules. But first, let's see how your cells make large molecules out of smaller ones.

? Identify the chemical groups that do *not* contain carbon.

The hydroxyl, amino, and phosphate groups ●

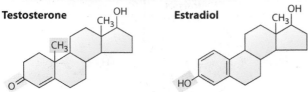

Testosterone **Estradiol**

▲ Figure 3.2   Differences in the chemical groups of sex hormones

3.3 Cells make large molecules from a limited set of small molecules

Given the rich complexity of life on Earth, we might expect there to be an enormous diversity of types of molecules. Remarkably, however, the important molecules of all living things—from bacteria to elephants—fall into just four main classes: carbohydrates, lipids, proteins, and nucleic acids. On a molecular scale, molecules of three of these classes—carbohydrates, proteins, and nucleic acids—can be gigantic; in fact, biologists call them **macromolecules**. For example, a protein may consist of thousands of atoms. How does a cell make such a huge molecule?

Cells make most of their macromolecules by joining smaller molecules into chains called **polymers** (from the Greek *polys*, many, and *meros*, part). A polymer is a long molecule consisting of many identical or similar building blocks strung together, much as a train consists of a chain of cars. The building blocks of polymers are called **monomers**.

Making Polymers   Cells link monomers together to form polymers by a **dehydration reaction**, a reaction that removes a molecule of water as two molecules become bonded together. Each monomer contributes part of the water molecule that is released during the reaction. As you can see on the left side of Figure 3.3, one monomer (the one at the right end of the short polymer in this example) loses a hydroxyl group and the other monomer loses a hydrogen atom to form H_2O. As this occurs, a new covalent bond forms, linking the two monomers. Dehydration reactions are the same regardless of the specific monomers and the type of polymer the cell is producing.

Breaking Polymers   Cells not only make macromolecules but also have to break them down. For example, most of the organic molecules in your food are in the form of polymers that are much too large to enter your cells. You must digest these polymers to make their monomers available to your cells. This digestion process is called **hydrolysis**. Essentially the reverse of a dehydration reaction, hydrolysis means to break (*lyse*) with water (*hydro-*). As the right side of Figure 3.3 shows, the bond between monomers is broken by the addition of a water molecule, with the hydroxyl group from the water attaching to one monomer and a hydrogen attaching to the adjacent monomer.

The lactose-intolerant individuals you learned about in the chapter introduction are unable to hydrolyze such a bond in the sugar lactose because they lack the enzyme lactase. Both dehydration reactions and hydrolysis require the help of enzymes to make and break bonds. **Enzymes** are specialized macromolecules that speed up chemical reactions in cells.

The Diversity of Polymers   The diversity of macromolecules in the living world is vast. Surprisingly, a cell makes all its thousands of different macromolecules from a small list of ingredients—about 40 to 50 common components and a few others that are rare. Proteins, for example, are built from only 20 kinds of amino acids. Your DNA is built from just four kinds of monomers called nucleotides. The key to the great diversity of polymers is arrangement—variation in the sequence in which monomers are strung together.

The variety in polymers accounts for the uniqueness of each organism. The monomers themselves, however, are essentially universal. Your proteins and those of a tree or an ant are assembled from the same 20 amino acids. Life has a simple yet elegant molecular logic: Small molecules common to all organisms are ordered into large molecules, which vary from species to species and even from individual to individual in the same species.

In the remainder of the chapter, we explore each of the four classes of large biological molecules. Like water and simple organic molecules, large biological molecules have unique emergent properties arising from the orderly arrangement of their atoms. As you will see, for these molecules of life, structure and function are inseparable.

> **?** Suppose you eat some cheese. What reactions must occur for the protein of the cheese to be broken down into its amino acid monomers and then for these monomers to be converted to proteins in your body?

● In digestion, the proteins are broken down into amino acids by hydrolysis. New proteins are formed in your body cells from these monomers in dehydration reactions.

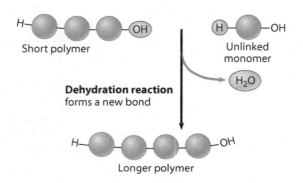

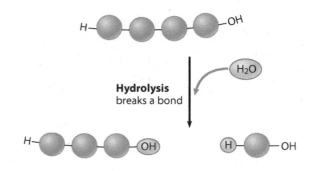

▲ Figure 3.3   Dehydration reaction building a polymer (left); Hydrolysis breaking down a polymer (right)

▷ Carbohydrates

3.4 Monosaccharides are the simplest carbohydrates

Let's start our survey of large biological molecules with **carbohydrates**, the class of molecules that range from small sugar molecules, such as those dissolved in soft drinks, to large polysaccharides, such as the starch molecules we consume in pasta and potatoes.

Simple sugars, or **monosaccharides** (from the Greek *monos*, single, and *sacchar*, sugar), are the monomers of carbohydrates. The honey shown in **Figure 3.4A** consists mainly of monosaccharides called glucose and fructose. These and other single-unit sugars can be hooked together by dehydration reactions to form more complex sugars and polysaccharides.

Monosaccharides generally have molecular formulas that are some multiple of CH_2O. For example, the formula for **glucose**, a common monosaccharide of central importance in the chemistry of life, is $C_6H_{12}O_6$. **Figure 3.4B** illustrates the molecular structure of glucose, with its carbons numbered 1 to 6. This structure also shows the two trademarks of a sugar: a number of hydroxyl groups (—OH) and a carbonyl group (> C=O, highlighted in blue). The hydroxyl groups make a sugar an alcohol, and the carbonyl group, depending on its location, makes it either an aldehyde sugar (glucose) or a ketone sugar (fructose).

If you count the numbers of different atoms in the fructose molecule in Figure 3.4B, you will find that its molecular formula is $C_6H_{12}O_6$, identical to that of glucose. Thus, glucose and fructose are isomers; they differ only in the arrangement of their atoms (in this case, the positions of the carbonyl groups). Because the shape of molecules is so important, seemingly minor differences like this give isomers different properties, such as how they react with other molecules. These differences also make fructose taste considerably sweeter than glucose.

The carbon skeletons of both glucose and fructose are six carbon atoms long. Other monosaccharides may have three to seven carbons. Five-carbon sugars, called pentoses, and six-carbon sugars, called hexoses, are among the most common. (Note that most names for sugars end in *-ose*. Also, as you saw with the enzyme lactase, which digests the sugar lactose, the names for most enzymes end in *-ase*.)

It is convenient to draw sugars as if their carbon skeletons were linear, but in aqueous solutions, most five- and six-carbon sugars form rings, as shown for glucose in **Figure 3.4C**. To form the glucose ring, carbon 1 bonds to the oxygen attached to carbon 5. As shown in the middle representation, the ring diagram of glucose and other sugars may be abbreviated by not showing the carbon atoms at the corners of the ring. Also, the bonds in the ring are often drawn with varied thickness, indicating that the ring is a relatively flat structure with attached atoms extending above and below it. The simplified ring symbol on the right is often used in this book to represent glucose.

Monosaccharides, particularly glucose, are the main fuel molecules for cellular work. Because cells release energy from glucose when they break it down, an aqueous solution of glucose (often called dextrose) may be injected into the bloodstream of sick or injured patients; the glucose provides an immediate energy source to tissues in need of repair. Cells also use the carbon skeletons of monosaccharides as raw material for making other kinds of organic molecules, such as amino acids and fatty acids. Sugars not used in these ways may be incorporated into disaccharides and polysaccharides, as we see next.

? **Write the formula for a monosaccharide that has three carbons.**

● $C_3H_6O_3$

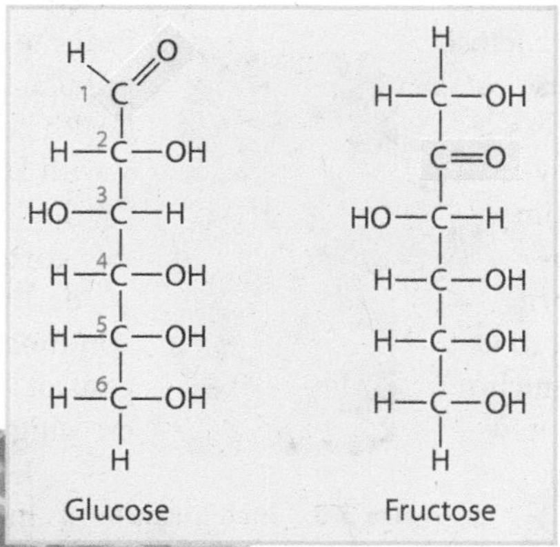

◀ **Figure 3.4B** Structures of glucose and fructose

Try This Identify the two functional groups that are characteristic of a monosaccharide.

Glucose

Fructose

▲ **Figure 3.4A** Bees with honey, a mixture of two monosaccharides

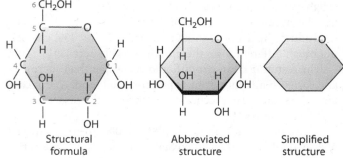

Structural formula

Abbreviated structure

Simplified structure

▲ **Figure 3.4C** Three representations of the ring form of glucose

3.5 Two monosaccharides are linked to form a disaccharide

Cells construct a **disaccharide** from two monosaccharide monomers by a dehydration reaction. Figure 3.5 shows how maltose, also called malt sugar, is formed from two glucose monomers. One monomer gives up a hydroxyl group and the other gives up a hydrogen atom. As H_2O is released, an oxygen atom is left, linking the two monomers. Malt sugar, which is common in germinating seeds, is used in making beer, malt whiskey, and malted milk candy.

Sucrose is the most common disaccharide. It is made of a glucose monomer linked to a fructose monomer. Transported in plant sap, sucrose provides a source of energy and raw materials to all the parts of the plant. We extract it from the stems of sugarcane or the roots of sugar beets to use as table sugar.

> **?** Lactose, as you read in the chapter introduction, is the disaccharide sugar in milk. It is formed from glucose and galactose. The formula for both these monosaccharides is $C_6H_{12}O_6$. What is the formula for lactose?
>
> ● $C_{12}H_{22}O_{11}$

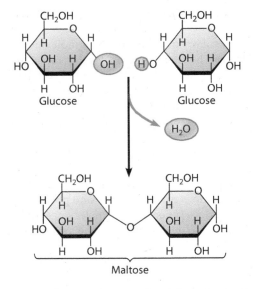

▲ **Figure 3.5** Disaccharide formation by a dehydration reaction

---

3.6 What is high-fructose corn syrup, and is it to blame for obesity?

CONNECTION

If you want to sweeten your coffee or tea, you probably reach for sugar—the disaccharide sucrose. But if you drink sodas, you're probably consuming the monosaccharides of sucrose in the form of high-fructose corn syrup. In fact, if you look at the label of almost any processed food, you will see high-fructose corn syrup listed as one of the ingredients (Figure 3.6).

What is high-fructose corn syrup (HFCS)? Let's start with the corn syrup part. The main carbohydrate in corn is starch, a polysaccharide built from glucose monomers. Industrial processing hydrolyzes starch into these monomers, producing corn syrup. Glucose, however, does not taste as sweet to us as sucrose. Fructose, on the other hand, tastes much sweeter than both glucose and sucrose. When a new process was developed in the 1970s that used an enzyme to rearrange the atoms of glucose into the sweeter isomer, fructose (see Figure 3.4B), the high-fructose corn syrup industry was born. (High-fructose corn syrup is a bit of a misnomer, because the fructose is combined with regular corn syrup to produce a mixture of about 55% fructose and 45% glucose, not much different from the proportions in sucrose.)

The resulting clear, goopy liquid is cheaper than sucrose and easier to mix into drinks and processed food. And it contains the same monosaccharides as sucrose, the disaccharide it is replacing. So is there a problem with HFCS? Some point to circumstantial evidence. From 1980 to 2000, the incidence of obesity doubled in the United States. In that same time period, the consumption of HFCS more than tripled, whereas the consumption of refined cane and beet sugar decreased 21%.

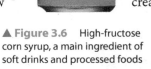

▲ **Figure 3.6** High-fructose corn syrup, a main ingredient of soft drinks and processed foods

Is high-fructose corn syrup to blame for the current "obesity epidemic" with its attendant increases in type 2 diabetes, high blood pressure, and other chronic diseases associated with increased weight? Does this *correlation* between increased HFCS consumption and increased obesity indicate *causation*? In spite of alarming claims in the popular press, most scientific studies have not shown health consequences associated with replacing sucrose with HFCS. Data also show that some countries with high obesity rates consume little high-fructose corn syrup. And although HFCS consumption has declined somewhat in recent years, obesity rates continue to rise, with almost 36% of U.S. adults now considered obese. Alternative hypotheses for our increasing obesity abound, including the fact that, from 1980 to 2000, the U.S. per capita daily caloric intake increased 23%.

It does not appear that high-fructose corn syrup is the "smoking gun" responsible for the obesity crisis. There is solid evidence, however, that overconsumption of sugar and/or HFCS along with dietary fat and decreased physical activity contribute to weight gain. In addition, high sugar consumption tends to replace eating more varied and nutritious foods. For good health, you require proteins, fats, vitamins, and minerals, as well as complex carbohydrates, the topic of the next module.

> **?** How is high-fructose corn syrup made from corn?
>
> ● Corn starch is hydrolyzed to glucose; then enzymes convert glucose to fructose. This fructose is combined with corn syrup to produce HFCS.

3.7 Polysaccharides are long chains of sugar units

Polysaccharides are macromolecules, polymers of hundreds to thousands of monosaccharides linked together by dehydration reactions. Polysaccharides may function as storage molecules or as structural compounds. **Figure 3.7** illustrates three common types: starch, glycogen, and cellulose.

Starch, a storage polysaccharide in plants, consists of long chains of glucose monomers. Starch molecules coil into a helical shape and may be unbranched (as shown in the figure) or branched. Starch granules serve as carbohydrate "banks" from which plant cells can withdraw glucose for energy or building materials. Humans and most other animals have enzymes that can hydrolyze plant starch to glucose. Potatoes and grains, such as wheat, corn, and rice, are the major sources of starch in the human diet.

Animals store glucose in a polysaccharide called **glycogen**. Glycogen is more highly branched than starch, as shown in the figure. Most of your glycogen is stored as granules in your liver and muscle cells, which hydrolyze the glycogen to release glucose when it is needed.

Cellulose, the most abundant organic compound on Earth, is a major component of the tough walls that enclose plant cells. Cellulose is also a polymer of glucose, but its monomers are linked together in a different orientation. (Carefully compare the oxygen "bridges" highlighted in yellow in the figure between glucose monomers in starch, glycogen, and cellulose.) Arranged parallel to each other, cellulose molecules are joined by hydrogen bonds, forming cable-like microfibrils. Layers of microfibrils combine with other polymers, producing strong support for trees and the structures we build with lumber.

Animals do not have enzymes that can hydrolyze the glucose linkages in cellulose. Therefore, cellulose is not a nutrient for humans, although it does contribute to digestive health. The cellulose that passes unchanged through your digestive tract is referred to as "insoluble fiber." Fresh fruits, vegetables, and whole grains are rich in fiber.

Some microorganisms do have enzymes that can hydrolyze cellulose. Cows and termites house such microorganisms in their digestive tracts and are thus able to derive energy from cellulose. Decomposing fungi also digest cellulose, helping to recycle its chemical elements within ecosystems.

Chitin is a structural polysaccharide used by insects and crustaceans to build their exoskeleton, the hard case enclosing the animal. Chitin is also found in the cell walls of fungi.

Almost all carbohydrates are hydrophilic owing to the many hydroxyl groups attached to their sugar monomers (see Figure 3.4B). Thus, cotton bath towels, which are mostly cellulose, are quite water absorbent due to the water-loving nature of cellulose. As you'll see next, not all biological molecules "love water."

> **?** **Compare and contrast starch and cellulose, two plant polysaccharides.**
>
> ● Both are polymers of glucose, but the bonds between glucose monomers have different shapes. Starch functions mainly for sugar storage. Cellulose is a structural polysaccharide that is the main material of plant cell walls.

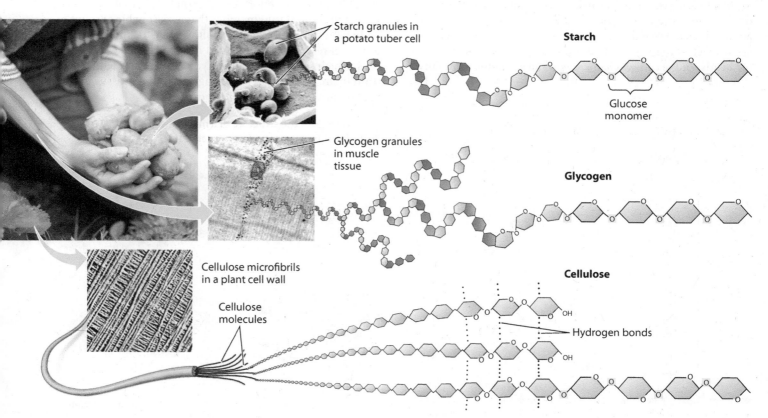

▲ **Figure 3.7** Polysaccharides of plants and animals

Starch granules in a potato tuber cell

Glycogen granules in muscle tissue

Cellulose microfibrils in a plant cell wall

Cellulose molecules

Starch

Glucose monomer

Glycogen

Cellulose

OH

Hydrogen bonds

OH

▷ Lipids

3.8 Fats are lipids that are mostly energy-storage molecules

Lipids are a diverse group of molecules that are classified together because they share one trait: They do not mix well with water. In contrast to carbohydrates and most other biological molecules, lipids are **hydrophobic** (water-fearing). You can see this chemical behavior in an unshaken bottle of salad dressing. The oil (a type of lipid) separates from the vinegar (which is mostly water).

Lipids also differ from carbohydrates, proteins, and nucleic acids in that they are neither huge macromolecules nor polymers built from similar monomers. In this and the next few modules, we consider the structures and functions of three important types of lipids: fats, phospholipids, and steroids.

A **fat** is a large lipid made from two kinds of smaller molecules: glycerol and fatty acids. Shown at the top in **Figure 3.8A**, glycerol consists of three carbons, each bearing a hydroxyl group (—OH). A fatty acid consists of a carboxyl group (the functional group that gives these molecules the name fatty *acid*, —COOH) and a hydrocarbon chain, usually 16 or 18 carbon atoms in length. The nonpolar C—H bonds in the hydrocarbon chains are the reason fats are hydrophobic.

Figure 3.8A shows how one fatty acid molecule can link to a glycerol molecule by a dehydration reaction. Linking three fatty acids to glycerol produces a fat, as illustrated in **Figure 3.8B**. A synonym for fat is *triglyceride*, a term you may see on food labels or on medical tests for fat in the blood.

A fatty acid whose hydrocarbon chain contains one or more double bonds is called an **unsaturated fatty acid**. Each carbon atom connected by a double bond has one fewer hydrogen atom attached to it. These double bonds usually cause kinks (or bends) in the carbon chain, as you can see in the third fatty acid in Figure 3.8B. A fatty acid that has no double bonds in its hydrocarbon chain has the maximum number of hydrogen atoms attached to each carbon atom (its carbons are "saturated" with hydrogen) and is called a **saturated fatty acid**.

Most animal fats are saturated: Their hydrocarbon chains—the "tails" of their fatty acids—lack double bonds and thus pack closely together, making them solid at room temperature (**Figure 3.8C**). In contrast, the fats of plants and fishes generally contain unsaturated fatty acids. The kinks in their unsaturated fatty acid tails prevent them from packing tightly together. Thus, unsaturated fats are usually liquid at room temperature and are referred to as oils. When you see "hydrogenated vegetable oils" on a margarine label, it means that unsaturated fats have been converted to saturated fats by adding hydrogen. Unfortunately, the process of hydrogenation also creates **trans fats**, a form of fat that recent research associates with health risks. We will discuss some of that research in Module 3.9.

The main function of fats is long-term energy storage. A gram of fat stores more than twice as much energy as a gram of polysaccharide. For immobile plants, the bulky energy storage form of starch is not a problem. (Vegetable oils are generally obtained from seeds, where more compact energy storage is a benefit.) Mobile animals, such as humans, can get around much more easily carrying their energy stores in the form of fat. Of course, the downside of this energy-packed storage form is that it takes more effort for a person to "burn off" excess fat.

It is important to remember that a reasonable amount of body fat is both normal and healthy. You stock these long-term fuel reserves in specialized reservoirs called adipose cells, which swell and shrink as you deposit and withdraw fat from them. In addition to storing energy, fatty tissue cushions vital organs and insulates the body.

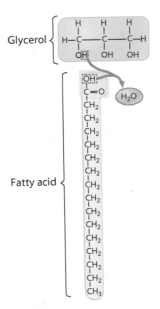

▲ **Figure 3.8A** A dehydration reaction that will link a fatty acid to glycerol

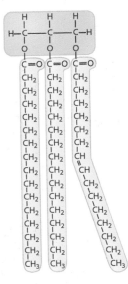

▲ **Figure 3.8B** A fat molecule (triglyceride) consisting of three fatty acids linked to glycerol

? **How does the structure of a monounsaturated fat differ from a polyunsaturated fat?**

● A monounsaturated fat has a fatty acid with a single double bond in its carbon chain. A polyunsaturated fat contains a fatty acid with more than one double bond.

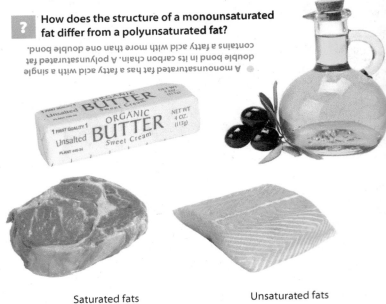

Saturated fats

Unsaturated fats

▲ **Figure 3.8C** Types of fats

3.9 Scientific studies document the health risks of trans fats

SCIENTIFIC THINKING

In the previous module, you learned about the difference between vegetable oils and animal fats and their unsaturated versus saturated fatty acids. In the 1890s, a process was invented that added hydrogen atoms to the double-bonded carbon atoms of unsaturated fats, producing partially hydrogenated vegetable oils. These new fats had several desirable traits: They didn't spoil as quickly as oils and could withstand repeated reheating for frying. In addition, in the 1950s and 1960s, scientific studies began to associate saturated fats with an increased risk of heart disease, leading to a public health campaign to reduce consumption of animal fats (such as butter) and replace them with unsaturated oils and the supposedly healthier partially hydrogenated vegetable oils (such as margarine).

Jump ahead to the 1990s, and partially hydrogenated oils were found in myriad foods—cookies, crackers, snacks, baked goods, and fried foods. But new research began to show that the trans fats produced in the process of hydrogenation were an even greater health risk than were saturated fats. One study estimated that eliminating trans fats from the food supply could prevent up to one in five heart attacks! In 2006, the U.S. Food and Drug Administration required the listing of trans fat on food labels. Because foods sold in restaurants and schools do not come with labels, many cities and states since have passed laws to eliminate trans fats in these foods. And an increasing number of countries have banned trans fats.

The scientific studies establishing the risks of trans fats were of two types: experimental and observational. In experimental controlled feeding trials, the diets of participants contained different proportions of saturated, unsaturated, and partially hydrogenated fats. The hypothesis of these studies was that trans fats adversely affect cardiovascular health; the prediction was that the more trans fats in the diet, the greater the risk. But how does one measure risk? Should the study proceed until participants start having heart attacks? For both ethical and practical reasons, controlled feeding trials are usually fairly short in duration, involve only limited dietary changes, generally use healthy individuals, and measure intermediary risk factors, such as changes in cholesterol levels, rather than actual disease outcomes.

Many scientific studies on dietary health effects are observational. The advantages of such studies are that they can extend over a longer time period, use a more representative population, and measure disease outcomes as well as risk factors. Observational studies may be retrospective (looking backward): Present health status is documented, and participants report their prior eating habits. Two difficulties with retrospective studies are that people may not accurately remember and report their dietary histories, and anyone who has already died, say, of a heart attack, is not included in the study. Prospective studies, on the other hand, look forward. Researchers conducting such studies enlist a study group, quantify participants' health attributes, and then collect data on the group over many years. Diet, lifestyle habits, risk factors, and disease outcomes can all be recorded and then analyzed.

TABLE 3.9

RISK OF HEART DISEASE ASSOCIATED WITH INCREASES IN SPECIFIC TYPES OF FAT CONSUMED

Variable	Relative Risk*
Saturated fat (each increase of 5% of energy)	1.17
Monounsaturated fat (each increase of 5% of energy)	0.81
Polyunsaturated fat (each increase of 5% of energy)	0.62
Trans fat (each increase of 2% of energy	1.93

* A relative risk (RR) of 1 means that there is no difference in risk of coronary heart disease when compared to an equivalent intake of carbohydrate; RR of less than 1 means there is a decreased risk; RR greater than 1, there is a greater risk.

Data from F. B. Hu et al. Dietary fat intake and the risk of coronary heart disease in women, *New England Journal of Medicine* 337: 1491–9 (1997).

A landmark example of a prospective study is the Nurses' Health Study, begun in 1976 with more than 120,000 female nurses. In a portion of the study that looked at dietary fat intake, 80,082 women were followed from 1980 to 1994. The researchers estimated the relative risk of coronary heart disease associated with the intake of different types of fats. As you can see in **Table 3.9**, for each 5% increase in energy consumed in the form of saturated fat, as compared to an equivalent energy intake from carbohydrates, the relative risk rises to 1.17—or a 17% increase in the risk of heart disease. For each 2% increase in the amount of energy consumed in the form of trans fat, however, there is a 93% increase in risk. Trans fats are indeed a greater health risk than saturated fats.

Based on an accumulation of scientific evidence from many studies, U.S. governmental agencies have revised their policies—from promoting partially hydrogenated vegetable oils as a healthful alternative to saturated fats in the middle of the 20th century to today regulating and increasingly banning the trans fats that are produced when such oils are hydrogenated. Such changes in policy reflect changes in our understanding based on current research. Scientific knowledge both expands and is revised as new questions are asked, new studies are done, and new evidence accumulates.

In the next module, we consider two other important types of lipids: phospholipids and steroids.

Data from D. Mozaffarian et al., Trans fatty acids and cardiovascular disease, *The New England Journal of Medicine* 354: 1601–13 (2006).

? How does the relative risk of coronary heart disease change with a 5% increase in polyunsaturated fat in the diet?

The relative risk drops to 0.62. In other words, there is a 38% decrease in risk.

3.10 Phospholipids and steroids are important lipids with a variety of functions

Cells could not exist without **phospholipids**, the major component of cell membranes. Phospholipids are structurally similar to fats, except that they contain only two fatty acids attached to glycerol instead of three. As shown in Figure 3.10A, a negatively charged phosphate group (shown as a yellow circle in the figure and linked to another small molecule) is attached to glycerol's third carbon.

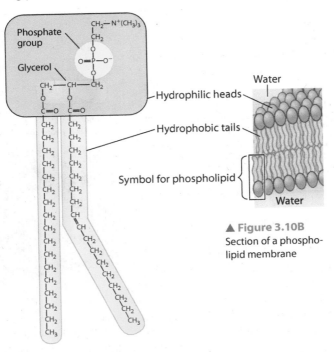

Phosphate group
Glycerol

Water
—Hydrophilic heads
—Hydrophobic tails
Symbol for phospholipid
Water

▲ Figure 3.10B
Section of a phospholipid membrane

▲ **Figure 3.10A** Chemical structure of a phospholipid molecule

Try This Explain why the gray region of this phospholipid is hydrophilic and why the yellow tails are hydrophobic.

The structure of phospholipids provides a classic example of how form fits function. The two ends of a phospholipid have different relationships with water, resulting in the aggregation of multiple phospholipid molecules into a membrane (Figure 3.10B). The hydrophobic tails of the fatty acids cluster together in the center, excluded from water, and the hydrophilic phosphate heads face the watery environment on either side of the membrane. Each gray-headed, yellow-tailed structure in the membrane shown here represents a phospholipid; this visual representation is used throughout this book. (We will explore the structure and function of biological membranes in more detail in Chapter 5.)

Steroids are lipids in which the carbon skeleton contains four fused rings, as shown in the structural formula of cholesterol in Figure 3.10C. (The diagram omits the carbons making up the rings and most of the chain and also their attached hydrogen atoms.) **Cholesterol** is a common component in animal cell membranes and is also the precursor for making other steroids, including sex hormones. Different steroids vary in the chemical groups attached to the rings, as you saw in Figure 3.2. Too much cholesterol in the blood may contribute to atherosclerosis.

? **Compare the structure of a phospholipid with that of a fat (triglyceride).**

● A phospholipid has two fatty acids and a phosphate group attached to glycerol. Three fatty acids are attached to the glycerol of a fat molecule.

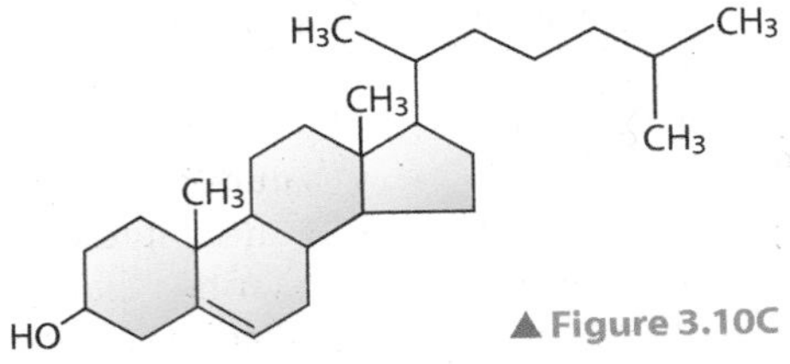

▲ **Figure 3.10C** Cholesterol, a steroid

3.11 Anabolic steroids pose health risks

CONNECTION

Anabolic steroids are synthetic variants of the male hormone testosterone. Testosterone causes a general buildup of muscle and bone mass in males during puberty and maintains masculine traits throughout life. Because anabolic steroids structurally resemble testosterone, they also mimic some of its effects. (The word *anabolic* comes from *anabolism*, the building of substances by the body.)

Anabolic steroids are used to treat general anemia and diseases that destroy body muscle. Some athletes use these drugs to build up their muscles quickly and enhance their performance. But at what cost? Steroid abuse may cause violent mood swings ("roid rage"), depression, liver damage or cancer, and high cholesterol levels and blood pressure. Use of these drugs often makes the body reduce its output of natural male sex hormones, which

can cause shrunken testicles, reduced sex drive, infertility, and breast enlargement in men. Use in women has been linked to menstrual cycle disruption and development of masculine characteristics. An effect in teens is that bones may stop growing. Despite the risks, some athletes continue to abuse synthetic steroids, and unscrupulous chemists, trainers, and coaches try to find ways to avoid their detection. Meanwhile, the U.S. Congress, professional sports authorities, and high school and college athletic programs ban the use of anabolic steroids, implement drug testing, and penalize violators in an effort to keep the competition fair and protect the health of athletes.

? **Explain why fats and steroids, which are structurally very different, are both classed as lipids?**

● Fats and steroids are hydrophobic molecules, the key characteristic of lipids.

3.12 Proteins have a wide range of functions and structures

Nearly every dynamic function in your body depends on proteins. A **protein** is a polymer of small building blocks called amino acids. Of all of life's molecules, proteins are structurally and functionally the most elaborate and varied.

You have tens of thousands of different proteins in your body. What do they all do? Probably their most important role is as enzymes, the chemical catalysts that speed and regulate virtually all chemical reactions in your cells. Lactase, which you read about in the chapter introduction, is just one example of an enzyme.

Other types of proteins include transport proteins that are embedded in cell membranes and move sugar molecules and other nutrients into your cells. Moving through your blood stream are defensive proteins, such as the antibodies of the immune system, and signal proteins, such as many of the hormones and other chemical messengers that help coordinate your body's activities. Receptor proteins built into cell membranes receive and transmit such signals into your cells.

Muscle cells are packed with contractile proteins, and structural proteins are found in the fibers that make up your tendons and ligaments. Indeed, the structural protein collagen, which forms the long, strong fibers of connective tissues, accounts for 40% of the protein in your body.

Some proteins are storage proteins, which supply amino acids to developing embryos. The proteins found in eggs and seeds are examples.

The functions of all of these different types of proteins depend on their individual shapes. **Figure 3.12A** shows a ribbon model of lysozyme, an enzyme found in your sweat, tears, and saliva. Lysozyme consists of one long polymer of amino acids, represented by the purple ribbon. Lysozyme's general shape is called globular. This overall shape is more apparent in **Figure 3.12B**, a space-filling model of lysozyme. In that model, the colors represent the different atoms of carbon, oxygen, nitrogen, and hydrogen. The barely visible yellow balls represent sulfur atoms that form the stabilizing bonds shown as yellow lines in the ribbon model. Most enzymes and many other proteins are globular. Structural proteins, such as those making up hair, tendons, and ligaments, are typically long and thin and are called fibrous proteins. **Figure 3.12C** shows a spider's web, made up of fibrous silk proteins. The structural arrangement within these proteins makes each silk fiber stronger than a steel strand of the same weight.

Descriptions such as *globular* and *fibrous* refer to a protein's general shape. Each protein also has a much more specific shape. The coils and twists of lysozyme's ribbon in Figure 3.12A may appear haphazard, but they represent the molecule's specific, three-dimensional

shape. Nearly all proteins must recognize and bind to some other molecule to function. Lysozyme can destroy bacterial cells, but first it must bind to molecules on the bacterial cell surface. Lysozyme's specific shape enables it to recognize and attach to its molecular target, which fits into the groove you see on the right in the figures.

The dependence of protein function on a protein's shape becomes clear when a protein is altered. In a process called **denaturation**, a protein unravels, losing its specific shape and, as a result, its function. Excessive heat can denature many proteins. For example, visualize what happens when you fry an egg. Heat quickly denatures the clear proteins surrounding the yolk, making them solid, white, and opaque.

Given the proper cellular environment, a newly synthesized amino acid chain spontaneously folds into its functional shape. What happens if a protein doesn't fold correctly? Many diseases, such as Alzheimer's and Parkinson's, involve an accumulation of misfolded proteins. Prions are infectious misshapen proteins that are associated with serious degenerative brain diseases such as mad cow disease (see Module 10.21). Such diseases reinforce the theme that structure fits function: A protein's unique three-dimensional shape

▲ **Figure 3.12C** Fibrous silk proteins of a spider's web

determines its proper functioning. In the next two modules, we'll learn how a protein's structure takes shape.

? **Why does a denatured protein no longer function normally?**

● The function of each protein is a consequence of its specific shape, which is lost when a protein denatures.

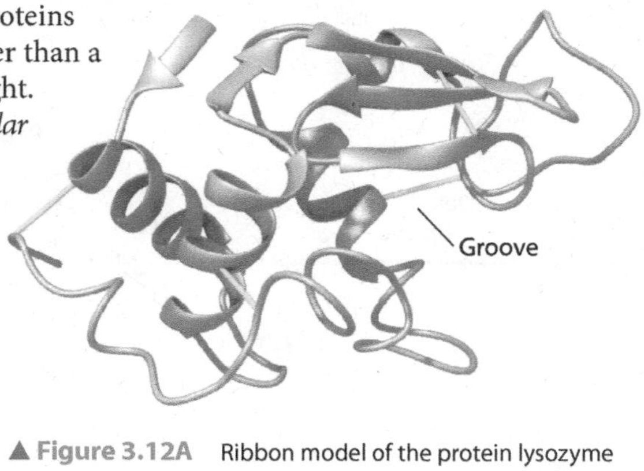

▲ **Figure 3.12A** Ribbon model of the protein lysozyme

Groove

▲ **Figure 3.12B** Space-filling model of the protein lysozyme

Groove

3.13 Proteins are made from amino acids linked by peptide bonds

Now let's see what the monomers of proteins look like. **Amino acids** all have an amino group and a carboxyl group (which makes it an acid, hence the name amino *acid*). As you

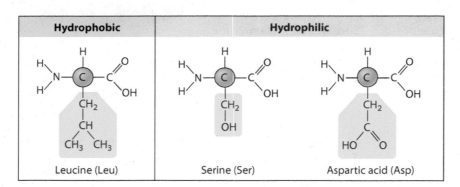

can see in the general structure shown in **Figure 3.13A**, both of these functional groups are covalently bonded to a central carbon atom. Also bonded to this carbon is a hydrogen atom. The fourth bond of the central carbon is to a variable chemical group symbolized by the letter R. In the simplest amino acid (glycine), the R group is just a hydrogen atom. In all others, the R group consists of one or more carbon atoms with various functional groups attached.

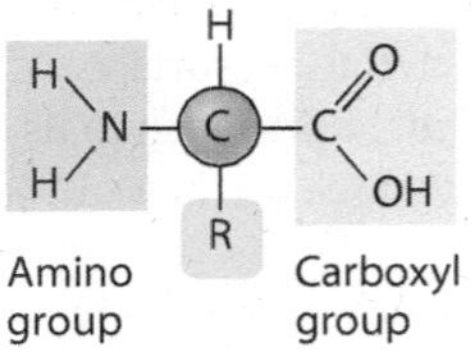

▲ Figure 3.13A General structure of an amino acid

All 20 amino acids are included in Appendix 3, grouped according to whether their R groups are hydrophobic or hydrophilic. **Figure 3.13B** shows representatives of these two main types. Hydrophobic amino acids have nonpolar R groups—note the nonpolar C—H bonds in the R group of leucine (abbreviated Leu) shown in the figure. The R groups of hydrophilic amino acids may be polar or charged. R groups that contain acidic or basic groups are charged at the pH of a cell. Indeed, the amino and carboxyl groups attached to the central carbon of all amino acids are also usually ionized at cellular pH (see ionized forms in Table 3.2).

Now that we have examined amino acids, let's see how they are linked to form polymers. Can you guess? Cells join amino acids together in a dehydration reaction that links the carboxyl group of one amino acid to the amino group of the next amino acid as a water molecule is removed (**Figure 3.13C**). The resulting covalent linkage is called a **peptide bond**. The product of the reaction shown in the figure is called a *di*peptide, because it was made from *two* amino acids. Additional amino acids can be added by the same process to form a chain of amino acids, a **polypeptide**.

How is it possible to make thousands of different kinds of proteins from just 20 amino acids? The answer has to do with sequence. You know that thousands of English words can be made by varying the sequence of letters and word length. Although the protein "alphabet" is slightly smaller (just 20 "letters," rather than 26), the "words" are much longer. Most polypeptides are at least 100 amino acids in length; some are 1,000 or more. Each polypeptide has a unique sequence of amino acids.

But a long polypeptide chain of specific sequence is not the same as a protein, any more than a long strand of yarn is the same as a sweater that can be knit from that yarn. What are the stitches that coil and fold a polypeptide chain into a unique three-dimensional shape? This is where the R groups of the constituent amino acids play their role in influencing protein structure. Hydrophobic amino acids may cluster together in the center of a globular protein, while hydrophilic amino acids face the outside, helping proteins dissolve in the aqueous solution of a cell. Hydrogen bonds and ionic bonds between hydrophilic R groups help determine a protein's shape, as do covalent bonds called disulfide bridges between sulfur atoms in some R groups. (Look back at the yellow lines in Figure 3.12A.) The unique sequence of the various types of amino acids in a polypeptide determines how a protein takes shape. Let's visualize this process in the next module.

? By what process do you digest the proteins you eat into their individual amino acids?

● By hydrolysis, adding a molecule of water back to break each peptide bond

Hydrophobic	Hydrophilic	
Leucine (Leu)	Serine (Ser)	Aspartic acid (Asp)

▲ Figure 3.13B Examples of amino acids with hydrophobic and hydrophilic R groups

Try This Point out the bonds and functional groups that make the R groups of these three amino acids either hydrophobic or hydrophilic.

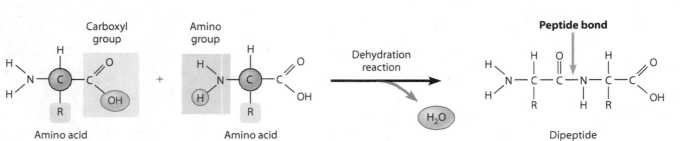

▲ Figure 3.13C Peptide bond formation

3.14 A protein's functional shape results from four levels of structure

The **primary structure** of a protein is the precise sequence of amino acids in the polypeptide chain. Segments of the chain then coil or fold into local patterns called **secondary structure**. The overall three-dimensional shape of a protein is called **tertiary structure**. Proteins with more than one polypeptide chain have **quaternary structure.**

To help you visualize how these structural levels are superimposed on each other to form a functional protein, let's look at transthyretin, an important transport protein found in your blood. Its specific shape enables it to transport vitamin A and one of the thyroid hormones throughout your body.

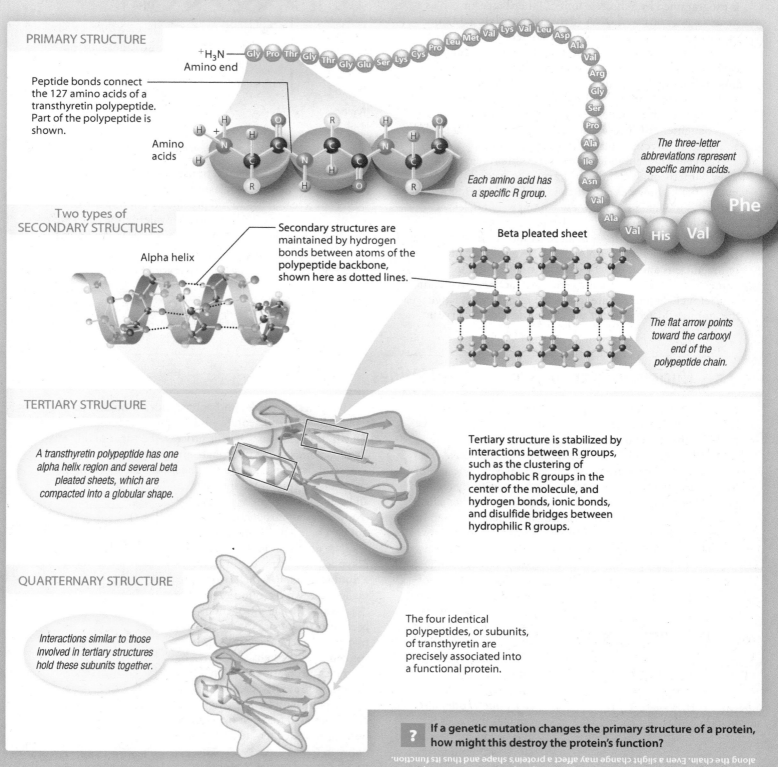

PRIMARY STRUCTURE

^+H_3N — Amino end

Peptide bonds connect the 127 amino acids of a transthyretin polypeptide. Part of the polypeptide is shown.

Amino acids

Each amino acid has a specific R group.

The three-letter abbreviations represent specific amino acids.

Two types of **SECONDARY STRUCTURES**

Alpha helix

Secondary structures are maintained by hydrogen bonds between atoms of the polypeptide backbone, shown here as dotted lines.

Beta pleated sheet

The flat arrow points toward the carboxyl end of the polypeptide chain.

TERTIARY STRUCTURE

A transthyretin polypeptide has one alpha helix region and several beta pleated sheets, which are compacted into a globular shape.

Tertiary structure is stabilized by interactions between R groups, such as the clustering of hydrophobic R groups in the center of the molecule, and hydrogen bonds, ionic bonds, and disulfide bridges between hydrophilic R groups.

QUARTERNARY STRUCTURE

Interactions similar to those involved in tertiary structures hold these subunits together.

The four identical polypeptides, or subunits, of transthyretin are precisely associated into a functional protein.

? If a genetic mutation changes the primary structure of a protein, how might this destroy the protein's function?

● Primary structure determines the secondary and tertiary structure due to the chemical nature of the polypeptide backbone and R groups of the amino acids positioned along the chain. Even a slight change may affect a protein's shape and thus its function.

▷ Nucleic Acids

3.15 DNA and RNA are the two types of nucleic acids

As we just saw, the primary structure of a polypeptide determines the shape of a protein. But what determines the primary structure? The amino acid sequence of a polypeptide is programmed by a discrete unit of inheritance known as a **gene**. Genes consist of **DNA (deoxyribonucleic acid)**, one of the two types of polymers called **nucleic acids**. The name *nucleic* comes from their location in the nuclei of eukaryotic cells. The genetic material that humans and other organisms inherit from their parents consists of DNA. Unique among molecules, DNA provides directions for its own replication. Thus, as a cell divides, its genetic instructions are passed to each daughter cell. These instructions program all of a cell's activities by directing the synthesis of proteins.

The genes present in DNA do not build proteins directly. They work through an intermediary—the second type of nucleic acid, known as **ribonucleic acid (RNA)**. **Figure 3.15** illustrates the main roles of these two types of nucleic acids in the production of proteins. In the nucleus of a eukaryotic cell, a gene directs the synthesis of an RNA molecule. We say that DNA is transcribed into RNA. The RNA molecule moves out of the nucleus and interacts with the protein-building machinery of the cell. There, the gene's instructions, written in "nucleic acid language," are translated into "protein language," the amino acid sequence of a polypeptide. (In prokaryotic

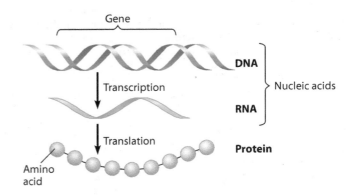

▲ Figure 3.15   The flow of genetic information in the building of a protein

cells, which lack nuclei, both transcription and translation take place within the cytoplasm of the cell.)

Recent research has found previously unknown types of RNA molecules that play many other roles in the cell. (We return to the functions of DNA and RNA later in the book.)

> **?**   **How are the two types of nucleic acids functionally related?**
>
> ● The hereditary material of DNA contains the instructions for the primary structure of polypeptides. RNA is the intermediary that conveys those instructions to the protein-making machinery that assembles amino acids in the designated order.

3.16 Nucleic acids are polymers of nucleotides

The monomers that make up nucleic acids are **nucleotides**. As indicated in **Figure 3.16A**, each nucleotide contains three parts. At the center of a nucleotide is a five-carbon sugar (blue); the sugar in DNA is deoxyribose, whereas RNA has a slightly different sugar called ribose. Linked to one side of the sugar in both types of nucleotides is a negatively charged phosphate group (yellow). Linked to the sugar's other side is a nitrogenous base (green), a molecular structure containing nitrogen and carbon. (The nitrogen atoms tend to take up H$^+$ in aqueous solutions, which explains why it is called a nitrogenous *base*.) Each DNA nucleotide has one of four different nitrogenous bases: adenine (A), thymine (T), cytosine (C), and guanine (G). Thus, all genetic information is written in a four-letter alphabet. RNA nucleotides also contain the bases A, C, and G; but the base uracil (U) is found instead of thymine.

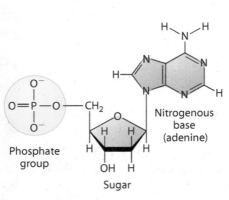

▲ Figure 3.16A   A nucleotide

Like polysaccharides and polypeptides, a nucleic acid polymer—a polynucleotide—is built from its monomers by dehydration reactions. In this process, the sugar of one nucleotide bonds to the phosphate group of the next monomer. The result is a repeating sugar-phosphate backbone in the polymer, as represented by the blue and yellow ribbon in **Figure 3.16B**. (Note that the nitrogenous bases are not part of the backbone.)

RNA usually consists of a single polynucleotide strand, but DNA is a **double helix**, in which two polynucleotides wrap around each other (**Figure 3.16C**). The nitrogenous bases protrude from the two sugar-phosphate backbones and pair in the center of the helix. As shown by their diagrammatic shapes in the figure, A always pairs with T, and C always pairs with G. The two DNA chains are held together by hydrogen bonds (indicated by the dotted lines) between their paired bases. These bonds are individually weak, but

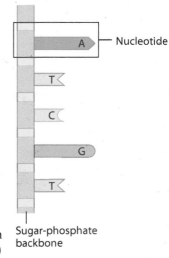

▲ Figure 3.16B   Part of a polynucleotide

collectively they zip the two strands together into a very stable double helix. Most DNA molecules have thousands or even millions of base pairs.

Because of the base-pairing rules, the two strands of the double helix are said to be *complementary*, each a predictable counterpart of the other. Thus, if a stretch of nucleotides on one strand has the base sequence –AGCACT–, then the same stretch on the other strand must be –TCGTGA–. Complementary base pairing is the key to how a cell makes two identical copies of each of its DNA molecules every time it divides. Thus, the structure of DNA accounts for its function of transmitting genetic information whenever a cell reproduces. The same base-pairing rules (with the exception that U nucleotides of RNA pair with A nucleotides of DNA) also

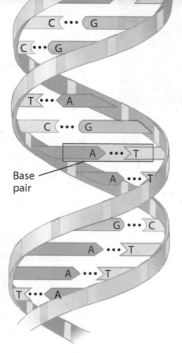

Base
pair

account for the precise transcription of information from DNA to RNA. (The details of gene transcription and translation are covered in detail in Chapter 10.)

An organism's genes determine the proteins and thus the structures and functions of its body. Let's return to the subject of the chapter introduction—lactose intolerance—to conclude our study of biological molecules. (In the next chapter, we move up in the biological hierarchy to the level of the cell.)

? **What roles do complementary base pairing play in the functioning of nucleic acids?**

● Complementary base pairing makes possible the precise replication of DNA, ensuring that genetic information is faithfully transmitted every time a cell divides. It also ensures that RNA molecules carry accurate instructions for the synthesis of proteins.

▲ **Figure 3.16C** DNA double helix

3.17 Lactose tolerance is a recent event in human evolution

EVOLUTION CONNECTION

As you'll recall from the chapter introduction, the majority of people stop producing the enzyme lactase in early childhood and thus do not easily digest the milk sugar lactose. Researchers were curious about the genetic and evolutionary basis for the regional distribution of lactose tolerance and intolerance.

What does evolution have to do with drinking milk?

In 2002, a group of scientists completed a study of the genes of 196 lactose-intolerant adults of African, Asian, and European descent. They determined that lactose intolerance is actually the human norm. It is "lactose tolerance" that represents a relatively recent mutation in the human genome.

The ability to make lactase into adulthood is concentrated in people of northern European descent, and the researchers speculated that lactose tolerance became widespread among this group because it offered a survival advantage. In northern Europe's relatively cold climate, only one harvest a year is possible. Therefore, animals were a main source of food for early humans in that region. Cattle were first domesticated in northern Europe about 9,000 years ago (Figure 3.17). With milk and other dairy products at hand year-round, natural selection would have favored anyone with a mutation that kept the lactase gene switched on into adulthood.

Researchers wondered whether the lactose tolerance mutation found in Europeans might be present in other cultures that kept dairy herds. Indeed, a 2006 study compared the genetic makeup and lactose tolerance of 43 ethnic groups in East Africa. The researchers identified three mutations, all different from each other and from the European mutation, that keep the lactase gene permanently turned on. The

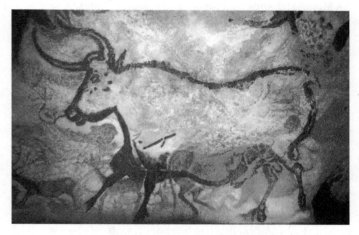

▲ **Figure 3.17** A prehistoric European cave painting of cattle

mutations appear to have occurred beginning around 7,000 years ago, around the time that archaeological evidence shows the domestication of cattle in these African regions.

Mutations that conferred a selective advantage, such as surviving cold winters or withstanding drought by drinking milk, spread rapidly in these early pastoral peoples. Their evolutionary and cultural history is thus recorded in their genes and in their continuing ability to digest milk.

Data from S. A. Tishkoff et al., Convergent adaptation of human lactase persistence in Africa and Europe, *Nature Genetics* 39: 31–40 (2006).

? **Explain how lactose tolerance involves three of the four major classes of biological macromolecules.**

● Lactose, milk sugar, is a carbohydrate that is hydrolyzed by the enzyme lactase, a protein. The ability to make this enzyme and the regulation of when it is made is coded for in DNA, a nucleic acid.

CHAPTER **3** REVIEW

For practice quizzes, BioFlix animations, MP3 tutorials, video tutors, and more study tools designed for this textbook, go to

Mastering Biology®

Reviewing the Concepts

Introduction to Organic Compounds (3.1–3.3)

3.1 Life's molecular diversity is based on the properties of carbon. Carbon's ability to bond with four other atoms is the basis for building large and diverse organic compounds. Hydrocarbons are composed of only carbon and hydrogen. Isomers have the same molecular formula but different structures.

3.2 A few chemical groups are key to the functioning of biological molecules. Hydrophilic functional groups give organic molecules specific chemical properties.

3.3 Cells make large molecules from a limited set of small molecules.

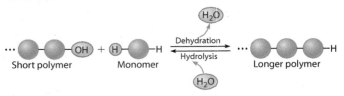

Carbohydrates (3.4–3.7)

3.4 Monosaccharides are the simplest carbohydrates. A monosaccharide has a formula that is a multiple of CH_2O and contains hydroxyl groups and a carbonyl group.

3.5 Two monosaccharides are linked to form a disaccharide.

3.6 What is high-fructose corn syrup, and is it to blame for obesity? HFCS, a mixture of glucose and fructose derived from corn, is commonly added to drinks and processed foods.

3.7 Polysaccharides are long chains of sugar units. Starch and glycogen are storage polysaccharides; cellulose is structural, found in plant cell walls. Chitin is a component of insect exoskeletons and fungal cell walls.

Lipids (3.8–3.11)

3.8 Fats are lipids that are mostly energy-storage molecules. Lipids are diverse, hydrophobic compounds composed largely of carbon and hydrogen. Fats (triglycerides) consist of glycerol linked to three fatty acids. Saturated fatty acids are found in animal fats; unsaturated fatty acids are typical of plant oils.

3.9 Scientific studies document the health risks of trans fats.

3.10 Phospholipids and steroids are important lipids with a variety of functions. Phospholipids are components of cell membranes. Steroids include cholesterol and some hormones.

3.11 Anabolic steroids pose health risks.

Proteins (3.12–3.14)

3.12 Proteins have a wide range of functions and structures. Proteins are involved in almost all of a cell's activities; as enzymes, they regulate chemical reactions.

3.13 Proteins are made from amino acids linked by peptide bonds. Protein diversity is based on different sequences of amino acids, monomers that contain an amino group, a carboxyl group, an H atom, and an R group, all attached to a central carbon. The R groups distinguish 20 amino acids, each with specific properties.

3.14 A protein's functional shape results from four levels of structure. A protein's primary structure is the sequence of amino acids in its polypeptide chain. Its secondary structure is the coiling or folding of the chain, stabilized by hydrogen bonds. The tertiary structure is the overall three-dimensional shape of a polypeptide, resulting from interactions among R groups. Proteins made of more than one polypeptide have quaternary structure.

Nucleic Acids (3.15–3.17)

3.15 DNA and RNA are the two types of nucleic acids. DNA and RNA serve as the blueprints for proteins and thus control the life of a cell. DNA is the molecule of inheritance.

3.16 Nucleic acids are polymers of nucleotides. Nucleotides are composed of a sugar, a phosphate group, and a nitrogenous base. DNA is a double helix; RNA is a single polynucleotide chain.

3.17 Lactose tolerance is a recent event in human evolution. Mutations in DNA have led to lactose tolerance in several human groups whose ancestors raised dairy cattle.

Connecting the Concepts

1. Complete the table to help review the structures and functions of the four classes of organic molecules.

Classes of Molecules and Their Components	Functions	Examples
Carbohydrates — Monosaccharide	Energy for cell, raw material	a. _____
	b. _____	Starch, glycogen
	Plant cell support	c. _____
Lipids (don't form polymers) — Glycerol, Fatty acid, Components of a fat molecule	Energy storage	d. _____
	e. _____	Phospholipids
	Hormones	f. _____
Proteins — g. _____ h. _____ i. _____ Amino acid	j. _____	Lactase
	k. _____	Hair, tendons
	l. _____	Muscle proteins
	Transport	m. _____
	Communication	Signal proteins
	n. _____	Antibodies
	Storage	Proteins in seeds
	Receive signals	Receptor protein
Nucleic Acids — o. _____ p. _____ Nucleotide q. _____	Heredity	r. _____
	s. _____	DNA and RNA

Testing Your Knowledge

Level 1: Knowledge/Comprehension

2. A glucose molecule is to starch as (*Explain your answer.*)
   a. a steroid is to a lipid.
   b. a protein is to an amino acid.
   c. a nucleic acid is to a polypeptide.
   d. a nucleotide is to a nucleic acid.
3. What makes a fatty acid an acid?
   a. It does not dissolve in water.
   b. It is capable of bonding with other molecules to form a fat.
   c. It has a carboxyl group that can donate an H^+ to a solution.
   d. It contains only two oxygen atoms.
4. Cows can derive nutrients from cellulose because
   a. they produce enzymes that recognize the shape of the glucose-glucose bonds and hydrolyze them.
   b. they re-chew their cud to break down cellulose fibers.
   c. their digestive tract contains prokaryotes that can hydrolyze the bonds of cellulose.
   d. they convert cellulose to starch and can digest starch.
5. Of the following functional groups, which is/are polar, tending to make organic compounds hydrophilic?
   a. carbonyl
   b. amino
   c. hydroxyl
   d. all of the above
6. Unsaturated fats
   a. have double bonds in their fatty acid chains.
   b. have fewer fatty acid molecules per fat molecule.
   c. are associated with greater health risks than are saturated fats.
   d. are more common in animals than in plants.

Level 2: Application/Analysis

7. A shortage of phosphorus in the soil would make it especially difficult for a plant to manufacture
   a. DNA.
   b. proteins.
   c. cellulose.
   d. sucrose.
8. Which of the following substances is a major component of the cell membrane of a fungus?
   a. cellulose
   b. chitin
   c. cholesterol
   d. phospholipids
9. Which structural level of a protein would be *least* affected by a disruption in hydrogen bonding?
   a. primary structure
   b. secondary structure
   c. tertiary structure
   d. quaternary structure
10. Circle and name the functional groups in this organic molecule. What type of compound is this? For which class of macromolecules is it a monomer?

11. Most proteins are soluble in the aqueous environment of a cell. Knowing that, where in the overall three-dimensional shape of a protein would you expect to find amino acids with hydrophobic R groups?
12. Sucrose is broken down in your intestine to the monosaccharides glucose and fructose, which are then absorbed into your blood. What is the name of this type of reaction? Using this diagram of sucrose, show how this would occur.

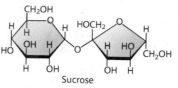
Sucrose

Level 3: Synthesis/Evaluation

13. The diversity of life is staggering. Yet the molecular logic of life is simple and elegant: Small molecules common to all organisms are ordered into unique macromolecules. Explain why carbon is central to this diversity of organic molecules. How do carbon skeletons, chemical groups, monomers, and polymers relate to this molecular logic of life?

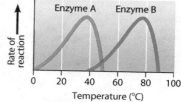

14. How can a cell make many different kinds of proteins out of only 20 amino acids? Of the myriad possibilities, how does the cell "know" which proteins to make?
15. Given that the function of egg yolk is to nourish and support the developing chick, explain why egg yolks are so high in fat, protein, and cholesterol.
16. Enzymes usually function best at an optimal pH and temperature. The following graph shows the effectiveness of two enzymes at various temperatures.

   a. At which temperature does enzyme A perform best? Enzyme B?
   b. One of these enzymes is found in humans and the other in thermophilic (heat-loving) bacteria. Which enzyme would you predict comes from which organism?
   c. From what you know about enzyme structure, explain why the rate of the reaction catalyzed by enzyme A slows down at temperatures above 40°C (140°F).

17. **SCIENTIFIC THINKING** Another aspect of the Nurses' Health Study introduced in Module 3.9 looked at the percentage of change in the risk of coronary heart disease associated with substituting one dietary component for another. These results estimated that replacement of 5% of energy from saturated fat in the diet with unsaturated fats would reduce the risk by 42%, and that the replacement of 2% of energy from trans fat with unsaturated fats would reduce the risk by 53%. Explain what these numbers mean.

Answers to all questions can be found in Appendix 4.

A Tour of the Cell

? How has our knowledge
of cells grown?

You can probably identify the blue blobs in this beautiful micrograph as the nuclei of the cells it depicts. But did you know that the brightly colored strands you also see form a cell's skeleton? These structures are part of a system of protein fibers called the cytoskeleton. Much like the way your skeleton provides support and also enables you to move, the cytoskeleton provides structural support to a cell and allows some cells to crawl and others to swim. But even stationary cells have movement: Many of their internal parts bustle about, often traveling on cytoskeletal "roads." Later in the chapter you will learn more about the cytoskeleton and how our knowledge of its structures and functions has grown. As you will see, our understanding of nature often goes hand in hand with the invention and refinement of instruments that extend our senses. This certainly applies to how cells were first discovered.

In 1665, Robert Hooke used a crude microscope to examine a piece of cork. Hooke compared the structures he saw to "little rooms"—*cellulae* in Latin—and the term *cell* stuck. His contemporary, Antoni van Leeuwenhoek, working with more refined lenses, examined numerous subjects, from

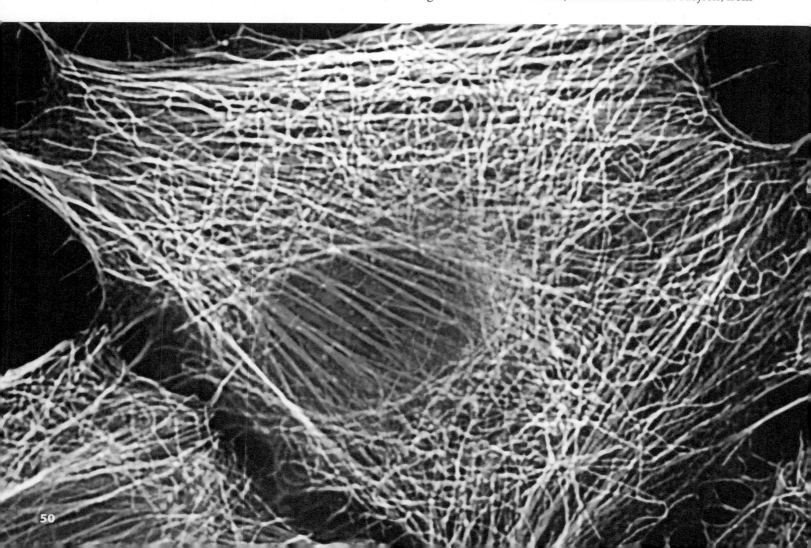

blood and sperm to pond water. He produced drawings and enthusiastic descriptions of his discoveries, such as the tiny "animalcules, very prettily a-moving" he found in the scrapings from his teeth.

Since the days of Hooke and Leeuwenhoek, improved microscopes and techniques have vastly expanded our view of the cell. For example, fluorescently colored stains reveal the cytoskeleton in the cells pictured below. In this chapter, you will see many micrographs using such techniques, and they will often be paired with drawings that help emphasize specific details.

Neither drawings nor micrographs allow you to see the dynamic nature of living cells. For that, you need to look through a microscope or view videos. As you study the images in this chapter, keep in mind that the parts of a cell are moving and interacting. Indeed, the phenomenon we call life emerges from the interactions of the many components of a cell.

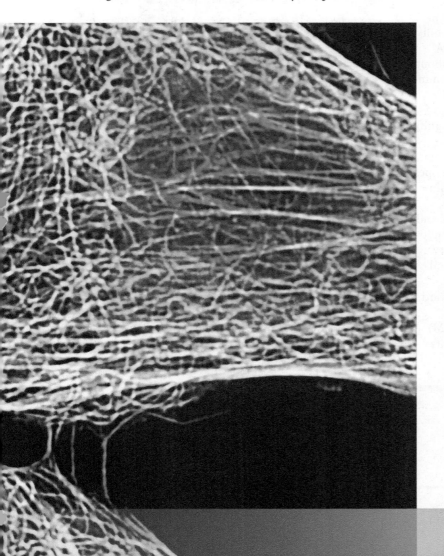

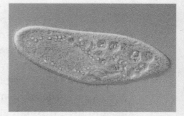

BIG IDEAS

Introduction to the Cell
(4.1–4.4)

Microscopes reveal the structures of cells—the fundamental units of life.

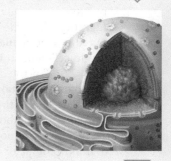

The Nucleus and Ribosomes
(4.5–4.6)

A cell's genetic instructions are housed in the nucleus and carried out by ribosomes.

The Endomembrane System
(4.7–4.12)

The endomembrane system participates in the manufacture, distribution, and breakdown of materials.

Energy-Converting Organelles
(4.13–4.15)

Mitochondria in all eukaryotic cells and chloroplasts in plant cells function in energy processing.

The Cytoskeleton and Cell Surfaces
(4.16–4.22)

The cytoskeleton and extracellular components provide support, motility, and functional connections.

▷ Introduction to the Cell

4.1 Microscopes reveal the world of the cell

Before microscopes were first used in the 1600s, no one knew that living organisms were composed of the tiny units we call cells. The first microscopes were light microscopes, like the ones you may use in a biology laboratory. In a **light microscope (LM)**, visible light is passed through a specimen, such as a microorganism or a thin slice of animal or plant tissue, and then through glass lenses. The lenses bend the light in such a way that the image of the specimen is magnified as it is projected into your eye or a camera.

Magnification is the increase in an object's image size compared with its actual size. **Figure 4.1A** shows a micrograph of a single-celled organism called *Paramecium*. The notation "LM 230✕" printed along the right edge tells you that this photograph was taken through a light microscope and that the image is 230 times the actual size of the organism. This *Paramecium* is about 0.33 millimeter in length. **Table 4.1** shows the most common units of length that biologists use.

An important factor in microscopy is resolution, a measure of the clarity of an image. Resolution is the ability to distinguish two nearby objects as separate. For example, what you see as a single star in the sky may be resolved as twin stars with a telescope. Each optical instrument—be it an eye, a telescope, or a microscope—has a limit to its resolution. The human eye can distinguish points as close together as 0.1 millimeter (mm), about the size of a very fine grain of sand. A typical light microscope cannot resolve detail finer than about 0.2 micrometer (μm), about the size of the smallest bacterium. No matter how many times the image of such a small cell is magnified, the light microscope cannot resolve the details of its structure. Indeed, light microscopes can effectively magnify objects only about 1,000 times.

From the time that Hooke discovered cells in 1665 until the middle of the 1900s, biologists had only light microscopes for viewing cells. With these microscopes and various staining techniques to increase contrast between parts of cells, these early biologists discovered microorganisms, animal and plant cells, and even some structures within cells. By the mid-1800s, this accumulation of evidence led to the **cell theory**, which states that all living things are composed of cells and that all cells come from other cells.

Our knowledge of cell structure took a giant leap forward as biologists began using the electron microscope in the 1950s. Instead of using light, an **electron microscope (EM)** focuses a beam of electrons through a specimen or onto its

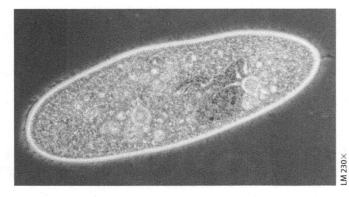

▲ **Figure 4.1A** Light micrograph of a unicellular organism, *Paramecium*

LM 230✕

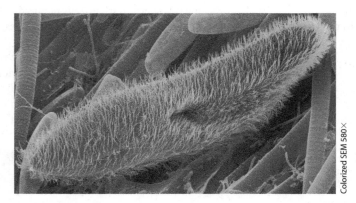

▲ **Figure 4.1B** Scanning electron micrograph of *Paramecium*

Colorized SEM 580✕

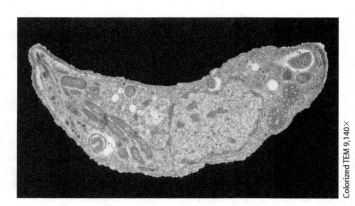

▲ **Figure 4.1C** Transmission electron micrograph of *Toxoplasma* (This parasite of cats can be transmitted to humans, causing the disease toxoplasmosis.)

Colorized TEM 9,140✕

Try This Describe a major difference between the *Paramecium* in Figure 4.1B and the protist in this figure. (*Hint*: Compare the notations along the right sides of the micrographs.)

surface. Electron microscopes can distinguish biological structures as small as about 2 nanometers (nm), a 100-fold improvement over the light microscope. This high resolution has enabled biologists to explore cell ultrastructure, the complex internal anatomy of a cell. **Figures 4.1B** and **4.1C** show images produced by two kinds of electron microscopes.

TABLE 4.1 | METRIC MEASUREMENT EQUIVALENTS

1 meter (m) = 100 cm = 1,000 mm = 39.4 inches

1 centimeter (cm) = 10^{-2} (1/100) m = 0.4 inch

1 millimeter (mm) = 10^{-3} (1/1,000) m = 10^{-1} (1/10) cm

1 micrometer (μm) = 10^{-6} m = 10^{-3} mm

1 nanometer (nm) = 10^{-9} m = 10^{-3} μm

Biologists use the **scanning electron microscope (SEM)** to study the detailed architecture of cell surfaces. The SEM uses an electron beam to scan the surface of a cell or other sample, which is usually coated with a thin film of gold. The beam excites electrons on the surface, and these electrons are then detected by a device that translates their pattern into an image projected onto a video screen. The scanning electron micrograph in Figure 4.1B highlights the numerous cilia on *Paramecium*, projections it uses for movement. Notice the indentation, called the oral groove, through which food enters the cell. As you can see, the SEM produces images that look three-dimensional.

The **transmission electron microscope (TEM)** is used to study the details of internal cell structure. The TEM aims an electron beam through a very thin section of a specimen, just as a light microscope aims a beam of light through a specimen. The section is stained with atoms of heavy metals, which attach to certain cellular structures more than others. Electrons are scattered by these more dense parts, and the image is created by the pattern of transmitted electrons. Instead of using glass lenses, both the SEM and TEM use electromagnets as lenses to bend the paths of the electrons, magnifying and focusing the image onto a monitor. The transmission electron micrograph in Figure 4.1C shows internal details of a protist called *Toxoplasma*. SEMs and TEMs are initially black and white but are often artificially colorized, as they are in these figures, to highlight or clarify structural features.

Electron microscopes have truly revolutionized the study of cells and their structures. Nonetheless, they have not replaced the light microscope: Electron microscopes cannot be used to study living specimens because the methods used to prepare the specimen kill the cells. For a biologist studying a living process, such as the movement of *Paramecium*, a light microscope equipped with a video camera is more suitable than either an SEM or a TEM.

There are different types of light microscopy, and major technical advances in the past several decades have greatly expanded our ability to visualize cells. **Figure 4.1D** shows *Paramecium* as seen using differential interference contrast microscopy. This optical technique amplifies differences in density so that the structures in living cells appear almost three-dimensional. Other techniques use fluorescent stains that selectively bind to various cellular molecules (see the chapter introduction).

You will see many beautiful and illuminating examples of microscopy in this textbook. But even with the magnification

shown beside each micrograph, it is often hard to imagine just how small cells are. **Figure 4.1E** shows the size range of cells compared with objects both larger and smaller and the optical instrument that allows us to view them. Notice that the scale along the left side of the figure is logarithmic to accommodate the range of sizes shown. Starting at the top with 10 meters (m), each reference measurement marks a 10-fold decrease in length. Most cells are between 1 and 100 μm in diameter (yellow region of the figure) and are therefore visible only with a microscope. Certain bacteria are as small as 0.2 μm and can barely be seen with a light microscope, whereas bird eggs are large enough to be seen with the unaided eye. A single nerve cell running from the base of your spinal cord to your big toe may be 1 m in length, although it is so thin you would still need a microscope to see it. In the next module, we explore why cells are so small.

? Which type of microscope would you use to study (a) the changes in shape of a living human white blood cell; (b) the finest details of surface texture of a human hair; (c) the detailed structure of an organelle in a liver cell?

● (a) Light microscope; (b) scanning electron microscope; (c) transmission electron microscope

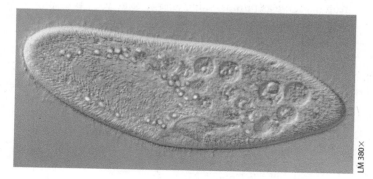

▲ **Figure 4.1D** Differential interference contrast micrograph of *Paramecium*

LM 380×

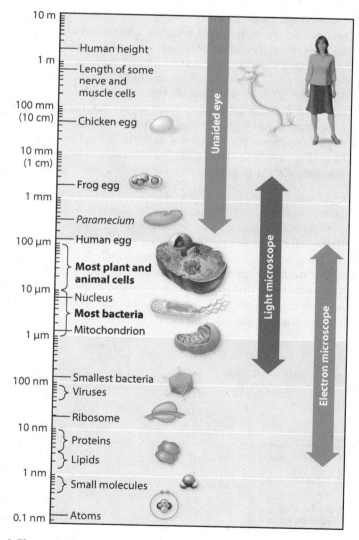

10 m	
1 m	Human height
100 mm (10 cm)	Length of some nerve and muscle cells
10 mm (1 cm)	Chicken egg
1 mm	Frog egg
100 μm	*Paramecium*
	Human egg
10 μm	**Most plant and animal cells**
	Nucleus
1 μm	**Most bacteria**
	Mitochondrion
100 nm	Smallest bacteria
	Viruses
10 nm	Ribosome
	Proteins
1 nm	Lipids
	Small molecules
0.1 nm	Atoms

Unaided eye
Light microscope
Electron microscope

▲ **Figure 4.1E** The size range of cells and related objects

4.2 The small size of cells relates to the need to exchange materials across the plasma membrane

As you saw in Figure 4.1E, most cells are microscopic. Are there advantages to being so small? The logistics of carrying out a cell's functions appear to set both lower and upper limits on cell size. At minimum, a cell must be large enough to house enough DNA, protein molecules, and structures to survive and reproduce. But why aren't most cells as large as chicken eggs? The maximum size of a cell is influenced by geometry—the need to have a surface area large enough to service the volume of a cell. Active cells have a huge amount of traffic across their outer surface. A chicken egg cell isn't very active, but once a chick embryo starts to develop, the egg is divided into many microscopic cells, each bounded by a membrane that allows the essential flow of oxygen, nutrients, and wastes across its surface.

Surface-to-Volume Ratio   Large cells have more surface area than small cells, but they have a much smaller surface area relative to their volume than small cells. **Figure 4.2A** illustrates this by comparing one large cube to 27 small ones. Using arbitrary units of measurement, the total volume is the same in both cases: 27 units³ (height × width × length). The total surface areas, however, are quite different. A cube has six sides; thus, its surface area is six times the area of each side (height × width). The surface area of the large cube is 54 units², while the total surface area of all 27 cubes is 162 units² (27 × 6 × 1 × 1), three times greater than the surface area of the large cube. Thus, we see that the smaller cubes have a much greater surface-to-volume ratio than the large cube. How about those neurons that extend from the base of your spine to your toes? Very thin, elongated shapes also provide a large surface area relative to a cell's volume.

The Plasma Membrane   So what is a cell's surface like? And how does it control the traffic of molecules across it? The **plasma membrane** forms a flexible boundary between the living cell and its surroundings. For a structure that separates life from nonlife, this membrane is amazingly thin. It would take a stack of more than 8,000 plasma membranes to equal the thickness of this page. And, as you have come to expect with all things biological, the structure of the plasma membrane correlates with its function.

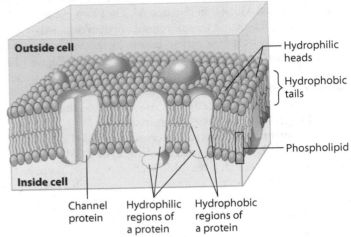

▲ **Figure 4.2B**   A plasma membrane: a phospholipid bilayer with associated proteins

The structure of phospholipid molecules is well suited to their role as a major constituent of biological membranes. Each phospholipid is composed of two distinct regions—a head with a negatively charged phosphate group and two nonpolar fatty acid tails (see Module 3.10). Phospholipids group together to form a two-layer sheet called a phospholipid bilayer. As you can see in **Figure 4.2B**, the phospholipids' hydrophilic (water-loving) heads face outward, exposed to the aqueous solutions on both sides of a membrane. Their hydrophobic (water-fearing) tails point inward, mingling together and shielded from water. Embedded in this lipid bilayer are diverse proteins, floating like icebergs in a phospholipid sea. The regions of the proteins within the center of the membrane are hydrophobic; the exterior sections exposed to water are hydrophilic.

Now let's see how the properties of the phospholipid bilayer and the proteins suspended in it relate to the plasma membrane's job as a traffic cop, regulating the flow of material into and out of the cell. Nonpolar molecules, such as O_2 and CO_2, can easily move across the membrane's hydrophobic interior. Some of the membrane's proteins form channels (tunnels) that shield ions and polar molecules as they pass through the hydrophobic center of the membrane. Still other proteins serve as pumps, using energy to actively transport molecules into or out of the cell.

We will return to the structure and function of biological membranes later (see Chapter 5). In the next module, we consider other features common to all cells and take a closer look at the prokaryotic cells of domains Bacteria and Archaea.

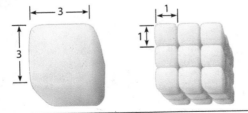

Total volume	27 units³	27 units³
Total surface area	54 units²	162 units²
Surface-to-volume ratio	2	6

▲ **Figure 4.2A**   Effect of cell size on surface area

?   To convince yourself that a small cell has a greater surface area relative to volume than a large cell, compare the surface-to-volume ratios of the large cube and one of the small cubes in Figure 4.2A.

● Large cube: 54/27 = 2; small cube: 6/1 = 6 (surface area is 1 × 1 × 6 sides = 6 units²; volume is 1 × 1 × 1 unit³)

4.3 Prokaryotic cells are structurally simpler than eukaryotic cells

Cells are of two distinct types: prokaryotic and eukaryotic. The microorganisms placed in domains Bacteria and Archaea consist of **prokaryotic cells**. These organisms are known as prokaryotes. All other forms of life (protists, fungi, plants, and animals) are placed in domain Eukarya and are composed of **eukaryotic cells**. They are referred to as eukaryotes.

Eukaryotic cells are distinguished by having a membrane-enclosed nucleus, which houses most of their DNA, and many membrane-enclosed organelles that perform specific functions. Prokaryotic cells are smaller and simpler in structure.

Both types of cells, however, share certain basic features. In addition to being bounded by a plasma membrane, the interior of all cells is filled with a thick, jellylike fluid called **cytosol**, in which cellular components are suspended. All cells have one or more **chromosomes**, which carry genes made of DNA. They also contain **ribosomes**, tiny structures that make proteins according to instructions from the genes. The inside of both types of cells is called the **cytoplasm**. However, in eukaryotic cells, this term refers only to the region between the nucleus and the plasma membrane.

Figure 4.3 explores the structure of a generalized prokaryotic cell. Notice that the DNA is coiled into a region called the **nucleoid** ("nucleus-like"), but no membrane surrounds the DNA. The ribosomes of prokaryotes (shown here in brown) are smaller and differ somewhat from those of eukaryotes. These molecular differences are the basis for the action of some antibiotics, such as tetracycline and streptomycin, which target prokaryotic ribosomes. Thus, protein synthesis

can be blocked for the bacterium that's invaded you, but not for you, the eukaryote who is taking the drug.

Outside the plasma membrane (shown here in gray) of most prokaryotes is a fairly rigid, chemically complex cell wall (orange). The wall protects the cell and helps maintain its shape. Some antibiotics, such as penicillin, prevent the formation of these protective walls. Again, because your cells don't have such walls, these antibiotics can kill invading bacteria without harming your cells. Certain prokaryotes have a sticky outer coat called a capsule (yellow) around the cell wall, helping to glue the cells to surfaces or to other cells in a colony. In addition to capsules, some prokaryotes have surface projections. Short projections help attach prokaryotes to each other or their substrate. Longer projections called **flagella** (singular, *flagellum*) propel a prokaryotic cell through its liquid environment.

It takes an electron microscope to see the internal details of any cell, and this is especially true of prokaryotic cells. Notice that the TEM of the bacterium in Figure 4.3 has a magnification of 4,700×. Most prokaryotic cells are about one-tenth the size of a typical eukaryotic cell (see Figure 1.3). (Prokaryotes will be described in more detail later; see Chapter 16.) Eukaryotic cells are the main focus of this chapter, so we turn to these next.

? **List three features that are common to prokaryotic and eukaryotic cells. List three features that differ.**

● Both types of cells have plasma membranes, chromosomes containing DNA, and ribosomes. Prokaryotic cells are smaller, do not have a nucleus that houses their DNA or other membrane-enclosed organelles, and have smaller, somewhat different ribosomes.

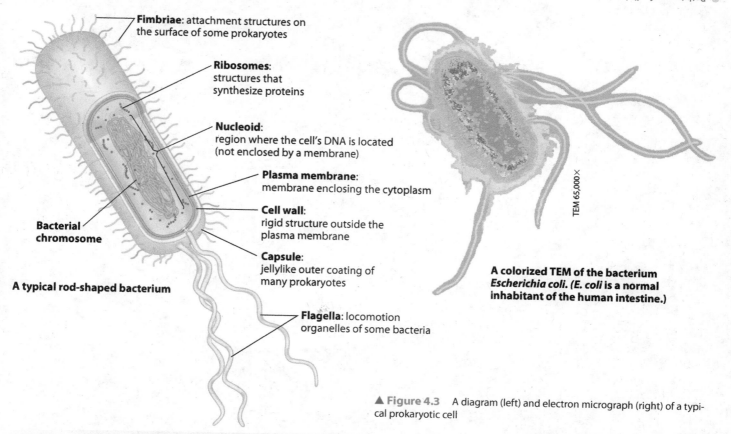

Fimbriae: attachment structures on the surface of some prokaryotes

Ribosomes: structures that synthesize proteins

Nucleoid: region where the cell's DNA is located (not enclosed by a membrane)

Plasma membrane: membrane enclosing the cytoplasm

Cell wall: rigid structure outside the plasma membrane

Capsule: jellylike outer coating of many prokaryotes

Bacterial chromosome

A typical rod-shaped bacterium

Flagella: locomotion organelles of some bacteria

TEM 65,000×

A colorized TEM of the bacterium *Escherichia coli*. (*E. coli* is a normal inhabitant of the human intestine.)

▲ **Figure 4.3** A diagram (left) and electron micrograph (right) of a typical prokaryotic cell

4.4 Eukaryotic cells are partitioned into functional compartments

All eukaryotic cells—whether from animals, plants, protists, or fungi—are fundamentally similar to one another and profoundly different from prokaryotic cells. Let's look at an animal cell and a plant cell as representatives of the eukaryotes.

Figure 4.4A is a diagram of a generalized animal cell, and Figure 4.4B shows a generalized plant cell. We color-code the various organelles and other structures in the diagrams for easier identification, and you will see miniature versions of these cells to orient you during our in-depth tour in the rest of the chapter. But no cells would look exactly like these. For one thing, cells have multiple copies of all of these structures (except for the nucleus). Your cells have hundreds of mitochondria and millions of ribosomes. A plant cell may have 30 chloroplasts packed inside. Cells also have different shapes and relative proportions of cell parts, depending on their specialized functions.

The nucleus is the most obvious difference between a prokaryotic and eukaryotic cell. A eukaryotic cell also contains various other **organelles** ("little organs"), which perform specific functions in the cell. Just as the cell itself is wrapped in a membrane made of phospholipids and proteins that perform various functions, each organelle is bounded by a membrane with a lipid and protein composition that suits its function.

The organelles and other structures of eukaryotic cells can be organized into four basic functional groups: (1) The nucleus and ribosomes carry out the genetic control of the cell. (2) Organelles involved in the manufacture, distribution, and breakdown of molecules include the endoplasmic reticulum, Golgi apparatus, lysosomes, vacuoles, and peroxisomes. (3) Mitochondria in all cells and chloroplasts in plant cells function in energy processing. (4) Structural support, movement, and communication between cells are the functions of the cytoskeleton, plasma membrane, and plant cell wall. The cellular components identified in these two figures will be examined in detail in the modules that follow.

In essence, the internal membranes of a eukaryotic cell partition it into compartments. Many of the chemical

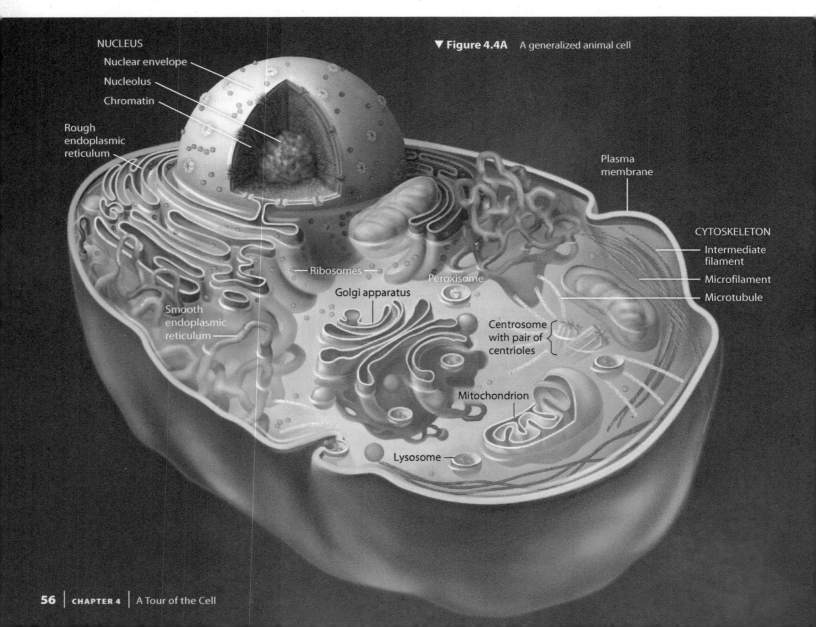

▼ Figure 4.4A A generalized animal cell

NUCLEUS
Nuclear envelope
Nucleolus
Chromatin
Rough endoplasmic reticulum
Smooth endoplasmic reticulum
Ribosomes
Golgi apparatus
Peroxisome
Plasma membrane
CYTOSKELETON
Intermediate filament
Microfilament
Microtubule
Centrosome with pair of centrioles
Mitochondrion
Lysosome

activities of cells—collectively, **cellular metabolism**—occur within organelles. In fact, many enzymes essential for metabolic processes are built into the membranes of organelles. The fluid-filled spaces within organelles are important as sites where specific chemical conditions are maintained. These conditions vary among organelles and favor the metabolic processes occurring in each. For example, while a part of the endoplasmic reticulum is engaged in making hormones, neighboring peroxisomes may be detoxifying harmful compounds and making hydrogen peroxide (H_2O_2) as a poisonous by-product of their activities. But because the H_2O_2 is confined within the peroxisomes, where it is converted to H_2O by resident enzymes, the rest of the cell is protected.

Except for lysosomes and centrosomes, the organelles and other structures of animal cells are found in plant cells. Also, although some animal cells have flagella or cilia (not shown in Figure 4.4A), among plants, only the sperm cells of a few species have flagella.

A plant cell (Figure 4.4B) also has some structures that an animal cell lacks. For example, a plant cell has a rigid, rather thick cell wall. Cell walls protect cells and help maintain their shape. Chemically different from prokaryotic cell walls, plant cell walls contain the polysaccharide cellulose. Plasmodesmata (singular, plasmodesma) are cytoplasmic channels through cell walls that connect adjacent cells. An important organelle found in plant cells is the chloroplast, where photosynthesis occurs. Unique to plant cells is a large central vacuole, a compartment that stores water and a variety of chemicals.

Eukaryotic cells contain nonmembranous structures as well. The cytoskeleton, which you were introduced to in the chapter introduction, is composed of different types of protein fibers that extend throughout the cell. These networks provide for support and movement. And ribosomes occur throughout the cytosol, as they do in prokaryotic cells. In addition, eukaryotic cells have many ribosomes attached to membranes.

After you preview these cell diagrams, let's move to the first stop on our detailed tour of the eukaryotic cell—the nucleus.

? **Identify the structures in the plant cell that are not present in the animal cell.**

⬤ Chloroplasts, central vacuole, cell wall, and plasmodesmata

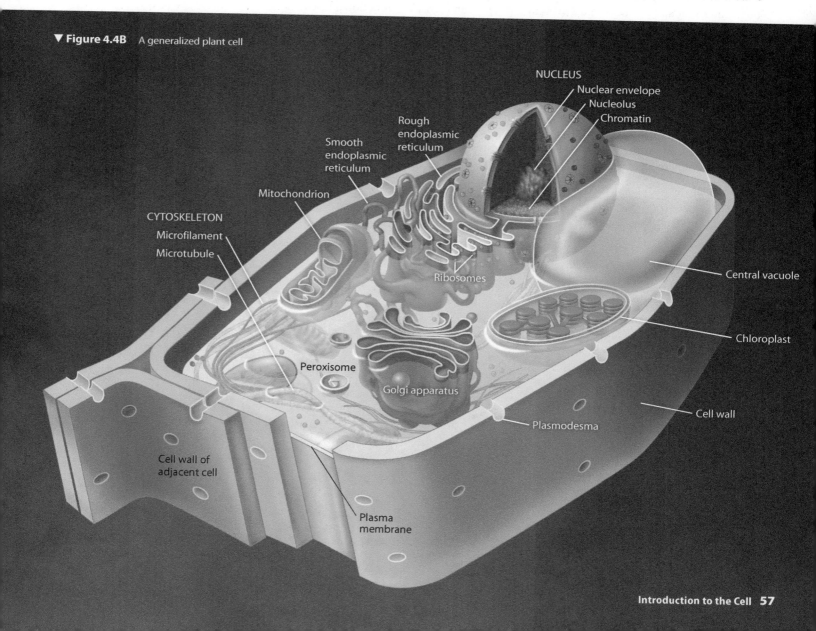

▼ **Figure 4.4B** A generalized plant cell

NUCLEUS
Nuclear envelope
Nucleolus
Chromatin

Rough endoplasmic reticulum

Smooth endoplasmic reticulum

Mitochondrion

CYTOSKELETON
Microfilament
Microtubule

Ribosomes

Central vacuole

Chloroplast

Peroxisome

Golgi apparatus

Cell wall

Plasmodesma

Cell wall of adjacent cell

Plasma membrane

4.5 The nucleus contains the cell's genetic instructions

You just saw a preview of the many intricate structures that can be found in a eukaryotic cell. A cell must build and maintain these structures and also process energy to support its work of transport, movement, and communication. But who is in charge of this bustling factory? Who stores the master plans, gives the orders, changes course in response to environmental input, and, when called on, makes another factory just like itself? The cell's nucleus functions as this command center.

The **nucleus** contains the cell's genetic instructions encoded in DNA. These master plans control the cell's activities by directing protein synthesis. The DNA is associated with many proteins and organized into structures called chromosomes. The proteins help coil these long DNA molecules. Indeed, the DNA of the 46 chromosomes in one of your cells laid end to end would stretch to a length of more than 2 m, but it must coil up to fit into a nucleus only 5 μm in diameter. When a cell is not dividing, this complex of proteins and DNA, called **chromatin**, appears as a diffuse mass within the nucleus, as shown in the TEM (right half) and diagram (left half) of a nucleus in **Figure 4.5**.

As a cell prepares to divide, the DNA is copied so that each daughter cell can later receive an identical set of genetic instructions. Just prior to cell division, the thin chromatin fibers coil up further, becoming thick enough to be visible with a light microscope as the familiar separate structures you would probably recognize as chromosomes.

Enclosing the nucleus is a double membrane called the **nuclear envelope**. Each of the two membranes is a separate phospholipid bilayer with associated proteins. Similar in function to the plasma membrane, the nuclear envelope controls the flow of materials into and out of the nucleus. As you can see in the diagram of a nucleus in Figure 4.5, the nuclear envelope is perforated with protein-lined pores. These pores regulate the entry and exit of large molecules and also connect with the cell's network of membranes called the endoplasmic reticulum.

The **nucleolus**, a prominent structure in the nucleus, is the site where a special type of RNA called ribosomal RNA(rRNA) is synthesized according to instructions in the DNA. Proteins brought in from the cytoplasm are assembled with this rRNA to form the subunits of ribosomes. These subunits then exit to the cytoplasm, where they will join to form functional ribosomes.

Another type of RNA, messenger RNA (mRNA), directs protein synthesis. Essentially, mRNA is a transcription of protein-synthesizing instructions written in a gene's DNA (see Figure 10.7). The mRNA moves into the cytoplasm, where ribosomes translate it into the amino acid sequences of proteins. Let's look at ribosomes next.

? **Describe the processes that occur in the nucleus.**

● DNA is copied and passed on to daughter cells in cell division; rRNA is made and ribosomal subunits assembled; protein-making instructions in DNA are transcribed into mRNA.

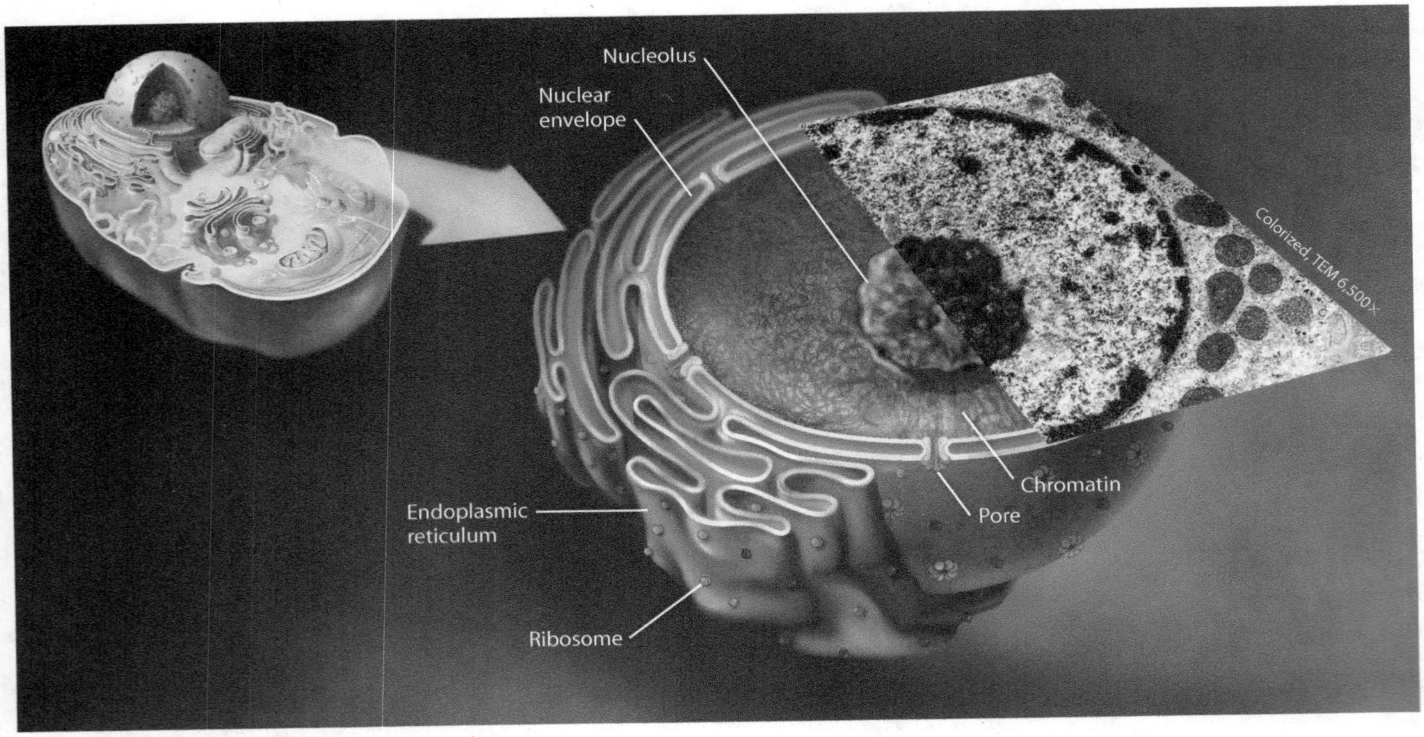

▲ **Figure 4.5** A diagram with a superimposed TEM of the nucleus

Nucleolus
Nuclear envelope
Colorized, TEM 6,500×
Chromatin
Pore
Endoplasmic reticulum
Ribosome

4.6 Ribosomes make proteins for use in the cell and for export

If the nucleus is the cell's command center, then ribosomes are the machines that carry out those commands. Ribosomes are the cellular components that use instructions from the nucleus, written in mRNA, to build proteins. Cells that make a lot of proteins have a large number of ribosomes. For example, a cell in your pancreas that produces digestive enzymes may contain a few million ribosomes. What other structure would you expect to be prominent in cells that are active in protein synthesis? Remember that the nucleolus in the nucleus is the site where the subunits of ribosomes are assembled.

As shown in **Figure 4.6**, ribosomes are found in two locations in the cell. Free ribosomes are suspended in the cytosol, while bound ribosomes are attached to the outside of the endoplasmic reticulum or nuclear envelope. Free and bound ribosomes are structurally identical, and they can move about and function in either location.

Most of the proteins made on free ribosomes function within the cytosol; examples are enzymes that catalyze the first steps of sugar breakdown for cellular respiration. In Module 4.8, you will see how bound ribosomes make proteins that will be inserted into membranes, packaged in certain organelles, or exported from the cell.

At the bottom right in Figure 4.6, you see how ribosomes interact with messenger RNA (carrying the instructions from a gene) to build a protein. The nucleotide sequence of an mRNA molecule is translated into the amino acid sequence of a polypeptide. (Protein synthesis is explored in more detail in Chapter 10.) Next let's look at more of the manufacturing equipment of the cell.

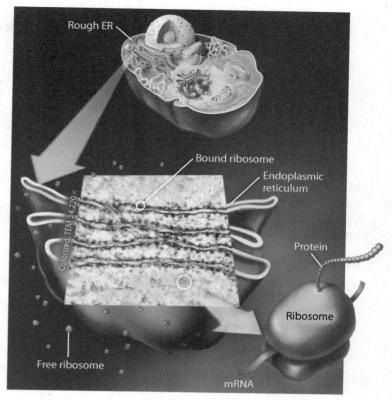

▲ **Figure 4.6** The locations and structure of ribosomes

? **What role do ribosomes play in carrying out the genetic instructions of a cell?**

● Ribosomes synthesize proteins according to the instructions of messenger RNA, which was transcribed from DNA in the nucleus.

▷ The Endomembrane System

4.7 Many organelles are connected in the endomembrane system

Ribosomes may be a cell's protein-making machines, but running a factory as complex as a cell requires infrastructure and many different departments that perform separate but related functions. Internal membranes, a distinguishing feature of eukaryotic cells, are involved in most of a cell's functions. Many of the membranes of the eukaryotic cell are part of an **endomembrane system**. Some of these membranes are physically connected and others are linked when tiny **vesicles** (sacs made of membrane) transfer membrane segments between them.

The endomembrane system includes the nuclear envelope, endoplasmic reticulum, Golgi apparatus, lysosomes, vacuoles, and the plasma membrane. (The plasma membrane is not exactly an *endo* membrane in physical location, but it is related to the other membranes by the transfer of vesicles). Many of these organelles interact in the synthesis, distribution, storage, and export of molecules.

The largest component of the endomembrane system is the **endoplasmic reticulum (ER)**, an extensive network of flattened sacs and tubules. (The term *endoplasmic* means "within the cytoplasm," and *reticulum* is Latin for "little net.") The ER is a prime example of the direct and indirect interrelatedness of parts of the endomembrane system. As shown in Figure 4.5 on the facing page, membranes of the ER are continuous with the nuclear envelope. And when vesicles bud from the ER, they travel to many other components of the endomembrane system.

The tubules and sacs of the ER enclose a space that is separate from the cytosol. Dividing the cell into functional compartments, each of which may require different conditions, is an important aspect of the endomembrane system.

? **Which structure includes all others in the list: rough ER, smooth ER, endomembrane system, nuclear envelope?**

● Endomembrane system

4.8 The endoplasmic reticulum is a biosynthetic workshop

One of the major manufacturing sites in a cell is the endo-plasmic reticulum. The diagram in **Figure 4.8A** shows a cut-away view of the interconnecting membranes of the smooth and rough ER, which can be distinguished in the superim-posed electron micrograph. **Smooth endoplasmic reticulum** is called *smooth* because its outer surface lacks attached ribo-somes. **Rough endoplasmic reticulum** has bound ribosomes that stud the outer surface of the membrane; thus, it appears *rough* in the electron micrograph.

Smooth ER The smooth ER of various cell types functions in a variety of metabolic processes. Enzymes of the smooth ER are important in the synthesis of lipids, including oils, phos-pholipids, and steroids. In vertebrates, for example, cells of the ovaries and testes synthesize the steroid sex hormones. These cells are rich in smooth ER, a structural feature that fits their function by providing ample machinery for steroid synthesis.

Our liver cells also have large amounts of smooth ER, with enzymes that help process drugs, alcohol, and other poten-tially harmful substances. The sedative phenobarbital and other barbiturates are examples of drugs detoxified by these enzymes. As liver cells are exposed to such chemicals, the amount of smooth ER and its detoxifying enzymes increases, thereby increasing the rate of detoxification and thus the body's tolerance to the drugs. The result is a need for higher doses of a drug to achieve a particular effect, such as seda-tion. Also, because detoxifying enzymes often cannot distin-guish among related chemicals, the growth of smooth ER in response to one drug can increase the need for higher doses of other drugs. Barbiturate abuse, for example, can decrease the effectiveness of certain antibiotics and other useful drugs.

Smooth ER has yet another function, the storage of calcium ions. In muscle cells, for example, a specialized smooth ER membrane pumps calcium ions into the interior of the ER. When a nerve signal stimulates a muscle cell, cal-cium ions rush from the smooth ER into the cytosol and trig-ger contraction of the cell.

Rough ER Many types of cells secrete proteins produced by ribosomes attached to rough ER. An example of a secretory protein is insulin, a hormone produced and secreted by cer-tain cells of the pancreas and transported in the bloodstream. Type 1 diabetes results when these cells are destroyed and a lack of insulin disrupts glucose metabolism in the body.

Figure 4.8B follows the synthesis, modification, and pack-aging of a secretory protein. ① As the polypeptide is synthe-sized by a bound ribosome following the instructions of an mRNA, it is threaded into the cavity of the rough ER. As it enters, the new protein folds into its three-dimensional shape. ② Short chains of sugars are often linked to the polypeptide, making the molecule a **glycoprotein** (*glyco* means "sugar"). ③ When the molecule is ready for export from the ER, it is packaged in a **transport vesicle**, a vesicle that moves from one part of the cell to another. ④ This vesicle buds off from the ER membrane.

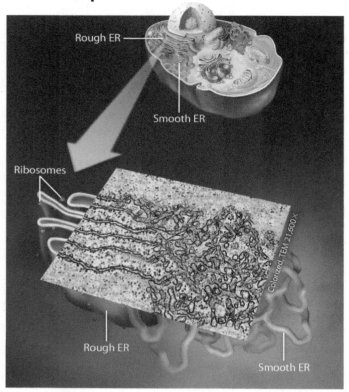

▲ **Figure 4.8A** A diagram and TEM of smooth and rough endoplasmic reticulum

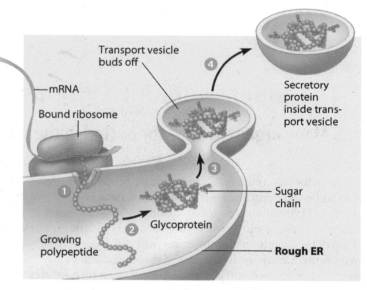

▲ **Figure 4.8B** Synthesis and packaging of a secretory protein by the rough ER

Try This Explain where the protein-making instructions carried by the mRNA came from.

The vesicle now carries the protein to the Golgi apparatus for further processing. From there, a transport vesicle con-taining the finished molecule makes its way to the plasma membrane and releases its contents from the cell.

In addition to making secretory proteins, rough ER is a membrane-making machine for the cell. It grows in place by adding membrane proteins and phospholipids to its own membrane. As polypeptides destined to be membrane proteins grow from bound ribosomes, they are inserted into the ER membrane. Phospholipids are made by enzymes of the rough ER and also inserted into the membrane. Thus, the ER membrane grows, and portions of it are transferred to other components of the endomembrane system in the form of transport vesicles.

Now let's follow a transport vesicle carrying products of the rough ER to the Golgi apparatus.

? Explain why we say that the endoplasmic reticulum is a biosynthetic workshop.

● The ER produces a huge variety of molecules, including phospholipids for cell membranes, steroid hormones, and proteins (synthesized by bound ribosomes) for membranes, other organelles, and secretion by the cell.

4.9 The Golgi apparatus modifies, sorts, and ships cell products

After leaving the ER, many transport vesicles travel to the **Golgi apparatus**. Using a light microscope and a staining technique he developed, Italian scientist Camillo Golgi discovered this membranous organelle in 1898. The electron microscope confirmed his discovery more than 50 years later, revealing a stack of flattened sacs, looking much like a pile of pita bread. A cell may contain many, even hundreds, of these stacks. The number of Golgi stacks correlates with how active the cell is in secreting proteins—a multistep process that, as you have just seen, is initiated in the rough ER.

The Golgi apparatus serves as a molecular warehouse and processing station for products manufactured by the ER. You can follow these activities in **Figure 4.9**. Note that the flattened Golgi sacs are not connected, as are ER sacs. ❶ One side of a Golgi stack serves as a receiving dock for transport vesicles produced by the ER. ❷ A vesicle fuses with a Golgi sac, adding its membrane and contents to the "receiving" side. ❸ Products of the ER are modified as a Golgi sac progresses through the stack. ❹ The "shipping" side of the Golgi

functions as a depot, dispatching its products in vesicles that bud off and travel to other sites.

How might ER products be processed during their transit through the Golgi? Various Golgi enzymes modify the carbohydrate portions of the glycoproteins made in the ER, removing some sugars and substituting others. Molecular identification tags, such as phosphate groups, may be added that help the Golgi sort molecules into different batches for different destinations.

Finished secretory products, packaged in transport vesicles, move to the plasma membrane for export from the cell. Alternatively, finished products may become part of the plasma membrane itself or part of another organelle, such as a lysosome, which we discuss next.

? What is the relationship of the Golgi apparatus to the ER in a protein-secreting cell?

● The Golgi receives transport vesicles budded from the ER that contain proteins synthesized by bound ribosomes. The Golgi finishes processing the proteins and dispatches transport vesicles to the plasma membrane, where the proteins are secreted.

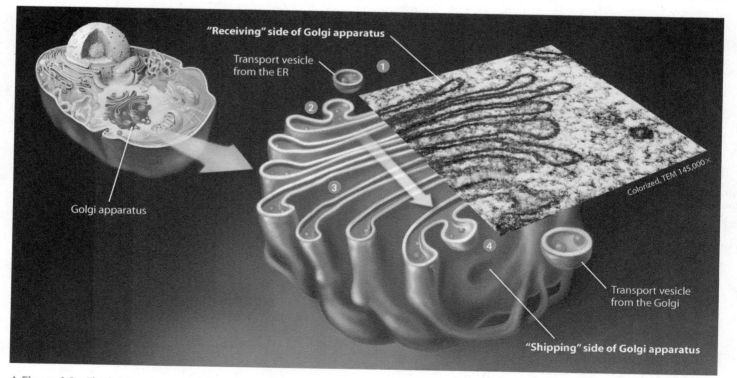

"Receiving" side of Golgi apparatus

Transport vesicle from the ER

❶ ❷ ❸ ❹

Golgi apparatus

Colorized, TEM 145,000×

Transport vesicle from the Golgi

"Shipping" side of Golgi apparatus

▲ **Figure 4.9** The Golgi apparatus receiving, processing, and shipping products

4.10 Lysosomes are digestive compartments within a cell

A **lysosome** is a membrane-enclosed sac of digestive enzymes. The name *lysosome* is derived from two Greek words meaning "breakdown body." The enzymes and membranes of lysosomes are made by rough ER and processed in the Golgi apparatus. Illustrating a main theme of eukaryotic cell structure—compartmentalization—a lysosome provides an acidic environment for its enzymes, while safely isolating them from the rest of the cell.

Lysosomes have several types of digestive functions. Many protists engulf food particles into membranous sacs called food vacuoles. As Figure 4.10A shows, lysosomes fuse with food vacuoles and digest the food. The nutrients are then released into the cytosol. Our white blood cells engulf bacteria and then destroy them using lysosomes. Lysosomes also serve as recycling centers. Cells enclose damaged organelles or small amounts of cytosol in membrane sacs. A lysosome fuses with such a vesicle (Figure 4.10B) and dismantles its contents, making organic molecules available for reuse. With the help of lysosomes, a cell continually renews itself.

The cells of people with inherited lysosomal storage diseases lack one or more lysosomal enzymes. The lysosomes become engorged with undigested material, eventually interfering with cellular function. In Tay-Sachs disease, for example, a lipid-digesting enzyme is missing, and brain cells become impaired by an accumulation of lipids. Fortunately, lysosomal storage diseases are rare, as they are often fatal in early childhood.

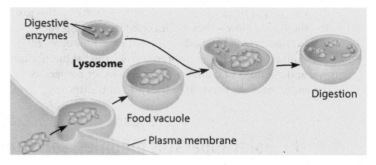

▲ **Figure 4.10A**   Lysosome fusing with a food vacuole and digesting food, after which nutrients are released to the cytosol

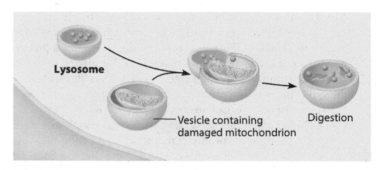

▲ **Figure 4.10B**   Lysosome fusing with a vesicle containing a damaged organelle and then digesting and recycling its contents

? **How is a lysosome like a recycling center?**

● It breaks down damaged organelles and recycles their molecules.

4.11 Vacuoles function in the general maintenance of the cell

Vacuoles are large vesicles that have a variety of functions. In Figure 4.10A, you saw how a food vacuole forms as a cell ingests food. Figure 4.11A shows two contractile vacuoles in the protist *Paramecium*, looking somewhat like wheel hubs with radiating spokes. The "spokes" collect water from the cell, and the hub expels it to the outside. Freshwater protists constantly take in water from their environment. Without a way to get rid of the excess water, the cell would swell and burst.

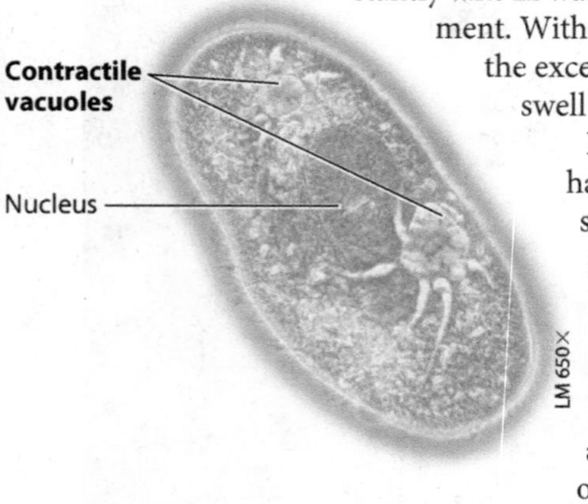

In plants, some vacuoles have a digestive function similar to that of lysosomes in animal cells. Vacuoles in flower petals contain pigments that attract pollinating insects. Vacuoles may also contain poisons or unpalatable compounds that protect the plant against herbivores;

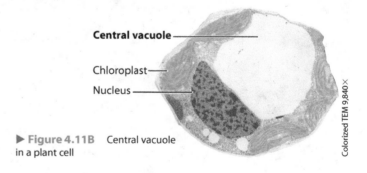

Central vacuole

Chloroplast

Nucleus

Colorized TEM 9,840×

▶ **Figure 4.11B**   Central vacuole in a plant cell

examples include nicotine, caffeine, and various chemicals we use as pharmaceutical drugs.

Figure 4.11B shows a plant cell's large **central vacuole**, which helps the cell grow in size by absorbing water and enlarging. It also stockpiles vital chemicals and may act as a trash can, safely storing toxic waste products.

? **Is a food vacuole part of the endomembrane system? Explain.**

● Yes; it forms by pinching in from the plasma membrane, which is part of the endomembrane system.

Contractile vacuoles

Nucleus

LM 650×

▲ **Figure 4.11A**   Contractile vacuoles in *Paramecium*, a unicellular eukaryote

4.12 A review of the structures involved in manufacturing and breakdown

Figure 4.12 summarizes the relationships within the endomembrane system. You can see the direct *structural* connections between the nuclear envelope, rough ER, and smooth ER. The red arrows show the *functional* connections, as membranes and proteins produced by the ER travel in transport vesicles to the Golgi and on to other destinations. Some vesicles develop into lysosomes or vacuoles. Others travel to and fuse with the plasma membrane, secreting their contents and adding their membrane to the plasma membrane.

Peroxisomes (see Figures 4.4A and B) are metabolic compartments that do not originate from the endomembrane system. In fact, how they are related to other organelles is still unknown. Some peroxisomes break down fatty acids to be used as cellular fuel. In your liver, peroxisomes detoxify harmful compounds. In these processes, enzymes transfer hydrogen from the compounds to oxygen, producing hydrogen peroxide (H_2O_2). Other enzymes in the peroxisome convert this toxic by-product to water—another example of the importance of a cell's compartmental structure.

A cell requires a continuous supply of energy to perform the work of life. Next we consider two organelles that act as cellular power stations—mitochondria and chloroplasts.

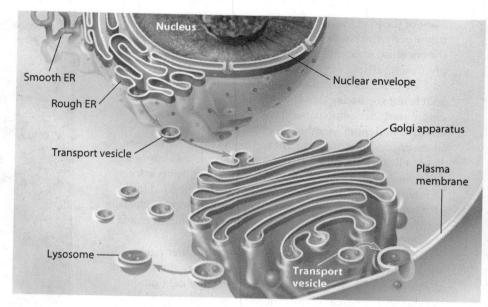

▲ **Figure 4.12**   Review of the endomembrane system

Try This Explain the role of transport vesicles in the endomembrane system.

? **How do transport vesicles help tie together the endomembrane system?**

● Transport vesicles move membranes and the substances they enclose between components of the endomembrane system.

▷ Energy-Converting Organelles

4.13 Mitochondria harvest chemical energy from food

Mitochondria (singular, *mitochondrion*) are organelles that carry out cellular respiration in nearly all eukaryotic cells, converting the chemical energy of foods such as sugars to the chemical energy of the molecule called ATP (adenosine triphosphate). ATP is the main energy source for cellular work.

A mitochondrion is enclosed by two membranes, each a phospholipid bilayer with a unique collection of embedded proteins **(Figure 4.13)**. The mitochondrion has two internal compartments. The first is the intermembrane space, the narrow region between the inner and outer membranes. The inner membrane encloses the second compartment, the **mitochondrial matrix**, which contains mitochondrial DNA and ribosomes, as well as enzymes that catalyze some of the reactions of cellular respiration. The inner membrane is highly folded and contains many embedded protein molecules that function in ATP synthesis. The folds, called **cristae**, increase the membrane's surface area, enhancing the mitochondrion's ability to produce ATP.

? **What is cellular respiration?**

● A process that converts the chemical energy of sugars and other food molecules to the chemical energy of ATP

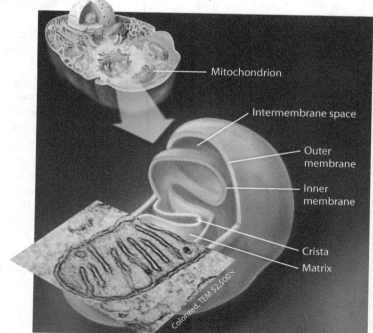

▲ **Figure 4.13**   The mitochondrion, site of cellular respiration

4.14 Chloroplasts convert solar energy to chemical energy

Most of the living world runs on the energy provided by photosynthesis, the conversion of light energy from the sun to the chemical energy of sugar molecules. **Chloroplasts** are the photosynthesizing organelles of plants and algae.

This organelle carries out complex, multistep processes, so it is not surprising that internal membranes partition the chloroplast into compartments (Figure 4.14). It is enclosed by an inner and outer membrane separated by a thin intermembrane space. The compartment inside the inner membrane holds a thick fluid called **stroma**, which contains chloroplast DNA and ribosomes as well as many enzymes. A network of interconnected sacs called **thylakoids** is suspended in the stroma. The sacs are often stacked like poker chips; each stack is called a **granum** (plural, *grana*). The compartment inside the thylakoids is called the thylakoid space.

The thylakoids are the chloroplast's solar power packs—the sites where the green chlorophyll molecules embedded in thylakoid membranes trap solar energy. In the next module, we explore the origin of mitochondria and chloroplasts.

? **Which membrane in a chloroplast appears to be the most extensive? Why might this be so?**

● The thylakoid membranes contain chlorophyll for photosynthesis.

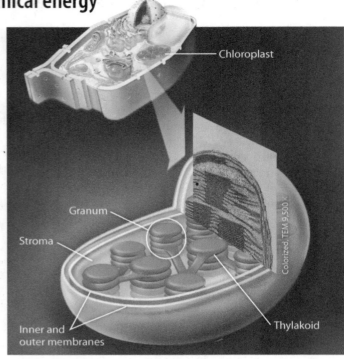

▲ **Figure 4.14**   The chloroplast, site of photosynthesis

4.15 Mitochondria and chloroplasts evolved by endosymbiosis

EVOLUTION CONNECTION

Mitochondria and chloroplasts contain a single circular DNA molecule, similar in structure to a prokaryotic chromosome, and ribosomes more similar to prokaryotic ribosomes than to eukaryotic ones. Interestingly, both organelles reproduce in a cell by a process resembling that of certain prokaryotes.

The **endosymbiont theory** states that mitochondria and chloroplasts were formerly small prokaryotes that began living within larger cells. These prokaryotes may have gained entry to the larger cell as undigested prey or parasites (Figure 4.15).

We can hypothesize how the symbiosis could have been beneficial. In a world that was becoming increasingly aerobic from the oxygen-generating photosynthesis of prokaryotes, a host would have benefited from an endosymbiont that was able to use oxygen to release large amounts of energy from organic molecules. Over the course of evolution, the host cell and its endosymbiont merged into a single organism—a eukaryotic cell with a mitochondrion. If one of these cells acquired a photosynthetic prokaryote, the prokaryote could provide the host cell with nourishment. An increasingly interdependent host and endosymbiont, over many generations, could become a eukaryotic cell containing chloroplasts.

? **All eukaryotes have mitochondria, but not all have chloroplasts. What is the evolutionary explanation?**

● The first endosymbiosis would have given rise to eukaryotic cells containing mitochondria. A second endosymbiotic event gave rise to cells containing chloroplasts as well as mitochondria.

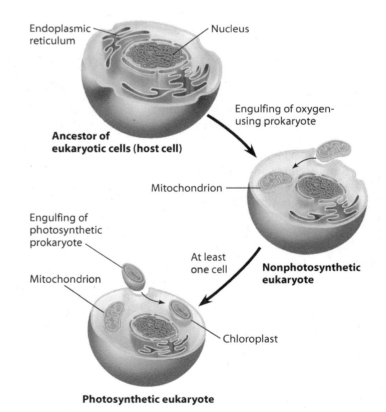

▲ **Figure 4.15**   Endosymbiotic origin of mitochondria and chloroplasts

4.16 The cell's internal skeleton helps organize its structure and activities

As you saw in the chapter introduction, networks of protein fibers extend throughout a cell. Collectively called the **cytoskeleton**, these fibers play a major role in organizing the structures and activities of the cell. And like a skeleton, they provide for structural support as well as movement, including both the internal movement of cell parts and the swimming or crawling motility of some cells.

Three main kinds of fibers make up the cytoskeleton: microtubules, the thickest fiber; microfilaments, the thinnest; and intermediate filaments, in between in thickness. **Figure 4.16** shows three micrographs of cells of the same type, each stained with a different fluorescent dye that selectively highlights one of these types of fibers.

Microtubules are straight, hollow tubes composed of globular proteins called tubulins. As indicated in the bottom left of Figure 4.16, microtubules elongate by the addition of tubulin proteins. They are readily disassembled, and their subunits can be reused elsewhere in the cell. In animal cells, microtubules grow out from a region near the nucleus called the **centrosome**, which contains a pair of centrioles, each composed of a ring of microtubules (see Figure 4.4A). Plant cells lack centrosomes with centrioles and organize microtubules by other means.

Microtubules shape and support the cell and also act as tracks along which organelles equipped with motor proteins move. For example, a lysosome might use its motor protein "feet" to "walk" along a microtubule to reach a food vacuole. Microtubules also guide the movement of chromosomes when cells divide, and they are the main components of cilia and flagella. We will return to the structure of these locomotive appendages in Module 4.18.

Intermediate filaments are found in the cells of most animals. They are made of various fibrous proteins that supercoil into cables. Intermediate filaments reinforce cell shape and anchor some organelles. For example, the nucleus typically sits in a cage made of intermediate filaments. While microtubules may be disassembled and reassembled elsewhere, intermediate filaments are often more permanent fixtures in the cell. The outer layer of your skin consists of dead skin cells packed full of intermediate filaments.

Microfilaments, also called actin filaments, are solid rods composed mainly of globular proteins called actin, arranged in a twisted double chain (bottom right of Figure 4.16). Microfilaments form a three-dimensional network just inside the plasma membrane that helps support the cell's shape. This is especially important for animal cells, which lack cell walls.

Microfilaments are also involved in cell movements. Actin filaments and thicker filaments made of a type of motor protein called myosin interact to cause contraction of muscle cells (see Figure 30.9B). Localized contractions brought about by actin and myosin are involved in the amoeboid (crawling) movement of the protist *Amoeba* and some of your white blood cells.

In the next module, we survey some of the techniques that led to the discovery of the cytoskeleton.

? Which component of the cytoskeleton is most important in (a) holding the nucleus in place within the cell; (b) guiding transport vesicles from the Golgi to the plasma membrane; (c) contracting muscle cells?

● (a) Intermediate filaments; (b) microtubules; (c) microfilaments

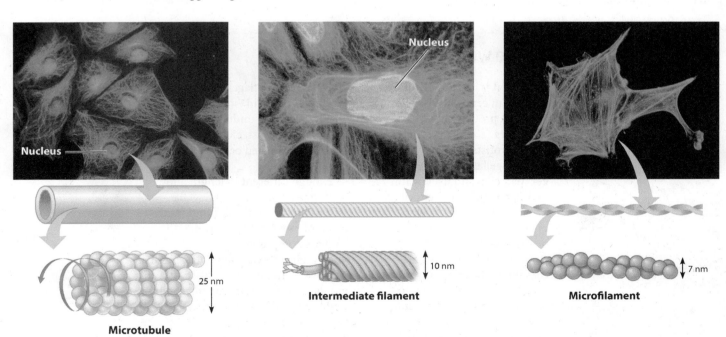

▲ **Figure 4.16**   Three types of fibers of the cytoskeleton: microtubules labeled with green fluorescent molecules (left), intermediate filaments labeled yellow-green (center), and microfilaments labeled red (right)

4.17 Scientists discovered the cytoskeleton using the tools of biochemistry and microscopy

SCIENTIFIC THINKING

As you learned in Module 4.1, improvements in microscopes and staining techniques led to the discovery of organelles. But biologists originally thought that these structures floated freely in the cell. Let's trace the progressive sequence of new techniques that led to the discovery of microfilaments, the component of the cytoskeleton built from actin.

In the 1940s, biochemists first isolated and identified the proteins actin and myosin from muscle cells. In 1954, scientists, using newly developed techniques of microscopy, established how filaments of actin and myosin interact in muscle contraction. In the next decade, researchers developed a technique to stain and identify actin filaments with the electron microscope. Imagine their surprise when they found actin not just in the muscle cells they were studying but also in other cells present in their samples. Further study identified actin filaments in all types of cells.

Today we take for granted our ability to "see" the cytoskeleton (as you saw in the chapter introduction). But intact networks of microfilaments were not visualized in cells until 1974. Using a technique called immunofluorescence microscopy, scientists developed antibody proteins that would bind to actin and attached fluorescent molecules to

How has our knowledge of cells grown?

them. When fluorescent molecules absorb light, they "glow" because they emit light of a specific wavelength or color.

When injected into cells, the fluorescent antibodies revealed a remarkable and beautiful web of microfilaments. **Figure 4.17** shows how different fluorescent tags can attach to various components of the cytoskeleton.

Researchers then tagged actin proteins themselves with fluorescent molecules and injected them into living cells. Instead of just marking where proteins are found, this technique, known as molecular cytochemistry, enabled scientists to visualize the dynamic behavior of cytoskeletal proteins in living cells.

In the early 1980s, biologists first paired a video camera with a microscope. Suddenly they could "watch" what was happening in cells over time and follow the changing architecture of the cytoskeleton.

As scientists develop new techniques, our understanding of the structure and function of the cytoskeleton will continue to grow.

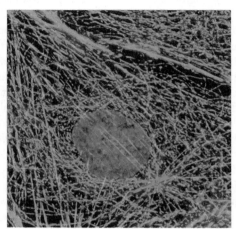

▲ **Figure 4.17**   A fluorescence micrograph of the cytoskeleton (microtubules are green, microfilaments are red)

> **?** What is the difference between immunofluorescence microscopy and molecular cytochemistry?

● In the former, fluorescently labeled antibodies show the locations of specific molecules. In the latter, the molecules themselves are labeled, and their behavior within a living cell can be tracked.

4.18 Cilia and flagella move when microtubules bend

The role of the cytoskeleton in movement is clearly seen in the motile appendages that protrude from certain cells. The short, numerous appendages that propel protists such as *Paramecium* (see Figure 4.1B) are called **cilia** (singular, *cilium*). Other protists may move using flagella, which are longer than cilia and usually limited to one or a few per cell.

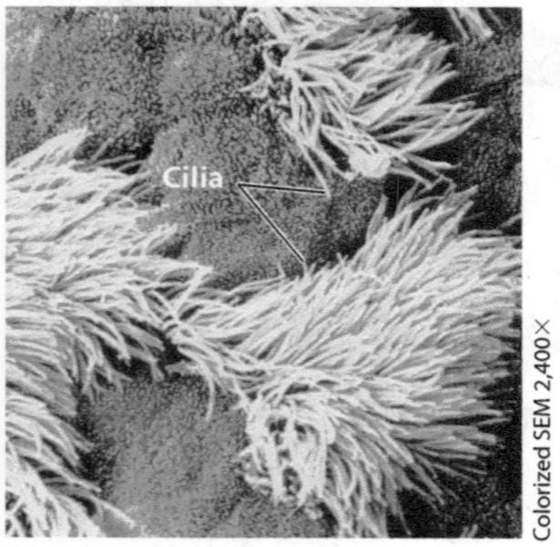

Some cells of multicellular organisms also have cilia or flagella. For example, **Figure 4.18A** shows cilia on cells lining the trachea (windpipe). These cilia sweep mucus containing trapped debris out of your lungs. (This cleaning function is impaired by cigarette smoke, which paralyzes the cilia.) Most animals and

some plants have flagellated sperm. A flagellum, shown in **Figure 4.18B**, propels the cell by an undulating whiplike motion. In contrast, cilia work more like the coordinated oars of a rowing team.

Though different in length and beating pattern, cilia and flagella have a common structure and mechanism of movement (**Figure 4.18C**). Both are composed of microtubules wrapped in an extension of the plasma membrane. In nearly all eukaryotic cilia and flagella, a ring of nine microtubule doublets surrounds a central pair of microtubules. This arrangement is called the "9 + 2" pattern. The microtubule assembly is anchored in the cell by a

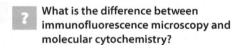

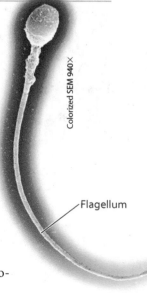

Colorized SEM 940×

Flagellum

▲ **Figure 4.18B**   Undulating flagellum on a human sperm cell

Cilia

Colorized SEM 2,400×

▲ **Figure 4.18A**   Cilia on cells lining the respiratory tract

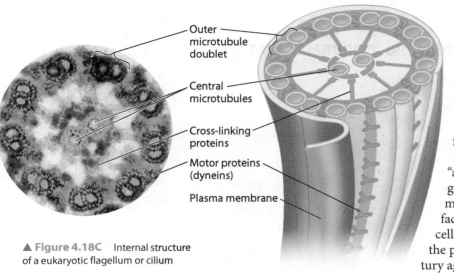

Outer microtubule doublet

Central microtubules

Cross-linking proteins

Motor proteins (dyneins)

Plasma membrane

Colorized TEM 290,000×

▲ **Figure 4.18C** Internal structure of a eukaryotic flagellum or cilium

basal body (not shown in the figure), which is structurally very similar to a centriole. In fact, in humans and many other animals, the basal body of the fertilizing sperm's flagellum enters the egg and becomes a centriole.

How does the microtubule assembly shown in Figure 4.18C produce the movement of cilia and flagella? Large motor proteins called dyneins (red in the figure) are attached along each outer microtubule doublet. A dynein protein has two "feet" that "walk" along an adjacent doublet. The walking

movement is coordinated so that it happens on one side at a time. The microtubules are held together by flexible cross-linking proteins (purple in the diagram). If the doublets were not held in place, they would slide past each other. Instead, the "walking" of the dynein feet causes the microtubules—and consequently the cilium or flagellum—to bend.

A cilium may also serve as a signal-receiving "antenna" for the cell. Cilia with this function are generally nonmotile (they lack the central pair of microtubules), and there is only one per cell. In fact, in vertebrate animals, it appears that almost all cells have what is called a *primary cilium*. Although the primary cilium was discovered more than a century ago, its importance to embryonic development, sensory reception, and cell function is only now being recognized. Defective primary cilia have been linked to polycystic kidney disease and other human disorders.

? **Primary ciliary dyskinesia (PCD), also known as immotile cilia syndrome, is a fairly rare disease in which cilia and flagella are lacking motor proteins. PCD is characterized by recurrent respiratory tract infections and immotile sperm. How would you explain these seemingly unrelated symptoms?**

● Without motor proteins, microtubules cannot bend. Thus cilia cannot cleanse the respiratory tract, and sperm cannot swim.

4.19 The extracellular matrix of animal cells functions in support and regulation

The plasma membrane is usually regarded as the boundary of the cell, but most cells synthesize and secrete materials that are external to the plasma membrane. These extracellular structures are essential to many cell functions.

Animal cells produce an **extracellular matrix (ECM)** (Figure 4.19). This elaborate layer helps hold cells together in tissues and protects and supports the plasma membrane. The main components of the ECM are glycoproteins, proteins bonded with carbohydrates. The most abundant glycoprotein is collagen, which forms strong fibers outside the cell. In fact, collagen accounts for about 40% of the protein in your body. The collagen fibers are embedded in a network woven from other types of glycoproteins. Large complexes form when hundreds of small glycoproteins connect to a central long polysaccharide molecule (shown as green in the figure). The ECM may attach to the cell through other glycoproteins that then bind to membrane proteins called **integrins**. Integrins span the membrane, attaching on the other side to proteins connected to microfilaments of the cytoskeleton.

As their name implies, integrins have the function of integration: They transmit signals between the ECM and the cytoskeleton. Thus, the cytoskeleton can influence the organization of the ECM and vice versa. For example, research shows that the ECM can regulate a cell's behavior, directing the path along which embryonic cells move and even influencing the activity of genes through the signals it relays. Genetic changes in cancer cells may result in a change in the composition of

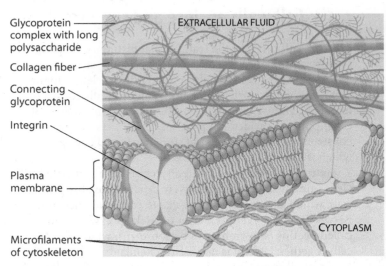

Glycoprotein complex with long polysaccharide

Collagen fiber

Connecting glycoprotein

Integrin

Plasma membrane

Microfilaments of cytoskeleton

EXTRACELLULAR FLUID

CYTOPLASM

▲ **Figure 4.19** The extracellular matrix (ECM) of an animal cell

the ECM they produce, causing such cells to lose their connections and spread to other tissues.

? **Referring to Figure 4.19, describe the structures that provide support to the plasma membrane.**

● The membrane is attached through membrane proteins (integrins) to microfilaments in the cytoskeleton and collagen fibers of the ECM.

4.20 Three types of cell junctions are found in animal tissues

Neighboring cells in animal tissues often adhere, interact, and communicate through specialized junctions between them. Figure 4.20 uses cells lining the digestive tract to illustrate three types of cell junctions. (The projections at the top of the cells increase the surface area for absorption of nutrients.)

At tight junctions, the plasma membranes of neighboring cells are knit tightly together by proteins. Tight junctions prevent leakage of fluid across a layer of cells. The dotted green arrows show how tight junctions prevent the contents of the digestive tract from leaking into surrounding tissues.

Anchoring junctions function like rivets, fastening cells together into strong sheets. Intermediate filaments made of sturdy proteins anchor these junctions in the cytoplasm. Anchoring junctions are common in tissues subject to stretching or mechanical stress, such as skin and muscle.

Gap junctions, also called communicating junctions, are channels that allow small molecules to flow through protein-lined pores between cells. The flow of ions through gap junctions in the cells of heart muscle coordinates their contraction. Gap junctions are common in embryos, where communication between cells is essential for development.

? A muscle tear injury would probably involve the rupture of which type of cell junction?

Anchoring junction ●

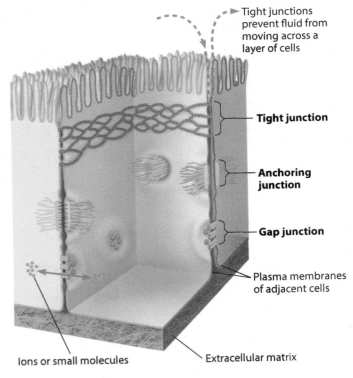

Tight junctions prevent fluid from moving across a layer of cells

Tight junction

Anchoring junction

Gap junction

Plasma membranes of adjacent cells

Ions or small molecules

Extracellular matrix

▲ Figure 4.20 Three types of cell junctions in animal tissues

4.21 Cell walls enclose and support plant cells

The **cell wall** is one of the features that distinguishes plant cells from animal cells. This rigid extracellular structure not only protects the cells but also provides the skeletal support that keeps plants upright on land. Plant cell walls consist of fibers of cellulose (see Figure 3.7) embedded in a matrix of other polysaccharides and proteins. This fibers-in-a-matrix construction resembles that of steel-reinforced concrete, which is also noted for its strength.

Figure 4.21 shows the layered structure of plant cell walls. Cells initially lay down a relatively thin and flexible primary wall, which allows the growing cell to continue to enlarge. Between adjacent cells is a layer of sticky polysaccharides called pectins (shown here in dark brown), which glue the cells together. (Pectin is used to thicken jams and jellies.) When a cell stops growing, it strengthens its wall. Some cells add a secondary wall deposited in laminated layers next to the plasma membrane. Wood consists mainly of secondary walls, which are strengthened with rigid molecules called lignin.

Despite their thickness, plant cell walls do not totally isolate the cells from each other. Figure 4.21 shows the numerous channels that connect adjacent plant cells, called **plasmodesmata** (singular, *plasmodesma*). Cytosol passing through the plasmodesmata allows water and other small molecules to freely move from cell to cell. Through

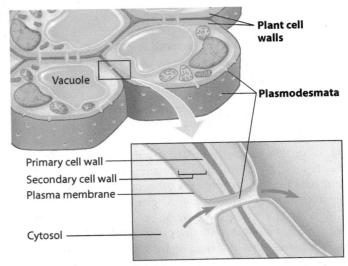

Plant cell walls

Vacuole

Plasmodesmata

Primary cell wall

Secondary cell wall

Plasma membrane

Cytosol

▲ Figure 4.21 Plant cell walls and plasmodesmata

plasmodesmata, the cells of a plant tissue share water, nourishment, and chemical messages.

? Which animal cell junction is analogous to a plasmodesma?

A gap junction ●

4.22 Review: Eukaryotic cell structures can be grouped on the basis of four main functions

Congratulations: You have completed the grand tour of the cell. In the process, you have been introduced to many important cell structures. To provide a framework for this information and reinforce the theme that structure is correlated with function, we have grouped the eukaryotic cell structures into four categories by general function, as reviewed in Table 4.22.

The first category is genetic control. Here we include the nucleus that houses a cell's genetic instructions and the ribosomes that produce the proteins coded for in those instructions. The second category includes organelles of the endomembrane system that are involved in the manufacture, distribution, and breakdown of materials. The third category includes the two energy-processing organelles, mitochondria and chloroplasts. And the fourth category—structural support, movement, and intercellular communication—includes the cytoskeleton, extracellular structures, and connections between cells.

Within most of these categories, a structural similarity underlies the general function of each component. Manufacturing depends heavily on a network of structurally and functionally connected membranes. All the organelles involved in the breakdown or recycling of materials are membranous sacs, inside of which enzymatic digestion can safely occur. In the energy-processing category, expanses of metabolically active membranes and intermembrane compartments within the organelles enable chloroplasts and mitochondria to perform the complex energy conversions that power the cell. Even in the diverse fourth category, there is a common structural theme in the various protein fibers of most of these cellular systems.

We can summarize further by noting that the overall structure of a cell is closely related to its specific function. Thus, cells that produce proteins for export contain a large quantity of ribosomes and rough ER, while muscle cells are packed with microfilaments, myosin motor proteins, and mitochondria. And, finally, let us emphasize that these cellular structures form an integrated team—with the property of life emerging at the level of the cell from the coordinated functions of the team members.

> **?** How do mitochondria, smooth ER, and the cytoskeleton all contribute to the contraction of a muscle cell?

● Mitochondria supply energy in the form of ATP. The smooth ER helps regulate contraction by the uptake and release of calcium ions. Microfilaments function in the actual contractile apparatus.

TABLE 4.22 | EUKARYOTIC CELL STRUCTURES AND FUNCTIONS

1. Genetic Control

Structure	Function
Nucleus 	DNA replication, RNA synthesis; assembly of ribosomal subunits (in nucleolus)
Ribosomes	Polypeptide (protein) synthesis

2. Manufacturing, Distribution, and Breakdown

Structure	Function
Rough ER	Synthesis of membrane lipids and proteins, secretory proteins, and hydrolytic enzymes; formation of transport vesicles
Smooth ER 	Lipid synthesis; detoxification in liver cells; calcium ion storage
Golgi apparatus	Modification and sorting of macromolecules; formation of lysosomes and transport vesicles
Lysosomes (in animal cells and some protists)	Digestion of ingested food or bacteria and recycling of a cell's damaged organelles and macromolecules
Vacuoles	Digestion (food vacuole); storage of chemicals and cell enlargement (central vacuole); water balance (contractile vacuole)
Peroxisomes (not part of endomembrane system)	Diverse metabolic processes, with breakdown of toxic hydrogen peroxide by-product

3. Energy Processing

Structure	Function
Mitochondria 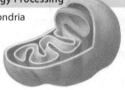	Conversion of chemical energy in food to chemical energy of ATP
Chloroplasts (in plants and algae)	Conversion of light energy to chemical energy of sugars

4. Structural Support, Movement, and Communication Between Cells

Structure	Function
Cytoskeleton (microfilaments, intermediate filaments, and microtubules) 	Maintenance of cell shape; anchorage for organelles; movement of organelles within cells; cell movement (crawling, muscle contraction, bending of cilia and flagella)
Plasma membrane	Regulate traffic in and out of cell
Extracellular matrix (in animals)	Support; regulation of cellular activities
Cell junctions	Communication between cells; binding of cells in tissues
Cell walls (in plants)	Support and protection; binding of cells in tissues

Reviewing the Concepts

Introduction to the Cell (4.1–4.4)

4.1 Microscopes reveal the world of the cell. The light microscope can display living cells. The greater magnification and resolution of the scanning and transmission electron microscopes reveal the ultrastructure of cells.

4.2 The small size of cells relates to the need to exchange materials across the plasma membrane. The microscopic size of most cells provides a large surface-to-volume ratio. The plasma membrane is a phospholipid bilayer with embedded proteins.

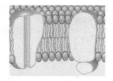

4.3 Prokaryotic cells are structurally simpler than eukaryotic cells. All cells have a plasma membrane, DNA, ribosomes, and cytosol. Prokaryotic cells lack organelles.

4.4 Eukaryotic cells are partitioned into functional compartments. Membrane-enclosed organelles compartmentalize a cell's activities.

The Nucleus and Ribosomes (4.5–4.6)

4.5 The nucleus contains the cell's genetic instructions. The nucleus houses the cell's DNA, which directs protein synthesis via messenger RNA. Subunits of ribosomes are assembled in the nucleolus.

4.6 Ribosomes make proteins for use in the cell and for export. Composed of ribosomal RNA and proteins, ribosomes synthesize proteins according to directions from DNA.

The Endomembrane System (4.7–4.12)

4.7 Many organelles are connected in the endomembrane system.

4.8 The endoplasmic reticulum is a biosynthetic workshop. The ER is a membranous network of tubes and sacs. Smooth ER synthesizes lipids and processes toxins. Rough ER produces membranes, and ribosomes on its surface make membrane and secretory proteins.

4.9 The Golgi apparatus modifies, sorts, and ships cell products. The Golgi apparatus consists of stacks of sacs in which products of the ER are processed and then sent to other organelles or to the cell surface.

4.10 Lysosomes are digestive compartments within a cell. Lysosomes house enzymes that break down ingested substances and damaged organelles for recycling.

4.11 Vacuoles function in the general maintenance of the cell. Some protists have contractile vacuoles. Plant cells contain a large central vacuole that stores molecules and wastes and facilitates growth.

4.12 A review of the structures involved in manufacturing and breakdown. The organelles of the endomembrane system are interconnected structurally and functionally.

Energy-Converting Organelles (4.13–4.15)

4.13 Mitochondria harvest chemical energy from food.

4.14 Chloroplasts convert solar energy to chemical energy.

4.15 Mitochondria and chloroplasts evolved by endosymbiosis. These organelles originated from prokaryotic cells that became residents in a host cell.

The Cytoskeleton and Cell Surfaces (4.16–4.22)

4.16 The cell's internal skeleton helps organize its structure and activities. The cytoskeleton includes microfilaments, intermediate filaments, and microtubules. Their functions include muscle contraction, anchorage and movement of organelles, and maintenance of cell shape.

4.17 Scientists discovered the cytoskeleton using the tools of biochemistry and microscopy.

4.18 Cilia and flagella move when microtubules bend. Eukaryotic cilia and flagella are locomotor appendages made of microtubules in a "9 + 2" arrangement.

4.19 The extracellular matrix of animal cells functions in support and regulation. The ECM consists mainly of glycoproteins, which bind tissue cells together, support the membrane, and communicate with the cytoskeleton.

4.20 Three types of cell junctions are found in animal tissues. Tight junctions bind cells to form leakproof sheets. Anchoring junctions rivet cells into strong tissues. Gap junctions allow substances to flow from cell to cell.

4.21 Cell walls enclose and support plant cells. Plant cell walls are made largely of cellulose. Plasmodesmata are connecting channels between cells.

4.22 Review: Eukaryotic cell structures can be grouped on the basis of four main functions. These functions are (1) genetic control; (2) manufacturing, distribution, and breakdown; (3) energy processing; and (4) structural support, movement, and communication between cells.

Connecting the Concepts

1. Label the structures in this diagram of an animal cell. Review the functions of each of these organelles.

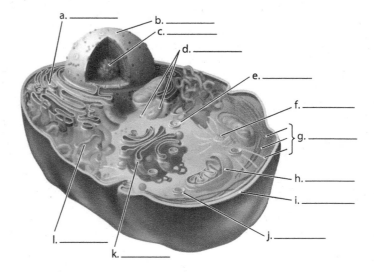

a. _____
b. _____
c. _____
d. _____
e. _____
f. _____
g. _____
h. _____
i. _____
j. _____
k. _____
l. _____

Testing Your Knowledge

Level 1: Knowledge/Comprehension

2. The ultrastructure of a chloroplast is best studied using a
   a. light microscope.
   b. scanning electron microscope.
   c. transmission electron microscope.
   d. light microscope and fluorescent dyes.
3. The cells of an ant and an elephant are, on average, the same small size; an elephant just has more of them. What is the main advantage of small cell size? (*Explain your reasoning.*)
   a. A small cell has a larger plasma membrane surface area than does a large cell.
   b. Small cells can better take up sufficient nutrients and oxygen to service their cell volume.
   c. It takes less energy to make an organism out of small cells.
   d. Small cells require less oxygen than do large cells.
4. Which of the following clues would tell you whether a cell is prokaryotic or eukaryotic?
   a. the presence or absence of a rigid cell wall
   b. whether or not the cell is partitioned by internal membranes
   c. the presence or absence of ribosomes
   d. Both a and b are important clues.
5. Which of the following is one of the major components of the plasma membrane of a plant cell?
   a. phospholipids
   b. cellulose fibers
   c. collagen fibers
   d. pectins
6. What four cellular components are shared by prokaryotic and eukaryotic cells?
7. Describe two different ways in which cilia can function in organisms.

Level 2: Application/Analysis

Choose from the following cells for questions 8–11:
   a. pancreatic cell that secretes digestive enzymes
   b. ovarian cell that produces estrogen (a steroid hormone)
   c. muscle cell in the thigh of a long-distance runner
   d. white blood cell that engulfs bacteria

8. In which cell would you find the most lysosomes?
9. In which cell would you find the most smooth ER?
10. In which cell would you find the most rough ER?
11. In which cell would you find the most mitochondria?
12. In what ways do the internal membranes of a eukaryotic cell contribute to the functioning of the cell?
13. Is this statement true or false? "Animal cells have mitochondria; plant cells have chloroplasts." Explain your answer, and describe the functions of these organelles.
14. Describe the structure of the plasma membrane of an animal cell. What would be found directly inside and outside the membrane?
15. Imagine a spherical cell with a radius of 10 μm. What is the cell's surface area in μm^2? Its volume, in μm^3? (*Note*: For a sphere of radius r, surface area $= 4\pi r^2$ and volume $= \pi r^3$. Remember that the value of π is 3.14.) What is the ratio of surface area to volume for this cell? Now do the same calculations for a second cell, this one with a radius of 20 μm. Compare the surface-to-volume ratios of the two cells. How is this comparison significant to the functioning of cells?

16. Describe the pathway of the protein hormone insulin from its gene to its export from a cell of your pancreas.

Level 3: Synthesis/Evaluation

17. How might the phrase "ingested but not digested" be used in a description of the endosymbiotic theory?
18. Cilia are found on cells in almost every organ of the human body, and the malfunction of cilia is involved in several human disorders. During embryological development, for example, cilia generate a leftward flow of fluid that initiates the left-right organization of the body organs. Some individuals with primary ciliary dyskinesia (see Module 4.18 checkpoint question) exhibit *situs inversus*, in which internal organs such as the heart are on the wrong side of the body. Explain why this reversed arrangement may be a symptom of PCD.
19. **SCIENTIFIC THINKING** Microtubules often produce movement through their interaction with motor proteins. But in some cases, microtubules move cell components when the length of the microtubule changes. Through a series of experiments, researchers determined that microtubules grow and shorten as tubulin proteins are added or removed from their ends. Other experiments showed that microtubules make up the spindle apparatus that "pulls" chromosomes toward opposite ends (poles) of a dividing cell. The figures below describe a clever experiment done in 1987 to determine whether a spindle microtubule shortens (depolymerizes) at the end holding a chromosome or at the pole end of a dividing cell.

    Experimenters labeled the microtubules of a dividing cell from a pig kidney with a yellow fluorescent dye. As shown on the left half of the diagram below, they then marked a region halfway along the microtubules by using a laser to eliminate the fluorescence from that region. They did not mark the other side of the spindle (right side of the figure).

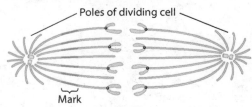

Poles of dividing cell

Mark

The figure below illustrates the results they observed as the chromosomes moved toward the opposite poles of the cell.

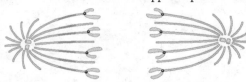

Describe these results. What would you conclude about where the microtubules depolymerize from comparing the length of the microtubules on either side of the mark? How could the experimenters determine whether this is the mechanism of chromosome movement in all cells?

Source: G. J. Gorbsky et al. Chromosomes move poleward in anaphase along stationary microtubules that coordinately disassemble from their kinetochore ends, *Journal of Cell Biology* 104:9–18 (1987).

Answers to all questions can be found in Appendix 4.

The Working Cell

The illustration below is beautiful and intriguing—but what does it represent? This computer model shows a small section of a membrane in a human cell; notice the water molecules (depicted with red and gray balls) streaming single file across the membrane. Notice also the phospholipids that make up the lipid bilayer of this membrane: The yellow balls represent the phosphate heads and the green squiggles are the fatty acid tails of the phospholipids. The blue ribbons embedded in the membrane represent regions of a membrane protein called aquaporin that function as water channels. Just one molecule of this protein enables billions of water molecules to flow through the membrane every second—many more than could wander through the lipid bilayer on their own.

Aquaporins are common in cells involved in water balance. For example, your kidneys must filter and reabsorb many liters of water a day, and aquaporins are vital to their proper functioning. There are rare cases of people with defective aquaporins whose kidneys can't reabsorb water and must drink 20 liters of water every day to prevent dehydration. On the other hand, if kidney cells have

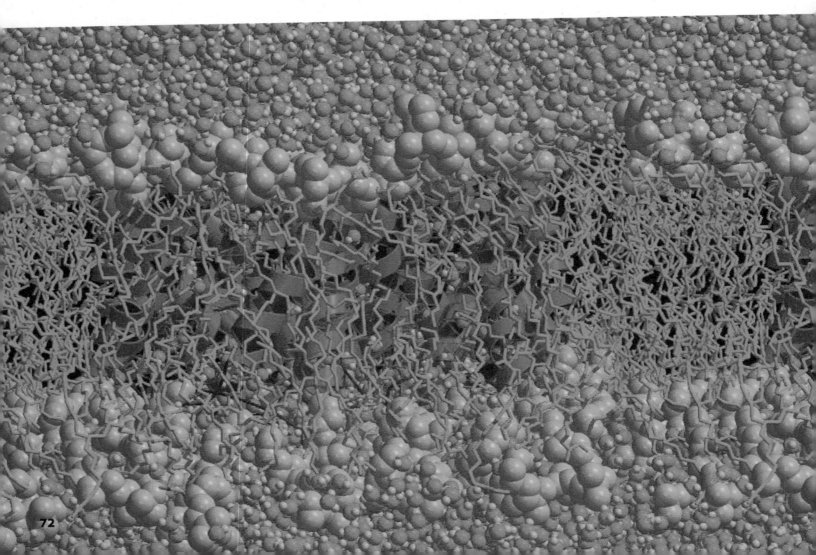

too many aquaporins, excess water is reabsorbed and body tissues may swell. A common complication of pregnancy is fluid retention, and it is likely caused by increased synthesis of aquaporin proteins. Later in the chapter you will learn about the serendipitous discovery of these water channels.

But aquaporins are only one example of how the plasma membrane and its proteins enable cells to survive and function. We begin this chapter by examining membranes. A cell expends energy to build membranes, and many of a membrane's functions require energy. A cell's energy conversions involve enzymes, which control all of its chemical reactions. Indeed, everything that is depicted in this computer model of water molecules zipping through a membrane relates to how working cells use membranes, energy, and enzymes—which are the topics of this chapter.

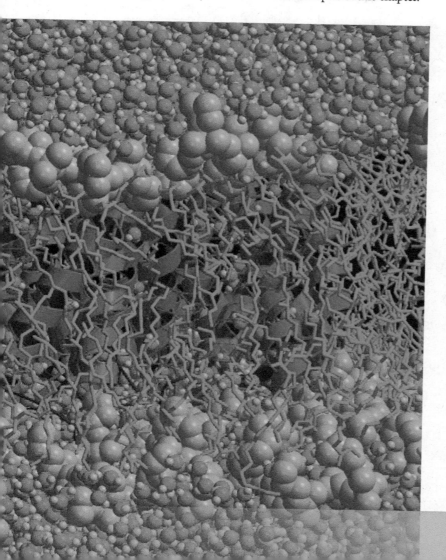

BIG IDEAS

Membrane Structure and Function
(5.1–5.9)

A cell membrane's structure enables its many functions, such as regulating traffic across the membrane.

Energy and the Cell
(5.10–5.12)

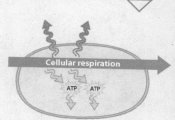

A cell's metabolic reactions transform energy, using ATP to drive cellular work.

How Enzymes Function
(5.13–5.16)

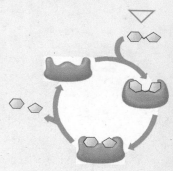

Enzymes speed up a cell's chemical reactions and provide precise control of metabolism.

VISUALIZING THE CONCEPTS

5.1 Membranes are fluid mosaics of lipids and proteins with many functions

Biologists use the **fluid mosaic model** to describe a membrane's structure—diverse protein molecules suspended in a fluid phospholipid bilayer. This module illustrates the structure and function of a plasma membrane, the boundary that encloses a living cell. Like all cellular membranes, the plasma membrane exhibits **selective permeability**; that is, it allows some substances to cross more easily than others. But the plasma membrane does more than just regulate the exchange of materials. This figure will help you visualize all the activity taking place in and across the membranes of two adjacent cells.

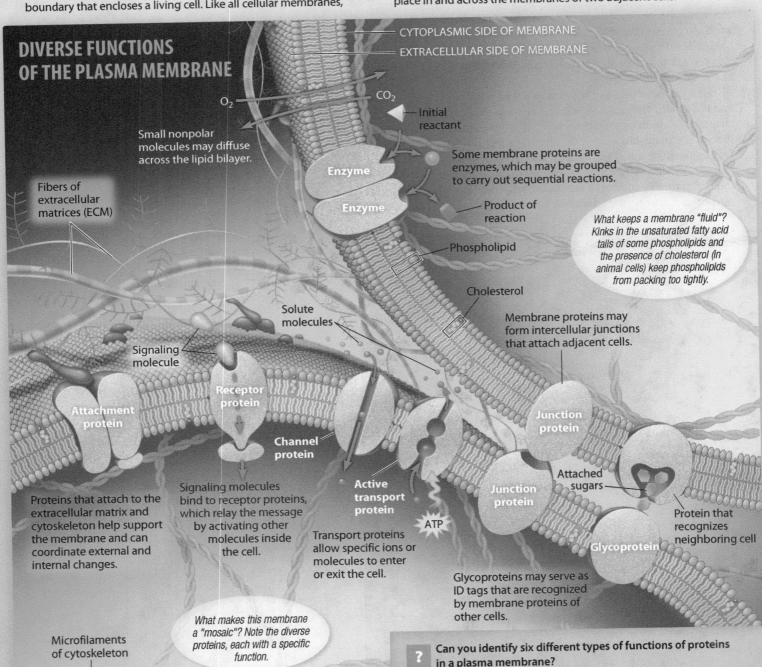

DIVERSE FUNCTIONS OF THE PLASMA MEMBRANE

CYTOPLASMIC SIDE OF MEMBRANE
EXTRACELLULAR SIDE OF MEMBRANE

O_2

CO_2

Initial reactant

Small nonpolar molecules may diffuse across the lipid bilayer.

Some membrane proteins are enzymes, which may be grouped to carry out sequential reactions.

Enzyme

Enzyme

Product of reaction

Fibers of extracellular matrices (ECM)

Phospholipid

What keeps a membrane "fluid"? Kinks in the unsaturated fatty acid tails of some phospholipids and the presence of cholesterol (in animal cells) keep phospholipids from packing too tightly.

Cholesterol

Membrane proteins may form intercellular junctions that attach adjacent cells.

Solute molecules

Signaling molecule

Receptor protein

Junction protein

Attachment protein

Channel protein

Attached sugars

Proteins that attach to the extracellular matrix and cytoskeleton help support the membrane and can coordinate external and internal changes.

Signaling molecules bind to receptor proteins, which relay the message by activating other molecules inside the cell.

Active transport protein

Transport proteins allow specific ions or molecules to enter or exit the cell.

ATP

Junction protein

Protein that recognizes neighboring cell

Glycoprotein

Glycoproteins may serve as ID tags that are recognized by membrane proteins of other cells.

Microfilaments of cytoskeleton

What makes this membrane a "mosaic"? Note the diverse proteins, each with a specific function.

? **Can you identify six different types of functions of proteins in a plasma membrane?**

● Attachment to the cytoskeleton and ECM, signal reception and relay, enzymatic activity, cell–cell recognition, intercellular joining, and transport

5.2 The spontaneous formation of membranes was a critical step in the origin of life

Phospholipids, the key ingredients of biological membranes, were probably among the first organic molecules that formed from chemical reactions on early Earth (see Module 15.2). These lipids could spontaneously self-assemble into simple membranes, as can be demonstrated in a test tube. When a mixture of phospholipids and water is shaken, the phospholipids organize into bilayers surrounding water-filled bubbles (Figure 5.2). This assembly requires neither genes nor other information beyond the properties of the phospholipids themselves.

The formation of membrane-enclosed collections of molecules would have been a critical step in the evolution of the first cells. A membrane can enclose a solution that is different in composition from its surroundings. A plasma membrane that allows cells to regulate their chemical exchanges with the environment is a basic requirement for life. Indeed, all cells are enclosed by a plasma membrane that is similar in structure and function—illustrating the evolutionary unity of life.

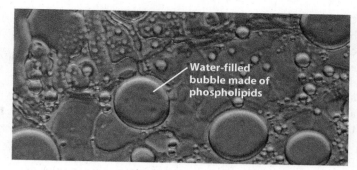

Water-filled bubble made of phospholipids

▲ Figure 5.2   Artificial membrane-bounded sacs

? In the origin of a cell, why would the formation of a simple lipid bilayer membrane not be sufficient? What else would have to be part of such a membrane?

● The membrane would need embedded proteins that could regulate the movement of substances into and out of the cell.

5.3 Passive transport is diffusion across a membrane with no energy investment

Molecules have a type of energy called thermal energy, due to their constant motion. One result of this motion is **diffusion**, the tendency for particles of any substance to spread out into the available space. How might diffusion affect the movement of substances into or out of a cell?

The figures to the right will help you visualize diffusion across a membrane. **Figure 5.3A** shows a solution of green dye separated from pure water by an artificial membrane. Assume that this membrane has microscopic pores through which dye molecules can move. Thus, we say the membrane is permeable to the dye. Although each molecule moves randomly, there will be a *net* movement from the side of the membrane where dye molecules are more concentrated to the side where they are less concentrated. Put another way, the dye diffuses down its **concentration gradient**. Eventually, the solutions on both sides will have equal concentrations of dye. At this dynamic equilibrium, molecules still move back and forth, but there is no *net* change in concentration on either side of the membrane.

Figure 5.3B illustrates the important point that two or more substances diffuse independently of each other; that is, each diffuses down its own concentration gradient.

Because a cell does not have to do work when molecules diffuse across its membrane, such movement across a membrane is called **passive transport**. Much of the traffic across cell membranes occurs by diffusion. For example, diffusion down concentration gradients is the sole means by which oxygen (O_2), essential for metabolism, enters your cells and carbon dioxide (CO_2), a metabolic waste, passes out of them.

Both O_2 and CO_2 are small, nonpolar molecules that diffuse easily across the phospholipid bilayer of a membrane. But can ions and polar molecules also diffuse across the

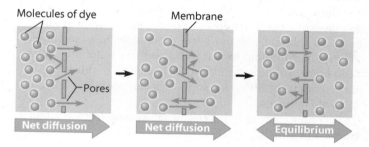

Molecules of dye   Membrane

Pores

Net diffusion   Net diffusion   Equilibrium

▲ Figure 5.3A   Diffusion of one type of molecule across a membrane

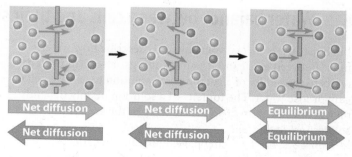

Net diffusion   Net diffusion   Equilibrium
Net diffusion   Net diffusion   Equilibrium

▲ Figure 5.3B   Diffusion of two types of molecules across a membrane
Try This   Explain why these two types of molecules are moving in opposite directions.

hydrophobic interior of a membrane? They can if they are moving down their concentration gradients and if they have transport proteins to help them cross.

? Why is diffusion across a membrane called passive transport?

● The cell does not expend energy to transport substances that are diffusing down their concentration gradients.

5.4 Osmosis is the diffusion of water across a membrane

One of the most important substances that crosses membranes by passive transport is water. In the next module, we consider the critical balance of water between a cell and its environment. But first let's explore a physical model of the diffusion of water across a selectively permeable membrane, a process called **osmosis**. Remember that a selectively permeable membrane allows some substances to cross more easily than others.

The top of Figure 5.4 shows what happens if a membrane permeable to water but not to a solute (such as glucose) separates two solutions that have different concentrations of solute. (A solute is a substance that dissolves in a liquid solvent. The resulting mixture is a solution.) The solution on the right side initially has a higher concentration of solute than that on the left. As you can see, water crosses the membrane until the solute concentrations are more nearly equal on both sides.

In the close-up view at the bottom of Figure 5.4, you can see what happens at the molecular level. Polar water molecules cluster around hydrophilic (water-loving) solute molecules. The effect is that on the right side, there are fewer water molecules that are *free* to cross the membrane. The less concentrated solution on the left has fewer solute molecules but more *free* water molecules available to move. There is a net movement of water down its own concentration gradient, from the solution with more free water molecules (and lower solute concentration) to that with fewer free water molecules (and higher solute concentration). The result of this water movement is the difference in water levels you see at the top right of Figure 5.4.

Let's now apply to living cells what we have learned about osmosis in artificial systems.

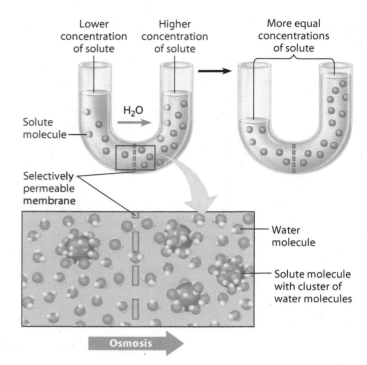

▲ Figure 5.4 Osmosis, the diffusion of water across a membrane

Try This Identify the solution that has more free water molecules. Predict which way water will move.

? Indicate the direction of net water movement between two solutions—a 0.5% sucrose solution and a 2% sucrose solution—separated by a membrane not permeable to sucrose.

● From the 0.5% sucrose solution (lower solute concentration) to the 2% sucrose solution (higher solute concentration)

5.5 Water balance between cells and their surroundings is crucial to organisms

Biologists use a special vocabulary to describe how water will move between a cell and its surroundings. The term **tonicity** refers to the ability of a surrounding solution to cause a cell to gain or lose water. The tonicity of a solution mainly depends on its concentration of solutes relative to the concentration of solutes inside the cell.

Figure 5.5, on the facing page, illustrates the effects of placing animal and plant cells in solutions of various tonicities.

When an animal cell, such as the red blood cell shown in the top center of the figure, is immersed in a solution that is **isotonic** to the cell (*iso*, same, and *tonos*, tension), the cell's volume remains constant. The solute concentration of a cell and its isotonic environment are essentially equal, and the cell gains water at the same rate that it loses it. In your body, red blood cells are transported in the isotonic plasma of the blood. Intravenous (IV) fluids administered in hospitals must also be isotonic to blood cells. The body cells of most animals are bathed in an extracellular fluid that is isotonic to the cells. And seawater is isotonic to the cells of many marine animals, such as sea stars and crabs.

What happens when an animal cell is placed in a **hypotonic** solution (*hypo*, below), a solution with a solute concentration lower than that of the cell? As shown in the upper left of the figure, the cell gains water, swells, and may burst (lyse) like an overfilled balloon. The upper right shows the opposite case—an animal cell placed in a **hypertonic** solution (*hyper*, above), a solution with a higher solute concentration. In which direction will water move? The cell shrivels and can die from water loss.

For an animal to survive in a hypotonic or hypertonic environment, it must have a way to prevent excessive uptake or loss of water and regulate the solute concentration of its body fluids. The control of water balance is called **osmoregulation**. For example, a freshwater fish, which lives in a hypotonic environment, takes up water by osmosis across the cells of its gills. Its kidneys work constantly to remove excess water from the body.

Water balance issues are somewhat different for the cells of plants, prokaryotes, and fungi because of their cell walls. As shown in the bottom of Figure 5.5, in a hypotonic environment a plant cell is turgid (very firm), which is the healthy state for most plant cells. Although the plant cell swells as water enters by osmosis, the cell wall exerts a back pressure, called turgor pressure, which prevents the cell from taking in too much water and bursting. Plants that are not woody, such as most houseplants, depend on their turgid cells for mechanical support. In contrast, when a plant cell is surrounded by an isotonic solution, there is no net movement of water into the cell, and the cell is flaccid (limp).

In a hypertonic environment (bottom right), a plant cell is no better off than an animal cell. As a plant cell loses water, it shrivels, and its plasma membrane pulls away from the cell wall. This process, called plasmolysis, causes the plant to wilt and can be lethal to the cell and the plant. The walled cells of bacteria and fungi also plasmolyze in hypertonic environments. Thus, meats and other foods can be preserved with

| Hypotonic solution (lower solute levels) | Isotonic solution (equal solute levels) | Hypertonic solution (higher solute levels) |

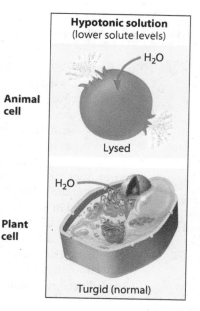 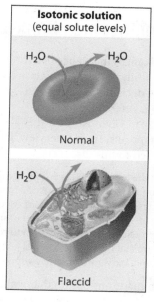 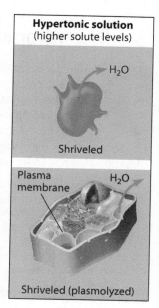

Animal cell — Lysed / Normal / Shriveled

Plant cell — Turgid (normal) / Flaccid / Shriveled (plasmolyzed)

▲ **Figure 5.5** How animal and plant cells react to changes in tonicity

concentrated salt solutions because the cells of food-spoiling bacteria or fungi become plasmolyzed and eventually die.

In the next module, we explore how water and other polar solutes move across cell membranes.

? Explain the function of the contractile vacuoles in a freshwater *Paramecium* (shown in Figure 4.11A) in terms of what you have just learned about water balance in cells.

● The pond water in which *Paramecium* lives is hypotonic to the cell. The contractile vacuoles expel the water that constantly enters the cell by osmosis.

5.6 Transport proteins can facilitate diffusion across membranes

Recall that nonpolar molecules, such as O_2 and CO_2, can dissolve in the lipid bilayer of a membrane and diffuse through it with ease. But how do polar or charged substances make it past the hydrophobic center of a membrane? Hydrophilic molecules and ions require the help of specific transport proteins to move across a membrane. This assisted transport, called **facilitated diffusion**, is a type of passive transport because it does not require energy. As in all passive transport, the driving force is the concentration gradient.

Figure 5.6 shows a common type of transport protein, which provides a channel that specific molecules or ions use as a passageway through a membrane. Another type of transport protein binds its passenger, changes shape, and releases the transported molecule on the other side. In both cases, the transport protein helps a specific substance diffuse across the membrane down its concentration gradient and, thus, requires no input of energy.

Substances that use facilitated diffusion for crossing cell membranes include a number of sugars, amino acids, ions—and even water. The water molecule is very small, but because it is polar (see Module 2.6), its diffusion through a membrane's hydrophobic interior is relatively slow. For many cells, this slow diffusion of water is adequate. Cells such as plant

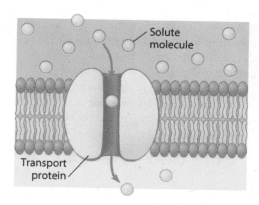

◀ **Figure 5.6** Transport protein providing a channel for the diffusion of a specific solute across a membrane

Solute molecule

Transport protein

cells, red blood cells, and the cells lining your kidney tubules, however, have greater water-permeability needs. As you saw in the chapter introduction, the very rapid diffusion of water into and out of such cells is made possible by a protein channel called an **aquaporin**. In the next module, we explore the discovery of these transport proteins.

? How do transport proteins contribute to a membrane's selective permeability?

● Because they are specific for the solutes they transport, the numbers and kinds of transport proteins affect a membrane's permeability to various solutes.

5.7 Research on another membrane protein led to the discovery of aquaporins

SCIENTIFIC THINKING

Sometimes major advances in science occur when a scientist is studying something else but makes the wise decision to explore an unexpected finding. Peter Agre received the 2003 Nobel Prize in Chemistry for this sort of discovery of aquaporins. In an interview, Dr. Agre described his research that led to this discovery:

How can water flow through a membrane?

> When I joined the faculty at the Johns Hopkins School of Medicine, I began to study the Rh blood antigens. Rh is of medical importance . . . when Rh-negative mothers have Rh-positive babies. Membrane-spanning proteins are really messy to work with. But we worked out a method to isolate the Rh protein. Our sample seemed to consist of two proteins, but we were sure that the smaller one was just a break-down product of the larger one. We were completely wrong.

Dr. Agre's research team made antibodies that would specifically bind to and label this smaller protein. They found two interesting results: The antibody did not bind to any part of the Rh protein, indicating that the smaller protein wasn't part of the Rh protein. And the antibody did bind in huge quantities to red blood cells, showing that this new protein is one of the most abundant proteins in red cell membranes. Agre and his team also determined that the protein was identical to and even more abundant in certain kidney cells. But they didn't know what this protein did.

A colleague suggested that the protein might be the elusive water channel that physiologists had predicted would explain the rapid transport of water in some cells. To test this hypothesis, the researchers injected messenger RNA for the protein into frog eggs, whose plasma membranes are known to be quite water impermeable. Biochemical tests showed that within 72 hours, the frog egg cells had translated the mRNA into the new protein. They transferred a group of RNA-injected frog eggs and a control group of eggs injected with only a buffer solution to a hypotonic solution and monitored the eggs with videomicroscopy. The osmotic swelling of RNA-injected and control cells is plotted in **Figure 5.7**. The experimental egg cells exploded in three minutes; the control eggs showed minimal swelling, even for time periods exceeding an hour. The researchers concluded that the newly discovered protein enabled the rapid movement of water into the cells.

Since the results of that experiment were reported in 1992, much research has been done on aquaporins, determining their structure and dynamic functioning. The chapter introduction presented a model of aquaporin structure. Molecular biophysicists have produced computer simulations that show water molecules flipping their way single file through an aquaporin. Such simulations have revealed how aquaporins allow only water molecules to pass through them. Aquaporins have been found in bacteria, plants, and animals, and evolutionary biologists are tracing the relationships of these various aquaporins. Medical researchers study the function and occasional malfunction of aquaporins in the human kidney, lungs, brain, and lens of the eye. The serendipitous discovery of aquaporins has led to a broad range of scientific research.

? **Why are aquaporins important in kidney cells?**

● Kidney cells must reabsorb a large amount of water when producing urine.

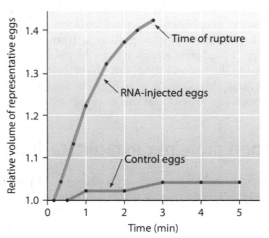

Source: Adaptation of Figure 2A from "Appearance of Water Channels in Xenopus Oocytes Expressing Red Cell CHIP28 Protein" by Gregory Preston et al., from *Science*, April 1992, Volume 256(5055). Copyright © 1992 by AAAS. Reprinted with permission.

▲ **Figure 5.7** Osmotic swelling of representative aquaporin RNA-injected and control-injected oocytes following transfer to a hypotonic medium

5.8 Cells expend energy in the active transport of a solute

In **active transport**, a cell must expend energy to move a solute *against* its concentration gradient—that is, across a membrane toward the side where the solute is more concentrated. The energy molecule ATP (described in more detail in Module 5.12) supplies the energy for most active transport.

Active transport allows a cell to maintain internal concentrations of small molecules and ions that are different from concentrations in its surroundings. For example, the inside of an animal cell has a higher concentration of potassium ions (K^+) and a lower concentration of sodium ions (Na^+) than the solution outside the cell. The generation of nerve signals depends on these concentration differences, which a transport protein called the sodium-potassium pump maintains by actively moving Na^+ out of the cell and K^+ into the cell.

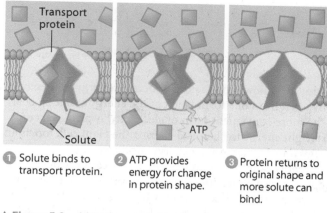

① Solute binds to transport protein.

② ATP provides energy for change in protein shape.

③ Protein returns to original shape and more solute can bind.

▲ **Figure 5.8** Active transport of a solute across a membrane

Figure 5.8 shows a simple model of an active transport system that pumps a solute out of the cell against its concentration gradient. ① The process begins when solute molecules on the cytoplasmic side of the plasma membrane attach to specific binding sites on the transport protein. ② With energy provided by ATP, the transport protein changes shape in such a way that the solute is released on the other side of the membrane. ③ The transport protein returns to its original shape, ready for its next passengers.

> **?** Cells actively transport Ca^{2+} out of the cell. Is calcium more concentrated inside or outside of the cell? Explain.

● Outside: Active transport moves calcium against its concentration gradient.

5.9 Exocytosis and endocytosis transport large molecules across membranes

So far, we've focused on how water and small solutes enter and leave cells. The story is different for large molecules.

A cell uses the process of **exocytosis** (from the Greek *exo*, outside, and *kytos*, cell) to export bulky materials such as proteins or polysaccharides. A transport vesicle filled with macromolecules buds from the Golgi apparatus and moves to the plasma membrane (see Figure 4.12). Once there, the vesicle fuses with the plasma membrane, and the vesicle's contents spill out of the cell when the vesicle membrane becomes part of the plasma membrane. For example, the cells in your pancreas that manufacture the hormone insulin secrete it into the extracellular fluid by exocytosis, where it is picked up by the bloodstream.

Endocytosis (*endo*, inside) is a transport process through which a cell takes in large molecules. **Figure 5.9** shows two kinds of endocytosis. The top diagram illustrates **phagocytosis**, or "cellular eating." A cell engulfs a particle by wrapping extensions called pseudopodia around it and packaging it within a membrane-enclosed sac called a vacuole. The vacuole then fuses with a lysosome, whose hydrolytic enzymes digest the contents of the vacuole (see Figure 4.10A). Protists such as amoeba take in food particles this way, and some of your white blood cells engulf invading bacteria via phagocytosis.

The bottom diagram illustrates **receptor-mediated endocytosis**, which enables a cell to acquire specific solutes. Receptor proteins for specific molecules are embedded in regions of the membrane that are lined by a layer of coat proteins. The plasma membrane indents to form a coated pit, whose receptor proteins pick up particular molecules from the extracellular fluid. The coated pit pinches closed to form a vesicle, which then releases the molecules into the cytoplasm.

Your cells use receptor-mediated endocytosis to take in cholesterol from the blood for synthesis of membranes and as a precursor for other steroids. Cholesterol circulates in the blood in particles called low-density lipoproteins (LDLs). LDLs bind to receptor proteins and then enter cells by

Phagocytosis

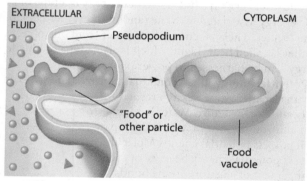

Receptor-mediated endocytosis

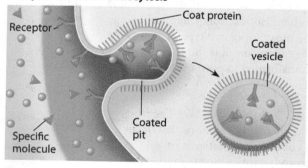

▲ **Figure 5.9** Two kinds of endocytosis

endocytosis. In humans with the inherited disease familial hypercholesterolemia, LDL receptor proteins are defective or missing. Cholesterol accumulates to high levels in the blood, leading to atherosclerosis, the buildup of fatty deposits in the walls of blood vessels (see Module 9.11).

> **?** As a cell grows, its plasma membrane expands. Does this involve endocytosis or exocytosis? Explain.

● Exocytosis: When a transport vesicle fuses with the plasma membrane, its contents are released and the vesicle membrane adds to the plasma membrane.

5.10 Cells transform energy as they perform work

The title of this chapter is "The Working Cell." But just what type of work does a cell do? You just learned that a cell can actively transport substances across membranes. The cell also builds those membranes and the proteins embedded in them. A cell is a miniature chemical factory in which thousands of reactions occur within a microscopic space. Some of these reactions release energy; others require energy. But before you can understand how the cell works, you must have a basic knowledge of energy.

Forms of Energy   **Energy** is the capacity to cause change or to perform work. There are two basic forms of energy: kinetic energy and potential energy. **Kinetic energy** is the energy of motion. Moving objects can perform work by transferring motion to other matter. For example, the movement of your legs can push bicycle pedals, turning the wheels and moving you and your bike up a hill. **Thermal energy** is a type of kinetic energy associated with the random movement of atoms or molecules. Thermal energy in transfer from one object to another is called **heat**. Light, which is also a type of kinetic energy, can be harnessed to power photosynthesis.

Potential energy, the second main form of energy, is energy that matter possesses as a result of its location or structure. Water behind a dam and you on your bicycle at the top of a hill possess potential energy. Molecules possess potential energy because of the arrangement of electrons in the bonds between their atoms. **Chemical energy** is the potential energy available for release in a chemical reaction. Chemical energy is the most important type of energy for living organisms; it is the energy that can be transformed to power the work of the cell.

Energy Transformations   The study of energy transformations that occur in a collection of matter is called **thermodynamics**. Scientists use the word *system* for the matter under study and refer to the rest of the universe—everything outside the system—as the *surroundings*. A system can be an electric power plant, a single cell, or the entire planet. An organism is an open system; that is, it exchanges both energy and matter with its surroundings.

The **first law of thermodynamics**, also known as the law of energy conservation, states that the energy in the universe is constant. Energy can be transferred and transformed, but it cannot be created or

destroyed. A power plant does not create energy; it merely converts it from one form (such as the energy stored in coal) to the more convenient form of electricity. A plant cell converts light energy to chemical energy; the plant cell, too, is an energy transformer, not an energy producer.

If energy cannot be destroyed, then why can't organisms simply recycle their energy? It turns out that during every transfer or transformation, some energy becomes unavailable to do work—it is converted to thermal energy (random molecular motion) and released as heat. Scientists use a quantity called **entropy** as a measure of disorder, or randomness. The more randomly arranged a collection of matter is, the greater its entropy. According to the **second law of thermodynamics**, energy conversions increase the entropy (disorder) of the universe.

Figure 5.10 compares a car and a cell to show how energy can be transformed and how entropy increases as a result. Automobile engines and cells use the same basic process to make the chemical energy of their fuel available for work. The engine mixes oxygen with gasoline in an explosive chemical reaction that pushes the pistons, which eventually move the wheels. The waste products emitted from the exhaust pipe are carbon dioxide and water, energy-poor, simple molecules. Only about

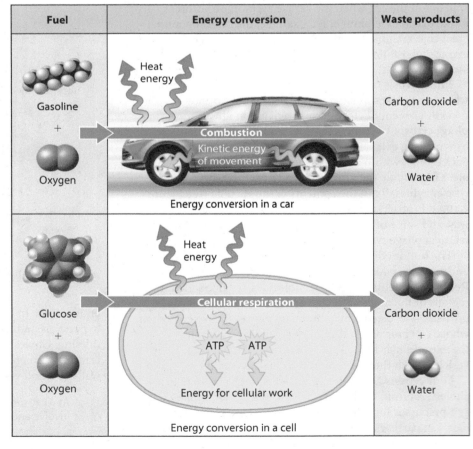

▲ **Figure 5.10**   Energy transformations in a car and a cell

25% of the energy stored in gasoline is converted to the kinetic energy of the car's movement; the rest is lost as heat.

Cells also use oxygen in reactions that release energy from fuel molecules. In the process called **cellular respiration**, the chemical energy stored in organic molecules is used to produce ATP, which the cell can use to perform work. Just like for the car, the waste products are carbon dioxide and water. Cells are more efficient than cars, however, converting about 34% of the chemical energy in their fuel to energy for cellular work. The other 66% generates heat, which explains why vigorous exercise makes you so warm.

According to the second law of thermodynamics, energy transformations result in the universe becoming more disordered. How, then, can we account for biological order?

Although the intricate structures of a cell correspond to a decrease in entropy, their production is accomplished at the expense of ordered forms of matter and energy taken in from the surroundings. As shown in Figure 5.10, cells extract the chemical energy of glucose and return disordered heat and lower-energy carbon dioxide and water to the surroundings. In a thermodynamic sense, a cell is an island of low entropy in an increasingly random universe.

? **How does the second law of thermodynamics explain the diffusion of a solute across a membrane?**

Diffusion across a membrane results in equal concentrations of solute, which is a more disordered arrangement (higher entropy) than a high concentration on one side and a low concentration on the other.

5.11 Chemical reactions either release or store energy

Chemical reactions are of two types: exergonic or endergonic. An **exergonic reaction** releases energy (*exergonic* means "energy outward"). As Figure 5.11A shows, an exergonic reaction begins with reactants whose covalent bonds contain more potential energy than those in the products. The reaction releases to the surroundings an amount of energy equal to the difference in potential energy between the reactants and the products.

Consider what happens when wood burns. One of the major components of wood is cellulose, a large energy-rich carbohydrate composed of many glucose monomers. Burning wood releases the energy of glucose as heat and light. Carbon dioxide and water are the products of the reaction.

As you learned in Module 5.10, cells release energy from fuel molecules in the process called cellular respiration. Burning and cellular respiration are alike in being exergonic. They differ in that burning is essentially a one-step process that releases all of a substance's energy at once. Cellular respiration, on the other hand, involves many steps, each a separate chemical reaction; you can think of it as a "slow burn." Some of the energy released by cellular respiration escapes as heat, but a substantial amount is stored in ATP, the immediate source of energy for a cell.

Endergonic reactions require a net input of energy and yield products that are rich in potential energy (*endergonic* means "energy inward"). As shown in Figure 5.11B, an endergonic reaction starts with reactants that contain relatively little potential energy. Energy is absorbed from the surroundings as the reaction occurs, so the products of an endergonic reaction contain more chemical energy than the reactants did.

Photosynthesis, the process by which plant cells make sugar, is an example of an endergonic process. Photosynthesis starts with energy-poor reactants (carbon dioxide and water molecules) and, using energy absorbed from sunlight, produces energy-rich sugar molecules.

Living cells carry out thousands of exergonic and endergonic reactions. The total of an organism's chemical reactions is called **metabolism**. We can picture a cell's metabolism as a road map of thousands of chemical reactions arranged as intersecting highways or metabolic pathways. A **metabolic pathway** is a series of chemical reactions that either builds a

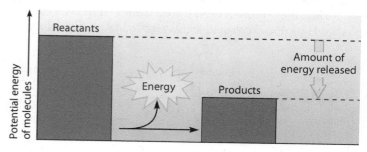

▲ **Figure 5.11A**   Exergonic reaction, energy released

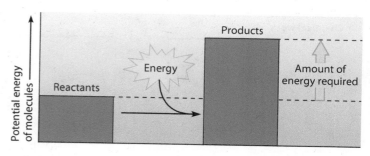

▲ **Figure 5.11B**   Endergonic reaction, energy required

complex molecule or breaks down a complex molecule into simpler compounds. The "slow burn" of cellular respiration is an example of a metabolic pathway in which a sequence of reactions slowly releases the potential energy stored in sugar.

All of an organism's activities require energy, which is obtained from sugar and other molecules by the exergonic reactions of cellular respiration. Cells then use that energy in endergonic reactions to make molecules and do the work of the cell. **Energy coupling**—the use of energy released from exergonic reactions to drive endergonic reactions—is crucial in all cells. ATP molecules are the key to energy coupling. In the next module, we explore the structure and function of ATP.

? **Cellular respiration is an exergonic process. Remembering that energy must be conserved, what do you think becomes of the energy extracted from food during this process?**

Some of it is stored in ATP molecules; the rest is released as heat.

5.12 ATP drives cellular work by coupling exergonic and endergonic reactions

ATP powers nearly all forms of cellular work. The abbreviation ATP stands for adenosine triphosphate, and as **Figure 5.12A** shows, ATP consists of an organic molecule called adenosine and a triphosphate tail of three phosphate groups (each symbolized by Ⓟ). All three phosphate groups are negatively charged (see Table 3.2). These like charges are crowded together, and their mutual repulsion makes the triphosphate tail of ATP the chemical equivalent of a compressed spring.

As a result, the bonds connecting the phosphate groups are unstable and can readily be broken by hydrolysis, the addition of water. Notice in Figure 5.12A that when the bond to the third group breaks, a phosphate group leaves ATP—which becomes ADP (adenosine diphosphate)—and energy is released.

Thus, the hydrolysis of ATP is exergonic—it releases energy. How does a cell couple this reaction to an endergonic

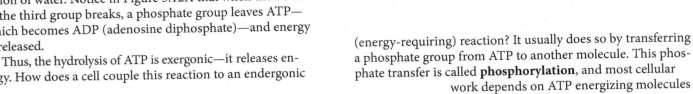

▲ **Figure 5.12C** The ATP cycle

(energy-requiring) reaction? It usually does so by transferring a phosphate group from ATP to another molecule. This phosphate transfer is called **phosphorylation**, and most cellular work depends on ATP energizing molecules by phosphorylating them.

What types of work does a cell do? As **Figure 5.12B** shows, the chemical, transport, and mechanical work of a cell are all driven by ATP. In chemical work, the phosphorylation of reactants provides energy to drive the endergonic synthesis of products. In transport work, ATP drives the active transport of solutes across a membrane against their concentration gradients by phosphorylating transport proteins. And in an example of mechanical work, the transfer of phosphate groups to special motor proteins in muscle cells causes the proteins to change shape and pull on other protein filaments, in turn causing the cells to contract.

ATP is a renewable resource. A cell uses and regenerates ATP continuously. **Figure 5.12C** shows the ATP cycle. Each side of this cycle illustrates energy coupling. Energy released in exergonic reactions, such as the breakdown of glucose during cellular respiration, is used to generate ATP from ADP. In this endergonic process, a phosphate group is bonded to ADP, forming ATP. The hydrolysis of ATP releases energy that drives endergonic reactions. The ATP cycle runs at an astonishing pace. In fact, a working muscle cell may consume and regenerate 10 million ATP molecules each second.

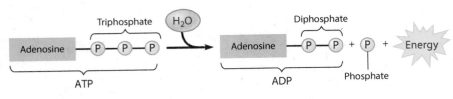

▲ **Figure 5.12A** The hydrolysis of ATP yielding ADP, a phosphate group, and energy.

Chemical work

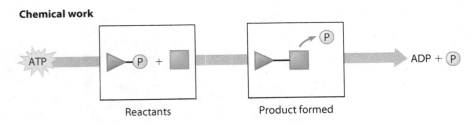

Reactants   Product formed

Transport work

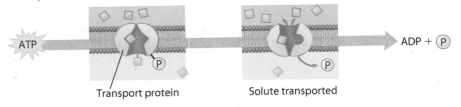

Transport protein   Solute transported

Mechanical work

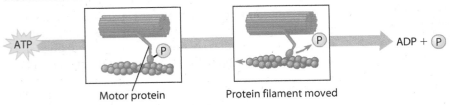

Motor protein   Protein filament moved

▲ **Figure 5.12B** How ATP powers cellular work

Try This Examine this figure and identify the way in which all three types of cellular work are similar.

> **?** Explain how ATP transfers energy from exergonic to endergonic processes in the cell.

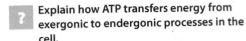

● Exergonic processes phosphorylate ADP to form ATP. ATP transfers energy to endergonic processes by phosphorylating other molecules.

5.13 Enzymes speed up the cell's chemical reactions by lowering energy barriers

Your room gets messier; water flows downhill; sugar crystals dissolve in your coffee. Ordered structures tend toward disorder, and high-energy systems tend to change toward a more stable state of low energy. Proteins, DNA, carbohydrates, lipids—most of the complex molecules of your cells are rich in potential energy. Why don't these high-energy, ordered molecules spontaneously break down into less ordered, lower-energy molecules? They remain intact for the same reason that wood doesn't normally burst into flames or the gas in an automobile's gas tank doesn't spontaneously explode.

There is an energy barrier that must be overcome before a chemical reaction can begin. Energy must be absorbed to contort or weaken bonds in reactant molecules so that they can break and new bonds can form. We call this the **activation energy** (because it activates the reactants). We can think of activation energy as the amount of energy needed for reactant molecules to move "uphill" to a higher-energy, unstable state so that the "downhill" part of a reaction can begin.

The activation energy barrier protects the highly ordered molecules of your cells from spontaneously breaking down. But now we have a dilemma. Life depends on countless chemical reactions that constantly change a cell's molecular makeup. Most of the essential reactions of metabolism must occur quickly and precisely for a cell to survive. How can the specific reactions that a cell requires get over that energy barrier?

One way to speed reactions is to add heat. Heat speeds up molecules and agitates atoms so that bonds break more easily and reactions can proceed. Certainly, adding a match to kindling will start a fire, and the firing of a spark plug ignites gasoline in an engine. But heating a cell would speed up all chemical reactions, not just the necessary ones, and too much heat would kill the cell.

The answer to this dilemma lies in **enzymes**—molecules that function as biological catalysts, increasing the rate of a reaction without being consumed by the reaction. Almost all enzymes are proteins. (Some RNA molecules can also function as enzymes.) An enzyme speeds up a reaction by lowering the activation energy needed for a reaction to begin. Figure 5.13 compares a reaction without an enzyme (left) and with an enzyme (right). Notice how much easier it is for the reactant to get over the activation energy barrier when an enzyme is involved. In the next module, we explore how the structure of an enzyme enables it to lower the activation energy, allowing a reaction to proceed.

? The graph below illustrates the course of a reaction with and without an enzyme. Which curve represents the enzyme-catalyzed reaction? What energy changes are represented by the lines labeled a, b, and c?

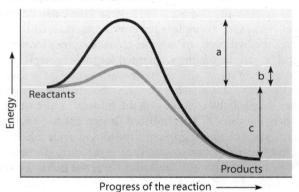

● The lower (red) curve. Line a is the activation energy without enzyme; b is the activation energy with enzyme; c is the change in energy between reactants and products, which is the same for both the catalyzed and uncatalyzed reactions.

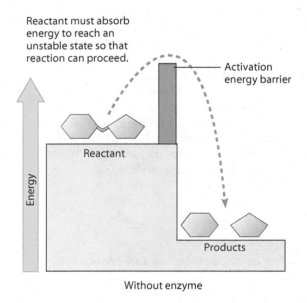

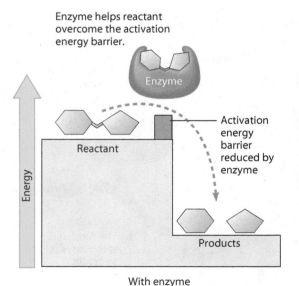

▲ **Figure 5.13**   The effect of an enzyme in lowering the activation energy

5.14 A specific enzyme catalyzes each cellular reaction

You just learned that an enzyme catalyzes a reaction by lowering the activation energy barrier. How does it do that? With the aid of an enzyme, the bonds in a reactant are contorted into the higher-energy, unstable state from which the reaction can proceed. Without an enzyme, the activation energy barrier might never be breached. For example, a solution of sucrose (table sugar) can sit for years at room temperature with no appreciable hydrolysis into its components glucose and fructose. But if we add a small amount of the enzyme sucrase, all the sucrose will be hydrolyzed within seconds.

An enzyme is very selective in the reaction it catalyzes. As a protein, an enzyme has a unique three-dimensional shape, and that shape determines the enzyme's specificity. The specific reactant that an enzyme acts on is called the enzyme's **substrate**. A substrate fits into a region of the enzyme called the **active site**—typically a pocket or groove on the surface of the enzyme. Enzymes are specific because only specific substrate molecules fit into their active sites.

The Catalytic Cycle   Figure 5.14 illustrates the catalytic cycle of an enzyme. Our example is the enzyme sucrase, which catalyzes the hydrolysis of sucrose. (Most enzymes have names that end in -ase, and many are named for their substrate.) ❶ The enzyme starts with an empty active site. ❷ Sucrose enters the active site, attaching by weak bonds. The active site changes shape slightly, embracing the substrate more snugly, like a firm handshake. This **induced fit** may contort substrate bonds or place chemical groups of the amino acids making up the active site in position to catalyze the reaction. (In reactions involving two or more reactants, the active site holds the substrates in the proper orientation for a reaction to occur.)

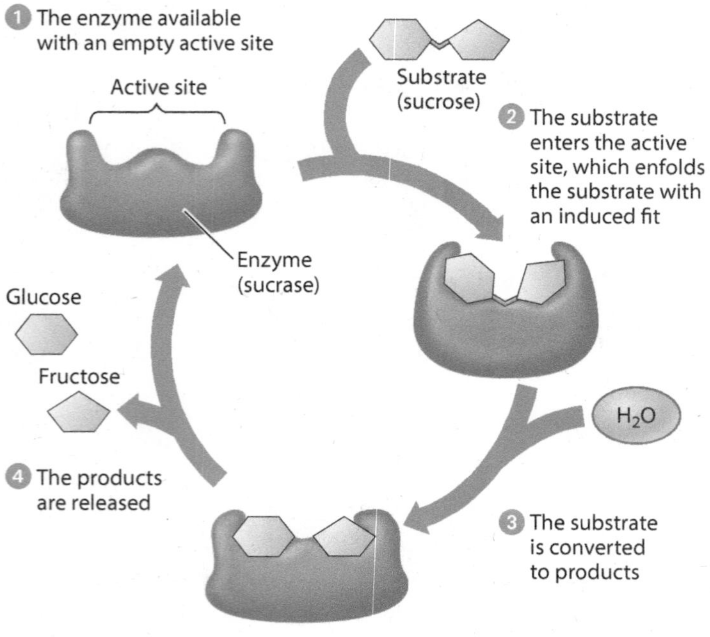

❸ The strained bond of sucrose reacts with water, and the substrate is converted (hydrolyzed) to the products glucose and fructose. ❹ The enzyme releases the products and emerges unchanged from the reaction. Its active site is now available for another substrate molecule, and another round of the cycle can begin. A single enzyme molecule may act on thousands or even millions of substrate molecules per second.

Optimal Conditions for Enzymes   As with all proteins, an enzyme's shape is central to its function, and this three-dimensional shape is affected by the environment. For every enzyme, there are optimal conditions under which it is most effective. Temperature, for instance, affects molecular motion, and an enzyme's optimal temperature produces the highest rate of contact between reactant molecules and the enzyme's active site. Higher temperatures denature the enzyme, altering its specific shape and destroying its function. Most human enzymes work best at 35–40°C (95–104°F), close to our normal body temperature of 37°C. Prokaryotes that live in hot springs, however, contain enzymes with optimal temperatures of 70°C (158°F) or higher. Scientists make use of the enzymes of these bacteria in a technique that rapidly replicates DNA sequences from small samples (see Module 12.12).

The optimal pH for most enzymes is near neutrality, in the range of 6–8. There are exceptions, of course. Pepsin, a digestive enzyme in your stomach, works best at pH 2. Such an environment would denature most enzymes, but the structure of pepsin is most stable and active in this acidic environment.

Cofactors   Many enzymes require nonprotein helpers called **cofactors**, which bind to the active site and function in catalysis. The cofactors of some enzymes are inorganic, such as the ions of zinc, iron, and copper. If the cofactor is an organic molecule, it is called a **coenzyme**. Most vitamins are important in nutrition because they function as coenzymes or raw materials from which coenzymes are made. For example, folic acid is a coenzyme for a number of enzymes involved in the synthesis of nucleic acids.

Chemical chaos would result if all of a cell's metabolic pathways were operating simultaneously. A cell must tightly control when and where its various enzymes are active. It does this either by switching on or off the genes that encode specific enzymes (as you will learn in Chapter 11) or by regulating the activity of enzymes once they are made. We explore this second mechanism in the next module.

❶ The enzyme available with an empty active site

Active site

Enzyme (sucrase)

Substrate (sucrose)

❷ The substrate enters the active site, which enfolds the substrate with an induced fit

Glucose

Fructose

H_2O

❹ The products are released

❸ The substrate is converted to products

▲ **Figure 5.14**   The catalytic cycle of an enzyme

? **Explain how an enzyme speeds up a specific reaction.**

● An enzyme lowers the activation energy needed for a reaction when its specific substrate enters its active site. With an induced fit, the enzyme strains bonds that need to break or positions substrates in an orientation that aids the conversion of reactants to products.

5.15 Enzyme inhibition can regulate enzyme activity in a cell

A chemical that interferes with an enzyme's activity is called an inhibitor. Scientists have learned a great deal about enzyme function by studying the effects of such chemicals. Some inhibitors resemble the enzyme's normal substrate and compete for entry into the active site. As shown in the lower left of **Figure 5.15A**, such a **competitive inhibitor** reduces an enzyme's productivity by blocking substrate molecules from entering the active site. Competitive inhibition can be overcome by increasing the concentration of the substrate, making it more likely that a substrate molecule rather than an inhibitor will be nearby when an active site becomes vacant.

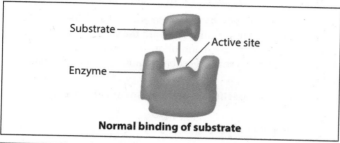

Normal binding of substrate

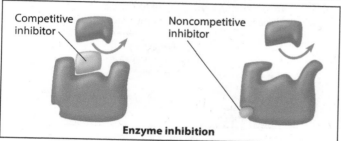

Enzyme inhibition

▲ **Figure 5.15A**   How inhibitors interfere with substrate binding

In contrast, a **noncompetitive inhibitor** does not enter the active site. Instead, it binds to a site elsewhere on the enzyme, and its binding changes the enzyme's shape so that the active site no longer fits the substrate (lower right of Figure 5.15A).

Although enzyme inhibition sounds harmful, cells use inhibitors as important regulators of cellular metabolism. Many of a cell's chemical reactions are organized into metabolic pathways in which a molecule is altered in a series of steps, each catalyzed by a specific enzyme, to form a final product. If a cell is producing more of that product than it needs, the product may act as an inhibitor of one of the enzymes early in the pathway. **Figure 5.15B** illustrates this sort of inhibition, called **feedback inhibition**. Because only weak interactions bind inhibitor and enzyme, this inhibition is reversible. When the product is used up by the cell, the enzyme is no longer inhibited and the pathway functions again.

In the next module, we explore some uses that people make of enzyme inhibitors.

?   **Explain an advantage of feedback inhibition to a cell.**

● It prevents the cell from wasting valuable resources by synthesizing more of a particular product than is needed.

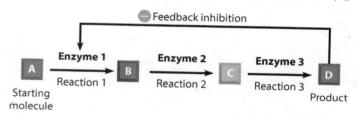

▲ **Figure 5.15B**   Feedback inhibition of a metabolic pathway in which product D acts as an inhibitor of enzyme 1

5.16 Many drugs, pesticides, and poisons are enzyme inhibitors

CONNECTION

Many beneficial drugs act as enzyme inhibitors. Ibuprofen (**Figure 5.16**) is a common drug that inhibits an enzyme involved in the production of prostaglandins—messenger molecules that increase the sensation of pain and inflammation. Other drugs that function as enzyme inhibitors include some blood pressure medicines and antidepressants. Many antibiotics work by inhibiting enzymes of disease-causing bacteria. Penicillin, for example, blocks the active site of an enzyme that many bacteria use in making cell walls. Protease inhibitors are HIV drugs that target a key viral enzyme. And many cancer drugs are inhibitors of enzymes that promote cell division.

Humans have developed enzyme inhibitors as pesticides, and occasionally as deadly poisons for use in warfare. Poisons

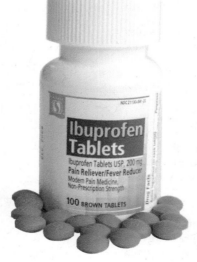

▲ **Figure 5.16**   Ibuprofen, an enzyme inhibitor

often attach to an enzyme by covalent bonds, making the inhibition irreversible. Poisons called nerve gases bind in the active site of an enzyme vital to the transmission of nerve impulses. The inhibition of this enzyme leads to rapid paralysis of vital functions and death. Pesticides such as malathion and parathion are toxic to insects (and dangerous to the people who apply them) because they also irreversibly inhibit this enzyme. Interestingly, some drugs reversibly inhibit this same enzyme and are used in anesthesia and treatment of certain diseases.

?   **What determines whether enzyme inhibition is reversible or irreversible?**

● If the inhibitor binds to the enzyme with covalent bonds, the inhibition is usually irreversible. When weak chemical interactions bind inhibitor and enzyme, the inhibition is reversible.

CHAPTER 5 REVIEW

For practice quizzes, BioFlix animations, MP3 tutorials, video tutors, and more study tools designed for this textbook, go to

MasteringBiology®

Reviewing the Concepts

Membrane Structure and Function (5.1–5.9)

5.1 Membranes are fluid mosaics of lipids and proteins with many functions. The proteins embedded in a membrane's phospholipid bilayer perform various functions.

5.2 The spontaneous formation of membranes was a critical step in the origin of life.

5.3 Passive transport is diffusion across a membrane with no energy investment. Solutes diffuse across membranes down their concentration gradients.

5.4 Osmosis is the diffusion of water across a membrane.

5.5 Water balance between cells and their surroundings is crucial to organisms. Cells shrink in a hypertonic solution and swell in a hypotonic solution. In isotonic solutions, animal cells are normal, but plant cells are flaccid.

5.6 Transport proteins can facilitate diffusion across membranes.

5.7 Research on another membrane protein led to the discovery of aquaporins.

5.8 Cells expend energy in the active transport of a solute.

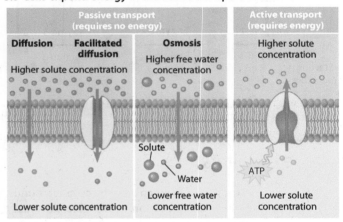

5.9 Exocytosis and endocytosis transport large molecules across membranes. A vesicle may fuse with the membrane and expel its contents (exocytosis), or the membrane may fold inward, enclosing material from the outside (endocytosis).

Energy and the Cell (5.10–5.12)

5.10 Cells transform energy as they perform work. Kinetic energy is the energy of motion. Potential energy is energy stored in the location or structure of matter and includes chemical energy. According to the laws of thermodynamics, energy can change form but cannot be created or destroyed, and energy transfers or transformations increase disorder, or entropy, with some energy being lost as heat.

5.11 Chemical reactions either release or store energy. Exergonic reactions release energy. Endergonic reactions require energy and yield products rich in potential energy. Metabolism encompasses all of a cell's chemical reactions.

5.12 ATP drives cellular work by coupling exergonic and endergonic reactions. The transfer of a phosphate group from ATP is involved in chemical, transport, and mechanical work.

How Enzymes Function (5.13–5.16)

5.13 Enzymes speed up the cell's chemical reactions by lowering energy barriers. Enzymes are protein catalysts that decrease the activation energy needed to begin a reaction.

5.14 A specific enzyme catalyzes each cellular reaction. An enzyme's substrate fits specifically in its active site.

5.15 Enzyme inhibition can regulate enzyme activity in a cell. A competitive inhibitor competes with the substrate for the active site. A noncompetitive inhibitor alters an enzyme's function by changing its shape. Feedback inhibition helps regulate metabolism.

5.16 Many drugs, pesticides, and poisons are enzyme inhibitors.

Connecting the Concepts

1. Fill in the following concept map to review the processes by which molecules move across membranes.

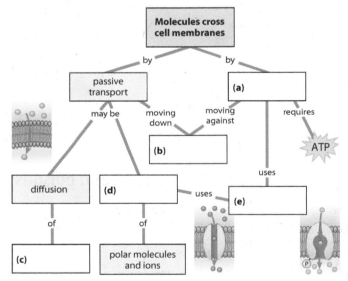

2. Label the parts of the following diagram illustrating the catalytic cycle of an enzyme.

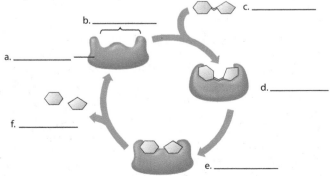

Testing Your Knowledge

Level 1: Knowledge/Comprehension

3. Which best describes the structure of a cell membrane?
   a. proteins between two bilayers of phospholipids
   b. proteins embedded in a bilayer of phospholipids
   c. a bilayer of protein coating a layer of phospholipids
   d. cholesterol embedded in a bilayer of phospholipids

4. A plant cell placed in distilled water will _____; an animal cell placed in distilled water will _____.
   a. burst . . . burst
   b. become flaccid . . . shrivel
   c. become turgid . . . be normal in shape
   d. become turgid . . . burst

5. The sodium concentration in a cell is 10 times less than the concentration in the surrounding fluid. How can the cell move sodium out of the cell? (*Explain your answer.*)
   a. passive transport
   b. receptor-mediated endocytosis
   c. active transport
   d. facilitated diffusion

6. The synthesis of ATP from ADP and Ⓟ
   a. stores energy in a form that can drive cellular work.
   b. involves the hydrolysis of a phosphate bond.
   c. transfers a phosphate, priming a protein to do work.
   d. is an exergonic process.

7. Facilitated diffusion across a membrane requires _____ and moves a solute _____ its concentration gradient.
   a. transport proteins . . . up (against)
   b. transport proteins . . . down
   c. energy and transport proteins . . . up
   d. energy and transport proteins . . . down

8. What are the main types of cellular work? How does ATP provide the energy for this work?

Level 2: Application/Analysis

9. Why is the barrier of the activation energy beneficial for cells? Explain how enzymes lower activation energy.
10. Relate the laws of thermodynamics to living organisms.
11. How do the components and structure of cell membranes relate to the functions of membranes?
12. Sometimes inhibitors can be harmful to a cell; often they are beneficial. Explain.

Level 3: Synthesis/Evaluation

13. Cells lining kidney tubules function in the reabsorption of water from urine. In response to chemical signals, they reversibly insert additional aquaporins into their plasma membranes. In which of these situations would your tubule cells have the most aquaporins: after a long run on a hot day, right after a large meal, or after drinking a large bottle of water? Explain.

14. **SCIENTIFIC THINKING** Mercury is known to inhibit the permeability of water channels. To help establish that the protein isolated by Agre's group was a water channel (see Module 5.7), the researchers incubated groups of RNA-injected oocytes (which then made aquaporin proteins) in four different solutions: plain buffer, low concentration and high concentration of a mercury chloride ($HgCl_2$) solution, and a low concentration of a mercury solution followed by an agent (ME)

known to reverse the effects of mercury. The water permeability of the cells was determined by the rate of their osmotic swelling. Interpret the results of this experiment, which are presented in the graph below.

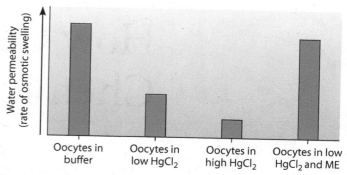

Data from G. M. Preston et al., Appearance of water channels in *Xenopus* oocytes expressing red cell CHIP28 protein, *Science* 256: 3385–7 (1992).

Control oocytes not injected with aquaporin RNA were also incubated with buffer and the two concentrations of mercury. Predict what the results of these treatments would be.

15. A biologist performed two series of experiments on lactase, the enzyme that hydrolyzes lactose to glucose and galactose. First, she made up 10% lactose solutions containing different concentrations of enzyme and measured the rate at which galactose was produced (grams of galactose per minute). Results of these experiments are shown in Table A below. In the second series of experiments (Table B), she prepared 2% enzyme solutions containing different concentrations of lactose and again measured the rate of galactose production.

Table A Rate and Enzyme Concentration					
Lactose concentration	10%	10%	10%	10%	10%
Enzyme concentration	0%	1%	2%	4%	8%
Reaction rate	0	25	50	100	200

Table B Rate and Substrate Concentration					
Lactose concentration	0%	5%	10%	20%	30%
Enzyme concentration	2%	2%	2%	2%	2%
Reaction rate	0	25	50	65	65

   a. Graph and explain the relationship between the reaction rate and the enzyme concentration.
   b. Graph and explain the relationship between the reaction rate and the substrate concentration. How and why did the results of the two experiments differ?

16. Organophosphates (organic compounds containing phosphate groups) are commonly used as insecticides to improve crop yield. Organophosphates typically interfere with nerve signal transmission by inhibiting the enzymes that degrade transmitter molecules. They affect humans and other vertebrates as well as insects. Thus, the use of organophosphate pesticides poses some health risks. On the other hand, these molecules break down rapidly upon exposure to air and sunlight. As a consumer, what level of risk are you willing to accept in exchange for an abundant and affordable food supply?

Answers to all questions can be found in Appendix 4.

6

How Cells Harvest Chemical Energy

A baby's first cry! This welcome sound shows that the baby is breathing and taking in oxygen. But why is oxygen necessary for life? Oxygen is a reactant in cellular respiration—the process that breaks down sugar and other food molecules and generates ATP, the energy currency of cells.

Cellular respiration occurred in this baby's cells before she was born, but the oxygen and sugar her cells required were delivered from her mother's blood. Now this baby takes in her own oxygen—although she still can't obtain her own food. The process of cellular

Can brown fat keep a newborn warm and help keep an adult thin?

respiration produces heat as well as ATP, which helps maintain a warm body temperature. But if this baby is exposed to the cold, she can't keep herself warm. If you get cold, you put on more clothes, move to a warmer place, or shiver—generating heat as your contracting muscles increase their production of ATP and heat. This baby can't do any of those things yet. Instead, along her back she has a layer of a special kind of "baby fat," called brown fat, that helps keep her warm. The cells of brown fat have a "short circuit" in their cellular respiration—they consume oxygen and burn fuel, but generate only heat, not ATP.

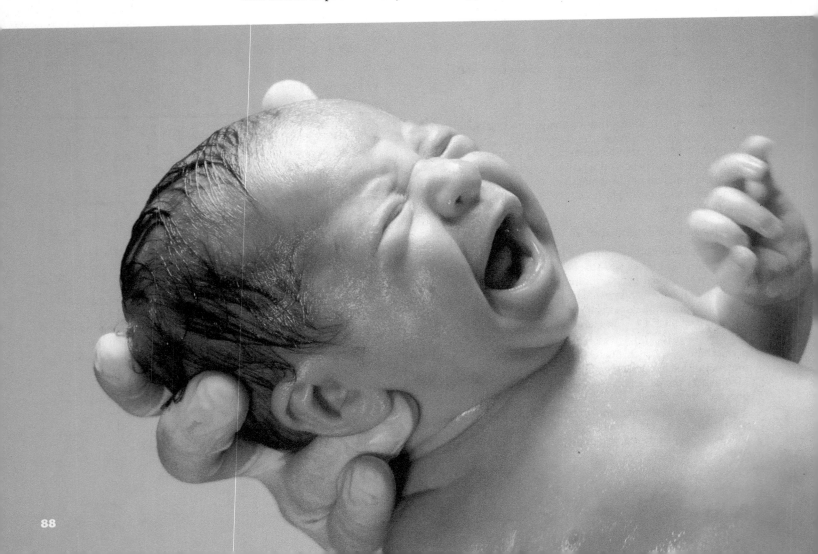

Scientists have long known that brown fat is important for heat production in small mammals, hibernating bears, and newborn infants. Studies have also shown brown fat to be involved in weight regulation in mice. As you will learn later in the chapter, brown fat deposits have only recently been discovered in adult humans. Scientists are now exploring whether this heat-generating, calorie-burning tissue may be tapped in the fight against obesity.

We begin this chapter with an overview of cellular respiration and then focus on its stages: glycolysis, the citric acid cycle, and oxidative phosphorylation. We also consider fermentation, an extension of glycolysis that has deep evolutionary roots. We complete the chapter with a comparison of the metabolic pathways that break down and build up the organic molecules of your body.

BIG IDEAS

Cellular Respiration: Aerobic Harvesting of Energy
(6.1–6.5)

Cellular respiration oxidizes fuel molecules and generates ATP for cellular work.

Stages of Cellular Respiration
(6.6–6.12)

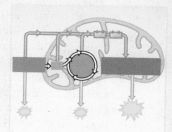

The main stages of cellular respiration are glycolysis, the citric acid cycle, and oxidative phosphorylation.

Fermentation: Anaerobic Harvesting of Energy
(6.13–6.14)

Fermentation regenerates NAD^+, allowing glycolysis and ATP production to continue without oxygen.

Connections Between Metabolic Pathways
(6.15–6.16)

The breakdown pathways of cellular respiration intersect with biosynthetic pathways.

▷ Cellular Respiration: Aerobic Harvesting of Energy

6.1 Photosynthesis and cellular respiration provide energy for life

Life requires energy. In almost all ecosystems, that energy ultimately comes from the sun. (Photosynthesis, the process by which the sun's energy is captured, will be explored later, in Chapter 7.) **Figure 6.1** illustrates how photosynthesis and cellular respiration together provide energy for living organisms. In photosynthesis, which takes place in a plant cell's chloroplasts, the energy of sunlight is used to rearrange the atoms of carbon dioxide (CO_2) and water (H_2O) to produce sugar and oxygen (O_2). In **cellular respiration**, O_2 is consumed as sugar is broken down to CO_2 and H_2O; the cell captures the energy released in ATP. Cellular respiration takes place in the mitochondria of almost all eukaryotic cells—in the cells of plants, animals, fungi, and protists. (Although prokaryotes don't have mitochondria, some do break down sugar in a similar type of oxygen-using respiration.)

This figure also shows that in these energy conversions, some energy is lost as heat. Life on Earth is solar powered, and energy makes a one-way trip through an ecosystem. Chemicals, however, are recycled. The CO_2 and H_2O released by cellular respiration are converted through photosynthesis to sugar and O_2, which are then used in respiration.

> **?** What is misleading about the following statement? "Plant cells perform photosynthesis, and animal cells perform cellular respiration."
>
> ● The statement implies that cellular respiration does not occur in plant cells. In fact, almost all eukaryotic cells use cellular respiration to obtain energy for their cellular work.

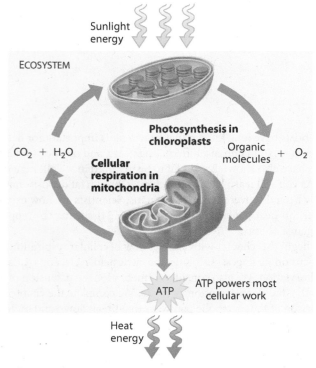

▲ **Figure 6.1** The connection between photosynthesis and cellular respiration

6.2 Breathing supplies O₂ for use in cellular respiration and removes CO₂

We often use the word *respiration* as a synonym for "breathing," the meaning of its Latin root. In that case, respiration refers to an exchange of gases: An organism obtains O_2 from its environment and releases CO_2 as a waste product. Biologists also define respiration as the aerobic (oxygen-requiring) harvesting of energy from food molecules by cells. This process is called cellular respiration to distinguish it from breathing.

Breathing and cellular respiration are closely related. As the runner in **Figure 6.2** breathes in air, her lungs take up O_2 and pass it to her bloodstream. The bloodstream carries the O_2 to her muscle cells. Mitochondria in the muscle cells use the O_2 in cellular respiration to harvest energy from glucose and other organic molecules and generate ATP. Muscle cells use ATP to fuel contractions. The runner's bloodstream and lungs also perform the vital function of disposing of the CO_2 waste, which is produced in cellular respiration. You can see the roles of O_2 and CO_2 in the equation for cellular respiration at the bottom of the figure.

> **?** How is your breathing related to your cellular respiration?
>
> ● In breathing, CO_2 and O_2 are exchanged between your lungs and the air. In cellular respiration, cells use the O_2 obtained through breathing to break down fuel, releasing CO_2 as a waste product.

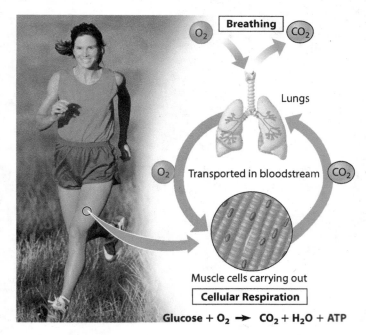

▲ **Figure 6.2** The connection between breathing and cellular respiration

6.3 Cellular respiration banks energy in ATP molecules

You breathe air and eat food to supply your cells with the reactants for cellular respiration—the process that generates ATP for cellular work.

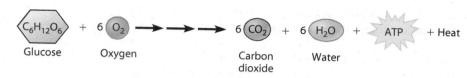

$$C_6H_{12}O_6 + 6\ O_2 \longrightarrow 6\ CO_2 + 6\ H_2O + ATP + Heat$$

Glucose Oxygen Carbon dioxide Water

▲ **Figure 6.3** Summary equation for cellular respiration

The chemical equation in **Figure 6.3** summarizes cellular respiration. The simple sugar glucose ($C_6H_{12}O_6$) is the fuel that cells use most often, although other organic molecules can also be "burned" in cellular respiration. The equation tells us that the atoms of the reactant molecules $C_6H_{12}O_6$ and O_2 are rearranged to form the products CO_2 and H_2O. In this exergonic (energy-releasing) process, the chemical energy of the bonds in glucose is released and stored (or "banked") in the chemical bonds of ATP (see Module 5.12). The series of arrows in Figure 6.3 indicates that cellular respiration consists of many steps, not just a single reaction.

Cellular respiration can produce up to 32 ATP molecules for each glucose molecule, a capture of about 34% of the energy originally stored in glucose. The rest of the energy is released as heat (see Module 5.10). This may seem inefficient, but it compares very well with the efficiency of most energy-conversion systems. For instance, the average automobile engine is able to convert only about 25% of the energy in gasoline to the kinetic energy of movement. And, as you learned in the chapter introduction, heat released in cellular respiration helps maintain your warm body temperature.

How great are the energy needs of a cell? If ATP could not be regenerated through cellular respiration, you would use up nearly your body weight in ATP each day. Let's consider the energy requirements for various human activities next.

? **Why are sweating and other body-cooling mechanisms necessary during vigorous exercise?**

The demand for ATP is supported by an increased rate of cellular respiration, but about 66% of the energy released from food produces heat instead of ATP.

6.4 The human body uses energy from ATP for all its activities

CONNECTION

Your body requires a continuous supply of energy just to stay alive—to keep your heart pumping and to keep you breathing. Your brain especially requires a huge amount of energy; its cells burn about 120 grams (g)—a quarter of a pound!—of glucose a day, accounting for about 15% of total oxygen consumption. Maintaining brain cells and other life-sustaining activities uses as much as 75% of the energy a person takes in as food during a typical day.

Above and beyond the energy you need for body maintenance, cellular respiration provides energy for voluntary activities. **Figure 6.4** shows the amount of energy it takes to perform some of these activities. The energy units are **kilocalories (kcal)**, a measure of the quantity of heat required to raise the temperature of 1 kilogram (kg) of water by 1°C. (The "Calories" listed on food packages are actually kilocalories, usually signified by a capital C.) The values shown do not include the energy the body consumes for its basic life-sustaining activities. Even sleeping or lying quietly requires energy for metabolism.

The U.S. National Academy of Sciences estimates that the average adult needs to take in food that provides about 2,200 kcal of energy per day, although the number varies based on age, sex, and activity level. A balance of energy intake and expenditure is required to maintain a healthy weight. Now we begin the study of how cells liberate the energy stored in fuel molecules to produce the ATP used to power the work of your cells and thus the activities of your body.

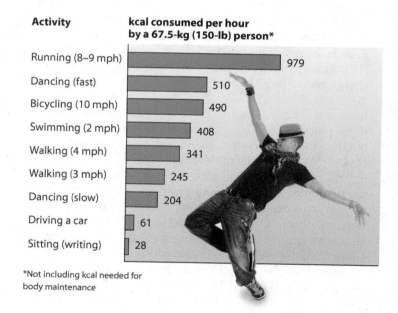

Activity	kcal consumed per hour by a 67.5-kg (150-lb) person*
Running (8–9 mph)	979
Dancing (fast)	510
Bicycling (10 mph)	490
Swimming (2 mph)	408
Walking (4 mph)	341
Walking (3 mph)	245
Dancing (slow)	204
Driving a car	61
Sitting (writing)	28

*Not including kcal needed for body maintenance

▲ **Figure 6.4** Energy consumed by various activities

? **Walking at 3 mph, how far would you have to travel to "burn off" the equivalent of an extra slice of pizza, which has about 475 kcal? How long would that take?**

You would have to walk about 6 miles, which would take you about 2 hours. (Now you understand why the most effective exercise for losing weight is pushing away from the table!)

6.5 Cells capture energy from electrons "falling" from organic fuels to oxygen

How do your cells extract energy from glucose? The answer involves the transfer of electrons during chemical reactions.

Redox Reactions   During cellular respiration, electrons are transferred from glucose to oxygen, releasing energy. Oxygen attracts electrons very strongly, and an electron loses potential energy when it is transferred to oxygen. If you burn a cube of sugar, this electron "fall" happens very rapidly, releasing energy in the form of heat and light. Cellular respiration is a more controlled descent of electrons—more like rolling down an energy hill, with energy released in small amounts that can be stored in the chemical bonds of ATP.

The movement of electrons from one molecule to another is an oxidation-reduction reaction, or **redox reaction** for short. In a redox reaction, the loss of electrons from one substance is called **oxidation**, and the addition of electrons to another substance is called **reduction**. A molecule is said to become oxidized when it loses one or more electrons and reduced when it gains one or more electrons. Because an electron transfer requires both a donor and an acceptor, oxidation and reduction always go together.

In the cellular respiration equation in **Figure 6.5A** below, you cannot see any electron transfers. What you do see are changes in the location of hydrogen atoms. These hydrogen movements represent electron transfers because each hydrogen atom consists of an electron (e^-) and a proton (hydrogen ion, or H^+). Glucose ($C_6H_{12}O_6$) loses hydrogen atoms (electrons) as it becomes oxidized to CO_2; simultaneously, O_2 gains hydrogen atoms (electrons) as it becomes reduced to H_2O. As they pass from glucose to oxygen, the electrons lose energy, some of which cells capture.

NADH and Electron Transport Chains   An important player in the process of oxidizing glucose is a coenzyme called **NAD$^+$**, which accepts electrons and becomes reduced to NADH. NAD$^+$ (nicotinamide adenine dinucleotide) is an organic molecule that cells make from the vitamin niacin and use to shuttle electrons in redox reactions. The top equation in **Figure 6.5B** depicts the oxidation of an organic molecule. We show only its three carbons (⚫) and a few of its other atoms. An enzyme called dehydrogenase strips two hydrogen atoms from this molecule. Simultaneously, as shown in the lower equation, NAD$^+$ picks up the two electrons (⊖) and becomes reduced to NADH. One hydrogen ion (H$^+$) also becomes part of the NADH, and the other is released. (NADH

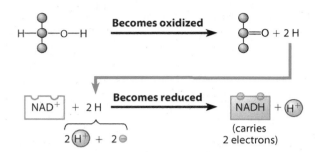

▲ **Figure 6.5B**   A pair of redox reactions occurring simultaneously

Try This   Circle the two atoms that will be removed from the molecule on the left as it becomes oxidized to the molecule on the right. Explain why we say that a hydrogen atom consists of a hydrogen ion (H^+) and an electron.

is represented throughout this chapter as a light brown box carrying two blue electrons.)

Using the energy hill analogy for electrons rolling from glucose to oxygen, the transfer of electrons from an organic molecule to NAD$^+$ is just the beginning. **Figure 6.5C** shows NADH delivering these electrons to a string of electron carrier molecules, shown here as purple ovals, that lead down the hill. At the bottom of the hill is oxygen (O_2), which accepts two electrons, picks up two H^+, and becomes reduced to water.

These carrier molecules form an **electron transport chain**. In a cell, they are built into the inner membrane of a mitochondrion. Through a series of redox reactions, electrons are passed from carrier to carrier, releasing energy in amounts small enough to be used by the cell to make ATP.

With an understanding of this basic mechanism of electron transfer and energy release, we can now explore cellular respiration in more detail.

?   What chemical characteristic of the element oxygen accounts for its function in cellular respiration?

● Oxygen is extremely electronegative (see Module 2.6), making it very powerful in pulling electrons down the electron transport chain.

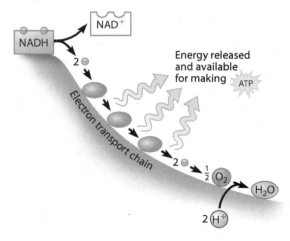

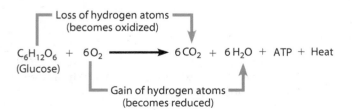

▲ **Figure 6.5A**   Rearrangement of hydrogen atoms (with their electrons) in the redox reactions of cellular respiration

▲ **Figure 6.5C**   Electrons releasing energy for ATP synthesis as they roll down an energy hill from NADH through an electron transport chain to O_2

6.6 Overview: Cellular respiration occurs in three main stages

Cellular respiration consists of a sequence of many chemical reactions that we can divide into three main stages. **Figure 6.6** gives an overview of these stages and shows where they occur in a eukaryotic cell. (In prokaryotic cells that use aerobic respiration, these steps occur in the cytosol, and the electron transport chain is built into the plasma membrane.)

Stage 1: Glycolysis (shown with a teal background throughout this chapter) occurs in the cytosol of the cell. Glycolysis begins cellular respiration by breaking glucose into two molecules of a three-carbon compound called pyruvate.

Stage 2: Pyruvate oxidation and the **citric acid cycle** (shown in shades of orange) take place within the mitochondria. Pyruvate is oxidized to a two-carbon compound. The citric acid cycle then completes the breakdown of glucose to carbon dioxide. Thus, the CO_2 that you exhale is formed in the mitochondria of your cells during this second stage of respiration.

As suggested by the smaller ATP symbols in the diagram, the cell makes a small amount of ATP during glycolysis and the citric acid cycle. The main function of these first two stages, however, is to supply the third stage of respiration with electrons (shown with gold arrows).

Stage 3: Oxidative phosphorylation (purple background) involves electron transport and a process known as chemiosmosis. NADH and a related electron carrier, $FADH_2$ (flavin adenine dinucleotide), shuttle electrons to an electron transport chain embedded in the inner mitochondrial membrane. Most of the

ATP produced by cellular respiration is generated by oxidative phosphorylation, which uses the energy released by the downhill fall of electrons from NADH and $FADH_2$ to oxygen to phosphorylate ADP. (Recall from Module 5.12 that cells generate ATP by adding a phosphate group to ADP.)

What couples the electron transport chain to ATP synthesis? As the electron transport chain passes electrons down the energy hill, it also pumps hydrogen ions (H^+) across the inner mitochondrial membrane into the narrow intermembrane space. The result is a concentration gradient of H^+ across the membrane. In **chemiosmosis**, the potential energy of this concentration gradient is used to make ATP. The details of this process are explored in Module 6.10.

The small amount of ATP produced in glycolysis and the citric acid cycle is made by substrate-level phosphorylation, a process we discuss in the next module. In the next several modules, we look more closely at the stages of cellular respiration and the mechanisms of ATP synthesis.

? Of the three main stages of cellular respiration, which is the only one that uses oxygen?

● Oxidative phosphorylation, in which the electron transport chain ultimately transfers electrons to oxygen

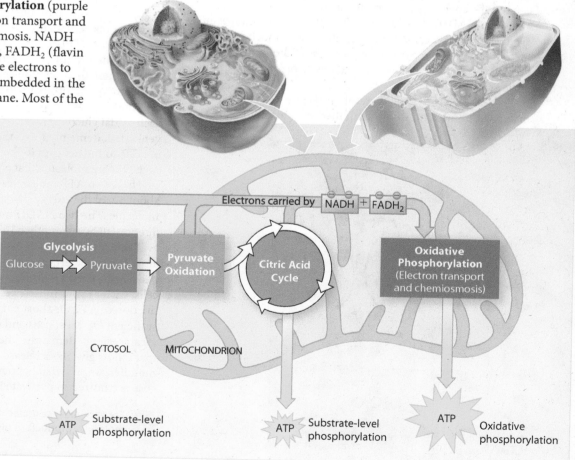

▶ **Figure 6.6** An overview of cellular respiration

6.7 Glycolysis harvests chemical energy by oxidizing glucose to pyruvate

Now that you have been introduced to the major players and processes, it's time to focus on the individual stages of cellular respiration. The term for the first stage, *glycolysis*, means "splitting of sugar" (*glyco*, sweet, and *lysis*, split), and that's exactly what happens during this phase.

Figure 6.7A below gives an overview of glycolysis, which begins with a single molecule of glucose and concludes with two molecules of pyruvate. (Pyruvate is the ionized form of pyruvic acid.) Each ⚫ represents a carbon atom in the molecules; glucose has six carbons, and these same six carbons end up in the two molecules of pyruvate (three carbons in each). The straight arrow shown running from glucose to pyruvate actually represents nine chemical steps, each catalyzed by its own enzyme. As these reactions occur, two molecules of NAD$^+$ are reduced to two molecules of NADH, and a net gain of two molecules of ATP is produced.

Figure 6.7B illustrates how ATP is formed in glycolysis by the process called **substrate-level phosphorylation**. In this process, an enzyme transfers a phosphate group (Ⓟ) from a substrate molecule directly to ADP, forming ATP. You will come across substrate-level phosphorylation again in our discussion of the citric acid cycle, in which a small amount of ATP is generated by this process.

The oxidation of glucose to pyruvate during glycolysis releases energy, which is stored in ATP and in NADH. The cell can use the energy in ATP immediately, but for it to use the energy in NADH, electrons from NADH must pass down an electron transport chain located in the inner mitochondrial membrane. And the pyruvate molecules still hold most of the energy of glucose; these molecules will be oxidized in the citric acid cycle.

Let's take a closer look at glycolysis. **Figure 6.7C**, on the next page, names and shows simplified structures for all the

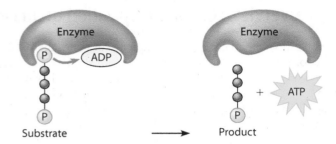

▲ **Figure 6.7B** Substrate-level phosphorylation: transfer of a phosphate group from a substrate to ADP, producing ATP

organic compounds that form in the nine chemical reactions of glycolysis. Commentary on the left highlights the main features of these reactions.

Compounds that form between the initial reactant, glucose, and the final product, pyruvate, are known as **intermediates**. Glycolysis is an example of a metabolic pathway in which each chemical step feeds into the next one. For instance, the intermediate glucose 6-phosphate is the product of step 1 and the reactant for step 2. Similarly, fructose 6-phosphate is the product of step 2 and the reactant for step 3. Also essential are the specific enzymes that catalyze each chemical step; however, the figure does not include the enzymes.

As indicated in Figure 6.7C, the steps of glycolysis can be grouped into two main phases. Steps ❶–❹, the energy investment phase, actually *consume* energy. In this phase, two molecules of ATP are used to energize a glucose molecule, which is then split into two small sugars. The figure follows each of these three-carbon sugars through the second phase.

Steps ❺–❾, the energy payoff phase, *yield* energy for the cell. In this phase, two NADH molecules are produced for each initial glucose molecule, and four ATP molecules are generated. Remember that the first phase used two molecules of ATP, so the net gain to the cell is two ATP molecules for each glucose molecule that enters glycolysis.

These two ATP molecules from glycolysis account for only about 6% of the energy that a cell can harvest from a glucose molecule. The two NADH molecules generated during step 5 represent about another 16%, but their stored energy is not available for use without oxygen. Some organisms—yeasts and certain bacteria, for instance—can satisfy their energy needs with the ATP produced by glycolysis alone. And some cells, such as your muscle cells, may use this anaerobic production of ATP for short periods when they do not have sufficient O_2. Most cells and organisms, however, have far greater energy demands. The stages of cellular respiration that follow glycolysis release much more energy. In the next modules, we see what happens in most organisms after glucose is oxidized to pyruvate in glycolysis.

? **For each glucose molecule processed, what are the net molecular products of glycolysis?**

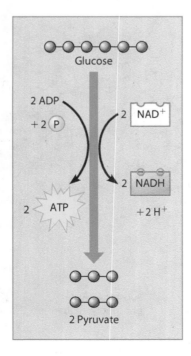

▶ **Figure 6.7A**
An overview
of glycolysis

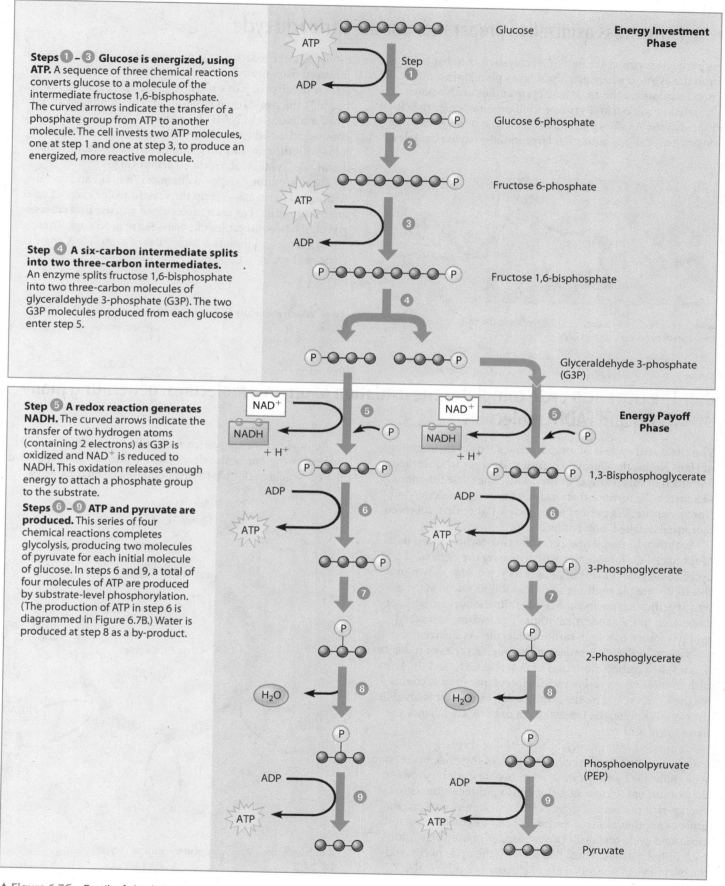

Steps ❶–❸ Glucose is energized, using ATP. A sequence of three chemical reactions converts glucose to a molecule of the intermediate fructose 1,6-bisphosphate. The curved arrows indicate the transfer of a phosphate group from ATP to another molecule. The cell invests two ATP molecules, one at step 1 and one at step 3, to produce an energized, more reactive molecule.

Step ❹ A six-carbon intermediate splits into two three-carbon intermediates. An enzyme splits fructose 1,6-bisphosphate into two three-carbon molecules of glyceraldehyde 3-phosphate (G3P). The two G3P molecules produced from each glucose enter step 5.

Step ❺ A redox reaction generates NADH. The curved arrows indicate the transfer of two hydrogen atoms (containing 2 electrons) as G3P is oxidized and NAD$^+$ is reduced to NADH. This oxidation releases enough energy to attach a phosphate group to the substrate.

Steps ❻–❾ ATP and pyruvate are produced. This series of four chemical reactions completes glycolysis, producing two molecules of pyruvate for each initial molecule of glucose. In steps 6 and 9, a total of four molecules of ATP are produced by substrate-level phosphorylation. (The production of ATP in step 6 is diagrammed in Figure 6.7B.) Water is produced at step 8 as a by-product.

Glucose

Glucose 6-phosphate

Fructose 6-phosphate

Fructose 1,6-bisphosphate

Glyceraldehyde 3-phosphate (G3P)

1,3-Bisphosphoglycerate

3-Phosphoglycerate

2-Phosphoglycerate

Phosphoenolpyruvate (PEP)

Pyruvate

Energy Investment Phase

Energy Payoff Phase

▲ **Figure 6.7C** Details of glycolysis

6.8 Pyruvate is oxidized in preparation for the citric acid cycle

As pyruvate forms at the end of glycolysis, it is transported from the cytosol, where glycolysis takes place, into a mitochondrion, where the citric acid cycle and oxidative phosphorylation will occur. Pyruvate itself does not enter the citric acid cycle. As shown in **Figure 6.8**, it first undergoes some major chemical "grooming." A large, multi-enzyme complex

catalyzes three reactions: ❶ A carboxyl group (—COO⁻) is removed from pyruvate and given off as a molecule of CO_2 (this is the first step in which CO_2 is released during respiration); ❷ the two-carbon compound remaining is oxidized while a molecule of NAD⁺ is reduced to NADH; and ❸ a compound called coenzyme A, derived from a B vitamin, joins with the two-carbon group to form a molecule called acetyl coenzyme A, abbreviated **acetyl CoA**.

These grooming steps—a chemical "haircut and conditioning" of pyruvate—set up the second major stage of cellular respiration. For each molecule of glucose that enters glycolysis, two molecules of pyruvate are produced. These are oxidized, and then two molecules of acetyl CoA enter the citric acid cycle.

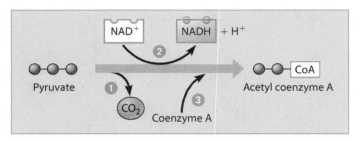

▲ **Figure 6.8** The link between glycolysis and the citric acid cycle: the oxidation of pyruvate to acetyl CoA

? **Which molecule in Figure 6.8 has been reduced?**

● NAD⁺ has been reduced to NADH.

6.9 The citric acid cycle completes the oxidation of organic molecules, generating many NADH and FADH₂ molecules

The citric acid cycle is often called the Krebs cycle in honor of Hans Krebs, the German-British researcher who worked out much of this pathway in the 1930s. The cycle functions as a metabolic furnace that oxidizes the acetyl CoA derived from pyruvate. We present an overview figure first, followed by a more detailed look at this cycle.

As shown in **Figure 6.9A**, only the two-carbon acetyl part of the acetyl CoA molecule actually enters the citric acid cycle; coenzyme A splits off and is recycled. Not shown in this figure are the multiple steps that follow, each catalyzed by a specific enzyme located in the mitochondrial matrix or embedded in the inner membrane. The two-carbon acetyl group is joined to a four-carbon molecule. As the resulting six-carbon molecule is processed through a series of redox reactions, two carbon atoms are removed as CO_2, and the four-carbon molecule is regenerated; this regeneration accounts for the word *cycle*. The six-carbon compound first formed in the cycle is citrate, the ionized form of citric acid; hence the name *citric acid cycle*.

Compared with glycolysis, the citric acid cycle pays big energy dividends to the cell. Each turn of the cycle makes one ATP molecule by substrate-level phosphorylation (shown at the bottom of Figure 6.9A). But it also produces four other energy-rich molecules: three NADH molecules and one molecule of another electron carrier, FADH₂. Remember that the citric acid cycle processes two molecules of acetyl CoA for each initial glucose. Thus, two turns of the cycle occur, and the overall yield per molecule of glucose is 2 ATP, 6 NADH, and 2 FADH₂.

So how many energy-rich molecules have been produced by processing one molecule of glucose through glycolysis and the citric acid cycle? Up to this point, the cell has gained a

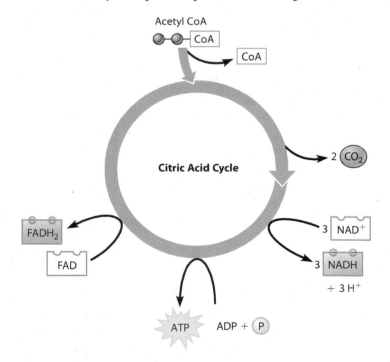

▲ **Figure 6.9A** An overview of the citric acid cycle

Try This Remember that 2 acetyl CoA are produced from each glucose. Use this figure to determine the per-glucose return from the citric acid cycle.

total of 4 ATP (all from substrate-level phosphorylation), 10 NADH, and 2 FADH$_2$. For the cell to be able to harvest the energy banked in NADH and FADH$_2$, these molecules must shuttle their high-energy electrons to an electron transport chain. There the energy from the *oxidation* of organic molecules is used to *phosphorylate* ADP to ATP—hence the name *oxidative phosphorylation*. Before we look at how oxidative phosphorylation works, you may want to examine the inner workings of the citric acid cycle in **Figure 6.9B**, below.

? What is the total number of NADH and FADH$_2$ molecules generated during the complete breakdown of one glucose molecule to six molecules of CO$_2$? (Hint: Combine the outputs discussed in Modules 6.7–6.9.)

● 10 NADH: 2 from glycolysis; 2 from the oxidation of pyruvate; 6 from the citric acid cycle; and 2 FADH$_2$ from the citric acid cycle. (Did you remember to double the output after to the sugar-splitting step of glycolysis?)

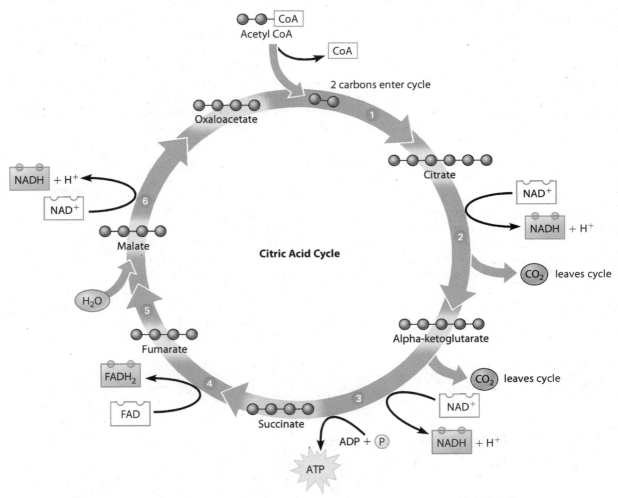

Step ①
Acetyl CoA stokes the furnace.

A turn of the citric acid cycle begins (top center) as enzymes strip the CoA portion from acetyl CoA and combine the remaining two-carbon group with the four-carbon molecule oxaloacetate (top left) already present in the mitochondrion. The product of this reaction is the six-carbon molecule citrate. All the acid compounds in this cycle exist in the cell in their ionized form, hence the suffix *-ate.*

Steps ② – ③
NADH, ATP, and CO$_2$ are generated during redox reactions.

Successive redox reactions harvest energy by stripping hydrogen atoms from citrate and then alpha-ketoglutarate and producing energy-laden NADH molecules. In two places, an intermediate compound loses a CO$_2$ molecule. Energy is harvested by substrate-level phosphorylation of ADP to produce ATP. A four-carbon compound called succinate emerges at the end of step 3.

Steps ④ – ⑥
Further redox reactions generate FADH$_2$ and more NADH.

Succinate is oxidized as the electron carrier FAD is reduced to FADH$_2$. Fumarate is converted to malate, which is then oxidized as one last NAD$^+$ is reduced to NADH. One turn of the citric acid cycle is completed with the regeneration of oxaloacetate, which is then ready to start the next cycle by accepting an acetyl group from acetyl CoA.

▲ **Figure 6.9B**   A closer look at the citric acid cycle. (Remember that the cycle runs two times for each glucose molecule oxidized.)

6.10 Most ATP production occurs by oxidative phosphorylation

Your main objective in this chapter is to learn how cells harvest the energy of glucose to make ATP. But so far, you've seen the production of only 4 ATP per glucose molecule. Now it's time for the big energy payoff. The final stage of cellular respiration is oxidative phosphorylation, which uses the electron transport chain and chemiosmosis—a process introduced in Module 6.6. Oxidative phosphorylation clearly illustrates the concept of structure fitting function: The arrangement of electron carriers built into a membrane makes it possible to create an H^+ concentration gradient across the membrane and then use the energy of that gradient to drive ATP synthesis.

Figure 6.10A shows how an electron transport chain is arranged in the inner membrane of the mitochondrion. The folds (cristae) of this membrane enlarge its surface area, providing space for thousands of copies of the chain. Also embedded in the membrane are multiple copies of an enzyme complex called **ATP synthase**, which synthesizes ATP.

Electron Transport Chain Starting on the left in Figure 6.10A, the gold arrow traces the transport of electrons from the shuttle molecules NADH and $FADH_2$ through the electron transport chain to oxygen, the final electron acceptor. It is in this end stage of cellular respiration that oxygen finally steps in to play its critical role. Each oxygen atom ($\frac{1}{2}O_2$) accepts 2 electrons from the chain and picks up 2 H^+ from the surrounding solution, forming H_2O. You can see that happening in the center right of the figure.

Most of the carrier molecules of the chain reside in four main protein complexes (labeled I to IV in the diagram), while two mobile carriers transport electrons between the complexes. All of the carriers bind and release electrons in redox reactions, passing electrons down the "energy hill." Three of the protein complexes use the energy released from these electron transfers to actively transport H^+ across the membrane, from where H^+ is less concentrated to where it is more concentrated. The green vertical arrows show H^+ being transported from the matrix of the mitochondrion into the narrow intermembrane space.

Chemiosmosis Recall that chemiosmosis is a process that uses the energy stored in a hydrogen ion gradient across a membrane to drive ATP synthesis. **Figure 6.10B** shows the role of ATP synthase in chemiosmosis. The H^+ concentration gradient across the membrane stores potential energy, much the way a dam stores energy by holding back the elevated water behind it. The energy stored by a dam can be harnessed to do work (such as generating electricity)

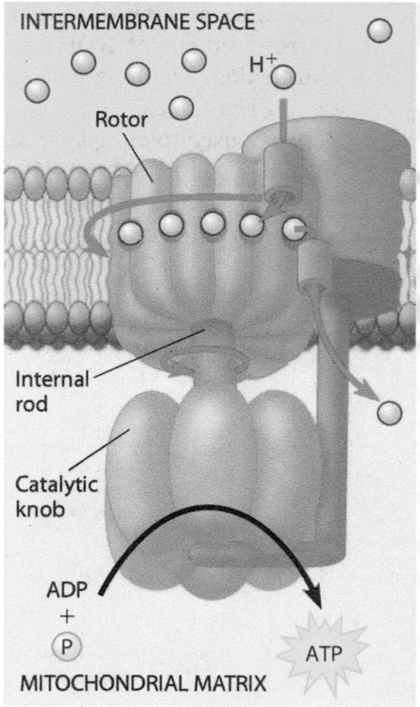

▲ **Figure 6.10B** ATP synthase—a molecular rotary motor

Try This Identify the power source that runs this motor. Explain where this "power" comes from.

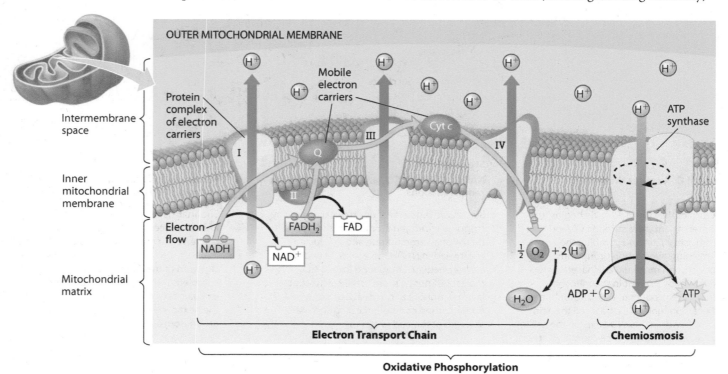

▲ **Figure 6.10A** Oxidative phosphorylation: electron transport and chemiosmosis in a mitochondrion

when the water is allowed to rush downhill, turning giant wheels called turbines. The ATP synthases built into the inner mitochondrial membrane act like miniature turbines, with the rush of H^+ ions down their concentration gradient turning the wheels. Indeed, ATP synthase is considered the smallest molecular rotary motor known in nature.

As Figure 6.10B shows, hydrogen ions move one by one into binding sites within this protein complex (the rotor), causing it to spin. After once around, they are spit out into the mitochondrial matrix. The spinning rotor turns an internal rod, which activates sites in the catalytic knob that phosphorylate ADP to ATP.

We will make a final tally of ATP production in Module 6.12. But first, let's consider how cellular respiration can sometimes be used primarily to generate heat.

> **?** **What effect would an absence of oxygen (O_2) have on the process illustrated in Figure 6.10A?**
>
> ⦿ Without oxygen to "pull" electrons down the electron transport chain, the energy stored in NADH and FADH$_2$ could not be harnessed for ATP synthesis.

6.11 Scientists have discovered heat-producing, calorie-burning brown fat in adults

SCIENTIFIC THINKING

Ordinary body fat, called white fat, has little metabolic activity. Each cell is filled with a single large droplet of fat. Brown fat, on the other hand, actively burns energy. You learned in the chapter introduction that brown fat helps keep infants warm. Brown fat is named for its color, which comes from the brownish mitochondria that pack its cells. These mitochondria are unique in that they can burn fuel and produce heat without making ATP.

Can brown fat keep a newborn warm and help keep an adult thin?

How can they do that? Look back at Figure 6.10A and imagine ion channels spanning the inner mitochondrial membrane that allow H^+ to flow freely across the membrane. Such channels would dissipate the H^+ gradient that the electron transport chain had produced. Without that gradient, ATP synthase could not make ATP, and all the energy from the burning of fuel molecules would be released as heat. The mitochondria of brown fat cells have just such channels.

Until recently, brown fat in humans was thought to disappear after infancy. The presence of unidentified tissue in the PET scans of cancer patients, however, caused researchers to question that conclusion. Could the tissues in the scans be brown fat? To test that hypothesis, researchers analyzed 3,640 PET-CT scans that had been performed on 1,972 patients for various diagnostic reasons. PET is a technique that identifies areas with high uptake of radioactively labeled glucose, and CT scans can detect adipose (fat) tissue. The combined PET-CT scans revealed small areas in the neck and chest of some patients that fit the criteria for brown fat—adipose tissue that was metabolically active (burning glucose). The researchers correlated the presence or absence of brown fat with patients' sex, age, weight, and other parameters, including the outdoor temperature. The results showed that 7.5% of the women and 3% of the men examined had deposits of brown fat. The tissues were found to be more prevalent both in patients who were thinner and when the scans had been taken in cold weather.

As is typical in science, the results from one study led to new questions and new research. Is brown fat activated by cold temperatures and, thus, could a much higher percentage of adults have brown fat than shown in scans of patients who were presumably *not* cold? Is the prevalence of this fat-burning tissue in thinner individuals related to why some people are thin and others are obese?

A second study involving 24 men looked at the presence and activity of brown fat during cold exposure. Ten participants were classified as lean (based on a BMI [body mass index] of less than 25) and 14 were identified as overweight or obese. Combined PET-CT scans were taken of all research participants following a two-hour exposure at 16°C (60.8°F). The scans of all but one participant (the one with the highest BMI) revealed activated brown fat tissues. As shown in **Figure 6.11**, the measured brown fat activity of the lean group was significantly higher than that of the overweight/obese group.

These results indicate that brown fat may be present in most people, and, when activated by cold, the brown fat of lean individuals is more active (burns more calories). What questions does this study raise? Does the more active brown fat of thin individuals help keep them thin? Are there other ways to turn on brown fat besides exposure to cold? Could brown fat be a target for obesity-fighting drugs?

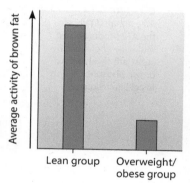

▲ **Figure 6.11** Activity level of brown fat of lean and overweight/obese participants after cold exposure

Data from W. D. van Marken Lichtenbelt et al., Cold-activated brown adipose tissue in healthy men, *New England Journal of Medicine* 360: 1500–8 (2009).

Research continues on brown fat and on the signals (temperature, hormonal, and nervous) that activate it. But as the popular press reports this potential link between calorie-burning brown fat and weight loss, be prepared to see new diets, supplements, exercise routines, and perhaps even cold spa treatments that promise to rev up your brown fat furnace. As always when evaluating such information, look for the science behind those claims.

Data from A. M. Cypess et al., Identification and importance of brown adipose tissue in adult humans, *New England Journal of Medicine* 360: 1509–17 (2009).

> **?** **The initial study discussed identified brown fat in less than 10% of the patients whose scans were analyzed. The second study identified brown fat in 96% of participants. What accounts for this difference?**
>
> ⦿ Brown fat is activated in response to cold temperature, and the second study involved cold treatment.

6.12 Review: Each molecule of glucose yields many molecules of ATP

Let's review what you have learned about cellular respiration by following the oxidation of one molecule of glucose. Starting on the left in **Figure 6.12**, glycolysis, which occurs in the cytosol, oxidizes glucose to two molecules of pyruvate, produces 2 NADH, and produces a net of 2 ATP by substrate-level phosphorylation. Within the mitochondrion, the oxidation of 2 pyruvate yields 2 NADH and 2 acetyl CoA. The 2 acetyl CoA feed into the citric acid cycle, which yields 6 NADH and 2 FADH$_2$, as well as 2 ATP by substrate-level phosphorylation. NADH and FADH$_2$ deliver electrons to the electron transport chain, where they are finally passed to O$_2$, forming H$_2$O. The electron transport chain pumps H$^+$ into the intermembrane space. The resulting H$^+$ gradient is tapped by ATP synthase to produce about 28 molecules of ATP by oxidative phosphorylation (according to current experimental data). Thus, the total yield of ATP molecules per glucose is about 32.

The number of ATP molecules cannot be stated exactly for several reasons. The NADH produced in glycolysis passes its electrons across the mitochondrial membrane to either NAD$^+$ or FAD. Because FADH$_2$ adds its electrons farther along the electron transport chain (see Figure 6.10A), it contributes less to the H$^+$ gradient and thus generates less ATP. In addition, some of the energy of the H$^+$ gradient may be used for work other than ATP production, such as the active transport of pyruvate into the mitochondrion.

Because most of the ATP generated by cellular respiration results from oxidative phosphorylation, the ATP yield depends on an adequate supply of oxygen to the cell. Without oxygen to function as the final electron acceptor, electron transport and ATP production stop. But as we see next, some cells can oxidize organic fuel and generate ATP *without* oxygen.

> **?** Explain where O$_2$ is used and CO$_2$ is produced in cellular respiration.

O$_2$ accepts electrons at the end of the electron transport chain. CO$_2$ is released during the oxidation of intermediate compounds in pyruvate oxidation and the citric acid cycle.

► Figure 6.12
An estimated tally of the ATP produced per molecule of glucose by substrate-level and oxidative phosphorylation in cellular respiration

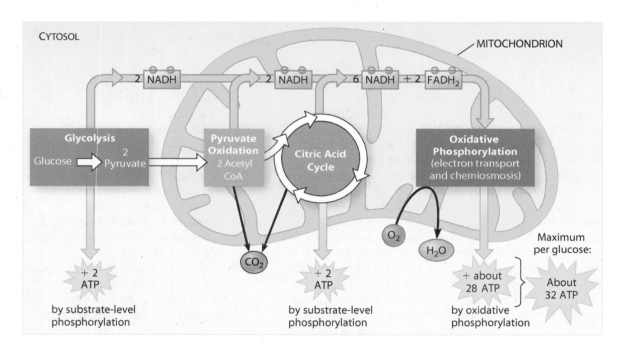

▷ Fermentation: Anaerobic Harvesting of Energy

6.13 Fermentation enables cells to produce ATP without oxygen

Fermentation is a way of harvesting chemical energy that does not require oxygen. The metabolic pathway that generates ATP during fermentation is glycolysis, the same pathway that functions in the first stage of cellular respiration. Remember that glycolysis uses no oxygen; it simply generates a net gain of 2 ATP while oxidizing glucose to two molecules of pyruvate and reducing NAD$^+$ to NADH. The yield of 2 ATP

is certainly a lot less than the possible 32 ATP per glucose generated during aerobic respiration, but it is enough to keep your muscles contracting for a short period of time when oxygen is scarce. And many microorganisms supply all their energy needs with the 2 ATP per glucose yield of glycolysis.

There is more to fermentation, however, than just glycolysis. To oxidize glucose in glycolysis, NAD$^+$ must be present as an electron acceptor. This is no problem under aerobic conditions, because the cell regenerates its pool of NAD$^+$ when NADH passes its electrons into the mitochondrion, to be transported to the electron transport chain. Fermentation provides an anaerobic path for recycling NADH back to NAD$^+$.

Lactic Acid Fermentation One common type of fermentation is called **lactic acid fermentation**. Your muscle cells and certain bacteria can regenerate NAD$^+$ by this process, as illustrated in **Figure 6.13A**. You can see that NADH is oxidized back to NAD$^+$ as pyruvate is reduced to lactate (the ionized form of lactic acid). Muscle cells can switch to lactic acid fermentation when the need for ATP outpaces the delivery of O$_2$ via the bloodstream. The lactate that builds up in muscle cells during strenuous exercise was previously thought to cause muscle fatigue and pain, but research now indicates that increased levels of other ions may be to blame. In any case, the lactate is gradually carried away by the blood to the liver, where it is converted back to pyruvate and oxidized in the mitochondria of liver cells.

The dairy industry uses lactic acid fermentation by bacteria to make cheese and yogurt. Other types of microbial fermentation turn soybeans into soy sauce and cabbage into sauerkraut.

Alcohol Fermentation For thousands of years, people have used **alcohol fermentation** in brewing, winemaking, and baking. Yeasts are single-celled fungi that normally use aerobic respiration to process their food. But they are also able to survive in anaerobic environments. Yeasts and certain bacteria recycle their NADH back to NAD$^+$ while converting pyruvate to CO$_2$ and ethanol **(Figure 6.13B)**. The CO$_2$ provides the bubbles in beer and champagne. Bubbles of CO$_2$ generated by baker's yeast cause bread dough to rise. Ethanol (ethyl alcohol), the two-carbon end product, is toxic to the organisms that produce it. Yeasts release their alcohol wastes to their surroundings, where it usually diffuses away. When yeasts are confined in a wine vat, they die when the alcohol concentration reaches 14%.

Types of Anaerobes Unlike muscle cells and yeasts, many prokaryotes that live in stagnant ponds and deep in the soil are *obligate anaerobes*, meaning they require anaerobic conditions and are poisoned by oxygen. Yeasts and many other bacteria are facultative anaerobes. A *facultative anaerobe* can make ATP either by fermentation or by oxidative phosphorylation, depending on whether O$_2$ is available. On the cellular level, our muscle cells behave as facultative anaerobes.

For a facultative anaerobe, pyruvate is a fork in the metabolic road. If oxygen is available, the organism will always use the more productive aerobic respiration. Thus, to make wine and beer, yeasts must be grown anaerobically so that they will ferment sugars and produce ethanol. For this reason, the wine barrels and beer fermentation vats in **Figure 6.13C** are designed to keep air out.

> **?** A glucose-fed yeast cell is moved from an aerobic environment to an anaerobic one. For the cell to continue generating ATP at the same rate, how would its rate of glucose consumption need to change?
>
> ● The cell would have to consume glucose at a rate about 16 times the consumption rate in the aerobic environment (2 ATP per glucose molecule is made by fermentation versus 32 ATP by cellular respiration).

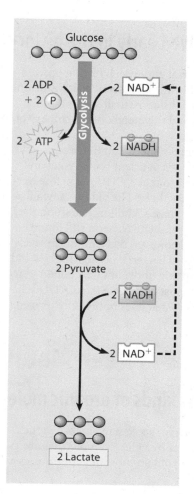

▲ **Figure 6.13A** Lactic acid fermentation: NAD$^+$ is regenerated as pyruvate is reduced to lactate

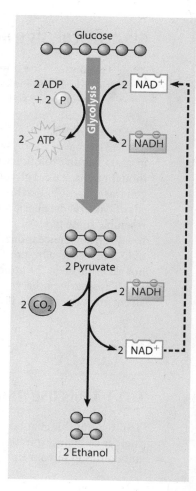

▲ **Figure 6.13B** Alcohol fermentation: NAD$^+$ is regenerated as pyruvate is broken down to CO$_2$ and ethanol

▲ **Figure 6.13C** Wine barrels and beer fermentation vats

6.14 Glycolysis evolved early in the history of life on Earth

Glycolysis is the universal energy-harvesting process of life. If you looked inside a bacterial cell, inside one of your body cells, or inside virtually any other living cell, you would find the metabolic machinery of glycolysis.

The role of glycolysis in both fermentation and respiration has an evolutionary basis. Ancient prokaryotes are thought to have used glycolysis to make ATP long before oxygen was present in Earth's atmosphere. The oldest known fossils of bacteria date back more than 3.5 billion years, and they resemble some types of photosynthetic bacteria still found today. The evidence indicates, however, that significant levels of O_2, formed as a by-product of bacterial photosynthesis, did not accumulate in the atmosphere until about 2.7 billion years ago. Thus, early prokaryotes most likely generated ATP exclusively from glycolysis, a process that does not require oxygen.

The fact that glycolysis is the most widespread metabolic pathway found in Earth's organisms today suggests that it evolved very early in the history of life. The location of glycolysis within the cell also implies great antiquity; the pathway does not require any of the membrane-enclosed organelles of the eukaryotic cell, which evolved about a billion years after the prokaryotic cell. Glycolysis is a metabolic heirloom from early cells that continues to function in fermentation and as the first stage in the breakdown of organic molecules by cellular respiration.

? **List some of the characteristics of glycolysis that indicate that it is an ancient metabolic pathway.**

Glycolysis occurs universally (functioning in both fermentation and respiration), does not require oxygen, and does not occur in a membrane-enclosed organelle.

▷ Connections Between Metabolic Pathways

6.15 Cells use many kinds of organic molecules as fuel for cellular respiration

Throughout this chapter, we have spoken of glucose as the fuel for cellular respiration. But free glucose molecules are not common in your diet. You obtain most of your calories as carbohydrates (such as sucrose and other disaccharide sugars and starch, a polysaccharide), fats, and proteins. You consume all three of these classes of organic molecules when you eat a handful of peanuts, for instance.

Figure 6.15 uses color-coded arrows to illustrate how a cell can use these three types of molecules to make ATP. A wide range of carbohydrates can be funneled into glycolysis, as indicated by the blue arrows on the far left of the diagram. For example, enzymes in your digestive tract hydrolyze starch to glucose, which is then broken down by glycolysis and the citric acid cycle. Similarly, glycogen, the polysaccharide stored in your liver and muscle cells, can be hydrolyzed to glucose to serve as fuel between meals.

Fats make excellent cellular fuel because they contain many hydrogen atoms and thus many energy-rich electrons. As the diagram shows (tan arrows), a cell first hydrolyzes fats to glycerol and fatty acids. It then converts the glycerol to glyceraldehyde 3-phosphate (G3P), one of the intermediates in glycolysis. The fatty acids are broken into two-carbon fragments that enter the citric acid cycle as acetyl CoA. A gram of fat yields more than twice as much ATP as a gram of carbohydrate. Because so many calories are stockpiled in each gram of fat, you must expend a large amount of energy to burn fat stored in your body. This helps explain why it is so difficult for a dieter to lose excess fat.

Proteins (purple arrows in Figure 6.15) can also be used for

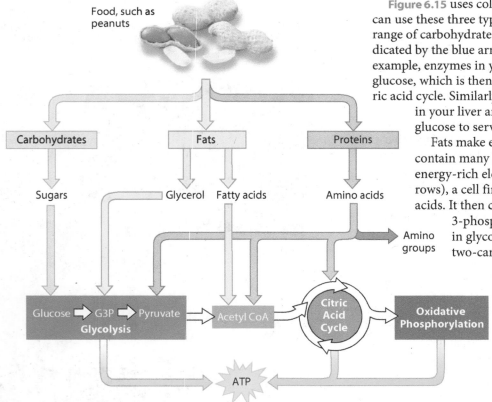

▲ Figure 6.15 Pathways that break down various food molecules

fuel, although your body preferentially burns sugars and fats first. To be oxidized as fuel, proteins must first be digested to their constituent amino acids. Typically, a cell will use most of these amino acids to make its own proteins. Enzymes can convert excess amino acids to intermediates of glycolysis or the citric acid cycle, and their energy is then harvested by cellular respiration. During the conversion, the amino groups are stripped off and later disposed of in urine.

? Animals store most of their energy reserves as fats, not as polysaccharides. What is the advantage of this mode of storage for an animal?

● Most animals are mobile and benefit from a compact and concentrated form of energy storage. Also, because fats are hydrophobic, they can be stored without extra water associated with them (see Module 3.8).

6.16 Organic molecules from food provide raw materials for biosynthesis

Not all food molecules are destined to be oxidized as fuel for making ATP. Food also provides the raw materials your cells use for biosynthesis—the production of organic molecules using energy-requiring metabolic pathways. A cell must be able to make its own molecules to build its structures and perform its functions. Some raw materials, such as amino acids, can be incorporated directly into your macromolecules. However, your cells also need to make molecules that are not present in your food. Indeed, glycolysis and the citric acid cycle function as metabolic interchanges that enable your cells to convert some kinds of molecules to others as you need them.

Figure 6.16 outlines the pathways by which your cells can make three classes of organic molecules using some of the intermediate molecules of glycolysis and the citric acid cycle. By comparing Figures 6.15 and 6.16, you can see clear connections between the energy-harvesting pathways of cellular respiration and the biosynthetic pathways used to construct the organic molecules of the cell.

Basic principles of supply and demand regulate these pathways. If there is an excess of a certain amino acid, for example, the pathway that synthesizes it is switched off. The most common mechanism for this control is feedback inhibition: The end product inhibits an enzyme that catalyzes an early step in the pathway (see Module 5.15). Feedback inhibition also controls cellular respiration. If ATP accumulates in a cell, it inhibits an early enzyme in glycolysis, slowing down respiration and conserving resources. On the other hand, the same enzyme is activated by a buildup of ADP in the cell, signaling the need for more energy.

The cells of all living organisms—including those of the panda shown in Figure 6.16 and the plants they eat—have the ability to harvest energy from the breakdown of organic molecules. When the process is cellular respiration, the atoms of the starting materials end up in carbon dioxide and water. In contrast, the ability to make organic molecules from carbon dioxide and water is not universal. Animal cells lack this ability, but plant cells can actually produce organic molecules from inorganic ones using the energy of sunlight in the process of photosynthesis. (We explore photosynthesis in Chapter 7.)

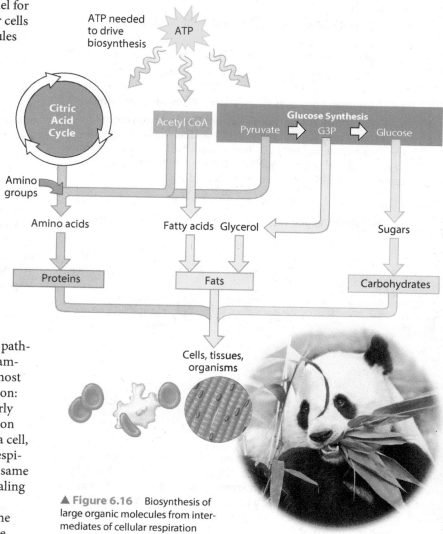

▲ Figure 6.16   Biosynthesis of large organic molecules from intermediates of cellular respiration

? Explain how someone can gain weight and store fat even when on a low-fat diet. (Hint: Look for G3P and acetyl CoA in Figures 6.15 and 6.16.)

● If caloric intake is excessive, body cells use metabolic pathways to convert the excess to fat. The glycerol and fatty acids of fats are made from G3P and acetyl CoA, respectively, both produced from the oxidation of carbohydrates.

CHAPTER **6** REVIEW

For practice quizzes, BioFlix animations, MP3 tutorials, video
tutors, and more study tools designed for this textbook, go to

MasteringBiology®

Reviewing the Concepts

Cellular Respiration: Aerobic Harvesting of Energy (6.1–6.5)

6.1 Photosynthesis and cellular respiration provide energy for life. Photosynthesis uses solar energy to produce glucose and O_2 from CO_2 and H_2O. In cellular respiration, O_2 is consumed during the breakdown of glucose to CO_2 and H_2O, and energy is released.

6.2 Breathing supplies O_2 for use in cellular respiration and removes CO_2.

6.3 Cellular respiration banks energy in ATP molecules.

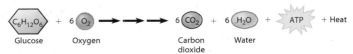

$C_6H_{12}O_6$ + 6 O_2 → 6 CO_2 + 6 H_2O + ATP + Heat
Glucose   Oxygen   Carbon   Water
                            dioxide

6.4 The human body uses energy from ATP for all its activities.

6.5 Cells capture energy from electrons "falling" from organic fuels to oxygen. Electrons removed from fuel molecules (oxidation) are transferred to NAD^+ (reduction). NADH passes electrons to an electron transport chain. As electrons "fall" from carrier to carrier and finally to O_2, energy is released.

Stages of Cellular Respiration (6.6–6.12)

6.6 Overview: Cellular respiration occurs in three main stages.

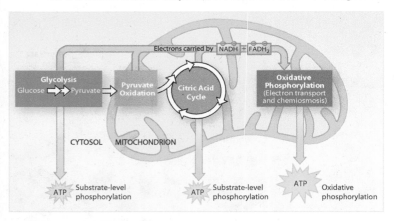

6.7 Glycolysis harvests chemical energy by oxidizing glucose to pyruvate. ATP is used to prime a glucose molecule, which is split in two. These three-carbon intermediates are oxidized to two molecules of pyruvate, yielding a net of 2 ATP and 2 NADH. ATP is formed by substrate-level phosphorylation, in which a phosphate group is transferred from an organic molecule to ADP.

6.8 Pyruvate is oxidized in preparation for the citric acid cycle. The oxidation of pyruvate yields acetyl CoA, CO_2, and NADH.

6.9 The citric acid cycle completes the oxidation of organic molecules, generating many NADH and $FADH_2$ molecules. For each turn of the cycle, two carbons from acetyl CoA are added and 2 CO_2 are released.

6.10 Most ATP production occurs by oxidative phosphorylation. In mitochondria, electrons from NADH and $FADH_2$ are passed down the electron transport chain to O_2, which picks up H^+ to form water. Energy released by these redox reactions is used to pump H^+ into the intermembrane space. In chemiosmosis, the H^+ gradient drives H^+ back through ATP synthase complexes in the inner membrane, synthesizing ATP.

6.11 Scientists have discovered heat-producing, calorie-burning brown fat in adults.

6.12 Review: Each molecule of glucose yields many molecules of ATP. Substrate-level phosphorylation and oxidative phosphorylation produce up to 32 ATP molecules for every glucose molecule oxidized in cellular respiration.

Fermentation: Anaerobic Harvesting of Energy (6.13–6.14)

6.13 Fermentation enables cells to produce ATP without oxygen. Under anaerobic conditions, muscle cells, yeasts, and certain bacteria produce ATP by glycolysis. NAD^+ is recycled from NADH as pyruvate is reduced to lactate (lactic acid fermentation) or alcohol and CO_2 (alcohol fermentation).

6.14 Glycolysis evolved early in the history of life on Earth. Glycolysis occurs in the cytosol of the cells of nearly all organisms and is thought to have evolved in ancient prokaryotes.

Connections Between Metabolic Pathways (6.15–6.16)

6.15 Cells use many kinds of organic molecules as fuel for cellular respiration.

6.16 Organic molecules from food provide raw materials for biosynthesis. Cells use intermediates from cellular respiration and ATP for biosynthesis of other organic molecules. Metabolic pathways are often regulated by feedback inhibition.

Connecting the Concepts

1. Fill in the blanks in this summary map to help you review the key concepts of cellular respiration.

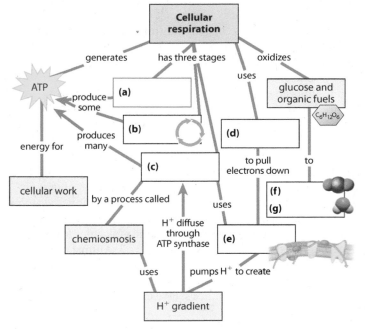

Testing Your Knowledge

Level 1: Knowledge/Comprehension

2. A biochemist wanted to study how various substances were used in cellular respiration. In one experiment, she allowed a mouse to breathe air containing O_2 "labeled" by a particular isotope. In the mouse, the labeled oxygen first showed up in
   a. ATP.
   b. NADH.
   c. CO_2.
   d. H_2O.

3. In glycolysis, _____ is oxidized and _____ is reduced.
   a. NAD^+ . . . glucose
   b. glucose . . . oxygen
   c. ATP . . . ADP
   d. glucose . . . NAD^+

4. Which of the following is the most immediate source of energy for making most of the ATP in your cells?
   a. the transfer of (P) from intermediate substrates to ADP
   b. the movement of H^+ across a membrane down its concentration gradient
   c. the splitting of glucose into two molecules of pyruvate
   d. electrons moving through the electron transport chain

5. Which of the following is a true distinction between cellular respiration and fermentation?
   a. NADH is oxidized by passing electrons to the electron transport chain in respiration only.
   b. Only respiration oxidizes glucose.
   c. Substrate-level phosphorylation is unique to fermentation; cellular respiration uses oxidative phosphorylation.
   d. Fermentation is the metabolic pathway found in prokaryotes; cellular respiration is unique to eukaryotes.

Level 2: Application/Analysis

6. The poison cyanide binds to an electron carrier within the electron transport chain and blocks the movement of electrons. When this happens, glycolysis and the citric acid cycle soon grind to a halt as well. Why do you think these other two stages of cellular respiration stop? (*Explain your answer.*)
   a. They run out of ATP.
   b. Unused O_2 interferes with cellular respiration.
   c. They run out of NAD^+ and FAD.
   d. Electrons are no longer available.

7. In which of the following is the first molecule becoming reduced to the second molecule?
   a. pyruvate → acetyl CoA
   b. pyruvate → lactate
   c. glucose → pyruvate
   d. $NADH + H^+$ → $NAD^+ + 2 H$

8. Which of the three stages of cellular respiration is considered the most ancient? Explain your answer.

9. Compare and contrast fermentation as it occurs in your muscle cells and in yeast cells.

10. Explain how your body can convert excess carbohydrates in the diet to fats. Can excess carbohydrates be converted to protein? What else must be supplied?

11. An average adult human requires 2,200 kcal of energy per day. Suppose your diet provides an average of 2,300 kcal per day. How many hours per week would you have to walk to burn off the extra calories? Swim? Run? (See Figure 6.4.)

12. Your body makes NAD^+ and FAD from two B vitamins, niacin and riboflavin. The Recommended Dietary Allowance for niacin is 20 mg and for riboflavin, 1.7 mg. These amounts are thousands of times less than the amount of glucose your body needs each day to fuel its energy needs. Why is the daily requirement for these vitamins so small?

Level 3: Synthesis/Evaluation

13. In the citric acid cycle, an enzyme oxidizes malate to oxaloacetate, with the production of NADH and the release of H^+. You are studying this reaction using a suspension of bean cell mitochondria and a blue dye that loses its color as it takes up H^+. You know that the higher the concentration of malate, the more rapid the decolorization of the dye. You set up reaction mixtures with mitochondria, dye, and three different concentrations of malate (0.1 mg/L, 0.2 mg/L, and 0.3 mg/L). Which of the following graphs represents the results you would expect, and why?

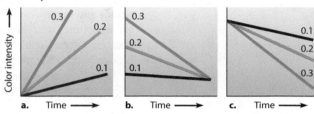

14. ATP synthase enzymes are found in the prokaryotic plasma membrane and in the inner membrane of a mitochondrion. What does this suggest about the evolutionary relationship of this eukaryotic organelle to prokaryotes?

15. **SCIENTIFIC THINKING** Several studies have found a correlation between the activity levels of brown fat tissue in research participants following exposure to cold and their percentage of body fat (see Module 6.11). Devise a graph that would present the results from such a study, labeling the axes and drawing a line to show whether the results show a positive or negative correlation between the variables. Propose two hypotheses that could explain these results.

16. For a short time in the 1930s, some physicians prescribed low doses of a compound called dinitrophenol (DNP) to help patients lose weight. This unsafe method was abandoned after some patients died. DNP uncouples the chemiosmotic machinery by making the inner mitochondrial membrane leaky to H^+. Explain how this drug could cause profuse sweating, weight loss, and possibly death.

17. Explain how the mechanism of brown fat metabolism is similar to the effect that the drug DNP described above has on mitochondria. Pharmaceutical companies may start targeting brown fat for weight loss drugs. How might such drugs help patients lose weight? What dangers might such drugs pose?

Answers to all questions can be found in Appendix 4.

7

Photosynthesis: *Using Light to Make Food*

Will global climate change make you itch?

If you are among the 80% of people allergic to poison ivy, the thick patch of three-leaved plants pictured below may make you want to scrub with soap and water and rush to find calamine lotion. A close encounter with this noxious weed often leads to itchy and oozing blisters that can last for weeks. The allergic component of poison ivy sap, urushiol, binds to skin, clothing, and pet fur on contact, where it remains active until washed off. Even dead leaves or vines retain active urushiol for several years.

Poison ivy is found throughout much of North America, often growing along the ground in both woods and open areas. It can also grow as a vine, climbing high up trees with its lateral branches that are sometimes mistaken for tree limbs. The rhymes "hairy vine, no friend of mine" and "raggy rope, don't be a dope" help alert hikers to the danger around them when the characteristic shiny leaves are hidden high in the tree foliage.

Like all plants, poison ivy produces energy for its growth by photosynthesis, the process that converts light energy to the chemical energy of sugar. Photosynthesis removes CO_2 from the

atmosphere and stores it in plant matter. The burning of sugar in the cellular respiration of almost all organisms releases CO_2 back to the environment. Burning fossil fuels and deforestation also release CO_2, and these activities are contributing to the current rise in atmospheric CO_2 and the accompanying global climate change. How might higher CO_2 levels affect plant growth? Unfortunately, many studies indicate that weeds grow faster under such conditions than do our crop plants or trees. Later in the chapter we will discuss one such study concerning the growth of poison ivy.

But first, let's learn how photosynthesis works. We begin with some basic concepts and then look more closely at the two stages of photosynthesis: the light reactions and the Calvin cycle. Finally, we explore ways in which photosynthesis affects our global environment.

BIG IDEAS

An Introduction to Photosynthesis
(7.1–7.5)

Plants and other photoautotrophs use the energy of sunlight to convert CO_2 and H_2O to sugar and O_2.

The Light Reactions: Converting Solar Energy to Chemical Energy
(7.6–7.9)

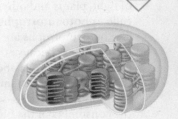

In the thylakoids of a chloroplast, the light reactions generate ATP and NADPH.

The Calvin Cycle: Reducing CO_2 to Sugar
(7.10–7.11)

The Calvin cycle, which takes place in the stroma of the chloroplast, uses ATP and NADPH to reduce CO_2 to sugar.

The Global Significance of Photosynthesis
(7.12–7.14)

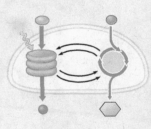

Photosynthesis provides the energy and building material for ecosystems. It also affects global climate and the ozone layer.

▷ An Introduction to Photosynthesis

7.1 Photosynthesis fuels the biosphere

Life on Earth is solar powered. The chloroplasts in plant cells capture light energy that has traveled 150 million kilometers from the sun. Through the process of **photosynthesis**, plants use solar energy to convert CO_2 and H_2O to sugars and other organic molecules, and they release O_2 as a by-product. Plants are **autotrophs** (meaning "self-feeders" in Greek) in that they make their own food. Autotrophs not only feed themselves, but they are the ultimate source of organic molecules for almost all other organisms. Because they use the energy of light, plants and other photosynthesizers are specifically called **photoautotrophs**.

Photoautotrophs are often referred to as the producers of the biosphere because they produce its food supply. (In Chapter 16, you will learn about chemoautotrophs—prokaryotes that use inorganic chemicals as their energy source and are the producers in deep-sea vent communities.) Producers feed the consumers of the biosphere—the **heterotrophs** that cannot make their own food but must consume plants or animals or decompose organic material (*hetero* means "other"). You and almost all other heterotrophs are completely dependent on photoautotrophs for the raw materials and organic fuel necessary to maintain life and for the oxygen required to burn that fuel in cellular respiration.

Photoautotrophs not only feed us; they also clothe us (think cotton), house us (think wood), and provide energy for warmth, light, transport, and manufacturing. The fossil fuels we use as energy sources represent stores of the sun's energy captured by photoautotrophs in the far distant past.

The photographs shown on this page illustrate some of the diversity among today's photoautotrophs. On land, plants, such as those in the tropical forest in **Figure 7.1A**, are the producers. In aquatic environments, photoautotrophs include unicellular and multicellular algae, as well as photosynthetic prokaryotes. **Figure 7.1B** shows kelp, a large alga that forms extensive underwater "forests" off the coast of California. **Figure 7.1C** is a micrograph of cyanobacteria, which are important producers in freshwater and marine ecosystems.

In this chapter, we focus on photosynthesis in plants, which takes place in chloroplasts. The remarkable ability of these organelles to harness light energy and use it to drive the synthesis of organic compounds emerges from their structural organization: Photosynthetic pigments and enzymes are grouped together in membranes or compartments, facilitating the complex series of chemical reactions in photosynthesis. Photosynthetic bacteria have infolded regions of the plasma membrane containing such clusters of pigments and enzymes. In fact, according to the widely accepted theory of endosymbiosis, chloroplasts originated from a photosynthetic prokaryote that took up residence inside a eukaryotic cell (see Module 4.15).

Let's begin our study of photosynthesis with an overview of the location and structure of plant chloroplasts.

> **?** What do "self-feeding" photoautotrophs require from the environment to make their own food?

● Light, carbon dioxide, and water.

▲ **Figure 7.1A** Tropical forest plants

▲ **Figure 7.1B** Kelp, a large, multicellular alga

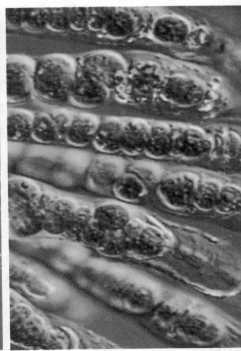

▲ **Figure 7.1C** Cyanobacteria (photosynthetic bacteria) LM 980X

7.2 Photosynthesis occurs in chloroplasts in plant cells

All green parts of a plant have chloroplasts in their cells, but leaves are the major sites of photosynthesis in most plants. Indeed, a section of leaf with a top surface area of 1 mm² has about a half million chloroplasts. A leaf's green color comes from **chlorophyll**, a light-absorbing pigment in the chloroplasts that plays a central role in converting solar energy to chemical energy.

Figure 7.2 zooms in on a leaf to show the actual sites of photosynthesis. As you can see in the leaf cross section, chloroplasts are concentrated in the cells of the **mesophyll**, the green tissue in the interior of the leaf. Carbon dioxide enters the leaf, and oxygen exits, by way of tiny pores called **stomata** (singular, *stoma*, meaning "mouth"). Water absorbed by the roots is delivered to the leaves in veins. Leaves also use veins to export sugar to roots and other parts of the plant.

As you will notice in the light micrograph of a single mesophyll cell, each cell has numerous chloroplasts. A typical mesophyll cell has about 30 to 40 chloroplasts. The bottom drawing and the electron micrograph show the structures in a single chloroplast. Membranes in the chloroplast form the framework within which many of the reactions of photosynthesis occur, just as mitochondrial membranes are the site for much of the energy-harvesting machinery in cellular respiration (see Module 6.10). In the chloroplast, an envelope of two membranes encloses an inner compartment, which is filled with a thick fluid called **stroma**. Suspended in the stroma is a system of interconnected membranous sacs, called **thylakoids**, which enclose another internal compartment, called the thylakoid space. (As you will see later, this thylakoid space plays a role analogous to the intermembrane space of a mitochondrion in the generation of ATP.) In many places, thylakoids are concentrated in stacks called grana (singular, *granum*). Built into the thylakoid membranes are the chlorophyll molecules that capture light energy. The thylakoid membranes also house much of the machinery that converts light energy to chemical energy, which is used in the stroma to make sugar.

Later in the chapter, we examine the function of these structures in more detail. But first, let's look more closely at the general process of photosynthesis.

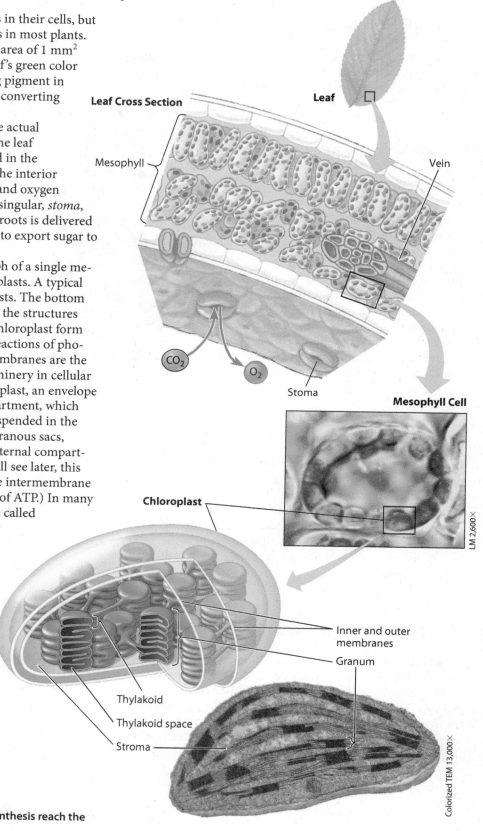

▲ Figure 7.2   Zooming in on the location and structure of chloroplasts

? **How do the reactant molecules of photosynthesis reach the chloroplasts in leaves?**

● CO₂ enters leaves through stomata, and H₂O enters the roots and is carried to leaves through veins.

7.3 Scientists traced the process of photosynthesis using isotopes

The leaves of plants that live in lakes and ponds are often covered with bubbles like the ones shown in **Figure 7.3**. The bubbles are oxygen gas (O_2) produced during photosynthesis. But where does this O_2 come from?

The overall process of photosynthesis has been known since the 1800s: In the presence of light, green plants produce sugar and oxygen from carbon dioxide and water. Consider the basic equation for photosynthesis:

$$6\ CO_2 + 6\ H_2O \rightarrow C_6H_{12}O_6 + 6\ O_2$$

Looking at this equation, you can understand why scientists hypothesized that photosynthesis first splits carbon dioxide ($CO_2 \rightarrow C + O_2$), releasing oxygen gas, and then adds water (H_2O) to the carbon to produce sugar. In the 1930s, this idea was challenged by C. B. van Niel, who was working with photosynthesizing bacteria that produce sugar from CO_2 but do not release O_2 in the process. These bacteria obviously did not split CO_2 in their photosynthesis. He hypothesized that in plants, it is H_2O that is split, with the hydrogen becoming incorporated into sugar and the O_2 released as gas.

In the 1950s, scientists confirmed van Niel's hypothesis by using a heavy isotope of oxygen, O-18, to follow the fate of oxygen atoms during photosynthesis. Isotopes are atoms with differing numbers of neutrons: O-18 has two more neutrons in the nucleus of its atom than the more common isotope O-16. The summary of the results of these experiments follows. (Note that these equations are slightly more detailed than the equation written above because, as it turns out, water is both a reactant and a product in photosynthesis.)

▲ **Figure 7.3** Oxygen bubbles on the leaves of an aquatic plant

Experiment 1: $6\ CO_2 + 12\ H_2O \rightarrow C_6H_{12}O_6 + 6\ H_2O + 6\ O_2$

Experiment 2: $6\ CO_2 + 12\ H_2O \rightarrow C_6H_{12}O_6 + 6\ H_2O + 6\ O_2$

The red type in the equations above denotes the source and ending location of O-18, the tracer used in these experiments. In experiment 1, a plant given CO_2 containing O-18 gave off no labeled (containing O-18) oxygen gas. But in experiment 2, a plant given H_2O containing O-18 did produce labeled O_2. What did these experiments show? As you can see, the O_2 released during photosynthesis comes from water and not from CO_2. Additional experiments have revealed that the oxygen atoms from CO_2 and the hydrogen atoms from the reactant H_2O molecules end up in both the sugar molecule and the H_2O molecules that are formed as a product.

The synthesis of sugar in photosynthesis involves numerous chemical reactions. Working out the details of these reactions also involved the use of isotopes, in this case, radioactive isotopes. In the mid-1940s, American biochemist Melvin Calvin and his colleagues began using radioactive C-14 to trace the sequence of intermediates formed in the cyclic pathway that produces sugar from CO_2. (See Module 2.3 to review radioactive isotopes.) They worked for 10 years to elucidate this cycle, which is now called the Calvin cycle. Calvin received the Nobel Prize in 1961 for this work.

> **?** Photosynthesis produces billions of tons of carbohydrate a year. Where does most of the mass of this huge amount of organic matter come from?
>
> ● Mostly from CO_2 in the air, which provides both the carbon and oxygen in carbohydrate. Water supplies only the hydrogen.

7.4 Photosynthesis is a redox process, as is cellular respiration

What actually happens when CO_2 and water are converted to sugar and O_2? Photosynthesis is a redox (oxidation-reduction) process, just as cellular respiration is (see Module 6.5). As indicated in the summary equation for photosynthesis (**Figure 7.4A**), CO_2 becomes reduced to sugar as electrons, along with hydrogen ions (H^+) from water, are added to it. Meanwhile, water molecules are oxidized; that is, they lose

electrons, along with hydrogen ions. Recall that oxidation and reduction always go hand in hand.

Now compare the food-producing equation for photosynthesis with the energy-releasing equation for cellular respiration (**Figure 7.4B**). Cellular respiration harvests energy stored in a glucose molecule by oxidizing the sugar and reducing O_2 to H_2O. This process involves a number of energy-releasing

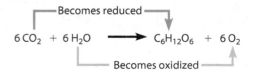

▲ **Figure 7.4A** Photosynthesis (uses light energy)

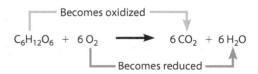

▲ **Figure 7.4B** Cellular respiration (releases chemical energy)

redox reactions, with electrons losing potential energy as they are passed down an electron transport chain to O_2. Along the way, the mitochondrion uses some of the energy to synthesize ATP.

In contrast, the food-producing redox reactions of photosynthesis require energy. The potential energy of electrons increases as they move from H_2O to CO_2 during photosynthesis. The light energy captured by chlorophyll molecules

in the chloroplast provides this energy boost. Photosynthesis converts light energy to chemical energy and stores it in the chemical bonds of sugar molecules, which can provide energy for later use or raw materials for biosynthesis.

> **?** Which redox process, photosynthesis or cellular respiration, is endergonic? (*Hint*: See Module 5.11.)

Photosynthesis

7.5 The two stages of photosynthesis are linked by ATP and NADPH

The equation for photosynthesis is a simple summary of a rather complex process. Photosynthesis occurs in two stages, each with multiple steps. Let's begin our study of photosynthesis with an overview of the two stages. **Figure 7.5** shows the inputs and outputs of the light reactions and the Calvin cycle and how these two stages are related.

The **light reactions**, which occur in the thylakoids, include the steps that convert light energy to chemical energy and release O_2. Water is split, providing a source of electrons and giving off O_2 as a by-product. Light energy absorbed by chlorophyll molecules built into the thylakoid membranes is used to drive the transfer of electrons and H^+ from water to the electron acceptor **NADP$^+$**, reducing it to NADPH. NADPH is first cousin to NADH, which transports electrons in cellular respiration; the two differ only in the extra phosphate group in NADPH. NADPH temporarily stores electrons and hydrogen ions and provides "reducing power" to the Calvin cycle. The light reactions also generate ATP from ADP and a phosphate group.

In summary, the light reactions absorb solar energy and convert it to chemical energy stored in both ATP and NADPH. Notice that these reactions produce no sugar; sugar is not made until the Calvin cycle, which is the second stage of photosynthesis.

The **Calvin cycle** occurs in the stroma of the chloroplast. It is a cyclic series of reactions that assembles sugar molecules using CO_2 and the energy-rich products of the light reactions. The incorporation of carbon from CO_2 into organic compounds, shown in the figure as CO_2 entering the Calvin cycle, is called **carbon fixation**. After carbon fixation, the carbon compounds are reduced to sugars.

As the figure suggests, it is NADPH produced by the light reactions that provides the electrons for reducing carbon compounds in the Calvin cycle. And ATP from the light reactions provides chemical energy that powers several of the steps of the Calvin cycle. The Calvin cycle is sometimes referred to as the dark reactions, or light-independent

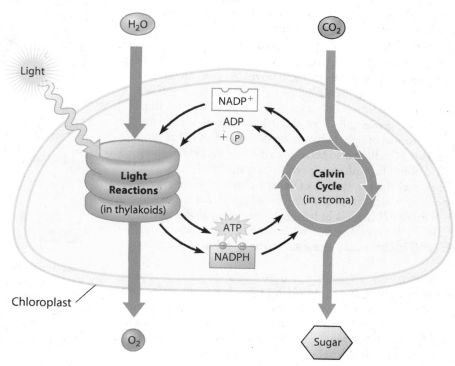

▲ **Figure 7.5** An overview of the two stages of photosynthesis in a chloroplast

Try This Relate the summary equation for photosynthesis to this overview diagram.

reactions, because none of the steps requires light directly. However, in most plants, the Calvin cycle occurs during daylight, when the light reactions power the cycle's sugar assembly line by supplying it with NADPH and ATP.

The word *photosynthesis* encapsulates the two stages. *Photo*, from the Greek word for "light," refers to the light reactions; *synthesis*, meaning "putting together," refers to sugar construction by the Calvin cycle. In the next several modules, we look at these two stages in more detail. But first, let's consider some of the properties of light, the energy source that powers photosynthesis.

> **?** For chloroplasts to produce sugar from carbon dioxide in the dark, they would need to be supplied with _____ and _____.

ATP . . . NADPH

▷ The Light Reactions: Converting Solar Energy to Chemical Energy

7.6 Visible radiation absorbed by pigments drives the light reactions

What do we mean when we say that photosynthesis is powered by light energy from the sun?

The Nature of Sunlight   Sunlight is a type of energy called electromagnetic energy or radiation. Electromagnetic energy travels in space as rhythmic waves analogous to those made by a pebble dropped in a puddle of water. The distance between the crests of electromagnetic waves is called a **wavelength**. **Figure 7.6A** shows the **electromagnetic spectrum**, the full range of electromagnetic wavelengths from the very short gamma rays to the very long-wavelength radio waves. As you can see in the center of the figure, visible light—the radiation your eyes see as different colors—is only a small fraction of the spectrum. It consists of wavelengths from about 380 nm to about 750 nm.

The model of light as waves explains many of light's properties. However, light also behaves as discrete packets of energy called photons. A **photon** has a fixed quantity of energy, and the shorter the wavelength of light, the greater the energy of its photons. In fact, the photons of wavelengths that are shorter than those of visible light have enough energy to damage molecules such as proteins and nucleic acids. This is why ultraviolet (UV) radiation can cause sunburns and skin cancer.

Photosynthetic Pigments   **Figure 7.6B** shows what happens to visible light in the chloroplast. Light-absorbing molecules called pigments, built into the thylakoid membranes, absorb some wavelengths of light and reflect or transmit other wavelengths. We do not see the absorbed wavelengths; their energy has been absorbed by pigment molecules. What we see when we look at a leaf are the green wavelengths that are not absorbed but are transmitted and reflected by the pigments.

Different pigments absorb light of different wavelengths, and chloroplasts contain more than one type of pigment. Chlorophyll *a*, which participates directly in the light

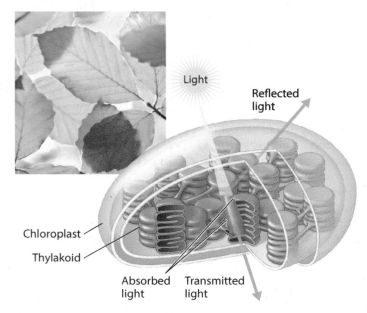

▲ **Figure 7.6B**   The interaction of light with chlorophyll in a chloroplast

Try This   Use this diagram to explain why leaves are green.

reactions, absorbs mainly blue-violet and red light. It looks blue-green because it reflects mainly green light. A very similar molecule, chlorophyll *b*, absorbs mainly blue and orange light and reflects (appears) olive green. Chlorophyll *b* broadens the range of light that a plant can use by conveying absorbed energy to chlorophyll *a*, which then puts the energy to work in the light reactions.

Chloroplasts also contain pigments called carotenoids, which are various shades of yellow and orange. The spectacular colors of fall foliage in certain parts of the world are due partly to the yellow-orange hues of longer-lasting carotenoids that show through once the green chlorophyll breaks down. Carotenoids may broaden the spectrum of colors that can drive photosynthesis. However, a more important function seems to be photoprotection: Some carotenoids absorb and dissipate excessive light energy that would otherwise damage chlorophyll or interact with oxygen to form reactive oxidative molecules that can damage cell molecules. Similar carotenoids, which we obtain from carrots and other vegetables and fruits, have a photoprotective role in our eyes.

Each type of pigment absorbs certain wavelengths of light because it is able to absorb the specific amounts of energy in those photons. Next we see what happens when a pigment molecule such as chlorophyll absorbs a photon of light.

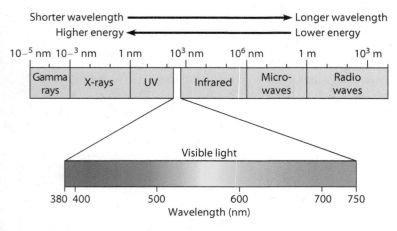

▲ **Figure 7.6A**   The electromagnetic spectrum and the wavelengths of visible light

 What color of light is least effective at driving photosynthesis? Explain.

● Green, because it is mostly transmitted and reflected—not absorbed—by photosynthetic pigments.

7.7 Photosystems capture solar energy

Energy cannot be created or destroyed, but it can be transferred or transformed (see Module 5.10). Let's examine how light energy can be transformed to other types of energy. When a pigment molecule absorbs a photon of light, one of the pigment's electrons jumps to an energy level farther from the nucleus. In this location, the electron has more potential energy, and we say that the electron has been raised from a ground state to an excited state. The excited state, like all high-energy states, is unstable. Generally, when isolated pigment molecules absorb light, their excited electrons drop back down to the ground state in a billionth of a second, releasing their excess energy as heat. This conversion of light energy to heat is what makes a black car so hot on a sunny day (black pigments absorb all wavelengths of light).

Some isolated pigments, including chlorophyll, emit light as well as heat after absorbing photons. We can demonstrate this phenomenon in the laboratory with a chlorophyll solution, as shown on the left in **Figure 7.7A**. When brightly illuminated, the chlorophyll emits photons of light that produce a reddish after-glow called fluorescence. The right side of Figure 7.7A illustrates what happens in fluorescence: An absorbed photon boosts an electron of chlorophyll to an excited state, from which it falls back to the ground state, emitting its energy as heat and light.

But chlorophyll behaves very differently in isolation than it does in an intact chloroplast. In their native habitat of the thylakoid membrane, chlorophyll and other pigments that absorb photons transfer the energy to other pigment molecules and eventually to a special pair of chlorophyll molecules. This pair passes off an excited electron to a neighboring molecule before it has a chance to drop back to the ground state.

In the thylakoid membrane, chlorophyll molecules are organized along with other pigments and proteins into clusters called photosystems (**Figure 7.7B**). A **photosystem** consists of a number of light-harvesting complexes surrounding a reaction-center

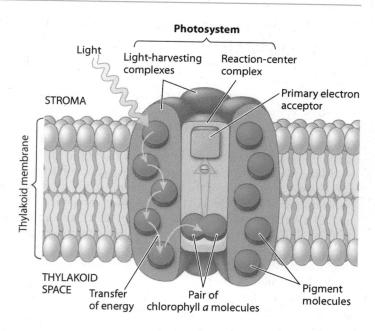

▲ **Figure 7.7B**   A light-excited pair of chlorophyll molecules in the reaction center of a photosystem passing an excited electron to a primary electron acceptor

complex. A light-harvesting complex contains various pigment molecules bound to proteins. Collectively, the light-harvesting complexes function as a light-gathering antenna. The pigments absorb photons and pass the energy from molecule to molecule, somewhat like a human "wave" at a sporting event, until it reaches the reaction center. The reaction-center complex contains a pair of special chlorophyll *a* molecules and a molecule called the primary electron acceptor, which is capable of accepting electrons and becoming reduced. The solar-powered transfer of an electron from the reaction-center chlorophyll *a* pair to the primary electron acceptor is the first step in the transformation of light energy to chemical energy in the light reactions.

Two types of photosystems have been identified, and they cooperate in the light reactions. They are referred to as photosystem I and photosystem II, in order of their discovery, although photosystem II actually functions first in the sequence of steps that make up the light reactions. Each photosystem has a characteristic reaction-center complex, with a special pair of chlorophyll *a* molecules associated with a particular primary electron acceptor. Now let's see how the two photosystems work together in the light reactions to generate ATP and NADPH.

?   **Compared with a solution of isolated chlorophyll, why do intact chloroplasts release less heat and fluorescence when illuminated?**

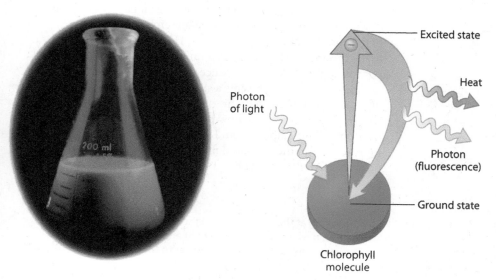

▲ **Figure 7.7A**   A solution of chlorophyll glowing red when illuminated (left); a diagram of an isolated, light-excited chlorophyll molecule that releases heat and a photon of red light when it falls back to ground state (right)

● In the chloroplasts, a light-excited electron from the reaction-center chlorophyll molecules is trapped by a primary electron acceptor rather than giving up its energy as heat and light.

7.8 Two photosystems connected by an electron transport chain generate ATP and NADPH

You have just seen how light energy can boost an electron of chlorophyll *a* in the reaction center of a photosystem to an excited state, from which it is captured by a primary electron acceptor. But how do these captured electrons lead to the production of ATP and NADPH? Part of the explanation is found in the arrangement of photosystems II and I in the thylakoid membrane and their connection via an electron transport chain. Another part of the explanation involves the flow of electrons removed from H_2O through these components to NADPH. And the final part of the explanation, the synthesis of ATP, is linked (as it is in cellular respiration) to an electron transport chain pumping H^+ into a membrane compartment, from which the ions flow through an ATP synthase embedded in the membrane.

To unpack this rather complicated system, let's start with the simple mechanical analogy illustrated in **Figure 7.8**. Starting on the left, you see that the large yellow photon mallet provides the energy to boost an electron from photosystem II to a higher energy level, where it is caught by the primary electron acceptor standing on the platform. The electron is loaded onto an electron transport chain "ramp" leading to photosystem I. (Recall that photosystem II precedes photosystem I in the light reactions.) As electrons roll down the ramp, they release energy that is used for the production of ATP. When an electron reaches photosystem I, another photon mallet pumps it up to a higher energy level, where it is caught by a primary electron acceptor on the photosystem I platform. From there, the photoexcited electrons are thrown into a bucket to produce NADPH. This construction analogy shows how the coupling of two photosystems and an electron transport chain can transform the energy of light to the chemical energy of ATP and NADPH.

The simple analogy in Figure 7.8 does leave a few important unanswered questions: What is the source of the electrons that are moving through the photosystems to NADPH? Don't the light reactions produce O_2—where does that happen? And how does the flow of electrons down that ramp produce ATP?

The electrons that end up reducing $NADP^+$ to NADPH originally come from water. An enzyme in the thylakoid space splits H_2O into 2 electrons, 2 hydrogen ions (H^+), and 1 oxygen atom ($\frac{1}{2} O_2$). The H^+ stay in the thylakoid space. The oxygen atom immediately joins with another oxygen to form O_2. As you learned in Module 7.3, water is the source of the O_2 produced in photosynthesis, and these oxygen molecules diffuse out of the thylakoids, the chloroplast, and the plant cell, finally exiting the leaf through its stomata. The all-important electrons from water are passed, one by one, to the reaction center chlorophyll *a* molecules in photosystem II, replacing the photoexcited electron that was just captured by the primary electron acceptor. From photosystem II, the electrons pass through an electron transport chain to the reaction center chlorophyll *a* molecules in photosystem I, again replacing photoexcited electrons that had been captured by its primary electron acceptor. Although the illustration shows these electrons being dropped in a bucket, they actually are passed through a short electron transport chain to $NADP^+$, reducing it to NADPH.

Now that we have accounted for NADPH and O_2, all that is left is ATP. Making ATP in the light reactions involves an electron transport chain and chemiosmosis—the same players and process you met in the synthesis of ATP in cellular respiration. Recall that in chemiosmosis, the potential energy of a concentration gradient of H^+ across a membrane powers ATP synthesis. This gradient is created when an electron transport chain uses the energy released as it passes electrons down the chain to pump H^+ across a membrane. The energy of the concentration gradient drives H^+ back across the membrane through ATP synthase, spinning this rotary motor and phosphorylating ADP to produce ATP (see Figure 6.10B).

The next module presents a slightly more realistic model of the light reactions than this mechanical analogy, which should help you visualize how photosystem II, the electron transport chain, photosystem I, and ATP synthase function together within the thylakoid membranes of a chloroplast to produce NADPH and ATP.

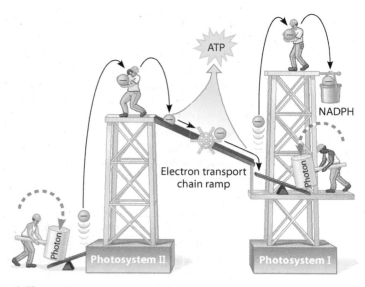

▲ **Figure 7.8** A mechanical analogy of the light reactions

> **?** Looking at the model of the light reactions in Figure 7.8, explain why two photons of light are required in the movement of electrons from water to NADPH.

● One photon excites an electron from photosystem II, which is then passed down an electron transfer chain to photosystem I. A second photon excites an electron from photosystem I, which is then used in the reduction of $NADP^+$ to NADPH.

7.9 The light reactions take place within the thylakoid membranes

The diagram below shows the relationship between chloroplast structure and function in the light reactions. Depicted here is a small portion of a thylakoid sac showing how the two photosystems and electron transport chain are embedded in a thylakoid membrane. All of the components shown here are present in numerous copies in each thylakoid. Moving from left to right, you can see how light energy absorbed by the

two photosystems drives the flow of electrons from water to NADPH. The electron transport chain helps to produce the concentration gradient of H^+ across the thylakoid membrane, which drives H^+ through ATP synthase, producing ATP. Because the initial energy input is light (*photo-*), this chemiosmotic production of ATP is called **photophosphorylation**.

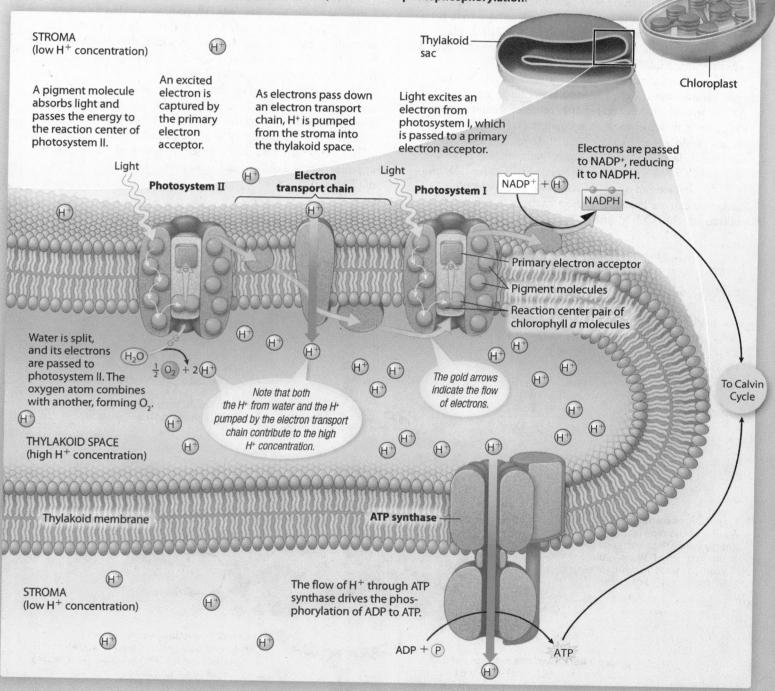

STROMA (low H^+ concentration)

Thylakoid sac

Chloroplast

A pigment molecule absorbs light and passes the energy to the reaction center of photosystem II.

An excited electron is captured by the primary electron acceptor.

As electrons pass down an electron transport chain, H^+ is pumped from the stroma into the thylakoid space.

Light excites an electron from photosystem I, which is passed to a primary electron acceptor.

Electrons are passed to $NADP^+$, reducing it to NADPH.

Light

Photosystem II

Electron transport chain

Light

Photosystem I

$NADP^+$ + NADPH

Primary electron acceptor

Pigment molecules

Reaction center pair of chlorophyll *a* molecules

Water is split, and its electrons are passed to photosystem II. The oxygen atom combines with another, forming O_2.

H_2O $\frac{1}{2} O_2$ + 2 H^+

Note that both the H^+ from water and the H^+ pumped by the electron transport chain contribute to the high H^+ concentration.

The gold arrows indicate the flow of electrons.

To Calvin Cycle

THYLAKOID SPACE (high H^+ concentration)

Thylakoid membrane

ATP synthase

STROMA (low H^+ concentration)

The flow of H^+ through ATP synthase drives the phosphorylation of ADP to ATP.

ADP + P

H^+

ATP

? What is the advantage of the light reactions producing NADPH and ATP on the stroma side of the thylakoid membrane?

● The Calvin cycle, which uses the NADPH and ATP, occurs in the stroma.

7.10 ATP and NADPH power sugar synthesis in the Calvin cycle

The Calvin cycle functions like a sugar factory within a chloroplast. The inputs to this all-important food-making process are CO$_2$ (from the air) and ATP and NADPH (both generated by the light reactions). ATP is used as an energy source and NADPH provides high-energy electrons for reducing CO$_2$ to sugar. The output of the Calvin cycle is an energy-rich, three-carbon sugar, glyceraldehyde 3-phosphate (G3P). A plant cell uses G3P to make glucose, the disaccharide sucrose, and other organic molecules as needed.

Figure 7.10 outlines the steps of the Calvin cycle. It is called a cycle because, like the citric acid cycle in cellular respiration, the starting material is regenerated after molecules enter and leave the cycle. In this case, the starting material is a five-carbon sugar named ribulose bisphosphate (RuBP). To make a molecule of G3P, the cycle must turn three times, incorporating three molecules of CO$_2$. We show the cycle starting with three CO$_2$ molecules so that we end up with a complete G3P molecule.

As you can see in step 1, carbon fixation, the enzyme rubisco attaches CO$_2$ to RuBP. (Recall that carbon fixation

refers to the initial incorporation of CO$_2$ into organic compounds.) This unstable six-carbon molecule splits into two three-carbon molecules. In step 2, reduction, ATP and NADPH are used to reduce the three-carbon molecule to G3P.

For this to be a cycle, RuBP must be regenerated. In step 3, release of one molecule of G3P, you can see that for every three CO$_2$ molecules fixed, one G3P molecule leaves the cycle as product. In step 4, regeneration of RuBP, the remaining five G3P molecules are rearranged, using energy from ATP, to regenerate three molecules of RuBP.

Note that for the net synthesis of one G3P molecule, the Calvin cycle consumes nine ATP and six NADPH molecules, which were provided by the light reactions. Neither the light reactions nor the Calvin cycle alone can make sugar from CO$_2$. Photosynthesis is an emergent property of the structural organization of a chloroplast, which integrates the two stages of photosynthesis.

> **?** To synthesize one glucose molecule, the Calvin cycle uses _____ CO$_2$, _____ ATP, and _____ NADPH. Explain why this high number of ATP and NADPH molecules is consistent with the value of glucose as an energy source.

● 6 ... 18 ... 12. Glucose is a highly reduced molecule, storing lots of potential energy in its electrons. The more energy a molecule stores, the more energy and reducing power required to produce that molecule.

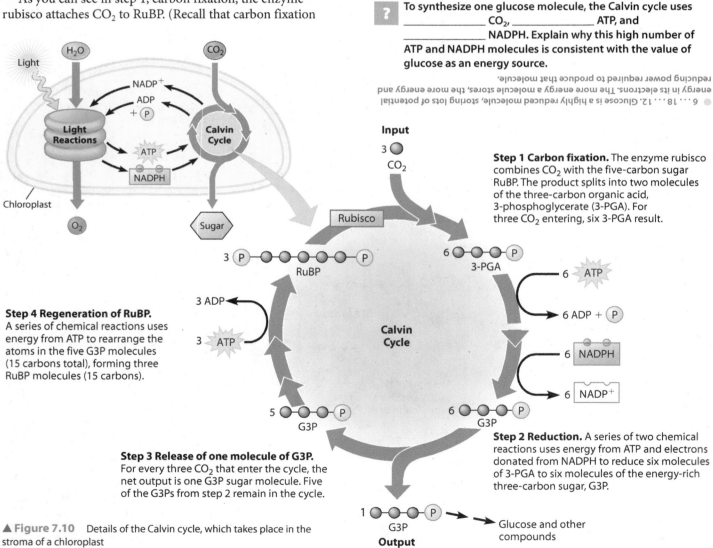

Step 1 Carbon fixation. The enzyme rubisco combines CO$_2$ with the five-carbon sugar RuBP. The product splits into two molecules of the three-carbon organic acid, 3-phosphoglycerate (3-PGA). For three CO$_2$ entering, six 3-PGA result.

Step 2 Reduction. A series of two chemical reactions uses energy from ATP and electrons donated from NADPH to reduce six molecules of 3-PGA to six molecules of the energy-rich three-carbon sugar, G3P.

Step 3 Release of one molecule of G3P. For every three CO$_2$ that enter the cycle, the net output is one G3P sugar molecule. Five of the G3Ps from step 2 remain in the cycle.

Step 4 Regeneration of RuBP. A series of chemical reactions uses energy from ATP to rearrange the atoms in the five G3P molecules (15 carbons total), forming three RuBP molecules (15 carbons).

▲ Figure 7.10 Details of the Calvin cycle, which takes place in the stroma of a chloroplast

7.11 Other methods of carbon fixation have evolved in hot, dry climates

EVOLUTION CONNECTION

As you learned in the previous module, the first step of the Calvin cycle is carbon fixation. Most plants use CO_2 directly from the air, and carbon fixation occurs when the enzyme rubisco adds CO_2 to RuBP (see step 1 of Figure 7.10). Such plants are called C_3 **plants** because the first product of carbon fixation is the three-carbon compound 3-PGA. C_3 plants are widely distributed; they include such important agricultural crops as soybeans, oats, wheat, and rice. One problem that farmers face in growing C_3 plants is that hot, dry weather can decrease crop yield. In response to such conditions, plants close their stomata, the pores in their leaves. This adaptation reduces water loss and helps prevent dehydration, but it also prevents CO_2 from entering the leaf and O_2 from exiting. As a result, CO_2 levels get very low in the leaf and photosynthesis slows. And the O_2 released from the light reactions begins to accumulate, creating another problem.

As O_2 builds up in a leaf, rubisco adds O_2 instead of CO_2 to RuBP. A two-carbon product of this reaction is then broken down in the cell. This process is called **photorespiration** because it occurs in the light and, like respiration, it consumes O_2 and releases CO_2. But unlike cellular respiration, it uses ATP instead of producing it; and unlike photosynthesis, it yields no sugar. Photorespiration can, however, drain away as much as 50% of the carbon fixed by the Calvin cycle.

According to one hypothesis, photorespiration is an evolutionary relic from when the atmosphere had less O_2 than it does today. In the ancient atmosphere that prevailed when rubisco first evolved, the inability of the enzyme's active site to exclude O_2 would have made little difference. It is only after O_2 became so concentrated in the atmosphere that the "sloppiness" of rubisco presented a problem. New evidence also indicates that photorespiration may play a protective role when the products of the light reactions build up in a cell (as occurs when the Calvin cycle slows due to a lack of CO_2).

C_4 Plants   In some plant species found in hot, dry climates, alternate modes of carbon fixation have evolved that minimize photorespiration and optimize the Calvin cycle. C_4 **plants** are so named because they first fix CO_2 into a four-carbon compound. When the weather is hot and dry, a C_4 plant keeps its stomata mostly closed, thus conserving water. It continues making sugars by photosynthesis using the pathway and the two types of cells shown on the left side of **Figure 7.11**. An enzyme in the mesophyll cells has a high affinity for CO_2 and can fix carbon even when the CO_2 concentration in the leaf is low. The resulting four-carbon compound then acts as a carbon shuttle; it moves into bundle-sheath cells, which are packed around the veins of the leaf, and releases CO_2. Thus, the CO_2 concentration in these cells remains high enough for the Calvin cycle to make sugars and avoid photorespiration. Corn and sugarcane are examples of agriculturally important C_4 plants.

CAM Plants   A second photosynthetic adaptation has evolved in pineapples, many cacti, and other succulent (water-storing)

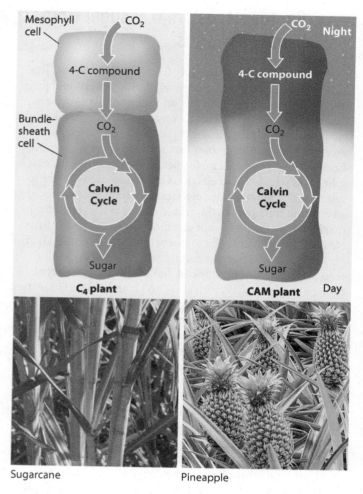

▲ **Figure 7.11**   Adaptations for photosynthesis in hot, dry climates

Try This   Use these diagrams to explain the differences between C_4 and CAM photosynthesis.

plants, such as aloe and jade plants. Called **CAM plants**, these species are adapted to very dry climates. A CAM plant (right side of Figure 7.11) conserves water by opening its stomata and admitting CO_2 only at night. CO_2 is fixed into a four-carbon compound, which banks CO_2 at night and releases it during the day. Thus, the Calvin cycle can operate, even with the leaf's stomata closed during the day.

In C_4 plants, carbon fixation and the Calvin cycle occur in different types of cells. In CAM plants, these processes occur in the same cells, but at different times of the day. Keep in mind that CAM, C_4, and C_3 plants all eventually use the Calvin cycle to make sugar from CO_2. The C_4 and CAM pathways are two evolutionary adaptations that minimize photorespiration and maximize photosynthesis in hot, dry climates.

?   **Why would you expect photorespiration on a hot, dry day to occur less in C_4 and CAM plants than in C_3 plants?**

● Because of their initial fixing of carbon, both C_4 and CAM plants can supply rubisco with CO_2. When a C_3 plant closes its stomata, CO_2 levels drop and O_2 rises, making it more likely that rubisco will add O_2 to RuBP.

7.12 Photosynthesis makes sugar from CO₂ and H₂O, providing food and O₂ for almost all living organisms

Now that we have made our way from photons to food, let's step back and review the process of photosynthesis and then discuss its importance. Starting on the left of the overview diagram shown in **Figure 7.12**, you see a summary of the light reactions, which occur in the thylakoid membranes. Two photosystems in the membranes capture solar energy, energizing electrons in chlorophyll molecules. Simultaneously, water is split, O₂ is released, and electrons are funneled to the photosystems. The photoexcited electrons are transferred through an electron transport chain, where energy is harvested to make ATP by the process of chemiosmosis, and finally to NADP⁺, reducing it to the high-energy compound NADPH.

The chloroplast's sugar factory is the Calvin cycle, the second stage of photosynthesis. In the stroma, the enzyme rubisco combines CO₂ with RuBP. ATP and NADPH are used to reduce 3-PGA to G3P. Sugar molecules made from G3P serve as a plant's own food supply.

About 50% of the carbohydrate made by photosynthesis is consumed as fuel for cellular respiration in the mitochondria of plant cells. Sugars also serve as starting material for making other organic molecules, such as a plant's proteins and lipids. Many glucose molecules are linked together to make cellulose, the main component of cell walls. Cellulose is the most abundant organic molecule in a plant—and probably on the surface of the planet. Most plants make much more food each day than they need. They store the excess in roots, tubers, seeds, and fruits.

Plants (and other photosynthesizers) not only feed themselves but also are the ultimate source of food for virtually all other organisms. Humans and other animals make none of their own food and are totally dependent on the organic matter made by photosynthesizers. Even the energy we acquire when we eat meat was originally captured by photosynthesis. The energy in a steak, for instance, came from sunlight that was originally converted to a chemical form in the grasses eaten by cattle.

The collective productivity of the tiny chloroplasts is truly amazing: Photosynthesis makes an estimated 150 billion metric tons of carbohydrate per year (about 165 billion tons). That's equivalent in mass to a stack of about 100 trillion copies of this textbook—10 stacks of books reaching from Earth to the sun!

The products of photosynthesis provide us with more than just food. For most of human history, burning plant material has been a major source of heat, light, and cooking fuel. The use of fossil fuels is a relatively recent development, and these sources of energy come from the remains of ancient organisms that removed CO₂ from the atmosphere by photosynthesis over the course of hundreds of millions of years. The burning of these ancient carbon stores is increasing the atmospheric level of CO₂, which has risen more than 40% since 1850, the start of the Industrial Revolution, changing the global climate and affecting current-day photosynthesizers. In the next module, we explore how scientists study the effects of rising CO₂ levels on plants.

> **?** Explain this statement: No process is more important to the welfare of life on Earth than photosynthesis.

● Photosynthesis is the ultimate source of the food for almost all organisms and the oxygen they need for cellular respiration.

▶ **Figure 7.12** A summary of photosynthesis

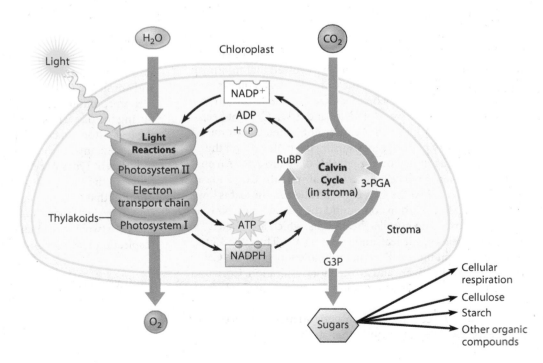

7.13 Rising atmospheric levels of carbon dioxide and global climate change will affect plants in various ways

How is the increase in atmospheric carbon dioxide affecting Earth's climate? First, let's consider the role of CO_2 as a so-called greenhouse gas. As you probably know, greenhouses are used to grow plants when the weather outside is too cold. Solar radiation can pass through their transparent walls, and much of the heat that accumulates inside is trapped.

An analogous process, called the **greenhouse effect**, operates on a global scale. Solar radiation passes through the atmosphere and warms Earth's surface. Heat radiating from the warmed planet is absorbed by greenhouse gases, such as CO_2, water vapor, and methane, which then reflect some of the heat back to Earth. Without this natural heating effect, the average air temperature would be a frigid $-18°C$ ($-0.4°F$), and most life as we know it could not exist. But this insulating blanket of greenhouse gases is starting to warm Earth *too* much.

Increasing concentrations of greenhouse gases have been linked to **global climate change**, of which one major aspect is global warming. The predicted consequences of global climate change include melting of polar ice, rising sea levels, extreme weather patterns, droughts, increased extinction rates, and the spread of tropical diseases. Indeed, many of these effects are already being documented.

How may global climate change affect plants? You might predict that, as a raw material for photosynthesis, increasing CO_2 levels would increase plant productivity. Indeed, research has documented such an increase, although results often indicate that the growth rates of weeds, such as the poison ivy described in the chapter introduction, increase more than those of crop plants and trees.

How do scientists study the effects of increasing CO_2 on plants? As is so often the case, scientists use different types of experiments to test their hypotheses. Many experiments are done in small growth chambers in which variables can be carefully controlled. But the availability of facilities and resources often limits such studies in scope and length. Some creative researchers have made use of study areas that naturally vary in CO_2 levels, such as comparing plant diversity and growth in experimental plots set in urban, suburban, and country locations.

Other scientists are turning to long-term field studies that include large-scale manipulations of CO_2 levels. In the Free-Air CO_2 Enrichment (FACE) experiment set up in Duke University's experimental forest, scientists monitored the effects of elevated CO_2 levels on an intact forest ecosystem over a period of 15 years. Six study sites were established, each 30 m in diameter and ringed by 16 towers (Figure 7.13A). In three of the plots, the towers released air containing CO_2 concentrations about 1½ times

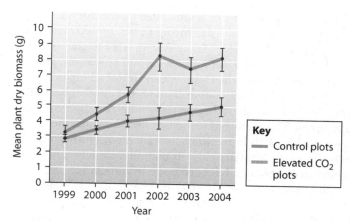

Source: Adaptation of Figure 1A from "Biomass and Toxicity Responses of Poison Ivy (*Toxicodendron Radicans*) to Elevated Atmospheric CO_2," by Jacqueline E. Mohan, et al., from *PNAS*, June 2006, Volume 103(24). Copyright © 2006 by National Academy of Sciences. Reprinted with permission.

▲ **Figure 7.13B** The mean poison ivy biomass in control plots and elevated CO_2 plots (with error bars showing the variation around the mean)

present-day levels. Monitoring instruments on a tall tower in the center of each plot adjusted the distribution of CO_2 to maintain a stable concentration. All other factors, such as temperature, precipitation, and wind patterns, varied normally for both experimental plots and adjacent control plots.

Figure 7.13B shows some results from a study that compared the growth of poison ivy in experimental and control plots. The poison ivy in the elevated CO_2 plots showed an average annual growth increase of 149% compared to control plots. This increase is much greater than the increase for woody plants that similar studies have documented. Indeed, over a 12-year monitoring period, the trees in the FACE experimental plots produced only about 15% more wood per year than those in the control plots.

Will global climate change make you itch?

There was one other significant finding of the poison ivy study. A chemical analysis showed that the high-CO_2 plants produced a more potent form of poison ivy's allergenic compound. Thus, poison ivy is predicted to become both more abundant and more toxic ("itchy") as CO_2 levels rise.

▲ **Figure 7.13A** Large-scale experiment in the Duke University Experimental Forest on the effects of elevated CO_2 concentration. (Rings of towers emit CO_2-enriched air in three of the plots.)

? **Describe three research methods that scientists use to test the hypothesis that increasing CO_2 levels will affect the growth of plants.**

● Laboratory growth chambers, field studies in areas where CO_2 levels vary naturally, and large-scale field studies in which CO_2 levels are manipulated

7.14 Scientific research and international treaties have helped slow the depletion of Earth's ozone layer

The importance of science is illustrated by the story of how synthetic chemicals were destroying Earth's protective ozone layer and how the work of many scientists led to changes in worldwide environmental policies. As you now know, photosynthesis produces the O_2 on which almost all organisms depend for cellular respiration. This O_2 has another benefit: High in the atmosphere, high-energy solar radiation converts it to ozone (O_3). Acting as sunscreen for the planet, the ozone layer shields Earth from ultraviolet radiation. The balance between ozone formation and its natural destruction in the atmosphere, however, has been upset by human actions.

Chlorofluorocarbons (CFCs) are chemicals developed in the 1930s that became widely used in aerosol sprays, refrigerators, and Styrofoam production. In 1970, a scientist wondered whether CFCs were accumulating in the environment and sent a homemade detector on a boat trip to Antarctica. He found CFCs in the air all along the journey. When he reported his findings at a scientific meeting in 1972, two chemists, Sherwood Rowland and Mario Molina, further wondered what happened to CFCs once they entered the atmosphere. A search of the literature found that these chemicals were not broken down in the lower atmosphere.

But the intense solar radiation in the upper atmosphere could break down CFCs, releasing chlorine atoms. Molina learned that chlorine reacts with ozone, reducing it to O_2. Other reactions liberate the chlorine, allowing it to destroy more ozone. In 1974, Molina and Rowland published their work predicting that the release of CFCs would damage the ozone layer.

As other researchers tested the CFC-ozone depletion hypothesis, the evidence accumulated, and more people became concerned about ozone depletion. Others worried about the economic impact of banning CFCs, and many chemical manufacturers mounted a campaign to cast doubt on the Molina-Rowland hypothesis in any way they could.

Then, in 1985, scientists from the British Antarctic Survey published their observations that the ozone level above Antarctica had decreased drastically. A reanalysis of data collected by the National Aeronautics and Space Administration (NASA) over that period confirmed a gigantic hole in the ozone layer. This hole has appeared every spring over Antarctica since the late 1970s and continues today. Figure 7.14A shows an image produced from atmospheric data from 2012. Dark blue colors show where there is the least ozone. The ozone depletion turned out to be much greater than had been predicted by Molina and Rowland. How could that be explained?

Susan Solomon (Figure 7.14B), with the National Oceanic and Atmospheric Administration (NOAA), developed a hypothesis that the unique ice clouds that develop during the cold winter in Antarctica could be involved in speeding up the reactions that destroy ozone. The then 30-year-old scientist led two research expeditions to the Antarctic. The data that she and her team collected indicated that chemical reactions occurring on the icy particles when the spring sun hits them made CFCs destroy ozone at an astonishing rate. Once the clouds warm and disperse, these reactions slow.

Further laboratory tests and field measurements taken from the ground, balloons, and airplanes supported Solomon's hypothesis. In response to these scientific findings, the first treaty to address Earth's environment was signed in 1987. In the original Montreal Protocol, more than two dozen nations agreed to phase out CFCs. As research continued to establish the extent and danger of ozone depletion, these agreements were strengthened in 1990, and now nearly 200 nations participate in the protocol. In 1995, Molina and Rowland shared a Nobel Prize for their work in determining how CFCs were damaging the atmosphere.

Global emissions of CFCs are near zero now, but because these compounds are so stable, recovery of the ozone layer is not expected until around 2060. Meanwhile, unblocked UV radiation is predicted to increase skin cancer and cataracts, as well as damage crops and phytoplankton in the oceans.

In addition to being ozone destroyers, CFCs are also potent greenhouse gases. The phaseout of CFCs has avoided what would have been the equivalent of adding 10 gigatons of CO_2 to the atmosphere. (For comparison, the Kyoto Protocol of 1997 set a 2012 target of a reduction of 2 gigatons of CO_2 emissions.)

Whether an environmental problem involves CFCs or CO_2, the scientific research is often complicated and the solutions complex. The connections between science, technology, and society, so clearly exemplified by the work of the scientists studying the ozone layer, are a major theme of this book.

▲ Figure 7.14B Susan Solomon at her cold research site

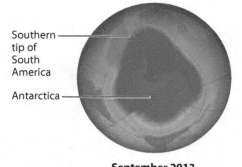

Southern tip of South America

Antarctica

September 2012

▲ Figure 7.14A The ozone hole in the Southern Hemisphere, fall 2012

? Where does the ozone layer come from, and why is it so important to life on Earth?

High in the atmosphere, radiation from the sun converts O_2 to ozone. The ozone layer absorbs potentially damaging UV radiation before it can reach Earth's surface.

CHAPTER **7** REVIEW

For practice quizzes, BioFlix animations, MP3 tutorials, video tutors, and more study tools designed for this textbook, go to

MasteringBiology®

Reviewing the Concepts

An Introduction to Photosynthesis (7.1–7.5)

7.1 Photosynthesis fuels the biosphere. Plants, algae, and some bacteria are photoautotrophs, the producers of food consumed by virtually all heterotrophic organisms.

7.2 Photosynthesis occurs in chloroplasts in plant cells. Chloroplasts are surrounded by a double membrane and contain stacks of thylakoids and a thick fluid called stroma.

7.3 Scientists traced the process of photosynthesis using isotopes. Experiments using both heavy and radioactive isotopes helped determine the details of the process of photosynthesis.

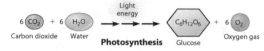

$$6\ CO_2 + 6\ H_2O \xrightarrow[\textbf{Photosynthesis}]{\text{Light energy}} C_6H_{12}O_6 + 6\ O_2$$

Carbon dioxide · Water · · Glucose · Oxygen gas

7.4 Photosynthesis is a redox process, as is cellular respiration. In photosynthesis, H_2O is oxidized and CO_2 is reduced.

7.5 The two stages of photosynthesis are linked by ATP and NADPH. The light reactions occur in the thylakoids, producing ATP and NADPH for the Calvin cycle, which takes place in the stroma.

The Light Reactions: Converting Solar Energy to Chemical Energy (7.6–7.9)

7.6 Visible radiation absorbed by pigments drives the light reactions. Certain wavelengths of visible light are absorbed by chlorophyll and other pigments. Carotenoids also function in photoprotection from excessive light.

7.7 Photosystems capture solar energy. Thylakoid membranes contain photosystems, each consisting of light-harvesting complexes and a reaction-center complex. A primary electron acceptor receives photoexcited electrons from chlorophyll.

7.8 Two photosystems connected by an electron transport chain generate ATP and NADPH. Electrons shuttle from photosystem II to photosystem I, providing energy to make ATP, and then reduce $NADP^+$ to NADPH. Photosystem II regains electrons as water is split and O_2 released.

7.9 The light reactions take place within the thylakoid membranes. In photophosphorylation, the electron transport chain pumps H^+ into the thylakoid space. The concentration gradient drives H^+ back through ATP synthase, powering the synthesis of ATP.

The Calvin Cycle: Reducing CO_2 to Sugar (7.10–7.11)

7.10 ATP and NADPH power sugar synthesis in the Calvin cycle. The steps of the Calvin cycle include carbon fixation, reduction, release of G3P, and regeneration of RuBP. Using carbon from CO_2, electrons from NADPH, and energy from ATP, the cycle constructs G3P, which is used to build glucose and other organic molecules.

7.11 Other methods of carbon fixation have evolved in hot, dry climates. In C_3 plants, a drop in CO_2 and rise in O_2 when stomata close divert the Calvin cycle to photorespiration. C_4 plants and CAM plants first fix CO_2 into four-carbon compounds that provide CO_2 to the Calvin cycle even when stomata close on hot, dry days.

The Global Significance of Photosynthesis (7.12–7.14)

7.12 Photosynthesis makes sugar from CO_2 and H_2O, providing food and O_2 for almost all living organisms.

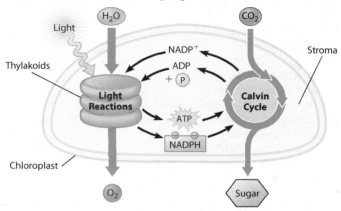

7.13 Rising atmospheric levels of carbon dioxide and global climate change will affect plants in various ways. Scientists study the effects of rising CO_2 levels using laboratory growth chambers and field studies. Long-term field projects enable scientists to assess the effects of CO_2 levels on natural ecosystems.

7.14 Scientific research and international treaties have helped slow the depletion of Earth's ozone layer. Solar radiation converts O_2 high in the atmosphere to ozone (O_3), which shields organisms from damaging UV radiation. Industrial chemicals called CFCs caused dangerous thinning of the ozone layer, but international restrictions on CFC use are allowing its recovery.

Connecting the Concepts

1. Complete this summary map of photosynthesis.

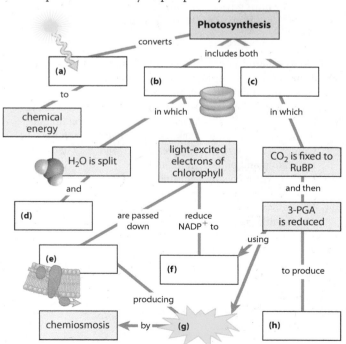

Testing Your Knowledge

Level 1: Knowledge/Comprehension

2. In photosynthesis, _____ is oxidized and _____ is reduced.
   a. water . . . oxygen
   b. carbon dioxide . . . water
   c. water . . . carbon dioxide
   d. glucose . . . carbon dioxide

3. Which of the following are produced by reactions that take place in the thylakoids and consumed by reactions in the stroma?
   a. CO_2 and H_2O
   b. ATP and NADPH
   c. ATP, NADPH, and CO_2
   d. ATP, NADPH, and O_2

4. When light strikes chlorophyll molecules in the reaction-center complex, they lose electrons, which are ultimately replaced by
   a. splitting water.
   b. oxidizing NADPH.
   c. the primary electron acceptor.
   d. the electron transport chain.

5. The reactions of the Calvin cycle are not directly dependent on light, but they usually do not occur at night. Why? (*Explain your answer.*)
   a. It is often too cold at night for these reactions to take place.
   b. Carbon dioxide concentrations decrease at night.
   c. The Calvin cycle depends on products of the light reactions.
   d. Plants usually close their stomata at night.

6. Which of the following does *not* occur during the Calvin cycle?
   a. carbon fixation
   b. oxidation of NADPH
   c. consumption of ATP
   d. release of oxygen

7. Why is it difficult for C_3 plants to carry out photosynthesis in very hot, dry environments such as deserts?
   a. The light is too intense and destroys the pigment molecules.
   b. The closing of stomata keeps CO_2 from entering and O_2 from leaving the plant.
   c. They must rely on photorespiration to make ATP.
   d. CO_2 builds up in the leaves, blocking carbon fixation.

Level 2: Application/Analysis

8. How is photosynthesis similar in C_4 plants and CAM plants?
   a. In both cases, the light reactions and the Calvin cycle are separated in both time and location.
   b. Both types of plants make sugar without the Calvin cycle.
   c. In both cases, rubisco is not used to fix carbon initially.
   d. Both types of plants make most of their sugar in the dark.

9. Compare and describe the roles of CO_2 and H_2O in cellular respiration and photosynthesis.

10. Explain why a poison that inhibits an enzyme of the Calvin cycle will also inhibit the light reactions.

11. What do plants do with the sugar they produce in photosynthesis?

Level 3: Synthesis/Evaluation

12. The following diagram compares the chemiosmotic synthesis of ATP in mitochondria and chloroplasts. Identify the components that are shared by both organelles and indicate which side of the membrane has the higher H^+ concentration. Then label on the right the locations within the chloroplast.

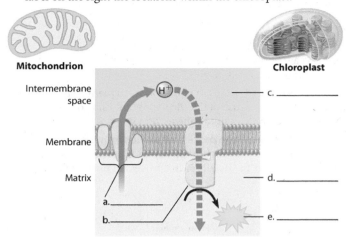

13. Continue your comparison of electron transport and chemiosmosis in mitochondria and chloroplasts. In each case,
    a. where do the electrons come from?
    b. how do the electrons get their high potential energy?
    c. what picks up the electrons at the end of the chain?
    d. how is the energy given up by the electrons used?

14. **SCIENTIFIC THINKING** Will global climate change make you sneeze as well as itch? Scientists studying the effects of rising CO_2 levels have looked at ragweed, whose pollen is the primary allergen for fall hay fever. They grew ragweed in three levels of CO_2: a pre-industrial concentration of 280 ppm, a year 2000 level of 370 ppm, and a projected level of 600 ppm. They found that pollen production increased by 131% and 320% in the plants exposed to the recent and projected CO_2 levels, respectively. What was the hypothesis of this experiment? Do the results support the hypothesis? Given what you know about global climate change, what other variables would you like to test, and what other measurements would you like to take?

15. Most experts agree that global climate change is already occurring and that global warming will increase rapidly in this century. Recent international negotiations, however, including a 2012 meeting in Doha, Qatar, have yet to reach a global consensus on how to reduce greenhouse gas emissions. Some countries have resisted taking action because a very few scientists and policymakers think that the warming trend may be just a random fluctuation and/or not related to human activities or that cutting CO_2 emissions would sacrifice economic growth. Do you think we need more evidence before taking action? Or is it better to act now to reduce CO_2 emissions? What are the possible costs and benefits of each of these two strategies?

Answers to all questions can be found in Appendix 4.

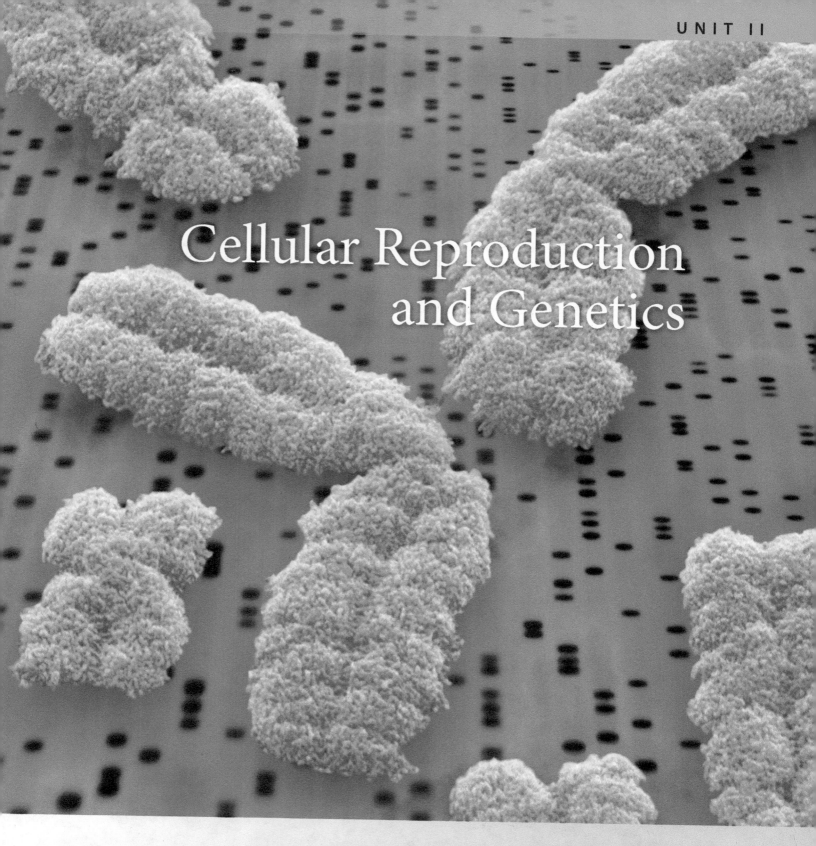

Cellular Reproduction and Genetics

The Cellular Basis of Reproduction and Inheritance

The photo below shows a cancer cell dividing. Cancer cells start as normal body cells, but genetic mutations cause them to lose the ability to regulate the tempo of their own division. Like a car careening downhill without brakes, unconstrained body cells will likely wreak havoc. If left untreated, cancer cells will continue to divide and spread, invading other tissues, disrupting organ function, and eventually killing the host.

How can cancer be stopped? Most cancer treatments seek to disrupt one or more steps in cell division. Some anticancer drugs target dividing DNA; others disrupt the cellular structures that assist in cell division. Recent advances in cancer therapy have sought to match particular patients with specific therapies. For example, about two-thirds of human breast tumors contain cells that bear receptors for the sex hormone estrogen, which enhances breast cell division, thereby accelerating the growth of the tumor. Patients with such tumors may be treated with tamoxifen, a drug that specifically blocks estrogen receptors. Women who lack estrogen receptors on their tumor cells (about one-third of breast cancer patients)

? Can cancer therapy be personalized?

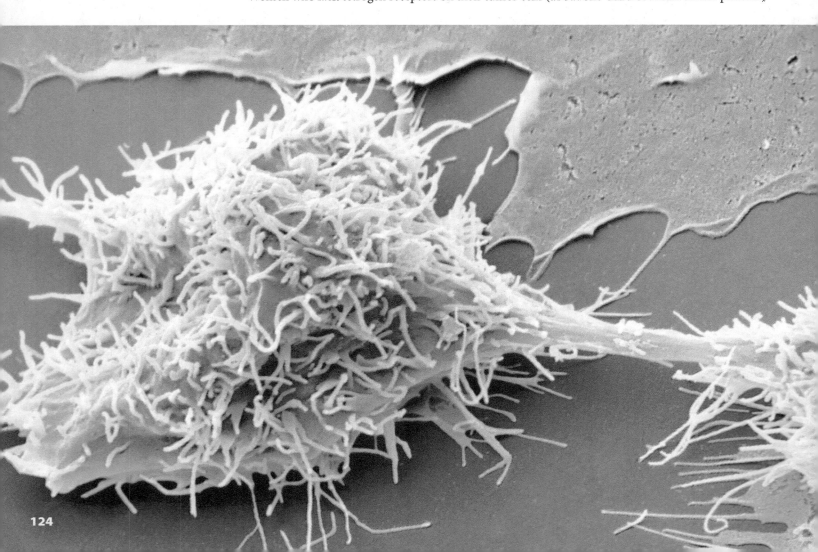

will not respond to this therapy. As more is learned about the underlying biology of cancer cells, cancer therapy will become even more personalized, with the most reliable drugs chosen for each patient.

Although uncontrolled cell division in cancer cells is harmful, normal cell division is necessary in all forms of life. Some organisms, such as single-celled prokaryotes, reproduce themselves via cell division, creating two genetically identical offspring. In the bodies of all multicellular organisms, cell division allows for growth, replacement of damaged cells, and development of an embryo into an adult. In sexually reproducing organisms, eggs and sperm are produced by a particular type of cell division. In this chapter, we discuss the two main types of cell division—mitosis and meiosis—and explore how they function within organisms.

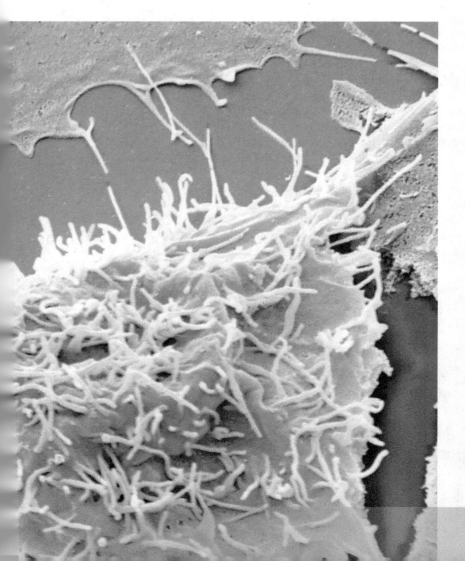

BIG IDEAS

Cell Division and Reproduction
(8.1–8.2)

Cell division underlies many of life's important processes.

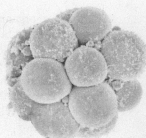

The Eukaryotic Cell Cycle and Mitosis
(8.3–8.10)

Cells produce genetic duplicates through an ordered, tightly controlled series of steps.

Meiosis and Crossing Over
(8.11–8.17)

The process of meiosis produces genetically varied haploid gametes from diploid cells.

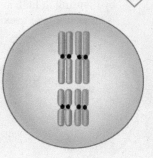

Alterations of Chromosome Number and Structure
(8.18–8.23)

Errors in cell division can produce organisms with abnormal numbers of chromosomes.

▷ Cell Division and Reproduction

8.1 Cell division plays many important roles in the lives of organisms

The ability of organisms to reproduce their own kind is the characteristic that best distinguishes living things from non-living matter (see Module 1.1 to review the characteristics of life). Only amoebas produce more amoebas, only people make more people, and only maple trees produce more maple trees. However, reproduction actually occurs much more often at the cellular level. When a cell undergoes reproduction, or **cell division**, the two "daughter" cells that result are genetically identical to each other and to the original "parent" cell. (Biologists traditionally use the word *daughter* in this context; it does not imply gender.) Before the parent cell splits into two, it duplicates its **chromosomes**, the structures that contain most of the cell's DNA. Then, during the division process, one set of chromosomes is distributed to each daughter cell. As a rule, the daughter cells receive identical sets of chromosomes from the lone, original parent cell. Each offspring cell will thus be genetically identical to the other and to the original parent cell.

Sometimes, cell division results in the reproduction of a whole organism. Many single-celled organisms, such as pro-karyotes or the eukaryotic yeast cell in **Figure 8.1A**, reproduce by dividing in half, and the offspring are genetic replicas. This is an example of **asexual reproduction**, the creation of ge-netically identical offspring by a single parent, without the participation of sperm and egg. Many multicel-lular organisms can reproduce asexually as well. For example, some sea star species have the ability to grow new individ-uals from fragmented pieces (**Figure 8.1B**). And if you've ever grown a houseplant from a clip-ping, you've observed asex-ual reproduction

▲ **Figure 8.1B**   A sea star reproducing asexually via fragmentation and regeneration of the body from the fragmented arm

Colorized TEM 5,000×

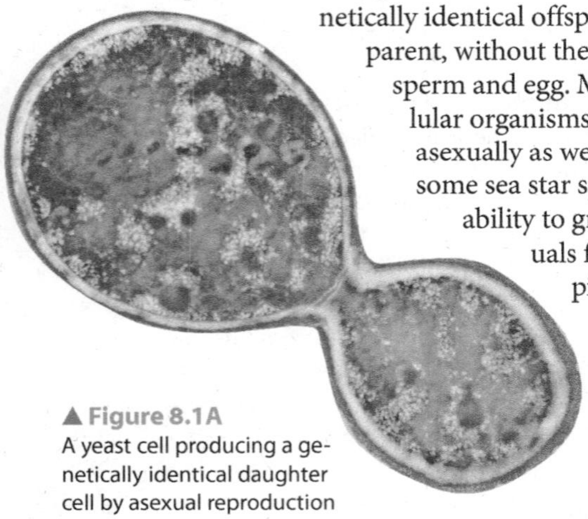

▲ **Figure 8.1A**
A yeast cell producing a ge-netically identical daughter cell by asexual reproduction

in plants (**Figure 8.1C**). In asexual reproduc-tion, there is one simple principle of inheritance: The lone parent and each of its offspring have identical genes.

Sexual reproduction is different; it requires fertilization of an egg by a sperm. The production of gametes—egg and sperm— involves a particular type of cell division that occurs only in reproductive organs (testes and ovaries in humans). A gamete has only half as many chromosomes as the parent cell that gave rise to it (see Module 8.13), and these chromosomes contain unique combinations of genes. Therefore, offspring produced by sexual reproduction gener-ally resemble their parents more closely than they resemble unrelated in-dividuals of the same species, but they are not identical to their parents or (with the ex-ception of identical twins) to each other (**Figure 8.1D**). Each offspring inherits a unique combination of genes from its two parents, and this one-and-only set of genes programs a unique combination of traits. As a result, sexual reproduction can produce great variation among offspring.

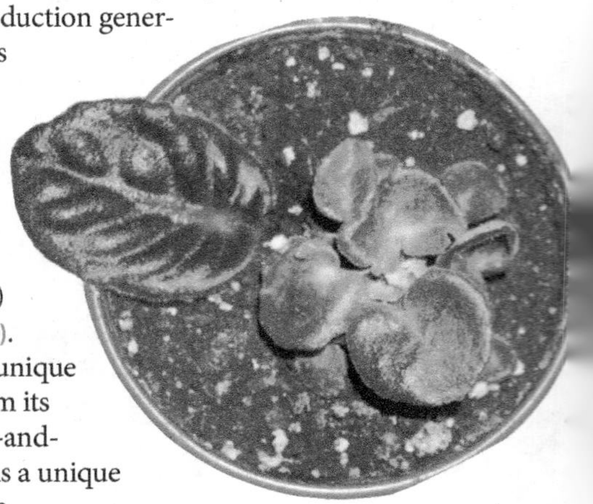

▲ **Figure 8.1C**   An African violet re-producing asexually from a cutting (the large leaf on the left)

▼ **Figure 8.1D** Sexual reproduc-tion produces offspring with unique combinations of genes

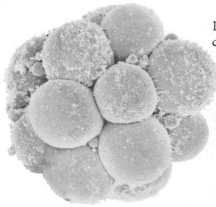

▲ Figure 8.1E Dividing cells in an early human embryo

In multicellular organisms, cell division plays other important roles, in addition to the production of gametes. Cell division enables sexually reproducing organisms to develop from a single cell—the fertilized egg, or zygote (Figure 8.1E)—into an adult organism. All of the trillions of cells in your body arose via repeated cell divisions that began in your mother's body with a single fertilized egg cell. After an organism is fully grown, cell division continues to function in renewal and repair, replacing cells that die from normal wear and tear or from accidents. Within your body, millions of cells must divide every second to replace damaged or lost cells (Figure 8.1F). For example, dividing cells within your epidermis continuously replace dead cells that slough off the surface of your skin.

The type of cell division responsible for the growth and maintenance of multicellular organisms and for asexual reproduction involves a process called mitosis. The production of egg and sperm cells involves a different type of cell division called meiosis. In the remainder of this chapter, you will learn the details of both mitosis and meiosis. To start, we'll look briefly at prokaryotic cell division.

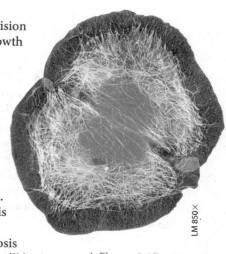

▲ Figure 8.1F A human kidney cell dividing

? **What function does cell division play in an amoeba (a single-celled protist)? What functions does it play in your body?**

● Reproduction; development, growth, and repair

8.2 Prokaryotes reproduce by binary fission

Prokaryotes (single-celled bacteria and archaea) reproduce by a type of cell division called **binary fission**, a term that means "dividing in half." In typical prokaryotes, the majority of genes are carried on a single circular DNA molecule that, with associated proteins, constitutes the organism's

chromosome. Although prokaryotic chromosomes are much smaller than those of eukaryotes, duplicating them in an orderly fashion and distributing the copies equally to two daughter cells are still formidable tasks. Consider, for example, that when stretched out, the chromosome of the bacterium *Escherichia coli* (*E. coli*) is about 500 times longer than the cell itself. It is no small achievement to accurately replicate this molecule when it is coiled and packed inside the cell.

Figure 8.2A illustrates binary fission in a prokaryote. ❶ As the chromosome is duplicating, the copies move toward the opposite ends of the cell. ❷ Meanwhile, the cell elongates. ❸ When chromosome duplication is complete and the cell has reached about twice its initial size, the plasma membrane grows inward and more cell wall is made, which eventually divides the parent cell into two daughter cells (Figure 8.2B).

? **Why is binary fission classified as asexual reproduction?**

● Because the genetically identical offspring inherit their DNA from a single parent

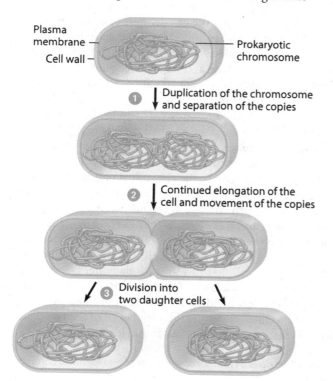

▲ Figure 8.2A Binary fission of a prokaryotic cell

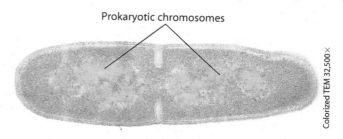

▲ Figure 8.2B An electron micrograph of a bacterium in a late stage of dividing

8.3 The large, complex chromosomes of eukaryotes duplicate with each cell division

Eukaryotic cells, in general, are more complex and much larger than prokaryotic cells. In addition, eukaryotic cells usually have many more genes, the units of information that specify an organism's inherited traits. Human cells, for example, carry just under 21,000 genes, versus about 3,000 for a typical bacterium. Almost all the genes in the cells of humans, and in all other eukaryotes, are found in the cell nucleus, grouped into multiple chromosomes. (The exceptions include genes on the small DNA molecules within mitochondria and, in plants, within chloroplasts.) Each eukaryotic species has a characteristic number of chromosomes in each cell nucleus. For example, human body cells have 46 chromosomes, while the body cells of a dog have 78 and those of a hedgehog have 90.

Each eukaryotic chromosome consists of one long DNA molecule—bearing hundreds or thousands of genes—and a number of protein molecules, which are attached to the DNA. The proteins help maintain the chromosome's structure and control the activity of its genes. Together, the entire complex—consisting of roughly equal amounts of DNA and protein—is called **chromatin**.

Most of the time, chromatin exists as a diffuse mass of long, thin fibers that, if stretched out, would be far too long to fit in a cell's nucleus. In fact, the total length of DNA in just one of your cells exceeds your height! Chromatin in this state is too thin to be seen using a light microscope.

As a cell prepares to divide, its chromatin coils up, forming tight, distinct chromosomes that are visible under a light microscope. Why is it necessary for a cell's chromosomes to be compacted in this way? Imagine an analogy from your own life: Your belongings are spread throughout your home, but as you prepare to move, you gather them up and pack them into small containers to make them more easily sorted and transported. Similarly, before a cell can undergo division, it must compact all its DNA into manageable packages. Figure 8.3A is a micrograph of a plant cell that is about to divide; each thick

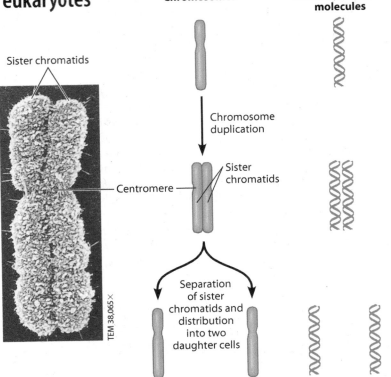

Figure 8.3B   Chromosome duplication and distribution

purple thread is actually an individual chromosome consisting of a single DNA molecule tightly wrapped around proteins.

The chromosomes of a eukaryotic cell are duplicated before they condense and the cell divides. The DNA molecule of each chromosome is replicated (as you'll learn in Chapter 10), and new protein molecules attach as needed to maintain the chromosome's structure and regulate its genes. Each chromosome now consists of two copies called **sister chromatids**, joined copies of the original chromosome (Figure 8.3B). The two sister chromatids are attached together along their lengths by proteins and are cinched especially tightly at a region called the **centromere** (visible as a narrow "waist" near the center of each chromosome shown in the figure).

When the cell divides, the sister chromatids of a duplicated chromosome separate from each other. Once separated from its sister, each chromatid is considered an individual chromosome, and it is identical to the cell's original chromosome. During cell division, one of the newly separated chromosomes goes to one daughter cell, and the other goes to the other daughter cell. In this way, each daughter cell receives a complete and identical set of chromosomes. In humans, for example, a typical dividing cell has 46 duplicated chromosomes (and thus 92 chromatids), and each of the two daughter cells that results from it has 46 single chromosomes.

▶ **Figure 8.3A**
A plant cell (from an African blood lily (*Scadoxus multiflorus*) just before cell division

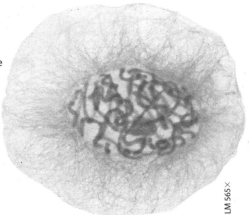

LM 565×

? **When does a chromosome consist of two identical chromatids?**

● When the cell is preparing to divide and has duplicated its chromosomes but before the duplicates actually separate

8.4 The cell cycle includes growing and division phases

How do chromosome duplication and cell division fit into the life of a cell—and the life of an organism? As discussed in Module 8.1, all life depends on cell division: Cell division is the basis of reproduction for every organism; it enables a multicellular organism to grow to adult size; and it replaces worn-out or damaged cells, keeping the total number of cells in an adult animal relatively constant. In your body, for example, millions of cells must divide every second to maintain the total number of about 10 trillion cells. Some cells divide once a day, others less often; and highly specialized cells, such as mature muscle cells, do not divide at all. The fact that some mature cells never divide explains why some kinds of damage—such as the death of cardiac muscle during a heart attack or the death of brain cells during a stroke—can never be reversed.

The process of cell division is a key component of the **cell cycle**, an ordered sequence of events that extends from the instant a cell is first formed from a dividing parent cell until its own division into two cells. The cell cycle consists of two main stages: a growing stage (called interphase), during which the cell approximately doubles everything in its cytoplasm and precisely replicates its chromosomal DNA, and the actual cell division (called the mitotic phase).

As **Figure 8.4** indicates, most of the cell cycle is spent in **interphase**. This is an interval when a cell's metabolic activity is very high and the cell performs its normal functions. For example, a cell in your small intestine might release digestive enzymes and absorb nutrients. Your intestinal cell also grows in size during interphase, making more cytoplasm, increasing its supply of digestive proteins, and creating more cytoplasmic organelles (such as mitochondria and ribosomes). In addition, the cell duplicates its chromosomes during this period. Typically, interphase lasts for at least 90% of the total time required for the cell cycle.

Interphase (illustrated in the beige portion of the figure) can be divided into three subphases: the G_1 phase ("first gap"), the S phase ("synthesis" of DNA—also known as DNA replication), and the G_2 phase ("second gap"). During all three subphases, the cell grows. The chromosomes are duplicated during the S phase: At the beginning of the S phase, each chromosome is single. At the end of this subphase, after DNA replication, the chromosomes are doubled, each consisting of two sister chromatids joined along their lengths. During the G_2 phase, the cell grows more as it completes preparations for cell division.

The **mitotic phase** (**M phase**; illustrated in the blue portion of the figure), the interval of the cell cycle when the cell physically divides, accounts for only about 10% of the total time required for the cell cycle. The mitotic phase is divided into two overlapping stages, called mitosis and cytokinesis. In **mitosis**, the nucleus and its contents—most important, the duplicated chromosomes—divide and are evenly distributed, forming two daughter nuclei. During **cytokinesis**, which usually begins before mitosis ends, the cytoplasm is divided in

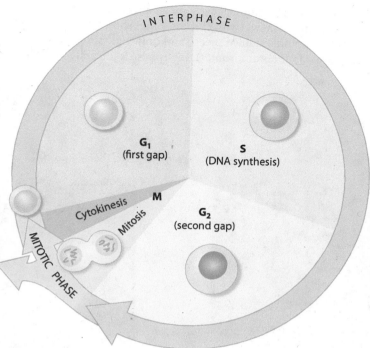

▲ **Figure 8.4**   The eukaryotic cell cycle

two. The combination of mitosis and cytokinesis produces two genetically identical daughter cells, each with a single nucleus, surrounding cytoplasm stocked with organelles, and a plasma membrane. Each newly produced daughter cell may then proceed through G_1 and repeat the cycle.

Mitosis is unique to eukaryotes and is the evolutionary solution to the problem of allocating an identical copy of the whole set of chromosomes to two daughter cells. Mitosis is a remarkably accurate mechanism. Experiments with yeast, for example, indicate that an error in chromosome distribution occurs only once in about 100,000 cell divisions.

The extreme accuracy of mitosis is essential to the development of your own body. You began as a single cell. Mitotic cell division ensures that all your body cells receive copies of the 46 chromosomes that were found in this original cell. Thus, every one of the trillions of cells in your body today can trace its ancestry back through mitotic divisions to that first cell produced when your father's sperm and mother's egg fused about nine months before your birth.

During the mitotic phase, a living cell viewed through a light microscope undergoes dramatic changes in the appearance of the chromosomes and other structures. In the next module, we'll use these visible changes as a guide to the stages of mitosis.

?   A researcher treats cells with a chemical that prevents DNA synthesis from starting. This treatment would trap the cells in which part of the cell cycle?

8.5 Cell division is a continuum of dynamic changes

Figure 8.5 illustrates the cell cycle for an animal cell using micrographs from a newt (with chromosomes shown in blue and the mitotic spindle stained green) and drawings (simplified to include just four chromosomes). Interphase is illustrated here, but the emphasis is on the dramatic changes that occur during cell division, the mitotic phase. Mitosis is a continuum, but biologists can distinguish five main stages: **prophase**, **prometaphase**, **metaphase**, **anaphase**, and **telophase**.

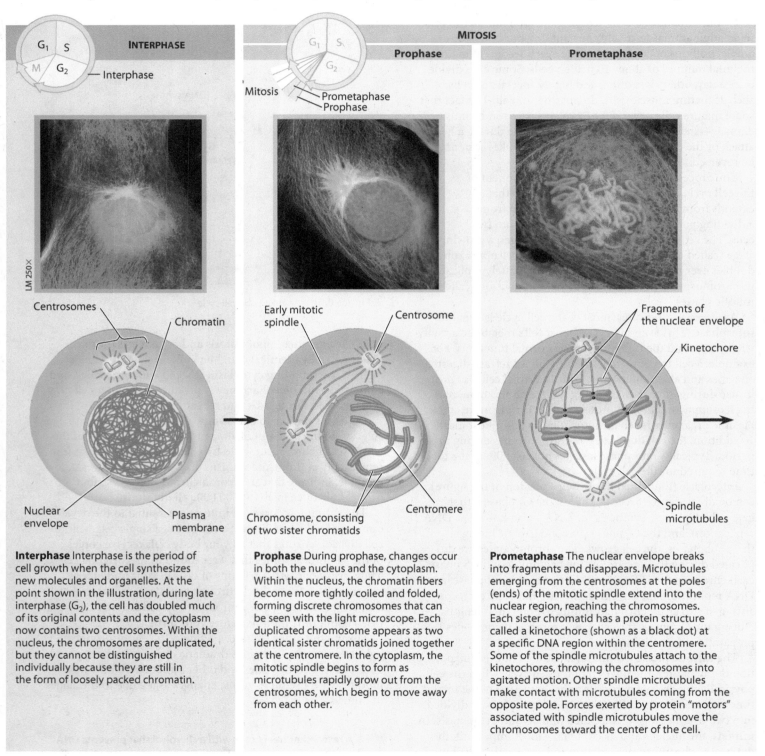

Interphase Interphase is the period of cell growth when the cell synthesizes new molecules and organelles. At the point shown in the illustration, during late interphase (G_2), the cell has doubled much of its original contents and the cytoplasm now contains two centrosomes. Within the nucleus, the chromosomes are duplicated, but they cannot be distinguished individually because they are still in the form of loosely packed chromatin.

Prophase During prophase, changes occur in both the nucleus and the cytoplasm. Within the nucleus, the chromatin fibers become more tightly coiled and folded, forming discrete chromosomes that can be seen with the light microscope. Each duplicated chromosome appears as two identical sister chromatids joined together at the centromere. In the cytoplasm, the mitotic spindle begins to form as microtubules rapidly grow out from the centrosomes, which begin to move away from each other.

Prometaphase The nuclear envelope breaks into fragments and disappears. Microtubules emerging from the centrosomes at the poles (ends) of the mitotic spindle extend into the nuclear region, reaching the chromosomes. Each sister chromatid has a protein structure called a kinetochore (shown as a black dot) at a specific DNA region within the centromere. Some of the spindle microtubules attach to the kinetochores, throwing the chromosomes into agitated motion. Other spindle microtubules make contact with microtubules coming from the opposite pole. Forces exerted by protein "motors" associated with spindle microtubules move the chromosomes toward the center of the cell.

▲ **Figure 8.5** The stages of cell division by mitosis

Try This Using simple drawings, illustrate the stages of mitosis for a cell that has six chromosomes.

The chromosomes are the stars of the mitotic drama. Their movements depend on the **mitotic spindle**, a football-shaped structure of microtubules and associated proteins that guides the separation of the two sets of daughter chromosomes. The spindle microtubules emerge from two **centrosomes**, microtubule-organizing regions in the cytoplasm of eukaryotic cells.

? You view an animal cell through a microscope and observe dense, duplicated chromosomes scattered throughout the cell. Which state of mitosis are you witnessing?

Prophase (because the chromosomes are condensed but not yet aligned)

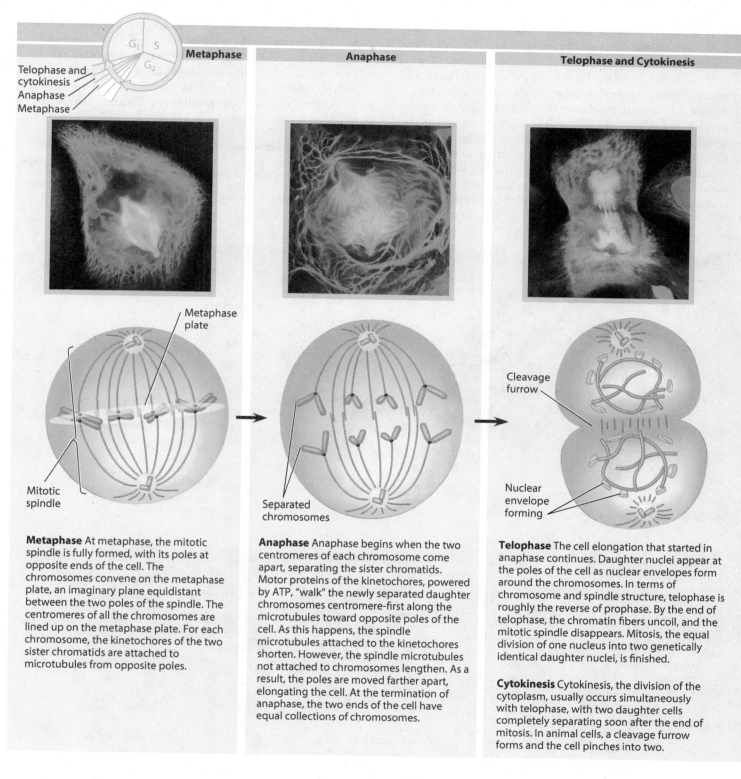

Metaphase At metaphase, the mitotic spindle is fully formed, with its poles at opposite ends of the cell. The chromosomes convene on the metaphase plate, an imaginary plane equidistant between the two poles of the spindle. The centromeres of all the chromosomes are lined up on the metaphase plate. For each chromosome, the kinetochores of the two sister chromatids are attached to microtubules from opposite poles.

Anaphase Anaphase begins when the two centromeres of each chromosome come apart, separating the sister chromatids. Motor proteins of the kinetochores, powered by ATP, "walk" the newly separated daughter chromosomes centromere-first along the microtubules toward opposite poles of the cell. As this happens, the spindle microtubules attached to the kinetochores shorten. However, the spindle microtubules not attached to chromosomes lengthen. As a result, the poles are moved farther apart, elongating the cell. At the termination of anaphase, the two ends of the cell have equal collections of chromosomes.

Telophase The cell elongation that started in anaphase continues. Daughter nuclei appear at the poles of the cell as nuclear envelopes form around the chromosomes. In terms of chromosome and spindle structure, telophase is roughly the reverse of prophase. By the end of telophase, the chromatin fibers uncoil, and the mitotic spindle disappears. Mitosis, the equal division of one nucleus into two genetically identical daughter nuclei, is finished.

Cytokinesis Cytokinesis, the division of the cytoplasm, usually occurs simultaneously with telophase, with two daughter cells completely separating soon after the end of mitosis. In animal cells, a cleavage furrow forms and the cell pinches into two.

8.6 Cytokinesis differs for plant and animal cells

As discussed in the previous module, cytokinesis typically overlaps with telophase. Given the differences between animal and plant cells—particularly the stiff cell wall in plant cells—it isn't surprising that cytokinesis proceeds differently for these two types of eukaryotic cells.

In animal cells, cytokinesis occurs by cleavage. As shown in Figure 8.6A, the first sign of cleavage in animal cells is the appearance of a **cleavage furrow**, a shallow groove in the cell surface. At the site of the furrow, the cytoplasm has a ring of microfilaments made of actin, associated with molecules of myosin. (Actin and myosin are the same proteins responsible for muscle contraction.) When the actin microfilaments interact with the myosin, the ring contracts. Contraction of the myosin ring is much like pulling a drawstring on a hooded sweatshirt: As the drawstring is pulled, the ring of the hood contracts inward, eventually pinching shut. Similarly, the cleavage furrow deepens and eventually pinches the parent cell in two, resulting in two completely separate daughter cells, each with its own nucleus and share of cytoplasm.

Cytokinesis is markedly different in plant cells, which possess stiff cell walls (Figure 8.6B). During telophase, membranous vesicles containing cell wall material collect at the middle of the parent cell. The vesicles fuse, forming a membranous disk called the **cell plate**. The cell plate grows outward, accumulating more cell wall materials as more vesicles fuse with it. Eventually, the membrane of the cell plate fuses with the plasma membrane, and the cell plate's contents join the parental cell wall. The result is two daughter cells, each bounded by its own plasma membrane and cell wall.

? **Contrast cytokinesis in animals with cytokinesis in plants.**

In animals, cytokinesis involves a cleavage furrow in which contracting microfilaments pinch the cell in two. In plants, it involves formation of a cell plate, a fusion of vesicles that forms new plasma membranes and new cell walls between the cells.

Cytokinesis

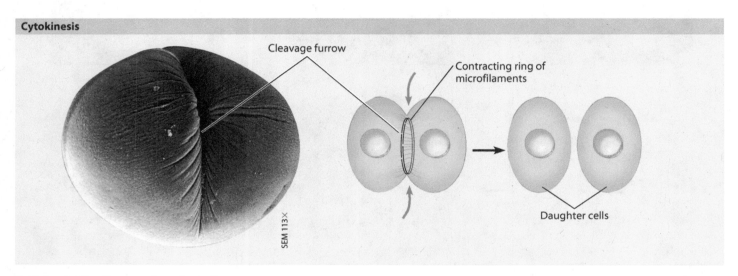

Cleavage furrow

Contracting ring of microfilaments

SEM 113×

Daughter cells

▲ Figure 8.6A   Cleavage of an animal cell

Cytokinesis

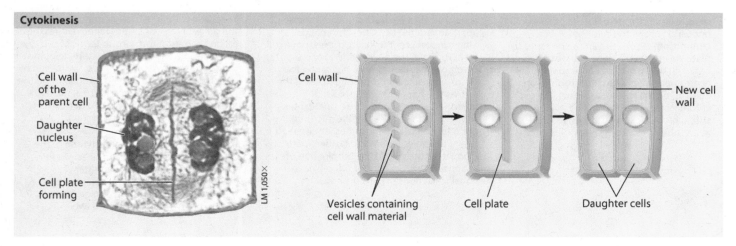

Cell wall of the parent cell

Daughter nucleus

Cell plate forming

LM 1,050×

Cell wall

Vesicles containing cell wall material

Cell plate

Daughter cells

New cell wall

▲ Figure 8.6B   Cell plate formation in a plant cell

8.7 Anchorage, cell density, and chemical growth factors affect cell division

For a plant or an animal to grow, develop normally, and maintain its tissues once fully grown, it must be able to control the timing of cell division in different parts of its body. For example, in your body, skin cells and the cells lining your digestive tract divide frequently, replacing cells that are constantly being abraded and sloughed off. In contrast, cells in your liver usually do not divide unless the liver is damaged.

By growing animal cells in culture, researchers have been able to identify many factors, both chemical and physical, that influence cell division. For example, most animal cells exhibit **anchorage dependence**; they must be in contact with a solid surface—such as the inside of a culture dish or the extracellular matrix of a tissue—to divide. One of the characteristics that distinguishes cancerous cells from normal body cells is their failure to exhibit anchorage dependence; they grow whether or not they are in contact with a suitable surface.

Another physical factor that can regulate growth rate is **density-dependent inhibition**, a phenomenon in which crowded cells stop dividing (Figure 8.7A). Animal cells growing on the surface of a dish multiply to form a single layer and usually stop dividing when they touch one another. If some cells are removed, those bordering the open space begin dividing again and continue until the vacancy is filled. What actually causes the inhibition of growth? Studies of cultured cells suggest that physical contact of cell-surface proteins between adjacent cells is responsible for inhibiting cell division. As with anchorage dependence, density-dependent inhibition fails in tumors; cancer cells continue to divide even at high densities, piling up on one another (bottom of Figure 8.7A).

Chemical factors can also influence the rate of cell growth. For example, when grown in the laboratory, cells fail to divide if an essential nutrient is left out of the culture medium. And most types of mammalian cells divide in culture only if certain specific growth factors are included. A **growth factor** is a protein secreted by certain body cells that stimulates other cells to divide (Figure 8.7B). Researchers have discovered at least 50 different growth factors that can trigger cell division. Different cell types respond specifically to certain growth factors or a combination of growth factors. For example, injury to the skin causes blood platelets to release a protein called platelet-derived growth factor. This protein promotes the rapid growth of connective tissue cells that help seal the wound. Another well-studied example is a protein called vascular endothelial growth factor (VEGF), which stimulates the growth of new blood vessels during fetal development and after injury. Interestingly, VEGF overproduction is a hallmark of many dangerous cancers; several anticancer drug therapies work by inhibiting the action of VEGF.

How do growth factors work? We will explore this question in the next module.

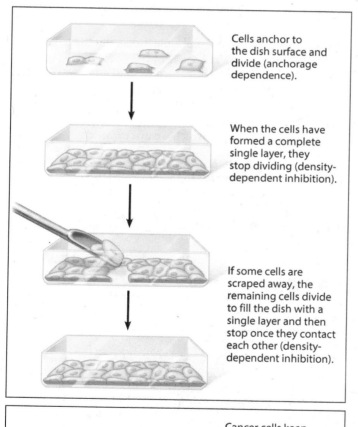

Cells anchor to the dish surface and divide (anchorage dependence).

When the cells have formed a complete single layer, they stop dividing (density-dependent inhibition).

If some cells are scraped away, the remaining cells divide to fill the dish with a single layer and then stop once they contact each other (density-dependent inhibition).

Cancer cells keep dividing even when they have filled a layer, forming a clump of overlapping cells.

▲ **Figure 8.7A** An experiment demonstrating density-dependent inhibition, using animal cells grown in culture

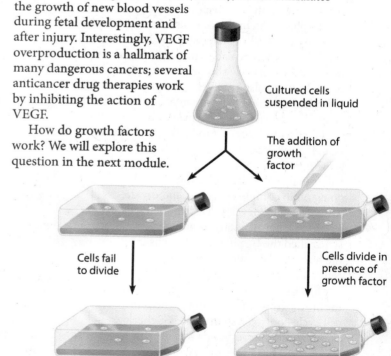

Cultured cells suspended in liquid

The addition of growth factor

Cells fail to divide

Cells divide in presence of growth factor

▲ **Figure 8.7B** An experiment demonstrating the effect of growth factors on the division of cultured animal cells

? Compared to a control culture, the cells in an experimental culture are fewer but much larger in size when they cover the dish surface and stop growing. What is a reasonable hypothesis for this difference?

● The experimental culture is deficient in one or more growth factors.

8.8 Growth factors signal the cell cycle control system

In a living animal, most cells are anchored in a fixed position and bathed in a solution of nutrients supplied by the blood, yet they usually do not divide unless they are signaled by other cells to do so. Growth factors are the main signals, and their role in promoting cell division leads us back to our earlier discussion of the cell cycle.

The sequential events of the cell cycle, represented by the circle in Figure 8.8A, are directed by a distinct cell cycle control system, represented by the gray circle in the center of the art. The thin gray bar extending from the circle represents the current position in the cell cycle. The **cell cycle control system** is a cyclically operating set of molecules in the cell that both triggers and coordinates key events in the cell cycle. The cell cycle is *not* like a row of falling dominoes, with each event causing the next one in line. Within the M phase, for example, metaphase does not automatically lead to anaphase. Instead, proteins of the cell cycle control system must trigger the separation of sister chromatids that marks the start of anaphase.

A checkpoint in the cell cycle is a critical control point where stop and go-ahead signals (represented by stop/go lights in the figure) can regulate the cycle. The default action in most animal cells is to halt the cell cycle at these checkpoints unless overridden by specific go-ahead signals.

The red and white gates in Figure 8.8A represent major checkpoints in the cell cycle: during the G_1 and G_2 subphases of interphase and in the M phase. Intracellular signals detected by the control system tell the system whether key cellular processes up to each point have been completed and whether the cell cycle should proceed past that point. The control system also receives messages from outside the cell, indicating general environmental conditions and the presence of specific signal molecules from other cells. For many cells, the G_1 checkpoint seems to be the most important in cell division. If a cell receives a go-ahead signal—for example, from a growth factor—at the G_1 checkpoint, it will usually enter the S phase, eventually going on to complete its cycle and divide. If such a signal never arrives, the cell will switch to a permanently nondividing state called the G_0 phase. Many cells in the human body, such as mature nerve cells and muscle cells, are in the G_0 phase.

Figure 8.8B shows a simplified model for how a growth factor might affect the cell cycle control system at the G_1 checkpoint. A cell that responds to a growth factor (▽) has molecules of a specific receptor protein in its plasma membrane. Binding of the growth factor to the receptor (◗) triggers a signal transduction pathway in the cell. A signal transduction pathway is a series of protein molecules that conveys a message (see Modules 5.1 and 11.10). In this case, that message leads to cell division. The "signals" are

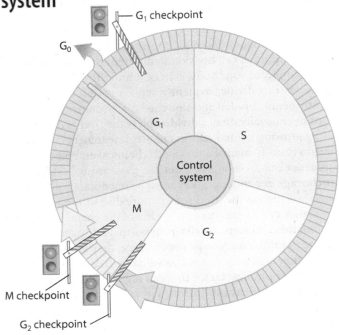

▲ Figure 8.8A   A schematic model for the cell cycle control system

changes that each protein molecule induces in the next molecule in the pathway. Via a series of relay proteins, a signal finally reaches the cell cycle control system and overrides the brakes that otherwise prevent progress of the cell cycle.

Research on the control of the cell cycle is one of the hottest areas in biology today. This research is leading to a better understanding of cancer, which we discuss next.

> **?** **At which of the three checkpoints described in this module do the chromosomes exist as duplicated sister chromatids?**
>
> ● G_2 and M checkpoints

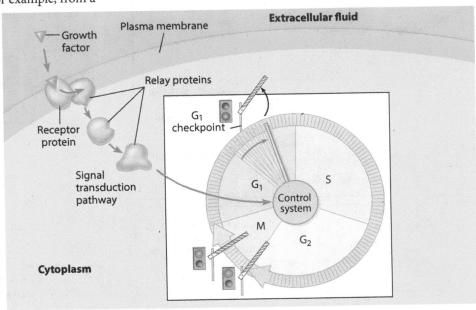

▲ Figure 8.8B   How a growth factor signals the cell cycle control system

8.9 Growing out of control, cancer cells produce malignant tumors

CONNECTION

Cancer, which claims the lives of one out of every five people in the United States, is a disease of the cell cycle. Cancer cells do not heed the normal signals that regulate the cell cycle; they divide excessively and invade other tissues of the body. If unchecked, cancer cells may continue to grow and spread until they kill the organism.

The abnormal behavior of cancer cells begins when a single cell undergoes transformation, a process that converts a normal cell to a cancer cell. Transformation occurs following a mutation in one or more genes that encode for proteins in the cell cycle control system. Because a transformed cell grows abnormally, the immune system usually recognizes it as such and destroys it. However, if the cell evades destruction, it may multiply to form a **tumor**, a mass of abnormally growing cells within otherwise normal tissue. If the abnormal cells remain at their original site, the lump is called a **benign tumor**. Benign tumors can cause problems if they grow in and disrupt certain organs, such as the brain, but often they can be completely removed by surgery or even (in cases in which they pose no imminent threat) left alone.

In contrast, a **malignant tumor** can spread into neighboring tissues and invade other parts of the body, displacing normal tissue and interrupting organ function as it grows (Figure 8.9). An individual with a malignant tumor is said to have **cancer**. Cancer cells may separate from the original tumor or secrete signal molecules that cause blood vessels to grow toward the tumor. A few tumor cells may then enter the blood and lymph vessels and move to other parts of the body, where they may proliferate and form new tumors. The spread of cancer cells beyond their original site is called **metastasis**.

Cancers are named according to the organ or tissue in which they originate. Liver cancer, for example, starts in liver tissue and may or may not spread from there. Carcinomas are cancers that originate in the external or internal coverings of the body, such as the skin or the lining of the intestine. Leukemia is a broad term covering a number of diseases that originate in immature white blood cells within the blood or bone marrow.

From studying cancer cells in culture, researchers have learned that cancer cells do not heed the normal signals that regulate the cell cycle. For example, many cancer cells have defective cell cycle control systems that proceed past checkpoints even in the absence of growth factors. Other cancer cells synthesize growth factors themselves, causing the cells to divide continuously. If cancer cells do stop dividing, they seem to do so at random points in the cell cycle, rather than at the normal cell cycle checkpoints. Moreover, in the

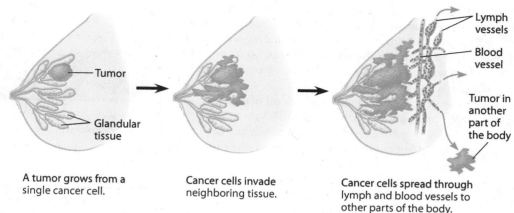

A tumor grows from a single cancer cell.

Cancer cells invade neighboring tissue.

Cancer cells spread through lymph and blood vessels to other parts of the body.

▲ **Figure 8.9** Growth and metastasis of a malignant tumor of the breast

laboratory, cancer cells are "immortal"; they can go on dividing indefinitely, as long as they have a supply of nutrients (whereas normal mammalian cells divide only about 20 to 50 times before they stop). A striking example of the immortality of cancer cells is a line that has been continuously multiplying in culture since 1951. Cells of this line are called HeLa cells, named for the original donor, Henrietta Lacks, who died of cervical cancer more than 60 years ago.

Luckily, many tumors can be successfully treated. A tumor that appears to be localized may be removed surgically. Alternatively, it can be treated with concentrated beams of high-energy radiation, which usually damages DNA in cancer cells more than it does in normal cells, perhaps because cancer cells have lost the ability to repair such damage. However, radiation also damages normal body cells, producing harmful side effects. For example, radiation damage to cells of the ovaries or testes can lead to sterility.

Chemotherapy is used to treat widespread or metastatic tumors. During periodic chemotherapy treatments, drugs are administered that disrupt specific steps in the cell cycle. For instance, the drug paclitaxel (trade name Taxol) freezes the mitotic spindle after it forms, which stops actively dividing cells from proceeding past metaphase. Vinblastin, a chemotherapeutic drug first obtained from the periwinkle plant, prevents the mitotic spindle from forming.

The side effects of chemotherapy are due to the drugs' effects on normal cells that rapidly divide. Nausea results from chemotherapy's effects on intestinal cells; hair loss comes from effects on hair follicle cells; and susceptibility to infection results from effects on immune cell production. (We will return to the topic of cancer—specifically, how mutations in genes that control cell division can lead to cancer—in Chapter 11.)

In the next module, you'll learn how understanding such mutations may aid in cancer treatment.

? What is metastasis?

● Metastasis is the spread of cancer cells from their original site of formation to other sites in the body.

8.10 Tailoring treatment to each patient may improve cancer therapy

SCIENTIFIC THINKING

Although several forms of cancer treatment are available, oncologists (doctors who treat cancer) have observed that different patients respond in drastically different ways to the same treatment. Medicines that are ineffective for most patients may have profound effects in a few, and vice versa.

Recently, researchers have amassed a flood of data about specific DNA mutations that disable the cell cycle control system and thereby promote the development of cancer. In addition, the time and cost required to sequence genes from a given individual have decreased dramatically. Thus, with increased understanding of DNA mutations and better access to gene sequencing, it is increasingly possible for physicians to personalize cancer treatment. The goal in moving toward personalized treatment is to identify and administer drugs that have the best chance of success in combating a given tumor's specific genetic profile.

Can cancer therapy be personalized?

A study that examined personalized cancer treatment was conducted at Memorial Sloan-Kettering Cancer Center in New York in 2012. Researchers sequenced the complete genome of tumor cells taken from a patient with metastasized bladder cancer. This patient, unlike most individuals with this type of cancer, responded well to a drug called everolimus. The researchers hoped that a genetic profile could provide insight into this unexpected result. Their next step was to identify 140 distinct mutations within the protein-coding genes of this patient's tumor cells. One of these mutations—in a gene called *TSC1*—affects a pathway that is targeted by the drug. The researchers hypothesized that mutations in this gene might be predictive of the drug's effect in cancer patients; those with the mutation would fare well when taking everolimus, whereas those who lack the mutation would not.

Because their hypothesis was based on a single case—and researchers are careful never to draw broad conclusions from

TABLE 8.10	NUMBERS OF CANCER PATIENTS RESPONDING TO THE DRUG EVEROLIMUS ($N = 13$)	
	Patients Responding to Everolimus	**Patients *Not* Responding to Everolimus**
Patients who had *TSC1* mutation	3	1
Patients who *did not* have *TSC1* mutation	1	8

Source: Data from G. Iyer et al., Genome sequencing identifies a basis for everolimus sensitivity, *Science* 338: 221 (2012).

just one case—the Sloan-Kettering researchers expanded their study by analyzing the *TSC1* gene in tumors from 13 additional bladder cancer patients. Their results (Table 8.10) suggest that the drug may indeed be most effective in patients who harbor mutations in the *TSC1* gene: three out of four patients with the mutation responded to the drug, whereas only one out of nine patients without the mutation responded.

Critics caution that the *TSC1* mutation is sufficiently rare that enough data to draw reliable conclusions may never be obtained. The nature of the evidence—scant and difficult to generalize—is typical of personalized cancer therapy trials. But small advances are continuously being made that may lead to improved treatment for a variety of cancer patients.

? Think critically about the data presented in Table 8.10: Which data in Table 8.10 do not support the hypothesis that everolimus works *only* in patients who harbor a *TSC1* mutation?

● One patient without the mutation responded to the drug, and one patient with the mutation did not respond to the drug.

▷ Meiosis and Crossing Over

8.11 Chromosomes are matched in homologous pairs

In humans, a typical body cell, called a **somatic cell**, has 46 chromosomes. When chromosomes from a cell in metaphase (when the chromosomes are most condensed) are viewed with a microscope, they can be arranged into matching pairs; Figure 8.11 illustrates one pair of metaphase chromosomes consisting of two joined sister chromatids. A human cell at metaphase contains 23 sets of duplicated chromosomes. Other species have different numbers of chromosomes, but these, too, usually occur in matched pairs. Moreover, when treated with special dyes, the chromosomes of a pair display matching staining patterns (represented by colored stripes in Figure 8.11).

Almost every chromosome has a twin that resembles it in length, centromere position, and staining (coloration)

pattern. The two chromosomes of such a matching pair are **homologous chromosomes** (or homologs) because each chromosome carries genes controlling the same inherited characteristics. For example, if a gene for freckles is located at a particular place, or **locus** (plural, *loci*), on one chromosome—within the

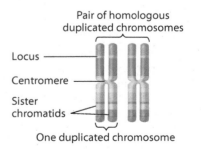

▲ Figure 8.11   A pair of homologous chromosomes

Try This   Cover the figure, then draw a pair of homologous chromosomes and label sister chromatids, the centromere, and one chromosome.

narrow orange band in our drawing—then the homologous chromosome has that same gene at that same locus. However, the two chromosomes of a homologous pair may have different versions of the same gene.

The two distinct chromosomes referred to as X and Y are an important exception to the general pattern of homologous chromosomes in human somatic cells. Human females have a homologous pair of X chromosomes (XX), but males have one X and one Y chromosome (XY). Only small parts of the

X and Y are homologous. Most of the genes carried on the X chromosome do not appear on the tiny Y, and the Y chromosome has genes not present on the X. Because they determine an individual's sex, the X and Y chromosomes are called **sex chromosomes**. Chromosomes other than sex chromosomes are called **autosomes**.

> **?** Are all of *your* chromosomes fully homologous?
>
> ● If you are female, yes. If you are male, no.

8.12 Gametes have a single set of chromosomes

The development of a fertilized egg into a new adult organism is one phase of a multicellular organism's **life cycle**, the sequence of stages leading from the adults of one generation to the adults of the next (Figure 8.12A). Having two sets of chromosomes, one inherited from each parent, is a key factor in the life cycle of all species that reproduce sexually.

Most animals and plants are said to be **diploid** organisms because all somatic cells contain pairs of homologous chromosomes. The total number of chromosomes is called the diploid number (abbreviated $2n$). For humans, the diploid number is 46; that is, $2n = 46$. The exceptions are the egg and sperm cells, collectively known as **gametes**. Each gamete has a single set of chromosomes: 22 autosomes plus a sex chromosome, either X or Y. A cell with a

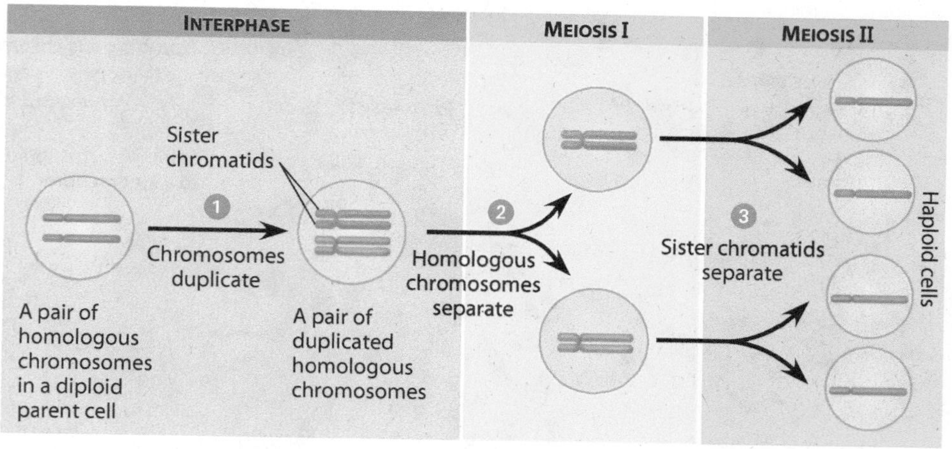

▲ **Figure 8.12B** How meiosis halves chromosome number through two sequential divisions

single chromosome set is called a **haploid** cell; it has only one member of each homologous pair. For humans, the haploid number (abbreviated n) is 23; that is, $n = 23$.

The human life cycle begins when a haploid sperm cell from the father fuses with a haploid egg cell from the mother in the process of **fertilization**. The resulting fertilized egg, called a **zygote**, has one set of homologous chromosomes from each parent, and so is diploid. As a human develops into an adult, mitosis of the zygote and its descendants generates all the somatic cells.

The only cells of the human body not produced by mitosis are the gametes. Gametes are made by a different form of cell division called meiosis, which occurs only in reproductive organs. Whereas mitosis produces daughter cells with the same number of chromosomes as the parent cell, meiosis reduces the chromosome number by half. Figure 8.12B tracks one pair of homologous chromosomes through the two divisions of meiosis. ❶ Each of the chromosomes is duplicated during interphase (before meiosis). ❷ The first division, meiosis I, segregates the two chromosomes of the homologous pair, packaging them in separate (haploid) daughter cells. But each chromosome is still doubled. ❸ Meiosis II separates the sister chromatids. Each of the four daughter cells is haploid and contains only a single chromosome from the homologous pair.

Next, we'll take a closer look at the process of meiosis.

> **?** How many autosomes are found in a human sperm cell? How many and which sex chromosomes?
>
> ● 22 autosomes plus either an X or Y sex chromosome

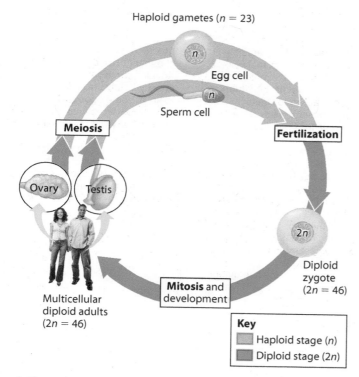

▲ **Figure 8.12A** The human life cycle

Key
- ▢ Haploid stage (*n*)
- ▮ Diploid stage (2*n*)

8.13 Meiosis reduces the chromosome number from diploid to haploid

Meiosis is a type of cell division that produces haploid gametes in diploid organisms. Two haploid gametes may then combine via fertilization to restore the diploid state in the zygote. Fertilization and meiosis alternate in sexual life cycles, which serves to maintain a constant number of chromosomes in each species from one generation to the next.

Many of the stages of meiosis closely resemble corresponding stages in mitosis. Meiosis, like mitosis, is preceded by the duplication of chromosomes. However, this single duplication is followed by not one but two consecutive cell divisions,

called meiosis I and meiosis II. Because one duplication of the chromosomes is followed by two divisions, the result is four daughter cells, each with half as many chromosomes as the parent cell. The illustrations in **Figure 8.13** show the two meiotic divisions for an animal cell with a diploid number of 6. The members of a pair of homologous chromosomes in Figure 8.13 (and later figures) are colored red and blue to help distinguish them. (Imagine that the red chromosomes were inherited from the mother and the blue chromosomes from the father.) One of the most important events in meiosis

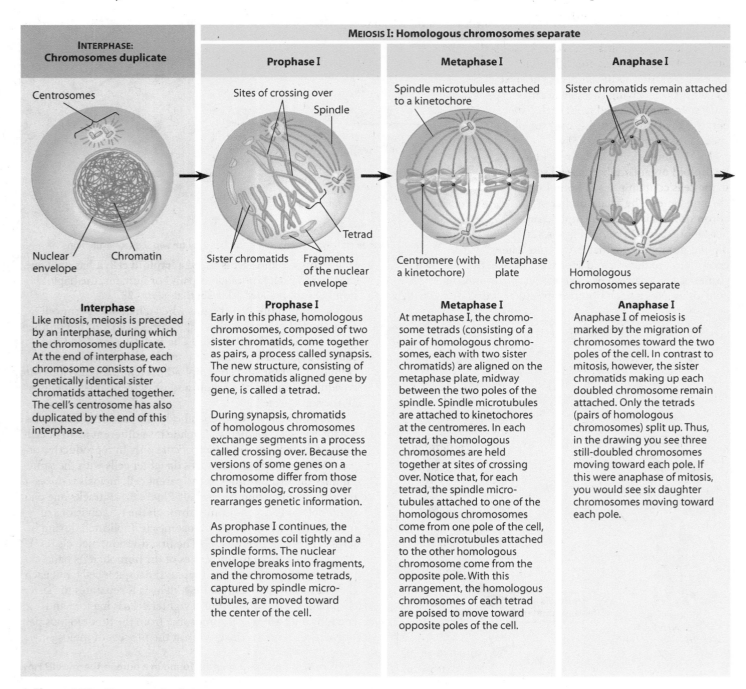

INTERPHASE: Chromosomes duplicate

Centrosomes

Nuclear envelope   Chromatin

MEIOSIS I: Homologous chromosomes separate

Prophase I

Sites of crossing over

Spindle

Tetrad

Sister chromatids   Fragments of the nuclear envelope

Metaphase I

Spindle microtubules attached to a kinetochore

Centromere (with a kinetochore)   Metaphase plate

Anaphase I

Sister chromatids remain attached

Homologous chromosomes separate

Interphase
Like mitosis, meiosis is preceded by an interphase, during which the chromosomes duplicate. At the end of interphase, each chromosome consists of two genetically identical sister chromatids attached together. The cell's centrosome has also duplicated by the end of this interphase.

Prophase I
Early in this phase, homologous chromosomes, composed of two sister chromatids, come together as pairs, a process called synapsis. The new structure, consisting of four chromatids aligned gene by gene, is called a tetrad.

During synapsis, chromatids of homologous chromosomes exchange segments in a process called crossing over. Because the versions of some genes on a chromosome differ from those on its homolog, crossing over rearranges genetic information.

As prophase I continues, the chromosomes coil tightly and a spindle forms. The nuclear envelope breaks into fragments, and the chromosome tetrads, captured by spindle microtubules, are moved toward the center of the cell.

Metaphase I
At metaphase I, the chromosome tetrads (consisting of a pair of homologous chromosomes, each with two sister chromatids) are aligned on the metaphase plate, midway between the two poles of the spindle. Spindle microtubules are attached to kinetochores at the centromeres. In each tetrad, the homologous chromosomes are held together at sites of crossing over. Notice that, for each tetrad, the spindle microtubules attached to one of the homologous chromosomes come from one pole of the cell, and the microtubules attached to the other homologous chromosome come from the opposite pole. With this arrangement, the homologous chromosomes of each tetrad are poised to move toward opposite poles of the cell.

Anaphase I
Anaphase I of meiosis is marked by the migration of chromosomes toward the two poles of the cell. In contrast to mitosis, however, the sister chromatids making up each doubled chromosome remain attached. Only the tetrads (pairs of homologous chromosomes) split up. Thus, in the drawing you see three still-doubled chromosomes moving toward each pole. If this were anaphase of mitosis, you would see six daughter chromosomes moving toward each pole.

▲ Figure 8.13   The stages of meiosis

occurs during prophase I. At this stage, four chromatids (two sets of sister chromatids) are aligned and physically touching each other. When in this configuration, nonsister chromatids may trade segments. As you will learn in Module 8.17, this exchange of chromosome segments—called crossing over— shuffles genes, making an important contribution to the genetic variability that results from sexual reproduction.

? A cell has the haploid number of chromosomes, but each chromosome has two chromatids. The chromosomes are arranged singly at the center of the spindle. What is the meiotic stage?

● Metaphase II (because the chromosomes line up two by two in metaphase I)

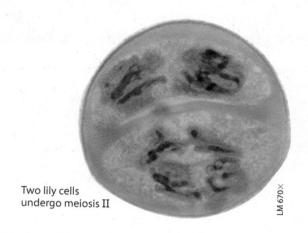

Two lily cells undergo meiosis II

LM 670×

MEIOSIS II: Sister chromatids separate

Telophase I and Cytokinesis	Prophase II	Metaphase II	Anaphase II	Telophase II and Cytokinesis

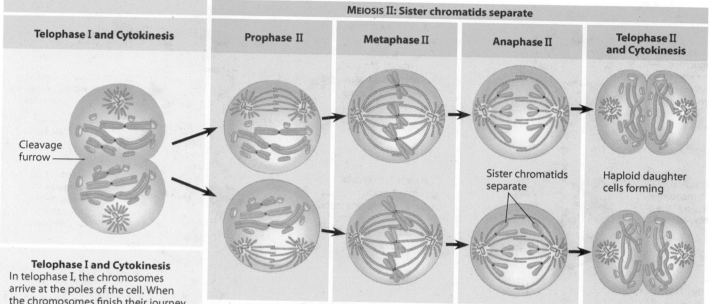

Cleavage furrow

Sister chromatids separate

Haploid daughter cells forming

Telophase I and Cytokinesis

In telophase I, the chromosomes arrive at the poles of the cell. When the chromosomes finish their journey, each pole of the cell has a haploid chromosome set, although each chromosome is still in duplicate form (with two sister chromatids) at this point. Usually, cytokinesis (division of the cytoplasm) occurs along with telophase I, and two haploid daughter cells are formed.

Following telophase I in some organisms, there is an interphase between telophase I and meiosis II. In other species, meiosis I immediately leads to meiosis II. In either case, no chromosome duplication occurs between telophase I and the onset of meiosis II.

Meiosis II

Meiosis II is essentially the same as mitosis. The important difference is that meiosis II starts with a haploid cell.

During prophase II, a spindle forms and moves the chromosomes toward the middle of the cell. During metaphase II, the chromosomes are aligned on the metaphase plate as they are in mitosis, with the kinetochores of the sister chromatids of each chromosome pointing toward opposite poles. In anaphase II, the centromeres of sister chromatids separate, and the sister chromatids of each pair, now individual chromosomes, move toward opposite poles of the cell. In telophase II, nuclei form at the cell poles, and cytokinesis occurs at the same time. There are now four daughter cells, each with the haploid number of (single) chromosomes.

8.14 Mitosis and meiosis have important similarities and differences

Carefully review this module, which compares mitosis and meiosis starting from a diploid parent cell with four chromosomes. Homologous chromosomes match in size. Color distinguishes the two chromosomes of each homologous pair.

MITOSIS		MEIOSIS I

Parent cell
(before chromosome duplication)
$2n = 4$
Chromosome duplication
(Occurs once, during S phase of preceding interphase)

Prophase

Duplicated chromosome (two sister chromatids)

In prophase of mitosis, each duplicated chromosome remains separate, while in prophase I of meiosis, chromosomes are associated with their homologs.

Prophase I

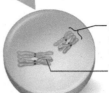

Homologous chromosomes come together in pairs

Site of crossing over between homologous (nonsister) chromatids

Metaphase

Individual chromosomes line up at the metaphase plate

In metaphase of mitosis, duplicated chromosomes line up singly, while in metaphase I of meiosis, duplicated homologous chromosomes line up in pairs.

Metaphase I

Tetrads (pairs of homologous chromosomes) line up at the metaphase plate

Anaphase Telophase

In anaphase of mitosis, sister chromatids separate, while in anaphase I of meiosis, pairs of homologous chromosomes separate.

Anaphase I Telophase I

Sister chromatids separate during anaphase

$2n$ $2n$

Homologous chromosomes separate during anaphase I; sister chromatids remain attached

$n = 2$

Mitosis involves one division of the nucleus and cytoplasm, while meiosis involves two divisions.

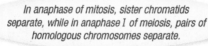

MEIOSIS II

Sister chromatids separate

Sister chromatids separate during anaphase II

n n n n

Result: Two genetically identical diploid cells
Used for: Growth, tissue repair, asexual reproduction

Result: Four genetically unique haploid cells
Used for: Sexual reproduction

? **Which stage of meiosis shown here most closely resembles mitosis?**

● The movement of chromosomes during meiosis II very closely matches mitosis (except with half as many chromosomes).

8.15 Independent orientation of chromosomes in meiosis and random fertilization lead to varied offspring

Offspring that result from sexual reproduction are highly varied (see Module 8.1); they are genetically different from their parents and from one another. How does this genetic variation result from meiosis?

Figure 8.15 illustrates one way: The arrangement of homologous chromosome pairs at metaphase I affects the resulting gametes. Once again, our example is from a diploid organism with four chromosomes (two homologous pairs, with one set larger than the other to help make them distinct), and red represents chromosomes inherited from the mother, whereas blue represents chromosomes inherited from the father.

Recall that joined homologous chromosomes form tetrads, a set of four chromatids. At metaphase, the orientation of these tetrads—whether the maternal or paternal chromosome is closer to a given pole—is as random as the flip of a coin. Thus, there is a 50% chance that a particular daughter cell will get the maternal chromosome of a certain homologous pair and a 50% chance that it will receive the paternal chromosome. In this example, there are two possible ways that the two tetrads can align during metaphase I. In possibility A, the tetrads are oriented with both red chromosomes on the same side of the metaphase plate. Therefore, the gametes produced in possibility A can each have either two red *or* two blue chromosomes (bottom row, combinations 1 and 2).

In possibility B, the tetrads are oriented differently (blue/red and red/blue). This arrangement produces gametes that each have one red and one blue chromosome. Furthermore, half the gametes have a big blue chromosome and a small red one (combination 3), and half have a big red chromosome and a small blue one (combination 4).

So we see that for this example, four chromosome combinations are possible in the gametes. In fact, the organism will produce gametes of all four types in equal quantities. For a species with more than two pairs of chromosomes, such as humans, *all* the chromosome pairs orient independently at metaphase I. (Chromosomes X and Y behave as a homologous pair in meiosis.)

For any species, the total number of combinations of chromosomes that meiosis can produce in gametes is 2^n, where n is the haploid number. For the organism in this figure, $n = 2$, so the number of chromosome combinations is 2^2, or 4. For a human ($n = 23$), there are 2^{23}, or about 8 million possible chromosome combinations! This means that each gamete you produce contains one of roughly 8 million possible combinations of chromosomes.

How many possibilities are there when a gamete from one individual unites with a gamete from another individual in fertilization? In humans, the random fusion of a single sperm with a single egg during fertilization will produce a zygote with any of about 64 trillion (8 million × 8 million) combinations of chromosomes! Although the random nature of fertilization adds a huge amount of potential variability to the offspring of sexual reproduction, there is in fact even more variety created during meiosis, as we see in the next two modules.

> **?** A particular species of worm has a diploid number of 10. How many chromosomal combinations are possible for gametes formed by meiosis?
>
> ● 32; $2n = 10$, so $n = 5$ and $2^5 = 32$

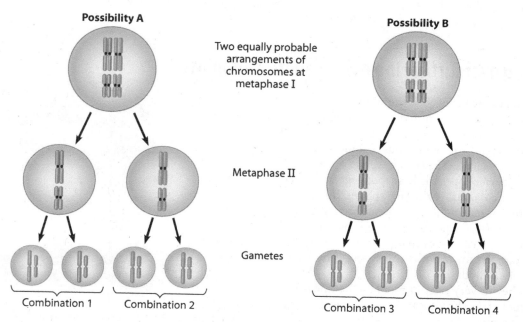

▲ **Figure 8.15** Results of the independent orientation of chromosomes at metaphase I

Possibility A

Two equally probable arrangements of chromosomes at metaphase I

Possibility B

Metaphase II

Gametes

Combination 1   Combination 2   Combination 3   Combination 4

8.16 Homologous chromosomes may carry different versions of genes

So far, we have focused on genetic variability in gametes and zygotes at the whole-chromosome level. We have yet to discuss the actual genetic information—the genes—contained in the chromosomes. The question we need to answer now is: What is the significance of the independent orientation of metaphase chromosomes at the level of genes?

Let's take a simple example, the single tetrad in Figure 8.16. The letters on the homologous chromosomes represent genes. Recall that homologous chromosomes have genes for the same characteristic at corresponding loci. Our example involves hypothetical genes controlling the appearance of mice. *C* and *c* indicate different versions of a gene for one characteristic, coat color; *E* and *e* are different versions of a gene for another characteristic, eye color. (As you'll learn in later chapters, different versions of a gene contain slightly different nucleotide sequences in the chromosomal DNA.)

Let's say that *C* represents the gene for a brown coat and that *c* represents the gene for a white coat. In the chromosome diagram, notice that *C* is at the same locus on the red chromosome as *c* is on the blue one. Likewise, gene *E* (for black eyes) is at the same locus as *e* (pink eyes).

The fact that homologous chromosomes can bear two different kinds of genetic information for the same characteristic (for instance, coat color) is what really makes gametes—and therefore offspring—different from one another. In our example, a gamete carrying a red chromosome would have genes specifying brown coat color and

black eye color, whereas a gamete with the homologous blue chromosome would have genes for white coat and pink eyes. Thus, we see that a tetrad can yield two genetically different kinds of gametes. In the next module, we go a step further and see how this same tetrad can actually yield *four* different kinds of gametes.

? In the tetrad of Figure 8.16, use labels to distinguish the pair of homologous chromosomes from sister chromatids.

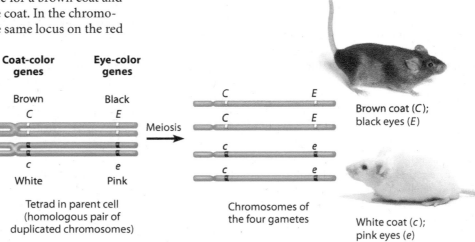

Brown coat (*C*); black eyes (*E*)

Chromosomes of the four gametes

White coat (*c*); pink eyes (*e*)

Coat-color genes   **Eye-color genes**

Brown   Black
C   *E*

Meiosis

c   *e*
White   Pink

Tetrad in parent cell (homologous pair of duplicated chromosomes)

▲ **Figure 8.16**   Differing genetic information (coat color and eye color) on homologous chromosomes

8.17 Crossing over further increases genetic variability

Crossing over is an exchange of corresponding segments between nonsister chromatids of homologous chromosomes. The micrograph and drawing in Figure 8.17A show the results of crossing over between two homologous chromosomes during prophase I of meiosis. The chromosomes are a tetrad. The sites of crossing over appear as X-shaped regions; each of these sites is called a **chiasma**. A chiasma (plural, *chiasmata*) is a place where two homologous (nonsister) chromatids are attached to each other. Figure 8.17B on the next page illustrates how crossing over can produce new combinations of genes, using as examples the hypothetical mouse genes mentioned in the previous module.

Crossing over begins very early in prophase I of meiosis. At that time, homologous chromosomes are paired all along their lengths, with a precise gene-by-gene alignment. Notice

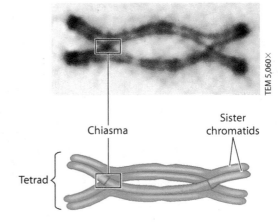

TEM 5,060×

Chiasma

Sister chromatids

Tetrad

▲ **Figure 8.17A**   Chiasmata, the sites of crossing over

at the top of the figure a tetrad with coat-color (*C, c*) and eye-color (*E, e*) genes labeled. ❶ The DNA molecules of two nonsister chromatids—one maternal (red) and one paternal (blue)—break at the same place. ❷ Immediately, the two broken chromatids join together in a new way (red to blue and blue to red). In effect, the two homologous segments trade places, or cross over, producing hybrid chromosomes (red/blue and blue/red) with new combinations of maternal and paternal genes. ❸ When the homologous chromosomes separate in anaphase I, each contains a new segment originating from its homolog. ❹ Finally, during anaphase II, the sister chromatids separate, each going to a different gamete.

In this example, if there were no crossing over, meiosis could produce only two genetic types of gametes. These would be the ones ending up with the "parental" types of chromosomes (either all blue or all red), carrying either genes *C* and *E* or genes *c* and *e*. These are the same two kinds of gametes we saw in Figure 8.16. With crossing over, two other types of gametes can result, ones that are part blue and part red. One of these carries genes *C* and *e* and the other carries genes *c* and *E*. Chromosomes with these combinations of genes would not exist if not for crossing over. They are called "recombinant" because they result from **genetic recombination**, the production of gene combinations different from those carried by the original parental chromosomes.

In meiosis in humans, an average of one to three crossover events occur per chromosome pair. Thus, if you were to examine a chromosome from one of your gametes, you would most likely find that it is not exactly like any one of your own chromosomes. Rather, it is probably a patchwork of segments derived from a pair of homologous chromosomes, in essence cut and pasted together to form a hybrid chromosome with a unique combination of genes.

We have now examined three sources of genetic variability in sexually reproducing organisms: independent orientation of chromosomes at metaphase I, random fertilization, and crossing over during prophase I of meiosis. The different versions of genes that homologous chromosomes may have at each locus originally arise from mutations (changes in the sequence of DNA), so mutations are ultimately responsible for genetic diversity in living organisms. Once these differences arise, reshuffling of the different versions during sexual reproduction increases genetic variation. (When we discuss natural selection and evolution in Unit III, we will see that this genetic variety in offspring is the raw material for natural selection.)

Our discussion of meiosis to this point has focused on the process as it normally occurs. In the next section, we consider some of the consequences of errors in the process.

? Describe how crossing over and the random alignment of homologous chromosomes on the metaphase I plate account for the genetic variation among gametes formed by meiosis.

● Crossing over creates recombinant chromosomes having a combination of genes that were originally on different, though homologous, chromosomes. Homologous chromosome pairs are oriented randomly at metaphase of meiosis I.

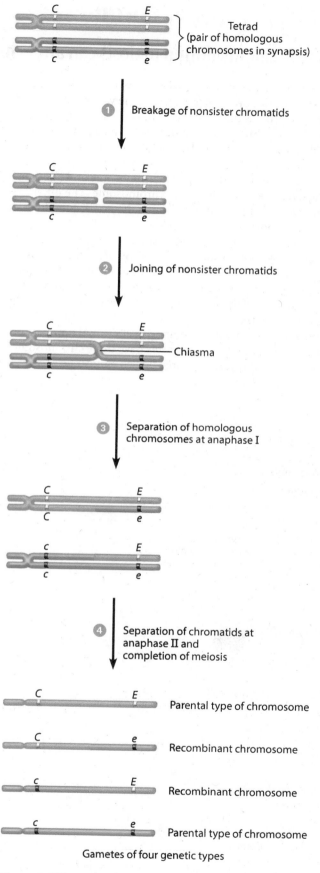

Tetrad (pair of homologous chromosomes in synapsis)

❶ Breakage of nonsister chromatids

❷ Joining of nonsister chromatids

Chiasma

❸ Separation of homologous chromosomes at anaphase I

❹ Separation of chromatids at anaphase II and completion of meiosis

Parental type of chromosome

Recombinant chromosome

Recombinant chromosome

Parental type of chromosome

Gametes of four genetic types

▲ **Figure 8.17B** How crossing over leads to genetic recombination

8.18 Accidents during meiosis can alter chromosome number

Within the human body, meiosis occurs repeatedly as the testes or ovaries produce gametes. In the vast majority of cases, the process distributes chromosomes to daughter cells without error. But there is an occasional mishap, called a **nondisjunction**, in which the members of a chromosome pair fail to separate. After a nondisjunction, one gamete receives two of the same type of chromosome and another gamete receives no copy of that chromosome. The other chromosomes (those not involved in the nondisjunction) are distributed normally.

Imagine a hypothetical organism whose diploid chromosome number is 4. In such an organism, the somatic cells are diploid ($2n = 4$), with two pairs of homologous chromosomes. Sometimes, a pair of homologous chromosomes does not separate during meiosis I (see left side of Figure 8.18). In this case, even though the rest of meiosis occurs normally, all the resulting gametes end up with abnormal numbers of chromosomes. Two of the gametes have three chromosomes; the other two gametes have only one chromosome each.

Alternatively, sometimes meiosis I procedes normally, but one pair of sister chromatids fails to separate during meiosis II (see right side of Figure 8.18). In this case, two of the resulting gametes are abnormal—one with an extra chromosome and one that is missing a chromosome; the other two gametes are normal.

If an abnormal gamete produced by nondisjunction unites with a normal gamete during fertilization, the result is a zygote with an abnormal number of chromosomes. Mitosis will then transmit the mistake to all embryonic cells. If the organism survived, it would most likely display a syndrome of disorders caused by the abnormal number of genes. Biologists can detect such syndromes by taking an inventory of the chromosomes in a person's cells, as we'll see next.

? **Explain how nondisjunction could result in a diploid gamete.**

● A diploid gamete would result if the nondisjunction affected all the chromosomes during one of the meiotic divisions.

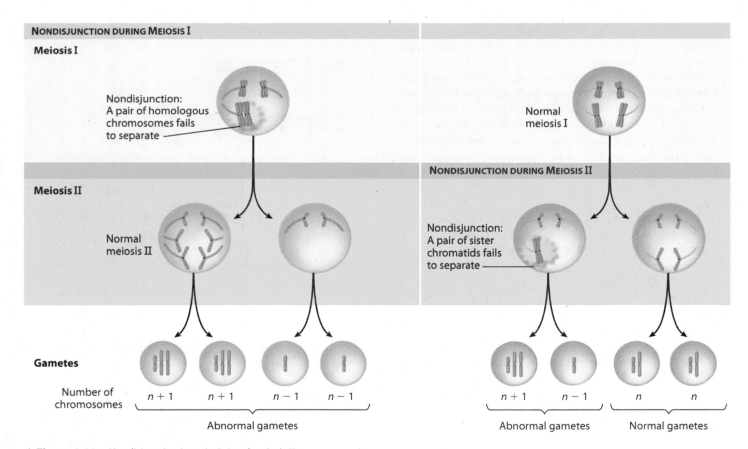

NONDISJUNCTION DURING MEIOSIS I

Meiosis I

Nondisjunction: A pair of homologous chromosomes fails to separate

Normal meiosis I

NONDISJUNCTION DURING MEIOSIS II

Meiosis II

Normal meiosis II

Nondisjunction: A pair of sister chromatids fails to separate

Gametes

Number of chromosomes · $n + 1$ · $n + 1$ · $n - 1$ · $n - 1$ · $n + 1$ · $n - 1$ · n · n

Abnormal gametes · Abnormal gametes · Normal gametes

▲ Figure 8.18 Nondisjunction in meiosis I and meiosis II

8.19 A karyotype is a photographic inventory of an individual's chromosomes

Chromosomal abnormalities can be readily detected in a **karyotype**, an ordered display of magnified images of an individual's chromosomes arranged in pairs. A karyotype shows the chromosomes condensed and doubled, as they appear in metaphase of mitosis.

To prepare a karyotype, scientists often use lymphocytes, a type of white blood cell. A blood sample is treated with a chemical that stimulates mitosis. After growing in culture for several days, the cells are treated with another chemical to arrest mitosis at metaphase, when the chromosomes, each consisting of two joined sister chromatids, are most highly condensed. Figure 8.19 outlines the steps of one method for the preparation of a karyotype from a blood sample.

The photograph on the right shows the karyotype of a normal human male. Images of the 46 chromosomes from a single diploid cell are arranged in 23 homologous pairs: autosomes numbered from 1 to 22 (starting with the largest) and one pair of sex chromosomes (X and Y in this case). The chromosomes have been stained to reveal band patterns, which are helpful in differentiating the chromosomes and in detecting structural abnormalities. Among the alterations that can be detected by karyotyping is trisomy 21, the basis of Down syndrome, which we discuss next.

? **How would the karyotype of a human female differ from the male karyotype in Figure 8.19?**

● Instead of an XY combination for the sex chromosomes, there would be a homologous pair of X chromosomes (XX).

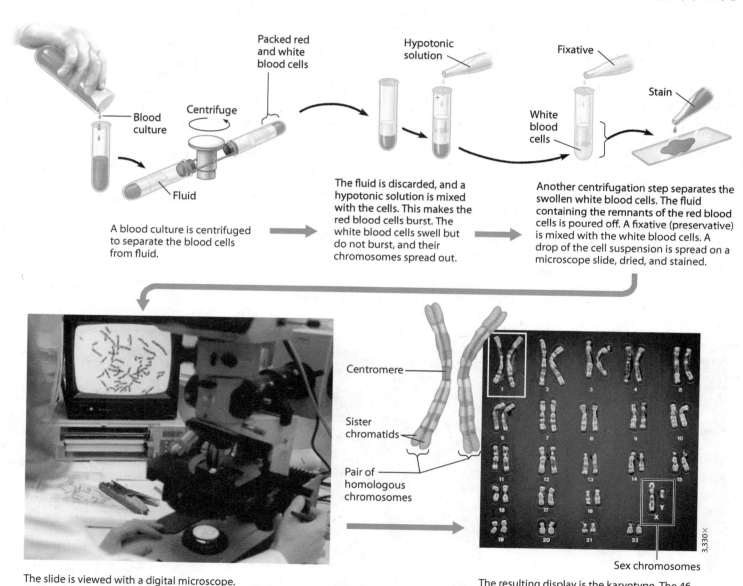

Packed red and white blood cells

Blood culture

Centrifuge

Fluid

A blood culture is centrifuged to separate the blood cells from fluid.

Hypotonic solution

The fluid is discarded, and a hypotonic solution is mixed with the cells. This makes the red blood cells burst. The white blood cells swell but do not burst, and their chromosomes spread out.

Fixative

White blood cells

Stain

Another centrifugation step separates the swollen white blood cells. The fluid containing the remnants of the red blood cells is poured off. A fixative (preservative) is mixed with the white blood cells. A drop of the cell suspension is spread on a microscope slide, dried, and stained.

Centromere

Sister chromatids

Pair of homologous chromosomes

3,330×

Sex chromosomes

The slide is viewed with a digital microscope. Software is used to electronically arrange the photographed chromosomes by size and shape.

The resulting display is the karyotype. The 46 chromosomes here include 22 pairs of autosomes and two sex chromosomes, X and Y. Each of the chromosomes consists of two sister chromatids joined along their lengths (as shown in the diagram).

▲ **Figure 8.19** Preparation of a karyotype from a blood sample

8.20 An extra copy of chromosome 21 causes Down syndrome

CONNECTION

The karyotype in Figure 8.19 shows the normal human complement of 23 pairs of chromosomes. Compare this figure with the karyotype shown in **Figure 8.20A**; besides having two X chromosomes (because it's from a female), notice that there are three number 21 chromosomes, making 47 chromosomes in total. This condition is called **trisomy 21**.

In most cases, an abnormal number of chromosomes is so harmful to development that an affected embryo is spontaneously aborted (miscarried) long before birth. But some aberrations in chromosome number, including trisomy 21, appear to upset the genetic balance less drastically, and individuals carrying such chromosomal abnormalities can survive into adulthood. Individuals with chromosomal abnormalities have a characteristic set of symptoms, collectively called a syndrome. A person with trisomy 21, for instance, has a condition called **Down syndrome**, named after John Langdon Down, a doctor who described the syndrome in 1866.

Trisomy 21 is the most common chromosome number abnormality. Affecting about one out of every 700 children, it is also the most common serious birth defect in the United States. Down syndrome includes characteristic facial features—frequently a round face, a skin fold at the inner corner of the eye, a flattened nose bridge, and small, irregular teeth—as well as short stature, heart defects, and susceptibility to respiratory infections, leukemia, and Alzheimer's disease.

People with Down syndrome usually have a life span shorter than normal. They also exhibit varying degrees of developmental disabilities. However, with proper care, many individuals with the syndrome live to middle age or beyond, and many are socially adept and are able to hold jobs. A few women with Down syndrome have had children, though nearly all men with the syndrome are sexually underdeveloped and sterile. Half the eggs produced by a woman with Down syndrome will have the extra chromosome 21, so there

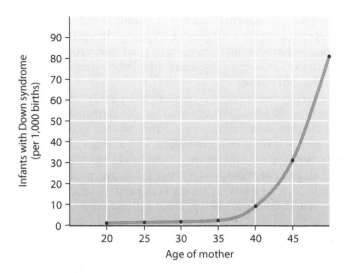

▲ **Figure 8.20B** Maternal age and incidence of Down syndrome

Source: Adapted from C. A. Huether et al., Maternal age specific risk rate estimates for Down syndrome among live births in whites and other races from Ohio and Metropolitan Atlanta, 1970–1989, *Journal of Medical Genetics* 35: 482–90 (1998).

is a 50% chance that she will transmit the syndrome to her child.

As indicated in **Figure 8.20B**, the incidence of Down syndrome in the offspring of normal parents increases markedly with the age of the mother. Down syndrome affects less than 0.05% of children (fewer than one in 2,000) born to women under age 30. The risk climbs to 1% (10 in 1,000) for mothers at age 40 and is even higher for older mothers. Prenatal screening for chromosomal defects in the embryo is now offered to all pregnant women.

? For mothers of age 47, the risk of having a baby with Down syndrome is about _____ per thousand births, or _____ %.

● 40 . . . 4

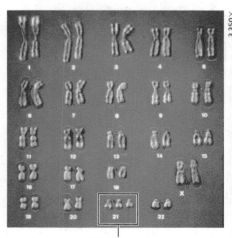

Trisomy 21

▲ **Figure 8.20A** A karyotype showing trisomy 21 and an individual with Down syndrome

8.21 Abnormal numbers of sex chromosomes do not usually affect survival

CONNECTION

Nondisjunction can result in abnormal numbers of sex chromosomes, X and Y. Unusual numbers of sex chromosomes seem to upset the genetic balance less than unusual numbers of autosomes. This may be because the Y chromosome is very small and carries relatively few genes. Furthermore, mammalian cells usually operate with only one functioning X chromosome because other copies of the chromosome become inactivated in each cell (as you'll learn in Module 11.2).

Table 8.21 lists the most common human sex chromosome abnormalities. An extra X chromosome in a male, making him XXY, occurs approximately once in every 1,000 live male births. Men with this disorder, called Klinefelter syndrome, have male sex organs, but the testes are abnormally small, the individual is sterile, and he often has female body characteristics. Affected individuals may have subnormal intelligence. Klinefelter syndrome is also found in individuals with more than three sex chromosomes, such as XXYY, XXXY, or XXXXY. These abnormal numbers of sex chromosomes result from multiple nondisjunctions; such men are more likely to have developmental disabilities than XY or XXY individuals.

Human males with an extra Y chromosome do not have any well-defined syndrome, although they tend to be taller than average. Females with an extra X chromosome cannot be distinguished from XX females except by karyotype.

Females who lack an X chromosome are designated XO; the O indicates the absence of a second sex chromosome. These women have Turner syndrome. They have a characteristic appearance, including short stature and often a web of skin extending between the neck and the shoulders. Women with Turner syndrome are sterile because their sex organs do not fully mature at adolescence. If left untreated, girls with Turner syndrome have poor development of breasts and other secondary sexual characteristics. Artificial administration of estrogen can alleviate these symptoms. Women with Turner syndrome have normal intelligence. The XO condition is the sole known case where having only 45 chromosomes is not fatal in humans.

? What is the total number of autosomes you would expect to find in the karyotype of a female with Turner syndrome?

44 (plus one sex chromosome)

TABLE 8.21 | ABNORMALITIES OF SEX CHROMOSOME NUMBER IN HUMANS

Sex Chromosomes	Syndrome	Origin of Nondisjunction	Frequency in Population
XXY	Klinefelter syndrome (male)	Meiosis in egg or sperm formation	1/1,000 live male births
XYY	None (normal male)	Meiosis in sperm formation	1/1,000 live male births
XXX	None (normal female)	Meiosis in egg or sperm formation	1/1,000 live female births
XO	Turner syndrome (female)	Meiosis in egg or sperm formation	1/2,500 live female births

8.22 New species can arise from errors in cell division

EVOLUTION CONNECTION

Errors in meiosis or mitosis do not always lead to problems. In fact, biologists hypothesize that such errors have been instrumental in the evolution of many species. Such new species are polyploid, meaning that they have more than two sets of homologous chromosomes in each somatic cell. At least half of all species of flowering plants are polyploid, including such crops as wheat, potatoes, and cotton.

Let's consider one scenario by which a diploid (2n) plant species might generate a tetraploid (4n) plant. Imagine that, like many plants, our diploid plant produces both sperm and egg cells and can self-fertilize. If meiosis fails to occur in the plant's reproductive organs and gametes are instead produced by mitosis, the gametes will be diploid. The union of a diploid (2n) sperm with a diploid (2n) egg during self-fertilization will produce a tetraploid (4n) zygote, which may develop into a mature tetraploid plant that can itself reproduce by self-fertilization. The tetraploid plants will constitute a new species, one that has evolved in just one generation. Although polyploid animal species are less common than polyploid plants, they are known to occur among the fishes and amphibians (Figure 8.22). Moreover, researchers in Chile have identified the first candidate for polyploidy among the mammals—the Viscacha rat (*Tympanoctomys barrerae*), a rodent whose cells seem to be tetraploid. Tetraploid organisms are sometimes strikingly different from their recent diploid ancestors. Scientists don't yet understand exactly how polyploidy brings about such differences.

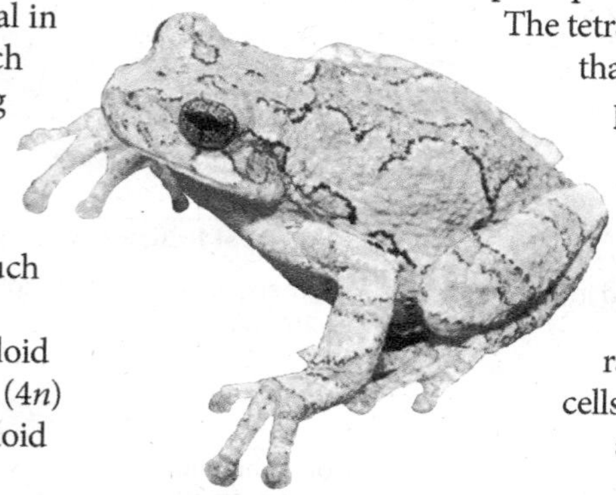

▲ Figure 8.22   The gray tree frog (*Hyla versicolor*), a tetraploid organism

? What is a polyploid organism?

An organism with more than two sets of homologous chromosomes in its body cells

8.23 Alterations of chromosome structure can cause birth defects and cancer

CONNECTION

Errors in meiosis or damaging agents such as radiation can cause a chromosome to break, which can lead to four types of changes in chromosome structure (**Figure 8.23A**). A **deletion** occurs when a chromosomal fragment (along with its genes) becomes detached. The "deleted" fragment may disappear from the cell, or it may become attached as an extra segment to its sister chromatid or a homologous chromosome, producing a **duplication**. A chromosomal fragment may also reattach to the original chromosome but in the reverse orientation, producing an **inversion**. A fourth possible result of chromosomal breakage is for the fragment to join a nonhomologous chromosome, a rearrangement called a **translocation**. As shown in the figure, a translocation may be reciprocal; that is, two nonhomologous chromosomes may exchange segments.

Inversions are less likely than deletions or duplications to produce harmful effects, because in inversions all genes are still present in their normal number. Many deletions in human chromosomes, however, cause serious physical and mental problems. One example is a specific deletion in chromosome 5 that causes *cri du chat* ("cat-cry") syndrome. A child born with this syndrome has severe developmental disabilities, a small head with unusual facial features, and a cry that sounds like the mewing of a distressed cat. Such individuals usually die in infancy or early childhood.

Like inversions, translocations may or may not be harmful. Some people with Down syndrome have only part of a third chromosome 21; as the result of a translocation, this partial chromosome is attached to another (nonhomologous) chromosome. Other chromosomal translocations have been implicated in certain cancers, including chronic myelogenous leukemia (CML). CML develops after a reciprocal translocation during mitosis of cells that will become white blood cells. In these cells, the exchange of a large portion of chromosome 22 with a small fragment from a tip of chromosome 9 produces a much shortened, easily recognized chromosome 22 (**Figure 8.23B**). Such an exchange causes cancer by activating a gene that leads to uncontrolled cell cycle progression.

Because the chromosomal changes in cancer are usually confined to somatic cells, cancer is not usually inherited. (We'll return to cancer in Chapter 11.) We continue our study of genetic principles (in Chapter 9), looking first at the historical development of the science of genetics and then at the rules governing the way traits are passed from parents to offspring.

? **How is reciprocal translocation different from crossing over?**

● Reciprocal translocation swaps chromosome segments between nonhomologous chromosomes. Crossing over exchanges corresponding segments between homologous chromosomes.

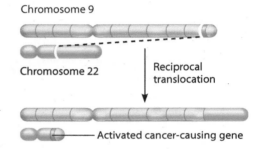

Chromosome 9

Chromosome 22

Reciprocal translocation

Activated cancer-causing gene

▲ **Figure 8.23B** The translocation associated with chronic myelogenous leukemia

Deletion	Inversion
A segment of a chromosome is removed	A segment of a chromosome is removed and then reinserted opposite to its original orientation
Duplication	**Reciprocal translocation**
A segment of a chromosome is copied and inserted into the homologous chromosome	Segments of two nonhomologous chromosomes swap locations with each other
Homologous chromosomes	Nonhomologous chromosomes

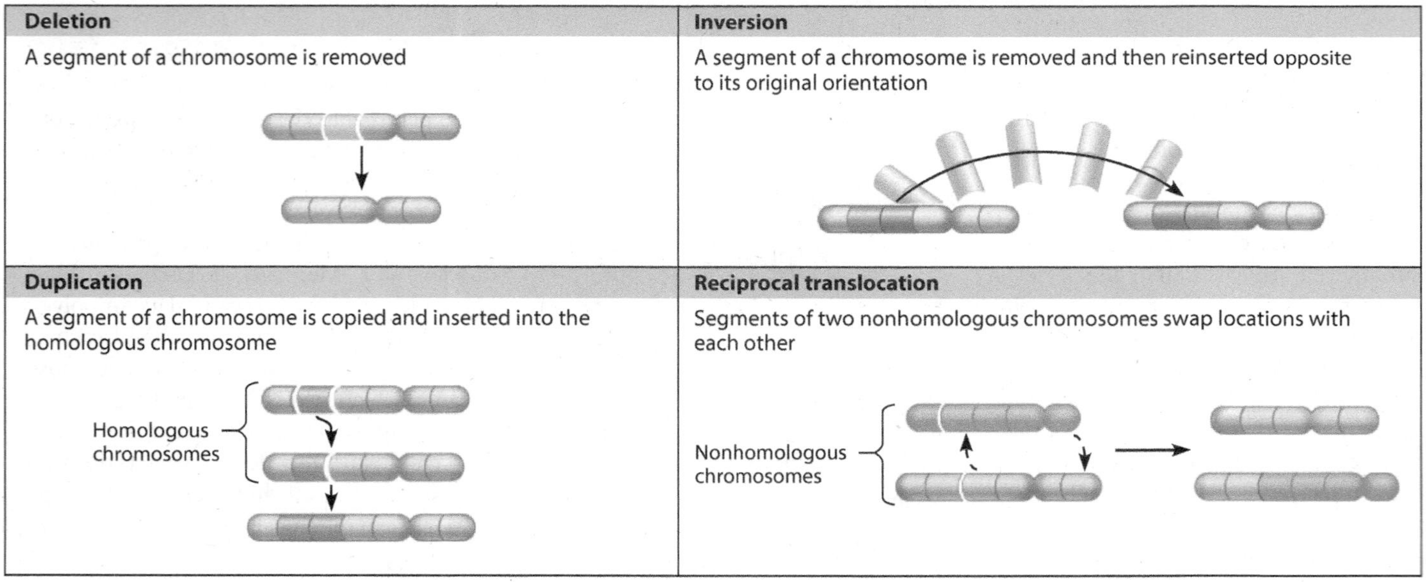

▲ **Figure 8.23A** Alterations of chromosome structure

CHAPTER 8 REVIEW

For practice quizzes, BioFlix animations, MP3 tutorials, video tutors, and more study tools designed for this textbook, go to

MasteringBiology®

Reviewing the Concepts

Cell Division and Reproduction (8.1–8.2)

8.1 Cell division plays many important roles in the lives of organisms. Cell division is at the heart of the reproduction of cells and organisms because cells originate only from preexisting cells. Some organisms reproduce through asexual reproduction, and in such instances their offspring are all genetic copies of the parent and identical to each other. Other organisms reproduce through sexual reproduction, creating a variety of offspring.

8.2 Prokaryotes reproduce by binary fission. Prokaryotic cells reproduce asexually by cell division. As the cell replicates its single chromosome, the copies move apart; the growing membrane then divides the cell.

The Eukaryotic Cell Cycle and Mitosis (8.3–8.10)

8.3 The large, complex chromosomes of eukaryotes duplicate with each cell division. A eukaryotic cell has many more genes than a prokaryotic cell, and they are grouped into multiple chromosomes in the nucleus. Each chromosome contains one long DNA molecule. Individual chromosomes are visible under a light microscope only when the cell is in the process of dividing; otherwise, chromosomes are thin, loosely packed chromatin fibers too small to be seen. Before a cell starts dividing, the chromosomes duplicate, producing sister chromatids (containing identical DNA) that are joined together along their lengths. Cell division involves the separation of sister chromatids and results in two daughter cells, each containing a complete and identical set of chromosomes.

8.4 The cell cycle includes growing and division phases.

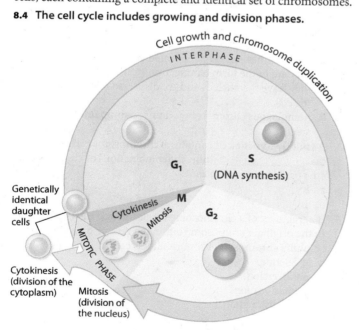

8.5 Cell division is a continuum of dynamic changes. Mitosis distributes duplicated chromosomes into two daughter nuclei. After the chromosomes are coiled up, a mitotic spindle made of microtubules moves the chromosomes to the middle of the cell. The sister chromatids then separate and move to opposite poles of the cell, at which point two new nuclei form.

8.6 Cytokinesis differs for plant and animal cells. Cytokinesis, in which the cell divides in two, overlaps the end of mitosis. In animals, cytokinesis occurs when a cell constricts, forming a cleavage furrow. In plants, a membranous cell plate forms and then splits the cell in two.

8.7 Anchorage, cell density, and chemical growth factors affect cell division. In laboratory cultures, most normal cells divide only when attached to a surface. The cultured cells continue dividing until they touch one another. Most animal cells divide only when stimulated by growth factors, and some do not divide at all. Growth factors stimulate other cells to divide.

8.8 Growth factors signal the cell cycle control system. A set of proteins within the cell controls the cell cycle. Signals affecting critical checkpoints in the cell cycle determine whether a cell will go through the complete cycle and divide. The binding of growth factors to specific receptors on the plasma membrane is usually necessary for cell division.

8.9 Growing out of control, cancer cells produce malignant tumors. Cancer cells divide excessively to form masses called tumors. Malignant tumors can invade other tissues. Radiation and chemotherapy are effective as cancer treatments because they interfere with cell division.

8.10 Tailoring treatment to each patient may improve cancer therapy. Determination of specific mutations within the cells of an individual tumor may aid in treatment. Although reliable data are scant today, such personalized medicine may prove to be an important treatment regimen in the future.

Meiosis and Crossing Over (8.11–8.17)

8.11 Chromosomes are matched in homologous pairs. The somatic (body) cells of each species contain a specific number of chromosomes; for example, human cells have 46, consisting of 23 pairs of homologous chromosomes. The chromosomes of a homologous pair of autosomes carry genes for the same characteristics at the same place, or locus.

8.12 Gametes have a single set of chromosomes. Cells with two sets of homologous chromosomes are diploid. Gametes—eggs and sperm—are haploid cells with a single set of chromosomes. Sexual life cycles involve the alternation of haploid and diploid stages.

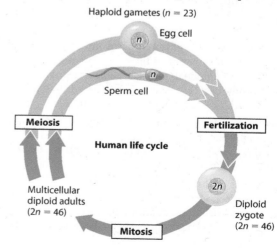

8.13 Meiosis reduces the chromosome number from diploid to haploid. Meiosis, like mitosis, is preceded by chromosome duplication, but in meiosis, the cell divides twice to form four daughter cells. The first division, meiosis I, starts with the pairing of homologous chromosomes. In crossing over, homologous chromosomes exchange corresponding segments. Meiosis I separates the members of each homologous pair and produces two daughter cells, each with one set of chromosomes. Meiosis II is essentially the same as mitosis: In each of the cells, the sister chromatids of each chromosome separate. The result is a total of four haploid cells.

8.14 Mitosis and meiosis have important similarities and differences. Both mitosis and meiosis begin with diploid parent cells that have chromosomes duplicated during the previous interphase. Mitosis produces two genetically identical diploid somatic daughter cells, whereas meiosis produces four genetically unique haploid gametes.

8.15 Independent orientation of chromosomes in meiosis and random fertilization lead to varied offspring. Each chromosome of a homologous pair differs at many points from the other member of the pair. Random arrangements of chromosome pairs at metaphase I of meiosis lead to many different combinations of chromosomes in eggs and sperm. Random fertilization of eggs by sperm greatly increases this variation.

8.16 Homologous chromosomes may carry different versions of genes. The differences between homologous chromosomes come from the fact that they can bear different versions of genes at corresponding loci.

8.17 Crossing over further increases genetic variability. Genetic recombination, which results from crossing over during prophase I of meiosis, increases variation still further.

Alterations of Chromosome Number and Structure (8.18–8.23)

8.18 Accidents during meiosis can alter chromosome number. An abnormal chromosome count is the result of nondisjunction, which can result from the failure of a pair of homologous chromosomes to separate during meiosis I or from the failure of sister chromatids to separate during meiosis II.

8.19 A karyotype is a photographic inventory of an individual's chromosomes. To prepare a karyotype, white blood cells are isolated, stimulated to grow, arrested at metaphase, and photographed under a microscope. The chromosomes are arranged into ordered pairs so that any chromosomal abnormalities can be detected.

8.20 An extra copy of chromosome 21 causes Down syndrome. Trisomy 21, the most common chromosome number abnormality, results in a condition called Down syndrome.

8.21 Abnormal numbers of sex chromosomes do not usually affect survival. Nondisjunction of the sex chromosomes during meiosis can result in individuals with a missing or extra X or Y chromosome. In some cases (such as XXY), this leads to syndromes; in other cases (such as XXX), the body is normal.

8.22 New species can arise from errors in cell division. Nondisjunction can produce polyploid organisms, organisms with extra sets of chromosomes. Such errors in cell division can be important in the evolution of new species.

8.23 Alterations of chromosome structure can cause birth defects and cancer. Chromosome breakage can lead to rearrangements—deletions, duplications, inversions, and translocations—that can produce genetic disorders or, if the changes occur in somatic cells, cancer.

Connecting the Concepts

1. Complete the following table to compare mitosis and meiosis.

	Mitosis	Meiosis
Number of chromosomal duplications		
Number of cell divisions		
Number of daughter cells produced		
Number of chromosomes in the daughter cells		
How the chromosomes line up during metaphase		
Genetic relationship of the daughter cells to the parent cell		
Functions performed in the human body		

Testing Your Knowledge

Level 1: Knowledge/Comprehension

2. If an intestinal cell in a grasshopper contains 24 chromosomes, then a grasshopper sperm cell contains _____ chromosomes.
   a. 6
   b. 12
   c. 24
   d. 48

3. Which of the following is *not* a function of mitosis in humans?
   a. repair of wounds
   b. growth
   c. production of gametes from diploid cells
   d. replacement of lost or damaged cells

4. It is difficult to observe individual chromosomes during interphase because
   a. the DNA has not been replicated yet.
   b. they are in the form of long, thin strands.
   c. they leave the nucleus and are dispersed to other parts of the cell.
   d. homologous chromosomes do not pair up until division starts.

5. A fruit fly somatic cell contains 8 chromosomes. This means that _____ different combinations of chromosomes are possible in its gametes.
   a. 8
   b. 16
   c. 32
   d. 64

6. If a fragment of a chromosome breaks off and then reattaches to the original chromosome but in the reverse direction, the resulting chromosomal abnormality is called
   a. a deletion.
   b. an inversion.
   c. a translocation.
   d. a nondisjunction.

Level 2: Application/Analysis

7. Which of the following phases of mitosis is essentially the opposite of prophase in terms of changes within the nucleus?
   a. telophase
   b. metaphase
   c. interphase
   d. anaphase

8. A biochemist measured the amount of DNA in cells growing in the laboratory and found that the quantity of DNA in a cell doubled
   a. between prophase and anaphase of mitosis.
   b. between the G_1 and G_2 phases of the cell cycle.
   c. during the M phase of the cell cycle.
   d. between prophase I and prophase II of meiosis.
9. A micrograph of a dividing cell from a mouse showed 19 chromosomes, each consisting of two sister chromatids. During which of the following stages of cell division could such a picture have been taken? (*Explain your answer.*)
   a. prophase of mitosis
   b. telophase II of meiosis
   c. prophase I of meiosis
   d. prophase II of meiosis
10. Cytochalasin B is a chemical that disrupts microfilament formation. This chemical would interfere with
    a. DNA replication.
    b. formation of the mitotic spindle.
    c. cleavage.
    d. formation of the cell plate.
11. Why are individuals with an extra chromosome 21, which causes Down syndrome, more numerous than individuals with an extra chromosome 3 or chromosome 16?
    a. There are probably more genes on chromosome 21 than on the others.
    b. Chromosome 21 is a sex chromosome and chromosomes 3 and 16 are not.
    c. Down syndrome is not more common, just more serious.
    d. Extra copies of the other chromosomes are probably fatal.
12. In the light micrograph below of dividing cells near the tip of an onion root, identify a cell in interphase, prophase, metaphase, anaphase, and telophase. Describe the major events occurring at each stage.

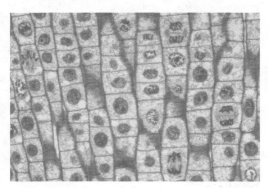

Level 3: Synthesis/Evaluation

13. An organism called a plasmodial slime mold is one large cytoplasmic mass with many nuclei. Explain how such a "megacell" could form.
14. Briefly describe how three different processes that occur during a sexual life cycle increase the genetic diversity of offspring.
15. Discuss the factors that control the division of eukaryotic cells grown in the laboratory. Cancer cells are easier to grow in the lab than other cells. Why do you suppose this is?
16. Compare cytokinesis in plant and animal cells. In what ways are the two processes similar? In what ways are they different?
17. Sketch a cell with three pairs of chromosomes undergoing meiosis, and show how nondisjunction can result in the production of gametes with extra or missing chromosomes.

18. Suppose you read in the newspaper that a genetic engineering laboratory has developed a procedure for fusing two gametes from the same person (two eggs or two sperm) to form a zygote. The article mentions that an early step in the procedure prevents crossing over from occurring during the formation of the gametes in the donor's body. The researchers are in the process of determining the genetic makeup of one of their new zygotes. Which of the following predictions do you think they would make? Justify your choice, and explain why you rejected each of the other choices.
    a. The zygote would have 46 chromosomes, all of which came from the gamete donor (its one parent), so the zygote would be genetically identical to the gamete donor.
    b. The zygote *could* be genetically identical to the gamete donor, but it is much more likely that it would have an unpredictable mixture of chromosomes from the gamete donor's parents.
    c. The zygote would not be genetically identical to the gamete donor, but it would be genetically identical to one of the donor's parents.
    d. The zygote would not be genetically identical to the gamete donor, but it would be genetically identical to one of the donor's grandparents.
19. Bacteria are able to divide on a faster schedule than eukaryotic cells. Some bacteria can divide every 20 minutes, while the minimum time required by eukaryotic cells in a rapidly developing embryo is about once per hour, and most cells divide much less often than that. State several testable hypotheses explaining why bacteria can divide at a faster rate than eukaryotic cells.
20. Red blood cells, which carry oxygen to body tissues, live for only about 120 days. Replacement cells are produced by cell division in bone marrow. How many cell divisions must occur each second in your bone marrow just to replace red blood cells? Here is some information to use in calculating your answer: There are about 5 million red blood cells per cubic millimeter (mm^3) of blood. An average adult has about 5 L (5,000 cm^3) of blood. (*Hint*: What is the total number of red blood cells in the body? What fraction of them must be replaced each day if all are replaced in 120 days?)
21. A mule is the offspring of a horse and a donkey. A donkey sperm contains 31 chromosomes and a horse egg cell contains 32 chromosomes, so the zygote contains a total of 63 chromosomes. The zygote develops normally. The combined set of chromosomes is not a problem in mitosis, and the mule combines some of the best characteristics of horses and donkeys. However, a mule is sterile; meiosis cannot occur normally in its testes (or ovaries). Explain why mitosis is normal in cells containing both horse and donkey chromosomes but the mixed set of chromosomes interferes with meiosis.
22. **SCIENTIFIC THINKING** The personalized cancer therapy study described in Module 8.10 began with a single bladder cancer patient. This patient, unlike many others, responded well to treatment with the drug everolimus. Many scientific studies begin with a detailed examination of an unusual case like this; the goal is to understand the underlying cause and use this information to understand (and help) more individuals. How could this approach be extended from the data presented in Table 8.10? Do you see any unusual results that could prompt another round of study? How might such a study be designed?

Answers to all questions can be found in Appendix 4.

Patterns of Inheritance

The people of Tibet occupy a high-altitude region of the Himalayan mountains and are renowned for their mountaineering skills. For centuries, westerners have marveled at their uncanny ability to live and work at altitudes above 13,000 feet, where the amount of oxygen that reaches the blood is 40% less than at sea level. Without extensive conditioning, most people from other regions can hardly walk under such conditions, let alone carry heavy loads.

What makes the Tibetan people so able to tolerate their harsh surroundings? The answer lies, at least in part, in their genes: Over the last several thousand years, the Tibetan population has accumulated several dozen genetic mutations that affect their circulatory and respiratory systems. Tibetans commonly have versions of these genes that are rare among their low-dwelling Chinese neighbors. A newborn with such mutations is three times more likely to survive a high-altitude infancy, an advantage that clearly increases fitness in this environment and so is favored by natural selection.

Are humans evolving?

In this chapter, we'll examine the rules that govern how inherited traits are passed from parents to offspring. We'll look at several different patterns of inheritance and investigate how we can predict the ratios of offspring with particular traits. Most important, we'll uncover a basic biological concept: how the behavior of chromosomes during gamete formation and fertilization (discussed in Chapter 8) accounts for the patterns of inheritance we observe. Along the way, we'll consider many examples of how genetic principles can help us understand the biology of humans, plants, and many other familiar creatures.

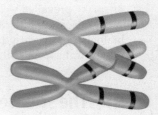

9.1 The study of genetics has ancient roots

Attempts to explain inheritance date back at least to the ancient Greek physician Hippocrates (Figure 9.1). He suggested that particles called "pangenes" travel from each part of an organism's body to the eggs or sperm and then are passed to the next generation; moreover, Hippocrates argued, changes that occur in the body during an organism's life are passed on in this way.

Hippocrates's idea is incorrect in several respects. The reproductive cells are not composed of particles from somatic (body) cells, and changes in somatic cells do not influence eggs and sperm. For instance, no matter how many years you endure orthodontic braces, cells in your mouth do not transmit genetic information to your gametes, and there is no higher likelihood that your offspring will have straight teeth just because you wore braces. This may seem like common sense today, but the idea that traits acquired during an individual's lifetime are passed on to offspring prevailed well into the 19th century.

By observing inheritance patterns in ornamental plants, biologists of the early 19th century established that offspring inherit traits from both parents. The favored explanation of

▲ **Figure 9.1** Hippocrates (approximately 460–370 BCE)

inheritance then became the "blending" hypothesis, the idea that the hereditary materials contributed by the male and female parents mix in forming the offspring similar to the way that blue and yellow paints blend to make green. For example, according to this hypothesis, after the genetic information for the colors of black and chocolate brown Labrador retrievers is blended, the colors should be as inseparable as paint pigments. But this is not what happens: Instead, the offspring of a purebred black Lab and a purebred brown Lab will all be black, but some of the dogs in the next generation will be brown (you'll learn why in Module 9.5). The blending hypothesis was finally rejected because it does not explain how traits that disappear in one generation can reappear in later ones.

? Imagine you have two different houseplants of the same species, one of which blooms with white flowers and the other with red flowers. Design a simple experiment to test the blending hypothesis.

● Cross the two plants and observe the resulting flower color in the offspring. The blending hypothesis predicts the appearance of pink flowers.

9.2 The science of genetics began in an abbey garden

Heredity is the transmission of traits from one generation to the next. The field of **genetics**, the scientific study of heredity, began in the 1860s, when an Augustinian monk named Gregor Mendel (Figure 9.2A) deduced the fundamental principles of genetics by breeding garden peas. Mendel lived and worked in an abbey in Brunn, Austria (now Brno, in the Czech Republic). His research was strongly influenced by his study of physics, mathematics, and chemistry at the University of Vienna; the research was both experimentally and mathematically rigorous, and these qualities were largely responsible for his success.

▲ **Figure 9.2A** Gregor Mendel

In a classic paper published in 1866, Mendel correctly argued that parents pass discrete "heritable factors" on to their offspring. (It is interesting to note that Mendel's landmark publication appeared just seven years after Darwin's 1859 publication of *The Origin of Species*, making the 1860s a banner decade in the development of modern biology.) Mendel stressed that the heritable factors, today called genes,

retain their individuality generation after generation. That is, genes are like playing cards: A deck may be shuffled, but the cards always retain their original identities, and no card is ever blended with another. Similarly, genes may be sorted, but each gene permanently retains its identity.

Mendel probably chose to study garden peas because they had short generation times, produced large numbers of offspring from each mating, and came in many readily distinguishable varieties. For example, one variety has purple flowers, and another variety has white flowers. A heritable feature that varies among individuals, such as flower color, is called a **character**. Each variant for a character, such as purple or white flowers, is called a **trait**. Perhaps the most important advantage of pea plants as an experimental model was that Mendel could strictly control matings. As **Figure 9.2B** shows, the petals of the pea flower almost completely enclose the reproductive organs: the stamens and carpel.

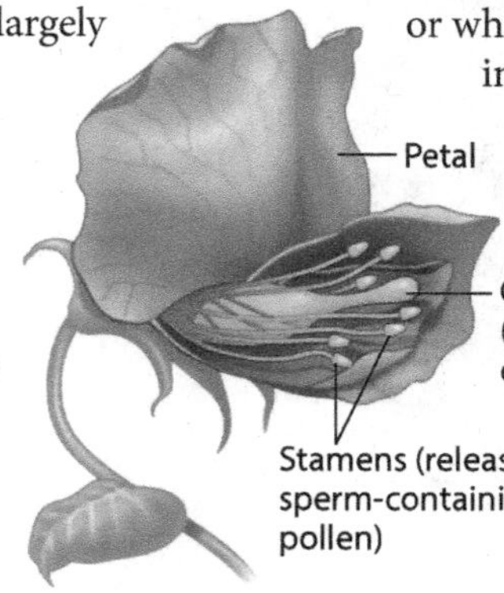

Petal

Carpel (contains eggs)

Stamens (release sperm-containing pollen)

◀ **Figure 9.2B** The anatomy of a garden pea flower (with one petal removed to improve visibility)

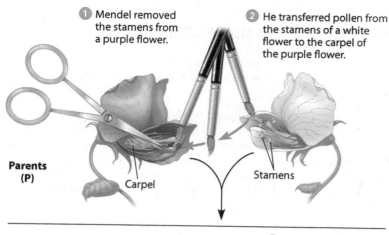

1 Mendel removed the stamens from a purple flower.

2 He transferred pollen from the stamens of a white flower to the carpel of the purple flower.

Parents (P)

Carpel

Stamens

3 The pollinated carpel matured into a pod.

4 Mendel planted seeds from the pod.

Offspring (F₁)

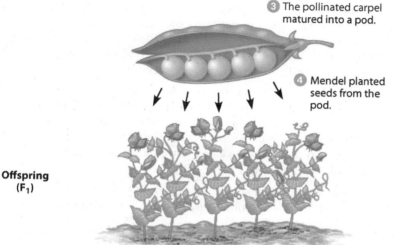

▲ **Figure 9.2C** Mendel's technique for cross-fertilization of pea plants

Consequently, pea plants usually are able to self-fertilize in nature. That is, sperm-carrying pollen grains released from the stamens land on the egg-containing carpel of the same flower. Mendel could ensure self-fertilization by covering a flower with a small bag so that no pollen from another plant could reach the carpel. When he wanted cross-fertilization (fertilization of one plant by pollen from a different plant), he used the method shown in **Figure 9.2C**. **1** He prevented self-fertilization by cutting off the immature stamens of a plant before they produced pollen. **2** To cross-fertilize the stamenless flower, he dusted its carpel with pollen from another plant. After pollination, **3** the carpel developed into a pod, containing seeds (peas) that **4** he later planted. The seeds grew into offspring plants. Through these methods, Mendel could always be sure of the parentage of new plants.

Mendel's success was due to his experimental approach and choice of organism and to his selection of characters to study. He chose to observe seven characters, each of which occurred as two distinct traits (**Figure 9.2D**). Mendel worked with his plants until he was sure he had **true-breeding** varieties—that is, varieties for which self-fertilization produced offspring all identical to the parent. For instance, he identified a purple-flowered variety that, when self-fertilized, produced offspring plants that all had purple flowers.

Mendel was then ready to ask what would happen when he crossed his different true-breeding varieties with each other. For example, what offspring would result if plants with purple flowers and plants with white flowers were cross-fertilized? The offspring of two different varieties are called **hybrids**, and the cross-fertilization itself is referred to as a hybridization, or simply a genetic **cross**. The true-breeding parents are called the **P generation** (P for parental), and their hybrid offspring are called the **F₁ generation** (F for *filial*, from the Latin word for "son"). When F₁ plants self-fertilize or fertilize each other, their offspring are the **F₂ generation**.

Mendel's quantitative analysis of the F₂ plants from thousands of genetic crosses allowed him to deduce the fundamental principles of heredity. We turn to Mendel's results next.

> **?** Describe three generations of your own family using the terminology of a genetic cross (P, F₁, F₂).
>
> ● The P generation is your grandparents, the F₁ your parents, and the F₂ is you (and any siblings).

Character	Traits	
	Dominant	**Recessive**
Flower color	Purple	White
Flower position	Axial	Terminal
Seed color	Yellow	Green
Seed shape	Round	Wrinkled
Pod shape	Inflated	Constricted
Pod color	Green	Yellow
Stem length	Tall	Dwarf

▲ **Figure 9.2D** The seven pea characters studied by Mendel

9.3 Mendel's law of segregation describes the inheritance of a single character

Mendel performed many experiments in which he tracked the inheritance of characters that occur in two forms, such as flower color. The results led him to formulate several hypotheses about inheritance. Let's look at some of his experiments and follow the reasoning that led to his hypotheses.

Figure 9.3A starts with a cross between a true-breeding pea plant with purple flowers and a true-breeding pea plant with white flowers. This is an example of a **monohybrid cross** because it follows just one character—flower color. Mendel observed that F_1 plants all had purple flowers. Was the white-flowered plant's genetic contribution to the hybrids lost? By mating the F_1 plants with each other, Mendel found the answer to be no. Out of 929 F_2 plants, 705 (about $\frac{3}{4}$) had purple flowers and 224 (about $\frac{1}{4}$) had white flowers. That is, there are about three plants with purple flowers for every one with white flowers, or a 3:1 ratio of purple to white. Mendel reasoned that the heritable factor for white flowers did not disappear in the F_1 plants but was masked when the purple-flower factor was present. He also deduced that the F_1 plants must have carried two factors for the flower-color character, one for purple and one for white. From these results and others, Mendel developed four hypotheses, described here using modern terminology, such as "gene" instead of "heritable factor."

1. *There are alternative versions of genes that account for variations in inherited characters.* For example, the gene for flower color in pea plants exists in two versions: one for purple and the other for white. Alternative versions of a gene are called **alleles**.

2. *For each character, an organism inherits two alleles, one from each parent.* These alleles may be identical or they may differ. An organism that has two identical alleles for a gene is said to be **homozygous** for that gene (and is a "homozygote" for that trait). An organism that has two different alleles for a gene is said to be **heterozygous** for that gene (and is a "heterozygote").

3. *If the two alleles of an inherited pair differ, then one determines the organism's appearance and is called the* **dominant allele**; *the other has no noticeable effect on the organism's appearance and is called the* **recessive allele**. Geneticists use uppercase italic letters to represent dominant alleles and lowercase italic letters to represent recessive alleles.

4. *A sperm or egg carries only one allele for each inherited character because allele pairs separate (segregate) from each other during the production of gametes.* This statement is called the **law of segregation**. When sperm and egg unite at fertilization, each contributes its allele, restoring the paired condition in the offspring.

Do Mendel's hypotheses account for the 3:1 ratio he observed in the F_2 generation? Figure 9.3B illustrates Mendel's law

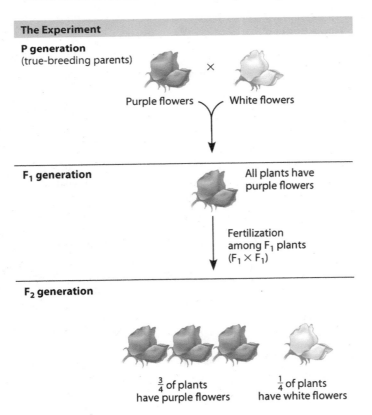

The Experiment

P generation
(true-breeding parents)

Purple flowers × White flowers

F₁ generation
All plants have purple flowers

Fertilization among F_1 plants ($F_1 \times F_1$)

F₂ generation

$\frac{3}{4}$ of plants have purple flowers

$\frac{1}{4}$ of plants have white flowers

▲ Figure 9.3A   A monohybrid cross that tracks one character (flower color)

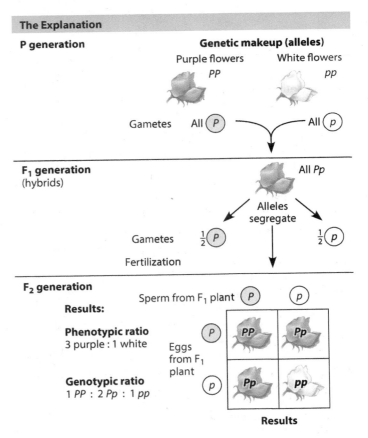

The Explanation

P generation

Genetic makeup (alleles)

Purple flowers — PP White flowers — pp

Gametes   All P All p

F₁ generation
(hybrids)

All Pp

Alleles segregate

Gametes $\frac{1}{2}$ P $\frac{1}{2}$ p

Fertilization

F₂ generation

Results:

Phenotypic ratio
3 purple : 1 white

Genotypic ratio
1 PP : 2 Pp : 1 pp

Sperm from F_1 plant P p

Eggs from F_1 plant P : PP Pp p : Pp pp

Results

▲ Figure 9.3B   An explanation of the crosses in Figure 9.3A

of segregation, which explains the inheritance pattern shown in Figure 9.3A. Mendel's hypotheses predict that when alleles segregate during gamete formation in the F_1 plants, half the gametes will receive a purple-flower allele (P) and the other half a white-flower allele (p). During pollination among the F_1 plants, the gametes unite randomly. An egg with a purple-flower allele has an equal chance of being fertilized by a sperm with a purple-flower allele or one with a white-flower allele (that is, a P egg may fuse with a P sperm or a p sperm). Because the same is true for an egg with a white-flower allele (a p egg with a P sperm or p sperm), there are a total of four equally likely combinations of sperm and egg in the F_2 generation.

The diagram at the bottom of Figure 9.3B, called a **Punnett square**, repeats the cross shown in Figure 9.3A in a way that highlights the four possible combinations of gametes and the resulting four possible offspring in the F_2 generation. Each square represents an equally probable product of fertilization. For example, the box in the upper right corner of the Punnett square shows the genetic combination resulting from a p sperm fertilizing a P egg.

According to the Punnett square, what will be the physical appearance of these F_2 offspring? One-fourth of the plants have two alleles specifying purple flowers (PP); clearly, these plants will have purple flowers. One-half (two-fourths) of the F_2 offspring have inherited one allele for purple flowers and one allele for white flowers (Pp); like the F_1 plants, these plants will also have purple flowers, the dominant trait. (Note that Pp and pP are equivalent and usually written as Pp.) Finally, one-fourth of the F_2 plants have inherited two alleles specifying white flowers (pp) and will express this recessive trait. Thus, Mendel's model accounts for the 3:1 ratio that he observed in the F_2 generation.

Because an organism's appearance does not always reveal its genetic composition, geneticists distinguish between an organism's physical traits, called its **phenotype** (such as purple or white flowers), and its genetic makeup, its **genotype** (in this example, PP, Pp, or pp). So now we see that Figure 9.3A shows just phenotypes, whereas Figure 9.3B shows both phenotypes and genotypes in our sample crosses. For the F_2 plants, the ratio of plants with purple flowers to those with white flowers (3:1) is called the phenotypic ratio. The genotypic ratio, as shown by the Punnett square, is 1PP : 2Pp : 1pp.

Mendel found that each of the seven characters he studied exhibited the same inheritance pattern: One parental trait disappeared in the F_1 generation, only to reappear in $\frac{1}{4}$ of the F_2 offspring. The mechanism underlying this inheritance pattern is stated by Mendel's law of segregation: *Pairs of alleles segregate (separate) during gamete formation; the fusion of gametes at fertilization creates allele pairs once again.* Research since Mendel's time has established that the law of segregation applies to all sexually reproducing organisms, including humans.

Later in this chapter, we'll return to Mendel and his experiments with pea plants (in Module 9.5). But first, we'll investigate how cell division (the topic of Chapter 8) fits with what we've learned about genetics so far.

? **How can two plants with different genotypes for a particular inherited character be identical in phenotype?**

● One could be homozygous for the dominant allele and the other heterozygous.

9.4 Homologous chromosomes bear the alleles for each character

Figure 9.4 shows a pair of homologous chromosomes. The chromosomes in a homologous pair—chromosomes that carry alleles of the same genes—are also called homologs. Recall that every diploid cell, whether from a pea plant or a person, has pairs of homologous chromosomes. One member of each pair comes from the organism's female parent and the other member of each pair comes from the male parent.

Each labeled band on the chromosomes in Figure 9.4 represents a gene **locus** (plural, *loci*), a specific location of a gene along the chromosome. You can see the connection between Mendel's law of segregation and homologous chromosomes: Alleles (alternative versions) of a gene reside at the same locus on homologous chromosomes. However, the two chromosomes may bear either identical alleles at a locus (as in the P/P and a/a loci) or different alleles (as in the B/b locus)—the organisms may be homozygous or heterozygous for the gene at any particular locus. We will return to the chromosomal basis of Mendel's law later in the chapter.

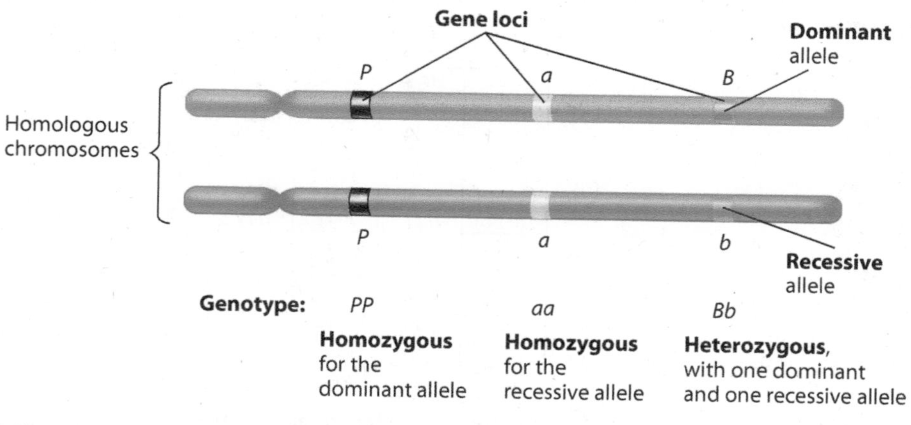

? **An individual is heterozygous, *Bb*, for a gene. According to the law of segregation, each gamete formed by this individual will have *either* the B allele *or* the b allele. Which step in the process of meiosis is the physical basis for this segregation of alleles? (*Hint*: See Figure 8.12.)**

● The B and b alleles are located at the same gene locus on homologous chromosomes, which separate during meiosis I and are packaged in separate gametes during meiosis II.

▲ Figure 9.4   Three gene loci on homologous chromosomes

9.5 The law of independent assortment is revealed by tracking two characters at once

Recall from Module 9.3 that Mendel deduced his law of segregation by following through the F_1 and F_2 generations one character from the P generation. From such monohybrid crosses, Mendel knew that the allele for round seed shape (designated R) was dominant to the allele for wrinkled seed shape (r) and that the allele for yellow seed color (Y) was dominant to the allele for green seed color (y). Mendel wondered: What would happen if he crossed plants that differ in both seed shape and seed color?

To find out, Mendel set up a **dihybrid cross**, a mating of parental varieties differing in two characters. Mendel crossed homozygous plants having round yellow seeds (genotype $RRYY$) with plants having wrinkled green seeds ($rryy$). Mendel knew that an $RRYY$ plant would produce only gametes with RY alleles; an $rryy$ plant would produce only gametes with ry alleles. Therefore, Mendel knew there was only one possible outcome for the F_1 generation: The union of RY and ry gametes would yield hybrids heterozygous for both characters ($RrYy$)—that is, dihybrids. All of these $RrYy$ offspring would have round yellow seeds, the double dominant phenotype.

The F_2 generation is trickier to predict. To find out if genes for seed color and shape would be transmitted as a package, Mendel crossed the $RrYy$ F_1 plants with each other. He hypothesized two outcomes from this experiment: Either the dihybrid cross would exhibit *dependent* assortment, with the alleles for seed color and seed shape inherited together as they came from the P generation, or it would exhibit *independent* assortment, with the genes inherited independently.

As shown on the left side of **Figure 9.5A**, the hypothesis of dependent assortment leads to the prediction that each F_2 plant would inherit one of two possible sperm (RY or ry) and one of two possible eggs (RY or ry), for a total of four combinations. The Punnett square shows that there could be only

two F_2 phenotypes—round yellow or wrinkled green—in a 3:1 ratio. However, when Mendel actually performed this cross, he did not obtain these results, thus refuting the hypothesis of dependent assortment.

The alternative hypothesis—that the genes would exhibit independent assortment—is shown on the right side of Figure 9.5A. This leads to the prediction that the F_1 plants would produce four different gametes: RY, rY, Ry, and ry. Each F_2 plant would inherit one of four possible sperm and one of four possible eggs, for a total of 16 possible combinations. Fertilization among these gametes would lead to four different seed phenotypes—round yellow, round green, wrinkled yellow, or wrinkled green—in a 9:3:3:1 ratio. In fact, Mendel observed such a ratio in the F_2 plants, indicating that each pair of alleles segregates independently of the other.

From the 9:3:3:1 ratio, we can see that there are 12 plants with round seeds to 4 with wrinkled seeds, and 12 yellow-seeded plants to 4 green-seeded ones. These 12:4 ratios each reduce to 3:1, which is the F_2 ratio for a monohybrid cross. In other words, an independent monohybrid cross is occurring for each of the two characters. Mendel tried his seven pea characters in various dihybrid combinations and always obtained data close to the predicted 9:3:3:1 ratio. These results supported the hypothesis that each pair of alleles segregates independently of other pairs of alleles during gamete formation. Put another way, the inheritance of one character has no effect on the inheritance of another. This is referred to as Mendel's **law of independent assortment**.

Figure 9.5B shows how this law applies to the inheritance of two characters controlled by separate genes in Labrador retrievers: black versus chocolate coat color and normal vision versus progressive retinal atrophy (PRA), an eye disorder that leads to blindness. Black Labs have at least one copy of an allele, B, that gives their hairs densely packed granules of a dark pigment. The B allele is dominant to the b allele, which leads to a less tightly packed distribution of pigment. As a result, the coats of dogs with genotype bb are chocolate in color. The

▼ Figure 9.5A
Two hypotheses for segregation in a dihybrid cross

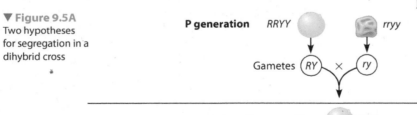

P generation: $RRYY$ $rryy$
Gametes: RY × ry

F₁ generation: $RrYy$

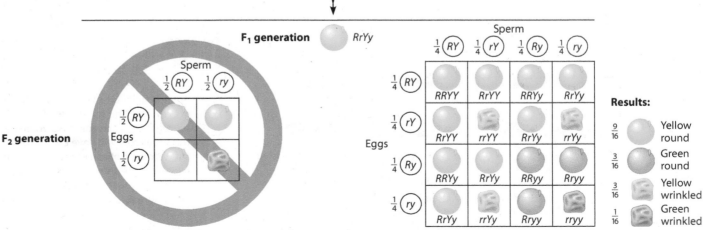

The hypothesis of dependent assortment
Not actually seen; hypothesis refuted

The hypothesis of independent assortment
Actual results; hypothesis supported

Results:

$\frac{9}{16}$	Yellow round
$\frac{3}{16}$	Green round
$\frac{3}{16}$	Yellow wrinkled
$\frac{1}{16}$	Green wrinkled

allele that causes PRA, *n*, is recessive to allele *N*, which is necessary for normal vision. Thus, only dogs of genotype *nn* become blind from PRA. In the top of this figure, blanks in the genotypes are used where a particular phenotype may result from multiple genotypes. For example, a black Lab may have either genotype *BB* or *Bb*, which we abbreviate as *B_*.)

The lower part of Figure 9.5B shows what happens when we mate two heterozygous Labs, both of genotype *BbNn*. The F_2 phenotypic ratio will be nine black dogs with normal eyes

to three black with PRA to three chocolate with normal eyes to one chocolate with PRA. These 9:3:3:1 results are analogous to the results in Figure 9.5A and demonstrate that the alleles for the *B* and *N* genes are inherited independently.

> **?** Predict the phenotypes of offspring obtained by mating a black Lab homozygous for both coat color and normal eyes with a chocolate Lab that is blind from PRA.

All offspring would be black with normal eyes (*BBNN × bbnn → BbNn*).

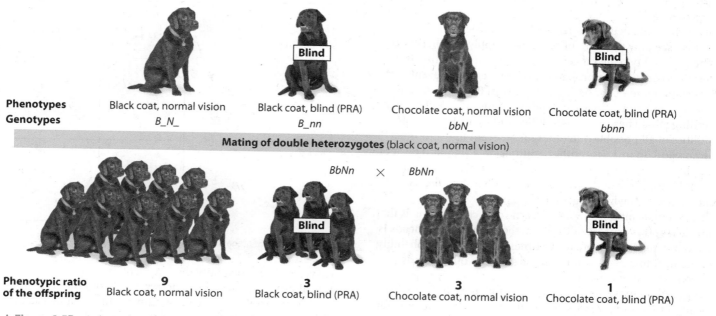

Phenotypes	Black coat, normal vision	Black coat, blind (PRA)	Chocolate coat, normal vision	Chocolate coat, blind (PRA)
Genotypes	*B_N_*	*B_nn*	*bbN_*	*bbnn*

Mating of double heterozygotes (black coat, normal vision)

BbNn × *BbNn*

Phenotypic ratio of the offspring	**9**	**3**	**3**	**1**
	Black coat, normal vision	Black coat, blind (PRA)	Chocolate coat, normal vision	Chocolate coat, blind (PRA)

▲ **Figure 9.5B**   Independent assortment of two genes in Labrador retrievers

Try This   Rewrite the cross shown in this figure using a Punnett square, like the one used in the previous figure. You should get the same results!

9.6 Geneticists can use a testcross to determine unknown genotypes

Suppose you have a chocolate Lab. Referring to Figure 9.5B, you can tell that its genotype must be *bb*. But what if you had a black Lab? It could have one of two possible genotypes—

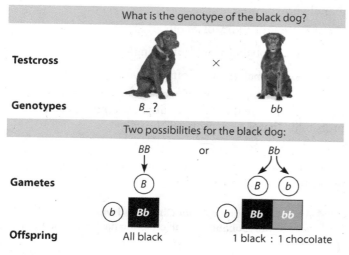

What is the genotype of the black dog?

Testcross		×
Genotypes	*B_?*	*bb*

Two possibilities for the black dog:

	BB	or	*Bb*
Gametes	*B*		*B* *b*

		b	**Bb**
Offspring	All black		1 black : 1 chocolate

▲ **Figure 9.6**   Using a testcross to determine genotype

BB or *Bb*—and there is no way to tell simply by looking at the dog. To determine your dog's genotype, you could perform a **testcross**, a mating between an individual of unknown genotype (your black Lab) and a homozygous recessive (*bb*) individual—in this case, a chocolate Lab.

Figure 9.6 shows the offspring that could result from such a mating. If, as shown on the bottom left, the black-coated parent's genotype is *BB*, all the offspring would be black because a cross between genotypes *BB* and *bb* can produce only *Bb* offspring. On the other hand, if the black parent is *Bb*, as shown on the bottom right, we would expect both black (*Bb*) and chocolate (*bb*) offspring. Thus, the appearance of the offspring reveals the original black dog's genotype.

To understand the results of any genetic cross, you need to understand the rules of probability, our next topic.

> **?** You use a testcross to determine the genotype of a Lab with normal eyes. Half of the offspring are normal and half develop PRA. What is the genotype of the normal parent?

Heterozygous (*Nn*)

9.7 Mendel's laws reflect the rules of probability

Mendel's strong background in mathematics served him well in his studies of inheritance. He understood, for instance, that the segregation of allele pairs during gamete formation and the re-forming of pairs at fertilization obey the rules of probability—the same rules that apply to the tossing of coins, the rolling of dice, and the drawing of cards. Mendel also appreciated the statistical nature of inheritance. He knew that he needed to obtain large samples—to count many offspring from his crosses—before he could begin to interpret inheritance patterns.

Let's see how the rules of probability apply to inheritance. The probability scale ranges from 0 to 1. An event that is certain to occur has a probability of 1, whereas an event that is certain *not* to occur has a probability of 0. For example, a tossed coin has a $\frac{1}{2}$ chance of landing heads and a $\frac{1}{2}$ chance of landing tails. These two possibilities add up to 1; the probabilities of all possible outcomes for an event to occur must always add up to 1. In another example, in a standard deck of 52 playing cards, the chance of drawing a jack of diamonds is $\frac{1}{52}$ and the chance of drawing any card other than the jack of diamonds is $\frac{51}{52}$, which together add up to 1.

An important lesson we can learn from coin tossing is that for each and every toss of the coin, the probability of heads is $\frac{1}{2}$. Even if heads has landed five times in a row, the probability of the next toss coming up heads is still $\frac{1}{2}$. In other words, the outcome of any particular toss is unaffected by what has happened on previous attempts. Each toss is an independent event. If two coins are tossed simultaneously, the outcome for each coin is an independent event, unaffected by the other coin. What is the chance that both coins will land heads up when tossed together? The probability of such a dual event is the product of the separate probabilities of the independent events; for the coins, $\frac{1}{2} \times \frac{1}{2} = \frac{1}{4}$. This statistical principle is called the **rule of multiplication**, and it holds true for independent events in genetics as well as coin tosses.

Figure 9.7 offers a visual analogy of a cross between F_1 Labrador retrievers that have the *Bb* genotype for coat color. The genetic cross is portrayed by the tossing of two coins that stand in for the two gametes (a dime for the egg and a penny for the sperm); the heads side of each coin stands for the dominant *B* allele and the tails side of each coin the recessive *b* allele. What is the probability that a particular F_2 dog will have the *bb* genotype? To produce a *bb* offspring, both egg and sperm must carry the *b* allele. The probability that an egg will have the *b* allele is $\frac{1}{2}$, and the probability that a sperm will have the *b* allele is also $\frac{1}{2}$. By the rule of multiplication, the probability that the two *b* alleles will come together at fertilization is $\frac{1}{2} \times \frac{1}{2} = \frac{1}{4}$. This is exactly the answer given by the Punnett square in Figure 9.7. If we know the genotypes of the parents, we can predict the probability for any genotype among the offspring.

Now consider the probability that an F_2 Lab will be heterozygous for the coat-color gene. As Figure 9.7 shows, there are two ways in which F_1 gametes can combine to produce a heterozygous offspring. The dominant (*B*) allele can come from the egg and the recessive (*b*) allele from the sperm, or

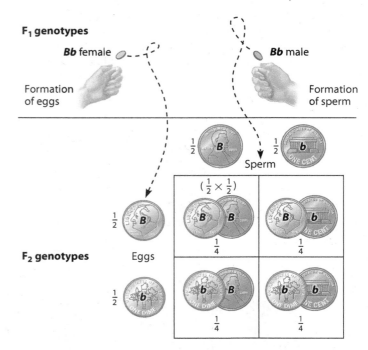

▲ **Figure 9.7** Segregation and fertilization as chance events

vice versa. The probability that an event can occur in two or more alternative ways can be determined from the sum of the separate probabilities of the alternatives; this is known as the **rule of addition**. Using this rule, we can calculate the probability of an F_2 heterozygote as $\frac{1}{4} + \frac{1}{4} = \frac{1}{2}$.

By applying the rules of probability to segregation and independent assortment, we can solve some rather complex genetics problems. For instance, we can predict the results of trihybrid crosses, in which three different characters are involved. Consider a cross between two organisms that both have the genotype *AaBbCc*. What is the probability that an offspring from this cross will be a recessive homozygote for all three genes (*aabbcc*)? Because each allele pair assorts independently, we can treat this trihybrid cross as three separate monohybrid crosses:

Aa × Aa: Probability of *aa* offspring $= \frac{1}{4}$

Bb × Bb: Probability of *bb* offspring $= \frac{1}{4}$

Cc × Cc: Probability of *cc* offspring $= \frac{1}{4}$

Because the segregation of each allele pair is an independent event, we use the rule of multiplication to calculate the probability that the offspring will be *aabbcc*:

$\frac{1}{4}aa \times \frac{1}{4} bb \times \frac{1}{4}cc = \frac{1}{64}$

We could reach the same conclusion by constructing a 64-section Punnett square, but that would take a lot of space!

> **?** A plant of genotype *AABbCC* is crossed with an *AaBbCc* plant. What is the probability of an offspring having the genotype *AABBCC*?

$\bullet$ ⅟₁₆ (that is, $\frac{1}{2} \times \frac{1}{4} \times \frac{1}{2}$)

9.8 Genetic traits in humans can be tracked through family pedigrees

Although Mendel developed his laws of inheritance while working with peas, these principles apply to the inheritance of many human traits just as well. How are human traits studied? We obviously cannot perform testcrosses on people, so geneticists must analyze the results of matings that have already occurred. First, a geneticist collects information about a family's history for a trait. This information is assembled into a family tree, called a **pedigree**, that describes the traits of parents and children across generations. Here, you can see a pedigree that traces the incidence of straight hairline versus a "widow's peak" (pointed) hairline through three generations of a hypothetical family. Notice that Mendel's laws and simple logic enable us to deduce the genotypes for nearly every person in the pedigree.

READING A PEDIGREE

A horizontal line connecting two people represents a mating.

KEY

Female Male
- ○ □ Widow's peak hairline trait
- ● ■ Straight hairline trait

H: widow's peak allele
h: straight allele

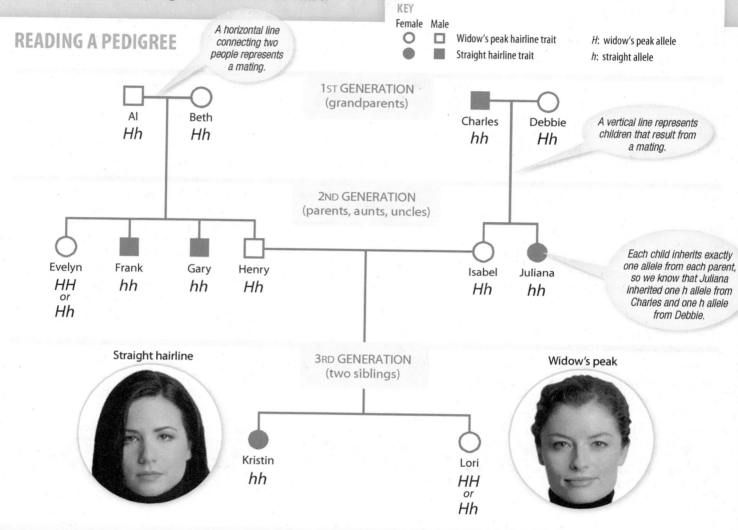

A vertical line represents children that result from a mating.

Each child inherits exactly one allele from each parent, so we know that Juliana inherited one *h* allele from Charles and one *h* allele from Debbie.

1ST GENERATION (grandparents)

Al *Hh* — Beth *Hh* Charles *hh* — Debbie *Hh*

2ND GENERATION (parents, aunts, uncles)

Evelyn *HH* or *Hh* Frank *hh* Gary *hh* Henry *Hh* Isabel *Hh* Juliana *hh*

3RD GENERATION (two siblings)

Straight hairline — Kristin *hh* Lori *HH* or *Hh* — Widow's peak

▶ Kristin has a straight hairline but neither of her parents (Henry and Isabel) do. This is only possible if the trait is recessive. We therefore know that Kristin and every other individual with a straight hairline must be homozygous recessive *hh*.

▶ Henry and Isabel must each have a copy of the *h* allele, because they each passed one on to daughter Kristin. And because they both have widow's peaks, they must each be heterozygous (*Hh*).

▶ Grandparents Al and Beth must both be *Hh* because they both had widow's peaks, but two of their sons (Frank and Gary) had straight hairlines and must therefore be *hh*.

▶ We cannot deduce the genotype of every member of the pedigree. Lori must have at least one *H* allele (since she has a widow's peak), but she could be either *HH* or *Hh*. We cannot distinguish between these two possibilities using the available data.

? If Lori had a child, which phenotype would allow her to deduce her own genotype for certain?

● If her child had a straight hairline (*hh*), then Lori would know that she herself must be *Hh*.

9.9 Many inherited traits in humans are controlled by a single gene

CONNECTION

In the previous module, you studied an example of a human character (widow's peak) controlled by simple dominant-recessive inheritance of one gene.

Figure 9.9A shows two more examples. (The genetic underpinnings of many other human characters, such as eye and hair color, are more complex and as yet poorly understood.) A trait being dominant does not mean that it is "normal" or more common than a recessive trait; **wild-type traits**—those seen most often in nature—are not necessarily specified by dominant alleles. Rather, dominance means that a heterozygote (*Aa*) displays the dominant phenotype. By contrast, the phenotype of a recessive allele is seen only in a homozygote (*aa*). Recessive traits may in fact be more common in the population than dominant ones. For example, the absence of freckles (a dominant trait) is more common than their presence. The term mutant trait refers to a trait that is less common in nature.

The genetic disorders listed in **Table 9.9** are known to be inherited as dominant or recessive traits controlled by a single gene. These human disorders show simple inheritance patterns like the traits Mendel studied in pea plants. The genes discussed in this module are all located on autosomes, chromosomes other than the sex chromosomes X and Y (see Module 8.11).

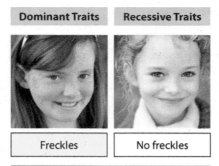

Dominant Traits	Recessive Traits
Freckles	No freckles

Normal pigmentation	Albinism

Key
- ☐ Wild-type (more common) trait
- ☐ Mutant (less common) trait

▲ **Figure 9.9A**   Examples of single-gene inherited traits in humans

Recessive Disorders   Thousands of human genetic disorders—ranging in severity from relatively mild, such as albinism, to invariably fatal, such as cystic fibrosis—are inherited as recessive traits. Remember that the dominant phenotype results from either the homozygous genotype *AA* or the heterozygous genotype *Aa*. Recessive phenotypes result only from the homozygous genotype *aa*. Most people who have recessive disorders are born to normal parents who are both heterozygotes—that is, those parents who are **carriers** of the recessive allele for the disorder but are phenotypically normal.

Using Mendel's laws, we can predict the fraction of affected offspring likely to result from a mating between two carriers (**Figure 9.9B**). Suppose two people who are heterozygous carriers for albinism (*Aa*) had a child. What is the probability that this child would display albinism? Each child of two carriers has a $\frac{1}{4}$ chance of inheriting two recessive alleles. To put it another way, we can say that about one-fourth of the children from such a mating are predicted to display albinism. We can also say that a child with normal pigmentation has a $\frac{2}{3}$ chance of being an *Aa* carrier; that is, on average, two out of three offspring with the pigmented phenotype will be carriers for albinism.

TABLE 9.9 | SOME AUTOSOMAL DISORDERS IN HUMANS

Disorder	Major Symptoms	Incidence	Comments
Recessive Disorders			
Albinism	Lack of pigment in the skin, hair, and eyes	1/22,000	Prone to skin cancer
Cystic fibrosis	Excess mucus in the lungs, digestive tract, liver; increased susceptibility to infections; death in early childhood unless treated	1/2,500 Caucasians	See Module 9.9
Phenylketonuria (PKU)	Accumulation of phenylalanine in blood; lack of normal skin pigment; developmental disabilities	1/10,000 in United States and Europe	See Module 9.10
Sickle-cell disease	Sickled red blood cells; damage to many tissues	1/400 African Americans	See Module 9.13
Tay-Sachs disease	Lipid accumulation in brain cells; mental deficiency; blindness; death in childhood	1/3,600 Jews from central Europe	See Module 4.10
Dominant Disorders			
Achondroplasia	Dwarfism	1/25,000	See Module 9.9
Huntington's disease	Developmental disabilities and uncontrollable movements; strikes in middle age	1/25,000	See Module 9.9
Hypercholesterolemia	Excess cholesterol in the blood; heart disease	1/500 are heterozygous	See Module 9.11

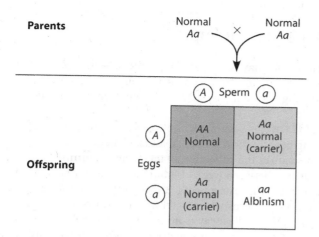

Parents Normal *Aa* × Normal *Aa*

Offspring Eggs

Sperm

	(A)	(a)
(A)	*AA* Normal	*Aa* Normal (carrier)
(a)	*Aa* Normal (carrier)	*aa* Albinism

▲ **Figure 9.9B** Offspring produced by parents who are both carriers for albinism, a recessive disorder

The most common lethal genetic disease in the United States is cystic fibrosis (CF). Affecting about 30,000 Americans, the recessive CF allele is carried by about one in 31 Americans. A person with two copies of this allele has cystic fibrosis, which is characterized by an excessive secretion of very thick mucus from the lungs and other organs. This mucus can interfere with breathing, digestion, and liver function and makes the person vulnerable to recurrent bacterial infections. Although there is no cure for CF, strict adherence to a daily health regimen—including gentle pounding on the chest and back to clear the airway, inhaled antibiotics, and a special diet—can have a profound impact on the health of the affected person. CF was once invariably fatal in childhood, but tremendous advances in treatment have raised the median survival age of Americans with CF to 37.

Cystic fibrosis is most common in Caucasians. In fact, most genetic disorders are not evenly distributed across all ethnic groups. Such uneven distribution is the result of prolonged geographic isolation of certain populations. Isolation (as with settlers of a new island, for example) can lead to matings between close blood relatives. People with recent common ancestors are more likely to carry the same recessive alleles than are unrelated people. Therefore, matings between close relatives may cause the frequency of a rare allele (and the disease it causes) to increase within that community. Geneticists have observed increased incidence of harmful recessive traits among many types of inbred animals. For example, the detrimental effects of inbreeding are seen in some endangered species that recovered from small populations (see Module 13.11). With the increased mobility in most human populations today, it is relatively unlikely that two people who carry a rare, harmful allele will meet and mate.

▲ **Figure 9.9C** Dr. Michael C. Ain, a specialist in the repair of bone defects caused by achondroplasia and related disorders

Dominant Disorders Although most harmful alleles are recessive, a number of human disorders are caused by dominant alleles. Some are harmless conditions, such as extra fingers and toes (called polydactyly) or webbed fingers and toes.

A more serious dominant disorder is achondroplasia, a form of dwarfism in which the head and torso of the body develop normally but the arms and legs are short (**Figure 9.9C**). The homozygous dominant genotype (*AA*) causes death of the embryo; therefore, only heterozygotes (*Aa*) have this disorder. (This also means that a person with achondroplasia has a 50% chance of passing the condition on to any children.) Therefore, all those who do not have achondroplasia, more than 99.99% of the population, are homozygous for the recessive allele (*aa*). This example makes it clear that a dominant allele is not necessarily more common in a population than a corresponding recessive allele.

Dominant alleles that cause lethal diseases are much less common than recessive alleles that cause lethal diseases. One reason is that the dominant lethal allele cannot be carried by heterozygotes without affecting them. Many lethal dominant alleles result from mutations in a sperm or egg that subsequently kill the embryo. And if the afflicted individual is born but does not survive long enough to reproduce, he or she will not pass on the lethal allele to future generations. This is in contrast to lethal recessive mutations, which are perpetuated from generation to generation by healthy heterozygous carriers.

A lethal dominant allele can escape elimination, however, if it does not cause death until a relatively advanced age. One such example is the allele that causes **Huntington's disease**, a degenerative disorder of the nervous system that usually does not appear until middle age. Once the deterioration of the nervous system begins, it is irreversible and inevitably fatal. Because the allele for Huntington's disease is dominant, any child born to a parent with the allele has a 50% chance of inheriting the allele and the disorder. This example makes it clear that a dominant allele is not necessarily "better" than a corresponding recessive allele.

Until relatively recently, the onset of symptoms was the only way to know if a person had inherited the Huntington's allele. This is no longer the case. A genetic test is now available that can detect the presence of the Huntington's allele in an individual's genome. This is one of several genetic tests currently available. We'll explore the topic of personal genetic screening in the next module.

? **Peter is a 30-year-old man whose father died of Huntington's disease. Neither Peter's mother nor a much older sister shows any signs of Huntington's. What is the probability that Peter has inherited Huntington's disease?**

● Since his father had the disease, there is a ½ chance that Peter received the gene. (The genotype of his sister is irrelevant.)

9.10 New technologies can provide insight into one's genetic legacy

Some prospective parents are aware that they have an increased risk of having a baby with a genetic disorder. For example, many pregnant women over age 35 know that they have a heightened risk of bearing children with Down syndrome (see Module 8.20), and some couples are aware that certain genetic diseases run in their families. These prospective parents may want to learn more about their own and their baby's genetic makeup. Modern technologies offer ways to obtain such information.

Genetic Testing   Because most children with recessive disorders are born to healthy parents, the genetic risk for many diseases is determined by whether the prospective parents are carriers of the recessive allele. For an increasing number of genetic disorders, including Tay-Sachs disease, sickle-cell disease, and one form of cystic fibrosis, tests are available that can distinguish between individuals who have no disease-causing alleles and those who are heterozygous carriers. Other parents may know that a dominant but late-appearing disease, such as Huntington's disease, runs in their family.

Such people may benefit from genetic tests for dominant alleles. Information from genetic testing (also called genetic screening) can inform decisions about family planning.

Fetal Testing   Several technologies are available for detecting genetic conditions in a fetus. Genetic testing before birth requires the collection of fetal cells. In **amniocentesis**, performed between weeks 14 and 20 of pregnancy, a physician carefully inserts a needle through the abdomen and into the mother's uterus while watching an ultrasound imager to guide the needle away from the fetus (**Figure 9.10A**, left). The physician extracts about 10 milliliters (2 teaspoons) of the amniotic fluid that bathes the developing fetus. Tests for genetic disorders can be performed on fetal cells that have been isolated from the fluid. These cells are usually cultured in the laboratory for several weeks. By then, enough dividing cells can be harvested to allow karyotyping (see Module 8.19) that will detect chromosomal abnormalities such as Down syndrome. Biochemical tests can also be performed on the cultured cells, revealing conditions such as Tay-Sachs disease.

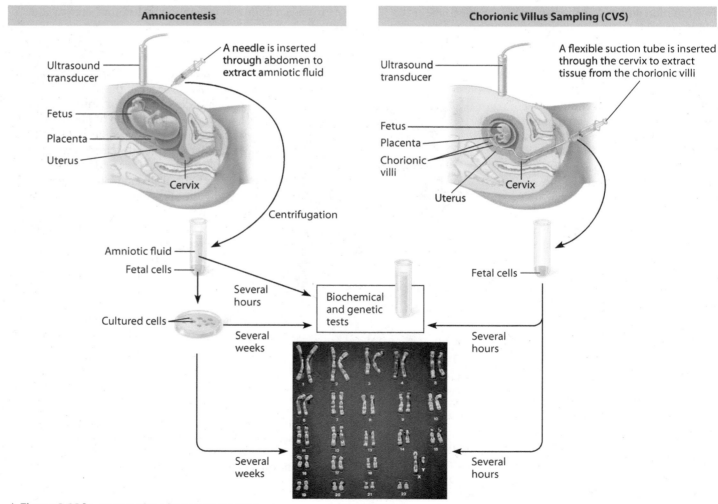

▲ **Figure 9.10A**   Testing a fetus for genetic disorders

In another procedure, **chorionic villus sampling (CVS)**, a physician extracts a tiny sample of chorionic villus tissue from the placenta, the organ that carries nourishment and wastes between the fetus and the mother. The tissue can be obtained using a narrow, flexible tube inserted through the mother's vagina and cervix into the uterus (Figure 9.10A, right). Results of karyotyping and some biochemical tests can be available within 24 hours. The speed of CVS is an advantage over amniocentesis. Another advantage is that CVS can be performed as early as the 8th week of pregnancy.

Unfortunately, both amniocentesis and CVS pose some risk of complications, such as maternal bleeding, miscarriage, or premature birth. Complication rates for amniocentesis and CVS are about 1% and 2%, respectively. Because of the risks, these procedures are usually reserved for situations in which the possibility of a genetic disease is significantly higher than average. Newer genetic screening procedures involve isolating tiny amounts of fetal cells or DNA released into the mother's bloodstream. Although few reliable tests are yet available using this method, this promising and complication-free technology may soon replace more invasive procedures.

Blood tests on the mother at 15 to 20 weeks of pregnancy can help identify fetuses at risk for certain birth defects—and thus candidates for further testing that may require more invasive procedures (such as amniocentesis). The most widely used blood test measures the mother's blood level of alpha-fetoprotein (AFP), a protein produced by the fetus. High levels of AFP may indicate a neural tube defect in the fetus. (The neural tube is an embryonic structure that develops into the brain and spinal cord.) Low levels of AFP may indicate Down syndrome. For a more complete risk profile, a woman's doctor may order a "triple screen test," which measures AFP as well as two other hormones produced by the placenta. Abnormal levels of these substances in the maternal blood may also point to a risk of Down syndrome.

Fetal Imaging   Other techniques enable a physician to examine a fetus directly for anatomical deformities. The most common procedure is **ultrasound imaging**, which uses sound waves to produce a picture of the fetus. **Figure 9.10B** shows an ultrasound scanner, which emits high-frequency sounds, beyond the range of hearing. When the sound waves bounce off the fetus, the echoes produce an image on the monitor. The inset image in Figure 9.10B shows a fetus at about 20 weeks. Traditional ultrasound imaging is noninvasive—no foreign objects are inserted into the mother's body—and has no known risk. Transvaginal ultrasound imaging—during which a probe is placed in the woman's vagina—can be used to provide clear images in early pregnancy. In another imaging method, fetoscopy, a needle-thin tube containing a fiber-optic viewing scope is inserted into the uterus. Fetoscopy can provide highly detailed images of the fetus but, unlike ultrasound, carries risk of complications.

Newborn Screening   Some genetic disorders can be detected at birth by simple tests that are now routinely performed in most hospitals in the United States. One common screening program is for phenylketonuria (PKU), a

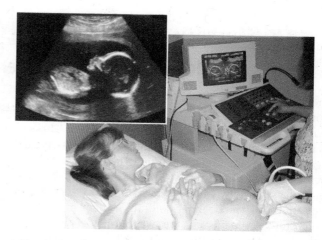

▲ **Figure 9.10B**   Traditional ultrasound scanning of a fetus

recessively inherited disorder that occurs in about one out of every 10,000 births in the United States. Children with this disease cannot properly break down the naturally occurring amino acid phenylalanine, and an accumulation of phenylalanine may lead to developmental disabilities. However, if the deficiency is detected in the newborn, a special diet low in phenylalanine can usually prevent symptoms. Unfortunately, few other genetic disorders are currently treatable.

Ethical Considerations   As new technologies such as fetal imaging and testing become more widespread, geneticists are working to make sure that they do not cause more problems than they solve. Consider the tests for identifying carriers of recessive diseases. Such information may enable people with family histories of genetic disorders to make informed decisions about having children. But these new methods for genetic screening pose problems, too. If confidentiality is breached, will carriers be stigmatized? For example, will they be denied health or life insurance, even though they themselves are healthy? Geneticists stress that patients seeking genetic testing should receive counseling both before and after to clarify their family history, to explain the test, and to help them cope with the results. But with a wealth of genetic information increasingly available, a full discussion of the meaning of the results might be time-consuming and costly, raising the question of who should pay for such counseling.

Couples at risk for conceiving children with genetic disorders may now learn a great deal about their unborn children. In particular, CVS gives parents a chance to become informed very early in pregnancy. What is to be done with such information? If fetal tests reveal a serious disorder, the parents must choose between terminating the pregnancy and preparing themselves for a baby with severe problems. Identifying a genetic disease early can give families time to prepare—emotionally, medically, and financially. The dilemmas posed by human genetics reinforce one of this book's central themes: the immense social implications of biology.

?   What is the primary benefit of genetic screening by CVS? What is the primary risk?

● CVS allows genetic screening to be performed very early in pregnancy and provides quick results, but it carries a risk of miscarriage.

9.11 Incomplete dominance results in intermediate phenotypes

Mendel's two laws explain inheritance in terms of discrete factors—genes—that are passed along from generation to generation according to simple rules of probability. These laws are valid for all sexually reproducing organisms, including garden peas, Labradors, and human beings. But just as the basic rules of musical harmony cannot account for all the rich sounds of a symphony, Mendel's laws stop short of explaining some patterns of genetic inheritance. In fact, for most sexually reproducing organisms, cases where Mendel's laws can strictly account for the patterns of inheritance are relatively rare. More often, the observed inheritance patterns are more complex, as we will see in this and the next four modules.

The F_1 offspring of Mendel's pea crosses always looked like one of the two parental varieties. In this situation—called **complete dominance**—the dominant allele has the same phenotypic effect whether present in one or two copies. But for some characters, the appearance of F_1 hybrids falls between the phenotypes of the two parental varieties, an effect called **incomplete dominance**. For instance, when red snapdragons are crossed with white snapdragons, all the F_1 hybrids have pink flowers (Figure 9.11A). This third phenotype results from flowers of the heterozygote having less red pigment than the red homozygotes.

As the Punnett square at the bottom of Figure 9.11A shows, the F_2 offspring appear in a phenotypic ratio of one red to two pink to one white, as the red and white alleles segregate during gamete formation in the pink F_1 hybrids. In incomplete dominance, the phenotypes of heterozygotes differ from the two homozygous varieties, and the genotypic ratio and the phenotypic ratio are both 1:2:1 in the F_2 generation.

We also see examples of incomplete dominance in humans. One case involves a recessive allele (h) that can cause hypercholesterolemia, dangerously high levels of cholesterol in the blood. Normal individuals are homozygous dominant (HH). Heterozygotes (Hh; about one in 500 people) have blood cholesterol levels about twice normal. They are unusually prone to atherosclerosis, the blockage of arteries by cholesterol buildup in artery walls, and they may have heart attacks from blocked heart arteries by their mid-30s. This form of the disease can often be controlled through changes in diet and by taking statins, a class of medications that can significantly lower blood cholesterol. Hypercholesterolemia is even more serious in homozygous recessive individuals (hh; about one in a million people). Homozygotes have about five times the normal amount of blood cholesterol and may have heart attacks as early as age 2. Homozygous hypercholesterolemia is harder to treat; options include high doses of statin drugs, organ surgeries or transplants, or physically filtering lipids from the blood.

Figure 9.11B illustrates the molecular basis for hypercholesterolemia. The dominant allele (H), which normal individuals carry in duplicate (HH), specifies a cell-surface receptor protein called an LDL receptor. Low-density lipoprotein (LDL, sometimes called "bad cholesterol") is transported in the blood. In certain cells, the LDL receptors mop up excess LDL particles from the blood and promote their breakdown. This process helps prevent the accumulation of cholesterol in arteries. Heterozygotes (Hh) have only half the normal

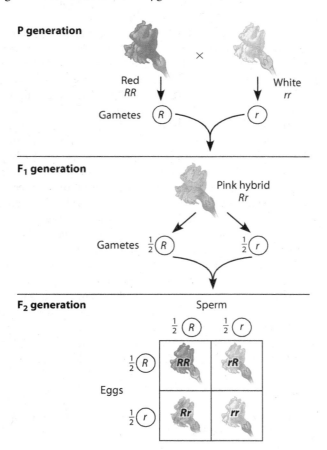

P generation

Red
RR

×

White
rr

Gametes (R) (r)

F₁ generation

Pink hybrid
Rr

Gametes ½(R) ½(r)

F₂ generation Sperm

½(R) ½(r)

½(R) | RR | rR |

Eggs

½(r) | Rr | rr |

▲ Figure 9.11A Incomplete dominance in snapdragon flower color

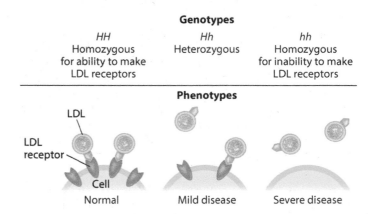

Genotypes

| *HH* | *Hh* | *hh* |
| Homozygous for ability to make LDL receptors | Heterozygous | Homozygous for inability to make LDL receptors |

Phenotypes

LDL

LDL receptor

Cell

Normal | Mild disease | Severe disease

▲ Figure 9.11B Incomplete dominance in human hypercholesterolemia number of LDL receptors, and homozygous recessives (*hh*) have none. A lack of receptors prevents the cells from removing much of the excess cholesterol from the blood. The resulting buildup of LDL in the blood can be lethal.

? **Why doesn't the cross shown in Figure 9.11A support the blending hypothesis (see Module 9.1)?**

● Although two of the F₂ offspring show a "blended" phenotype (pink flowers), the other two do not, and the white and red alleles are not lost to future generations.

9.12 Many genes have more than two alleles in the population

So far, we have discussed inheritance patterns involving only two alleles per gene (*H* versus *h*, for example). But most genes can be found in populations in more than two versions, known as multiple alleles. Although each individual carries, at most, two different alleles for a particular gene, in cases of multiple alleles, more than two possible alleles exist in the population.

For instance, the **ABO blood group** phenotype in humans involves three alleles of a single gene. Various combinations of three alleles—called I^A, I^B, and *i*—produce four phenotypes: A person's blood type may be A, B, AB, or O (**Figure 9.12**). These letters refer to two carbohydrates, designated A and B, that may be found on the surface of red blood cells. A person's red blood cells may be coated with carbohydrate A (in which case they are said to have type A blood), carbohydrate B (type B), both carbohydrates (type AB), or neither carbohydrate (type O). (In case you are wondering, the "positive" and "negative" notations on blood types—referred to as the Rh blood group system—are due to inheritance of a separate, unrelated gene.)

Matching compatible blood types is critical for safe blood transfusions. If a donor's blood cells have a carbohydrate (A or B) that is foreign to the recipient, then the recipient's immune system produces proteins called antibodies bind the foreign carbohydrates and cause the donor blood cells to clump together, potentially killing the recipient. The clumping reaction is also the basis of a blood-typing test performed

in the laboratory. In Figure 9.12, notice that AB individuals can receive blood from anyone without fear of clumping, making them "universal recipients," while donated type O blood never causes clumping, making those with type O blood "universal donors."

The four blood groups result from various combinations of the three different alleles: I^A (for an enzyme referred to as I, which adds carbohydrate A to red blood cells), I^B (which adds carbohydrate B), and *i* (which adds neither A nor B carbohydrate). Each person inherits one of these alleles from each parent. Because there are three alleles, there are six possible genotypes, as illustrated in the figure. Both the I^A and I^B alleles are dominant to the *i* allele. Thus, $I^A I^A$ and $I^A i$ people have type A blood, and $I^B I^B$ and $I^B i$ people have type B. Recessive homozygotes, *ii*, have type O blood, with neither carbohydrate. The I^A and I^B alleles are **codominant**: Both alleles are expressed in heterozygous individuals ($I^A I^B$), who have type AB blood. Be careful to distinguish codominance (the expression of both alleles) from incomplete dominance (the expression of one intermediate trait).

? **Maria has type O blood, and her sister has type AB blood. The girls know that both of their maternal grandparents are type A. What are the genotypes of the girls' parents?**

● Their mother is $I^A i$; their father is $I^B i$.

Blood Group (Phenotype)	Genotypes	Carbohydrates Present on Red Blood Cells	Antibodies Present in Blood	Reaction When Blood from Groups Below Is Mixed with Antibodies from Groups at Left			
				O	A	B	AB
A	$I^A I^A$ or $I^A i$	Carbohydrate A	Anti-B				
B	$I^B I^B$ or $I^B i$	Carbohydrate B	Anti-A				
AB	$I^A I^B$	Carbohydrate A and Carbohydrate B	None				
O	*ii*	Neither	Anti-A Anti-B				

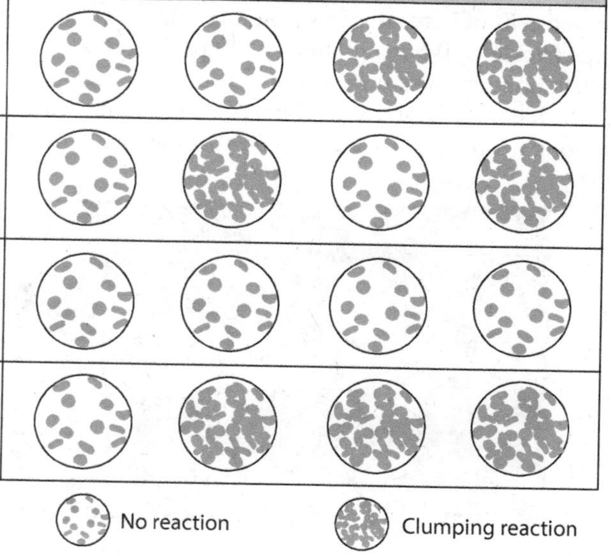

No reaction   Clumping reaction

▲ **Figure 9.12**   Multiple alleles for the ABO blood groups

9.13 A single gene may affect many phenotypic characters

All of our genetic examples to this point have been cases in which each gene specifies only one hereditary character. In many cases, however, one gene influences multiple characters, a property called **pleiotropy**.

An example of pleiotropy in humans is **sickle-cell disease** (sometimes called sickle-cell anemia). The direct effect of the sickle-cell allele is to make red blood cells produce abnormal hemoglobin proteins. These molecules tend to link together and crystallize, especially when the oxygen content of the blood is lower than usual because of high altitude, overexertion, or respiratory ailments. As the hemoglobin crystallizes, the normally disk-shaped red blood cells deform to a sickle shape with jagged edges (Figure 9.13A). Sickled cells are destroyed rapidly by the body, and their destruction may seriously lower the individual's red cell count, causing anemia and general weakening of the body. Also, because of their angular shape, sickled cells do not flow smoothly in the blood and tend to accumulate and clog tiny blood vessels. Blood flow to body parts is reduced, resulting in periodic fever, weakness, severe pain, and damage to various organs, including the heart, brain, and kidneys. The overall result is a disorder characterized by the cascade of symptoms shown in Figure 9.13B. Blood transfusions and drug treatment may relieve some of the symptoms, but there is no cure; sickle-cell disease kills about 100,000 people each year.

In most cases, only people who are homozygous for the sickle-cell allele have sickle-cell disease. Heterozygotes, who have one sickle-cell allele and one normal allele, are usually healthy—hence, the disease is considered recessive. However, in rare cases, heterozygotes may experience some effects of the disease when oxygen in the blood is severely reduced, such as at very high altitudes. Thus, at the organismal level, a heterozygote displays incomplete dominance for the sickle-cell trait, with a phenotype between the homozygous dominant and homozygous recessive phenotypes. At the molecular level, however, the two alleles are actually codominant; the blood cells of heterozygotes contain both normal and abnormal (sickle-cell) hemoglobins. A simple blood test can distinguish homozygotes from heterozygotes.

Sickle-cell disease is the most common inherited disorder among people of African descent, striking one in 400 African Americans. About one in ten African Americans is a heterozygous carrier. Among Americans of other ancestry, the sickle-cell allele is extremely rare.

One in ten is an unusually high frequency of carriers for an allele with such harmful effects in homozygotes. We might expect that the frequency of the sickle-cell allele in the population would be much lower because many homozygotes die before passing their genes to the next generation. The high frequency appears to be a vestige of the ancestral roots of African Americans. Sickle-cell disease is most common in tropical Africa, where the deadly disease malaria is also prevalent. The parasite that causes malaria spends part of its life cycle inside red blood cells. When it enters those of a person with the sickle-cell allele, it triggers sickling. The body destroys most of the sickled cells, killing the parasite with them. Consequently, sickle-cell carriers have increased resistance to malaria, and in many parts of Africa, they live longer and have more offspring than noncarriers who are exposed to malaria. In this way, malaria has kept the frequency of the sickle-cell allele relatively high in much of the African continent. To put it in evolutionary terms, as long as the environment harbors malaria, individuals with one sickle-cell allele will have a selective advantage.

? **Why is the sickle-cell trait considered codominant at the molecular level?**

● Codominance means that both traits are expressed; a carrier for the sickle-cell allele produces both normal and abnormal hemoglobin.

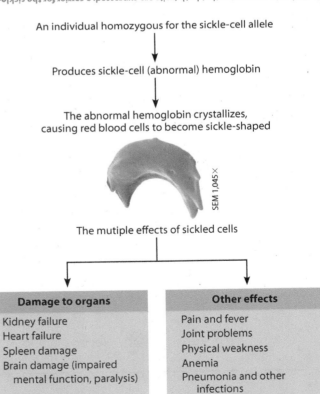

An individual homozygous for the sickle-cell allele

↓

Produces sickle-cell (abnormal) hemoglobin

↓

The abnormal hemoglobin crystallizes, causing red blood cells to become sickle-shaped

SEM 1,045×

The multiple effects of sickled cells

Damage to organs	Other effects
Kidney failure	Pain and fever
Heart failure	Joint problems
Spleen damage	Physical weakness
Brain damage (impaired mental function, paralysis)	Anemia
	Pneumonia and other infections

▲ Figure 9.13B   Sickle-cell disease, an example of pleiotropy

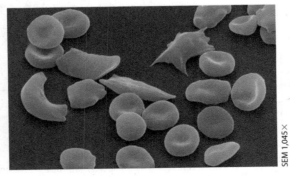

▲ Figure 9.13A   In this micrograph, you can see several jagged sickled cells in the midst of normal red blood cells.

SEM 1,045×

9.14 A single character may be influenced by many genes

Mendel studied genetic characters that could be classified on an either-or basis, such as purple or white flower color. However, many characters, such as human skin color and height, vary in a population along a continuum. Many such features result from **polygenic inheritance**, the additive effects of two or more genes on a single phenotypic character. (This is the opposite of pleiotropy, in which one gene affects several characters.)

Let's consider a hypothetical example. Assume that the continuous variation in human skin color is controlled by three genes that are inherited separately, like Mendel's pea genes. (Actually, this character is probably affected by a great many genes, but for our purposes we'll simplify.) The "dark-skin" allele for each gene (*A*, *B*, or *C*) contributes one "unit" of darkness to the phenotype and is incompletely dominant to the other allele (*a*, *b*, or *c*). An *AABBCC* person would be very dark, whereas an *aabbcc* individual would be very light. An *AaBbCc* person would have skin of an intermediate shade. Because the alleles have an additive effect, the genotype *AaBbCc* would produce the same skin color as any other genotype with just three dark-skin alleles, such as *AABbcc*, because both of these individuals have three "units" of darkness.

The Punnett square in **Figure 9.14** shows all possible genotypes from a mating of two triple heterozygotes (*AaBbCc*). The row of squares below the Punnett square shows the seven skin pigmentation phenotypes that would theoretically result from this mating. The seven bars in the graph at the bottom of the figure depict the relative numbers of each of the phenotypes in the F₂ generation. This hypothetical example shows how inheritance of three genes could lead to a wide variety of pigmentation phenotypes. As we will see in the next module, in actual human populations, skin color has even more variations than shown in the figure.

Up to this point in the chapter, we have presented four types of inheritance patterns that are extensions of Mendel's laws of inheritance: incomplete dominance, codominance, pleiotropy, and polygenic inheritance. It is important to realize that these patterns are extensions of Mendel's model, rather than exceptions to it. From Mendel's pea garden experiments came data supporting the idea that genes are transmitted according to the same rules of chance that govern the tossing of coins. This basic idea of genes as discrete units of inheritance holds true for all inheritance patterns, even the patterns that are more complex than the ones originally considered by Mendel. In the next module, we consider another important source of deviation from Mendel's standard model: the effect of the environment.

? An *AaBbcc* individual would be indistinguishable in phenotype from which of the following individuals: *AAbbcc*, *aaBBcc*, *AabbCc*, *Aabbcc*, or *aaBbCc*?

● All except *Aabbcc*

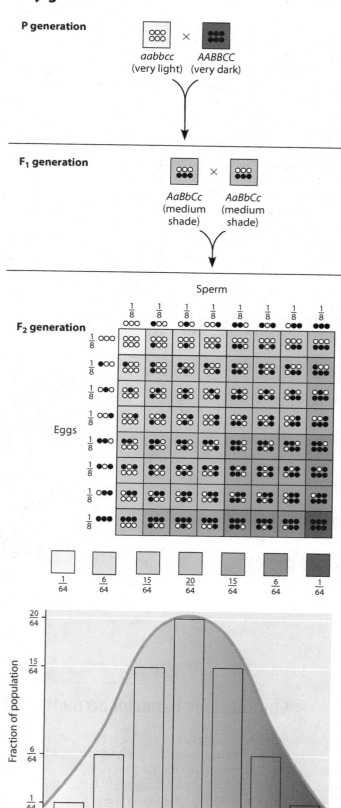

▲ **Figure 9.14** A model for polygenic inheritance of skin color

9.15 The environment affects many characters

In the previous module, we saw how a set of three hypothetical human skin-color genes could produce seven different phenotypes for skin color. But, of course, if we examine a real human population for skin color, we would see more shades than just seven. The true range might be similar to the entire spectrum of color under the bell-shaped curve in Figure 9.14. In fact, no matter how carefully we characterize the genes for skin color, a purely genetic description will always be incomplete. This is because skin color is also influenced by environmental factors, such as exposure to the sun (Figure 9.15A).

Many characters result from a combination of heredity and environment. For humans, nutrition influences height; exercise alters build; sun-tanning darkens the skin; experience improves performance on intelligence tests; and social and cultural forces greatly affect appearance. As geneticists learn more and more about our genes, it is becoming clear that many human characters—such as risk of heart disease and cancer and susceptibility to alcoholism and schizophrenia—are influenced by both genes and environment.

Whether human characters are more influenced by genes or by the environment—nature or nurture—is a very hotly contested debate. For some characters, such as the ABO blood group, a given genotype mandates a very specific phenotype, and the environment plays no role whatsoever. In contrast, how many red blood cells are circulating in your body is significantly influenced by environmental factors such as the altitude of your environment and your overall health.

It is important to realize that the individual features of any organism arise from a combination of genetic and environmental factors. Simply spending time with identical twins will convince anyone that environment, and not just genes, affects a person's traits (Figure 9.15B). Next, we turn to a discussion of the cellular basis of heredity: the behavior of chromosomes.

> **?** If most characters result from a combination of environment and heredity, why was Mendel able to ignore environmental influences in his pea plants?
>
> ● The characters he chose for study were all entirely genetically determined and all his test subjects were raised in a similar environment.

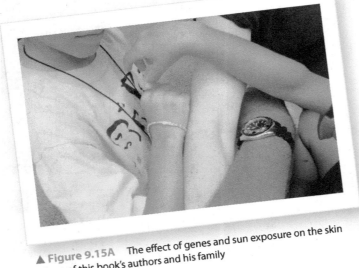

▲ Figure 9.15A The effect of genes and sun exposure on the skin of one of this book's authors and his family

▲ Figure 9.15B Varying phenotypes due to environmental factors in genetically identical twins

▷ The Chromosomal Basis of Inheritance

9.16 Chromosome behavior accounts for Mendel's laws

Mendel published his results in 1866, but biologists did not understand the significance of his work until long after he died. Cell biologists worked out the processes of mitosis and meiosis by the late 1800s (see Chapter 8 to review these processes). Then, around 1902, researchers began to notice parallels between the behavior of chromosomes and the behavior of Mendel's "heritable factors" (what we now call genes). By combining this new understanding of mitosis and meiosis with an increasing understanding of genes, one of biology's most important concepts was formulated: The **chromosome theory of inheritance** holds that genes occupy specific loci (positions) on chromosomes, and it is the chromosomes that undergo segregation and independent assortment during meiosis. Thus, it is the behavior of chromosomes during meiosis and fertilization that accounts for inheritance patterns.

We can see the chromosomal basis of Mendel's laws by following the fates of two genes during meiosis and fertilization in pea plants. In Figure 9.16, the genes for seed shape (alleles

R and r) and seed color (Y and y) are shown as black bars on different chromosomes. Notice that the Punnett square is repeated from Figure 9.5A; we will now follow the chromosomes to see how they account for the results of the dihybrid cross shown in the Punnett square. We start with the F_1 generation, in which all plants have the $RrYy$ genotype. To simplify the diagram, we show only two of the seven pairs of pea chromosomes and three of the stages of meiosis.

To see the chromosomal basis of the law of segregation (which states that pairs of alleles separate from each other during gamete formation via meiosis; see Module 9.3), let's follow just the homologous pair of long chromosomes, the ones carrying R and r, taking either the left or the right branch from the F_1 cell. Whichever arrangement the chromosomes assume at metaphase I, the two alleles segregate as the homologous chromosomes separate in anaphase I. And at the end of meiosis II, a single long chromosome ends up in each of the gametes. Fertilization then randomly recombines the two alleles, resulting in F_2 offspring that are $\frac{1}{4}$ RR, $\frac{1}{2}$ Rr,

and $\frac{1}{4}$ rr. The ratio of round to wrinkled phenotypes is thus 3:1 (12 round to 4 wrinkled), the ratio Mendel observed, as shown in the Punnett square in the figure.

To see the chromosomal basis of the law of independent assortment (which states that each pair of alleles sorts independently of other pairs of alleles during gamete formation; see Module 9.5), follow both the long and short (nonhomologous) chromosomes through the figure. Two alternative arrangements of tetrads can occur at metaphase I. The nonhomologous chromosomes (and their genes) assort independently, leading to four gamete genotypes. Random fertilization leads to the 9:3:3:1 phenotypic ratio in the F_2 generation.

> **?** Which of Mendel's laws have their physical basis in the following phases of meiosis: (a) the orientation of homologous chromosome pairs in metaphase I; (b) the separation of homologs in anaphase I?

(a) The law of independent assortment; (b) the law of segregation

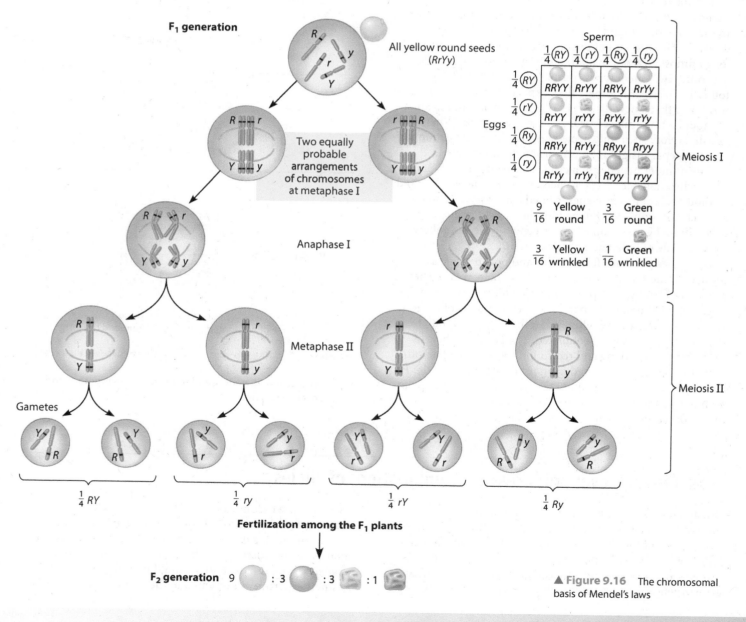

▲ **Figure 9.16** The chromosomal basis of Mendel's laws

9.17 Genes on the same chromosome tend to be inherited together

SCIENTIFIC THINKING

In 1908, British biologists William Bateson and Reginald Punnett (originator of the Punnett square) observed an inheritance pattern that seemed inconsistent with Mendelian laws. Bateson and Punnett were working with two characters in sweet peas: flower color and pollen shape. They crossed doubly heterozygous plants (*PpLl*) that exhibited the dominant traits: purple flowers (expression of the *P* allele) and long pollen grains (expression of the *L* allele). The corresponding recessive traits are red flowers (in *pp* plants) and round pollen (in *ll* plants).

The top part of **Figure 9.17** illustrates Bateson and Punnett's experiment. When they looked at just one of the two characters (that is, either cross *Pp* × *Pp* or cross *Ll* × *Ll*), they recorded a phenotypic ratio of approximately 3:1 for the offspring, in agreement with Mendel's law of segregation. However, when the biologists combined their data for the two characters, they did not see the 9:3:3:1 ratio predicted by Mendel's law of independent assortment. Instead, as shown in the table, they found a disproportionately large number of plants with just two of the predicted phenotypes: purple long (almost 75% of the total) and red round (about 14%). The other two phenotypes (purple round and red long) were found in far fewer numbers than expected. It is often the case in science that a new discovery begins with a "failure," an experiment with results contrary to those expected. When scientists explore such unexpected results, the investigation may lead to deeper insight than was originally anticipated.

The number of genes in a cell is far greater than the number of chromosomes; in fact, each chromosome has hundreds or thousands of genes. Genes located close together on the same chromosome tend to be inherited together and are called **linked genes**. Linked genes generally do not follow Mendel's law of independent assortment.

Sweet-pea genes for flower color and pollen shape are located on the same chromosome. Thus, meiosis in the heterozygous (*PpLl*) sweet-pea plant yields mostly two genotypes of gametes (*PL* and *pl*) rather than equal numbers of the four types of gametes that would result if the flower-color and pollen-shape genes were not linked. The large numbers of plants with purple long and red round traits in the Bateson-Punnett experiment resulted from fertilization among the *PL* and *pl* gametes. But what about the smaller numbers of plants with purple round and red long traits? As you will see in the next module, crossing over accounts for these offspring.

The Experiment

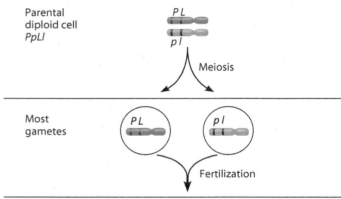

Phenotypes	Observed offspring	Prediction (9:3:3:1)
Purple long	284	215
Purple round	21	71
Red long	21	71
Red round	55	24

The Explanation: Linked Genes

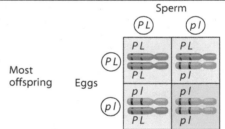

3 purple long : 1 red round
Not accounted for: purple round and red long

▲ **Figure 9.17** The experiment revealing linked genes in the sweet pea

? **Why do linked genes tend to be inherited together and not sort independently?**

Because they are located close together on the same chromosome

9.18 Crossing over produces new combinations of alleles

During meiosis, crossing over between homologous chromosomes produces new combinations of alleles in gametes (as we saw in Module 8.17). Using the experiment shown in Figure 9.17 as an example, **Figure 9.18A** reviews this process, showing that two linked genes can give rise to four different gamete genotypes. Gametes with genotypes *PL* and *pl* carry

parental-type chromosomes that have not been altered by crossing over. In contrast, gametes with genotypes *Pl* and *pL* are recombinant gametes. The exchange of chromosome segments during crossing over has produced new combinations of alleles. We can now understand the results of the Bateson-Punnett experiment presented in the previous module: The

▲ **Figure 9.18A** Review: the production of recombinant gametes

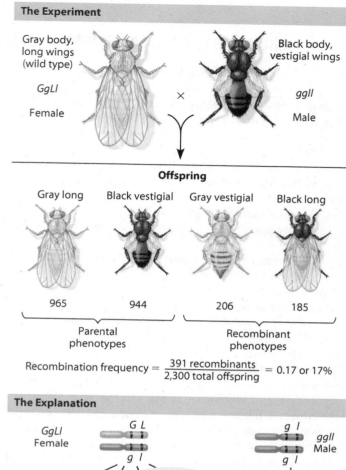

Gray body, long wings (wild type)

GgLl

Female

×

Black body, vestigial wings

ggll

Male

Offspring

Gray long   Black vestigial   Gray vestigial   Black long

965   944   206   185

Parental phenotypes   Recombinant phenotypes

$$\text{Recombination frequency} = \frac{391 \text{ recombinants}}{2,300 \text{ total offspring}} = 0.17 \text{ or } 17\%$$

▲ **Figure 9.18B**
Drosophila melanogaster

small fraction of offspring with recombinant phenotypes (purple round and red long) must have resulted from fertilization involving recombinant gametes.

The discovery of how crossing over creates gamete diversity confirmed the relationship between chromosome behavior and heredity. Some of the most important early studies of crossing over were performed in the laboratory of American embryologist Thomas Hunt Morgan in the early 1900s. Morgan and his colleagues used the fruit fly *Drosophila melanogaster* in many of their experiments (**Figure 9.18B**). *Drosophila* is a good research animal for genetic studies because it can be bred easily and inexpensively, producing each new generation in two weeks.

Figure 9.18C shows one of Morgan's experiments. This cross involves a wild-type fruit fly—recall from Module 9.8 that "wild-type" refers to the traits most common in nature, in this case, gray body and long wings—and a fly with a black body and vestigial wings. (Used here, the term *vestigial* describes the undeveloped, shrunken appearance of the wings and should not be confused with the evolutionary use of the word *vestigial*.) Morgan knew the genotypes of these flies from previous studies. Here we use the following gene symbols: *G* = gray body (dominant), *g* = black body (recessive), *L* = long wings (dominant), *l* = vestigial wings (recessive).

In mating a heterozygous gray fly with long wings (genotype *GgLl*) with a black fly with vestigial wings (genotype *ggll*), Morgan performed a testcross (see Module 9.6). If the genes were not linked, then independent assortment would produce offspring in a phenotypic ratio of 1:1:1:1 ($\frac{1}{4}$ gray body, long wings; $\frac{1}{4}$ black body, vestigial wings; $\frac{1}{4}$ gray body, vestigial wings; and $\frac{1}{4}$ black body, long wings). But because these genes are linked, Morgan obtained the results shown in the top part of Figure 9.18C: Most of the offspring had parental phenotypes, but 17% of the offspring flies were recombinants. The percentage of recombinant offspring among the total is called the **recombination frequency**.

The lower part of Figure 9.18C explains Morgan's results in terms of crossing over. A crossover between chromatids

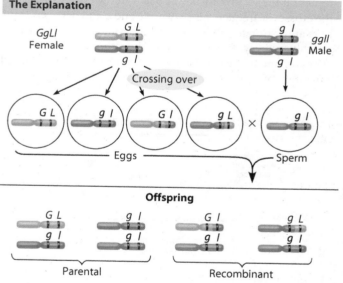

GgLl Female   *ggll* Male

Crossing over

Eggs   Sperm

Offspring

Parental   Recombinant

▲ **Figure 9.18C** A fruit fly experiment demonstrating the role of crossing over in inheritance

From T. H. Morgan and C. J. Lynch, The linkage of two factors in *Drosophila* that are not sex-linked, *Biological Bulletin* 23: 174–82 (1912).

of homologous chromosomes in parent *GgLl* broke linkages between the *G* and *L* alleles and between the *g* and *l* alleles, forming the recombinant chromosomes *Gl* and *gL*. Later steps in meiosis distributed the recombinant chromosomes to gametes, and random fertilization produced the four kinds of offspring Morgan observed.

? Return to the data in Figure 9.17. What is the recombination frequency between the flower-color and pollen-length genes?

11% (42/381)

9.19 Geneticists use crossover data to map genes

While working with *Drosophila*, Alfred H. Sturtevant, one of Morgan's students, developed a way to use crossover data to map gene loci. This technique is based on the assumption that the chance of crossing over is approximately equal at all points along a chromosome. Sturtevant hypothesized that the farther apart two genes are on a chromosome, the more points there are between them where crossing over can occur. (This assumption is not entirely accurate, but it is good enough to provide useful data.) With this principle in mind, Sturtevant began using recombination data from fruit fly crosses to assign relative positions of the genes on the chromosomes—that is, to map genes.

Figure 9.19A represents a part of the chromosome that carries the linked genes for black body (*g*) and vestigial wings (*l*) that we described in Module 9.18. This same chromosome also carries a gene that has a recessive allele (we'll call it *c*) determining cinnabar eye color, a brighter red than the wild-type color. Figure 9.19A shows the actual crossover (recombination) frequencies between these alleles, taken two at a time: 17% between the *g* and *l* alleles, 9% between *g* and *c*, and 9.5% between *c* and *l*. Sturtevant reasoned that these values represent the relative distances between the genes. Because the crossover frequencies between *g* and *c* and between *l* and *c* are approximately half that between *g* and *l*, gene *c* must lie roughly midway between *g* and *l*. Thus, the sequence of these genes on one of the fruit fly chromosomes must be *g-c-l*. Such a diagram of relative gene locations is called a **linkage map**.

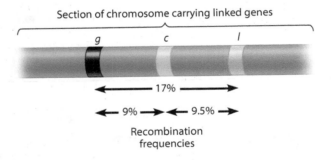

Section of chromosome carrying linked genes

g   c   l

◄————— 17% —————►

◄— 9% —►◄— 9.5% —►

Recombination frequencies

▲ **Figure 9.19A**   Mapping genes from crossover data

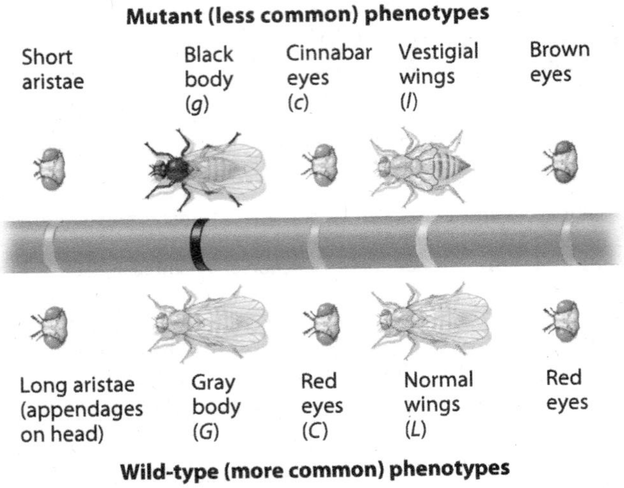

Mutant (less common) phenotypes

| Short aristae | Black body (*g*) | Cinnabar eyes (*c*) | Vestigial wings (*l*) | Brown eyes |

| Long aristae (appendages on head) | Gray body (*G*) | Red eyes (*C*) | Normal wings (*L*) | Red eyes |

Wild-type (more common) phenotypes

▲ **Figure 9.19B**   A partial linkage map of a fruit fly chromosome

Although based on some approximations, Sturtevant's method of mapping genes helped establish the relative positions of many other fruit fly genes. Eventually, enough data were accumulated to reveal that *Drosophila* has four groups of genes, corresponding to its four pairs of homologous chromosomes. Figure 9.19B is a genetic map showing just five of the gene loci on part of one chromosome: the loci labeled *g*, *c*, and *l* and two other traits, aristae and brown eyes.

The linkage-mapping method has proved valuable in establishing the relative positions of many genes in many organisms. The real beauty of the technique is that a wealth of information about genes can be learned simply by breeding and observing the organisms; no fancy equipment is required.

> **?** You design *Drosophila* crosses to provide recombination data for a gene not included in Figure 9.19A. The gene has recombination frequencies of 3% with the vestigial-wing (*l*) locus and 7% with the cinnabar-eye (*c*) locus. Where is it located on the chromosome?

● The gene is located between the vestigial and cinnabar loci, a bit closer to the vestigial-wing locus (because the vestigial-wing locus has a lower recombination frequency).

▷ Sex Chromosomes and Sex-Linked Genes

9.20 Chromosomes determine sex in many species

Many animals, including fruit flies and all mammals, have a pair of **sex chromosomes**, designated X and Y, that determine an individual's sex (Figure 9.20A). Among humans, individuals with one X chromosome and one Y chromosome are males; XX individuals are females. In addition, human males and females both have 44 autosomes (nonsex chromosomes). After meiosis, each gamete contains one sex chromosome and a haploid set of autosomes (22 in humans). All eggs

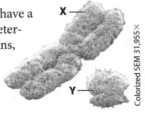

X

Y

Colorized SEM 31,955×

▲ **Figure 9.20A**   The human sex chromosomes

contain a single X chromosome. Of the sperm cells, half contain an X chromosome and half contain a Y chromosome. An offspring's sex depends on whether the sperm cell that fertilizes the egg bears an X chromosome or a Y chromosome (Figure 9.20B).

The genetic basis of sex determination in humans is not yet completely understood, but one gene on the Y chromosome plays a crucial role.

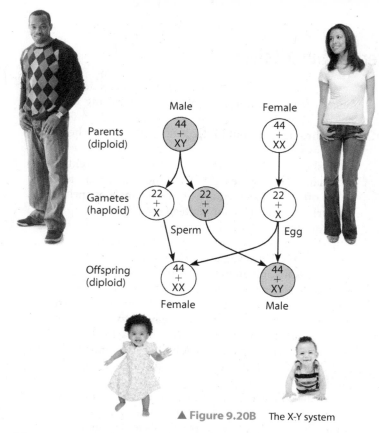

Male / Female

Parents (diploid): Male 44 + XY, Female 44 + XX

Gametes (haploid): 22 + X, 22 + Y (Sperm); 22 + X (Egg)

Offspring (diploid): 44 + XX (Female); 44 + XY (Male)

▲ Figure 9.20B The X-Y system

an X-O system, in which O stands for the absence of a sex chromosome. Females have two X chromosomes (XX); males have only one sex chromosome (XO). Males produce two classes of sperm: Half bear an X and half lack a sex chromosome. In this case, as in humans, sperm cells determine the sex of the offspring at fertilization.

In contrast to the X-Y and X-O systems, eggs determine sex in certain fishes, butterflies, and birds. The sex chromosomes in these animals are designated Z and W. Males have the genotype ZZ; females are ZW. In this system, sex is determined by whether the egg carries a Z or a W.

Some organisms lack sex chromosomes altogether. In most ants and bees, sex is determined by chromosome number rather than by sex chromosomes. Females develop from fertilized eggs and thus are diploid. Males develop from unfertilized eggs—they are fatherless—and are haploid.

Most animals have two separate sexes; that is, individuals are either male or female. Many plant species have sperm-bearing and egg-bearing flowers found on different individuals. Some plant species, such as date palms, have the X-Y system of sex determination; others, such as the wild strawberry, have the Z-W system. However, most plant species and some animal species have individuals that produce both sperm and eggs. In such species, all individuals have the same complement of chromosomes.

In Module 9.15, we discussed the role that environment plays in determining many characters. Among some animals, environment can even determine sex. For some species of reptiles, the temperature at which eggs are incubated during a specific period of embryonic development determines whether that embryo will develop into a male or female. For example, if green sea turtle hatchlings incubate above 30°C (86°F), nearly all the resulting turtles will be males. (Some worry that global climate change might therefore affect the makeup of turtle populations.) Such temperature-dependent sex determination is an extreme example of the environment affecting the phenotype of an individual.

This gene is called *SRY* (for sex-determining region of Y) and triggers testis development. In the absence of *SRY*, ovaries develop rather than testes. *SRY* codes for proteins that regulate other genes on the Y chromosome. These genes in turn produce proteins necessary for normal testis development.

The X-Y system is only one of several sex-determining systems (Table 9.20 summarizes three other systems). For example, grasshoppers, roaches, and some other insects have

TABLE 9.20 THREE SYSTEMS OF SEX DETERMINATION

System	Example Organism	Genetic Makeup	
		Males	Females
X-O		22 + X	22 + XX
Z-W		76 + ZZ	76 + ZW
Chromosome number		16	32

? King Henry VIII of England was quick to blame his wives for bearing him only daughters. Explain how, from a genetic point of view, his thinking was wrong.

● The male sperm bears either an X or Y, thereby determining the sex of the offspring; his wives' eggs always carried an X.

9.21 Sex-linked genes exhibit a unique pattern of inheritance

Besides bearing genes that determine sex, the sex chromosomes also contain genes for characters unrelated to femaleness or maleness. A gene located on either sex chromosome is called a **sex-linked gene**. Because the human X chromosome contains many more genes than the Y, the vast majority of sex-linked genes are on the X chromosome. Be careful not to confuse the term *sex-linked gene*, which refers to a gene on a sex chromosome, with the term *linked genes*, which refers to genes on the same chromosome that tend to be inherited together.

The figures in this module illustrate inheritance patterns for white eye color in the fruit fly, an X-linked recessive trait. Wild-type fruit flies have red eyes; white eyes are very rare (Figure 9.21A). We use the uppercase letter R for the dominant, wild-type, red-eye allele and r for the recessive white-eye allele. Because these alleles are carried on the X chromosome, we show them as superscripts to the letter X. Thus, red-eyed male fruit flies have the genotype $X^R Y$; white-eyed males are $X^r Y$. The Y chromosome does not have a gene locus for eye color; therefore, the male's phenotype results entirely from his single X-linked gene. In the female, $X^R X^R$ and $X^R X^r$ flies have red eyes, and $X^r X^r$ flies have white eyes.

A white-eyed male ($X^r Y$) will transmit his X^r to all of his female offspring but to none of his male offspring. This is because his female offspring, in order to be female, must inherit his X chromosome, but his male offspring must inherit his Y chromosome.

As shown in Figure 9.21B, when the female parent is a dominant homozygote ($X^R X^R$) and the male parent is $X^r Y$, all the offspring have red eyes, but the female offspring are all carriers of the allele for white eyes ($X^R X^r$). When those offspring are bred to each other, the classic 3:1 phenotypic ratio of red eyes to white eyes appears among the offspring (Figure 9.21C). However, there is a twist: The white-eyed trait shows up only in males. All the females have red eyes, whereas half the males have red eyes and half have white eyes. All females inherit at least one dominant allele (from their male parent); half of them are homozygous dominant, whereas the other half are heterozygous carriers, like their female parent. Among the males, half of them inherit the recessive allele their mother was carrying, producing the white-eye phenotype.

Because the white-eye allele is recessive, a female will have white eyes only if she receives that allele on both X chromosomes. For example, if a heterozygous female mates with a white-eyed male, there is a 50% chance that each offspring will have white eyes (resulting from genotype $X^r X^r$ or $X^r Y$), regardless of sex (Figure 9.21D). Female offspring with red eyes are heterozygotes, whereas red-eyed male offspring completely lack the recessive allele.

> **?** A white-eyed female *Drosophila* is mated with a red-eyed (wild-type) male. What result do you predict for the numerous offspring?
>
> ● All female offspring will be red-eyed but heterozygous ($X^R X^r$); all male offspring will be white-eyed ($X^r Y$).

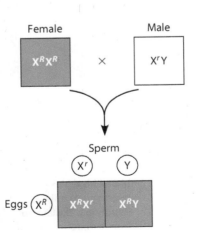

▲ Figure 9.21A   Fruit fly eye color determined by sex-linked gene

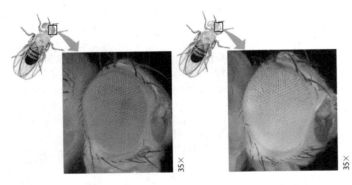

R = red-eye allele
r = white-eye allele

▲ **Figure 9.21B**   A homozygous, red-eyed female crossed with a white-eyed male

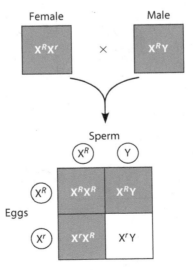

▲ **Figure 9.21C**   A heterozygous female crossed with a red-eyed male

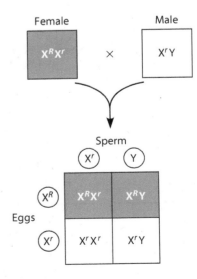

▲ **Figure 9.21D**   A heterozygous female crossed with a white-eyed male

9.22 Human sex-linked disorders affect mostly males

CONNECTION

A number of human conditions result from sex-linked recessive alleles located on the X chromosome. If a man inherits only one X-linked recessive allele—from his mother—the allele will be expressed. In contrast, a woman has to inherit two such alleles—one from each parent—to exhibit the trait. Thus, recessive X-linked traits are expressed much more frequently in men than in women.

Hemophilia is an X-linked recessive trait with a well-documented history. Hemophiliacs bleed excessively when injured because they lack one or more of the proteins required for blood clotting. A high incidence of hemophilia plagued the royal families of Europe. Queen Victoria (1819–1901) of England was a carrier of the hemophilia allele. She passed it on to one of her sons and two of her daughters. Through marriage, her daughters then introduced the disease into the families of Prussia, Russia, and Spain. The pedigree in **Figure 9.22** traces the disease through one branch of the royal family. As you can see, Alexandra, like her mother and grandmother, was a carrier, and Alexis had the disease.

Another human X-linked recessive disorder is Duchenne muscular dystrophy, a condition characterized by a progressive weakening of the muscles and loss of coordination. The first symptoms appear in early childhood, when the child begins to have difficulty standing up. Eventually, muscle tissue becomes severely wasted, the individual becomes wheelchair-bound, and normal breathing becomes difficult. Affected individuals rarely live past their early 20s. Researchers have

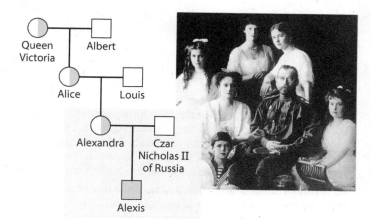

▲ **Figure 9.22** Hemophilia in the royal family of Russia

Try This Alexis must have had an X^h chromosome (because he had hemophilia). Use your finger to trace back this mutant chromosome through three generations of his ancestors.

traced the disorder to a recessive mutation in a gene on the X chromosome that codes for a muscle protein.

? **Neither Tom nor Sue has hemophilia, but their first son does. If the couple has a second child, what is the probability that he or she will also have the disease?**

● $\frac{1}{4}$ ($\frac{1}{2}$ chance of a male child × $\frac{1}{2}$ chance that he will inherit the mutant X)

9.23 The Y chromosome provides clues about human male evolution

EVOLUTION CONNECTION

As you learned in the chapter-opening story about Tibetans, our genes often bear evidence of recent human evolution. The Y chromosome can be particularly useful for tracing our evolutionary past because, barring mutations, the human Y chromosome passes essentially intact from father to son. By analyzing Y DNA, researchers can learn about the ancestry of human males.

In 2003, geneticists discovered that about 8% of males currently living in central Asia have Y chromosomes of striking genetic similarity. Further analysis traced their common genetic heritage to a single man living about 1,000 years ago. In combination with historical records, the data led to the speculation that the Mongolian ruler Genghis Khan (**Figure 9.23**) may be responsible for the spread of the telltale chromosome to nearly 16 million men living today. A similar study of Irish men suggested that nearly 10% of them were descendants of Niall of the Nine Hostages, a warlord who lived during the 5th century.

▲ **Figure 9.23** Genghis Khan

Another study of Y DNA seemed to confirm the claim by the Lemba people of southern Africa that they are descended from ancient Jews. Sequences of Y DNA distinctive of a particular Jewish priestly caste are found at high frequencies among the Lemba.

Are humans evolving?

The discovery of the sex chromosomes and their pattern of inheritance was one of many breakthroughs in understanding how genes are passed from one generation to the next. During the first half of the 20th century, geneticists rediscovered Mendel's work, reinterpreted his laws in light of chromosomal behavior during meiosis, and firmly established the chromosome theory of inheritance. This work set the stage for discoveries in molecular genetics, an area we explore in the next three chapters.

? **Why is the Y chromosome particularly useful in tracing recent human heritage?**

● Because it is passed directly from father to son, forming an unbroken chain of male lineage

CHAPTER 9 REVIEW

For practice quizzes, BioFlix animations, MP3 tutorials, video tutors and more study tools designed for this textbook, go to

MasteringBiology®

Reviewing the Concepts

Mendel's Laws (9.1–9.10)

9.1 The study of genetics has ancient roots.

9.2 The science of genetics began in an abbey garden. The science of genetics began with Gregor Mendel's quantitative experiments. Mendel crossed pea plants and traced traits from generation to generation. He hypothesized that there are alternative versions of genes (alleles), the units that determine heritable traits.

9.3 Mendel's law of segregation describes the inheritance of a single character. Mendel's law of segregation predicts that each set of alleles will separate as gametes are formed.

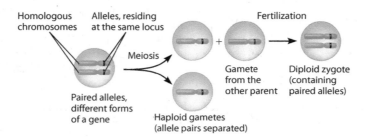

9.4 Homologous chromosomes bear the alleles for each character. When the two alleles of a gene in a diploid individual are different, the dominant allele determines the inherited trait, whereas the recessive allele has no effect.

9.5 The law of independent assortment is revealed by tracking two characters at once. Mendel's law of independent assortment states that the alleles of a pair segregate independently of other allele pairs during gamete formation.

9.6 Geneticists can use a testcross to determine unknown genotypes. The offspring of a testcross, a mating between an individual of unknown genotype and a homozygous recessive individual, can reveal the unknown's genotype.

9.7 Mendel's laws reflect the rules of probability. The rule of multiplication calculates the probability of two independent events both occurring. The rule of addition calculates the probability of an event that can occur in alternative ways.

9.8 Genetic traits in humans can be tracked through family pedigrees. The inheritance of many human traits follows Mendel's laws. Family pedigrees can help determine individual genotypes.

9.9 Many inherited disorders in humans are controlled by a single gene.

9.10 New technologies can provide insight into one's genetic legacy. Carrier screening, fetal testing, fetal imaging, and newborn screening can provide information for reproductive decisions but may create ethical dilemmas.

Variations on Mendel's Laws (9.11–9.15)

9.11 Incomplete dominance results in intermediate phenotypes. Mendel's laws are valid for all sexually reproducing species, but genotype often does not dictate phenotype in the simple way Mendel's laws describe.

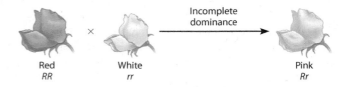

Red *RR* × White *rr* → Incomplete dominance → Pink *Rr*

9.12 Many genes have more than two alleles in the population. For example, the ABO blood group phenotype in humans is controlled by three alleles that produce a total of four phenotypes.

9.13 A single gene may affect many phenotypic characters.

Single gene → Pleiotropy → Multiple characters

9.14 A single character may be influenced by many genes.

Multiple genes → Polygenic inheritance → Single characters (such as skin color)

9.15 The environment affects many characters. Many traits are affected, in varying degrees, by both genetic and environmental factors.

The Chromosomal Basis of Inheritance (9.16–9.19)

9.16 Chromosome behavior accounts for Mendel's laws. Genes are located on chromosomes, whose behavior during meiosis and fertilization accounts for inheritance patterns.

9.17 Genes on the same chromosome tend to be inherited together. Such genes are said to be linked; they display non-Mendelian inheritance patterns.

9.18 Crossing over produces new combinations of alleles. Crossing over can separate linked alleles, producing gametes with recombinant chromosomes.

9.19 Geneticists use crossover data to map genes. Recombination frequencies can be used to map the relative positions of genes on chromosomes.

Sex Chromosomes and Sex-Linked Genes (9.20–9.23)

9.20 Chromosomes determine sex in many species. In mammals, a male has XY sex chromosomes, and a female has XX. The Y chromosome has genes for the development of testes, whereas an absence of the Y allows ovaries to develop. Other systems of sex determination exist in other animals and plants.

9.21 Sex-linked genes exhibit a unique pattern of inheritance. All genes on the sex chromosomes are said to be sex-linked. However, the X chromosome carries many genes unrelated to sex.

9.22 Human sex-linked disorders affect mostly males. Most sex-linked (X-linked) human disorders are due to recessive alleles and are seen mostly in males. A male receiving a single X-linked recessive allele from his mother will have the disorder; a female must receive the allele from both parents to be affected.

9.23 The Y chromosome provides clues about human male evolution. Because they are passed on intact from father to son, Y chromosomes can provide data about recent human evolutionary history.

Connecting the Concepts

1. Complete this concept map to help you review some key concepts of genetics.

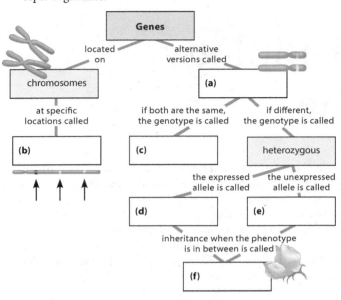

Testing Your Knowledge

Level 1: Knowledge/Comprehension

2. Whether an allele is dominant or recessive depends on
   a. how common the allele is, relative to other alleles.
   b. whether it is inherited from the mother or the father.
   c. whether it or another allele determines the phenotype when both are present.
   d. whether or not it is linked to other genes.

3. Edward was found to be heterozygous (Ss) for sickle-cell trait. The alleles represented by the letters S and s are
   a. linked.
   b. on homologous chromosomes.
   c. both present in each of Edward's sperm cells.
   d. on the same chromosome but far apart.

Level 2: Application/Analysis

4. Two fruit flies with eyes of the usual red color are crossed, and their offspring are as follows: 77 red-eyed males, 71 ruby-eyed males, 152 red-eyed females. The allele for ruby eyes is
   a. autosomal (carried on an autosome) and dominant.
   b. autosomal and recessive.
   c. sex-linked and dominant.
   d. sex-linked and recessive.

5. A man with type B blood and a woman who has type A blood could have children of which of the following phenotypes?
   a. A or B only
   b. AB only
   c. AB or O
   d. A, B, AB, or O

6. Tim and Jan both have freckles (see Module 9.9), but their son Mike does not. Show with a Punnett square how this is possible. If Tim and Jan have two more children, what is the probability that both will have freckles?

7. Both Tim and Jan (problem 6) have a widow's peak (see Module 9.8), but Mike has a straight hairline. What are their genotypes? What is the probability that Tim and Jan's next child will have freckles and a straight hairline?

8. In rabbits, black hair depends on a dominant allele, B, and brown hair on a recessive allele, b. Short hair is due to a dominant allele, S, and long hair to a recessive allele, s. If a true-breeding black short-haired male is mated with a brown long-haired female, describe their offspring. What will be the genotypes of the offspring? If two of these F_1 rabbits are mated, what phenotypes would you expect among their offspring? In what proportions?

9. A fruit fly with a gray body and red eyes (genotype $BbPp$) is mated with a fly having a black body and purple eyes (genotype $bbpp$). What ratio of offspring would you expect if the body-color and eye-color genes are on different chromosomes (unlinked)? When this mating is actually carried out, most of the offspring look like the parents, but 3% have a gray body and purple eyes, and 3% have a black body and red eyes. Are these genes linked or unlinked? What is the recombination frequency?

10. A series of matings shows that the recombination frequency between the black-body gene (problem 9) and the gene for dumpy (shortened) wings is 36%. The recombination frequency between purple eyes and dumpy wings is 41%. What is the sequence of these three genes on the chromosome?

11. A couple are both phenotypically normal, but their son suffers from hemophilia, a sex-linked recessive disorder. What fraction of their children are likely to suffer from hemophilia? What fraction are likely to be carriers?

Level 3: Synthesis/Evaluation

12. Why do more men than women have colorblindness?

13. In fruit flies, the genes for wing shape and body stripes are linked. In a fly whose genotype is $WwSs$, W is linked to S, and w is linked to s. Show how this fly can produce gametes containing four different combinations of alleles. Which are parental-type gametes? Which are recombinant gametes? How are the recombinants produced?

14. Adult height in humans is at least partially hereditary; tall parents tend to have tall children. But humans come in a range of sizes, not just tall and short. Which extension of Mendel's model accounts for the hereditary variation in human height?

15. Heather was surprised to discover she suffered from red-green colorblindness. She told her biology professor, who said, "Your father is colorblind, too, right?" How did her professor know this? Why did her professor not say the same thing to the colorblind males in the class?

16. In 1981, a stray black cat with unusual rounded, curled-back ears was adopted by a family in Lakewood, California. Suppose you owned the first curl cat and wanted to breed it to develop a true-breeding variety. Describe tests that would determine whether the curl gene is dominant or recessive and whether it is autosomal or sex-linked. Explain why you think your tests would be conclusive. Describe a test to determine that a cat is true-breeding.

17. **SCIENTIFIC THINKING** The breakthrough that led Bateson and Punnett to recognize the existence of linked genes (Module 9.17) was the appearance of unexpected results after they crossed double heterozygous pea plants ($PpLl$) with each other. Imagine that you have a group of Labrador retrievers that are all heterozygous for both coat color and blindness ($BbNn$). If you used this group of dogs to produce 160 puppies, how many puppies of each phenotype do you expect to get if the genes are not linked? How would the results differ if the genes are in fact linked?

Answers to all questions can be found in Appendix 4.

10 Molecular Biology of the Gene

? *Why are viral diseases such a constant threat?*

The electron micrograph below shows the 2009 H1N1 influenza virus, an infectious microbe that first appeared in a cluster of flu cases diagnosed in and near Mexico City. Once the threat had been identified, the city was virtually shut down in an effort to contain the outbreak. Despite these efforts, the new viral strain spread so quickly that within months the World Health Organization (WHO) declared H1N1 a pandemic (global epidemic). A vaccine against the 2009 H1N1 strain was rushed into production and became available in the fall of that year. By the time the WHO declared the pandemic over in August 2010, the disease had reached 207 countries, infecting more than 600,000 and killing an estimated 20,000 people.

The 2009 H1N1 influenza virus is just one example in a long, bleak history of human viral diseases. The flu virus, like all viruses, consists of a relatively simple structure of protein and nucleic acid (RNA in this case). Viruses share some of the characteristics of living organisms, but are generally not considered alive because they are not cellular and cannot reproduce on their own. So how

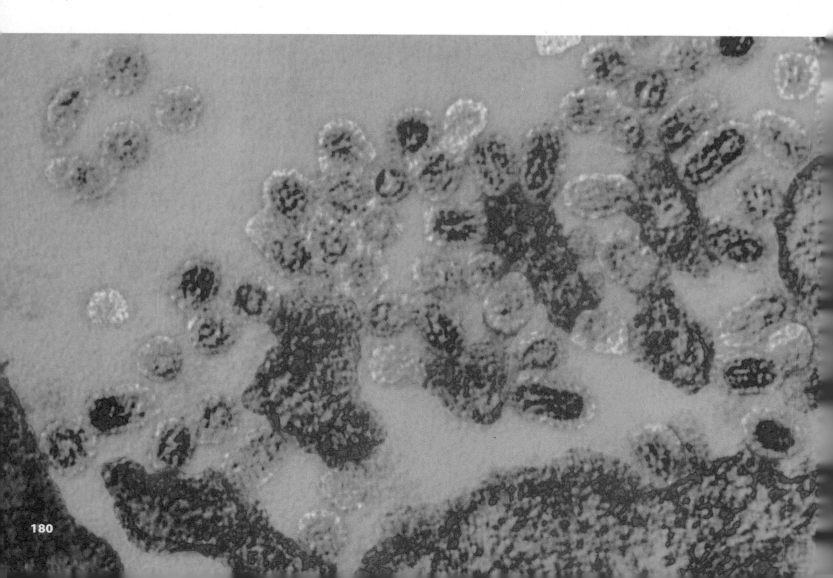

can such a simple pathogen evade the best efforts of the world's scientists? The key to the elusiveness of many viruses lies in their tendency to evolve rapidly. The 2009 H1N1 strain, for example, arose through genetic re-shuffling of multiple flu viruses, including ones that infect humans, birds, and pigs.

Combating any virus requires a detailed understanding of molecular biology, the study of DNA and how it serves as the basis of heredity. In fact, we owe our first glimpses of the functions of DNA, the molecule that controls hereditary traits, to the study of viruses. In this chapter, we'll explore the structure of DNA, how it replicates, and how it controls the cell by directing RNA and protein synthesis. We'll conclude by discussing the genetics of viruses and bacteria.

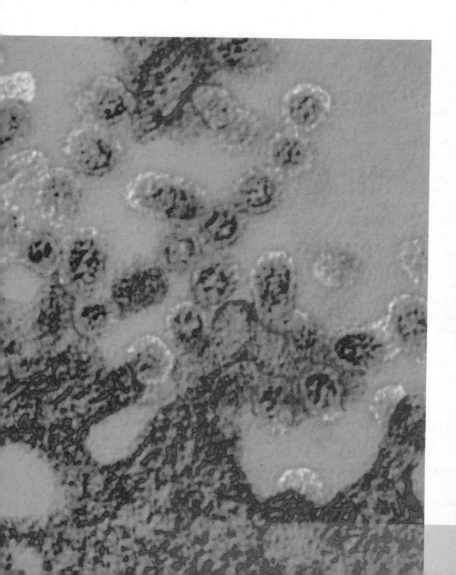

The Structure of the Genetic Material
(10.1–10.3)

A series of experiments established DNA as the molecule of heredity.

DNA Replication
(10.4–10.5)

Each DNA strand can serve as a template for another.

The Flow of Genetic Information from DNA to RNA to Protein
(10.6–10.16)

Genotype controls phenotype through the production of proteins.

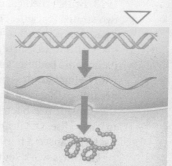

The Genetics of Viruses and Bacteria
(10.17–10.23)

Viruses and bacteria are useful model systems for the study of molecular biology.

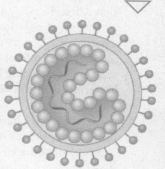

▷ The Structure of the Genetic Material

10.1 Experiments showed that DNA is the genetic material

SCIENTIFIC THINKING

Today, scientists routinely manipulate DNA in the laboratory and use it to change the heritable characteristics of cells. Early in the 20th century, however, the molecular basis for inheritance was a mystery. Biologists did know that genes were located on chromosomes. The two chemical components of chromosomes—DNA and protein—were therefore the leading candidates to be the genetic material. Until the 1940s, the case for proteins seemed stronger because proteins appeared to be more structurally complex: Proteins were known to be made from 20 different amino acid building blocks, whereas DNA was known to be made from just four kinds of nucleotides. It seemed logical that the more complex molecule would serve as the hereditary material. Biologists finally established the role of DNA in heredity through experiments with bacteria and the viruses that infect them. This breakthrough ushered in the field of **molecular biology**, the study of heredity at the molecular level.

We can trace the discovery of the genetic role of DNA to 1928. British medical officer Frederick Griffith was studying two strains (varieties) of a bacterium: a harmless strain and a pathogenic (disease-causing) strain that causes pneumonia. Griffith was surprised to find that when he killed the pathogenic bacteria and then mixed the bacterial remains with living harmless bacteria, some living bacterial cells became pathogenic. Furthermore, all of the descendants of the transformed bacteria inherited the newly acquired ability to cause disease. Clearly, some chemical component of the dead bacteria caused a heritable change in live bacteria.

Griffith's work set the stage for a race to discover the identity of the chemical basis of heredity. In 1952, American biologists Alfred Hershey and Martha Chase performed a very convincing set of experiments that showed DNA to be the genetic material of T2, a virus that infects the bacterium *Escherichia coli* (*E. coli*), a microbe normally found in the intestines of mammals (including humans). Viruses that exclusively infect bacteria are called **bacteriophages** ("bacteria-eaters"), or **phages** for short.

Hershey and Chase knew that T2 could reprogram its host cell to produce new phages, but they did not know what component of the virus conferred this capability. At the time, it was known that the structure of phage T2 consists solely of two types of molecules (**Figure 10.1A**): DNA (blue in the figure) and protein (gold). The researchers took advantage of this fact to devise an elegantly simple experiment that determined which of these molecules the phage transferred to *E. coli* during infection.

The Hershey and Chase experiment illustrates a point that arises repeatedly in the history of science: the importance of carefully designing an experiment and choosing the correct model organism to study. Like Mendel's garden peas (Module 9.2) and Morgan's fruit flies (Module 9.18), bacteriophage T2 had just the right properties (in this case, a simple

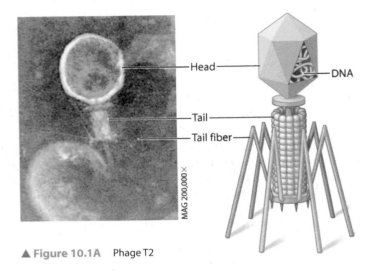

▲ **Figure 10.1A** Phage T2

structure consisting of just two contrasting elements) to allow for the design of a simple but conclusive experiment.

To begin, Hershey and Chase grew T2 with *E. coli* in a solution containing radioactive sulfur (shown in bright yellow in **Figure 10.1B**). Protein contains sulfur but DNA does not, so as new phages were made, the radioactive sulfur atoms were incorporated only into the proteins of the bacteriophage. The researchers grew a second batch of phages in a solution containing radioactive phosphorus (green). Because nearly all the phage's phosphorus is in DNA, this labeled only the phage DNA.

Armed with the two batches of labeled T2, Hershey and Chase were ready to perform the experiment outlined in Figure 10.1B. They allowed the two batches of T2 to infect separate samples of nonradioactive bacteria. Shortly after the onset of infection, they agitated the cultures in an ordinary kitchen blender to shake loose any parts of the phages that remained outside the bacterial cells. Then, they collected the mixtures in tubes and spun the tubes in a centrifuge. The cells were deposited as a solid pellet at the bottom of the centrifuge tubes, but phages and parts of phages—because they were lighter—remained suspended in the liquid. The researchers then measured the radioactivity in the pellet and in the liquid.

Hershey and Chase found that when the bacteria had been infected with T2 phages containing labeled protein, as in batch 1, the radioactivity ended up mainly in the solution within the centrifuge tube, which contained phages but not bacteria. This result suggested that the phage protein did not enter the cells. But when the bacteria had been infected with phages whose DNA was tagged, as in batch 2, most of the radioactivity was in the pellet of bacterial cells at the bottom of the centrifuge tube. Furthermore, when these bacteria were returned to a liquid growth medium, they soon lysed, or broke open, releasing new phages that contained some radioactive phosphorus in their DNA in their proteins.

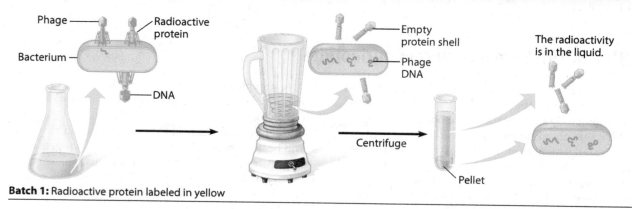

Batch 1: Radioactive protein labeled in yellow

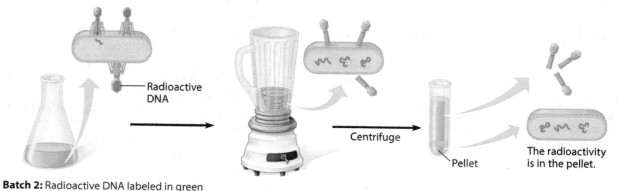

Batch 2: Radioactive DNA labeled in green

Hershey and Chase mixed radioactively labeled phages with bacteria. The phages infected the bacterial cells.	They agitated the cultures in a blender to separate the phages outside of the bacteria from the cells and their contents.	They centrifuged the mixture so that the bacteria formed a pellet at the bottom of the test tube.	Finally, they measured the radioactivity in the pellet and in the liquid.

▲ Figure 10.1B   The Hershey-Chase experiment

Figure 10.1C outlines our current understanding of the replication cycle of phage T2. After the virus ❶ attaches to the host bacterial cell, it ❷ injects its DNA into the host. Notice that virtually all of the viral protein (yellow) is left outside (which is why the radioactive protein did not show up in the host cells during the experiment shown at the top of Figure 10.1B). Once injected, the viral DNA causes the bacterial cells to ❸ produce new phage proteins and DNA molecules—indeed, complete new phages—which soon ❹ cause the cell to lyse, releasing the newly produced phages, which may then attach to other host bacterial cells. As

Hershey and Chase discovered, it is the viral DNA that contains the instructions for making phages.

Once DNA was shown to be the molecule of heredity, understanding its structure became the most important quest in biology. In the next two modules, we'll review the structure of DNA and discuss how it was discovered.

> ❓ What convinced Hershey and Chase that DNA, rather than protein, is the genetic material of phage T2?

⊙ Radioactively labeled phage DNA, but not labeled protein, entered the host cell during infection and directed the synthesis of new viruses.

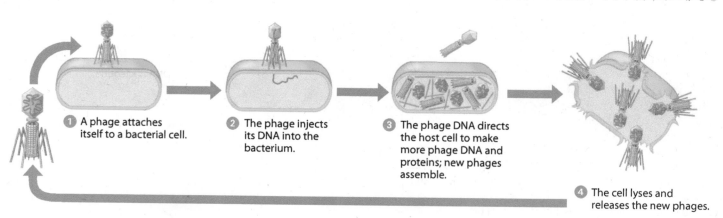

❶ A phage attaches itself to a bacterial cell.

❷ The phage injects its DNA into the bacterium.

❸ The phage DNA directs the host cell to make more phage DNA and proteins; new phages assemble.

❹ The cell lyses and releases the new phages.

▲ Figure 10.1C   A phage replication cycle

10.2 DNA and RNA are polymers of nucleotides

By the time Hershey and Chase performed their experiments, much was already known about DNA. Scientists had identified all its atoms and knew how they were bonded to one another. What was not understood was the specific three-dimensional arrangement of atoms that gave DNA its unique properties—the capacity to store genetic information, copy it, and pass it from generation to generation. However, only one year after Hershey and Chase published their results, scientists figured out the structure of DNA and the basic strategy of how it works. We will examine that momentous discovery in Module 10.3, but first, let's look at the underlying chemical structure of DNA and its chemical cousin, RNA.

DNA and RNA are nucleic acids, consisting of long chains (polymers) of chemical units (monomers) called **nucleotides** (see Module 3.16). **Figure 10.2A** shows four representations of various parts of the same molecule. At left is a view of a DNA double helix. One of the strands is opened up (center) to show two different views of an individual DNA **polynucleotide**, a nucleotide polymer (chain). The view on the far right zooms

in to a single nucleotide from the chain. Each type of DNA nucleotide has a different nitrogen-containing base: adenine (A), cytosine (C), thymine (T), or guanine (G). Because nucleotides can occur in a polynucleotide in any sequence and because polynucleotides can be very long, the number of possible polynucleotides is enormous. The chain shown in this figure has the sequence ACTGG, only one of many possible arrangements of the four types of nucleotides that make up DNA.

Looking more closely at our polynucleotide, we see in the center of Figure 10.2A that each nucleotide consists of three components: a nitrogenous base (in DNA: A, C, T, or G), a sugar (shown in blue), and a phosphate group (shown in yellow). The nucleotides are joined to one another by covalent bonds between the sugar of one nucleotide and the phosphate of the next, which forms a **sugar-phosphate backbone** with a repeating pattern of sugar-phosphate-sugar-phosphate. The nitrogenous bases are arranged like ribs that project from the backbone.

Examining a single nucleotide in even more detail (on the right in Figure 10.2A), you can see the chemical structure of its three components. The phosphate group has a phosphorus atom (P) at its center and is the source of the word *acid* in *nucleic acid*. The sugar has five carbon atoms, shown in red here for emphasis—four in its ring and one extending above the ring. The ring also includes an oxygen atom. The sugar is called deoxyribose because, compared with the sugar

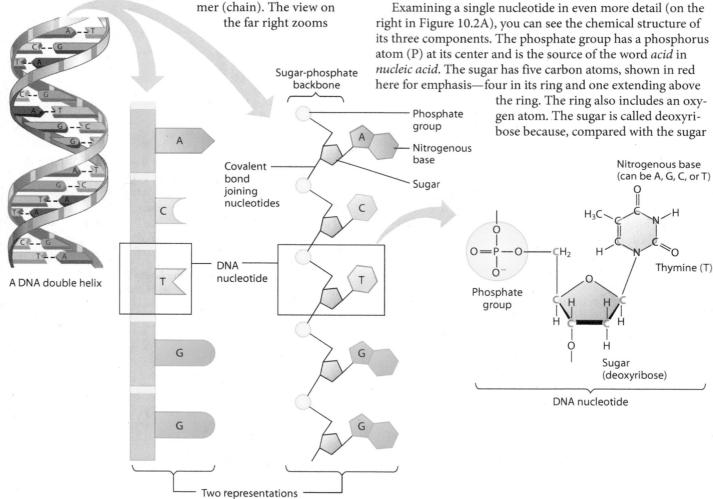

▲ **Figure 10.2A** Breaking down the structure of DNA

Try This Use your finger to trace each part of the nucleotide—sugar, phosphate, and base—in all four parts of this figure.

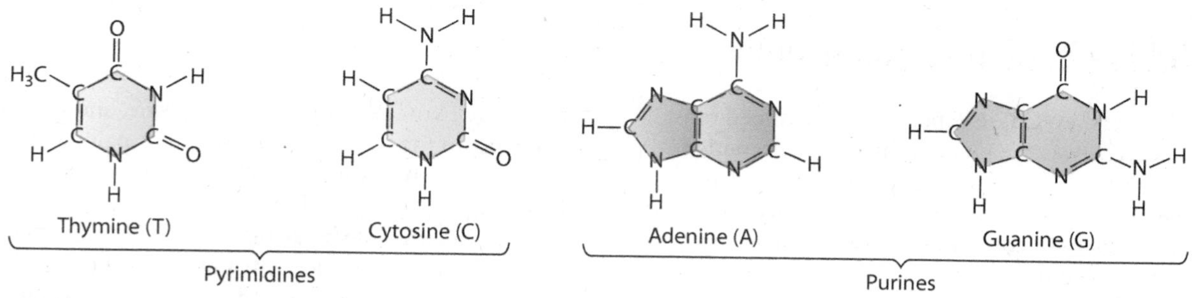

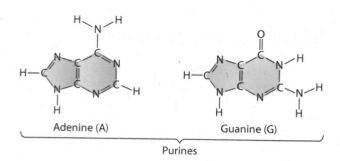

▲ **Figure 10.2B**   The nitrogenous bases of DNA

Thymine (T)   Cytosine (C)

Pyrimidines

Adenine (A)   Guanine (G)

Purines

ribose, it is missing an oxygen atom. Notice that the C atom in the lower right corner of the ring is bonded to an H atom instead of to an —OH group, as it is in ribose; see Figure 10.2C. Hence, DNA is "deoxy"—which means "without an oxygen"—compared to RNA.

The full name for **DNA** is **deoxyribonucleic acid**, with *nucleic* referring to DNA's location in the nuclei of eukaryotic cells. Each nitrogenous base (thymine, in our example at the right in Figure 10.2A) has a single or double ring consisting of nitrogen and carbon atoms with various functional groups attached (**Figure 10.2B**). Recall that a functional group is a chemical group that affects a molecule's function by participating in specific chemical reactions (see Module 3.2). In the case of DNA, the main role of the functional groups is to determine which other kind of bases each base can form hydrogen bonds with. For example, the NH_2 group hanging off cytosine is capable of forming a hydrogen bond to the C=O group hanging off guanine, but not with the NH_2 group protruding from adenine. The chemical groups of the bases are therefore responsible for DNA's most important property, which you will learn more about in the next module. In contrast to the acidic phosphate group, nitrogenous bases are basic—hence their name.

The four nucleotides found in DNA differ only in the structure of their nitrogenous bases. At this point, the structural details are not as important as the fact that the bases are of two types. **Thymine (T)** and **cytosine (C)** are single-ring structures called pyrimidines. **Adenine (A)** and **guanine (G)** are larger, double-ring structures called purines. The

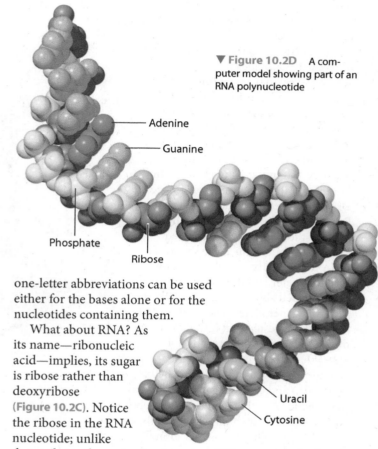

▼ **Figure 10.2D**   A computer model showing part of an RNA polynucleotide

Adenine

Guanine

Phosphate

Ribose

Uracil

Cytosine

one-letter abbreviations can be used either for the bases alone or for the nucleotides containing them.

What about RNA? As its name—ribonucleic acid—implies, its sugar is ribose rather than deoxyribose (**Figure 10.2C**). Notice the ribose in the RNA nucleotide; unlike deoxyribose, the sugar ring has an —OH group attached to the C atom at its lower-right corner. Another difference between RNA and DNA is that instead of thymine, RNA has a nitrogenous base called **uracil (U)**. (You can see the structure of uracil in Figure 10.2C; it is very similar to thymine.) Except for the presence of ribose and uracil, an RNA polynucleotide chain is identical to a DNA polynucleotide chain. **Figure 10.2D** is a computer graphic of a piece of RNA polynucleotide about 20 nucleotides long. In this three-dimensional view, each sphere represents an atom; notice that the color scheme is the same as in the other figures in this module. The yellow phosphate groups and blue ribose sugars make it easy to spot the sugar-phosphate backbone. In the next module, we'll see how two DNA polynucleotides join together in a molecule of DNA.

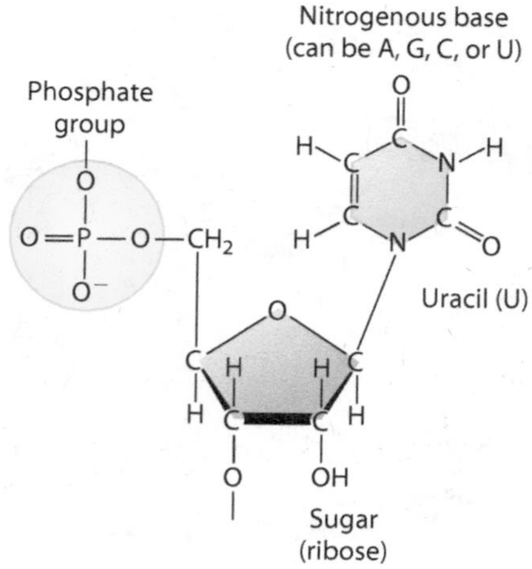

Phosphate group

Nitrogenous base (can be A, G, C, or U)

Uracil (U)

Sugar (ribose)

▲ **Figure 10.2C**   An RNA nucleotide

? **Compare and contrast DNA and RNA polynucleotides.**

● Both are polymers of nucleotides consisting of a sugar, a nitrogenous base, and a phosphate. In RNA, the sugar is ribose; in DNA, it is deoxyribose. Both RNA and DNA have the bases A, G, and C, but DNA has a T and RNA has a U.

10.3 DNA is a double-stranded helix

After the 1952 Hershey-Chase experiment convinced most biologists that DNA was the material that stored genetic information, a race was on to determine how the structure of this molecule could account for its role in heredity. By that time, the arrangement of covalent bonds in a nucleic acid polymer was well established, and researchers focused on discovering the three-dimensional shape of DNA. First to the finish line were two scientists who were relatively unknown at the time—American James D. Watson and Englishman Francis Crick.

The partnership that solved the puzzle of DNA structure began soon after Watson, a 23-year-old newly minted Ph.D., journeyed to Cambridge University in England, where the more senior Crick was studying protein structure with a technique called X-ray crystallography. While visiting the laboratory of Maurice Wilkins at King's College in London, Watson saw an X-ray image of DNA produced by Wilkins's colleague, Rosalind Franklin (Figure 10.3A). A careful study of the image enabled Watson to deduce the basic shape of DNA to be a helix (spiral) with a uniform diameter and the nitrogenous bases located above one another like a stack of dinner plates. The thickness of the helix suggested that it was made up of two polynucleotide strands, forming a **double helix**. But how were the nucleotides arranged in the double helix?

▲ Figure 10.3A   Rosalind Franklin and her X-ray image of DNA

Watson and Crick began trying to construct a wire model of a double helix that would conform both to Franklin's data and to what was then known about the chemistry of DNA (Figure 10.3B). They knew that Franklin had concluded that the sugar-phosphate backbones must be on the outside of the double helix, forcing the nitrogenous bases to swivel to the interior of the molecule. But how were the bases arranged in the interior of the double helix?

At first, Watson and Crick imagined that the bases paired like with like—for example, A with A and C with C. But that kind of pairing did not fit the X-ray data, which suggested that the DNA molecule has a uniform diameter. An A-A pair, with two double-ring bases, would be almost twice as wide as a C-C pair, made of two single-ring bases. It soon became apparent that a double-ringed base (purine) on one strand must always be paired with a single-ringed base (pyrimidine) on the opposite strand to produce a molecule of uniform thickness. After considerable trial and error, Watson and Crick realized that the chemical structures of the bases dictated the pairings even more specifically. As discussed in the previous module, each base has protruding functional groups that can best form hydrogen bonds with just one appropriate partner (to review the hydrogen bond, see Module 2.8). Adenine can

best form hydrogen bonds with thymine, and guanine with cytosine. In the biologist's shorthand, A pairs with T, and G pairs with C. A is also said to be "complementary" to T and G to C.

Watson and Crick's pairing scheme both fit what was known about the physical attributes and chemical bonding of DNA and explained some data obtained several years earlier by American biochemist Erwin Chargaff. Chargaff had discovered that the amount of adenine in the DNA of any one species was equal to the amount of thymine and that the amount of guanine was equal to that of cytosine. Chargaff's rules, as they are called, are explained by the fact that A on one of DNA's polynucleotide chains always pairs with T on the other polynucleotide chain, and G on one chain pairs only with C on the other chain.

You can picture the model of the DNA double helix proposed by Watson and Crick as a rope ladder with wooden rungs, with the ladder twisting into a spiral (Figure 10.3C). The side ropes represent the sugar-phosphate backbones, and the rungs represent pairs of nitrogenous bases joined by hydrogen bonds.

Figure 10.3D shows three representations of the double helix. The shapes of the base symbols in the ribbonlike diagram on the left indicate the bases' complementarity; notice that the shape of any kind of base matches only one other kind of base. In the center of the diagram is an atomic-level version showing four base pairs, with the helix untwisted and the hydrogen bonds specified by dotted

▲ Figure 10.3B   Watson and Crick in 1953 with their model of the DNA double helix

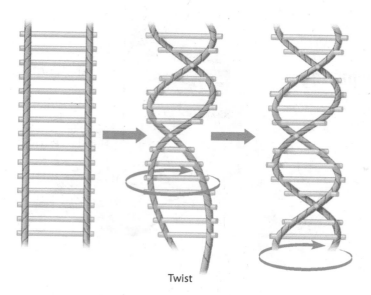

▲ Figure 10.3C A rope ladder analogy for the double helix

Twist

lines. Notice that a C-G base pair has functional groups that form three hydrogen bonds, whereas an A-T base pair has functional groups that form two hydrogen bonds. This difference means that C-G base pairs are somewhat stronger than A-T base pairs. You can see that the two sugar-phosphate backbones of the double helix are oriented in opposite directions. (Notice that the sugars on the two strands are upside down with respect to each other.) On the right is a computer graphic showing most of the atoms of part of a double helix. The atoms that compose the deoxyribose sugars are shown

as blue, phosphate groups as yellow, and nitrogenous bases as shades of green and orange.

Although the Watson-Crick base-pairing rules dictate the side-by-side combinations of nitrogenous bases that form the rungs of the double helix, they place no restrictions on the sequence of nucleotides along the length of a DNA strand. In fact, the sequence of bases can vary in countless ways, and each gene has a unique order of nucleotides, or base sequence.

In April 1953, Watson and Crick rocked the scientific world with a succinct paper explaining their molecular model for DNA in the British scientific journal *Nature*. In 1962, Watson, Crick, and Wilkins received the Nobel Prize for their work. (Sadly, Rosalind Franklin died in 1958 at the age of 38 and was thus ineligible for the prize.) Few milestones in the history of biology have had as broad an impact as the discovery of the double helix, with its A-T and C-G base pairing.

The Watson-Crick model gave new meaning to the words *genes* and *chromosomes*—and to the chromosome theory of inheritance (see Module 9.16). With a complete picture of DNA, we can see that the genetic information in a chromosome must be encoded in the nucleotide sequence of the molecule. One powerful aspect of the Watson-Crick model is that the structure of DNA suggests a molecular explanation for genetic inheritance, as we will see in the next module.

? Along one strand of a double helix is the nucleotide sequence GGCATAGGT. What is the complementary sequence for the other DNA strand?

● CCGTATCCA

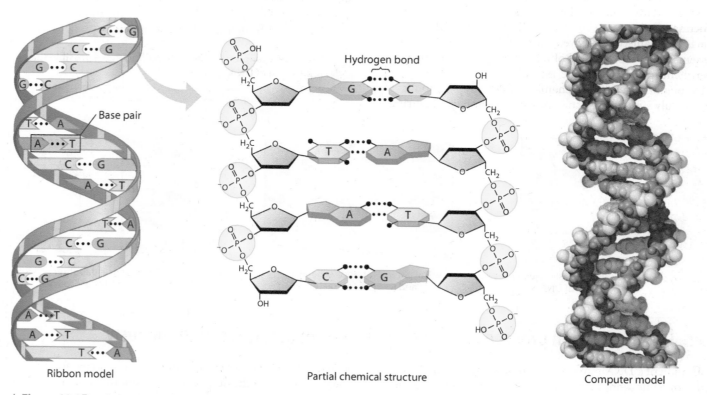

Ribbon model

Partial chemical structure

Computer model

▲ Figure 10.3D Three representations of DNA

▷ DNA Replication

10.4 DNA replication depends on specific base pairing

One of biology's overarching themes—the relationship between structure and function—is evident in the double helix. The idea that there is specific pairing of bases in DNA was the flash of inspiration that led Watson and Crick to the correct structure of the DNA molecule. At the same time, they saw the functional significance of the base-pairing rules.

The logic behind the Watson-Crick proposal for how DNA is copied—by specific pairing of complementary bases—is quite simple. You can see this by covering one of the strands in the parental DNA molecule in **Figure 10.4A**. You can determine the sequence of bases in the covered strand by applying the base-pairing rules to the unmasked strand: A pairs with T (and T with A), and G pairs with C (and C with G).

Watson and Crick predicted that a cell applies the same rules when copying its genes during each turn of the cell cycle (Module 8.3). As shown in Figure 10.4A, the two strands of parental DNA (blue) separate. Each strand becomes a template for the assembly of a complementary strand from a supply of free nucleotides (gray) available within the nucleus. The nucleotides line up one at a time along the template strand in accordance with the base-pairing rules. Enzymes link the nucleotides to form the new DNA strands. The completed new molecules, identical to the parental molecule, are known as daughter DNA (although no gender should be inferred).

Watson and Crick's model predicts that when a double helix replicates, each of the two daughter molecules will have one old strand from the parental molecule and one newly created strand. This model for DNA replication is known as the **semiconservative model** because half of the parental molecule is maintained (conserved) in each daughter molecule. The semiconservative model of replication was confirmed by experiments performed in the 1950s.

Although the general mechanism of DNA replication is conceptually simple, the actual process is complex, requiring

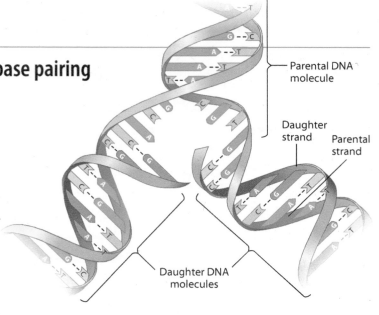

the coordination of more than a dozen enzymes and other proteins. Some of the complexity arises from the need for the helical DNA molecule to untwist as it replicates and for the two new strands to be made roughly simultaneously (**Figure 10.4B**). Another challenge is the speed of the process. *E. coli*, with about 4.6 million DNA base pairs, can copy its entire genome in less than an hour. Human cells, with more than 6 billion base pairs in 46 chromosomes, require only a few hours. Despite this speed, the process is amazingly accurate; typically, only about one DNA nucleotide per several billion is incorrectly paired. In the next module, we take a closer look at the mechanisms of DNA replication that allow it to proceed with such speed and accuracy.

▲ **Figure 10.4B**   The untwisting and replication of DNA

> **?** How does complementary base pairing make possible the replication of DNA?

● When the two strands of the double helix separate, free nucleotides can base-pair along each strand, leading to the synthesis of new complementary strands.

▶ **Figure 10.4A**
A template model for
DNA replication

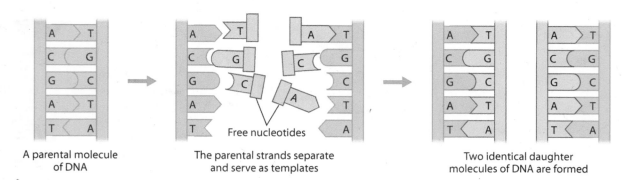

| A parental molecule of DNA | The parental strands separate and serve as templates | Two identical daughter molecules of DNA are formed |

Free nucleotides

10.5 DNA replication proceeds in two directions at many sites simultaneously

Replication of a DNA molecule begins at particular sites called origins of replication, short stretches of DNA having a specific sequence of nucleotides. Proteins that initiate DNA replication attach to the DNA at the origin of replication, separating the two strands of the double helix (**Figure 10.5A**). Replication then proceeds in both directions, creating replication

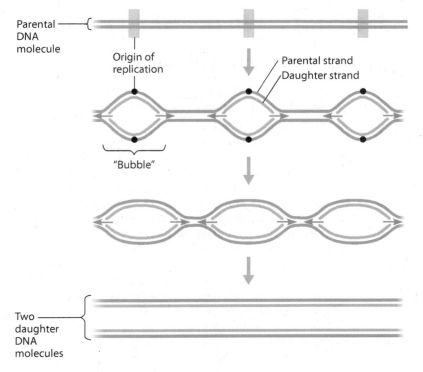

Parental DNA molecule

Origin of replication

Parental strand
Daughter strand

"Bubble"

Two daughter DNA molecules

▲ **Figure 10.5A** Multiple replication bubbles in DNA

"bubbles." The parental DNA strands (blue) open up as daughter strands (gray) elongate on both sides of each bubble. The DNA molecule of a eukaryotic chromosome has many origins where replication can start simultaneously. Thus, hundreds or thousands of bubbles can be present at once, shortening the total time needed for replication. Eventually, all the bubbles fuse, yielding two completed, double-stranded daughter DNA molecules (see the bottom of Figure 10.5A).

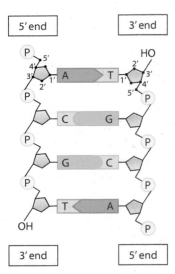

5′ end

3′ end

3′ end

5′ end

▲ **Figure 10.5B** The opposite orientations of DNA strands

Try This On each polynucleotide strand, identify one complete nucleotide by drawing a circle around it. Notice that in one strand, the phosphate is on top, and on the other strand, it's on the bottom.

Figure 10.5B shows the molecular building blocks of a tiny segment of DNA. Notice that the sugar-phosphate backbones run in opposite directions. As a result, each strand has a 3′ ("three-prime") end and a 5′ ("five-prime") end. The primed numbers refer to the carbon atoms of the nucleotide sugars. At one end of each DNA strand, the sugar's 3′ carbon atom is attached to an —OH group; at the other end, the sugar's 5′ carbon is attached to a phosphate group.

The opposite orientation of the strands is important in DNA replication. The enzymes that link DNA nucleotides to a growing daughter strand, called **DNA polymerases**, add

nucleotides only to the 3′ end of the strand, never to the 5′ end. Thus, a daughter DNA strand can only grow in the 5′ → 3′ direction. You see the consequences of this enzyme specificity in **Figure 10.5C**, where the forked structure represents one side of a replication bubble. One of the daughter strands (shown in gray) can be synthesized in one continuous piece by a DNA polymerase working toward the forking point of the parental DNA. However, to make the other daughter strand, polymerase molecules must work outward from the forking point. The only way this can be accomplished is if the new strand is synthesized in short pieces as the fork opens up. These pieces are called Okazaki fragments, after the Japanese husband and wife team of molecular biologists who discovered them. Another enzyme, called **DNA ligase**, then links, or ligates, the pieces together into a single DNA strand.

In addition to their roles in adding nucleotides to a DNA chain, DNA polymerases carry out a proofreading step that quickly removes nucleotides that have base-paired incorrectly during replication. DNA polymerases and DNA ligase are also involved in repairing DNA damaged by harmful radiation, such as ultraviolet light and X-rays, or toxic chemicals in the environment, such as those found in tobacco smoke.

DNA replication ensures that all the somatic cells in a multicellular organism carry the same genetic information. It is also the means by which genetic instructions are copied for the next generation of the organism. In the next module, we begin to pursue the connection between DNA instructions and an organism's phenotypic traits.

? **What is the function of DNA polymerase in DNA replication?**

● As free nucleotides base-pair to a parental DNA strand, the enzyme covalently bonds them to the 3′ end of a growing daughter strand.

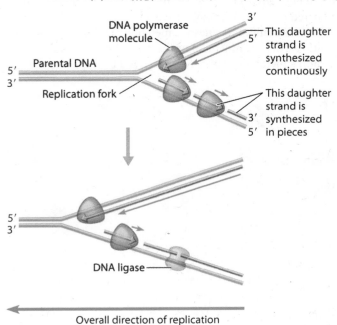

▲ **Figure 10.5C** How daughter DNA strands are synthesized

10.6 Genes control phenotypic traits through the expression of proteins

We can now define genotype and phenotype in terms of the structure and function of DNA. An organism's genotype, its genetic makeup, is the heritable information contained in the sequence of nucleotide bases in DNA. The phenotype is the organism's physical traits. So what is the molecular connection between genotype and phenotype?

The answer is that the DNA inherited by an organism specifies traits by dictating the synthesis of proteins. In other words, proteins are the links between genotype and phenotype. However, a gene does not build a protein directly. Rather, a gene dispatches instructions in the form of RNA, which in turn programs protein synthesis. This fundamental concept in biology is summarized in **Figure 10.6A**. The molecular "chain of command" is from DNA in the nucleus of the cell to RNA to protein synthesis in the cytoplasm. The two main stages are **transcription**, the synthesis of RNA under the direction of DNA, and **translation**, the synthesis of protein under the direction of RNA.

The relationship between genes and proteins was first proposed in 1909, when English physician Archibald Garrod suggested that genes dictate phenotypes through enzymes, proteins that catalyze chemical reactions. Garrod hypothesized that an inherited disease reflects a person's inability to make a particular enzyme. He gave as one example the hereditary condition called alkaptonuria, in which the urine is dark because it contains a chemical called alkapton. Garrod reasoned that most people have an enzyme that breaks down alkapton, whereas people with alkaptonuria inherited an inability to make the enzyme. Garrod's hypothesis was ahead of its time, but research conducted decades later supported his hypothesis. In the intervening years, biochemists accumulated evidence that cells make and break down biologically important molecules via metabolic pathways, as in the synthesis of an amino acid or the breakdown of a sugar. Each step in a metabolic pathway is catalyzed by a specific enzyme

(as we described in Unit I; see Module 5.15, for example). Therefore, individuals lacking one of the enzymes for a pathway are unable to complete it.

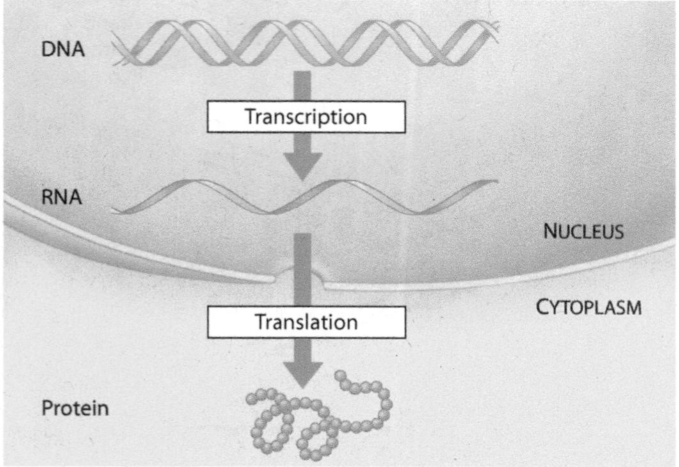

The major breakthrough in demonstrating the relationship between genes and enzymes came in the 1940s from the work of American geneticists George Beadle and Edward Tatum with the bread mold *Neurospora crassa* (**Figure 10.6B**). Beadle and Tatum studied strains of the mold that were unable to grow on a simple growth medium. Each of these so-called nutritional mutants turned out to lack an enzyme in a metabolic pathway that synthesized some molecule the mold needed, such as an amino acid. Beadle and Tatum also showed that each mutant was defective in a single gene. Accordingly, they hypothesized that the function of an individual gene is to dictate the production of a specific enzyme.

The "one gene–one enzyme hypothesis" has since been modified. First, it was extended beyond enzymes to include *all* types of proteins. For example, keratin (the structural protein of hair) and the hormone insulin are two examples of proteins that are not enzymes. In addition, many proteins are made from two or more polypeptide chains, with each polypeptide specified by its own gene. For example, hemoglobin, the oxygen-transporting protein in your red blood cells, is built from two kinds of polypeptides, encoded by two different genes. Thus, Beadle and Tatum's hypothesis is now stated as follows: The function of a gene is to dictate the production of a polypeptide.

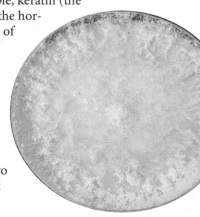

▲ **Figure 10.6B** The bread mold *Neurospora crassa* growing in a culture dish

Even this description is not entirely accurate, in that the RNA transcribed from some genes is not translated but nonetheless has important functions (you'll learn about two such kinds of RNA in Modules 10.11 and 10.12). In addition, many eukaryotic genes code for a set of polypeptides (rather than just one) by a process called alternative splicing (discussed in Module 11.4). The more biologists learn about the ways that genes act in cells, the more complicated the picture—and the very concept of a gene—becomes. This topic continues to be an active area of research within the biology community. But for now, we'll focus on genes that do code for polypeptides. The nature of that code is our next topic.

? What are the functions of transcription and translation?

DNA

Transcription

RNA

NUCLEUS

CYTOPLASM

Translation

Protein

▲ **Figure 10.6A** The flow of genetic information in a eukaryotic cell

● Transcription is the transfer of information from DNA to RNA. Translation is the use of the information in RNA to make a polypeptide.

10.7 Genetic information written in codons is translated into amino acid sequences

Genes provide the instructions for making specific proteins. But a gene does not build a protein itself. As you have learned, the bridge between DNA and protein synthesis is the nucleic acid RNA: DNA is transcribed into RNA, which is then translated into protein. Put another way, information within the cell flows as DNA → RNA → protein. This can be stated as: "DNA makes RNA makes protein."

Transcription and translation are linguistic terms, and it is useful to think of nucleic acids and proteins as having languages. To understand how genetic information passes from genotype to phenotype, we need to see how the chemical language of DNA is translated into the different chemical language of proteins.

What exactly is the language of nucleic acids? Both DNA and RNA are polymers made of nucleotide monomers strung together in specific sequences that convey information, much as specific sequences of letters convey information in written language. In DNA, there are four types of nucleotides, which differ in their nitrogenous bases (A, T, C, and G). The same is true for RNA, although it has the base U instead of T.

Figure 10.7 focuses on a small region of one gene (gene 3, shown in light blue) on a DNA molecule. DNA's language is written as a linear sequence of nucleotide bases on a polynucleotide, a sequence such as the one you see on the enlarged DNA segment in the figure. Specific sequences of bases, each with a beginning and an end, make up the genes on a DNA strand. A typical gene consists of hundreds or thousands of nucleotides in a specific sequence.

The pink strand underneath the enlarged DNA segment represents the results of transcription: an RNA molecule. The process is called transcription because the nucleic acid language of DNA has been rewritten (transcribed) as a sequence of bases on RNA. Notice that the language is still that of nucleic acids, although the nucleotide bases on the RNA molecule are complementary to those on the DNA strand. As we will see in Module 10.9, this is because the RNA was synthesized using the DNA as a template.

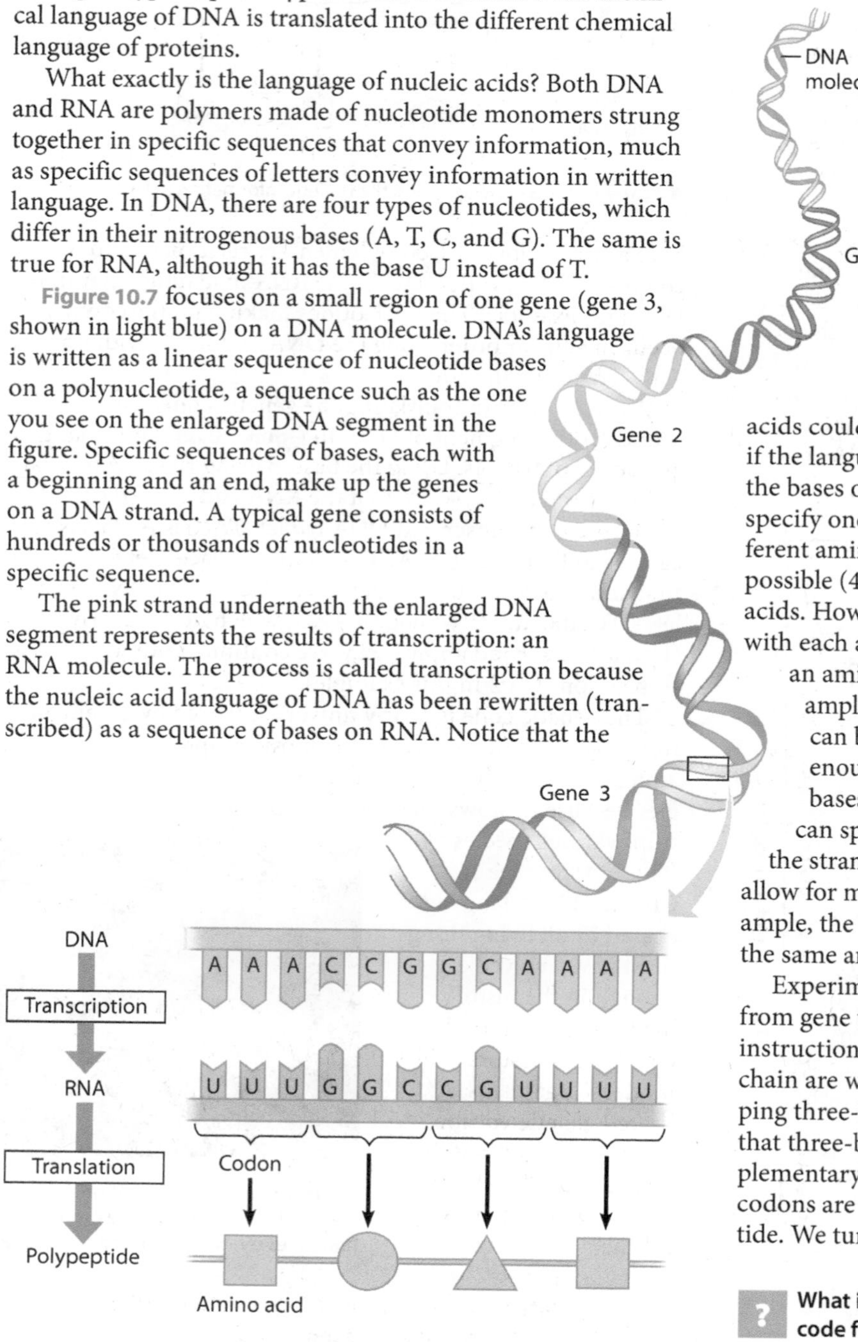

The purple chain at the bottom of Figure 10.7 represents the results of translation, the conversion of the nucleic acid language to the polypeptide language. Like nucleic acids, polypeptides are polymers, but the monomers that compose them are the 20 different kinds of amino acids. Again, the language is written in a linear sequence, and the sequence of nucleotides of the RNA molecule dictates the sequence of amino acids of the polypeptide. The RNA acts as a messenger carrying genetic information from DNA.

During translation, there is a change in language from the nucleotide sequence of the RNA to the amino acid sequence of the polypeptide. How is this translation achieved? Recall that there are only four different kinds of nucleotides in DNA (A, G, C, T) and in RNA (A, G, C, U). In translation, these four nucleotides must somehow specify all 20 amino acids. Consider if each single nucleotide base were to specify one amino acid. In this case, only four of the 20 amino acids could be accounted for, one for each type of base. What if the language consisted of two-letter code words? If we read the bases of a gene two at a time—AG, for example, could specify one amino acid, whereas AT could designate a different amino acid—then only 16 arrangements would be possible (4^2), which is still not enough to specify all 20 amino acids. However, if the base code in DNA consists of a triplet, with each arrangement of three consecutive bases specifying an amino acid—AGT specifies one amino acid, for example, while AGA specifies a different one—then there can be 64 (that is, 4^3) possible code words, more than enough to specify the 20 amino acids. Thus, triplets of bases are the smallest "words" of uniform length that can specify all the amino acids (see the brackets below the strand of RNA in Figure 10.7). Indeed, the 64 triplets allow for more than one to represent an amino acid. For example, the base triplets AAT and AAC could both code for the same amino acid.

Experiments have verified that the flow of information from gene to protein is based on a **triplet code**: The genetic instructions for the amino acid sequence of a polypeptide chain are written in DNA and RNA as a series of nonoverlapping three-base "words" called **codons**. Notice in the figure that three-base codons in the DNA are transcribed into complementary three-base codons in the RNA, and then the RNA codons are translated into amino acids that form a polypeptide. We turn to the codons themselves in the next module.

DNA molecule

Gene 1

Gene 2

Gene 3

DNA

Transcription

A A A C C G G C A A A A

RNA

U U U G G C C G U U U U

Translation

Codon

Polypeptide

Amino acid

? **What is the minimum number of nucleotides necessary to code for 100 amino acids?**

▲ **Figure 10.7** Transcription and translation of codons

10.8 The genetic code dictates how codons are translated into amino acids

During the 1960s, molecular biologists used a series of elegant experiments to crack the **genetic code**, the amino acid translations of each of the nucleotide triplets. The first codon was deciphered in 1961 by American biochemist Marshall Nirenberg. He synthesized an artificial RNA molecule by linking together identical RNA nucleotides having uracil as their only base. No matter where this message started or stopped, it could contain only one type of triplet codon: UUU. Nirenberg added this "poly-U" to a test-tube mixture containing ribosomes and the other ingredients required for polypeptide synthesis. His artificial system translated the poly-U into a polypeptide containing a single kind of amino acid, phenylalanine (Phe). Thus, Nirenberg learned that the RNA codon UUU specifies the amino acid phenylalanine. By variations on this method, the amino acids specified by all the codons were soon determined.

As shown in **Figure 10.8A**, 61 of the 64 triplets code for amino acids. The triplet AUG (green box in the figure) has a dual function: It codes for the amino acid methionine (Met) and also can provide a signal for the start of a polypeptide chain. Three codons (UAA, UGA, and UAG, shown in red) do not designate amino acids but serve as stop codons that mark the end of translation.

Notice in Figure 10.8A that there is redundancy in the code but no ambiguity. For example, although codons UUU and UUC both specify phenylalanine (redundancy), neither of them ever represents any other amino acid (no ambiguity). The codons in the figure are the triplets found in RNA. They

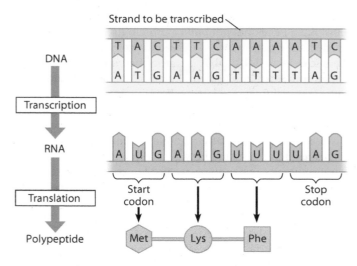

▲ **Figure 10.8B** Deciphering the genetic information in DNA

have a straightforward, complementary relationship to the codons in DNA, with UUU in the RNA matching AAA in the DNA, for example. The nucleotides making up the codons occur in a linear order along the DNA and RNA, with no gaps separating the codons.

As an exercise in translating the genetic code, consider the 12-nucleotide segment of DNA in **Figure 10.8B**. Let's read this as a series of triplets. Using the base-pairing rules (with U in RNA instead of T), we see that the RNA codon corresponding to the first transcribed DNA triplet, TAC, is AUG. As you can see in Figure 10.8A, AUG specifies, "Place Met as the first amino acid in the polypeptide." The second DNA triplet, TTC, dictates RNA codon AAG, which designates lysine (Lys) as the second amino acid. We continue until we reach a stop codon (UAG in this example).

The genetic code is nearly universal, shared by organisms from the simplest bacteria to the most complex plants and animals. Such universality is key to modern DNA technologies because it allows scientists to mix and match genes from various species (**Figure 10.8C**; see Chapter 12). A language shared by all living things must have evolved early enough in the history of life to be present in the common ancestors of all modern organisms. A shared genetic vocabulary is a reminder of the evolutionary kinship that connects all life on Earth.

▲ **Figure 10.8C** The cat on the left was engineered to express a protein that fluoresces red when exposed to UV light

Second base of RNA codon

	U	C	A	G	
U	UUU ⎤ UUC ⎦ Phe UUA ⎤ UUG ⎦ Leu	UCU ⎤ UCC ⎥ UCA ⎥ UCG ⎦ Ser	UAU ⎤ UAC ⎦ Tyr UAA Stop UAG Stop	UGU ⎤ UGC ⎦ Cys UGA Stop UGG Trp	U C A G
C	CUU ⎤ CUC ⎥ CUA ⎥ CUG ⎦ Leu	CCU ⎤ CCC ⎥ CCA ⎥ CCG ⎦ Pro	CAU ⎤ CAC ⎦ His CAA ⎤ CAG ⎦ Gln	CGU ⎤ CGC ⎥ CGA ⎥ CGG ⎦ Arg	U C A G
A	AUU ⎤ AUC ⎥ Ile AUA ⎦ AUG Met or start	ACU ⎤ ACC ⎥ ACA ⎥ ACG ⎦ Thr	AAU ⎤ AAC ⎦ Asn AAA ⎤ AAG ⎦ Lys	AGU ⎤ AGC ⎦ Ser AGA ⎤ AGG ⎦ Arg	U C A G
G	GUU ⎤ GUC ⎥ GUA ⎥ Val GUG ⎦	GCU ⎤ GCC ⎥ GCA ⎥ GCG ⎦ Ala	GAU ⎤ GAC ⎦ Asp GAA ⎤ GAG ⎦ Glu	GGU ⎤ GGC ⎥ GGA ⎥ GGG ⎦ Gly	U C A G

First base of RNA codon (left side) *Third base of RNA codon* (right side)

▲ **Figure 10.8A** The genetic code used to translate RNA codons to amino acids

Try This Identify the DNA triplet that produces an RNA start codon, and identify the three DNA triplets that produce an RNA stop codon.

? Translate the RNA sequence CCAUUUACG into the corresponding amino acid sequence.

Pro-Phe-Thr

10.9 Transcription produces genetic messages in the form of RNA

In eukaryotic cells, transcription, the transfer of genetic information from DNA to RNA, occurs in the nucleus. Here we focus on transcription in prokaryotic cells, which is a simpler process than in eukaryotes.

After separation of the two DNA strands, one strand serves as a template for a new RNA molecule; the other DNA strand is unused. The transcription enzyme **RNA polymerase** moves along the gene, forming a new RNA strand by following the base-pairing rules—but remember that in RNA, uracil replaces thymine. A specific nucleotide sequence called a **promoter** acts as a binding site for RNA polymerase and determines where transcription starts and on which strand. RNA polymerase adds RNA nucleotides until it reaches a sequence of DNA bases called the **terminator**, which signals the end of the gene.

TRANSCRIPTION OF A GENE

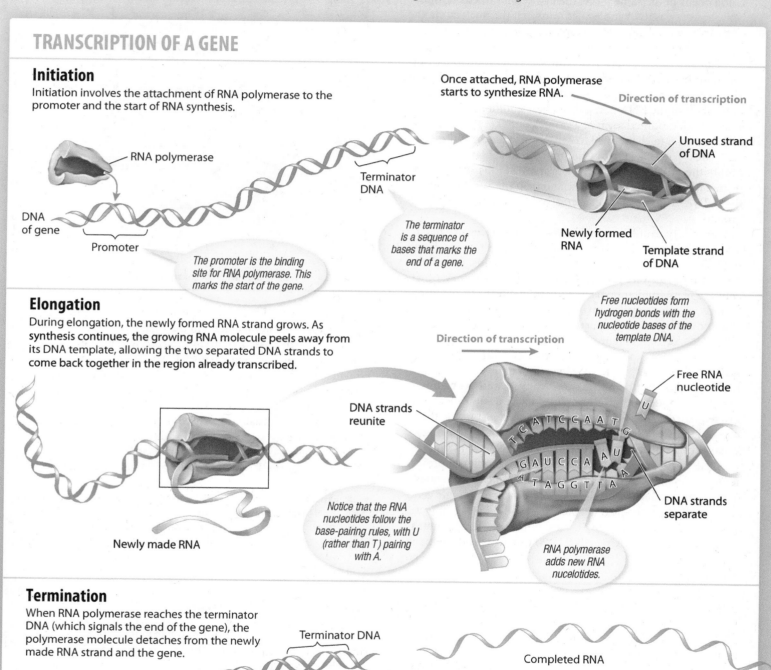

Initiation

Initiation involves the attachment of RNA polymerase to the promoter and the start of RNA synthesis.

RNA polymerase

DNA of gene

Promoter

The promoter is the binding site for RNA polymerase. This marks the start of the gene.

Terminator DNA

The terminator is a sequence of bases that marks the end of a gene.

Once attached, RNA polymerase starts to synthesize RNA.

Direction of transcription

Unused strand of DNA

Newly formed RNA

Template strand of DNA

Elongation

During elongation, the newly formed RNA strand grows. As synthesis continues, the growing RNA molecule peels away from its DNA template, allowing the two separated DNA strands to come back together in the region already transcribed.

Newly made RNA

Direction of transcription

DNA strands reunite

Notice that the RNA nucleotides follow the base-pairing rules, with U (rather than T) pairing with A.

Free nucleotides form hydrogen bonds with the nucleotide bases of the template DNA.

Free RNA nucleotide

DNA strands separate

RNA polymerase adds new RNA nucelotides.

T C A T C C A A T G
G A U C C A U A
A T A G G T T A

Termination

When RNA polymerase reaches the terminator DNA (which signals the end of the gene), the polymerase molecule detaches from the newly made RNA strand and the gene.

Terminator DNA

Completed RNA

RNA polymerase detaches

? How does RNA polymerase recognize the start and end of the gene?

Special DNA sequences mark the start (promoter) and end (terminator) of a gene.

10.10 Eukaryotic RNA is processed before leaving the nucleus as mRNA

The kind of RNA that encodes amino acid sequences is called **messenger RNA (mRNA)** because it conveys genetic messages from DNA to the translation machinery of the cell. Messenger RNA is transcribed from DNA, and the information in the mRNA is then translated into polypeptides. In prokaryotic cells, which lack nuclei, transcription and translation occur in the same place: the cytoplasm. In eukaryotic cells, however, mRNA molecules must exit the nucleus via the nuclear pores and enter the cytoplasm, where the machinery for polypeptide synthesis is located.

Before leaving the nucleus as mRNA, eukaryotic transcripts are modified, or processed, in several ways (Figure 10.10). One kind of RNA processing is the addition of extra nucleotides to the ends of the RNA transcript. These additions include a small cap (a modified form of a G nucleotide) at the 5′ end and a long tail (a chain of 50 to 250 A nucleotides) at the 3′ end. The cap and tail (yellow in the figure) facilitate the export of the mRNA from the nucleus, protect the mRNA from degradation by cellular enzymes, and help ribosomes bind to the mRNA. The cap and tail themselves are not translated into protein.

Another type of RNA processing is made necessary in eukaryotes by noncoding stretches of nucleotides that interrupt the nucleotides that actually code for amino acids. It is as if nonsense words were randomly interspersed in a story. Most genes of plants and animals include such internal noncoding regions, which are called **introns** ("intervening sequences"). The coding regions—the parts of a gene that are expressed—are called **exons**. As Figure 10.10 shows, both exons (shown in a darker color) and introns (in a lighter color) are transcribed from DNA into RNA. However, before the RNA leaves the nucleus, the introns are removed, and the exons are joined to produce an mRNA molecule with a continuous coding sequence. (The short noncoding regions just inside the cap and tail are considered parts of the first and last exons.) This cutting-and-pasting process is called **RNA splicing**. In most cases, RNA splicing is catalyzed by a complex of proteins and small RNA molecules. RNA splicing also provides a means to produce multiple polypeptides from a single gene (as we will see in the next chapter; see Module 11.4). In fact, RNA splicing is believed to play a significant role in humans in allowing our approximately 21,000 genes to produce many

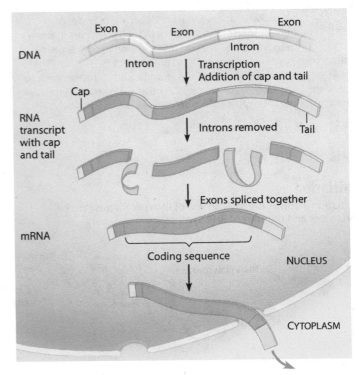

▲ **Figure 10.10**   The production of eukaryotic mRNA

thousands more polypeptides. This is accomplished by varying the exons that are included in the final mRNA.

As we have discussed, translation is a conversion between different languages—from the nucleic acid language to the protein language—and it involves more elaborate machinery than transcription. The first important ingredient required for translation is the processed mRNA. Once it is present, the machinery used to translate mRNA requires enzymes and sources of chemical energy, such as ATP. In addition, translation requires two heavy-duty components: ribosomes and a kind of RNA called transfer RNA, the subject of the next module.

> **?** **Explain why most eukaryotic genes are longer than the mRNA that leaves the nucleus.**
>
> ● These genes have introns, noncoding sequences of nucleotides that are spliced out of the initial RNA transcript to produce mRNA.

10.11 Transfer RNA molecules serve as interpreters during translation

Translation of any language into another language requires an interpreter, someone or something that can recognize the words of one language and convert them to another. Translation of a genetic message carried in mRNA into the amino acid language of proteins also requires an interpreter. To convert the three-letter "words" of nucleic acids (codons) to the amino acid "words" of proteins, a cell uses a molecular interpreter, a special type of RNA called **transfer RNA (tRNA)**.

A cell that is producing proteins has in its cytoplasm a supply of amino acids, either obtained from food or manufactured by the cell. But amino acids themselves cannot recognize the codons in the mRNA. It is up to the cell's molecular interpreters, tRNA molecules, to match amino acids to the appropriate codons to form the new polypeptide. To perform this task, tRNA molecules must carry out two functions: (1) picking up the appropriate amino acids and (2) recognizing

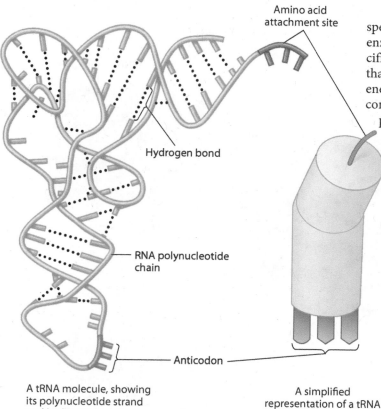

Amino acid attachment site

Hydrogen bond

RNA polynucleotide chain

Anticodon

A tRNA molecule, showing its polynucleotide strand and hydrogen bonding

A simplified representation of a tRNA

▲ **Figure 10.11A** The structure of tRNA

Each amino acid is joined to the correct tRNA by a specific enzyme. There is a family of 20 versions of these enzymes, one enzyme for each amino acid. Each enzyme specifically binds one type of amino acid to all tRNA molecules that code for that amino acid, using a molecule of ATP as energy to drive the reaction. The resulting amino acid–tRNA complex can then furnish its amino acid to a growing polypeptide chain, a process that we describe in Module 10.12.

The computer graphic in **Figure 10.11B** shows a tRNA molecule (green) and an ATP molecule (yellow) bound to the enzyme molecule (blue). (To help you see the two distinct molecules, the tRNA molecule is shown with a stick representation, while the enzyme is shown as space-filling spheres.) In this figure, you can see the proportional sizes of these three molecules. The amino acid that would attach to the tRNA is not shown; it would be less than half the size of the ATP.

Once an amino acid is attached to its appropriate tRNA, it can be incorporated into a growing polypeptide chain. This is accomplished within ribosomes, the cellular structures directly responsible for the synthesis of protein. We examine ribosomes in the next module.

? **What is an anticodon, and what is its function?**

● It is the base triplet of a tRNA molecule that couples the tRNA to a complementary codon in the mRNA. This is a key step in translating mRNA to polypeptide.

the appropriate codons in the mRNA. The unique structure of tRNA molecules enables them to perform both tasks.

Figure 10.11A shows two representations of a tRNA molecule. The structure on the left shows the backbone and bases, with hydrogen bonds between bases shown as dotted lines. The structure on the right is a simplified schematic that emphasizes the most important parts of the structure. Notice from the structure on the left that a tRNA molecule is made of a single strand of RNA—one polynucleotide chain— consisting of about 80 nucleotides. By twisting and folding upon itself, tRNA forms several double-stranded regions in which short stretches of RNA base-pair with other stretches via hydrogen bonds. A single-stranded loop at one end of the folded molecule contains a special triplet of bases called an **anticodon**. The anticodon triplet is complementary to a codon triplet on mRNA. During translation, the anticodon on the tRNA recognizes a particular codon on the mRNA by using base-pairing rules. At the other end of the tRNA molecule is a site where one specific kind of amino acid attaches.

In the modules that follow, we represent tRNA with the simplified shape shown on the right in Figure 10.11A. This shape emphasizes the two parts of the molecule—the anticodon and the amino acid attachment site—that give tRNA its ability to match a particular nucleic acid word (a codon in mRNA) with its corresponding protein word (an amino acid). Although all tRNA molecules are similar, there is a slightly different variety of tRNA for each amino acid.

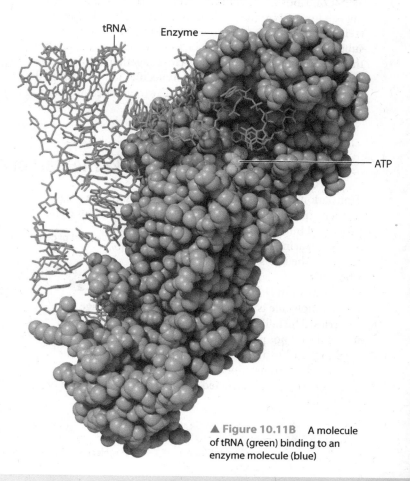

tRNA

Enzyme

ATP

▲ **Figure 10.11B** A molecule of tRNA (green) binding to an enzyme molecule (blue)

10.12 Ribosomes build polypeptides

We have now looked at many of the components a cell needs to carry out translation: instructions in the form of mRNA molecules, tRNA to interpret the instructions, a supply of amino acids and enzymes (for attaching amino acids to tRNA), and ATP for energy. The final components are the **ribosomes**, structures in the cytoplasm that coordinate the functioning of mRNA and tRNA and catalyze the synthesis of polypeptides (Figure 10.12). A ribosome consists of two subunits—a large subunit and a small subunit—each made up of proteins and a kind of RNA called **ribosomal RNA (rRNA)**.

The ribosomes of bacteria and eukaryotes are very similar in function, but those of eukaryotes are slightly larger and different in composition. The differences are medically significant. Certain antibiotic drugs can inactivate bacterial ribosomes while leaving eukaryotic ribosomes unaffected. These drugs, such as tetracycline and streptomycin, are used to combat bacterial infections.

The simplified drawings on the right side of Figure 10.12 indicate how tRNA anticodons and mRNA codons fit together on ribosomes. A fully assembled ribosome has a binding site for mRNA on the small subunit and binding sites (referred to as the P site and the A site) for tRNA on the large subunit. The subunits of the ribosome act like a vise, holding the tRNA and mRNA molecules close together, allowing the amino acids carried by the tRNA molecules to be connected into a polypeptide chain. In the next two modules, we examine the steps of translation in detail.

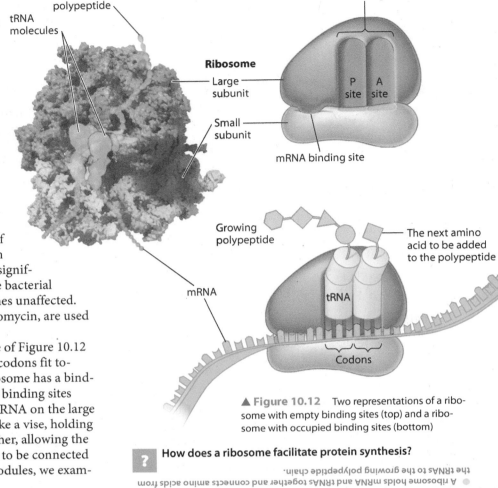

▲ Figure 10.12 Two representations of a ribosome with empty binding sites (top) and a ribosome with occupied binding sites (bottom)

? **How does a ribosome facilitate protein synthesis?**

● A ribosome holds mRNA and tRNAs together and connects amino acids from the tRNAs to the growing polypeptide chain.

10.13 An initiation codon marks the start of an mRNA message

Translation can be divided into the same three phases as transcription: initiation, elongation, and termination. The process of initiation brings together the mRNA, a tRNA bearing the first amino acid, and the two subunits of a ribosome.

As shown in Figure 10.13A, an mRNA molecule is longer than the genetic message it carries. The light pink nucleotides at either end of the molecule are not part of the message but help the mRNA to bind to the ribosome. The initiation process establishes exactly where translation will begin, ensuring that the mRNA codons are translated into the correct sequence of amino acids.

Initiation occurs in two steps (Figure 10.13B). ❶ An mRNA molecule binds to a small ribosomal subunit. A special initiator tRNA base-pairs with the specific codon, called the **start codon**, where translation is to begin on the mRNA molecule. The initiator tRNA carries the amino acid methionine (Met); its anticodon, UAC, base-pairs with the start codon, AUG. ❷ Next, a large ribosomal subunit binds to the small one, creating a functional ribosome. The initiator tRNA fits into one of the two tRNA binding

▲ Figure 10.13A   A molecule of eukaryotic mRNA

sites on the ribosome. This site, called the **P site**, will hold the growing polypeptide. The other tRNA binding site, called the **A site**, is shown vacant and ready for the next amino-acid-bearing tRNA.

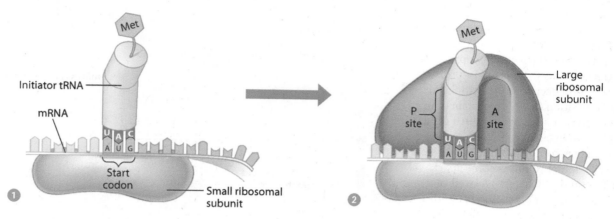

▲ **Figure 10.13B**   The initiation of translation

10.14 Elongation adds amino acids to the polypeptide chain until a stop codon terminates translation

Once initiation is complete, amino acids are added one by one to the previous amino acid. Each addition occurs in a three-step elongation process (**Figure 10.14**). ❶ The antico-don of an incoming tRNA molecule, carrying its amino acid, pairs with the mRNA codon in the A site of the ribosome. ❷ The polypeptide separates from the tRNA in the P site and attaches by a new peptide bond to the amino acid carried by the tRNA in the A site. The ribosome catalyzes formation of the peptide bond, adding one more amino acid to the growing polypeptide chain. ❸ Then, the P site tRNA (which is now lacking an amino acid) leaves the ribo-some, and the ribosome translocates (moves) the remaining tRNA (which holds the growing polypeptide) from the A site to the P site. The codon and anticodon remain hydrogen-bonded, and the mRNA and tRNA move as a unit. This movement brings into the A site the next mRNA codon to be translated, and the process can start again with step 1.

Elongation continues until a **stop codon** reaches the ribo-some's A site. As discussed earlier, stop codons—UAA, UAG, and UGA—do not code for amino acids but instead act as signals to stop translation. This is the termination stage of translation. The completed polypeptide is freed from the last tRNA, and the ribosome splits back into its separate subunits.

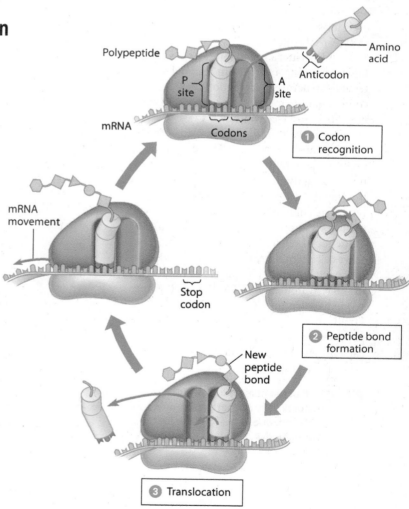

▲ **Figure 10.14**   Polypeptide elongation; the small green arrows indicate movement

10.15 Review: The flow of genetic information in the cell is DNA → RNA → protein

Figure 10.15 summarizes the flow of genetic information from DNA to RNA to protein. ➊ In transcription (DNA → RNA), the mRNA is synthesized on a DNA template. In eukaryotic cells, transcription occurs in the nucleus, and the messenger RNA is processed before it travels to the cytoplasm. In prokaryotes, transcription occurs in the cytoplasm.

➋–➎ Translation (RNA → protein) can be divided into four steps, all of which occur in the cytoplasm in eukaryotic cells. When the polypeptide is complete at the end of step 5, the two ribosomal subunits come apart, and the tRNA and mRNA are released (not shown in this figure). Translation is rapid; a single ribosome can make an average-sized polypeptide in less than a minute. Typically, an mRNA molecule is translated simultaneously by a number of ribosomes. Once the start codon emerges from the first ribosome, a second ribosome can attach to it; thus, several ribosomes may trail along on the same mRNA molecule.

As it is made, a polypeptide coils and folds, assuming a three-dimensional shape, its tertiary structure. Several polypeptides may come together, forming a protein with quaternary structure (see Module 3.14).

What is the overall significance of transcription and translation? These are the main processes whereby genes control the structures and activities of cells—or, more broadly, the way the genotype produces the phenotype. The chain of command originates with the information in a gene, a specific linear sequence of nucleotides in DNA. The gene serves as a template, dictating transcription of a complementary sequence of nucleotides in mRNA. In turn, mRNA dictates the linear sequence of amino acids in a polypeptide. Finally, the proteins that form from the polypeptides determine the appearance and the capabilities of the cell and organism.

? Which of the following molecules or structures does not participate directly in translation: ribosomes, transfer RNA, messenger RNA, DNA?

● DNA

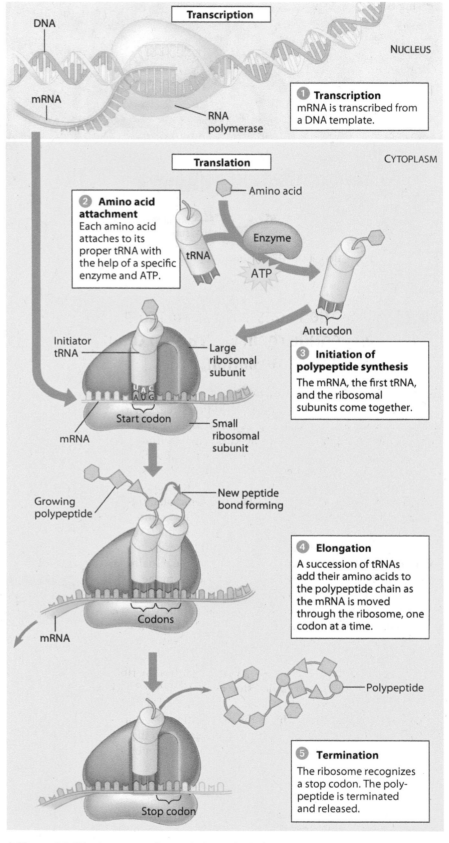

Transcription

DNA

NUCLEUS

mRNA

RNA polymerase

➊ Transcription
mRNA is transcribed from a DNA template.

CYTOPLASM

Translation

Amino acid

➋ Amino acid attachment
Each amino acid attaches to its proper tRNA with the help of a specific enzyme and ATP.

tRNA

Enzyme

ATP

Anticodon

Initiator tRNA

Large ribosomal subunit

➌ Initiation of polypeptide synthesis
The mRNA, the first tRNA, and the ribosomal subunits come together.

U A C
A U G

Start codon

mRNA

Small ribosomal subunit

Growing polypeptide

New peptide bond forming

➍ Elongation
A succession of tRNAs add their amino acids to the polypeptide chain as the mRNA is moved through the ribosome, one codon at a time.

Codons

mRNA

Polypeptide

➎ Termination
The ribosome recognizes a stop codon. The polypeptide is terminated and released.

Stop codon

▲ Figure 10.15   A summary of transcription and translation

10.16 Mutations can affect genes

Many inherited traits can be understood in molecular terms. For instance, sickle-cell disease can be traced to a change in a single amino acid in one of the polypeptides in the hemoglobin protein (see Module 9.13). This difference is caused by a single nucleotide difference in the DNA coding for that polypeptide (Figure 10.16A). In the double helix, one nucleotide *pair* is changed.

Any change in the nucleotide sequence of a cell's DNA is called a **mutation**. Mutations can involve large regions of a chromosome or just a single nucleotide pair, as in sickle-cell disease.

Mutations within a gene can be divided into two general categories: nucleotide substitutions and nucleotide insertions or deletions (Figure 10.16B). A nucleotide substitution is the replacement of one nucleotide and its base-pairing partner with another pair of nucleotides. For example, in the second row in Figure 10.16B, A replaces G in the fourth codon of the mRNA. What effect can a substitution have? Because the genetic code is redundant, some substitution mutations have no effect at all. For example, if a mutation causes an mRNA codon to change from GAA to GAG, no change in the protein product would result because GAA and GAG both code for the same amino acid (Glu; see Figure 10.8A). Such a change is called a **silent mutation**.

In contrast, a **missense mutation** changes one amino acid to another one. For example, if a mutation causes an mRNA codon to change from GGC to AGC, as in the second row of Figure 10.16B, the resulting protein will have a serine (Ser) instead of a glycine (Gly) at this position. Some missense mutations have little or no effect on the resulting protein, but others, as in the case of sickle-cell disease, prevent the protein from performing its normal function.

Some substitutions, called **nonsense mutations**, change an amino acid codon into a stop codon. For example, if an AGA (Arg) codon is changed to a UGA (stop) codon, the result will be a prematurely terminated protein, which probably will not function properly.

Mutations involving the insertion or deletion of one or more nucleotides in a gene, called **frameshift mutations**, often have disastrous effects. Because mRNA is read as a series of nucleotide triplets (codons) during translation, adding or subtracting nucleotides may alter the reading frame (triplet grouping) of the genetic message. All the nucleotides

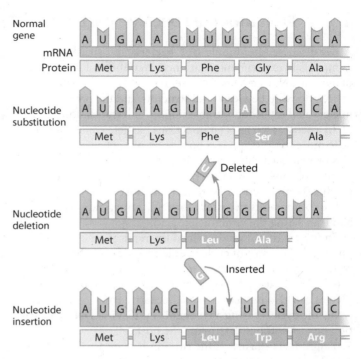

▲ **Figure 10.16B**   Types of mutations and their effects

after the insertion or deletion will be regrouped into different codons (Figure 10.16B, bottom two rows). Consider this example in the English language: The red cat ate the big rat. Deleting the second letter produces an entirely nonsensical message: Ter edc ata tet heb igr at. Frameshift mutations will most likely produce a nonfunctional polypeptide.

The production of mutations, called **mutagenesis**, can occur in a number of ways. Spontaneous mutations result from errors during DNA replication or recombination. Other mutations are caused by physical or chemical agents called **mutagens**. High-energy radiation, such as X-rays or ultraviolet light, is a physical mutagen. One class of chemical mutagens consists of chemicals that are similar to normal DNA bases but pair incorrectly or are otherwise disruptive when incorporated into DNA. For example, the anti-AIDS drug AZT works because its structure is similar enough to thymine that viral polymerases incorporate it into newly synthesized DNA but different enough that the drug blocks further replication.

Occasionally, a mutation leads to a protein that enhances the success of the mutant organism and its descendants. Much more often, mutations are harmful to an organism. Mutations are, however, an important source of the rich diversity of genes in the living world, a diversity that makes evolution by natural selection possible. And within the laboratory, mutations are essential tools for geneticists, creating the different alleles needed for genetic research.

? **How could a single nucleotide substitution result in a shortened protein product?**

● A substitution that changed an amino acid codon into a stop codon would produce a prematurely terminated polypeptide.

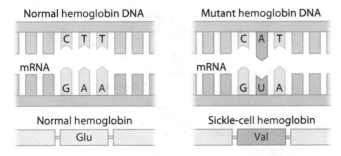

▲ **Figure 10.16A**   The molecular basis of sickle-cell disease

▷ The Genetics of Viruses and Bacteria

10.17 Viral DNA may become part of the host chromosome

As we discussed in Module 10.1, bacteria and viruses served as models in experiments that uncovered the molecular details of heredity. Now let's take a closer look at viruses, focusing on the relationship between viral structure and the processes of nucleic acid replication, transcription, and translation.

In a sense, a **virus** is an infectious particle consisting of little more than "genes in a box": a bit of nucleic acid wrapped in a protein coat called a **capsid** and, in some cases, a membrane envelope. Viruses are parasites that can replicate (reproduce) only inside cells. In fact, the host cell provides most of the components necessary for replicating, transcribing, and translating the viral nucleic acid.

In Figure 10.1C, we described the replication cycle of phage T2. This sort of cycle is called a **lytic cycle** because it results in the lysis (breaking open) of the host cell and the release of the viruses that were produced within the cell. Some phages can also replicate by an alternative route called the lysogenic cycle. During a **lysogenic cycle**, viral DNA replication occurs without destroying the host cell.

Figure 10.17 illustrates the two kinds of cycles for a phage called lambda that infects *E. coli*. Both cycles begin when the phage DNA ❶ enters the bacterium and ❷ forms a loop. The DNA then embarks on one of the two pathways. In the lytic cycle (left), ❸ lambda's DNA immediately turns the cell into a virus-producing factory, and ❹ the cell soon lyses

and releases its viral products, which may then infect another cell.

In the lysogenic cycle, ❺ viral DNA is inserted by genetic recombination into the bacterial chromosome. Once inserted, the phage DNA is referred to as a **prophage**, and most of its genes are inactive. ❻ Every time the *E. coli* cell prepares to divide, it replicates the phage DNA along with its own chromosome and passes the copies on to daughter cells. A single infected bacterium can thereby quickly give rise to a large population of bacterial cells that all carry a prophage. The lysogenic cycle enables viruses to spread without killing the host cells on which they depend. The prophages may remain in the bacterial cells indefinitely. Occasionally, however, an environmental signal—typically, one that indicates an unfavorable turn in the environment, such as an increase in radiation, drought, or certain toxic chemicals—triggers a switchover from the lysogenic cycle to the lytic cycle. This causes the viral DNA to be excised from the bacterial chromosome, eventually leading to death of the host cell.

Sometimes, the few prophage genes active in a lysogenic bacterium can cause medical problems. For example, the bacteria that cause diphtheria, botulism, and scarlet fever would be harmless to people if it were not for the prophage genes they carry. Certain of these genes direct the bacteria to produce the toxins responsible for making people ill. In the next module, we will explore viruses that infect animals and plants.

> **?** Describe one way a virus can perpetuate its genes without destroying its host cell. What is this type of replication cycle called?

● Some viruses can insert their DNA into a chromosome of the host cell, which replicates the viral genes when it replicates its own DNA prior to cell division. This is called the lysogenic cycle.

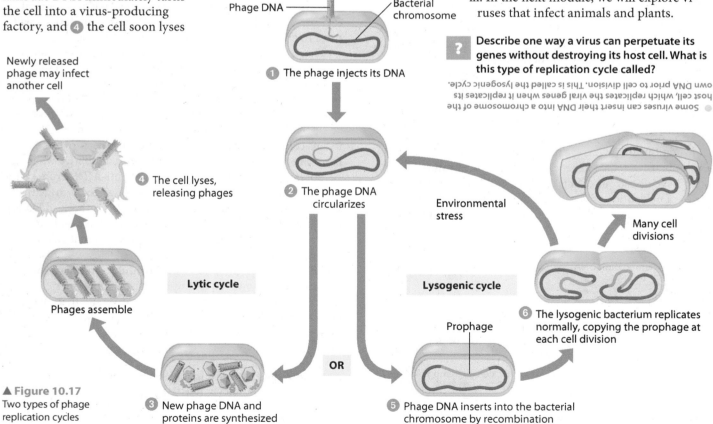

Phage
Attaches to cell
Phage DNA
Bacterial chromosome

❶ The phage injects its DNA

Newly released phage may infect another cell

❹ The cell lyses, releasing phages

❷ The phage DNA circularizes

Environmental stress

Many cell divisions

Phages assemble

Lytic cycle

Lysogenic cycle

Prophage

❻ The lysogenic bacterium replicates normally, copying the prophage at each cell division

OR

▲ **Figure 10.17**
Two types of phage replication cycles

❸ New phage DNA and proteins are synthesized

❺ Phage DNA inserts into the bacterial chromosome by recombination

10.18 Many viruses cause disease in animals and plants

CONNECTION

Viruses can cause disease in both animals and plants. A typical animal virus has a membranous outer envelope and projecting spikes of glycoprotein (protein molecules with attached sugars). The envelope helps the virus enter and leave the host cell. Many animal viruses have RNA rather than DNA as their genetic material. Examples of RNA viruses include those that cause the common cold, measles, mumps, polio, and AIDS. Examples of diseases caused by DNA viruses include hepatitis, chicken pox, and herpes infections.

Figure 10.18 shows the replication cycle of a typical enveloped RNA virus: the mumps virus. Once a common childhood disease characterized by fever and painful swelling of the salivary glands, mumps has become quite rare in industrialized nations thanks to widespread vaccination. When the mumps virus contacts a susceptible cell, the glycoprotein spikes attach to receptor proteins on the cell's plasma membrane. The viral envelope fuses with the cell's membrane, allowing the protein-coated RNA to ❶ enter the cytoplasm. ❷ Enzymes (not shown) then remove the protein coat. ❸ An enzyme that entered the cell as part of the virus uses the virus's RNA genome as a template for making complementary strands of RNA (shown in pink). The new strands have two functions: ❹ They serve as mRNA for the synthesis of new viral proteins, and they serve as templates for synthesizing new viral genome RNA. ❺ The new coat proteins assemble around the new viral RNA. ❻ Finally, the viruses leave the cell by cloaking themselves in the host cell's plasma membrane. Thus, the virus obtains its envelope from the host cell, leaving the cell without necessarily lysing it.

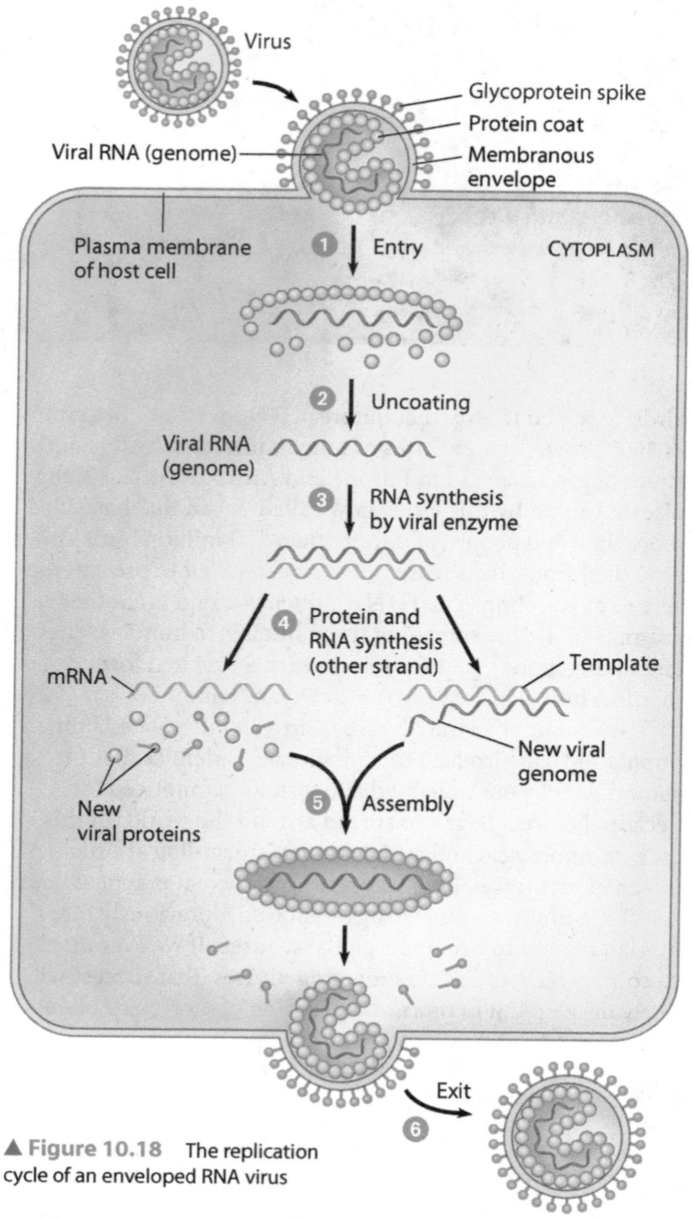

Not all animal viruses replicate in the cytoplasm. For example, herpesviruses—which cause chicken pox, shingles, cold sores, and genital herpes—are enveloped DNA viruses that replicate in the host cell's nucleus; they acquire their envelopes from the cell's nuclear membranes. While inside the nuclei of certain nerve cells, herpesvirus DNA may remain permanently dormant, without destroying these cells. From time to time, physical stress, such as a cold or sunburn, or emotional stress may stimulate the herpesvirus DNA to begin production of the virus, which then infects cells at the body's surface and causes unpleasant symptoms.

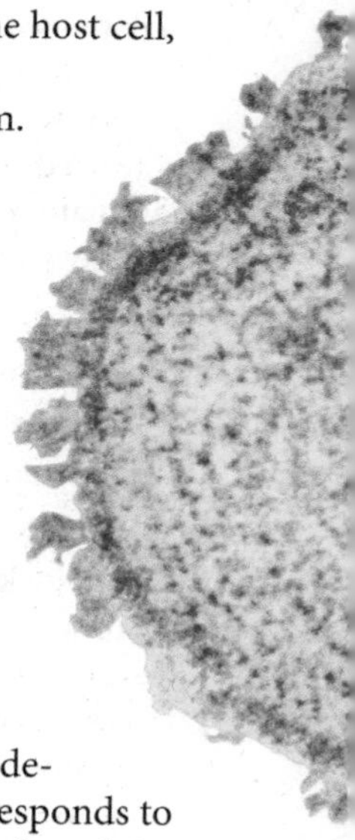

The amount of damage a virus causes our body depends partly on how quickly our immune system responds to fight the infection and partly on the ability of the infected tissue to repair itself. We usually recover completely from colds because our respiratory tract tissue can efficiently replace damaged cells by mitosis. In contrast, the poliovirus attacks nerve cells, which are not usually replaceable. The damage to such cells, unfortunately, is permanent. In such cases, we try to prevent the disease with vaccines.

Plants, like animals, are susceptible to viral infections. Viruses that infect plants can stunt plant growth and diminish crop yields. Most known plant viruses are RNA viruses. To infect a plant, a virus must first get past the plant's outer protective layer of cells (the epidermis). Once a virus enters a plant cell and begins replicating, it can spread throughout the entire plant through plasmodesmata, the cytoplasmic connections that penetrate the walls between adjacent plant cells (see Figure 4.21). Plant viruses may spread to other plants by insects, herbivores, humans, or farming tools. As with animal viruses, there are no cures for most viral diseases of plants. Agricultural scientists focus instead on preventing infections and on breeding resistant varieties of crop plants.

▲ Figure 10.18 The replication cycle of an enveloped RNA virus

? Explain how some viruses replicate without having DNA.

● The genetic material of these viruses is RNA, which is replicated inside the host cell by special enzymes encoded by the virus. The viral genome (or its complement) serves as mRNA for the synthesis of viral proteins.

10.19 Emerging viruses threaten human health

Emerging viruses are ones that seem to burst on to the scene, becoming apparent to the medical community quite suddenly. There are many familiar examples, such as the 2009 H1N1 influenza virus (discussed in the chapter introduction). Another example is **HIV** (human immunodeficiency virus), the virus that causes **AIDS** (acquired immunodeficiency syndrome). HIV appeared in New York and California in the early 1980s, seemingly out of nowhere. Yet another example is the deadly Ebola virus, recognized initially in 1976 in central Africa; it is one of several emerging viruses that cause hemorrhagic fever, an often fatal syndrome characterized by fever, vomiting, massive bleeding, and circulatory system collapse. A number of other dangerous newly recognized viruses cause encephalitis, inflammation of the brain. One example is the West Nile virus, which appeared in North America in 1999 and has since spread to all 48 contiguous U.S. states. West Nile virus is spread primarily by mosquitoes, which carry the virus in

Why are viral diseases such a constant threat?

blood sucked from one victim and can transfer it to another victim. West Nile virus cases surged in 2012, especially in Texas. Severe acute respiratory syndrome (SARS) first appeared in China in 2002. Within eight months, about 8,000 people were infected, and 10% died. Researchers quickly identified the infectious agent as a previously unknown, single-stranded RNA coronavirus, so named for its crownlike "corona" of spikes.

How do such viruses emerge suddenly, giving rise to new diseases? And why are viral diseases so hard to eradicate? Three processes contribute to the emergence of viral diseases: mutation, contact among species, and spread from isolated populations.

The mutation of existing viruses is a major source of new viral diseases. RNA viruses tend to have unusually high rates of mutation because errors in replicating their RNA genomes are not subject to the kind of proofreading and repair mechanisms that help reduce errors in DNA replication. Some mutations change existing viruses into new strains (genetic varieties) that can cause disease in individuals who have developed immunity to ancestral strains. That is why we need yearly flu vaccines: Mutations create new influenza virus strains to which previously vaccinated people have no immunity.

New viral diseases often arise from the spread of existing viruses from one host species to another. Scientists estimate that about three-quarters of new human diseases have originated in other animals. For example, in 1997, at least 18 people in Hong Kong were infected with a strain of flu virus called H5N1, which was previously seen only in birds. A mass culling of all of Hong Kong's 1.5 million domestic

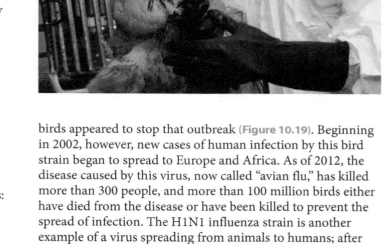

Colorized TEM 180,000×

▼ **Figure 10.19** A Hong Kong health-care worker prepares to cull a chicken to help prevent the spread of the avian flu virus (shown in the inset)

birds appeared to stop that outbreak (**Figure 10.19**). Beginning in 2002, however, new cases of human infection by this bird strain began to spread to Europe and Africa. As of 2012, the disease caused by this virus, now called "avian flu," has killed more than 300 people, and more than 100 million birds either have died from the disease or have been killed to prevent the spread of infection. The H1N1 influenza strain is another example of a virus spreading from animals to humans; after circulating among pigs for many years, a mutated form began to infect humans, creating the 2009 pandemic.

The spread of a viral disease from a small, isolated human population can also lead to widespread epidemics. For instance, AIDS went unnamed and virtually unnoticed for decades before it began to spread around the world. In this case, technological and social factors—including affordable international travel, blood transfusions, sexual practices, and the abuse of intravenous drugs—allowed a previously rare human disease to become a global scourge. If we ever manage to control HIV and other emerging viruses, that success will likely develop out of our understanding of molecular biology.

? **Why doesn't a flu shot one year give us immunity to flu in subsequent years?**

● Influenza viruses evolve rapidly by frequent mutation; thus, the strains that infect us later will most likely be different from the ones to which we've been vaccinated.

10.20 The AIDS virus makes DNA on an RNA template

HIV, the virus that causes AIDS, is an RNA virus with some special properties. In outward appearance, HIV resembles the flu or mumps virus (Figure 10.20A). Its membranous envelope and glycoprotein spikes enable HIV to enter and leave a host cell much the way the mumps virus does (see Figure 10.18). Notice, however, that HIV contains two identical copies of its RNA instead of one. HIV also has a different mode of replication. It is a **retrovirus**, an RNA virus that reproduces by means of a DNA molecule. Retroviruses are so named because they reverse the usual DNA → RNA flow of genetic information. These viruses carry molecules of an enzyme called **reverse transcriptase**, which catalyzes reverse transcription: the synthesis of DNA on an RNA template.

Figure 10.20B illustrates what happens after HIV RNA is uncoated in the cytoplasm of a host cell. ❶ Reverse transcriptase (⬤) uses the RNA as a template to make a DNA strand and then ❷ adds a second, complementary DNA strand. ❸ The resulting double-stranded viral DNA enters the cell's nucleus and inserts itself into the chromosomal

DNA, becoming a provirus (analogous to a prophage). The host's RNA polymerase ❹ transcribes the proviral DNA into RNA, which can then be ❺ translated by ribosomes into viral proteins. ❻ New viruses assembled from these components leave the cell and can infect other cells.

HIV infects and kills white blood cells that play important roles in the body's immune system. The loss of such cells causes the body to become susceptible to other infections that it would normally be able to fight off. Such secondary infections cause the syndrome (a collection of symptoms) that can kill an AIDS patient.

? Why is HIV reverse transcriptase a good target for anti-AIDS drug therapy?

● Reverse transcriptase is unique to HIV; we do not normally copy genetic information from RNA to DNA, so disabling reverse transcriptase would not affect a human.

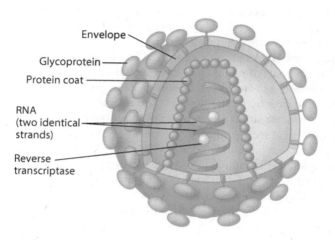

▲ **Figure 10.20A** A model of HIV structure

Envelope
Glycoprotein
Protein coat
RNA (two identical strands)
Reverse transcriptase

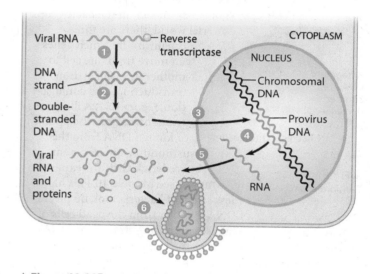

▲ **Figure 10.20B** The behavior of HIV nucleic acid in a host cell

Viral RNA — Reverse transcriptase
CYTOPLASM
NUCLEUS
DNA strand
Chromosomal DNA
Double-stranded DNA
Provirus DNA
Viral RNA and proteins
RNA

10.21 Viroids and prions are formidable pathogens in plants and animals

Viruses may be small and simple, but they are huge in comparison with another class of pathogens: viroids. **Viroids** are small, circular RNA molecules that infect plants. Unlike the nucleic acid of a virus, viroids do not encode proteins but can replicate in host plant cells, apparently using cellular enzymes. These small RNA molecules seem to interfere with regulatory systems that control plant growth. The typical signs of viroid diseases are abnormal development and stunted growth.

An important lesson to learn from viroids is that a single molecule can be an infectious agent. Viroids consist solely of nucleic acid, whose ability to be replicated is well known. Even more surprising are infectious proteins called **prions**, which cause a number of degenerative brain diseases in various animal species, including scrapie in sheep and goats, chronic wasting disease in deer and elk, mad cow disease (bovine

spongiform encephalopathy, or BSE), and Creutzfeldt-Jakob disease in humans (which is exceedingly rare).

A prion is thought to be a misfolded form of a protein normally present in brain cells. When a prion enters a cell containing the normal form of protein, the prion somehow converts the normal protein molecules to the misfolded prion versions. The abnormal proteins clump together, which may lead to loss of brain tissue (although *how* this occurs is the subject of much debate and ongoing research). There is no cure for prion diseases, and the only hope for developing effective treatments lies in understanding and preventing the process of infection.

? What makes prions different from all other known infectious agents?

● Prions are proteins and have no nucleic acid.

10.22 Bacteria can transfer DNA in three ways

By studying viral replication, researchers also learn about the mechanisms that regulate DNA replication and gene expression in living cells. Bacteria are equally valuable as microbial models in genetics research. As prokaryotic cells, bacteria allow researchers to investigate molecular genetics in the simplest living organisms.

Most of a bacterium's DNA is found in a single chromosome, a closed loop of DNA with associated proteins. In the diagrams here, we show the chromosome much smaller than it actually is relative to the cell. A bacterial chromosome is hundreds of times longer than its cell; it fits inside the cell because it is tightly folded.

Bacterial cells reproduce by replication of the bacterial chromosome followed by binary fission (see Module 8.2). Because binary fission is an asexual process involving only a single parent, the bacteria in a colony are genetically identical to the parental cell. But this does not mean that bacteria lack ways to produce new combinations of genes. In fact, in the bacterial world, there are three mechanisms by which genes can move from one cell to another: transformation, transduction, and conjugation. Figure 10.22A illustrates **transformation**, the uptake of foreign DNA from the surrounding environment.

In Frederick Griffith's experiments (see Module 10.1), a harmless strain of bacteria took up pieces of DNA left over from the dead cells of a disease-causing strain. The DNA from the pathogenic bacteria carried a gene that made the cells resistant to an animal's defenses, and when the previously harmless bacteria acquired this gene and replaced its own with the pathogenic version, it caused pneumonia in infected animals.

Bacteriophages, the viruses that infect bacteria, provide the second means of bringing together genes of different bacteria. The transfer of bacterial genes by a phage is called **transduction**. During a lytic infection, when new viruses are being assembled in an infected bacterial cell, a fragment of DNA belonging to the host cell may be mistakenly packaged within the phage's coat instead of, or along with, the phage's DNA. When the phage infects a new bacterial cell, the DNA stowaway from the former host cell is injected into the new host (Figure 10.22B).

Figure 10.22C is an illustration of what happens at the DNA level when two bacterial cells "mate." This physical union of two bacterial cells—of the same or different species—and the

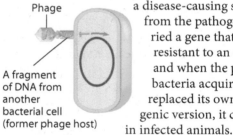

▲ Figure 10.22A Transformation

▲ Figure 10.22B Transduction

DNA enters cell

A fragment of DNA from another bacterial cell

Bacterial chromosome (DNA)

Phage

A fragment of DNA from another bacterial cell (former phage host)

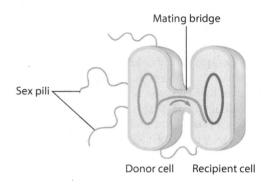

▲ Figure 10.22C   Conjugation

Mating bridge

Sex pili

Donor cell   Recipient cell

DNA transfer between them is called **conjugation**. The donor cell has hollow appendages called sex pili, one of which is attached to the recipient cell in the figure. After attachment, the pilus retracts, pulling the two cells together, much like a grappling hook. The donor then transfers DNA (light blue in the figure) to the recipient. The donor cell replicates its DNA as it transfers it, so the cell doesn't end up lacking any genes. The DNA replication is a special type that allows one copy to peel off and transfer into the recipient cell.

Once new DNA gets into a bacterial cell, by whatever mechanism, part of it may then integrate into the recipient's chromosome. As Figure 10.22D indicates, integration occurs by crossing over between the donor and recipient DNA molecules, a process similar to crossing over between eukaryotic chromosomes (see Module 8.17). Here we see that two crossovers result in a piece of the donated DNA replacing part of the recipient cell's original DNA. The leftover pieces of DNA are broken down and degraded, leaving the recipient bacterium with a recombinant chromosome.

As we'll see in the next module, the transfer of genetic material between bacteria has important medical consequences.

> **?** The three modes of gene transfer between bacteria are _____, which is transfer via a virus; _____, which is the uptake of DNA from the surrounding environment; and _____, which is bacterial "mating."
>
> ● transduction ··· transformation ··· conjugation

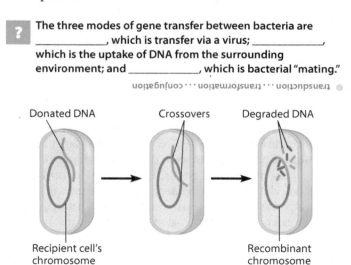

Donated DNA   Crossovers   Degraded DNA

Recipient cell's chromosome   Recombinant chromosome

▲ Figure 10.22D   The integration of donated DNA into the recipient cell's chromosome

10.23 Bacterial plasmids can serve as carriers for gene transfer

The ability of a donor *E. coli* cell to carry out conjugation is usually due to a specific piece of DNA called the **F factor** (F for *fertility*). The F factor carries about 25 genes for making sex pili and other requirements for conjugation; it also contains an origin of replication, where DNA replication starts.

Let's see how the F factor behaves during conjugation. In **Figure 10.23A**, the F factor (light blue) is integrated into the donor bacterium's chromosome. When this cell conjugates with a recipient cell, the donor chromosome starts replicating at the F factor's origin of replication, indicated in the figure by the blue dot on the DNA. The growing copy of the DNA peels off the chromosome and heads into the recipient cell. Thus, part of the F factor serves as the leading end of the transferred DNA, but right behind it are genes from the donor's original chromosome. The rest of the F factor stays in the donor cell. Once inside the recipient cell, the transferred donor genes can recombine with the corresponding part of the recipient chromosome by crossing over. If crossing over occurs, the recipient cell may be genetically changed, but it

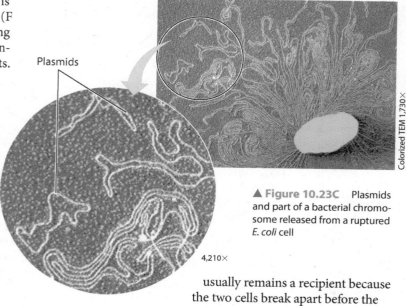

Plasmids

Colorized TEM 1,730×

▲ **Figure 10.23C** Plasmids and part of a bacterial chromosome released from a ruptured *E. coli* cell

4,210×

usually remains a recipient because the two cells break apart before the rest of the F factor transfers.

Alternatively, as **Figure 10.23B** shows, an F factor can exist as a **plasmid**, a small, circular DNA molecule separate from the bacterial chromosome. Every plasmid has an origin of replication, required for its replication within the cell. Some plasmids, including the F factor plasmid, can bring about conjugation and move to another cell. When the donor cell in Figure 10.23B mates with a recipient cell, the F factor replicates and at the same time transfers one whole copy of itself, in linear rather than circular form, to the recipient cell. The transferred plasmid re-forms a circle in the recipient cell, and the cell becomes a donor.

E. coli and other bacteria have many different kinds of plasmids. You can see several from one cell in **Figure 10.23C**, along with part of the bacterial chromosome, which extends in loops from the ruptured cell. Some plasmids carry genes that can affect the survival of the cell. Plasmids of one class, called **R plasmids**, pose serious problems for human medicine. Transferable R plasmids carry genes for enzymes that destroy antibiotics such as penicillin and tetracycline. Bacteria containing R plasmids are resistant (hence the designation R) to antibiotics that would otherwise kill them. The widespread use of antibiotics in medicine and agriculture has tended to kill off bacteria that lack R plasmids, whereas those with R plasmids have multiplied. As a result, an increasing number of bacteria that cause human diseases, such as food poisoning and gonorrhea, are becoming resistant to antibiotics (see Module 13.15).

We'll continue our study of molecular genetics and explore what is known about genes (see Chapter 11) and return to our discussion of plasmids (Chapter 12) in later chapters.

? **Plasmids are useful tools for genetic engineering. Can you guess why?**

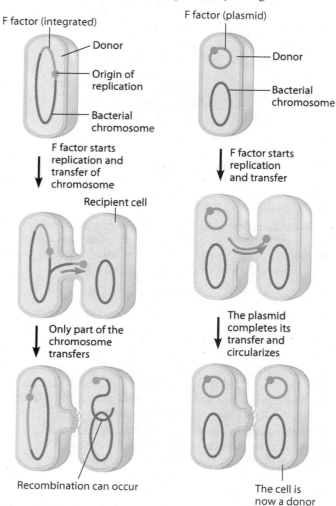

F factor (integrated)

Donor

Origin of replication

Bacterial chromosome

F factor starts replication and transfer of chromosome

Recipient cell

Only part of the chromosome transfers

Recombination can occur

▲ **Figure 10.23A** Transfer of chromosomal DNA by an integrated F factor

F factor (plasmid)

Donor

Bacterial chromosome

F factor starts replication and transfer

The plasmid completes its transfer and circularizes

The cell is now a donor

▲ **Figure 10.23B** Transfer of an F factor plasmid

● Scientists can take advantage of the ability of plasmids to carry foreign genes, to replicate, and to be inherited by progeny cells.

CHAPTER **10** REVIEW

For practice quizzes, BioFlix animations, MP3 tutorials, video tutors, and more study tools designed for this textbook, go to

MasteringBiology®

Reviewing the Concepts

The Structure of the Genetic Material (10.1–10.3)

10.1 Experiments showed that DNA is the genetic material. By carefully choosing their model organism, Hershey and Chase were able to show that certain phages (bacterial viruses) reprogram host cells to produce more phages by injecting their DNA.

10.2 DNA and RNA are polymers of nucleotides.

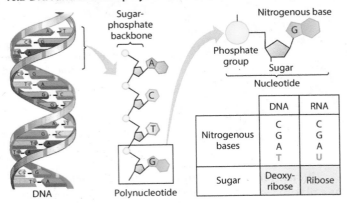

	DNA	RNA
Nitrogenous bases	C G A T	C G A U
Sugar	Deoxy-ribose	Ribose

10.3 DNA is a double-stranded helix. Watson and Crick worked out the three-dimensional structure of DNA: two polynucleotide strands wrapped around each other in a double helix. Hydrogen bonds between bases hold the strands together. Each base pairs with a complementary partner: A with T, G with C.

DNA Replication (10.4–10.5)

10.4 DNA replication depends on specific base pairing. DNA replication starts with the separation of DNA strands. Enzymes then use each strand as a template to assemble new nucleotides into a complementary strand.

10.5 DNA replication proceeds in two directions at many sites simultaneously. Using the enzyme DNA polymerase, the cell synthesizes one daughter strand as a continuous piece. The other strand is synthesized as a series of short pieces, which are then connected by the enzyme DNA ligase.

The Flow of Genetic Information from DNA to RNA to Protein (10.6–10.16)

10.6 Genes control phenotypic traits through the expression of proteins. The DNA of a gene—a linear sequence of many nucleotides—is transcribed into RNA, which is translated into a polypeptide.

10.7 Genetic information written in codons is translated into amino acid sequences. Codons are base triplets.

10.8 The genetic code dictates how codons are translated into amino acids. Nearly all organisms use an identical genetic code to convert the mRNA codons transcribed from a gene to the amino acid sequence of a polypeptide.

10.9 Transcription produces genetic messages in the form of RNA. In the nucleus, the DNA helix unzips, and RNA nucleotides line up and hydrogen-bond along one strand of the DNA, following the base-pairing rules.

10.10 Eukaryotic RNA is processed before leaving the nucleus as mRNA. Noncoding segments of RNA (introns) are spliced out, and a cap and tail are added to the ends of the mRNA.

10.11 Transfer RNA molecules serve as interpreters during translation. Translation takes place in the cytoplasm. A ribosome attaches to the mRNA and translates its message into a specific polypeptide, aided by transfer RNAs (tRNAs). Each tRNA is a folded molecule bearing a base triplet called an anticodon on one end and a specific amino acid attachment site at the other end.

10.12 Ribosomes build polypeptides. Made of rRNA and proteins, ribosomes have binding sites for tRNAs and mRNA.

10.13 An initiation codon marks the start of an mRNA message.

10.14 Elongation adds amino acids to the polypeptide chain until a stop codon terminates translation. As the mRNA moves one codon at a time relative to the ribosome, a tRNA with a complementary anticodon pairs with each codon, adding its amino acid to the growing polypeptide chain.

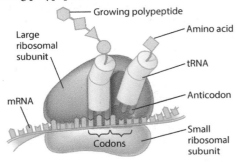

10.15 Review: The flow of genetic information in the cell is DNA → RNA → protein. The sequence of codons in DNA, via the sequence of codons in mRNA, spells out the primary structure of a polypeptide.

10.16 Mutations can affect genes. Mutations are changes in the genetic information of a cell, caused by errors in DNA replication or recombination, or by mutagens. Substituting, inserting, or deleting nucleotides alters a gene, with varying effects.

The Genetics of Viruses and Bacteria (10.17–10.23)

10.17 Viral DNA may become part of the host chromosome. Viruses are infectious particles that contain genes packaged in protein. When phage DNA enters a lytic cycle inside a bacterium, it is replicated, transcribed, and translated; the new viral DNA and protein molecules then assemble into new phages, which burst from the host cell. In the lysogenic cycle, phage DNA inserts into the host chromosome and is passed on to generations of daughter cells. Later, it may initiate phage production.

10.18 Many viruses cause disease in animals and plants. Flu viruses and most plant viruses have RNA, rather than DNA, as their genetic material. Some animal viruses steal a bit of host cell membrane as a protective envelope.

10.19 Emerging viruses threaten human health.

10.20 The AIDS virus makes DNA on an RNA template. HIV is a retrovirus: It uses RNA as a template for making DNA, which then inserts into a host chromosome.

10.21 Viroids and prions are formidable pathogens in plants and animals. Viroids are RNA molecules that can infect plants. Prions are infectious proteins that can cause brain diseases in animals.

10.22 Bacteria can transfer DNA in three ways. Bacteria can transfer genes from cell to cell by transformation, transduction, or conjugation.

10.23 Bacterial plasmids can serve as carriers for gene transfer. Plasmids are small, circular DNA molecules separate from the bacterial chromosome.

Connecting the Concepts

1. Check your understanding of the flow of genetic information through a cell by filling in the blanks.

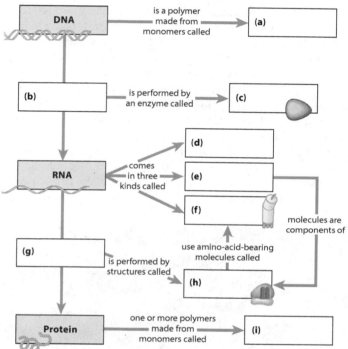

Testing Your Knowledge

Level 1: Knowledge/Comprehension

2. Which of the following correctly ranks the structures in order of size, from largest to smallest?
   a. gene-chromosome-nucleotide-codon
   b. chromosome-gene-codon-nucleotide
   c. nucleotide-chromosome-gene-codon
   d. chromosome-nucleotide-gene-codon

3. Describe the process of DNA replication: the ingredients needed, the steps in the process, and the final product.

4. What is the name of the process that produces RNA from a DNA template? What is the name of the process that produces a polypeptide from an RNA template?

Level 2: Application/Analysis

5. Scientists have discovered how to put together a bacteriophage with the protein coat of phage T2 and the DNA of phage lambda. If this composite phage were allowed to infect a bacterium, the phages produced in the host cell would have _____. (*Explain your answer.*)
   a. the protein of T2 and the DNA of lambda
   b. the protein of lambda and the DNA of T2

c. the protein and DNA of T2
   d. the protein and DNA of lambda

6. A geneticist found that a particular mutation had no effect on the polypeptide encoded by a gene. This mutation probably involved
   a. deletion of one nucleotide.
   b. alteration of the start codon.
   c. insertion of one nucleotide.
   d. substitution of one nucleotide.

7. Describe the process by which the information in a eukaryotic gene is transcribed and translated into a protein. Correctly use these words in your description: tRNA, amino acid, start codon, transcription, RNA splicing, exons, introns, mRNA, gene, codon, RNA polymerase, ribosome, translation, anticodon, peptide bond, stop codon.

Level 3: Synthesis/Evaluation

8. The nucleotide sequence of a DNA codon is GTA. A messenger RNA molecule with a complementary codon is transcribed from the DNA. In the process of protein synthesis, a transfer RNA pairs with the mRNA codon. What is the nucleotide sequence of the tRNA anticodon?
   a. CAT
   b. CUT
   c. GUA
   d. CAU

9. A cell containing a single chromosome is placed in a medium containing radioactive phosphate so that any new DNA strands formed by DNA replication will be radioactive. The cell replicates its DNA and divides. Then the daughter cells (still in the radioactive medium) replicate their DNA and divide, and a total of four cells are present. Sketch the DNA molecules in all four cells, showing a normal (nonradioactive) DNA strand as a solid line and a radioactive DNA strand as a dashed line.

10. The base sequence of the gene coding for a short polypeptide is CTACGCTAGGCGATTGACT. What would be the base sequence of the mRNA transcribed from this gene? Using the genetic code in Figure 10.8A, give the amino acid sequence of the polypeptide translated from this mRNA. (*Hint*: What is the start codon?)

11. Researchers working on the Human Genome Project have determined the nucleotide sequences of human genes and in many cases identified the proteins encoded by the genes. Knowledge of the nucleotide sequences of genes might be used to develop lifesaving medicines or treatments for genetic defects. In the United States, both government agencies and biotechnology companies have applied for patents on their discoveries of genes. In Britain, the courts have ruled that a naturally occurring gene cannot be patented. Do you think individuals and companies should be able to patent genes and gene products? Before answering, consider the following: What are the purposes of a patent? How might the discoverer of a gene benefit from a patent? How might the public benefit? What might be some positive and negative results of patenting genes?

12. **SCIENTIFIC THINKING** The success of an experiment often depends on choosing an appropriate organism to study. For example, Gregor Mendel was able to deduce the fundamental principles in genetics in part because of his choice of the pea plant. What properties of bacteriophage T2 allowed Hershey and Chase (Module 10.1) to identify DNA as the genetic materials in their famous experiment?

Answers to all questions can be found in Appendix 4.

11

How Genes Are Controlled

Even in a world in which cloning has become routine, the case of the baby banteng stands out. The Java banteng (*Bos javanicus*), shown below, is an endangered species of cattle native to Indonesia. Hunting and habitat destruction have reduced their wild population to just a few thousand.

Scientists obtained banteng skin tissue from "The Frozen Zoo," a facility in San Diego, California, where samples from rare or endangered animals are stored for conservation. Researchers inserted nuclei from these frozen skin cells into nucleus-free eggs from domestic beef cattle. The resulting embryos were implanted into surrogate domestic cows. Months later, two bantengs were born via Caesarian section, but one had to be euthanized within days. The other banteng survived, and as of 2013, remains a healthy inhabitant of the San Diego Zoo.

Although cloning mammals is now commonplace, one startling fact about the banteng makes this case unique: *The banteng that was cloned had died more than 20 years earlier.* Not only did this undertaking make the banteng the first successfully cloned endangered animal, it also demonstrated for the first time that well-preserved animals that have been dead for decades may be cloned using

? *Can life be rebooted?*

closely related animals as surrogates. Biologists hope that such efforts may increase the populations of threatened species or even recently extinct species.

How can a single cell be "rebooted" to develop into an entire organism? To be successful, the starting cell must contain a complete set of genes capable of directing the production of all the cell types in an organism. The development of different types of cells must therefore depend on turning on and off different genes in different cells—the control of gene expression.

We begin this chapter with examples of how and where cells may alter their patterns of gene expression. Next we look at the methods and applications of plant and animal cloning. Finally, we discuss cancer, a disease that can be caused by changes in gene expression.

BIG IDEAS

Control of Gene Expression
(11.1–11.11)
Cells can turn genes on and off through a variety of mechanisms.

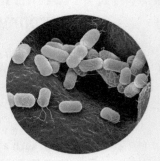

Cloning of Plants and Animals
(11.12–11.14)
Cloning demonstrates that many body cells retain their full genetic potential.

The Genetic Basis of Cancer
(11.15–11.18)
Changes in genes that control gene expression can lead to out-of-control cell growth.

▷ Control of Gene Expression

11.1 Proteins interacting with DNA turn prokaryotic genes on or off in response to environmental changes

Picture an *Escherichia coli* (*E. coli*) bacterium living in your intestine (**Figure 11.1A**). Its environment changes continuously, depending on your dietary whims. For example, if you eat a sweet roll for breakfast, the bacterium will be bathed in sugars and broken-down fats. Later, if you have a salad for lunch, the *E. coli*'s environment will change drastically. How can a bacterium cope with such a constantly shifting flow of resources?

The answer is that **gene regulation**—the turning on and off of genes—can help organisms respond to environmental changes. What does it mean to turn a gene on or off? Genes determine the nucleotide sequences of specific messenger RNA (mRNA) molecules (as we saw in Chapter 10), and mRNA in turn determines the sequences of amino acids in protein molecules (DNA → RNA → protein). Thus, a gene that is turned on is being transcribed into mRNA, and that message is being translated into specific protein molecules. The overall process by which genetic information flows from genes to proteins—that is, from genotype to phenotype—is called **gene expression**. The control of gene expression makes it possible for cells to produce specific kinds of proteins when and where they are needed.

Let's think back to our example of a bacterium living in your digestive system. It's no coincidence that we used *E. coli* as our example. Our earliest understanding of gene control came from studies of this bacterium by French biologists François Jacob and Jacques Monod. *E. coli* has a remarkable ability to change its metabolic activities in response to changes in its environment. For example, *E. coli* produces enzymes needed to metabolize a specific nutrient only when that nutrient is available. Bacterial cells that can conserve resources and energy have an advantage over cells that are unable to do so. Thus, natural selection has favored bacteria that express only the genes whose products are needed by the cell. Let's look at how the regulation of gene transcription helps *E. coli* efficiently use available resources.

The *lac* Operon   Imagine the bacterium in your intestine soon after you drink a glass of milk. One of the main nutrients in milk is the disaccharide sugar lactose. When lactose is plentiful in the intestine, *E. coli* makes the enzymes necessary to absorb the sugar and use it as an energy source. Conversely, when lactose is not plentiful, *E. coli* does not waste its energy producing these enzymes.

Recall that most enzymes are proteins; their production is an outcome of gene expression. *E. coli* can make

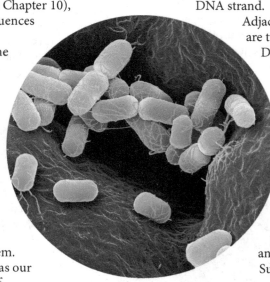

▲ **Figure 11.1A**   Cells of *E. coli* bacteria

lactose-utilization enzymes because it has genes that code for these enzymes. **Figure 11.1B** presents a model (first proposed in 1961 by Jacob and Monod) to explain how an *E. coli* cell can turn genes coding for lactose-utilization enzymes off or on, depending on whether lactose is available.

E. coli uses three enzymes to take up and start metabolizing lactose, and the genes coding for these three enzymes are regulated as a single unit. The DNA at the top of Figure 11.1B represents a small segment of the bacterium's chromosome. Notice that the three genes that code for the lactose-utilization enzymes (light blue) are situated next to each other along the DNA strand.

Adjacent to the group of lactose enzyme genes are two control sequences, short sections of DNA that help control the expression of these genes. One control sequence is a **promoter**, a site where the transcription enzyme, RNA polymerase, attaches and initiates transcription—in this case, transcription of all three lactose enzyme genes (as depicted in the bottom panel of Figure 11.1B). Between the promoter and the enzyme genes, a DNA control sequence called an **operator** acts as a switch. The operator determines whether RNA polymerase can attach to the promoter and start transcribing the genes.

Such a cluster of genes with related functions, along with the control sequences—in this instance, the entire stretch of DNA required for enzyme production—is called an **operon**; with rare exceptions, operons exist only in prokaryotes. The key advantage to the grouping of related genes into operons is that a single "on-off switch" can control the whole cluster. The operon discussed here is called the *lac* operon, short for lactose operon. When an *E. coli* bacterium encounters lactose, all the enzymes needed for its metabolism are made at once because the operon's genes are all controlled by a single switch, the operator. But what determines whether the operator switch is on or off?

The top panel of Figure 11.1B shows the *lac* operon in "off" mode, its status when there is no lactose in the cell's environment. Transcription is turned off because a protein called a **repressor** ( ) binds to the operator ( ) and physically blocks the attachment of RNA polymerase ( ) to the promoter ( ). On the left side of the figure, you can see where the repressor comes from. A gene called a **regulatory gene** (dark blue), located outside the operon, codes for the repressor. The regulatory gene is expressed continually, so the cell always has a small supply of repressor molecules.

Operon turned off (lactose is absent):

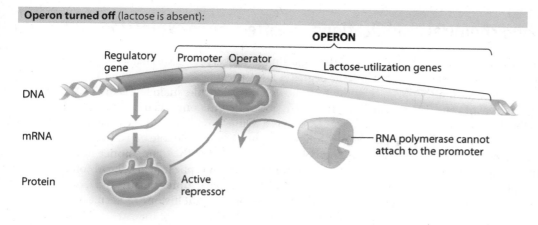

Operon turned on (lactose inactivates the repressor):

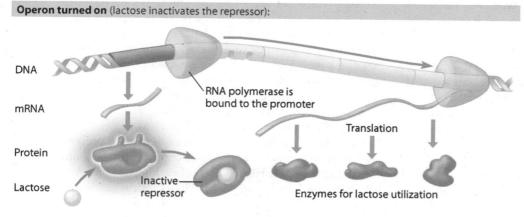

▲ **Figure 11.1B** The *lac* operon

Try This Compare the structure and function of the *lac* repressor protein when lactose is absent (top) and present (bottom).

How can an operon be turned on if its repressor is always present? As the bottom panel of Figure 11.1B indicates, lactose (○) interferes with the attachment of the *lac* repressor to the operator by binding to the repressor and changing its shape. With its new shape (◉), the repressor cannot bind to the operator, and the operator switch remains on. RNA polymerase is then able to bind to the promoter (because it is no longer being blocked) and from there transcribes the genes of the operon. The resulting mRNA carries coding sequences for all three enzymes needed for lactose metabolism. The cell can translate the message in this single mRNA into three separate polypeptides because the mRNA has multiple codons signaling the start and stop of translation.

The *lac* operon is so efficient that the addition of lactose to a bacterium's environment results in a thousandfold increase in lactose utilization enzymes in just 15 minutes. The newly produced mRNA and protein molecules will remain intact for only a short time before cellular enzymes break them down. When the synthesis of mRNA and protein stops because lactose is no longer present, the existing molecules are quickly degraded.

Other Kinds of Operons The *lac* operon is an example of an inducible operon (**Figure 11.1C**, left), one that is usually turned off but can be stimulated (induced) by a molecule—in this case, by lactose. Such operons usually operate as part of a pathway that breaks down a nutrient to simpler molecules. By producing the digestive enzymes only when the nutrient is available, the cell avoids wasting resources. A second type of operon, represented here by the *trp* operon, is called a repressible operon, because it is normally turned on but can be inhibited (repressed) when a specific molecule is present in abundance. In our example, the molecule is tryptophan (Trp), an amino acid essential for protein synthesis. *E. coli* can make tryptophan from scratch, using enzymes encoded in the *trp* operon. But *E. coli* will stop making tryptophan and simply absorb it from the surroundings whenever possible. When *E. coli* is bathed in tryptophan in the intestines (as occurs when you eat foods such as milk and poultry), the tryptophan binds to the repressor of the *trp* operon. This activates the *trp* repressor, enabling it to switch off the operon. Thus, this type of operon allows bacteria to stop making certain essential molecules when the molecules are already present in the environment, saving materials and energy for the cells.

Another type of operon control involves **activators**, proteins that turn operons *on* by binding to DNA and stimulating gene transcription. Activator proteins act by making it easier for RNA polymerase to bind to the promoter, rather than by blocking RNA polymerase, as repressors do. Activators help control a wide variety of operons.

Armed with a variety of operons regulated by repressors and activators, *E. coli* and other prokaryotes can thrive in frequently changing environments. Next we examine how more complex eukaryotes regulate their genes.

? A certain mutation in *E. coli* impairs the ability of the *lac* repressor to bind to the *lac* operator. How would this affect the cell?

● The cell would wastefully produce the enzymes for lactose metabolism continuously, even when lactose is not present.

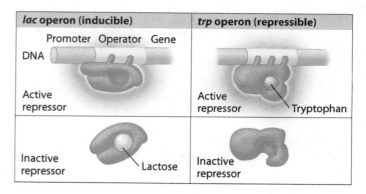

lac operon (inducible)	*trp* operon (repressible)

▲ **Figure 11.1C** Two types of repressor-controlled operons

11.2 Chromosome structure and chemical modifications can affect gene expression

The cells of all organisms, whether prokaryotes or eukaryotes, must be able to turn genes on and off in response to signals from their external and internal environments. All multicellular eukaryotes also require an additional level of gene control: During the repeated cell divisions that lead from a zygote to an adult in a multicellular organism, individual cells must undergo **differentiation**—that is, they must become specialized in structure and function, with each type of cell fulfilling a distinct role. Your body, for example, contains hundreds of different types of cells. What makes a kidney cell different from, say, a bone cell?

To perform its specialized role, each cell type must maintain a specific program of gene expression in which some genes are expressed and others are not. Almost all the cells in an organism contain an identical genome, yet the subset of genes expressed in each cell type is unique, reflecting its specific function. Each adult human cell expresses only a small fraction of its total genes at any given time. And even one particular cell type can change its pattern of gene expression over time in response to developmental signals or other changes in the environment.

The differences between cell types, therefore, are not due to different genes being present but instead due to selective gene expression. In this module, we begin our exploration of gene regulation in eukaryotes by looking at the structure of chromosomes.

DNA Packing The DNA of each human chromosome is thousands of times longer than the diameter of the nucleus. All of this DNA can fit within the nucleus because of an elaborate, multilevel system of packing, coiling, and folding. A crucial aspect of DNA packing is the association of the DNA with small proteins called **histones**. In fact, histone proteins account for about half the mass of eukaryotic chromosomes. (Prokaryotes have analogous proteins, but lack the degree of DNA packing seen in eukaryotes.)

Figure 11.2A shows a model for the main levels of DNA packing. At the left, notice that the unpacked double-helical molecule of DNA has a diameter of 2 nm. At the first level of packing, histones attach to the DNA double helix. In the electron micrograph near the top left of the figure, notice how the DNA-histone complex has the appearance of beads on a string. Each "bead," called a **nucleosome**, consists of DNA wound around a protein core of eight histone molecules. Short stretches of DNA, called linkers, are the "strings" that join consecutive "beads" of nucleosomes.

At the next level of packing, the beaded string is wrapped into a tight helical fiber with a diameter of 30 nm. This fiber coils further into a thick supercoil with a diameter of about 300 nm. Looping and folding can compact the DNA even more, as you can see in the metaphase chromosome on the right side of the figure. Figure 11.2A gives an overview of how successive levels of coiling and folding enable a huge amount of DNA to fit into a tiny cell nucleus.

DNA packing tends to block gene expression by preventing RNA polymerase and other transcription proteins from contacting the DNA. Higher levels of packing can therefore inactivate genes for the long term. Genes within highly compacted chromatin, as seen in mitotic chromosomes—such as the duplicated chromosome shown on the right side of the figure—and in varying regions of interphase chromosomes are generally not expressed at all.

Chemical Modifications and Epigenetic Inheritance Eukaryotic chromosomes can be chemically modified in ways that help regulate gene expression. For example, the addition of methyl (CH_3) groups to some of the amino acids in histone proteins can cause the chromosomes to become more

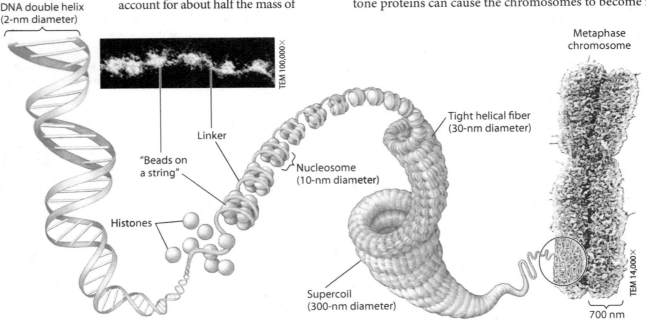

▲ Figure 11.2A   DNA packing in a eukaryotic chromosome

compact, leading to reduced transcription. Conversely, adding acetyl groups (—COCH$_3$) opens up the chromatin structure, promoting transcription.

DNA can also be chemically modified. For example, certain enzymes add a methyl group to DNA bases, usually cytosine, without changing the actual sequence of the bases. Individual genes are usually more heavily methylated in cells in which they are not expressed, and removing the extra methyl groups can turn on some of these genes. Thus, DNA methylation appears to play a role in turning genes off. At least in some species, DNA methylation seems to be essential for the long-term inactivation of genes. Such modifications are a normal and necessary mechanism for the regulation of gene expression, and improper methylation can lead to problems for the organism. For example, insufficient DNA methylation can lead to abnormal embryonic development in many species.

Once methylated, genes usually stay that way through successive cell divisions in a given individual. During replication, when a methylated stretch of DNA is duplicated, enzymes methylate the corresponding daughter strands to match. Methylation patterns are therefore passed on, allowing cells that form specialized tissues to keep a chemical record of what occurred during embryonic development. Thus, modifications to DNA and histones can be passed along to future generations of cells—that is, they can be inherited. Inheritance of traits transmitted by mechanisms not directly involving the nucleotide sequence is called **epigenetic inheritance**. Whereas mutations in the DNA are permanent changes, modifications to the chromatin, which do not affect the sequence of DNA itself, can be reversed by processes that are not yet fully understood.

Researchers are amassing more evidence for the importance of epigenetic information in the regulation of gene expression. Epigenetic variations might help explain differences in identical twins. For example, it is often the case that one identical twin acquires a genetically influenced disease, such as schizophrenia, but the other does not, despite their identical genomes. Researchers suspect that epigenetics may be behind such differences. Alterations in normal patterns of DNA methylation are seen in some cancers, where they are associated with inappropriate gene expression. Evidently, enzymes that modify chromatin structure are integral parts of the eukaryotic cell's machinery for regulating transcription.

X Inactivation

Gene regulation sometimes occurs at the whole chromosome level. For example, female mammals (including humans) inherit two X chromosomes, whereas males inherit only one. So why don't females make twice as much of the proteins encoded by genes on the X chromosome compared to the amounts in males? It turns out that in female mammals, one X chromosome in each somatic (body) cell is chemically modified and highly compacted, rendering it almost entirely inactive. Inactivation of an X chromosome involves modification of the DNA (by, for example, methylation) and the histone proteins that help compact it. A specific gene on the X chromosomes ensures that only one of them will be inactivated. This **X chromosome inactivation** is initiated early in embryonic development, when one of the two X chromosomes in each cell is inactivated at random. As a result, the cells of females and males have the same effective dose (one copy) of these genes. The inactive X in each cell of a female condenses into a compact object called a **Barr body**.

Which X chromosome is inactivated is a matter of chance in each embryonic cell, but once an X chromosome is inactivated, all descendant cells have the same copy turned off—an example of epigenetic inheritance. Consequently, females consist of a mosaic of two types of cells: those with the active X derived from the father and those with the active X derived from the mother. If a female is heterozygous for a gene on the X chromosome (a sex-linked gene; see Module 9.21), about half her cells will express one allele, while the others will express the alternate allele.

A striking example of this mosaic phenomenon is the tortoiseshell cat, which has orange and black patches of fur (Figure 11.2B). The relevant fur-color gene is on the X chromosome, and the tortoiseshell phenotype requires the presence of two different alleles, one for orange fur and one for black fur. Normally, only females can have both alleles because only they have two X chromosomes. If a female is heterozygous for the tortoiseshell gene, she will have the tortoiseshell phenotype. Orange patches are formed by populations of cells in which the X chromosome with the orange allele is active; black patches have cells in which the X chromosome with the black allele is active.

In this module, we have seen how the physical structure of chromosomes can affect which genes are expressed in a cell. In the next module, we discuss mechanisms for regulating genes in active, unpacked chromosomes.

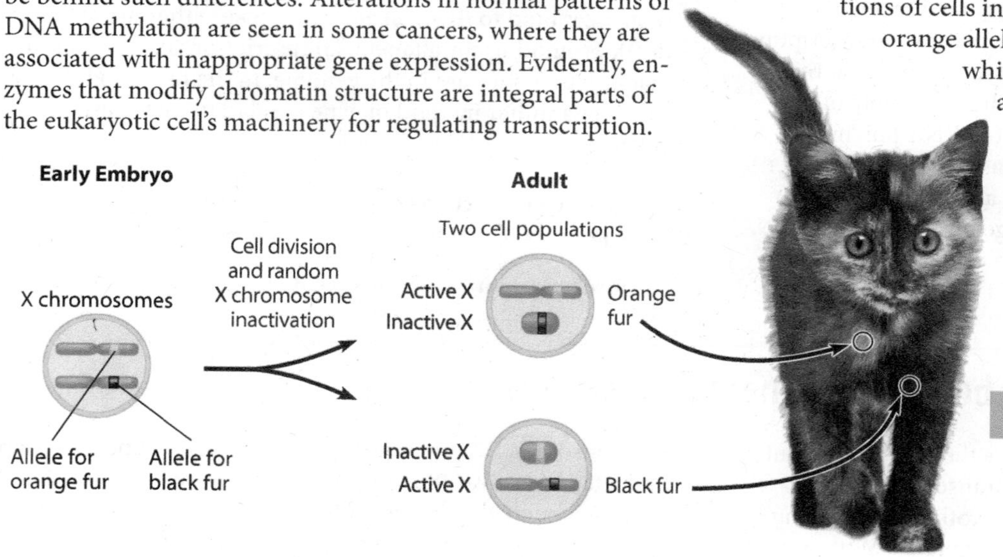

? In your body, a nerve cell has a very different structure and performs very different functions than a skin cell. Because the two cell types have the same genes, how can the cells be so different?

Early Embryo

X chromosomes

Allele for orange fur

Allele for black fur

Cell division and random X chromosome inactivation

Adult

Two cell populations

Active X
Inactive X → Orange fur

Inactive X
Active X → Black fur

▲ Figure 11.2B   A tortoiseshell pattern on a female cat, a result of X chromosome inactivation

● Each cell type must be expressing certain genes that are present in, but not expressed in, the other cell type.

11.3 Complex assemblies of proteins control eukaryotic transcription

The process of packing and unpacking of chromosomal DNA provides a coarse adjustment for eukaryotic gene expression by making a region of DNA either more or less available for transcription, the synthesis of RNA. The fine-tuning begins with the initiation of transcription. In both prokaryotes and eukaryotes, the initiation of transcription (whether transcription starts or not) is the most important stage for regulating gene expression.

Like prokaryotes (see Module 11.1), eukaryotes use regulatory proteins—activators and repressors—that bind to specific segments of DNA and either promote or block the binding of RNA polymerase, turning the transcription of genes on or off. However, most eukaryotic genes have individual promoters and other control sequences and are not clustered together as in operons.

The current model for the initiation of eukaryotic transcription features an intricate array of regulatory proteins that interact with DNA and with one another to turn genes on or off. In eukaryotes, activator proteins seem to be more important than repressors. A typical animal or plant cell needs to turn on (transcribe) only a small percentage of its genes, those required for the cell's specialized structure and function. Therefore, in multicellular eukaryotes, the "default" state for most genes seems to be "off." Important exceptions include housekeeping genes, those continually active in virtually all cells for routine activities such as glycolysis, which may be in an "on" state by default.

To function, eukaryotic RNA polymerase requires the assistance of proteins called **transcription factors**. In the model depicted in **Figure 11.3**, the first step in initiating gene transcription is the binding of activator proteins ( ) to DNA control sequences called **enhancers** ( ). In contrast to the operators found within prokaryotic operons, enhancers are usually located far away on the chromosome from the gene they help regulate. Next, a DNA-bending protein brings the bound activators closer to the promoter. Once the DNA is bent, the bound activators interact with other transcription factor proteins ( ), which then bind as a complex at the gene's promoter ( ). This large assembly of proteins facilitates the correct attachment of RNA polymerase to the promoter and the initiation of transcription. Only when the complete complex of proteins has assembled can the polymerase begin to move along the gene, producing an RNA strand. As shown in the figure, multiple enhancers and activators may be involved in turning on a single gene.

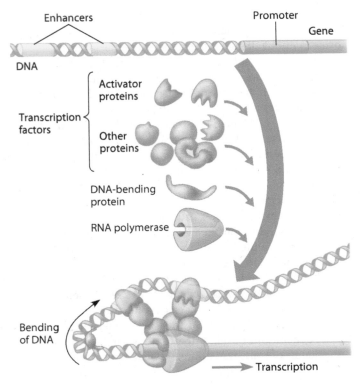

▲ **Figure 11.3** A model for the turning on of a eukaryotic gene

Try This Explain how enhancer sequences can promote transcription of a gene that is located far away on the DNA molecule.

Genes coding for the enzymes of a metabolic pathway are often scattered across different chromosomes. How can a eukaryotic cell turn on or off all functionally related genes at the same time? The key to coordinated gene expression in eukaryotes is often the association of a specific combination of control sequences with every gene of a particular metabolic pathway. Copies of the activators that recognize these control sequences bind to them all at once (because they are all identical), promoting simultaneous transcription of the genes, no matter where they are in the genome. In the next module, we consider another method of gene regulation that is unique to eukaryotes.

> ? **What must occur before RNA polymerase can bind to a promoter and transcribe a specific eukaryotic gene?**

Transcription factors must bind to enhancers to facilitate the attachment of RNA polymerase to the promoter.

11.4 Eukaryotic RNA may be spliced in more than one way

Although regulation of transcription is the most important step in gene regulation in most cells, transcription alone does not equal gene expression. Several other points along the path from DNA to protein can be regulated. Within a eukaryotic cell, for example, RNA transcripts are processed into mRNA before moving to the cytoplasm for translation by the ribosomes. RNA processing includes the addition of a cap and a tail, as well as the removal of any introns—noncoding DNA segments that interrupt the genetic message—and the splicing together of the remaining exons (see Module 10.10).

Some scientists hypothesize that the splicing process may help control the flow of mRNA from nucleus to cytoplasm because until splicing is completed, the RNA is attached to the molecules of the splicing machinery and cannot pass through the nuclear pores. Moreover, in some cases, the cell can carry out splicing in more than one way, generating different mRNA molecules from the same RNA transcript. Notice in **Figure 11.4**, for example, that one mRNA molecule ends up with the green exon and the other with the brown exon. With this sort of **alternative RNA splicing**, an organism can produce more than one type of polypeptide from a single gene.

One interesting example of two-way splicing is found in the *Drosophila* fruit fly, where the differences between males and females are largely due to different patterns of RNA splicing. In addition, researchers have found a gene in *Drosophila* that, through the alternate splicing of many exons, produces more than 17,500 proteins, each of which is found in the membrane of a different nerve cell where it acts as an identification marker. In humans, more than 90% of protein-coding genes appear to undergo alternate splicing.

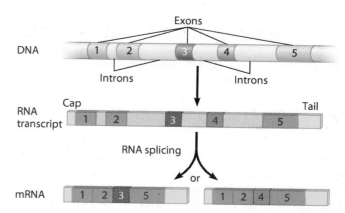

▲ Figure 11.4   The production of two different mRNAs from the same gene

? **How is it possible that just under 21,000 human genes can produce more than 100,000 polypeptides?**

● Through alternate splicing: Each kind of polypeptide is encoded by an mRNA molecule containing a different combination of exons.

11.5 Small RNAs play multiple roles in controlling gene expression

Genome research has revealed that only 1.5% of the human genome—and a similarly small percentage of the genomes of many other multicellular eukaryotes—codes for proteins. Another very small fraction of DNA consists of genes for ribosomal RNA and transfer RNA. Until recently, most of the remaining DNA was thought to be untranscribed and therefore considered to be lacking any genetic information. However, a flood of recent data has contradicted this view. It turns out that a significant amount of the genome is transcribed into functioning but non–protein-coding RNAs, including a variety of small RNAs. Although many questions about the functions of these RNAs remain unanswered, researchers are uncovering more evidence of their biological roles every day.

In 1993, researchers discovered small RNA molecules, called **microRNAs (miRNAs)**, that can bind to complementary sequences on mRNA molecules (**Figure 11.5**). Each miRNA, typically about 22 nucleotides long, ❶ forms a complex with one or more proteins. The miRNA-protein complex can ❷ bind to any mRNA molecule with 7 to 8 nucleotides of complementary sequence. ❸ Then the complex either degrades the target mRNA or blocks its translation. It has been estimated that miRNAs may regulate the expression of at least one-half of all human genes, a striking figure given that miRNAs were unknown 20 years ago.

Researchers can take advantage of miRNA to artificially control gene expression. For example, injecting miRNA into a cell can turn off expression of a gene with a sequence that matches the miRNA, a procedure called **RNA interference (RNAi)**. The RNAi pathway may have evolved as a natural defense against infection by certain viruses with RNA genomes (see Chapter 10). In 2006, two American researchers were awarded a Nobel Prize for their discovery and categorization of RNA interference.

Biologists are excited about these recent discoveries, which hint at a large, diverse population of RNA molecules in the cell that play crucial roles in regulating gene expression—and have gone largely unnoticed until very recently. Our new understanding may lead to important clinical applications. For example, in 2009, researchers discovered a particular miRNA that is essential for the proper functioning of the pancreas. Without it, insulin-producing beta cells die, which can lead to diabetes.

? **If a gene has the sequence AATTCGCG, what would be the sequence of an miRNA that turns off the gene?**

● The gene will be transcribed as the mRNA sequence UUAAGCGC; an miRNA of sequence AAUUCGCG would bind to and disable this mRNA.

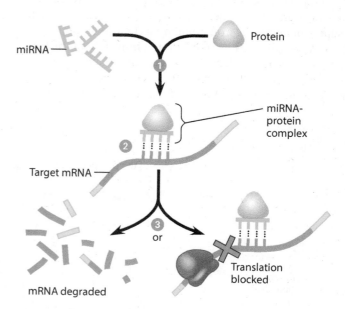

▲ Figure 11.5   Mechanisms of RNA interference

11.6 Later stages of gene expression are also subject to regulation

Even after a eukaryotic mRNA is fully processed and transported to the cytoplasm, there are several additional opportunities for regulation. Such control points include mRNA breakdown, initiation of translation, protein activation, and protein breakdown.

Breakdown of mRNA Molecules of mRNA do not remain intact forever. Enzymes in the cytoplasm eventually break them down, and the timing of this event is an important factor regulating the amounts of various proteins that are produced in the cell. Long-lived mRNAs can be translated into many more protein molecules than short-lived ones. Prokaryotic mRNAs have very short lifetimes; they are typically degraded by enzymes within a few minutes after their synthesis. This is one reason bacteria can change their protein production so quickly in response to environmental changes. In contrast, the mRNAs of eukaryotes have lifetimes from hours to weeks.

A striking example of long-lived mRNA is found in vertebrate red blood cells, which manufacture large quantities of the protein hemoglobin. In most species of vertebrates, the mRNAs for hemoglobin are unusually stable. They probably last as long as the red blood cells that contain them—about a month or a bit longer in reptiles, amphibians, and fishes—and are translated again and again. Mammals are an exception. When their red blood cells mature, they lose their ribosomes (along with their other organelles) and thus cease to make new hemoglobin. However, mammalian hemoglobin itself lasts about as long as the red blood cells last: around four months.

Initiation of Translation The process of translating an mRNA into a polypeptide also offers opportunities for regulation. Among the molecules involved in translation are a great many proteins that control the start of polypeptide synthesis. Red blood cells, for instance, have an inhibitory protein that prevents translation of hemoglobin mRNA unless the cell has a supply of heme, the iron-containing chemical group essential for hemoglobin function. (It is the iron atom of the heme group to which oxygen molecules actually attach.) By controlling the start of protein synthesis, cells can avoid wasting energy if the needed components are currently unavailable.

Protein Activation After translation is complete, some polypeptides require alterations before they become functional. Post-translational control mechanisms in eukaryotes often involve the cleavage (cutting) of a polypeptide to yield a smaller final product that is the active protein, able to carry out a specific function in the organism. In **Figure 11.6**, we see the example of the protein hormone insulin. Insulin is synthesized in the cells of the pancreas as one long polypeptide that has no hormonal activity. After translation is completed, the polypeptide folds up, and covalent bonds form between the sulfur (S) atoms of sulfur-containing amino acids (see Figure 3.12A, which shows S—S bonds in another protein). Two H atoms are lost as each S—S bond forms, linking together parts of the polypeptide in a specific way. Finally, a large center portion is cut away, leaving two shorter chains held together by the sulfur linkages. This combination of two shorter polypeptides is the form of insulin that functions as a hormone. By controlling the timing of such protein modifications, the rate of insulin synthesis can be fine-tuned.

Protein Breakdown The final control mechanism operating after translation is the selective breakdown of proteins. Although mammalian hemoglobin may last as long as the red blood cell housing it, the lifetimes of many other proteins are closely regulated. Some of the proteins that trigger metabolic changes in cells are broken down within a few minutes or hours. This regulation allows a cell to adjust the kinds and amounts of its proteins in response to changes in its environment. It also enables the cell to maintain its proteins in prime working order. Indeed, when proteins are damaged, they are usually broken down right away and replaced by new ones that function properly.

Over the last five modules, you have learned about several ways that eukaryotes can control gene expression. The next module summarizes all of these processes.

> **?** Review Figure 11.6. If the enzyme responsible for cleaving inactive insulin is deactivated, what effect will this have on the form and function of insulin?
>
> ⊙ The final molecule will have a shape different from that of active insulin and therefore will not be able to function as a hormone.

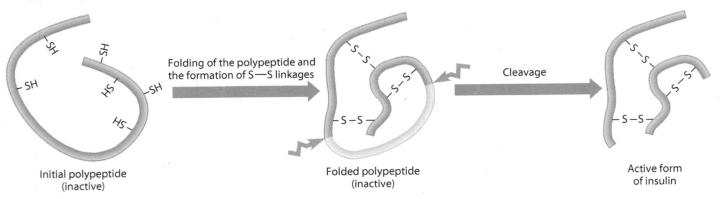

Initial polypeptide (inactive) → Folding of the polypeptide and the formation of S—S linkages → Folded polypeptide (inactive) → Cleavage → Active form of insulin

▲ **Figure 11.6** Protein activation: the role of polypeptide cleavage in producing the active insulin protein

11.7 Multiple mechanisms regulate gene expression in eukaryotes

This summary of eukaryotic gene expression highlights the multiple control points where the process can be turned on or off, speeded up, or slowed down. Although many control points are shown, only a few of them may be important for any particular protein.

Picture the pipes that carry water from a reservoir to your faucet. At various points, valves control the flow. Similarly, genetic information flows from a chromosome—a reservoir of genetic information—through several control points (shown as valves and described in the blue ovals) to an active protein in the cell's cytoplasm.

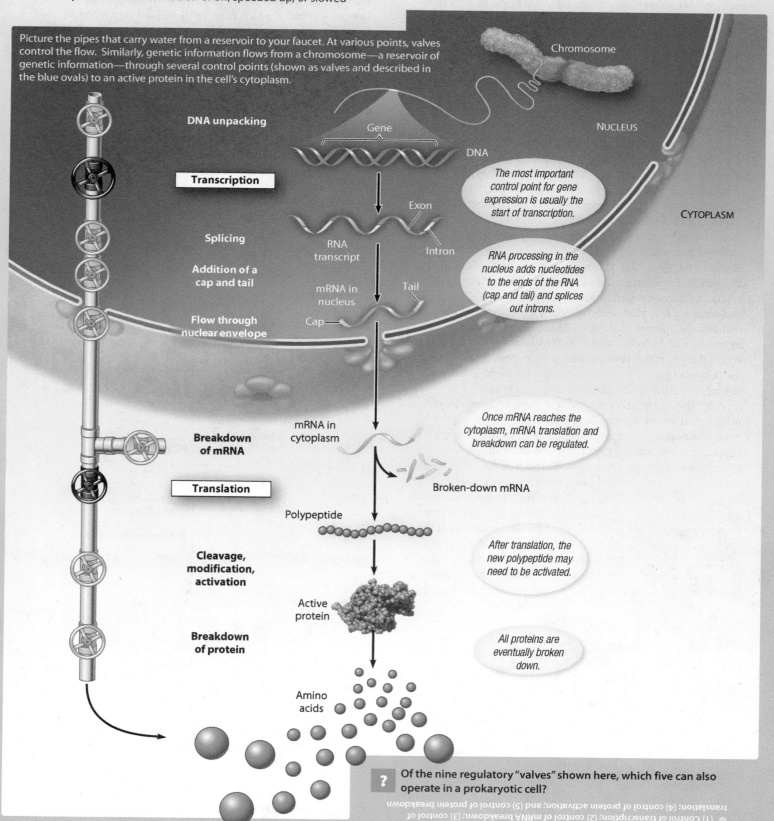

DNA unpacking

Transcription

Splicing

Addition of a cap and tail

Flow through nuclear envelope

Breakdown of mRNA

Translation

Cleavage, modification, activation

Breakdown of protein

Chromosome

NUCLEUS

Gene

DNA

Exon

RNA transcript

Intron

mRNA in nucleus

Tail

Cap

CYTOPLASM

The most important control point for gene expression is usually the start of transcription.

RNA processing in the nucleus adds nucleotides to the ends of the RNA (cap and tail) and splices out introns.

mRNA in cytoplasm

Broken-down mRNA

Once mRNA reaches the cytoplasm, mRNA translation and breakdown can be regulated.

Polypeptide

Active protein

After translation, the new polypeptide may need to be activated.

All proteins are eventually broken down.

Amino acids

? Of the nine regulatory "valves" shown here, which five can also operate in a prokaryotic cell?

● (1) Control of transcription; (2) control of mRNA breakdown; (3) control of translation; (4) control of protein activation; and (5) control of protein breakdown

11.8 Cell signaling and waves of gene expression direct animal development

In eukaryotes, cellular differentiation results from the selective turning on and off of genes. During the life cycle of a multicellular eukaryote, cellular differentiation by selective gene expression is most vital during the development of an embryo from a zygote. Waves of gene expression, with the protein products of one set of genes activating other sets of genes, are a common mechanism of development.

Some of the first glimpses into the relationship between gene expression and embryonic development came from studies of mutants of the fruit fly *Drosophila melanogaster* (see Module 9.18). Figure 11.8A shows the heads of two fruit flies. The one on the right, a mutant, developed in a strikingly abnormal way: It has two legs where its antennae should be! Research on this and other developmental mutants has led to the identification of many of the genes that program development in the normal fly. This genetic approach has revolutionized developmental biology.

Among the earliest events in fruit fly development are those that determine which end of the egg cell will become the head and which end will become the tail. As you can see in Figure 11.8B, ➊ these events occur in the ovaries of the mother fly and involve communication between an unfertilized egg cell and cells adjacent to it in its follicle (egg chamber). The back-and-forth signaling between the cells triggers expression of certain genes in the two cell types. ➋ One important result is the localization of a specific type of mRNA (shown in pink) at the end of the egg where the fly's head will develop, thus defining the animal's head-to-tail axis. (Similar events lead to the positioning of the top-to-bottom and side-to-side axes.)

After the egg is fertilized and laid, repeated rounds of mitosis transform the zygote into an embryo. The early embryo makes proteins that diffuse through its cell layers. Cell signaling—now among the cells of the embryo—helps drive the process of development. ➌ The result is the subdivision of the embryo's body into segments. At this point the finer details of the fly take shape. Protein products of some of the axis-specifying genes and segment-forming genes activate yet another set of genes,

called homeotic genes. A **homeotic gene** is a master control gene that regulates the "batteries" of other genes that determine the anatomy of parts of the body and in this example determine which body parts will develop where in the fly. For example, one set of homeotic genes in fruit flies instructs cells in the segments of the head and thorax (midbody) to form antennae and legs, respectively. ➍ The eventual outcome is an adult fly. Notice that the adult's body segments correspond to those of the embryo in step 3. It was mutation of a homeotic gene that was responsible for the abnormal fly in Figure 11.8A.

How can scientists study the expression of genes within living systems? In the next module, we'll look at how DNA technology can help elucidate gene expression in any cell.

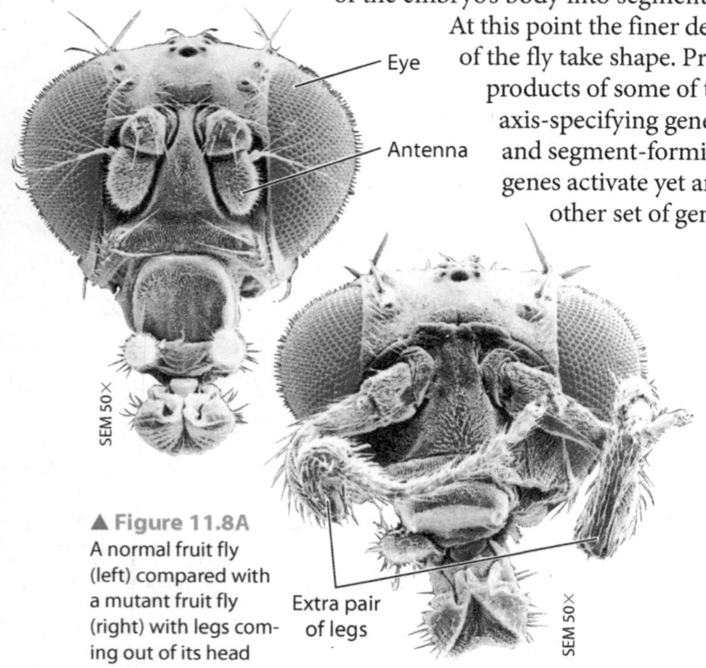

? What determines which end of a developing fruit fly will become the head?

● A specific kind of mRNA localizes at the end of the unfertilized egg that will become the head.

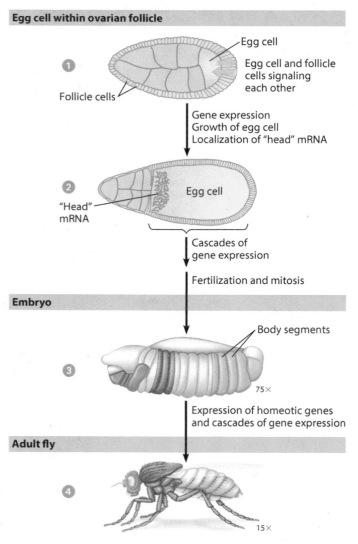

Egg cell within ovarian follicle

➊ Egg cell
Egg cell and follicle cells signaling each other
Follicle cells

Gene expression
Growth of egg cell
Localization of "head" mRNA

➋ Egg cell
"Head" mRNA

Cascades of gene expression

Fertilization and mitosis

Embryo

➌ Body segments
75×

Expression of homeotic genes and cascades of gene expression

Adult fly

➍ 15×

▲ Figure 11.8B   Key steps in the early development of head-tail axis in a fruit fly

Eye

Antenna

SEM 50×

SEM 50×

▲ Figure 11.8A
A normal fruit fly (left) compared with a mutant fruit fly (right) with legs coming out of its head

Extra pair of legs

11.9 Scientists use DNA microarrays to test for the transcription of many genes at once

Biologists today are working hard to learn how genes act together within a functioning organism. Now that a number of whole genomes have been sequenced (see Module 12.17), it is possible to study the expression of large groups of genes. For example, researchers can investigate which genes are transcribed in different situations, such as in different tissues or at different stages of development. They can also look for groups of genes that are expressed in a coordinated manner, with the aim of identifying networks of gene expression across an entire genome.

Genome-wide expression studies are made possible by DNA microarrays. A **DNA microarray** consists of a glass or plastic surface with tiny amounts of thousands of different kinds of single-stranded DNA fragments attached to microscopic wells in a tightly spaced array, or grid. (A DNA microarray is also called a DNA chip or gene chip by analogy to a computer chip.) Each fixed DNA fragment is obtained from a particular gene; a single microarray thus carries DNA from thousands of genes, perhaps even all the genes of an organism.

Figure 11.9 outlines how microarrays are used. ❶ A researcher collects all of the mRNA transcribed from genes in a particular type of cell at a given moment. ❷ This collection of mRNAs is mixed with reverse transcriptase (a viral enzyme that produces DNA from an RNA template; see Module 10.20) to produce a mixture of single-stranded DNA fragments. These fragments are called cDNAs (complementary DNAs) because each one is complementary to one of the mRNAs. The cDNAs are produced in the presence of nucleotides that have been modified to fluoresce (glow). The fluorescent cDNA collection thus represents all of the genes that are being actively transcribed in that particular cell at that particular time. ❸ A small amount of the fluorescently labeled cDNA mixture is added to each of the wells in the microarray. If a molecule in the cDNA mixture is complementary to a DNA fragment at a particular location on the grid, the cDNA molecule binds to it, becoming fixed there. ❹ After unbound cDNA is rinsed away, the remaining cDNA produces a detectable glow in the microarray. The pattern of glowing spots enables the researcher to determine which genes were being transcribed in the starting cells.

DNA microarrays hold great promise in medical research. Many cancers have a variety of subtypes with different patterns of gene expression that can be identified with DNA microarrays. For example, one study showed that DNA microarray data can classify different types of leukemia into specific subtypes based on the activity of 17 genes. This information can be used to predict which of several available regimens of chemotherapy is likely to be most effective. In addition, comparing patterns of gene expression in breast cancer tumors and noncancerous breast tissue has resulted in more informed and effective treatment protocols. Some oncologists predict that DNA microarrays will usher in a new era in which medical treatment is personalized to each patient (see Module 8.10).

DNA microarrays can also reveal general profiles of gene expression over the lifetime of an organism. For example, researchers performed DNA microarray experiments on more than 90% of the genes of the nematode worm *Caenorhabditis elegans* during every stage of its life cycle. The results showed that expression of nearly 60% of the *C. elegans* genes changed dramatically during development. This study supported the model held by most developmental biologists that embryonic development of multicellular eukaryotes involves a complex and elaborate program of gene expression, rather than simply the expression of a small number of important genes.

? **What can be learned from a DNA microarray?**

● Which genes are active (transcribed) in a particular sample of cells

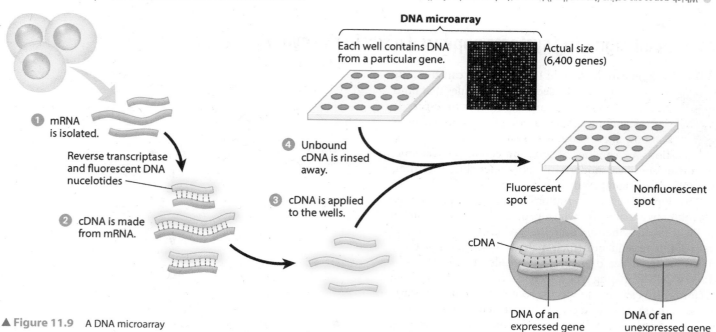

▲ **Figure 11.9**   A DNA microarray

11.10 Signal transduction pathways convert messages received at the cell surface to responses within the cell

Within a multicellular organism, cells must be able to communicate messages that will coordinate gene expression. Cell-to-cell signaling via proteins or other kinds of molecules carrying messages from signaling cells to receiving (target) cells is a key mechanism in the coordination of cellular activities. In most cases, a signaling molecule acts by binding to a receptor protein in the plasma membrane and initiating a signal transduction pathway in the target cell.

A **signal transduction pathway** is a series of molecular changes that converts a signal on a target cell's surface to a specific response inside the cell (Figure 11.10). ❶ The cell sending a message secretes a signaling molecule. ❷ This molecule binds to a specific receptor protein embedded in the target cell's plasma membrane. ❸ The binding activates the first in a series of relay proteins within the target cell. Each relay molecule activates another. ❹ The last relay molecule in the series activates a transcription factor that ❺ triggers transcription of a specific gene. ❻ Translation of the mRNA produces a protein that performs the function originally called for by the signal.

Signal transduction pathways are crucial to many cellular functions. Throughout your study of biology, you'll see the importance of signal transduction pathways again and again. We encountered them when we studied the cell cycle control system (Module 8.8); we'll revisit them when we discuss cancer later in this chapter (see, for example, Module 11.17); and we'll see how they relate to hormone function in animals and plants.

? To turn on a gene, must a signal molecule actually enter a target cell?

No, a signal molecule can bind to a receptor protein in the outer membrane of the target cell and trigger a signal transduction pathway that activates transcription factors

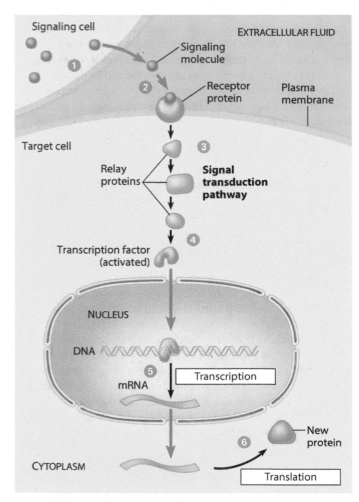

▲ Figure 11.10   A signal transduction pathway that turns on a gene

11.11 Cell-signaling systems appeared early in the evolution of life

EVOLUTION CONNECTION

As explained in Module 11.10, one cell can communicate with another by secreting molecules that bind to surface proteins on a target cell. How widespread are such signaling systems among Earth's organisms—and how ancient are these systems? To answer these questions, we can look at communication between microorganisms, because modern microbes offer clues regarding the role of cell signaling during the evolution of life on Earth.

One topic of cell "conversation" is sex—at least for the yeast *Saccharomyces cerevisiae*, which people have used for millennia to make bread, wine, and beer. Researchers have learned that cells of this yeast identify their mates by chemical signaling. There are two sexes, or mating types, called **a** and **α** (Figure 11.11). Cells of mating type **a** secrete a chemical signal called **a** factor, which can bind to specific receptor proteins on nearby **α** cells. At the same time, **α** cells secrete **α** factor, which binds to receptors on **a** cells. Without actually entering the target cells,

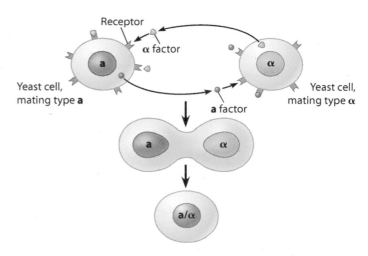

▲ Figure 11.11   Communication between mating yeast cells

the two mating factors cause the cells to grow toward each other and bring about other cellular changes. The result is the fusion, or mating, of two cells of opposite type. The resulting **a/α** cell contains all the genes of both original cells, a combination of genetic resources that provides advantages to the cell's descendants, which arise by subsequent cell divisions.

Extensive studies across different species have revealed that the molecular details of signal transduction in yeast and mammals are strikingly similar, even though the last common ancestor of these two groups of organisms lived more than a billion years ago. These similarities—and others more recently uncovered between signaling systems in bacteria and plants—suggest that early versions of the cell-signaling mechanisms used today evolved well before the first multicellular creatures appeared on Earth. Scientists think that signaling mechanisms evolved first in ancient prokaryotes and single-celled eukaryotes and then became adapted for new uses in their multicellular descendants.

? **In what sense is the joining of yeast mating types "sex"?**

● The process results in the creation of a diploid cell that is a genetic blend of two parental haploid cells.

▷ Cloning of Plants and Animals

11.12 Plant cloning shows that differentiated cells may retain all of their genetic potential

One of the most important take-home lessons from this chapter is that most cells express only a small percentage of their genes. If all genes are still present but some are turned off, have the unexpressed genes become permanently disabled? Or do all genes (even the unexpressed ones) retain the potential to be expressed?

One way to approach these questions is to determine if a differentiated cell can be stimulated to generate a whole new organism. In plants, this ability is common. In fact, if you have ever grown a plant from a small cutting, you've seen evidence that a differentiated plant cell can undergo cell division and give rise to all the tissues of an adult plant. On a larger scale, the technique described in **Figure 11.12** can be used to produce hundreds or thousands of genetically identical plants from the cells of a single plant. For example, when cells from a carrot are transferred to a culture medium, a single cell can begin dividing and eventually grow into an adult plant, a genetic replica of the original. Such an organism, produced through asexual reproduction from a single parent, is called a **clone**. In this context, the term clone refers to an individual created by asexual reproduction (that is, reproduction of a single individual that does not involve fusion of sperm and egg). The fact that a mature plant cell can dedifferentiate, or reverse its differentiation, and then give rise to all the different kinds of specialized cells of a new plant shows that differentiation does not necessarily involve irreversible changes in the plant's DNA.

Plant cloning is used extensively in agriculture. Seedless plants (such as seedless grapes and watermelons) cannot reproduce sexually, leaving cloning as the sole means of mass-producing these common foods. Other plants, such as orchids, reproduce poorly in artificial settings, leaving cloning as the only commercially practical means of production. In other cases, cloning has been used to reproduce a plant with desirable traits, such as high fruit yield or resistance to disease.

But is this sort of cloning possible in animals? A good indication that differentiation need not impair an animal cell's genetic potential is the natural process of **regeneration**, the regrowth of lost body parts. When a salamander loses a leg, for example, certain cells in the leg stump dedifferentiate, divide, and then redifferentiate, giving rise to a new leg. Many animals, especially among the invertebrates (sea stars, for example), can regenerate lost parts. In a few relatively simple animals (such as some sponges), isolated differentiated cells can dedifferentiate and then develop into an entire organism. Additional evidence for the complete genetic potential of animal cells comes from cloning experiments, our next topic.

? **How does the cloning of plants from differentiated cells support the view that differentiation is based on the control of gene expression rather than on irreversible changes in the genome?**

● Cloning shows that all the genes of a fully differentiated plant cell are still present.

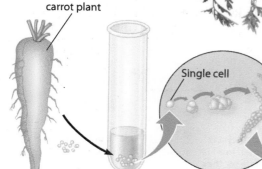

▶ **Figure 11.12**
Growth of a carrot plant from a differentiated root cell

Root of carrot plant

Single cell

Root cells cultured in growth medium

Cell division in culture

Plantlet

Adult plant

11.13 Biologists can clone animals via nuclear transplantation

SCIENTIFIC THINKING

Animal cloning has been achieved through **nuclear transplantation** (Figure 11.13). This method involves ① replacing the nucleus of an egg cell or a zygote with ② a nucleus removed from an adult somatic cell. If properly stimulated, the recipient cell may then begin to divide. ③ After a few days, repeated cell divisions form a blastocyst, a hollow ball of about 100 cells. ④ If the animal being cloned is a mammal, the blastocyst is then implanted into the uterus of a surrogate mother. The cloned animal will be genetically identical to the donor of the nucleus—in other words, a clone of the donor. This type of cloning is called **reproductive cloning** because it results in the birth of a new living individual.

Nuclear transplantation was first performed in the 1950s using cells from frog embryos. In later decades, scientists successfully cloned mammals starting from embryonic cells. However, investigators had success only with very young embryos; they found that the older a donor nucleus, the less chance it could be used to successfully clone an animal. In fact, attempts to clone using nuclei from adult cells failed repeatedly. Something within the nucleus of adult cells was preventing them from being "rebooted" into a cell that would give rise to a new, living animal.

A major breakthrough in cloning came in 1996 when Scottish researcher Ian Wilmut and his colleagues cloned a sheep named Dolly, the first mammal successfully cloned from an adult cell. How did they achieve success? Wilmut and his team hypothesized that the significant changes that occur to chromosomes over the cell cycle require that the phases of the donor nucleus and recipient egg be matched during nuclear transplantation. To achieve synchronization, the researchers grew both nucleus-donor mammary gland cells and nucleus-recipient egg cells in a growth medium that contained only 1/20th the normal nutrients. Faced with starvation, all of the cells switched into the dormant G_0 phase of the cell cycle (see Module 8.8). The researchers then removed the nuclei from the dormant eggs, fused these empty egg cells with nuclei from dormant udder cells, and zapped them with electricity to fuse and reboot them. After several days of growth, the resulting embryos were implanted in the uteruses of surrogate sheep mothers. One of the embryos developed into Dolly.

Can life be rebooted?

The pioneering cloning work of Wilmut and colleagues demonstrates how scientific success is often preceded by numerous failures. After decades of failures in previous experiments, the Scottish team produced a total of 277 zygotes, of which only 29 survived to implantation, resulting in just one live birth.

Dolly demonstrated that the differentiation of animal cells is achieved by changes in gene expression, rather than by permanent changes in the genes themselves. This conclusion has numerous practical implications. Since Dolly's landmark birth, researchers have cloned many other mammals, including mice, cats, horses, cows, mules, pigs, rabbits, ferrets, and dogs. Why bother cloning animals? Scientists working in agriculture are cloning farm animals with specific sets of desirable traits in the hope of creating high-yielding herds. The pharmaceutical industry is experimenting with cloning mammals for the production of potentially valuable drugs. For example, researchers have produced pig clones that lack a gene for a protein that can cause immune system rejection in humans. Organs from such pigs may one day be used in human patients who require life-saving transplants.

Conservation biologists hope that reproductive cloning can be used to restock the populations of endangered animals. In addition to the banteng discussed in the chapter introduction, other rare animals have been cloned, including a wild mouflon (a small European sheep), a gaur (an Asian ox), and gray wolves. Despite cloning's potential for increasing the numbers of endangered animals, some conservationists object, arguing that cloning may detract from efforts to preserve natural habitats. Such critics correctly point out that cloning does not increase genetic diversity and is therefore not as beneficial to endangered species as natural reproduction.

Another important consideration when cloning animals is the health of the offspring produced. An increasing body of evidence suggests that cloned animals may be less healthy than those arising from a fertilized egg. In 2003, Dolly was euthanized after suffering complications from a lung disease usually seen only in much older sheep. She was 6 years old, while her breed has a life expectancy of 12 years. Other cloned animals have exhibited arthritis, susceptibility to obesity, pneumonia, liver failure, and premature death. Recent research suggests that the methylation of chromatin (see Module 11.2) may be responsible for health problems in cloned animals. Researchers have found that the DNA in cells from cloned embryos often has different patterns of

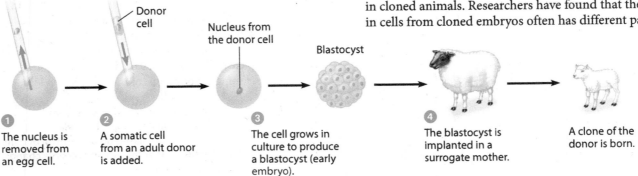

1 The nucleus is removed from an egg cell.

2 A somatic cell from an adult donor is added.

3 The cell grows in culture to produce a blastocyst (early embryo).

4 The blastocyst is implanted in a surrogate mother.

A clone of the donor is born.

▲ **Figure 11.13** Reproductive cloning via nuclear transplantation methylation than does the DNA in equivalent cells from normal embryos of the same species. Because DNA methylation helps regulate gene expression, misplaced methyl groups may interfere with the pattern of gene expression necessary for normal embryonic development. Researchers are investigating whether chromatin in a donor nucleus can be artificially "rejuvenated" to resemble that of a newly fertilized egg.

The successful cloning of mammals has heightened speculation that humans could be cloned. Critics point out that there are many obstacles—both practical and ethical—to human cloning. Practically, animal cloning is extremely difficult and inefficient. Only a small percentage of cloned embryos (usually less than 10%) develop normally, and those

cloned animals that do develop are less healthy than naturally born kin. Indeed, Dolly's creators have since predicted that their cloning technique will never be sufficiently efficient to attempt in humans. Ethically, the discussion about whether people should be cloned, and under what circumstances, is far from settled. Ethical questions also surround the outcomes of therapeutic cloning, our next topic.

? It took three sheep to create Dolly: A blackface sheep donated the egg, a white-faced sheep donated the mammary cells from which the nucleus was taken, and a blackface sheep served as surrogate. What color face should Dolly have?

● White, reflecting the genetic makeup of the nucleus donor

11.14 Therapeutic cloning can produce stem cells with great medical potential

CONNECTION

A blastocyst, made via natural sexual reproduction or produced via nuclear transplantation (see Figure 11.13), can provide **embryonic stem cells (ES cells)**. Within the embryo, ES cells differentiate to give rise to all the specialized cell types of the body. When grown in laboratory culture, embryonic stem cells can divide indefinitely. The right conditions—such as the presence of certain growth factors—can (hypothetically) induce changes in gene expression that cause differentiation of ES cells into a particular cell type (Figure 11.14). When the goal is to produce ES cells to use in therapeutic treatments, this process is called **therapeutic cloning**.

Embryonic stem cells are not the only stem cells available to researchers. Blood collected from the umbilical cord and placenta at birth contains stem cells that are partially differentiated. In 2005, doctors reported that an infusion of umbilical cord blood stem cells from a compatible (but unrelated) donor appeared to cure some babies of Krabbe's disease, a usually fatal inherited disorder of the nervous system. To date, however, most attempts at umbilical cord blood therapy have not been successful. At present, the American Academy of Pediatrics recommends cord blood banking only for babies born into families with a known genetic risk.

The adult body also has stem cells, which serve to replace nonreproducing specialized cells as needed. Because **adult stem cells** are farther along the road to differentiation than ES cells, they can give rise to only a few related types of cells. Adult animals have only tiny numbers of stem cells, but scientists are learning to identify and isolate these cells from various tissues and, in some cases, to grow them in culture. For example, bone marrow contains several types of stem cells, including one that can generate all the different kinds of blood cells. Adult stem cells from donor bone marrow have long been used as a source of immune system cells in patients whose own immune systems have been destroyed by genetic disorders or radiation treatments for cancer. More recently, clinical trials using bone marrow stem cells have shown slight success in promoting regeneration of heart tissue in patients whose hearts have been damaged by heart attacks.

The ultimate aim of therapeutic cloning is to supply cells for the repair of damaged or diseased organs. Some people

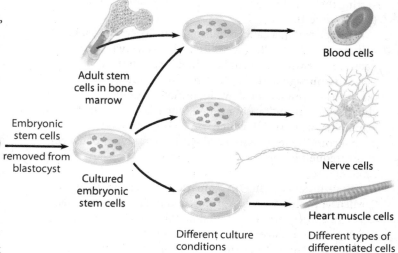

▲ Figure 11.14   Therapeutic cloning using stem cells

speculate, for example, that ES cells may one day be used to replace cells damaged by spinal cord injuries or heart attacks. In the future, a donor nucleus from a patient could allow production of embryonic stem cells that are an exact genetic match for that patient and are thus not rejected by his or her immune system.

Opinions vary widely about the morality of therapeutic cloning using embryonic stem cells, which require destruction of the embryo upon harvesting. Because no embryonic tissue is involved in their harvest, adult stem cells are less ethically problematic in therapy than ES cells. On the other hand, many researchers hypothesize that only the more versatile ES cells are likely to lead to groundbreaking advances in human health. The study of stem cells emphasizes the importance of understanding the control of gene expression. In the next section, we'll explore another important implication of gene regulation to human health: cancer.

? In nature, how do embryonic stem cells differ from adult stem cells?

● Embryonic cells give rise to all the different kinds of cells in the body. Adult stem cells generate only a few related types of cells.

▷ The Genetic Basis of Cancer

11.15 Cancer results from mutations in genes that control cell division

Cancer is a set of diseases in which the control mechanisms that normally limit cellular growth have malfunctioned (see Module 8.9). Scientists have learned that such malfunction is often due to changes in gene expression.

The abnormal behavior of cancer cells was observed years before anything was known about the cell cycle, its control, or the role genes play in making cells cancerous. One of the earliest clues to the cancer puzzle was the discovery, in 1911, of a virus that causes cancer in chickens. Recall that viruses are simply molecules of DNA or RNA surrounded by protein and in some cases a membranous envelope. Viruses that cause cancer can become permanent residents in host cells by inserting their nucleic acid into the DNA of host chromosomes (see Module 10.17).

The genes that a cancer-causing virus inserts into a host cell can make the cell cancerous. Such a gene, which can cause cancer when present in a single copy in the cell, is called an **oncogene** (from the Greek *onco*, tumor). Over the last century, researchers have identified a number of viruses that harbor cancer-causing genes. One example is the human papillomavirus (HPV), which can be transmitted through sexual contact and is associated with several types of cancer, most frequently cervical cancer.

Proto-oncogenes   In 1976, American molecular biologists J. Michael Bishop, Harold Varmus, and their colleagues made a startling discovery. They found that the cancer-causing chicken virus discovered in 1911 contains an oncogene that is an altered version of a normal chicken gene. Subsequent research has shown that the genomes of many animals, including humans, contain genes that can be converted to oncogenes. A normal gene that has the potential to become an oncogene is called a **proto-oncogene**. (These terms can be confusing, so

they bear repeating: a *proto-oncogene* is a normal, healthy gene that, if changed, can become a cancer-causing *oncogene*.) A cell can acquire an oncogene from a virus or from the mutation of one of its own proto-oncogenes.

Searching for their normal role, researchers found that many proto-oncogenes code for proteins that affect the cell cycle. When these proteins are functioning normally, in the right amounts at the right times, they help properly control cell division and cellular differentiation. But changes in these proteins can result in out-of-control growth.

How might a proto-oncogene—a gene that has an essential function in normal cells—become a cancer-causing oncogene? In general, an oncogene arises from a genetic change that leads to an increase either in the amount of the proto-oncogene's protein product or in the activity of each protein molecule. **Figure 11.15A** illustrates three kinds of changes in DNA that can produce oncogenes. Let's assume that the starting proto-oncogene codes for a growth factor, a protein that stimulates cell division. On the left in the figure, a mutation (shown in green) in the proto-oncogene creates an oncogene that codes for a hyperactive protein, one whose stimulating effect is stronger than normal. An error in DNA replication or recombination can generate multiple copies of the gene (as shown in the center of the figure), which are all transcribed and translated; the result is an excess of the normal stimulatory protein. On the right in the figure, the proto-oncogene has been moved from its normal location in the cell's DNA to another location. At its new site, the gene is under the control of a different promoter, one that causes it to be transcribed more often than normal; the normal protein is again made in excess. So in all three cases, normal gene expression is changed, and the cell is stimulated to divide excessively.

▶ **Figure 11.15A** Alternative ways to make oncogenes from a proto-oncogene (all leading to excessive cell growth)

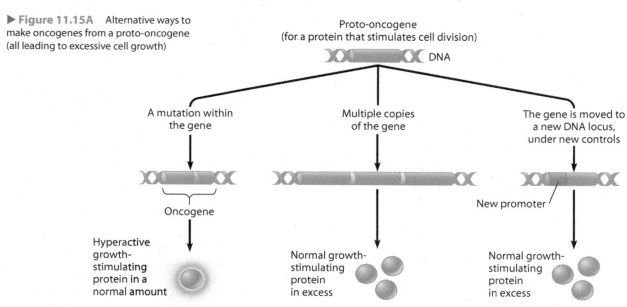

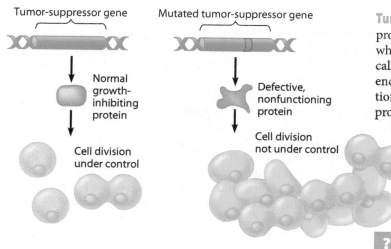

Tumor-suppressor gene

Mutated tumor-suppressor gene

Normal growth-inhibiting protein

Cell division under control

Defective, nonfunctioning protein

Cell division not under control

▲ Figure 11.15B   The effect of a mutation in a tumor-suppressor gene

Tumor-Suppressor Genes   In addition to genes whose products normally *promote* cell division, cells contain genes whose normal products *inhibit* cell division. Such genes are called **tumor-suppressor genes** because the proteins they encode help prevent uncontrolled cell growth. Any mutation that decreases the normal activity of a tumor-suppressor protein may contribute to the onset of cancer (**Figure 11.15B**). Scientists have also discovered a class of tumor-suppressor genes that function in the repair of damaged DNA. When these genes are mutated, other cancer-causing mutations are more likely to accumulate. How do such DNA mutations lead to the progression of disease? We consider that question next.

?   **How do proto-oncogenes relate to oncogenes?**

● A proto-oncogene is a normal gene that, if mutated, can become a cancer-causing oncogene.

11.16 Multiple genetic changes underlie the development of cancer

More than 100,000 Americans will be stricken by cancer of the colon (the main part of the large intestine) this year. One of the best-understood types of human cancer, colon cancer illustrates an important principle about how cancer develops: More than one somatic mutation is needed to produce a full-fledged cancer cell. As in many cancers, the development of malignant (spreading) colon cancer is a gradual process. (See Module 8.9 to review cancer terms.)

Figure 11.16A illustrates the gradual progression from somatic mutation to cancer using colon cancer as an example. ❶ Colon cancer begins when an oncogene arises or is activated through mutation, causing unusually frequent division of apparently normal cells in the colon lining. ❷ Later, additional DNA mutations, such as the inactivation of a tumor-suppressor gene, cause the growth of a small benign tumor (a polyp) in the colon wall. ❸ Still more mutations eventually lead to formation of a malignant tumor, a tumor that has the potential to metastasize (spread). The requirement for several mutations—the actual number is usually around six—explains why cancers can take a long time to develop.

Thus, the development of a malignant tumor is paralleled by a gradual accumulation of mutations that convert proto-oncogenes to oncogenes and knock out tumor-suppressor genes.

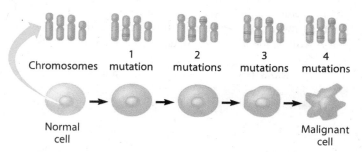

Chromosomes   1 mutation   2 mutations   3 mutations   4 mutations

Normal cell

Malignant cell

▲ Figure 11.16B   Accumulation of mutations in a cancer cell

Multiple changes must occur at the DNA level for a cell to become fully cancerous. In **Figure 11.16B**, colors distinguish the normal cell (tan) from cells with one or more mutations leading to increased cell division and cancer (red). Once a cancer-promoting mutation occurs (the red band on the chromosome), it is passed to all the descendants of the cell carrying it.

The fact that more than one somatic mutation is generally needed to produce a full-fledged cancer cell may help explain why the incidence of cancer increases with age. If cancer results from an accumulation of mutations that occur throughout life, then the longer we live, the more likely we are to develop cancer. Researchers are steadily cataloguing mutations that cause cancer and placing them in public databases. The hope is that such data will lead to improved treatment strategies and perhaps, someday, a cure.

?   **Epithelial cells, those that line body cavities, are frequently replaced and so divide more often than most other types of body cells. Will epithelial cells become cancerous more or less frequently than other types of body cells?**

● More frequent cell divisions will result in more frequent mutation and thus a greater chance of cancer.

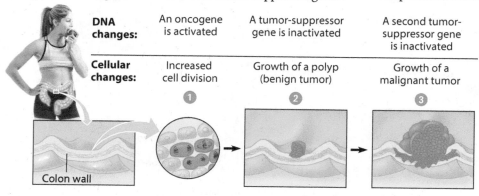

DNA changes:	An oncogene is activated	A tumor-suppressor gene is inactivated	A second tumor-suppressor gene is inactivated
Cellular changes:	Increased cell division	Growth of a polyp (benign tumor)	Growth of a malignant tumor
	❶	❷	❸

Colon wall

▲ Figure 11.16A   Stepwise development of a typical colon cancer

11.17 Faulty proteins can interfere with normal signal transduction pathways

The figures below (excluding, for the moment, the white boxes) illustrate two types of signal transduction pathways leading to the synthesis of proteins that influence the cell cycle. In **Figure 11.17A**, the pathway leads to the stimulation of cell division. The initial signal is a growth factor (●), and the target cell's ultimate response is the production of a protein that stimulates the cell to divide. By contrast, **Figure 11.17B** shows an inhibitory pathway, in which a growth-*inhibiting* factor (▽) causes the target cell to make a protein that inhibits cell division. In both cases, the newly made proteins function by interacting with components of the cell cycle control system.

Now, let's see what can happen when the target cell undergoes a cancer-causing mutation. The white box in Figure 11.17A shows the protein product of an oncogene resulting from mutation of a proto-oncogene called *ras*. The normal product of *ras* is a relay protein. Ordinarily, a stimulatory pathway like this will not operate unless the growth factor is available. However, an oncogene protein that is a hyperactive version of a protein in the pathway may trigger the pathway even in the absence of a growth factor. In this example, the oncogene protein is a hyperactive version of the *ras* relay protein that issues signals on its own.

The white box in Figure 11.17B indicates how a mutant tumor-suppressor protein can affect cell division. In this case, the mutation affects a gene called *p53*, which codes for an essential transcription factor. This mutation leads to the production of a faulty transcription factor, one that the signal transduction pathway cannot activate. As a result, the gene for the inhibitory protein at the bottom of the figure remains turned off, and excessive cell division may occur.

Mutations of the *ras* and *p53* genes have been implicated in many kinds of cancer. In fact, mutations in *ras* occur in about 30% of human cancers, and mutations in *p53* occur in more than 50%. As we see next, carcinogens are responsible for many mutations that lead to cancer.

? **Contrast the action of an oncogene with that of a cancer-causing mutation in a tumor-suppressor gene.**

● An oncogene encodes an abnormal protein that stimulates cell division via a signal transduction pathway; a mutant tumor-suppressor gene encodes a defective protein unable to function in a pathway that normally inhibits cell division.

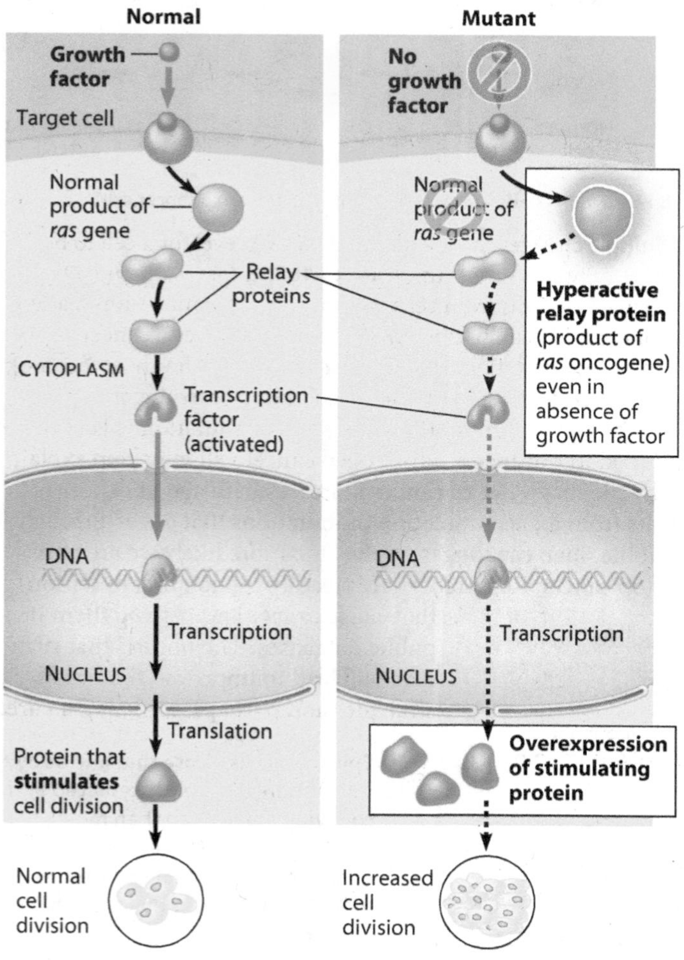

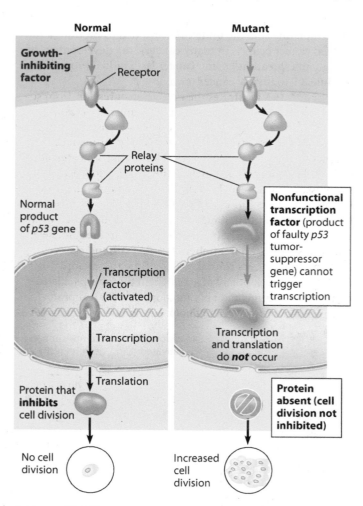

▲ **Figure 11.17A** A stimulatory signal transduction pathway and the effect of an oncogene protein

▲ **Figure 11.17B** An inhibitory signal transduction pathway and the effect of a faulty tumor-suppressor protein

11.18 Lifestyle choices can reduce the risk of cancer

CONNECTION

Cancer is the second-leading cause of death (after heart disease) in most industrialized nations. Death rates due to certain forms of cancer—including stomach, cervical, and uterine cancers—have decreased in recent years, but the overall cancer death rate is on the rise, currently increasing at about 1% per decade. Table 11.18 lists the most common cancers in the United States and associated risk factors for each.

The fact that multiple genetic changes are required to produce a cancer cell helps explain the observation that cancers can run in families. An individual inheriting an oncogene or a mutant allele of a tumor-suppressor gene is one step closer to accumulating the necessary mutations for cancer to develop than an individual without any such mutations.

But the majority of cancers are not associated with a mutation that is passed from parent to offspring; they arise from new mutations caused by environmental factors. Agents that alter DNA and make cells cancerous are called **carcinogens**. Most mutagens, substances that cause mutations, are carcinogens. Two of the most potent mutagens are X-rays and ultraviolet radiation in sunlight. X-rays are a significant cause of leukemia and brain cancer. Exposure to UV radiation from the sun is known to cause skin cancer, including a deadly type called melanoma.

The one substance known to cause more cases and types of cancer than any other single agent is tobacco. More people die of lung cancer (nearly 160,000 Americans in 2013) than any other form of cancer. Most tobacco-related cancers come from smoking, but the passive inhalation of secondhand smoke is also a risk. As Table 11.18 indicates, tobacco use, sometimes in combination with alcohol consumption, causes a number of other types of cancer in addition to lung cancer. In nearly all cases, cigarettes are the main culprit, but smokeless tobacco products, such as snuff and chewing tobacco, are linked to cancer of the mouth and throat.

How do carcinogens cause cancer? In many cases, the genetic changes that cause cancer result from decades of exposure to the mutagenic effects of carcinogens. Carcinogens can also produce their effect by promoting cell division. Generally, the higher the rate of cell division, the greater the chance for mutations resulting from errors in DNA replication or recombination. Some carcinogens seem to have both effects. For instance, the hormones linked to breast and uterine cancers promote cell division and may also cause mutations that lead to cancer. In other cases, several different agents, such as viruses and one or more carcinogens, may together produce cancer.

Avoiding carcinogens is not the whole story, because there is growing evidence that some food choices significantly reduce the risk of some cancers. For instance, eating 20–30 grams (g) of plant fiber daily—roughly equal to the amount of fiber in four slices of whole-grain bread, 1 cup of bran flakes, one apple, and ⅓ cup of carrots combined—and at the same time reducing animal fat intake may help prevent colon cancer. There is also evidence that other substances in fruits and vegetables, including vitamins C and E and certain

TABLE 11.18	CANCER IN THE UNITED STATES	
Cancer	**Risk Factors**	**New Cases 2013 (est.)**
Prostate	African heritage; possibly dietary fat	239,000
Breast	Estrogen	235,000
Lung	Tobacco smoke	228,000
Colon, rectum	High dietary fat; tobacco smoke; alcohol	143,000
Lymphomas	Viruses (for some types)	79,000
Melanoma of the skin	Ultraviolet light	77,000
Urinary bladder	Tobacco smoke	73,000
Kidney	Tobacco smoke	65,000
Uterus	Estrogen	62,000
Leukemias	X-rays; benzene; virus (for one type)	49,000
Pancreas	Tobacco smoke; obesity	45,000
Oral cavity	Tobacco in various forms; alcohol	41,000
Liver	Alcohol; hepatitis viruses	31,000
Brain and nerve	Trauma; X-rays	23,000
Ovary	Obesity; many ovulation cycles	22,000
Stomach	Table salt; tobacco smoke	22,000
Cervix	Sexually transmitted viruses; tobacco smoke	12,000
Total, including all other types		1,660,000

compounds related to vitamin A, may offer protection against a variety of cancers. Cabbage and its relatives, such as broccoli and cauliflower (see Figure 13.2), are thought to be especially rich in substances that help prevent cancer, although the identities of these substances are not yet established.

The battle against cancer is being waged on many fronts, and there is reason for optimism. It is especially encouraging that we can help reduce our risk of acquiring—and increase our chance of surviving—some of the most common forms of cancer by the choices we make in our daily life. Not smoking, exercising adequately, avoiding overexposure to the sun, and eating a high-fiber, low-fat diet can all help prevent cancer. Furthermore, seven types of cancer can be easily detected: cancers of the skin and oral cavity (via physical exam), breast (via self-exams and mammograms for higher-risk women), prostate (via rectal exam), cervix (via Pap smear), testes (via self-exam), and colon (via colonoscopy). Regular visits to the doctor can help identify tumors early, thereby significantly increasing the possibility of successful treatment.

? **Which of the most common cancers listed in Table 11.18 affect primarily males? Which affect primarily females?**

Males: prostate; females: breast, uterus, cervix

CHAPTER **11** REVIEW

For practice quizzes, BioFlix animations, MP3 tutorials, video tutors, and more study tools designed for this textbook, go to

MasteringBiology®

Reviewing the Concepts

Control of Gene Expression (11.1–11.11)

11.1 Proteins interacting with DNA turn prokaryotic genes on or off in response to environmental changes. In prokaryotes, genes for related enzymes are often controlled together in units called operons. Regulatory proteins bind to control sequences in the DNA and turn operons on or off in response to environmental changes.

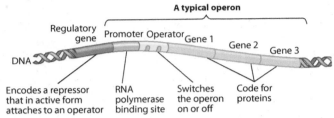

A typical operon

11.2 Chromosome structure and chemical modifications can affect gene expression. In multicellular eukaryotes, different types of cells make different proteins because different combinations of genes are active in each type. A chromosome contains DNA wound around clusters of histone proteins, forming a string of bead-like nucleosomes. DNA packing tends to block gene expression by preventing access of transcription proteins to the DNA. One example of DNA packing is X chromosome inactivation in the cells of female mammals. Chemical modification of DNA bases or histone proteins can result in epigenetic inheritance.

11.3 Complex assemblies of proteins control eukaryotic transcription. A variety of regulatory proteins interact with DNA and with each other to turn the transcription of eukaryotic genes on or off.

11.4 Eukaryotic RNA may be spliced in more than one way. After transcription, alternative RNA splicing may generate two or more types of mRNA from the same transcript.

11.5 Small RNAs play multiple roles in controlling gene expression. MicroRNAs, bound to proteins, can prevent gene expression by forming complexes with mRNA molecules.

11.6 Later stages of gene expression are also subject to regulation. The lifetime of an mRNA molecule helps determine how much protein is made, as do factors involved in translation. A protein may need to be activated in some way, and eventually the cell will break it down.

11.7 Multiple mechanisms regulate gene expression in eukaryotes. Gene expression can be regulated multiple ways within both the nucleus and cytoplasm.

11.8 Cell signaling and waves of gene expression direct animal development. A series of RNAs and proteins produced in the embryo control the development of an animal from a fertilized egg.

11.9 Scientists use DNA microarrays to test for the transcription of many genes at once. Scientists can use a DNA microarray to gather data about which genes are turned on or off in a particular cell. A glass slide containing DNA fragments from thousands of genes can be used to test which of those genes are being expressed in a particular cell type.

11.10 Signal transduction pathways convert messages received at the cell surface to responses within the cell.

11.11 Cell-signaling systems appeared early in the evolution of life. Similarities among organisms suggest that signal transduction pathways evolved early in the history of life on Earth.

Cloning of Plants and Animals (11.12–11.14)

11.12 Plant cloning shows that differentiated cells may retain all of their genetic potential. A clone is an individual created by asexual reproduction and thus genetically identical to a single parent.

11.13 Biologists can clone animals via nuclear transplantation. Inserting DNA from a donor cell into a nucleus-free host egg can result in an early embryo that is a clone of the DNA donor. Implanting a blastocyst into a surrogate mother can lead to the birth of a cloned mammal.

11.14 Therapeutic cloning can produce stem cells with great medical potential. The goal of therapeutic cloning is to produce embryonic stem cells. Such cells may eventually be used for a variety of therapeutic purposes. Like embryonic stem cells, adult stem cells can both perpetuate themselves in culture and give rise to differentiated cells. Unlike embryonic stem cells, adult stem cells normally give rise to only a limited range of cell types.

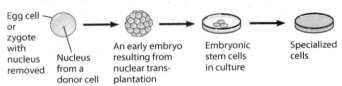

The Genetic Basis of Cancer (11.15–11.18)

11.15 Cancer results from mutations in genes that control cell division. Cancer cells, which divide uncontrollably, result from mutations in genes whose protein products affect the cell cycle. A mutation can change a proto-oncogene, a normal gene that helps control cell division, into an oncogene, which causes cells to divide excessively. Mutations that inactivate tumor-suppressor genes have similar effects.

11.16 Multiple genetic changes underlie the development of cancer. Cancers result from a series of genetic changes.

11.17 Faulty proteins can interfere with normal signal transduction pathways. Many proto-oncogenes and tumor-suppressor genes code for proteins active in signal transduction pathways regulating cell division.

11.18 Lifestyle choices can reduce the risk of cancer. Reducing exposure to carcinogens, which induce cancer-causing mutations, and making other lifestyle choices can help reduce cancer risk.

Connecting the Concepts

1. Complete the following concept map to test your knowledge of gene regulation.

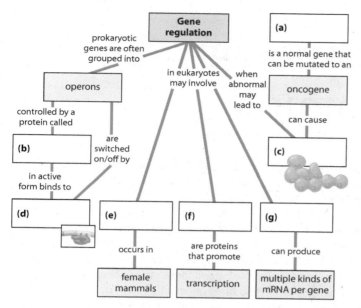

Testing Your Knowledge

Level 1: Knowledge/Comprehension

2. Which of the following methods of gene regulation do eukaryotes and prokaryotes have in common?
   a. elaborate packing of DNA in chromosomes
   b. activator and repressor proteins, which attach to DNA
   c. the addition of a cap and tail to mRNA after transcription
   d. *lac* and *trp* operons

3. A homeotic gene does which of the following?
   a. It serves as the ultimate control for prokaryotic operons.
   b. It regulates the expression of groups of other genes during development.
   c. It represses the histone proteins in eukaryotic chromosomes.
   d. It helps splice mRNA after transcription.

4. Which of the following is a valid difference between embryonic stem cells and the stem cells found in adult tissues?
   a. In laboratory culture, only adult stem cells are immortal.
   b. In nature, only embryonic stem cells give rise to all the different types of cells in the organism.
   c. Only adult stem cells can differentiate in culture.
   d. Embryonic stem cells are generally more difficult to grow in culture than adult stem cells.

Level 2: Application/Analysis

5. The control of gene expression is more complex in multicellular eukaryotes than in prokaryotes because _____. (*Explain your answer.*)
   a. eukaryotic cells are much smaller
   b. in a multicellular eukaryote, different cells are specialized for different functions
   c. prokaryotes are restricted to stable environments
   d. eukaryotes have fewer genes, so each gene must do several jobs

6. Your bone cells, muscle cells, and skin cells look different because
   a. each cell contains different kinds of genes.
   b. they are present in different organs.
   c. different genes are active in each kind of cell.
   d. they contain different numbers of genes.

7. All your cells contain proto-oncogenes, which can change into cancer-causing oncogenes. Why do cells possess such potential time bombs?
   a. Viruses infect cells with proto-oncogenes.
   b. Proto-oncogenes are genetic "junk" with no known function.
   c. Proto-oncogenes are unavoidable environmental carcinogens.
   d. Proto-oncogenes normally control cell division.

8. You obtain an egg cell from the ovary of a white mouse and remove the nucleus from it. You then obtain a nucleus from a liver cell from an adult black mouse. You use the methods of nuclear transplantation to insert the nucleus into the empty egg. After some prompting, the new zygote divides into an early embryo, which you then implant into the uterus of a brown mouse. A few weeks later, a litter of mice is born. What color will they be? Why?

9. Mutations can alter the function of the *lac* operon (see Module 11.1). Predict how the following mutations would affect the function of the operon in the presence and absence of lactose:
   a. Mutation of regulatory gene; repressor cannot bind to lactose.
   b. Mutation of operator; repressor will not bind to operator.
   c. Mutation of regulatory gene; repressor will not bind to operator.
   d. Mutation of promoter; RNA polymerase will not attach to promoter.

Level 3: Synthesis/Evaluation

10. A mutation in a single gene may cause a major change in the body of a fruit fly, such as an extra pair of legs or wings. Yet it probably takes the combined action of hundreds or thousands of genes to produce a wing or leg. How can a change in just one gene cause such a big change in the body?

11. A chemical called dioxin is produced as a by-product of some chemical manufacturing processes. This substance was present in Agent Orange, a defoliant sprayed on vegetation during the Vietnam War. There has been a continuing controversy over its effects on soldiers exposed to it during the war. Animal tests have suggested that dioxin can be lethal and can cause birth defects, cancer, organ damage, and immune system suppression. But its effects on humans are unclear, and even animal tests are inconclusive. Researchers have discovered that dioxin enters a cell and binds to a protein that in turn attaches to the cell's DNA. How might this mechanism help explain the variety of dioxin's effects? How might you determine whether a particular individual became ill as a result of exposure to dioxin?

12. **SCIENTIFIC THINKING** Each scientist works as part of a broader community of scientists, building on the work of others. Scientific advances often depend on the application of new technologies and/or on new techniques applied to an existing problem. What improvements to existing cloning methods did Wilmut make that allowed him to successfully clone Dolly the sheep from an adult cell?

Answers to all questions can be found in Appendix 4.

12 DNA Technology and Genomics

Papaya fruit, shown in the photograph below, are sweet and loaded with vitamin C. They are borne on a rapidly growing treelike plant (*Carica papaya*) that grows only in tropical climates. In Hawaii, papaya is both a dietary staple and a valuable export crop.

Although thriving today, Hawaii's papaya industry seemed doomed just a few decades ago. A deadly pathogen called the papaya ringspot virus (PRV) had spread throughout the islands and appeared poised to completely eradicate the papaya plant population. But scientists from the University of Hawaii were able to rescue the industry by creating new, genetically engineered PRV-resistant strains of papaya. Today, the papaya industry is once again vibrant—and the vast majority of Hawaii's papayas are genetically modified organisms (GMOs).

However, not everyone is happy about the circumstances surrounding the recovery of the Hawaiian papaya industry. Although genetically modified papayas are approved for consumption in the United States (as are many other GMO fruits and vegetables), some critics have raised safety concerns—for the people who eat them and for the environment. On three occasions over a three-year

? *Are genetically modified organisms safe?*

span, thousands of papaya trees on the big island of Hawaii were hacked down under the cover of darkness, presumably as a protest against GMO crops. Although few would condone such criminal behavior, should we in fact be concerned about the safety of GMO crops? This question continues to foster considerable debate and disagreement.

In addition to GMOs in our diet, DNA technologies affect our lives in many other ways: Gene cloning is used to produce medical and industrial products, DNA profiling has changed the field of forensic science, new technologies produce valuable data for biological research, and DNA can even be used to investigate historical questions. In this chapter, we'll discuss each of these applications. We'll also consider the specific techniques used, how they are applied, and some of the social, legal, and ethical issues that are raised by the new technologies.

▷ Gene Cloning

12.1 Genes can be cloned in recombinant plasmids

Although it may seem like a modern field, **biotechnology**, the manipulation of organisms or their components to make useful products, actually dates back to the dawn of civilization. Consider such ancient practices as the use of yeast to make beer, wine, and bread and the selective breeding of livestock, dogs, and other animals. But when people use the term *biotechnology* today, they are usually referring to **DNA technology**, modern laboratory techniques for studying and manipulating genetic material. Using these methods, scientists can, for instance, modify specific genes and move them between organisms as different as *Escherichia coli* bacteria, papaya, and fish.

In the 1970s, the field of biotechnology exploded with the invention of methods for making recombinant DNA in a test tube. **Recombinant DNA** is formed when scientists combine pieces of DNA from two different sources—often different species—*in vitro* (in a test tube) to form a single DNA molecule. Today, recombinant DNA technology is widely used for **genetic engineering**, the direct manipulation of genes for practical purposes. Scientists have genetically engineered bacteria to mass-produce a variety of useful chemicals, from cancer drugs to pesticides. Scientists have also transferred genes from bacteria into plants and from one animal species into another **(Figure 12.1A)**.

To manipulate genes in the laboratory, biologists often use bacterial **plasmids**, small, circular DNA molecules that replicate (duplicate) separately from the much larger bacterial chromosome (see Module 10.23). Plasmids typically carry only a few genes and are passed from one generation of bacteria to the next. Because plasmids are easily manipulated to carry virtually any genes, they are key tools for **gene cloning**, the production of many identical copies of a gene-carrying piece of DNA. Gene-cloning methods are central to the production of useful products via genetic engineering.

Consider a typical genetic engineering challenge: A molecular biologist at a pharmaceutical company has identified a gene that codes for a valuable product, a hypothetical substance called protein V. The biologist wants to manufacture the protein on a large scale. The biggest challenge in such an effort is of the "needle in a haystack" variety: The gene of interest is one relatively tiny segment embedded in a much longer DNA molecule. Figure 12.1B illustrates how the techniques of gene cloning can be used to find the desired gene and copy it.

To begin, the biologist isolates two kinds of DNA: ❶ a bacterial plasmid (usually from the bacterium *E. coli*) that

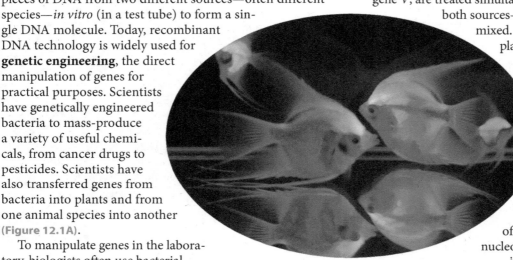

▲ **Figure 12.1A** Glowing angelfish produced by transferring a gene originally obtained from a jelly (cnidarian)

will serve as the **vector**, or gene carrier, and ❷ the DNA from another organism that includes the gene that codes for protein V (gene *V*) along with other, unwanted genes. The DNA containing gene *V* could come from a variety of sources, such as a different bacterium, a plant, a nonhuman animal, or even human tissue cells growing in laboratory culture.

❸ The researcher treats both the plasmid and the gene *V* source DNA with an enzyme that cuts DNA. An enzyme is chosen that cleaves the plasmid in only one place. ❹ The source DNA, which is usually much longer in sequence than the plasmid, may be cut into many fragments, one of which carries gene *V*. The figure shows the processing of just one DNA fragment and one plasmid, but actually, millions of plasmids and DNA fragments, most of which do not contain gene *V*, are treated simultaneously. ❺ The cut DNA from both sources—the plasmid and target gene—are mixed. The single-stranded ends of the plasmid base-pair with the complementary ends of the target DNA fragment (see Module 10.4 if you need a refresher on the DNA base-pairing rules). ❻ The enzyme **DNA ligase** joins the two DNA molecules by way of covalent bonds. This enzyme, which the cell normally uses in DNA replication (see Module 10.5), is a "DNA pasting" enzyme that catalyzes the formation of covalent bonds between adjacent nucleotides, joining the strands. The result is a recombinant DNA plasmid containing gene *V*, as well as many other recombinant DNA plasmids carrying other genes not shown here.

❼ The recombinant plasmid containing the targeted gene is mixed with bacteria. Under the right conditions, a bacterium takes up the plasmid DNA by transformation (see Module 10.22). ❽ The recombinant bacterium then reproduces to form a **clone** of cells, each carrying a copy of gene *V*. (In this context, the term *clone* refers to a group of identical cells descended from a single ancestral cell.) This step is the actual gene cloning. In our example, the biologist will eventually grow a cell clone large enough to produce protein *V* in marketable quantities.

❾ Gene cloning can be used to produce a variety of desirable products. Copies of the gene itself can be the immediate product, to be used in additional genetic engineering projects. For example, a pest-resistance gene present in one plant species might be cloned and transferred into plants of another species. Other times, the protein product of the cloned gene is harvested and used. For example, an enzyme that creates a faded look in blue jeans can be harvested in large quantities from bacteria carrying the cloned gene (in

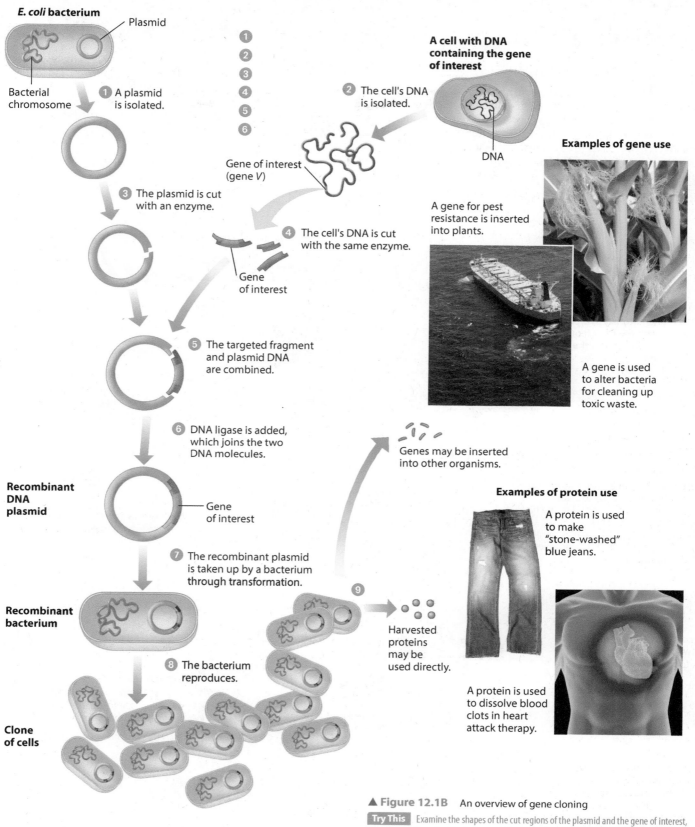

E. coli bacterium
Plasmid

Bacterial chromosome

1 A plasmid is isolated.

3 The plasmid is cut with an enzyme.

5 The targeted fragment and plasmid DNA are combined.

6 DNA ligase is added, which joins the two DNA molecules.

Recombinant DNA plasmid
Gene of interest

7 The recombinant plasmid is taken up by a bacterium through transformation.

Recombinant bacterium

8 The bacterium reproduces.

Clone of cells

1
2
3
4
5
6

A cell with DNA containing the gene of interest

2 The cell's DNA is isolated.

DNA

Gene of interest (gene V)

4 The cell's DNA is cut with the same enzyme.

Gene of interest

Genes may be inserted into other organisms.

9 Harvested proteins may be used directly.

Examples of gene use

A gene for pest resistance is inserted into plants.

A gene is used to alter bacteria for cleaning up toxic waste.

Examples of protein use

A protein is used to make "stone-washed" blue jeans.

A protein is used to dissolve blood clots in heart attack therapy.

▲ **Figure 12.1B** An overview of gene cloning

Try This Examine the shapes of the cut regions of the plasmid and the gene of interest, paying particular attention to the complementary shapes of the pieces that allow them to bond together.

other words, no stones are harmed in the making of stone-washed jeans!).

In the next four modules, we discuss the methods outlined in Figure 12.1B. You may find it useful to turn back to this summary figure as each technique is discussed.

? **In the example shown in Figure 12.1, what is the vector?**

● A plasmid isolated from an *E. coli* bacterium

12.2 Enzymes are used to "cut and paste" DNA

To understand how DNA is manipulated in the laboratory, you need to learn how enzymes cut and paste DNA. The cutting tools are bacterial enzymes called **restriction enzymes**. Biologists have identified hundreds of different restriction enzymes, each of which recognizes a particular short DNA sequence, which is called a **restriction site**. After a restriction enzyme binds to its restriction site, it cuts both strands of the DNA at precise points within the sequence—like a pair of highly specific molecular scissors—yielding pieces of DNA called

restriction fragments. All copies of a particular DNA molecule always yield the same set of DNA fragments when exposed to the same restriction enzyme. Once cut, fragments of DNA can be pasted together by the enzyme **DNA ligase**. The techniques outlined here form the basis of many genetic engineering procedures that involve combining DNA from different sources.

A restriction site is usually 4–8 nucleotide pairs long.

DNA   Restriction site
GAATTC
CTTAAG

Restriction enzyme

The restriction enzyme shown here, called EcoRI, is found naturally in *E. coli* bacteria. EcoRI recognizes the DNA sequence GAATTC and always cuts it the same way—between the bases A and G—producing restriction fragments.

G   AATTC
CTTAA   G

In bacteria, restriction enzymes play a defensive role, chopping up foreign DNA; the cell's own DNA is protected by the addition of methyl groups.

A piece of DNA from another source (the gene of interest) is cut by the same restriction enzyme and added to the first DNA. Both molecules of DNA are cut unevenly, yielding "sticky ends," single-stranded extensions from the double-stranded fragments.

Sticky end   Gene of interest
AATTC   G
G   CTTAA
Sticky end

The sticky ends from the two different DNA molecules are complementary to one another because they were cut by the same enzyme.

The complementary ends on the two different fragments stick together by base pairing.

GAATTC   GAATTC
CTTAAG   CTTAAG

Sticky ends are the key to joining restriction fragments from different sources: Hydrogen bonds (not shown) form base pairs that hold the two strands together.

DNA ligase

The temporary union between the DNA fragments is made permanent by DNA ligase, which creates new covalent bonds that join the sugar-phosphate backbones of the DNA strands.

Recombinant DNA

?   What are "sticky ends"?

Answer: Single-stranded regions whose unpaired bases can hydrogen-bond to the complementary sticky ends of other fragments created by the same restriction enzyme.

12.3 Cloned genes can be stored in genomic libraries

Each bacterial clone created using the procedure described in Figure 12.1B consists of identical cells with plasmids carrying one particular fragment of target DNA. A collection of cloned DNA fragments that includes an organism's entire genome is

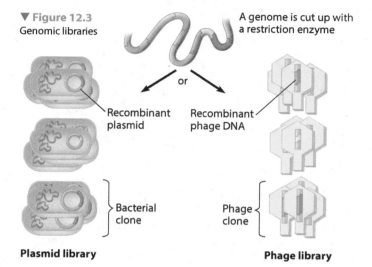

▼ **Figure 12.3** Genomic libraries

A genome is cut up with a restriction enzyme

or

Recombinant plasmid

Recombinant phage DNA

Bacterial clone

Phage clone

Plasmid library

Phage library

called a **genomic library**. On the left side of Figure 12.3, the red, yellow, and green DNA segments represent three of the thousands of different library "books" that are "shelved" in plasmids inside bacterial cells. A typical cloned DNA fragment is big enough to carry one or a few genes, and together, the fragments include the entire genome of the organism from which the DNA was derived.

Bacteriophages (also called phages)—viruses that infect bacteria—can also serve as vectors when cloning genes (Figure 12.3, right). When a phage is used as a vector, the DNA fragments are inserted into phage DNA molecules. The recombinant phage DNA can then be introduced into a bacterial cell through the normal infection process. Inside the cell, phage DNA is replicated, producing new phage particles carrying the foreign DNA. In the next module, we look at another source of DNA for cloning: eukaryotic mRNA.

? In what sense does a genomic library have multiple copies of each "book"?

● Each "book"—a piece of DNA from the genome that was the source of the library—is present in every recombinant bacterium or phage in a clone.

12.4 Reverse transcriptase can help make genes for cloning

Rather than starting with an entire eukaryotic genome, a researcher can focus on the genes expressed in a particular kind of cell by using its mRNA as the starting material for cloning (Figure 12.4). ❶ The chosen cells transcribe their genes within the nucleus and ❷ process the transcripts, removing introns and splicing exons together, producing mRNA. ❸ The researcher isolates the mRNA in a test tube. ❹ Single-stranded DNA transcripts are made from the mRNA using **reverse transcriptase**, a viral enzyme that can synthesize DNA from

an RNA template (gold in the figure; see Module 10.20). ❺ Another enzyme is added to break down the mRNA, and ❻ DNA polymerase (the enzyme that replicates DNA; see Module 10.5) is used to synthesize a second DNA strand.

The DNA that results from such a procedure, called **complementary DNA (cDNA)**, represents only the subset of genes that had been transcribed into mRNA in the starting cells. Among other purposes, such a cDNA library is useful for studying the genes responsible for the specialized functions of a particular cell type, such as brain or liver cells.

? Why is a cDNA gene made using reverse transcriptase often shorter than the natural form of the gene?

● Because cDNAs are made from spliced mRNAs, which lack introns

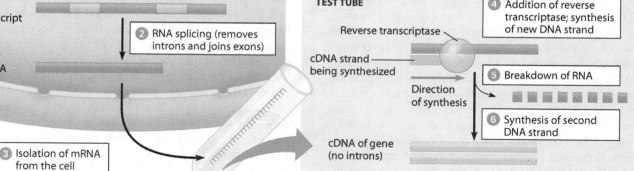

▲ **Figure 12.4** Making complimentary DNA (cDNA) from eukaryotic mRNA

CELL NUCLEUS

DNA of a eukaryotic gene — Exon | Intron | Exon | Intron | Exon

❶ Transcription

RNA transcript

❷ RNA splicing (removes introns and joins exons)

mRNA

❸ Isolation of mRNA from the cell

TEST TUBE

Reverse transcriptase

cDNA strand being synthesized

Direction of synthesis

cDNA of gene (no introns)

❹ Addition of reverse transcriptase; synthesis of new DNA strand

❺ Breakdown of RNA

❻ Synthesis of second DNA strand

12.5 Nucleic acid probes identify clones carrying specific genes

Often, the most difficult task in gene cloning is finding the right "books" in a genomic library—that is, identifying only the clones that contain a desired gene from among all those created. For example, a researcher might want to pull out just the clone of bacteria carrying what is depicted as the red gene in Figure 12.3. If bacterial clones containing a specific gene actually translate the gene into protein, they can be identified by testing for the protein product. However, not every desired gene produces detectable proteins. In such cases, researchers can also test directly for the gene itself.

Methods for detecting a gene directly depend on base pairing between the gene and a complementary sequence on another nucleic acid molecule, either DNA or RNA. When at least part of the nucleotide sequence of a gene is known, this information can be used to a researcher's advantage. For example, if we know that a gene contains the sequence TAGGCT, a biochemist can synthesize a short single strand of DNA with the complementary sequence (ATCCGA) and label it with a radioactive isotope or fluorescent tag. This labeled, complementary molecule is called a **nucleic acid probe** because it is used to find a specific gene or other nucleotide sequence within a mass of DNA. (In actual practice, probe molecules are considerably longer than six nucleotides.)

Figure 12.5 shows how a probe works. The DNA sample to be tested is treated with heat or chemicals to separate the DNA strands. When the radioactive DNA probe is added to these strands, it tags the correct molecules—that is, it finds the correct books in the genomic library—by hydrogen-bonding to the complementary sequence in the gene of interest. Such a probe can be simultaneously applied to many bacterial clones to screen all of them at once for a desired gene.

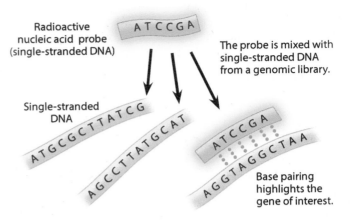

The probe is mixed with single-stranded DNA from a genomic library.

Base pairing highlights the gene of interest.

▲ **Figure 12.5** How a DNA probe tags a gene by base pairing

In one technique, a piece of filter paper is pressed against bacterial colonies (clones) growing on a petri dish. The filter paper picks up cells from each colony. A chemical treatment is used to break open the cells and separate the DNA strands. The DNA strands are then soaked in probe solution. Any bacterial colonies carrying the gene of interest will be tagged on the filter paper, marking them for easy identification. Once the researcher identifies a colony carrying the desired gene, the cells can be grown further, and the gene of interest, or its protein product, can be collected in large amounts.

> **?** How does a probe consisting of radioactive DNA or RNA enable a researcher to find the bacterial clones carrying a particular gene?
>
> The probe molecules bind to and label DNA only from the cells containing the gene of interest, which has a complementary DNA sequence.

▷ Genetically Modified Organisms

12.6 Recombinant cells and organisms can mass-produce gene products

Recombinant cells and organisms constructed by DNA technology are used to manufacture many useful products, chiefly proteins (Table 12.6, on the facing page). By transferring the gene for a desired protein into a bacterium, yeast, or other kind of cell that is easy to grow in culture, a genetic engineer can produce large quantities of proteins that are otherwise difficult to obtain. Bacteria—most commonly *E. coli*—are often the best organisms for manufacturing a protein product. Major advantages of bacteria include the plasmids and phages available for use as gene-cloning vectors and the fact that bacteria can be grown rapidly and cheaply in large tanks. Furthermore, bacteria can be engineered to produce large amounts of particular proteins and, in some cases, to secrete the proteins directly into their growth medium, simplifying the task of collecting and purifying the products. Bacteria are used for a wide variety of purposes, from producing valuable human drugs to enzymes used in making cheese and processed fruit juice.

Despite the advantages of using bacteria, it is sometimes desirable or necessary to use eukaryotic cells to produce a protein product. Often, the first-choice eukaryotic organism for protein production is the same yeast used in making bread and beer, *Saccharomyces cerevisiae*. As bakers and brewers have recognized for centuries, yeast cells are easy to grow. And like *E. coli*, yeast cells can take up foreign DNA and integrate it into their genomes. Yeast cells are often better than bacteria at synthesizing and secreting eukaryotic proteins, such as the hepatitis B vaccine. *S. cerevisiae* is currently used to produce a number of proteins. In certain cases, the same product—for example, interferons used in cancer research—can be made using either yeast or bacteria. In other cases, such as the hepatitis B vaccine, yeast alone is used.

The cells of choice for making some gene products come from mammals. Many proteins that mammalian cells

TABLE 12.6 — SOME PROTEIN PRODUCTS OF RECOMBINANT DNA TECHNOLOGY

Product	Made by	Use
Human insulin	E. coli	Treatment for diabetes
Human growth hormone (HGH)	E. coli	Treatment for growth defects
Epidermal growth factor (EGF)	E. coli	Treatment for burns, ulcers
Interleukin-2 (IL-2)	E. coli	Possible treatment for cancer
Bovine growth hormone (BGH)	E. coli	Improving weight gain in cattle
Cellulase	E. coli	Breaking down cellulose for animal feeds
Taxol	E. coli	Treatment for ovarian cancer
Interferons (alpha and gamma)	S. cerevisiae, E. coli	Possible treatment for cancer and viral infections
Hepatitis B vaccine	S. cerevisiae	Prevention of viral hepatitis
Erythropoietin (EPO)	Mammalian cells	Treatment for anemia
Factor VIII	Mammalian cells	Treatment for hemophilia
Tissue plasminogen activator (TPA)	Mammalian cells	Treatment for heart attacks and some strokes

▲ Figure 12.6A A goat carrying a gene for a human blood protein that is secreted in the milk

normally secrete are glycoproteins, proteins with chains of sugars attached. Because only mammalian cells can attach the sugars correctly, mammalian cells must be used for making these products. For example, recombinant mammalian cells growing in laboratory cultures are currently used to produce human erythropoietin (EPO), a hormone that stimulates the production of red blood cells. EPO can save lives as a treatment for anemia. However, EPO is also abused by some athletes who seek the advantage of artificially high levels of oxygen-carrying red blood cells (called "blood doping"). EPO is one of several drugs bicyclist Lance Armstrong and his teammates have admitted to abusing during his historic string of victories in the Tour de France bicycle race. After years of denial, Armstrong admitted his abuse of EPO (and other performance-enhancing substances) in 2012, leading to a lifetime ban from sanctioned athletic competition.

Recently, pharmaceutical researchers have been exploring the mass production of gene products by whole animals or plants rather than cultured cells. Genetic engineers have used recombinant DNA technology to insert genes for desired human proteins into other mammals, where the protein encoded by the recombinant gene may be secreted in the animal's milk. For example, a gene for antithrombin—a human protein that helps prevent inappropriate blood clotting—has been inserted into the genome of a goat (Figure 12.6A); isolated from the milk, the protein reduces the risk of life-threatening blood clots during surgery or childbirth. The sheep in Figure 12.6B have been genetically modified to produce a human protein called AAT; this protein can be supplied to patients to treat a hereditary form of emphysema. Other

mammals have been modified to serve as models for human diseases or to improve the health of livestock.

However, genetically engineered animals are difficult and costly to produce. Typically, a biotechnology company starts by injecting the desired DNA into a large number of embryos, which are then implanted into surrogate mothers. With luck, one or a few recombinant animals may result, but success rates for such procedures are very low. Once a recombinant organism is successfully produced, it may be cloned. The result can be a genetically identical herd—a grazing pharmaceutical "factory" of "pharm" animals that produce otherwise rare biological substances for medical use.

We continue an exploration of the medical applications of DNA technology in the next module.

? Why can't all human proteins be synthesized in E. coli?

● Because bacteria cannot correctly produce many eukaryotic (and mammalian) proteins, such as ones that require the attachment of sugar groups

▲ Figure 12.6B Sheep that have been genetically modified to produce a useful human protein

12.7 DNA technology has changed the pharmaceutical industry and medicine

CONNECTION

DNA technology, and gene cloning in particular, is widely used to produce medicines and to diagnose diseases.

Therapeutic Hormones Consider the first two products in Table 12.6 on the previous page—human insulin and human growth hormone. Insulin, normally secreted by the pancreas, is a hormone that helps regulate the levels of glucose in the blood. About 2 million Americans with diabetes depend on insulin injections. Before 1982, the main sources of this hormone were slaughtered pigs and cattle. Insulin extracted from these animals is chemically similar, but not identical, to human insulin, and it causes allergic reactions in some people. Genetic engineering has largely solved this problem by developing bacteria that synthesize and secrete the human form of insulin. In 1982, Humulin (Figure 12.7A)—human insulin produced by bacteria—became the first recombinant DNA drug approved by the U.S. Food and Drug Administration.

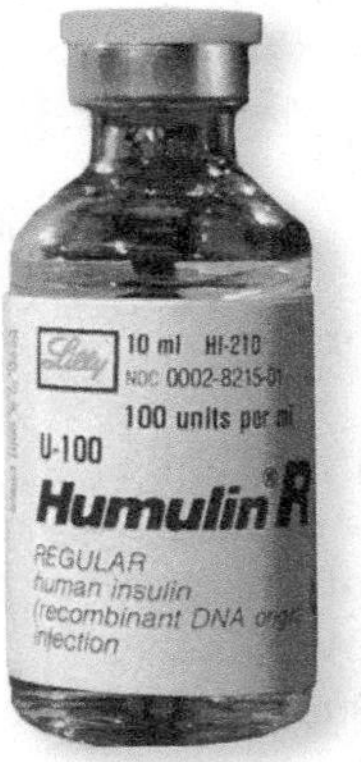

Treatment with human growth hormone (HGH) is a boon to children born with a form of dwarfism caused by inadequate amounts of HGH. Because growth hormones from other animals are not effective in humans, children with HGH deficiency historically have had to rely on scarce and expensive supplies from human cadavers. In 1985, however, molecular biologists made an artificial gene for HGH by joining a human DNA fragment to a chemically synthesized piece of DNA; using this gene, they were able to produce HGH in *E. coli*. HGH from recombinant bacteria is now widely used.

Another important pharmaceutical product produced by genetic engineering is tissue plasminogen activator (TPA). If administered soon after a heart attack, this protein helps dissolve blood clots and reduces the risk of subsequent heart attacks.

Diagnosis of Disease DNA technology can also serve as a diagnostic tool. Among the hundreds of genes for human diseases that have been identified are those for sickle-cell disease, hemophilia, cystic fibrosis, and Huntington's disease. Affected individuals with such diseases often can be identified before the onset of symptoms, even before birth. It is also possible to identify symptomless carriers of potentially harmful recessive alleles (see Module 9.9). In addition, DNA technology can pinpoint infections. For example, DNA analysis can help track down and identify elusive viruses such as HIV, the virus that causes AIDS.

Vaccines DNA technology is also helping medical researchers develop vaccines. A **vaccine** is a harmless variant (mutant) or derivative of a pathogen—usually a bacterium or virus—that is used to stimulate the immune system to mount a lasting defense against that pathogen, thereby preventing disease.

For many viral diseases (such as measles, mumps, and polio), prevention by vaccination is the only medical way to prevent illness among those exposed to the virus.

Genetic engineering can be used in several ways to make vaccines. One approach is to use genetically engineered cells or organisms to produce large amounts of a protein molecule that is found on the pathogen's outside surface. This method has been used to make the vaccine against hepatitis B, a disabling and sometimes fatal liver disease. Figure 12.7B shows a tank for growing yeast cells that have been engineered to carry the gene for the hepatitis B virus's surface protein. This protein, which is made by the yeast, will be the main ingredient of the vaccine.

Another way to use DNA technology in vaccine development is to make a harmless artificial mutant of the pathogen by altering one or more of its genes. When a harmless mutant is used as a so-called live vaccine, it multiplies in the body and may trigger a strong immune response. Artificial-mutant vaccines may cause fewer side effects than vaccines that have traditionally been made from natural mutants.

Yet another method for making vaccines uses a virus related to the one that causes smallpox. Smallpox was once a dreaded human disease, but it was eradicated worldwide in the 1970s by widespread vaccination with a harmless variant of the smallpox virus. Using this harmless virus, genetic engineers could replace some smallpox genes with genes that induce immunity to other diseases. In fact, the virus could be engineered to carry genes needed to vaccinate against several diseases simultaneously. In the future, one inoculation may prevent a dozen diseases.

Genetic engineering rapidly transformed the field of medicine and continues to do so today. But this new technology affects our lives in other ways, as we'll see next.

? Human growth hormone and insulin produced by DNA technology are used in the treatment of _____ and _____, respectively.

● dwarfism ... diabetes

▲ Figure 12.7A
Human insulin produced by bacteria

▲ Figure 12.7B Equipment used in the production of a vaccine against hepatitis B

12.8 Genetically modified organisms are transforming agriculture

CONNECTION

Since ancient times, people have selectively bred agricultural crops to make them more useful. Today, DNA technology is quickly replacing traditional breeding programs as scientists work to improve the productivity of agriculturally important plants and animals. Genetic engineers have produced many different varieties of **genetically modified organisms (GMOs)**, organisms that have acquired one or more genes by artificial means. If the new gene is from another organism, typically of another species, the recombinant organism is called a **transgenic organism**.

A common vector used to introduce new genes into plant cells is a plasmid from the soil bacterium *Agrobacterium tumefaciens* called the Ti plasmid (Figure 12.8A). ① With the help of a restriction enzyme and DNA ligase, the gene for the desired trait (indicated in red) is inserted into a modified version of the plasmid. ② Then the recombinant plasmid is put into a plant cell, where the DNA carrying the new gene integrates into one of the plant's chromosomes. ③ Finally, the recombinant cell is cultured and grown into a plant.

With an estimated 1 billion people facing malnutrition, GMO crops may be able to help a great many hungry people by improving food production, shelf life, pest resistance, and the nutritional value of crops. The story of the Hawaiian papaya industry (see the chapter introduction) provides one dramatic example. In India, the insertion of a natural but rare salinity-resistance gene has enabled new varieties of rice to grow in water three times as salty as seawater, allowing food to be grown in drought-stricken or flooded areas. Similar research is under way in Australia to help improve wheat yields in salty soil. Golden Rice, a transgenic variety created in 2000 with a few daffodil genes, produces yellow grains containing beta-carotene, which our body uses to make vitamin A (Figure 12.8B). A newer strain (Golden Rice 2) uses corn genes to boost beta-carotene levels even higher. Golden rice could help prevent vitamin A deficiency, which causes blindness in a quarter million children each year.

In addition to agricultural applications, genetic engineers are now creating plants that make human proteins for medical use. A recently developed transgenic rice strain harbors genes for milk proteins that can be used in rehydration formulas to treat infant diarrhea, a serious problem in developing countries. Other pharmaceutical trials under way involve using modified corn to treat cystic fibrosis, and duckweed to treat hepatitis. Although these trials seem promising, no plant-made drugs intended for use by humans have been approved.

Agricultural researchers are producing transgenic animals by injecting cloned genes directly into the nuclei of fertilized eggs. Some of the cells integrate the foreign DNA into their genomes. The engineered embryos are then surgically implanted into a surrogate mother. If an embryo develops successfully, the resulting animal will contain a gene from a third "parent"— the gene donor—which may even be of another species.

▲ Figure 12.8B   Golden Rice

The goals in creating a transgenic animal are often the same as the goals of traditional breeding—for instance, to make a sheep with better quality wool or a cow that will mature in less time. In 2006, researchers genetically modified pigs to carry a roundworm gene whose protein converts less healthy fatty acids to omega-3 fatty acids. Meat from the modified pigs contains four to five times as much healthy omega-3 fat as regular pork. Atlantic salmon have been genetically modified by the addition of a more active promoter of a growth hormone gene from Chinook salmon. Such fish can mature in half the time of conventional salmon and grow to twice the size. In late 2012, the FDA found that the modified salmon had no significant effect on humans or the environment, clearing an important hurdle to their sale as food. As of mid–2013, public hearings on whether to allow the salmon to become the first transgenic animal sold as food were ongoing. As we'll discuss next, some people worry that GMOs are not safe for human health or the environment.

? **What is the function of the Ti plasmid in the creation of transgenic plants?**

● It is used as the vector for introducing foreign genes into a plant cell.

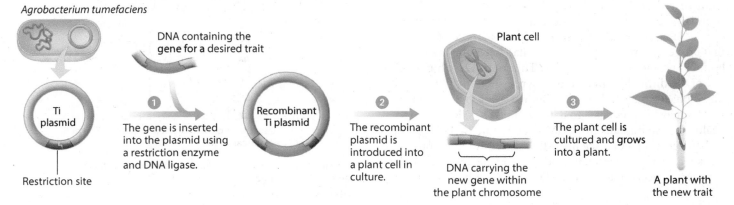

Agrobacterium tumefaciens

DNA containing the **gene for a** desired trait

Ti plasmid

Restriction site

① The gene is inserted into the plasmid using a restriction enzyme and DNA ligase.

Recombinant Ti plasmid

② The recombinant plasmid is introduced into a plant cell in culture.

Plant cell

DNA carrying the new gene within the plant chromosome

③ The plant cell is cultured and grows into a plant.

A plant with the new trait

▲ **Figure 12.8A**   Using the Ti plasmid to genetically engineer plants

12.9 Genetically modified organisms raise health concerns

SCIENTIFIC THINKING

As soon as scientists realized the power of DNA technology, they began to worry about potential dangers. Early concerns focused on the possibility that recombinant DNA technology might create new pathogens. To guard against rogue microbes, scientists developed a set of guidelines including strict laboratory safety and containment procedures, the genetic crippling of transgenic organisms to ensure that they cannot survive outside the laboratory, and a prohibition on certain dangerous experiments. Today, most public concern centers on GMOs used for food.

Are genetically modified organisms safe?

Human Safety Genetically modified organisms are used in crop production because they are more nutritious or because they are cheaper to produce. But do these advantages come at a cost to the health of people consuming GMOs? When investigating complex questions like this one, scientists often use multiple experimental methods. A 2012 animal study involved 104 pigs that were divided into two groups: The first was fed a diet containing 39% GMO corn and the other a closely related non-GMO corn. The health of the pigs was measured over the short term (31 days), the medium term (110 days), and the normal generational life span. The researchers reported no significant differences between the two groups and no traces of foreign DNA in the slaughtered pigs.

Although pigs are a good model organism for human digestion, critics argue that human data are required to draw conclusions about the safety of dietary GMOs for people. The results of one human study, conducted jointly by Chinese and American scientists, were published in 2012. Sixty-eight Chinese schoolchildren (ages 6–8) were fed Golden Rice, spinach (a natural source of beta-carotene), or a capsule containing pure beta-carotene. Over 21 days, blood samples were drawn to measure how much vitamin A the body produced from each food source. The data show that the beta-carotene in both Golden Rice and the capsules was converted to vitamin A in the body with similar efficiency, while the beta-carotene in spinach led to significantly less vitamin A (Figure 12.9). The results led researchers to conclude that GMO rice can indeed be effective in preventing vitamin A deficiency.

Despite its positive findings, this study caused an uproar. Chinese authorities called the study an unethical "scandal," complaining that U.S. scientists had used Chinese schoolchildren as laboratory subjects. The project leaders countered that proper permission and consent had been obtained in both China and the United States. The controversy highlights one of the difficulties in conducting research on human nutrition: Animal studies are of limited value, but human studies may be unethical. To date, no study has documented health risks in humans from GMO foods, and there is general agreement among scientists that the GMO foods on the market are safe. However, it is not yet possible to measure the long-term effects (if any) of GMOs on human health.

Environmental Safety Advocates of a cautious approach toward GMO crops fear that transgenic plants might pass their new genes to related species in nearby wild areas, disturbing the composition of the natural ecosystem. Critics of GMO crops can point to several studies that do indeed show unintended gene transfer from engineered crops to nearby wild relatives. But GMO advocates counter that no lasting or detrimental effects from such transfers have been demonstrated, and that some GMOs (such as bacteria engineered to break down oil spills) can actively help the environment.

Labeling Although the majority of several staple crops grown in the United States—including corn and soybeans—are genetically modified, products made from GMOs are not required to be labeled in any way. Chances are you ate a food containing GMOs today, but the lack of labeling means you probably can't say for certain. Labeling of foods containing more than trace amounts of GMOs is required in Europe, Japan, Australia, China, Russia, and other countries. Labeling advocates point out that the information would allow consumers to decide for themselves whether they wish to be exposed to GMO foods. Some biotechnology advocates, however, respond that similar demands were not made when "transgenic" crop plants produced by traditional breeding techniques were put on the market. For example, triticale (a crop used primarily in animal feed but also in some human foods) was created decades ago by combining the genomes of wheat and rye—two plants that do not interbreed in nature. Triticale is now sold worldwide without any special labeling.

Scientists and the public need to weigh the possible benefits versus risks on a case-by-case basis. The best scenario would be to proceed with caution, basing our decisions on sound scientific information rather than on either irrational fear or blind optimism.

? **Why might crop plants engineered to be resistant to weed killer pose a danger to the environment?**

The genes for herbicide resistance could transfer to closely related weeds, which could themselves then become resistant.

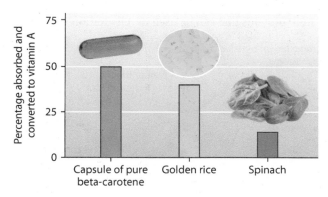

▲ **Figure 12.9** Vitamin A production after consumption of different sources of beta-carotene

Data from G. Tang et al., Beta-carotene in Golden Rice is as good as beta-carotene in oil at providing vitamin A to children, *American Journal of Clinical Nutrition* 96(3): 658–64 (2012).

12.10 Gene therapy may someday help treat a variety of diseases

CONNECTION

So far in this chapter, we have discussed transgenic viruses, bacteria, yeast, plants, and animals. What about transgenic humans? Why would anyone want to insert genes into a living person?

One reason to tamper with the human genome is the potential of **gene therapy**—alteration of a diseased individual's genes for therapeutic purposes. In people afflicted with disorders caused by a single defective gene, it might be possible to replace or supplement the defective gene by inserting a normal allele into cells of the tissue affected by the disorder. Once there, the normal allele might be expressed, potentially offering a permanent cure after just one treatment.

For gene therapy to be permanent, the normal allele would have to be transferred to cells that multiply throughout a person's life. Bone marrow cells, which include the stem cells that give rise to all the cells of the blood and immune system, are prime candidates (Figure 12.10). ❶ A gene from a healthy person is cloned, converted to an RNA version, and then inserted into the RNA genome of a harmless virus. ❷ Bone marrow cells are taken from the patient and infected with the recombinant virus. ❸ The virus inserts a DNA version of its genome, including the normal human gene, into the cells' DNA. ❹ The engineered cells are then injected back into the patient. If the procedure succeeds, the cells will multiply throughout the patient's life and produce a steady supply of the missing protein, curing the patient.

The promise of gene therapy thus far exceeds actual results, but there have been some successes. From 2000 to 2011, gene therapy cured 22 children with severe combined immunodeficiency (SCID), a fatal inherited disease caused by a defective gene that prevents development of the immune system, requiring patients to live within protective "bubbles." Unless treated with a bone marrow transplant, which is effective only 60% of the time, SCID patients quickly die from infections by microbes that most of us fend off. Although the gene therapy treatment cured the patients of SCID, there were some serious side effects: Four of the treated patients developed leukemia, and one died after the inserted gene turned the blood cells cancerous.

A 2009 gene therapy trial involved a disease called Leber's congenital amaurosis (LCA). People with one form of LCA produce abnormal rhodopsin, a pigment that enables the eye to detect light. In such people, photoreceptor cells gradually die, causing progressive blindness. Researchers found that a single injection—containing a virus carrying the normal gene—into one eye of affected children improved vision in that eye, sometimes enough to allow normal functioning.

Gene therapy raises difficult ethical questions. Some critics suggest that tampering with human genes in any way will inevitably lead to eugenics, the deliberate effort to control the genetic makeup of human populations. Other observers see no fundamental difference between the transplantation of genes into somatic cells and the transplantation of organs.

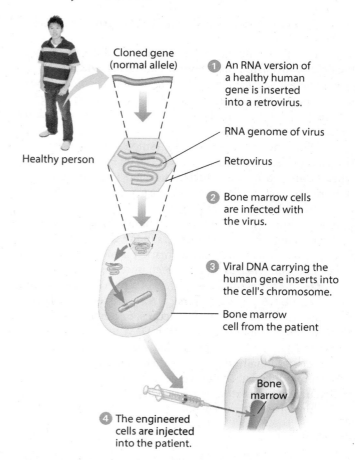

Healthy person

Cloned gene (normal allele)

❶ An RNA version of a healthy human gene is inserted into a retrovirus.

RNA genome of virus

Retrovirus

❷ Bone marrow cells are infected with the virus.

❸ Viral DNA carrying the human gene inserts into the cell's chromosome.

Bone marrow cell from the patient

Bone marrow

❹ The engineered cells are injected into the patient.

▲ **Figure 12.10** One type of gene therapy procedure

The implications of genetically manipulating gamete-forming cells or zygotes (already accomplished in lab animals) are more problematic. This possibility raises the most difficult ethical questions of all: Should we try to eliminate genetic defects in our children and their descendants? Should we interfere with evolution in this way? From a biological perspective, the elimination of unwanted alleles from the gene pool could backfire. Genetic variety is a necessary ingredient for the survival of a species as environmental conditions change with time. Genes that are damaging under some conditions may be advantageous under others (one example is the sickle-cell allele; see Module 9.13). Are we willing to risk making genetic changes that could be detrimental to our species in the future? We may have to face this question soon.

? **Why does bone marrow make a good target for gene therapy?**

● Bone marrow cells multiply throughout a person's life and contain stem cells that give rise to different kinds of blood cells.

▷ DNA Profiling

12.11 The analysis of genetic markers can produce a DNA profile

Modern DNA technology methods have rapidly transformed the field of **forensics**, the scientific analysis of evidence for crime scene investigations and other legal proceedings. The most important application to forensics is **DNA profiling**, the analysis of DNA samples to determine whether they came from the same individual.

Imagine that you have two DNA samples, perhaps one from a crime scene and one from a suspect. How do you test whether the two samples of DNA originate from the same person? You could compare the entire genomes found in the two samples, but such an approach would be extremely impractical, requiring a lot of time and money. Instead, scientists compare genetic markers, sequences in the genome that vary from person to person. A genetic marker is more likely to be a match between relatives than between unrelated individuals.

Figure 12.11 presents an overview of a typical investigation involving a DNA profile. ① First, DNA samples are isolated from the crime scene, suspects, victims, or other evidence. ② Next, selected markers from each DNA sample are amplified (copied many times), producing a large sample of DNA fragments. ③ Finally, the amplified DNA markers are compared, providing data about which samples are from the same individual. In the next four modules, we'll explore the methods behind these steps in detail.

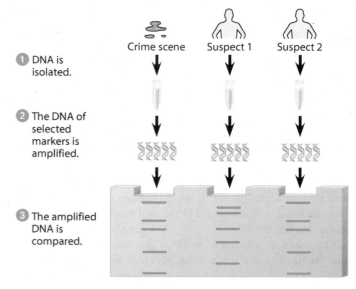

▲ **Figure 12.11**　An overview of DNA profiling

?　According to the data presented in Figure 12.11, which suspect left DNA at the crime scene?

Suspect 2: Notice that the number and location of the DNA markers in suspect 2's DNA and the crime scene DNA match.

12.12 The PCR method is used to amplify DNA sequences

The **polymerase chain reaction (PCR)** is a technique by which a specific segment of a DNA molecule can be targeted and quickly amplified in the laboratory. Starting with a minute sample, automated PCR can generate billions of copies of a DNA segment in just a few hours, producing enough DNA to allow a DNA profile to be constructed.

In principle, PCR is fairly simple (**Figure 12.12**). A repeated cycle brings about a chain reaction that doubles the population of identical DNA molecules during each round. The key to amplifying one particular segment of DNA and no others is the use of **primers**, short (usually 15–20 nucleotides long), chemically synthesized single-stranded DNA molecules with

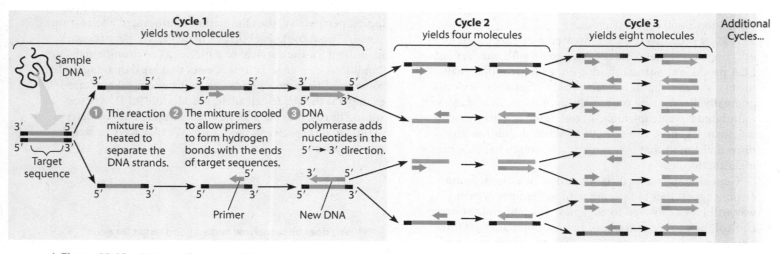

▲ **Figure 12.12**　DNA amplification by PCR

Try This　If each cycle takes 15 minutes, calculate the number of copies of the original DNA molecule that will be present after 6 hours.

sequences that are complementary to sequences at each end of the target sequence. One primer is complementary to one strand at one end of the target sequence; the second primer is complementary to the other strand at the other end of the sequence. The primers thus bind to sequences that flank the target sequence, marking the start and end points for the segment of DNA being amplified.

1 In the first step of each PCR cycle, the reaction mixture is heated to separate the strands of the DNA double helices. **2** Next, the strands are cooled. As they cool, primer molecules hydrogen-bond to their target sequences on the DNA. **3** Then a heat-stable DNA polymerase builds new DNA strands by extending the primers in the $5' \rightarrow 3'$ direction. These three steps are repeated over and over, doubling the amount of DNA after each three-step cycle. A key prerequisite for automating PCR was the discovery of an unusual DNA polymerase, first isolated from a bacterium living in hot springs, that could withstand the heat at the start of each cycle. Without such a heat-stable polymerase, PCR would not be possible because standard DNA polymerases would denature (unfold) during the heating step of each cycle.

Only minute amounts of DNA need to be present in the starting material, and this DNA can even be in a partially degraded state. The key to the high sensitivity is the primers. Because the primers only bind the sequences associated with the target, the DNA polymerase duplicates only the desired segments of DNA. Other DNA will not be bound by primers and thus not copied by the DNA polymerase.

Devised in 1985, PCR has had a major impact on biological research and biotechnology. PCR has been used to amplify DNA from a wide variety of sources: fragments of ancient DNA from a mummified human, a 40,000-year-old frozen woolly mammoth, and a 30-million-year-old plant fossil; DNA from fingerprints or from tiny amounts of blood, tissue, or semen found at crime scenes; DNA from single embryonic cells for rapid prenatal diagnosis of genetic disorders; and DNA of viral genes from cells infected with viruses that are difficult to detect, such as HIV.

? Why does PCR amplify only one specific region of DNA rather than all of it?

● The primers mark the ends, ensuring that only the DNA within the region between is amplified.

12.13 Gel electrophoresis sorts DNA molecules by size

Many DNA technology applications rely on **gel electrophoresis**, a method that separates macromolecules—usually proteins or nucleic acids—on the basis of size, electrical charge, or other physical properties. A gel is a thin rectangle of jellylike material often made from agarose, a carbohydrate polymer extracted from seaweed. Because agarose contains a tangle of cable-like threads, it can act as a molecular sieve.

Figure 12.13 outlines how gel electrophoresis can be used to separate mixtures of DNA fragments obtained from three different sources. A DNA sample from each source is placed in a separate well (hole) at one end of a gel that is suspended in liquid. A negatively charged electrode from a power supply is attached near the end of the gel containing the DNA, and a positive electrode is attached near the far end. Because all nucleic acid molecules carry negative charges on their phosphate groups (PO_4^-; see Module 10.2), the DNA molecules all travel through the gel toward the positive pole. However,

longer DNA fragments are held back by the thicket of polymer fibers within the gel, so they move more slowly than the shorter fragments. Over time, shorter molecules move farther through the gel than longer fragments. Gel electrophoresis thus separates DNA fragments by length, with shorter molecules migrating toward the bottom faster.

When the current is turned off, a series of bands is left in each "lane" of the gel. Each band is a collection of DNA fragments of the same length. The bands can be made visible by staining, by exposure onto photographic film (if the DNA is radioactively labeled), or by measuring fluorescence (if the DNA is labeled with a fluorescent dye).

? What causes DNA molecules to move toward the positive pole during electrophoresis? Why do large molecules move more slowly than smaller ones?

● The negatively charged phosphate groups of the DNA are attracted to the positive pole; the gel restricts the movement of longer fragments more.

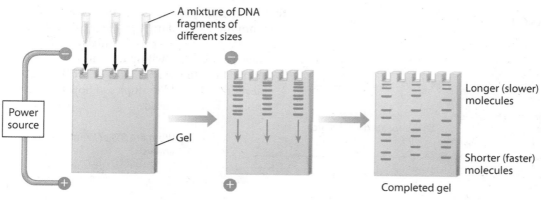

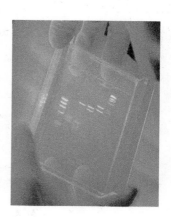

Longer (slower) molecules

Shorter (faster) molecules

Completed gel

Power source

Gel

A mixture of DNA fragments of different sizes

▲ **Figure 12.13** Gel electrophoresis of DNA

 **Try This** Explain why the shortest DNA molecules end up at the bottom of the gel.

12.14 Short tandem repeat analysis is commonly used for DNA profiling

Now that we've learned about DNA amplification by PCR and gel electrophoresis, let's see how these methods can be combined in DNA profiling. To create a DNA profile, a forensic scientist gathers data about a predefined set of genetic markers. The genetic markers most often used in DNA profiling are inherited variations in the lengths of repetitive DNA segments. **Repetitive DNA** consists of nucleotide sequences that are present in multiple copies in the genome; much of the DNA that lies between genes in humans is of this type. Some regions of repetitive DNA vary considerably from one individual to the next.

The repetitive DNA used in genetic DNA profiles consists of short sequences repeated many times in a row; such a series of repeats is called a **short tandem repeat (STR)**. For example, one person might have the sequence AGAT repeated 12 times in a row at one place in the genome, the sequence GATA repeated 45 times in a row at a second place, and so on. Another person has the same sequences at the same places but with different numbers of repeats. These stretches of repetitive DNA, like any genetic marker, are more likely to be an exact match between relatives than between unrelated individuals.

STR analysis is a method of DNA profiling that compares the lengths of STR sequences at specific sites in the genome. The current standard for DNA profiling in forensic and legal systems compares the number of repeats of specific four-nucleotide DNA sequences at 13 sites scattered throughout the genome. Each of these repeat sites, which typically contain from 3 to 50 four-nucleotide repeats in a row, vary widely from person to person. In fact, some of the STRs used in the standard procedure can be found in up to 80 different variations in the human population. In the United States, the number of repeats at each site is entered into a database called CODIS (Combined DNA Index System) administered by the Federal Bureau of Investigation (FBI). Law enforcement agencies around the world can access CODIS to search for matches to DNA samples they have obtained from crime scenes or suspects.

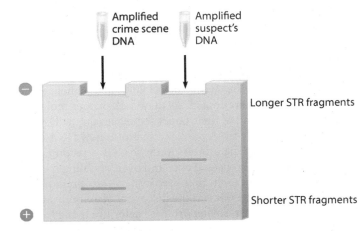

▲ **Figure 12.14B** DNA profiles generated from the STRs in Figure 12.14A

Consider the two samples of DNA shown in **Figure 12.14A**, where the top DNA was obtained at a crime scene and the bottom DNA from a suspect. The two segments have the same number of repeats at the first site: 7 repeats of the four-nucleotide DNA sequence AGAT (shown in orange). Notice, however, that they differ in the number of repeats at the second site: 8 repeats of GATA (shown in purple) in the crime scene DNA, compared with 13 repeats in the suspect's DNA. To create a DNA profile, a scientist uses PCR to specifically amplify the regions of DNA that include these STR sites. This can be done by using primers matching nucleotide sequences known to flank the STR sites. The resulting DNA molecules are then compared by gel electrophoresis.

Figure 12.14B shows a gel that could have resulted from the STR fragments in Figure 12.14A. The differences in the locations of the bands reflect the different lengths of the DNA fragments. (A gel from an actual DNA profile would typically contain more than just two bands in each lane.) This gel would provide evidence that the crime scene DNA did not come from the suspect. Notice that electrophoresis allows us to see similarities as well as differences between mixtures of DNA molecules. Thus, data from DNA profiling can provide evidence of either innocence or guilt.

Within the human population, so much variation exists within the 13 standard sites that a DNA profile made via STR analysis can definitely identify a single person from within the entire human population. In the next module, we'll examine several real-world examples of how this technology has been used.

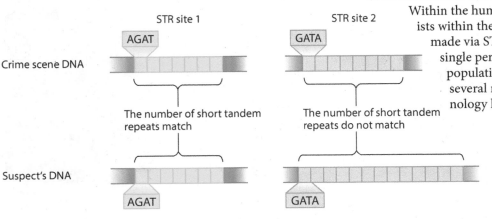

▲ **Figure 12.14A** Two representative STR sites from crime scene DNA samples

> **?** **What are STRs? What is STR analysis?**
>
> ● STRs are regions of the genome that contain varying numbers of sequential repeats of a short nucleotide sequence; STR analysis is a technique for determining whether two DNA samples have identical STRs.

12.15 DNA profiling has provided evidence in many forensic investigations

CONNECTION

When a violent crime is committed, body fluids or small pieces of tissue may be left at the crime scene or on the clothes of the victim or assailant. If rape has occurred, semen may be recovered from the victim. DNA profiling can match such samples to the person they came from with a high degree of certainty because the DNA sequence of every person is unique (except for identical twins). PCR amplification allows tissue samples comprising as few as 20 cells to be tested.

Since its introduction in 1986, DNA profiling has become a standard tool of forensics and has provided crucial evidence in many famous cases. DNA profiling first gained wide public attention during the O. J. Simpson murder trial, when DNA analysis proved that blood in Simpson's car belonged to the victims and that blood at the crime scene belonged to Simpson. (The jury in this case did not find the DNA evidence alone to be sufficient, and Simpson was found not guilty.) During the investigation that led to his impeachment, President Bill Clinton repeatedly denied that he had sexual relations with Monica Lewinsky—until DNA profiling proved that his semen was on her dress.

DNA evidence can prove innocence as well as guilt. Lawyers at the Innocence Project, a nonprofit organization dedicated to overturning wrongful convictions, have used DNA technology and legal work to exonerate more than 300 convicted criminals since 1989, including 17 who were on death row (Figure 12.15A). In more than a third of these cases, DNA profiling also identified the true perpetrators.

DNA profiling can also be used to identify victims. The largest such effort in history occurred after the terrorist attack on the World Trade Center on September 11, 2001. Forensic scientists, under the coordination of the Office of the Chief Medical Examiner of New York City, worked for years to identify more than 20,000 samples of victims' remains. DNA profiles of tissue samples from the disaster site were matched to DNA profiles from tissue known to be from the victims. If no sample of a victim's DNA was available, blood samples from close relatives were used to confirm identity through near matches. More than half of the identified victims at the World Trade Center site were recognized solely by DNA evidence, providing closure to many grieving families.

The use of DNA profiling extends beyond crimes. For instance, a comparison of the DNA of a child and the purported father can conclusively settle a question of paternity. Sometimes, paternity is of historical interest: DNA profiling proved that Thomas Jefferson or a close male relative of Jefferson's fathered a child with his slave Sally Hemings. Going back much further, one of the strangest cases of DNA

▲ Figure 12.15A   Earl Washington, a convicted murderer who was freed after 17 years in prison thanks to an STR analysis that proved his innocence

▲ Figure 12.15B   Cheddar Man and one of his modern-day descendants

profiling is that of Cheddar Man, a 9,000-year-old skeleton found in a cave near Cheddar, England (Figure 12.15B). DNA was extracted from his tooth and analyzed. The DNA profile showed that Cheddar Man was a direct ancestor—through approximately 300 generations—of a present-day schoolteacher who lived only a half mile from the cave!

Just how reliable is DNA profiling? When the standard CODIS set of 13 STR sites (see Module 12.14) is used, the probability of finding the same DNA profile in randomly selected, unrelated individuals is less than one in 10 billion. Put another way, a standard DNA profile can provide a statistical match of a particular DNA sample to just one living human. For this reason, DNA analyses are now accepted as compelling evidence by legal experts and scientists alike. In fact, DNA analysis on stored forensic samples has provided the evidence needed to solve many "cold cases" in recent years.

DNA analysis has also been used to probe the origin of non-human materials. For example, examination of DNA can prove the origin of food, as with a U.S. Fish and Wildlife Service program that tests caviar to determine if the fish eggs originate from the species claimed on the label. In addition, DNA profiling can help protect endangered species by conclusively providing the origin of contraband animal products, allowing for increased vigilance in endangered regions. Animals can also be the subject of research, as with a 2005 study that determined that DNA extracted from a 27,000-year-old Siberian mammoth was 98.6% identical to DNA from modern African elephants.

Although DNA profiling has provided definitive evidence in many investigations, the method is far from foolproof. Problems can arise from insufficient data, human error, or flawed evidence. Although the science behind DNA profiling is irrefutable, the human element remains a possible confounding factor.

? **In what way is DNA profiling valuable for determining innocence as well as guilt?**

● A DNA profile can prove with near certainty that a sample of DNA does or does not come from a particular individual. DNA profiling therefore can provide evidence in support of guilt or innocence.

12.16 RFLPs can be used to detect differences in DNA sequences

Recall that a genetic marker is a DNA sequence that varies in a population. Like different alleles of a gene, the DNA sequence at a specific place on a chromosome may exhibit small nucleotide differences, or polymorphisms (from the Greek for "many forms"). Geneticists have cataloged many single-base-pair variations in the genome. Such a variation found in at least 1% of the population is called a **single nucleotide polymorphism** (**SNP**, pronounced "snip"). SNPs occur on average about once in 100 to 300 base pairs in the human genome, both in the coding sequences of genes and in noncoding sequences between genes. Scientists have identified several million SNP sites, and more are discovered each year.

SNPs may alter a restriction site—the sequence recognized by a restriction enzyme. Such alterations change the lengths of the restriction fragments formed by that enzyme when it cuts the DNA. A sequence variation of this type is called a **restriction fragment length polymorphism** (**RFLP**, pronounced "rif-lip"). Thus, RFLPs can serve as genetic markers for particular loci in the genome. RFLPs have many uses. For example, disease-causing alleles can be diagnosed with reasonable accuracy if a closely linked RFLP marker has been found. Alleles for a number of genetic diseases were first detected by means of RFLPs in this indirect way.

Restriction fragment analysis involves two of the methods you have learned about: DNA fragments produced by restriction enzymes (Module 12.2) are sorted by gel electrophoresis (Module 12.13). The number of restriction fragments and their sizes reflect the specific sequence of nucleotides in the starting DNA.

At the top of Figure 12.16, you can see corresponding segments of DNA from two DNA samples prepared from human tissue. Notice that the DNA sequences differ by a single base pair (highlighted in yellow). In this case, the restriction enzyme cuts DNA between two cytosine (C) bases in the sequence CCGG and in its complement, GGCC. Because DNA from the first sample has two recognition sequences for the restriction enzyme, it is cleaved in two places, yielding three restriction fragments (labeled w, x, and y). DNA from the second sample, however, has only one recognition sequence and yields only two restriction fragments (z and y). Notice that the lengths of restriction fragments, as well as the number of fragments, differ, depending on the exact sequence of bases in the DNA.

To detect the differences between the collections of restriction fragments, we need to separate the restriction fragments in the two mixtures and compare their lengths. This process, called RFLP analysis, is accomplished through gel electrophoresis. As shown in the bottom of the figure, the three kinds of restriction fragments from sample 1 separate into three bands in the gel, whereas those from sample 2 separate into only two bands. Notice that the shortest fragment from sample 1 (y) produces a band at the same location as the identical short fragment from the sample 2. So you can see that electrophoresis allows us to see similarities as well as differences between mixtures of restriction fragments—and similarities

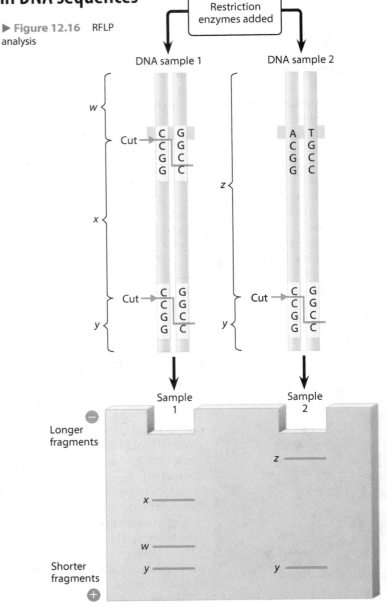

▶ Figure 12.16   RFLP analysis

as well as differences between the base sequences in DNA from two individuals. The restriction fragment analysis in Figure 12.16 clearly shows that the two DNA samples differ in sequence. Although RFLP analysis is rarely used today for identification, this method was vital in some of the earliest discoveries of disease-causing genes. For example, the gene for Huntington's disease was found after researchers used RFLPs to track a genetic marker that was closely associated with the disorder.

? You use a restriction enzyme to cut a DNA molecule that has three copies of the enzyme's recognition sequence clustered near one end. When you separate the restriction fragments by gel electrophoresis, how do you expect the bands to look?

● There should be three bands near the positive pole at the bottom of the gel (small fragments) and one band near the negative pole at the top of the gel (large fragment).

12.17 Genomics is the scientific study of whole genomes

By the 1980s, biologists were using RFLPs to map important genes in humans and some other organisms. But it didn't take long for biologists to think on a larger scale. In 1995, a team of scientists determined the nucleotide sequence of the entire genome of *Haemophilus influenzae*, a bacterium that can cause several human diseases, including pneumonia and meningitis. **Genomics**, the study of complete sets of genes (genomes) and their interactions, was born.

Since 1995, researchers have used the tools and techniques of DNA technology to develop more and more detailed maps of the genomes of a number of species. The first targets of genomics research were bacteria, which have relatively little DNA. The *H. influenza* genome, for example, contains only 1.8 million nucleotides and 1,709 genes. But soon, the attention of genomics researchers turned toward more complex organisms with much larger genomes. As of 2013, the genomes of nearly 7,000 species have been completed, and thousands more are in progress. Table 12.17 lists some of the completed genomes; for diploids, the size refers to the haploid genome. The majority of genomes under study are from prokaryotes, including *E. coli* and several thousand other bacteria (some of medical importance), and more than 200 Archaea. Over 300 eukaryotic species have been sequenced, including vertebrates, invertebrates, fungi, and plants.

Baker's yeast (*Saccharomyces cerevisiae*) was the first eukaryote to have its full sequence determined, and the roundworm *Caenorhabditis elegans* was the first multicellular organism. Other sequenced animals include the fruit fly (*Drosophila melanogaster*) and the laboratory mouse (*Mus musculus*), both model organisms for genetics research. Plants, such as one type of mustard (*Arabidopsis thaliana*,

an important research organism) and rice (*Oryza sativa*, one of the world's most economically important crops), have also been completed. Other recently completed eukaryotic genomes include sorghum (another important commercial crop), the honeybee, dog, wallaby (a marsupial), turkey, and bottlenose dolphin.

In 2005, researchers completed the genome sequence for our closest living relative on the evolutionary tree of life, the chimpanzee (*Pan troglodytes*). Comparisons with human DNA revealed that we share 96% of our genome with our closest animal relative. As you will see in Module 12.21, genomic scientists are currently finding and studying the important differences, shedding scientific light on the age-old question of what makes us human.

Why map so many genomes? Not only are all genomes of interest in their own right, but comparative analysis provides invaluable insights into the evolutionary relationships among organisms. Also, having maps of a variety of genomes helps scientists interpret the human genome. For example, when scientists find a nucleotide sequence in the human genome similar to a yeast gene whose function is known, they have a valuable clue to the function of the human sequence. In fact, the roles of several human disease-causing genes were determined by studying their yeast counterparts. Indeed, many genes of disparate organisms are being found to be astonishingly similar: Some researchers joke that fruit flies can even be thought of as "little people with wings."

? **Does a larger genome always correlate with more genes?**

● No. Compare, for example, the genomes of rice and mice.

TABLE 12.17 | SOME IMPORTANT COMPLETED GENOMES

Organism	Year Completed	Size of Haploid Genome (in Base Pairs)	Approximate Number of Genes
Haemophilus influenzae (bacterium)	1995	1.8 million	1,700
Saccharomyces cerevisiae (yeast)	1996	12 million	6,300
Escherichia coli (bacterium)	1997	4.6 million	4,400
Caenorhabditis elegans (nematode)	1998	100 million	20,100
Drosophila melanogaster (fruit fly)	2000	165 million	14,000
Arabidopsis thaliana (mustard plant)	2000	120 million	27,000
Mus musculus (mouse)	2001	2.6 billion	22,000
Oryza sativa (rice)	2002	430 million	42,000
Homo sapiens (humans)	2003	3.0 billion	21,000
Rattus norvegicus (lab rat)	2004	2.8 billion	25,000
Pan troglodytes (chimpanzee)	2005	3.1 billion	22,000
Macaca mulatta (macaque)	2007	2.9 billion	22,000
Macropus eugenii (wallaby)	2012	2.9 billion	18,000

12.18 The Human Genome Project revealed that most of the human genome does not consist of genes

CONNECTION

The **Human Genome Project (HGP)** was a massive, long-term scientific endeavor with the goals of determining the nucleotide sequence of all DNA in the human genome and identifying the location and sequence of every gene. The HGP began in 1990 and was completed in 2003. More than 99% of the human genome has been determined to 99.999% accuracy. (There remain a few hundred gaps of unknown sequences within the human genome that remain elusive.) The DNA sequences determined by the HGP and related projects have been deposited in a publicly available database called GenBank.

The chromosomes in the human genome—22 autosomes plus the X and Y sex chromosomes—contain approximately 3 billion nucleotide pairs of DNA. To get a sense of this much DNA, imagine that its nucleotide sequence is printed in letters (A, T, C, and G) like the letters in this book. At this size, the sequence would fill a stack of books 18 stories high! The biggest surprise from the HGP is the small number of human genes. The current estimate is just below 21,000 genes—very close to the number found in a microscopic worm. How, then, do we account for human complexity? Part of the answer may lie in alternative RNA splicing (see Module 11.4); scientists think that a typical human gene specifies several different polypeptides.

In humans, as in most complex eukaryotes, only a small amount of our total DNA (about 1.5%) is contained in genes that code for proteins, tRNAs, or rRNAs (**Figure 12.18**). Most multicellular eukaryotes have a huge amount of noncoding DNA; about 98.5% of human DNA is of this type. About one-quarter of our DNA consists of introns and gene control sequences such as promoters, enhancers, and microRNAs (see Chapter 11). The remaining noncoding DNA had been dubbed "junk DNA," a tongue-in-cheek way of saying that scientists don't fully understand its functions, but it is now generally accepted that much of this DNA probably plays some role. This stands in sharp contrast to a typical prokaryotic genome, in which the vast majority of DNA serves an obvious function; the human genome contains roughly 10,000 times more noncoding DNA than the *E. coli* genome.

Much of the DNA between genes consists of repetitive DNA, nucleotide sequences present in many copies in the genome. The repeated units of some of this DNA are short, such as the STRs used in DNA profiling (see Module 12.14). Stretches of DNA with thousands of short repetitions are also prominent at the centromeres and ends of chromosomes—called **telomeres**—suggesting that this DNA plays a role in chromosome structure.

In the second main type of repetitive DNA, each repeated unit is hundreds of nucleotides long, and the copies are scattered around the genome. Most of these sequences seem to be associated with **transposable elements** ("jumping genes"), DNA segments that can move or be copied from one location to another in a chromosome and even between chromosomes.

The potential benefits of having a complete map of the human genome are enormous. For instance, hundreds of disease-associated genes have been identified. One example is the gene that is mutated in an inherited type of Parkinson's disease, a debilitating brain disorder that causes tremors of increasing severity. Until recently, Parkinson's disease was not known to have a hereditary component. But data from the Human Genome Project mapped a small number of cases of Parkinson's disease to a specific gene. Interestingly, an altered version of the protein encoded by this gene has also been tied to Alzheimer's disease, suggesting a previously unknown link between these two brain disorders. Moreover, the same gene is also found in rats, where it plays a role in the sense of smell, and in zebra finches, where it is thought to be involved in song learning. Cross-species comparisons such as these may uncover clues about the role played by the normal version of the protein in the human brain. And such knowledge could eventually lead to treatment for the half million Americans with Parkinson's disease.

One interesting question about the Human Genome Project is, Whose genome was sequenced? The first human genome to be sequenced was actually a reference genome compiled from a group of individuals. At nearly the same time, a private biotechnology company sequenced the genome of the company's president. These representative sequences will serve as standards so that comparisons of individual differences and similarities can be made. Starting in 2007, the genomes of a number of other individuals—the first was James Watson, codiscoverer of the structure of DNA—have also been sequenced. These sequences are part of a larger effort to collect information on all of the genetic variations that affect human characteristics. As the amount of sequence data multiplies, the small differences that account for individual variation within our species will come to light.

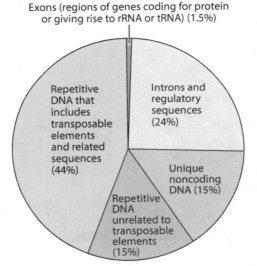

Exons (regions of genes coding for protein or giving rise to rRNA or tRNA) (1.5%)

Repetitive DNA that includes transposable elements and related sequences (44%)

Introns and regulatory sequences (24%)

Unique noncoding DNA (15%)

Repetitive DNA unrelated to transposable elements (15%)

▲ **Figure 12.18** Composition of the human genome

? The haploid human genome consists of about _____ base pairs and _____ genes spread over _____ different chromosomes (provide three numbers).

3 billion . . . 21,000 . . . 24 (22 autosomes plus 2 sex chromosomes)

12.19 The whole-genome shotgun method of sequencing a genome can provide a wealth of data quickly

Sequencing an entire genome is a complex task that requires careful work. The Human Genome Project proceeded through three stages that provided progressively more detailed views of the human genome. First, geneticists combined pedigree analyses of large families to map more than 5,000 genetic markers (mostly RFLPs) spaced throughout all of the chromosomes. The resulting low-resolution linkage map (see Module 9.19) provided a framework for mapping other markers and for arranging later, more detailed maps of particular regions. Next, researchers determined the number of base pairs between the markers in the linkage map. These data helped them construct a physical map of the human genome. Finally came the most arduous part of the project: determining the nucleotide sequences of the set of DNA fragments that had been mapped. Advances in automated DNA sequencing were crucial to this endeavor.

This three-stage approach is logical and thorough. However, in 1992, molecular biologist J. Craig Venter proposed an alternative strategy called the **whole-genome shotgun method** and set up the company Celera Genomics to implement it. His idea was essentially to skip the genetic and physical mapping stages and start directly with the sequencing step. In the whole-genome shotgun method, an entire genome is chopped by restriction enzymes into fragments that are cloned and sequenced in just one stage (Figure 12.19). High-performance computers running specialized mapping software can assemble the millions of overlapping short sequences into a single continuous sequence for every chromosome—an entire genome.

Today, the whole-genome shotgun approach is the method of choice for genomic researchers because it is fast and relatively inexpensive. However, recent research has revealed some limitations of this method, such as difficulties with repetitive sequences, suggesting that a hybrid approach that

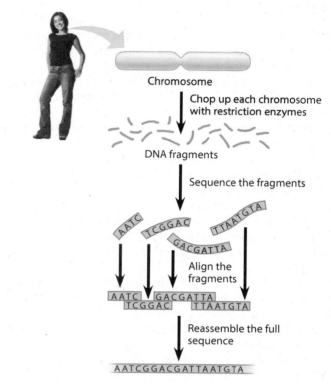

▲ Figure 12.19   The whole-genome shotgun method

combines whole-genome shotgunning with physical or genetic maps may prove to be the most useful method.

? **What are the primary advantages of the whole-genome shotgun method?**

● It is faster and cheaper than the three-stage method of genome sequencing.

12.20 Proteomics is the scientific study of the full set of proteins encoded by a genome

The successes in the field of genomics have encouraged scientists to begin similar systematic studies of the full protein sets (proteomes) encoded by genomes, an approach called **proteomics**. The number of different proteins in humans far exceeds the number of different genes—about 100,000 proteins versus about 21,000 genes. And because proteins, not genes, actually carry out most of the activities of the cell, scientists must study when and where proteins are produced in an organism and how they interact to understand the functioning of cells and organisms. Given the huge number of proteins and the myriad ways that their production can be controlled, assembling and analyzing proteomes pose many experimental challenges. Ongoing advances are beginning to provide the tools to meet those challenges.

Genomics and proteomics are enabling biologists to approach the study of life from an increasingly holistic (whole-system) perspective. Biologists are now compiling catalogs of genes and proteins—that is, listings of all the "parts" that contribute to the operation of cells, tissues, and organisms. As such catalogs become complete, researchers are shifting their attention from the individual parts to how these parts function together in biological systems.

? **If every protein is encoded by a gene, how can humans have many more proteins than genes?**

● The RNA transcribed from one gene may be spliced several different ways to produce different mRNAs that are translated into different proteins (see Module 11.4).

12.21 Genomes hold clues to human evolution

EVOLUTION CONNECTION

Scientists are accumulating genomic sequence data at an astonishing pace. As of 2013, the publicly accessible GenBank included DNA sequences totaling 150 billion base pairs, and this total is doubling every 18 months. Geneticists can now compare genome sequences from many species, allowing hypotheses about evolutionary relationships between those species to be tested. The more similar in sequence the same gene is in two species, the more closely related those species are in their evolutionary history.

The small number of genetic differences between closely related species makes it easier to correlate phenotypic differences between the species with particular genetic differences. The completion of the chimpanzee genome in 2005 has allowed us to compare our genome with that of our primate cousins. Such an analysis revealed that these two genomes differ by 1.2% in single-base substitutions. Researchers were surprised when they found a further 2.7% difference due to insertions or deletions of larger regions in the genome of one or the other species, with many of the insertions being duplications or other repetitive DNA. In fact, a third of the human duplications are not present in the chimpanzee genome, and some of these duplications contain regions associated with human diseases. All of these observations provide clues to the forces that might have swept the two genomes along different paths, but we don't have a complete understanding yet.

What about specific genes and types of genes that differ between humans and chimpanzees? Using evolutionary analyses, biologists have identified a number of genes that have evolved faster in humans. Among them are genes involved in defense against malaria and tuberculosis and a gene regulating brain size. One gene that changed rapidly in the human lineage is *FOXP2*, a gene implicated in speech and vocalization. Differences between the *FOXP2* gene in humans and chimpanzees may play a role in the ability of humans, but not chimpanzees, to communicate by speech.

Neanderthals (*Homo neanderthalensis*) were humans' closest relatives (Figure 12.21). First appearing at least 300,000 years ago, Neanderthals lived in Europe and Asia until suddenly going extinct a mere 30,000 years ago. Modern humans (*Homo sapiens*) first appeared in Africa around 200,000 years ago and spread into Europe and Asia around 50,000 years ago—meaning that modern humans and Neanderthals most likely comingled for some time.

A 2009 rough draft of a 60%-complete Neanderthal genome has, for the first time, allowed detailed genomic comparisons between two species in the genus *Homo*. Using 38,000-year-old thigh bone fossils of two *Homo neanderthalensis* females discovered in a Croatian cave, genomic analysis confirmed Neanderthals as a separate species and as our closest relatives (much closer than chimpanzees). Further comparisons, completed in 2010, suggested that Neanderthals and some *H. sapiens* probably did interbreed. Analysis of the sequence of the *FOXP2* gene showed that Neanderthals had the same allele as modern humans, hinting that Neanderthals may have had the ability to speak. Other genetic analyses of less complete Neanderthal genomes revealed one male to have an unusual allele for a pigment gene that would have given him pale skin and red hair. And, interestingly, analysis of the lactase gene suggests that Neanderthals, like the majority of modern humans, were lactose intolerant as adults (see Chapter 3).

Comparisons with Neanderthals and chimpanzees are part of a larger effort to learn more about the human genome. Other research efforts are extending genomic studies to many more species. These studies will advance our understanding of all aspects of biology, including health, ecology, and evolution. In fact, comparisons of the completed genome sequences of bacteria, archaea, and eukaryotes supported the theory that these are the three fundamental domains of life —a topic we discuss further in the next unit.

▲ Figure 12.21   Reconstruction of a Neanderthal female, based on a 36,000-year-old skull

? How can cross-species comparisons of the nucleotide sequences of a gene provide insight into evolution?

● Similarities in gene sequences correlate with evolutionary relatedness; greater genetic similarities reflect a more recent shared ancestry.

CHAPTER 12 REVIEW

For practice quizzes, BioFlix animations, MP3 tutorials, video tutors, and more study tools designed for this textbook, go to

MasteringBiology®

Reviewing the Concepts

Gene Cloning (12.1–12.5)

12.1 Genes can be cloned in recombinant plasmids. Gene cloning is one application of biotechnology, the manipulation of organisms or their components to make useful products. Researchers can manipulate bacterial plasmids so that they contain genes from other organisms. These recombinant DNA plasmids can then be inserted into bacteria. If the recombinant bacteria multiply into a clone, the foreign genes are also duplicated and copies of the gene or its protein product can be harvested.

12.2 Enzymes are used to "cut and paste" DNA. Restriction enzymes cut DNA at specific sequences, forming restriction fragments. DNA ligase "pastes" DNA fragments together.

12.3 Cloned genes can be stored in genomic libraries. Genomic libraries, sets of DNA fragments containing all of an organism's genes, can be constructed and stored for use in DNA technology applications.

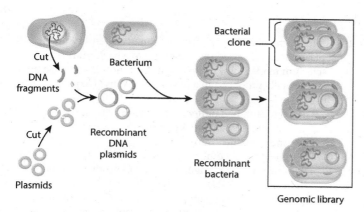

Genomic library

12.4 Reverse transcriptase can help make genes for cloning. cDNA libraries contain only the genes that are transcribed by a particular type of cell.

12.5 Nucleic acid probes identify clones carrying specific genes. A short, single-stranded molecule of labeled DNA or RNA can tag a desired gene in a library.

Genetically Modified Organisms (12.6–12.10)

12.6 Recombinant cells and organisms can mass-produce gene products. Bacteria, yeast, cell cultures, and whole animals can be used to make products for medical and other uses.

12.7 DNA technology has changed the pharmaceutical industry and medicine. Researchers use gene cloning to produce hormones, diagnose diseases, and produce vaccines.

12.8 Genetically modified organisms are transforming agriculture. A number of important crop plants are genetically modified.

12.9 Genetically modified organisms raise health concerns. Genetic engineering involves potential risks to human health and the environment.

12.10 Gene therapy may someday help treat a variety of diseases.

DNA Profiling (12.11–12.16)

12.11 The analysis of genetic markers can produce a DNA profile. DNA technology—methods for studying and manipulating genetic material—has revolutionized the field of forensics. DNA profiling can determine whether two samples of DNA come from the same individual.

12.12 The PCR method is used to amplify DNA sequences. The polymerase chain reaction (PCR) can be used to amplify a DNA sample. The use of specific primers that flank the desired sequence ensures that only a particular subset of the DNA sample will be copied.

12.13 Gel electrophoresis sorts DNA molecules by size.

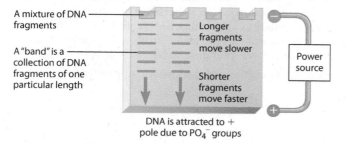

A mixture of DNA fragments

A "band" is a collection of DNA fragments of one particular length

Longer fragments move slower

Shorter fragments move faster

Power source

DNA is attracted to + pole due to PO$_4^-$ groups

12.14 Short tandem repeat analysis is commonly used for DNA profiling. Short tandem repeats (STRs) are stretches of DNA that contain short nucleotide sequences repeated many times in a row. DNA profiling by STR analysis involves amplifying 13 STRs.

12.15 DNA profiling has provided evidence in many forensic investigations. The applications of DNA profiling include helping to solve crimes, establishing paternity, and identify victims.

12.16 RFLPs can be used to detect differences in DNA sequences. Restriction fragment length polymorphisms (RFLPs) reflect differences in the sequences of DNA samples.

Genomics (12.17–12.21)

12.17 Genomics is the scientific study of whole genomes. Genomics researchers have sequenced many prokaryotic and eukaryotic genomes. Besides being of interest in their own right, nonhuman genomes can be compared with the human genome.

12.18 The Human Genome Project revealed that most of the human genome does not consist of genes. Data from the Human Genome Project (HGP) revealed that the human genome contains just under 21,000 genes and a huge amount of noncoding DNA, much of which consists of repetitive nucleotide sequences.

12.19 The whole-genome shotgun method of sequencing a genome can provide a wealth of data quickly. The HGP used genetic and physical mapping of chromosomes followed by DNA sequencing. Modern genomic analysis often uses the faster whole-genome shotgun method.

12.20 Proteomics is the scientific study of the full set of proteins encoded by a genome.

12.21 Genomes hold clues to human evolution.

Connecting the Concepts

1. Imagine you have found a small quantity of DNA. Fill in the following diagram, which outlines a series of DNA technology experiments you could perform to study this DNA.

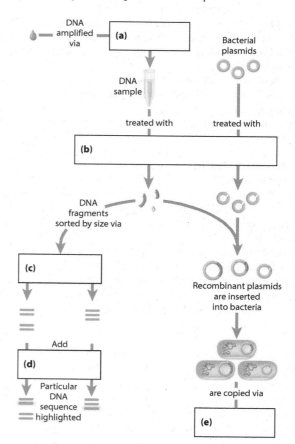

DNA amplified via **(a)**

Bacterial plasmids

DNA sample

treated with

treated with

(b)

DNA fragments sorted by size via

(c)

Add

(d)

Particular DNA sequence highlighted

Recombinant plasmids are inserted into bacteria

are copied via

(e)

Testing Your Knowledge

Level 1: Knowledge/Comprehension

2. Which of the following would be considered a transgenic organism?
   a. a bacterium that has received genes via conjugation
   b. a human given a corrected human blood-clotting gene
   c. a fern grown in cell culture from a single fern root cell
   d. a rat with rabbit hemoglobin genes

3. The DNA profiles used as evidence in a murder trial look something like supermarket bar codes. The pattern of bars in a DNA profile shows
   a. the order of bases in a particular gene.
   b. the presence of various-sized fragments of DNA.
   c. the presence of dominant or recessive alleles for particular traits.
   d. the order of genes along particular chromosomes.

4. A paleontologist has recovered a tiny bit of organic material from the 400-year-old preserved skin of an extinct dodo. She would like to compare DNA from the sample with DNA from living birds. Which of the following would be most useful for increasing the amount of DNA available for testing?
   a. restriction fragment analysis
   b. polymerase chain reaction
   c. molecular probe analysis
   d. electrophoresis

5. How many genes are there in a human sperm cell?
   a. 23
   b. 46
   c. about 21,000
   d. about 3 billion

Level 2: Application/Analysis

6. When a typical restriction enzyme cuts a DNA molecule, the cuts are uneven, giving the DNA fragments single-stranded ends. These ends are useful in recombinant DNA work because
   a. they enable a cell to recognize fragments produced by the enzyme.
   b. they serve as starting points for DNA replication.
   c. the fragments will bond to other fragments with complementary ends.
   d. they enable researchers to use the fragments as molecular probes.

7. Why does DNA profiling rely on comparing specific genetic markers rather than the entire genome?

8. Recombinant DNA techniques are used to custom-build bacteria for two main purposes: to obtain multiple copies of certain genes and to obtain useful proteins produced by certain genes. Give an example of each of these applications in medicine and agriculture.

9. A biochemist hopes to find a gene in human liver cells that codes for an important blood-clotting protein. She knows that the nucleotide sequence of a small part of the blood-clotting gene is CTGGACTGACA. Briefly outline a possible method she might use to isolate the desired gene.

Level 3: Synthesis/Evaluation

10. A biologist isolated a gene from a human cell, inserted it into a plasmid, and inserted the plasmid into a bacterium. The bacterium made a new protein, but it was nothing like the protein normally produced in a human cell. Why? (*Explain your answer.*)
    a. The bacterium had undergone transformation.
    b. The gene did not have sticky ends.
    c. The gene contained introns.
    d. The gene did not come from a genomic library.

11. Explain how you might engineer E. coli to produce human growth hormone (HGH) using the following: E. coli containing a plasmid, DNA carrying the gene for HGH, DNA ligase, a restriction enzyme, equipment for manipulating and growing bacteria, a method for extracting and purifying the hormone, and an appropriate DNA probe. (Assume that the human HGH gene lacks introns.)

12. What is left for genetic researchers to do now that the Human Genome Project has determined nearly complete nucleotide sequences for all of the human chromosomes? Explain.

13. Today, it is fairly easy to make transgenic plants and animals. What are some important safety and ethical issues raised by this use of recombinant DNA technology? What are some of the possible dangers of introducing genetically engineered organisms into the environment? What are some reasons for and against leaving decisions in these areas to scientists? To business owners and executives? What are some reasons for and against more public involvement? How might these decisions affect you? How do you think these decisions should be made?

14. In the not-too-distant future, gene therapy may be an option for the treatment and cure of some inherited disorders. What do you think are the most serious ethical issues that must be dealt with before human gene therapy is used on a large scale? Why do you think these issues are important?

15. The possibility of extensive genetic testing raises questions about how personal genetic information should be used. For example, should employers or potential employers have access to such information? Why or why not? Should the information be available to insurance companies? Why or why not? Is there any reason for the government to keep genetic files? Is there any obligation to warn relatives who might share a defective gene? Might some people avoid being tested for fear of being labeled genetic outcasts? Or might they be compelled to be tested against their wishes? Can you think of other reasons to proceed with caution?

16. **SCIENTIFIC THINKING** Scientists investigate hypotheses using a variety of methods, depending on the circumstances behind the research. Human nutrition studies (such as those studying whether GMO foods have any health effects) are particularly problematic. Can you design a hypothetical human nutrition study to test whether GMO corn is less healthy than traditional corn? Can you identify real-world problems that may interfere with your design and confound your results?

Answers to all questions can be found in Appendix 4.

Concepts of Evolution

13

How Populations Evolve

What does actor George Clooney have in common with George Washington, Ernest Hemingway, Christopher Columbus, and Mother Teresa? They all survived bouts with malaria, a disease caused by a protozoan parasite that is one of the worst killers in human history. In the 1960s, the World Health Organization (WHO) launched a campaign to eradicate malaria. Their

? How does evolution hinder attempts to eradicate disease?

strategy focused on killing the mosquitoes that carry the parasite from person to person. DDT, a widely used pesticide, was deployed in massive spraying operations. But in one location after another, early success was followed by rebounding mosquito populations in which resistance to DDT had evolved. Malaria continued to spread. Today, malaria causes more than a million deaths and 250 million cases of miserable illness each year.

Evolution has also hindered efforts to help malaria victims, such as the child shown in the photo below. At the same time that DDT was being celebrated as a miracle pesticide in the war against malaria, a drug called chloroquine was hailed as the miracle cure. But its effectiveness has diminished over

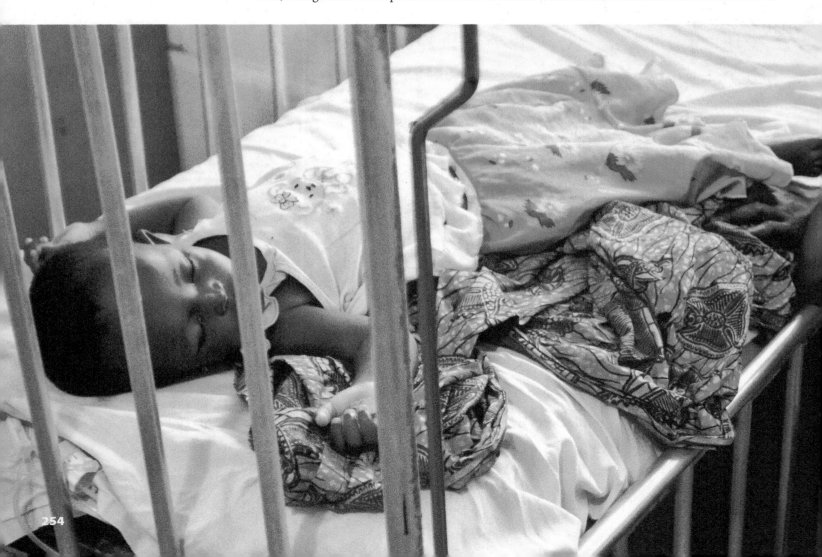

time, as resistance to the drug has evolved in parasite populations. In some regions, chloroquine is powerless against the disease. The most effective antimalarial drug now is artemisinin, a compound extracted from a plant used in traditional Chinese medicine. But the effectiveness of this drug will eventually succumb to the power of evolution, too. Cases of malaria that don't respond to artemisinin have already appeared in Southeast Asia.

An understanding of evolution informs all of biology, from exploring life's molecules to analyzing ecosystems. Applications of evolutionary biology are transforming fields as diverse as medicine, agriculture, and conservation biology. In this chapter, we begin our study of evolution with the enduring legacy of Charles Darwin's explanation for the unity and diversity of life. We also delve into the nitty-gritty of natural selection, the mechanism for evolution that Darwin proposed.

▷ Darwin's Theory of Evolution

13.1 A sea voyage helped Darwin frame his theory of evolution

If you have heard of the theory of evolution, you have probably heard of Charles Darwin. Although Darwin was born more than 200 years ago, his work had such an extraordinary impact that many biologists mark his birthday—February 12, the same as Abraham Lincoln's—with a celebration of his contributions to science. The publication of Darwin's best-known book, *On the Origin of Species by Means of Natural Selection*, commonly referred to as *The Origin of Species*, launched the era of evolutionary biology.

Darwin's Cultural and Scientific Context   Darwin's early career gave no hint of his future fame. As a boy, he was fascinated with nature. When not reading books about nature, he was fishing, hunting, and collecting insects. His father, an eminent physician, could see no future for his son as a naturalist and sent him to medical school. But Darwin, finding medicine boring and surgery before the days of anesthesia horrifying, quit medical school. His father then enrolled him at Cambridge University with the intention that he should become a clergyman. Thus, Darwin's education was typical for a young man of his social class.

The cultural and scientific context of his time also instilled Darwin with a conventional view of Earth and its life. Most scientists accepted the views of the Greek philosopher Aristotle, who generally held that species are fixed, permanent forms that do not evolve. Judeo-Christian culture fortified this idea with a literal interpretation of the biblical book of Genesis,

which tells the story of each form of life being individually created in its present-day form. In the 1600s, religious scholars used biblical accounts to estimate the age of Earth at 6,000 years. Thus, the idea that all living species came into being relatively recently and are unchanging in form dominated the intellectual climate of the Western world at the time.

Darwin's radical thinking stemmed from his post-college life, when he returned to his childhood interests rather than following the career path mapped out by his father. At the age of 22, Darwin took a position on HMS *Beagle*, a survey ship preparing for a long expedition to chart poorly known stretches of the South American coast (**Figure 13.1A**).

Darwin's Sea Voyage   As the ship's naturalist (field biologist), Darwin spent most of his time on shore collecting thousands of specimens of fossils and living plants and animals. He also kept detailed journals of his observations. For a naturalist from a small, temperate country, seeing the glorious diversity of unfamiliar life-forms on other continents was a revelation. He carefully noted the characteristics of plants and animals that made them well suited to such diverse environments as the jungles of Brazil, the grasslands of Argentina, the towering peaks of the Andes, and the desolate and frigid lands at the southern tip of South America.

Many of Darwin's observations indicated that geographic proximity is a better predictor of relationships among organism than similarity of environment. For example, the plants

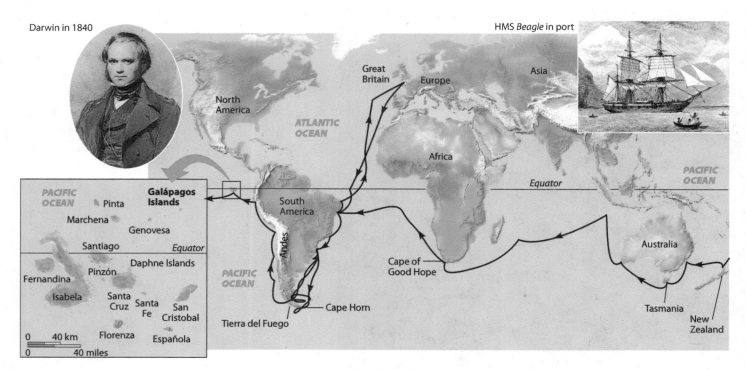

Darwin in 1840

HMS *Beagle* in port

▲ **Figure 13.1A**   The voyage of the *Beagle* (1831–1836), with insets showing a young Charles Darwin and the ship on which he sailed

and animals living in temperate regions of South America more closely resembled species living in tropical regions of that continent than species living in temperate regions of Europe. And the South American fossils Darwin found, though clearly species different from living ones, were distinctly South American in their resemblance to the contemporary plants and animals of that continent. For instance, he collected fossilized armor plates resembling those of living armadillo species. Paleontologists later reconstructed the creature to which the armor belonged—an extinct armadillo the size of a Volkswagen Beetle.

Darwin was particularly intrigued by the geographic distribution of organisms on the Galápagos Islands. The Galápagos are relatively young volcanic islands about 900 kilometers (540 miles) off the Pacific coast of South America. Most of the animals that inhabit these remote islands are found nowhere else in the world, but they resemble South American species. For example, Darwin noticed that Galápagos marine iguanas— with a flattened tail that aids in swimming—are similar to, but distinct from, land-dwelling iguanas on the islands and on the South American mainland (Figure 13.1B). Furthermore, each island had its own distinct variety of giant tortoise (Figure 13.1C), the strikingly unique inhabitant for which the islands were named (galápago means "tortoise" in Spanish).

While on his voyage, Darwin was strongly influenced by the newly published *Principles of Geology*, by Scottish geologist Charles Lyell. The book presented the case for an ancient Earth sculpted over millions of years by gradual geologic processes that continue today. Having witnessed an earthquake that raised part of the coastline of Chile almost a meter, Darwin realized that natural forces gradually changed Earth's surface and that these forces still operate. Thus, the growth of mountains as a result of earthquakes could account for the presence of marine snail fossils he collected on mountaintops in the Andes.

By the time Darwin returned to Great Britain five years after the *Beagle* first set sail, he had begun to seriously doubt that Earth and all its living organisms had been specially created only a few thousand years earlier. As he reflected on his observations, analyzed his collections, and discussed his work with colleagues, he concluded that the evidence was better explained by the hypothesis that present-day species are the descendants of ancient ancestors that they still resemble in some ways. Over time, differences gradually accumulated by a process that Darwin called "descent with modification," his

▲ **Figure 13.1B**   A marine iguana in the waters around the Galápagos Islands

▲ **Figure 13.1C**   A giant tortoise, one of the unique inhabitants of the Galápagos Islands

phrase for evolution. Darwin did not originate the concept of evolution; other scientists had explored the idea that organisms had changed over time. Unlike the others, however, Darwin also proposed a scientific mechanism for how life evolves, a process he called natural selection (see Module 1.7). He hypothesized that as the descendants of a remote ancestor spread into various habitats over millions and millions of years, they accumulated diverse modifications, or **adaptations**, that fit them to specific ways of life in their environment.

Darwin's Writings   By the early 1840s, Darwin had composed a long essay describing the major features of his theory of evolution by natural selection. He realized that his ideas would cause an uproar, however, and he delayed publishing his essay. Even as he procrastinated, Darwin continued to compile evidence in support of his hypothesis. In 1858, Alfred Wallace, a British naturalist doing fieldwork in Indonesia, conceived a hypothesis almost identical to Darwin's. Faced with the possibility that Wallace's work would be published first, Darwin finally released his essay to the scientific community.

The following year, Darwin published *The Origin of Species*, a book that supported his hypothesis with immaculate logic and hundreds of pages of evidence drawn from observations and experiments in biology, geology, and paleontology. The hypothesis of evolution set forth in *The Origin of Species* also generated predictions that have been tested and verified by more than 150 years of research. Consequently, scientists regard Darwin's concept of evolution by means of natural selection as a **theory**—a widely accepted explanatory idea that is broader in scope than a hypothesis, generates new hypotheses, and is supported by a large body of evidence.

Next, we examine lines of evidence for Darwin's theory of **evolution**, the idea that living species are descendants of ancestral species that were different from present-day ones. We then return to the second main point Darwin made in *The Origin of Species*, that natural selection is the mechanism for evolutionary change. With our current understanding of how this mechanism works, we extend Darwin's definition of evolution to include "genetic changes in a population from generation to generation."

   What was Darwin's phrase for evolution? What does it mean?

● Descent with modification. An ancestral species could diversify into many descendant species by the accumulation of adaptations to various environments.

13.2 The study of fossils provides strong evidence for evolution

Fossils—imprints or remains of organisms that lived in the past—document differences between past and present organisms and the fact that many species have become extinct. The organic substances of a dead organism usually decay rapidly, but the hard parts of an animal that are rich in minerals, such as the bones and teeth of vertebrates and the shells of clams and snails, may remain as fossils. For example, the fossilized skull in **Figure 13.2A** is from one of our early relatives, *Homo erectus*, who lived some 1.5 million years ago in Africa.

Some fossils are not the actual remnants of organisms. The 375-million-year-old fossils shown in **Figure 13.2B** are casts of ammonites, shelled marine animals related to the present-day nautilus (see Figure 18.9E). Casts form when a dead organism captured in sediment decomposes and leaves an empty mold that is later filled by minerals dissolved in water. The minerals harden, making a replica of the organism. Fossils may also be imprints that remain after the organism decays. Footprints, burrows, and fossilized feces (known as coprolites) provide evidence of an ancient organism's behavior.

In rare instances, an entire organism, including its soft parts, is encased in a medium that prevents bacteria and fungi from decomposing the corpse. Examples include insects trapped in amber (fossilized tree resin) and mammoths, bison, and even prehistoric humans frozen in ice or preserved in bogs.

Many fossils are found in fine-grained sedimentary rocks formed from the sand or mud that settles to the bottom of seas, lakes, swamps, and other aquatic habitats. New layers of sediment cover older ones and compress them into layers of rock called **strata** (singular, *stratum*). The fossils in a particular stratum provide a glimpse of some of the organisms that lived in the area at the time the layer formed. Because younger strata are on top of older ones, the relative ages of fossils can be determined by the layer in which they are found. Thus, the sequence in which fossils appear within layers of sedimentary rocks is a historical record of life on Earth.

Paleontologists (scientists who study fossils) sometimes gain access to very old fossils when erosion carves through upper (younger) strata, revealing deeper (older) strata that had been buried. **Figure 13.2C** shows strata of sedimentary rock at the Grand Canyon. The Colorado River has cut through more than 2,000 m (more than a mile) of rock, exposing sedimentary layers that can be read like huge pages from the book of life. Scan the canyon wall from rim to floor, and you look back through hundreds of millions of years. Each layer entombs fossils that represent some of the organisms from that period of Earth's history.

Of course, the **fossil record**—the chronicle of evolution over millions of years of geologic time engraved in the order in which fossils appear in rock strata—is incomplete. Many of Earth's organisms did not live in areas that favor fossilization. Many fossils that did form were in rocks later distorted or destroyed by geologic processes. Furthermore, not all fossils

▲ **Figure 13.2A** Skull of *Homo erectus*

▲ **Figure 13.2B**   Ammonite casts

▲ **Figure 13.2C**   Strata of sedimentary rock at the Grand Canyon

that have been preserved are accessible to paleontologists. Even with its limitations, however, the fossil record is remarkably detailed.

? **What types of animals do you think would be most represented in the fossil record? Explain your answer.**

● Animals with hard parts, such as shells or bones that readily fossilize, and those that lived in areas where sedimentary rock may form

13.3 Fossils of transitional forms support Darwin's theory of evolution

SCIENTIFIC THINKING

In *The Origin of Species*, Darwin predicted the existence of fossils of transitional forms linking very different groups of organisms. For example, if his hypothesis that whales evolved from land-dwelling mammals was correct, then fossils should show a series of changes in a lineage of mammals adapted to a fully aquatic habitat. Although Darwin lacked evidence with which to test this prediction, thousands of fossil discoveries have since shed light on the evolutionary origins of many groups of plants and animals, including the transition of fish to amphibian, the origin of birds from a lineage of dinosaurs, and the evolution of mammals from a reptilian ancestor. If Darwin were alive today, he would surely be delighted to know that evidence discovered over the past few decades has made the origin of whales from terrestrial mammals one of the best-documented evolutionary transitions to date.

Whales are cetaceans, a group that also includes dolphins and porpoises. They have forelimbs in the form of flippers but lack hind limbs (**Figure 13.3A**). If cetaceans evolved from four-legged land animals, then transitional forms should have reduced hind limb and pelvic bones. In the 1960s, observations of fossil teeth led paleontologists to hypothesize that whales were the descendants of primitive hoofed, wolflike carnivores. However, few fossil whales were available to study.

Beginning in the late 1970s, paleontologists unearthed an extraordinary series of transitional fossils in Pakistan and Egypt. The 50-million-year-old *Pakicetus* ("whale of Pakistan"; **Figure 13.3B**) was a carnivorous four-legged mammal that, remarkably, had distinctively cetacean ear structures. *Ambulocetus* ("walking whale"), roughly 48 million years old, was a perfect intermediate between modern whales and their land-dwelling ancestors. Its legs were short and sturdy. The wrist and elbow joints of the forelimbs suggested mobility on land, while a powerful tail and large, paddle-like hind feet suggested the ability to swim. Like *Pakicetus*, *Ambulocetus* had a whalelike ear, as did *Rodhocetus*, another mammal that apparently spent time both on land and in the water. The fossil genus *Dorudon*, which lived between 40 and 35 million

years ago, had completed the transition to aquatic life. The wrist and elbow joints of its paddle-like forelimbs could not have been used for walking, and its tiny hind limbs were not connected to the vertebral column.

The new fossil discoveries were consistent with the earlier hypothesis, and paleontologists became more firmly convinced that whales did indeed arise from a wolflike carnivore. But molecular biologists were testing an alternative hypothesis using DNA analysis to infer relationships among living animals. They found a close relationship between whales and hippopotamuses, which are members of a group of mostly herbivorous, cloven-hoofed mammals that includes pigs, deer, and camels. Consequently, these researchers hypothesized that whales and hippos were both descendants of a cloven-hoofed ancestor.

Paleontologists were taken aback by the contradictory results, but openness to new evidence is a hallmark of science. They turned their attention to seeking a fossil that would resolve the issue. Cloven-hoofed mammals have a unique ankle bone. If the ancestor of whales was a wolflike carnivore, then the shape of its ankle bone would be similar to most present-day mammals. Two fossils discovered in 2001 provided the answer. Both *Pakicetus* and *Rodhocetus* had the distinctive ankle bone of a cloven-hoofed mammal. Thus, as is often the case in science, scientists are becoming more certain about the evolutionary origin of whales as mounting evidence from different lines of inquiry converge.

? **What anatomical feature did scientists predict in fossils of species transitional between terrestrial and aquatic mammals?**

Reduced hind limb and pelvic bones ●

▲ **Figure 13.3A** A killer whale (*Orcinus orca*)

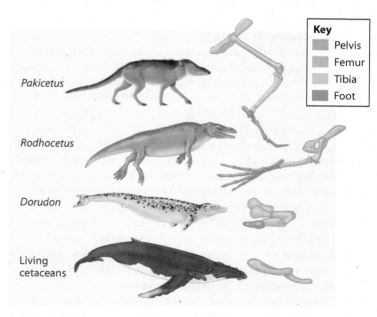

Key
■ Pelvis
■ Femur
■ Tibia
■ Foot

Pakicetus

Rodhocetus

Dorudon

Living cetaceans

▲ **Figure 13.3B** The transition to life in the sea

Try This List the animals shown, and describe how the structure of each animal's hind limbs reflects their function.

13.4 Homologies provide strong evidence for evolution

A second type of evidence for evolution comes from analyzing similarities among different organisms. Evolution is a process of descent with modification—characteristics present in an ancestral organism are altered over time by natural selection as its descendants face different environmental conditions. In other words, evolution is a remodeling process. As a result, related species can have characteristics that have an underlying similarity yet function differently. Similarity resulting from common ancestry is known as **homology**.

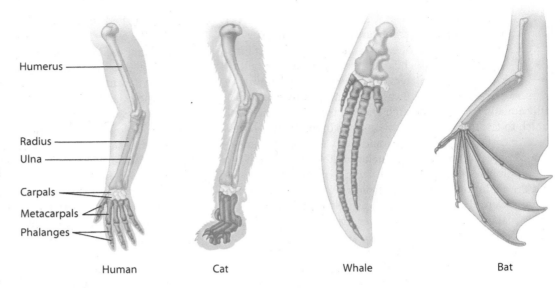

▲ **Figure 13.4A** Homologous structures: vertebrate forelimbs

Darwin cited the anatomical similarities among vertebrate forelimbs as evidence of common ancestry. As **Figure 13.4A** shows, the same skeletal elements make up the forelimbs of humans, cats, whales, and bats. The functions of these forelimbs differ. A whale's flipper does not do the same job as a bat's wing, so if these structures had been uniquely engineered, then we would expect that their basic designs would be very different. The logical explanation is that the arms, forelegs, flippers, and wings of these different mammals are variations on an anatomical structure of an ancestral organism that over millions of years has become adapted to different functions. Biologists call such anatomical similarities in different organisms **homologous structures**—features that often have different functions but are structurally similar because of common ancestry.

Because of advances in **molecular biology**, the study of the molecular basis of genes and gene expression, present-day scientists have a much deeper understanding of homologies than Darwin did. Just as your hereditary background is recorded in the DNA you inherit from your parents, the evolutionary history of each species is documented in the DNA inherited from its ancestral species. If two species have homologous genes with sequences that match closely, biologists conclude that these sequences must have been inherited from a relatively recent common ancestor. Conversely, the greater the number of sequence differences between species, the more distant is their last common ancestor. Molecular comparisons between diverse organisms have allowed biologists to develop hypotheses about the evolutionary divergence of major branches on the tree of life, as you learned in the previous module on the origin of whales.

Darwin's boldest hypothesis was that all life-forms are related. Molecular biology provides strong evidence for this claim: All forms of life use the same genetic language of DNA and RNA, and the genetic code—how RNA triplets are translated into amino acids—is essentially universal. Thus, it is likely that all species descended from common ancestors that used this code. Because of these homologies, bacteria engineered with human genes can produce human proteins such as insulin and human growth hormone (see Module 12.6). But molecular homologies go beyond a shared genetic code. For example, organisms as dissimilar as humans and bacteria share homologous genes inherited from a very distant common ancestor.

An understanding of homology can also explain observations that are otherwise puzzling. For example, comparing early stages of development in different animal species reveals similarities not visible in adult organisms. At some point in their development, all vertebrate embryos have a tail posterior to the anus, as well as structures called pharyngeal (throat) pouches. These pouches are homologous structures that ultimately develop to have very different functions, such as gills in fishes and parts of the ears and throat in humans. Note the pharyngeal pouches and tails of the bird embryo (left) and the human embryo (right) in **Figure 13.4B**.

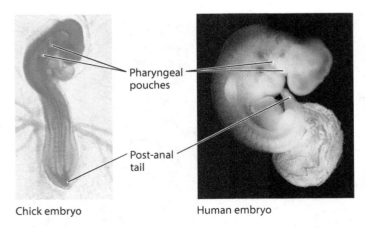

Chick embryo   Human embryo

▲ **Figure 13.4B** Homologous structures in vertebrate embryos

Some of the most interesting homologies are "leftover" structures that are of marginal or perhaps no importance to the organism. These **vestigial structures** are remnants of features that served important functions in the organism's ancestors. For example, the small pelvis and hind-leg bones of ancient whales are vestiges (traces) of their walking ancestors. The eye remnants that are buried under scales in blind species of cave fishes—a vestige of their sighted ancestors—are another example.

Organisms may also retain genes that have lost their function, even though homologous genes in related species are fully functional. Researchers have identified many of these inactive "pseudogenes" in humans. One such gene encodes an enzyme known as GLO that is used in making vitamin C.

Almost all mammals have a metabolic pathway to synthesize this essential vitamin from glucose. Although humans and other primates have functional genes for the first three steps in the pathway, the inactive GLO gene prevents vitamin C from being made—we must get sufficient amounts in our diet to maintain health.

Next we see how homologies help us trace evolutionary descent.

> **?** **What is homology? How does the concept of homology relate to molecular biology?**
>
> ● Homology is similarity in different species due to evolution from a common ancestor. Similarities in DNA sequences or proteins reflect the evolutionary relationship that is the basis of homology.

13.5 Homologies indicate patterns of descent that can be shown on an evolutionary tree

Darwin was the first to view the history of life as a tree, with multiple branchings from a common ancestral trunk to the descendant species at the tips of the twigs. Biologists represent these patterns of descent with an **evolutionary tree** (see Figure 14.1), although today they often turn the trees sideways.

Homologous structures, both anatomical and molecular, can be used to determine the branching sequence of such a tree. Some homologous characters, such as the genetic code, are shared by all species because they date to the deep ancestral past. In contrast, characters that evolved more recently are shared only within smaller groups of organisms. For example, all tetrapods (from the Greek *tetra*, four, and *pod*, foot) possess the same basic limb bone structure illustrated in Figure 13.4A, but their ancestors do not.

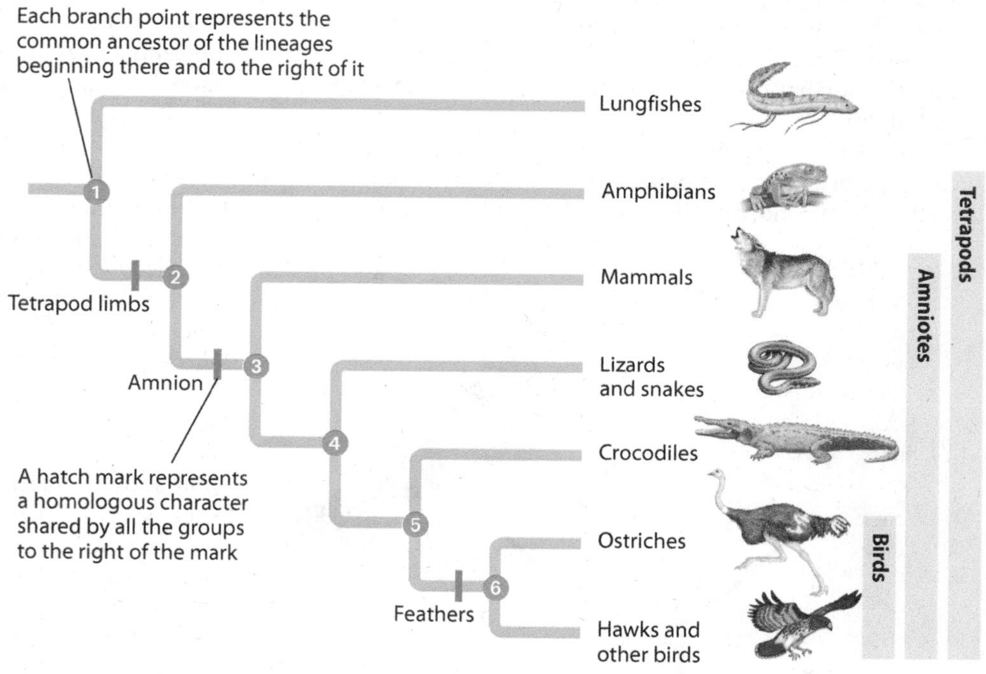

Each branch point represents the common ancestor of the lineages beginning there and to the right of it

Tetrapod limbs

Amnion

A hatch mark represents a homologous character shared by all the groups to the right of the mark

Feathers

Lungfishes
Amphibians
Mammals
Lizards and snakes
Crocodiles
Ostriches
Hawks and other birds

Tetrapods
Amniotes
Birds

▲ **Figure 13.5** An evolutionary tree for tetrapods and their closest living relatives, the lungfishes

Figure 13.5 is an evolutionary tree of tetrapods (amphibians, mammals, and reptiles, including birds) and their closest living relatives, the lungfishes. In this diagram, each branch point represents the common ancestor of all species that descended from it. For example, lungfishes and all tetrapods descended from ancestor **1**, whereas crocodiles and birds descended from ancestor **5**. Three homologies are shown by the purple hatch marks on the tree—tetrapod limbs, the amnion (a protective embryonic membrane), and feathers. Tetrapod limbs were present in ancestor **2** and hence are found in all of its descendants. The amnion was present only in ancestor **3** and thus is shared only by mammals and reptiles. Feathers were present only in ancestor **6** and hence are found only in birds.

Evolutionary trees are hypotheses reflecting our current understanding of patterns of evolutionary descent. Some trees, such as the one in Figure 13.5, are supported by a strong combination of fossil, anatomical, and molecular data. Others are more speculative because few data are available.

Now that you have learned about Darwin's view of evolution as descent with modification, let's examine the mechanism he proposed for how life evolves—natural selection.

> **?** **Refer to the evolutionary tree in Figure 13.5. Are crocodiles more closely related to lizards or birds?**
>
> ● Look for the most recent common ancestor of these groups. Crocodiles are more closely related to birds because they share a more recent common ancestor with birds (ancestor **5**) than with lizards (ancestor **4**).

13.6 Darwin proposed natural selection as the mechanism of evolution

Darwin's greatest contribution to biology was his explanation of *how* life evolves. Because he thought that species formed gradually over long periods of time, he knew that he would not be able to study the evolution of new species by direct observation. But he did have a way to gain insight into the process of incremental change—the practices used by plant and animal breeders.

All domesticated plants and animals are the products of selective breeding from wild ancestors. For example, the baseball-size tomatoes grown today are very different from their Peruvian ancestors, which were not much larger than blueberries, and dachshunds bear little resemblance to the wolves from which they were bred. Having conceived the notion that **artificial selection**—the selective breeding of domesticated plants and animals to promote the occurrence of desirable traits in the offspring—was the key to understanding evolutionary change, Darwin bred fancy pigeons (Figure 13.6) to gain firsthand experience. He also talked to farmers about livestock breeding. He learned that artificial selection has two essential components, variation and heritability.

Variation among individuals, for example, differences in coat type in a litter of puppies, size of corn ears, or milk production by the individual cows in a herd, allows the breeder to select the animals or plants with the most desirable combination of characters as breeding stock for the next generation. Heritability refers to the transmission of a trait from parent to offspring. Despite their lack of knowledge of the underlying genetics, breeders had long understood the importance of heritability in artificial selection.

Unlike most naturalists, who sought consistency of traits in order to classify organisms, Darwin was a careful observer of variations between individuals. He knew that individuals in natural populations have small but measurable differences. But what forces in nature played the role of the breeder by choosing which individuals became the breeding stock for the next generation?

Darwin found inspiration in an essay written by economist Thomas Malthus, who contended that much of human suffering—disease, famine, and war—was the consequence of human populations increasing faster than food supplies and other resources. Darwin applied Malthus's idea to populations of plants and animals. He deduced that the production of more individuals than the limited resources can support leads to a struggle for existence, with only some offspring surviving in each generation. Of the many eggs laid, young born, and seeds spread, only a tiny fraction complete development and leave offspring. The rest are eaten, starved, diseased, unmated, or unable to reproduce for other reasons. The essence of natural selection is this unequal reproduction. Individuals whose traits better enable them to obtain food or escape predators or tolerate physical conditions will survive and reproduce more successfully, passing these adaptive traits to their offspring.

Darwin reasoned that if artificial selection can bring about so much change in a relatively short period of time, then natural selection could modify species considerably over hundreds or thousands of generations. Over vast spans of time, many traits that adapt a population to its environment will accumulate. If the environment changes, however, or if individuals move to a new environment, natural selection will select for adaptations to these new conditions, sometimes producing changes that result in the origin of a completely new species in the process.

It is important to emphasize three key points about evolution by natural selection. First, although natural selection occurs through interactions between individual organisms and the environment, individuals do not evolve. Rather, it is the population—the group of organisms—that evolves over time as adaptive traits become more common in the group and other traits change or disappear.

Second, natural selection can amplify or diminish only heritable traits. Certainly, an organism may become modified through its own interactions with the environment during its lifetime, and those acquired characteristics may help the organism survive. But unless coded for in the genes of an organism's gametes, such acquired characteristics cannot be passed on to offspring. Thus, a championship female bodybuilder will not give birth to a muscle-bound baby.

▲ **Figure 13.6** Artificial selection: fancy pigeon varieties bred from the rock pigeon

Third, evolution is not goal directed; it does not lead to perfectly adapted organisms. Whereas artificial selection is a deliberate attempt by humans to produce individuals with specific traits, natural selection is the result of environmental factors that vary from place to place and over time. A trait that is favorable in one situation may be useless—or even detrimental—in different circumstances. And as you will see, adaptations are often compromises. Now let's look at some examples of natural selection.

13.7 Scientists can observe natural selection in action

Look at any natural environment, and you will see the products of natural selection—adaptations that suit organisms to their environment. But can we see natural selection in action?

Indeed, biologists have documented evolutionary change in thousands of scientific studies. A classic example comes from work that Peter and Rosemary Grant and their students did with finches in the Galápagos Islands over more than 30 years. As part of their research, they measured changes in beak size in a population of a ground finch species. These birds eat mostly small seeds. In dry years, when all seeds are in short supply, birds must eat more large seeds. Birds with larger, stronger beaks have a feeding advantage and greater reproductive success, and the Grants measured an increase in the average beak depth for the population. During wet years, smaller beaks are more efficient for eating the now abundant small seeds, and the Grants found a decrease in average beak depth.

An unsettling example of natural selection in action is the evolution of pesticide resistance in hundreds of insect species. Pesticides control insects and prevent them from eating crops or transmitting diseases. Whenever a new type of pesticide is used to control pests, the story is similar (**Figure 13.7**): A relatively small amount of poison initially kills most of the insects, but subsequent applications are less and less effective. The few survivors of the first pesticide wave are individuals that are genetically resistant, carrying an allele (alternative form of a gene, colored red in the figure) that somehow enables them to survive the chemical attack. So the poison kills most members of the population, leaving the resistant survivors to reproduce and pass the alleles for pesticide resistance to their offspring. The proportion of pesticide-resistant individuals thus increases in each generation.

The World Health Organization's campaign against malaria described in the chapter introduction is a real-world example of the evolution of pesticide resistance. Some mosquitoes in the populations that were sprayed with DDT carried an allele that codes for an enzyme that detoxifies the pesticide. When the presence of DDT changed the environment, the individuals carrying that allele survived to leave offspring, while nonresistant individuals did not. Thus, the process of natural selection defeated the efforts of WHO to control the spread of malaria by using DDT to kill mosquitoes.

These examples of evolutionary adaptation highlight two important points about natural selection. First, natural

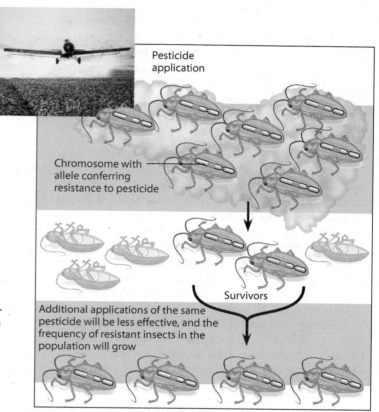

Pesticide application

Chromosome with allele conferring resistance to pesticide

Survivors

Additional applications of the same pesticide will be less effective, and the frequency of resistant insects in the population will grow

▲ **Figure 13.7** Evolution of pesticide resistance in an insect population

selection is more an editing process than a creative mechanism. A pesticide does not create new alleles that allow insects to survive. Rather, the presence of the pesticide leads to natural selection for insects in the population that already have those alleles. Second, natural selection is contingent on time and place: It favors those heritable traits in a varying population that fit the current, local environment. If the environment changes, different traits may be favored.

In the next few modules, we examine the genetic basis of evolution more closely.

13.8 Mutation and sexual reproduction produce the genetic variation that makes evolution possible

In *The Origin of Species*, Darwin provided evidence that life on Earth has evolved over time, and he proposed that natural selection, in favoring some heritable traits over others, was the primary mechanism for that change. But he could not explain the cause of variation among individuals, nor could he account for how those variations passed from parents to offspring.

Just a few years after the publication of *The Origin of Species*, Gregor Mendel wrote a groundbreaking paper on inheritance in pea plants (see Module 9.2). By breeding peas in his abbey garden, Mendel discovered the hereditary processes required for natural selection. Although the significance of Mendel's work was not recognized during his or Darwin's lifetime, its rediscovery in 1900 set the stage for understanding the genetic differences on which evolution is based.

Genetic Variation   You have no trouble recognizing your friends in a crowd. Each person has a unique genome, reflected in individual phenotypic variations such as appearance and other traits. Indeed, individual variation occurs in all species, as illustrated by the garter snakes in **Figure 13.8**. All four of these snakes were captured in one Oregon field. In addition to obvious physical differences, such as the snakes' colors and patterns, most populations have a great deal of phenotypic variation that can be observed only at the molecular level, such as an enzyme that detoxifies DDT.

Of course, not all variation in a population is heritable. The phenotype results from a combination of the genotype, which is inherited, and many environmental influences. For instance, if you have dental work to straighten and whiten your teeth, you will not pass your environmentally

produced smile to your offspring. Only the genetic component of variation is relevant to natural selection.

Many of the characters that vary in a population result from the combined effect of several genes. Polygenic inheritance produces characters that vary more or less continuously—in human height, for instance, from very short individuals to very tall ones (see Module 9.14). By contrast, other features, such as Mendel's purple and white pea flowers or human blood types, are determined by a single gene locus, with different alleles producing distinct phenotypes. But where do these alleles come from?

Mutation   New alleles originate by mutation, a change in the nucleotide sequence of DNA. Thus, mutation is the ultimate source of the genetic variation that serves as raw material for evolution. In multicellular organisms, however, only mutations in cells that produce gametes can be passed to offspring and affect a population's genetic variability.

A change as small as a single nucleotide in a protein-coding gene can have a significant effect on phenotype, as in sickle-cell disease (see Module 9.13). An organism is a refined product of thousands of generations of past selection, and a random change in its DNA is not likely to improve its genome any more than randomly changing some words on a page is likely to improve a story. In fact, mutation that affects a protein's function will probably be harmful. On rare occasions, however, a mutated allele may actually improve the adaptation of an individual to its environment and enhance its reproductive success. This kind of effect is more likely when the environment is changing in such a way that mutations that were once disadvantageous are favorable under the new conditions. For instance, mutations that endow houseflies with resistance to the pesticide DDT also reduce their growth rate. Before DDT was introduced, such mutations were a handicap to the flies that had them. But once DDT was part of the environment, the mutant alleles were advantageous, and natural selection increased their frequency in fly populations.

Chromosomal mutations that delete, disrupt, or rearrange many gene loci at once are almost certain to be harmful. But duplication of a gene or small pieces of DNA through errors in meiosis can provide an important source of genetic variation. If a repeated segment of DNA can persist over the generations, mutations may accumulate in the duplicate copies without affecting the function of the original gene, eventually leading to new genes with novel functions. This process may have played a major role in evolution. For

▲ Figure 13.8   Variation within a species of garter snakes

example, the remote ancestors of mammals carried a single gene for detecting odors that has since been duplicated repeatedly. As a result, mice have about 1,300 different olfactory receptor genes. It is likely that such dramatic increases helped early mammals by enabling them to distinguish among many different smells. And repeated duplications of genes that control development are linked to the origin of vertebrate animals from an invertebrate ancestor (see Module 15.11).

In prokaryotes, mutations can quickly generate genetic variation. Because bacteria multiply so rapidly, a beneficial mutation can increase in frequency in a matter of hours or days. And because bacteria are haploid, with a single allele for each gene, a new allele can have an effect immediately.

Mutation rates in animals and plants average about one in every 100,000 genes per generation. For these organisms, low mutation rates, long time spans between generations, and diploid genomes prevent most mutations from significantly affecting genetic variation from one generation to the next.

Sexual Reproduction In organisms that reproduce sexually, most of the genetic variation in a population results from the unique combination of alleles that each individual inherits. (Of course, the origin of those allele variations is past mutations.)

Fresh assortments of existing alleles arise every generation from three random components of sexual reproduction: crossing over, independent orientation of homologous chromosomes at metaphase I of meiosis, and random fertilization (see Modules 8.15 and 8.17). During meiosis, pairs of homologous chromosomes, one set inherited from each parent, trade some of their genes by crossing over. These homologous chromosomes separate into gametes independently of other chromosome pairs. Thus, gametes from any individual vary extensively in their genetic makeup. Finally, each zygote made by a mating pair has a unique assortment of alleles resulting from the random union of sperm and egg.

Now let's see why genetic variation is such an essential element of evolution.

> **?** What is the ultimate (original) source of genetic variation? What is the source of most genetic variation in a population that reproduces sexually?

Mutation; unique combinations of alleles resulting from sexual reproduction

---

13.9 Evolution occurs within populations

One common misconception about evolution is that individual organisms evolve during their lifetimes. It is true that natural selection acts on individuals: Each individual's combination of traits affects its survival and reproductive success. But the evolutionary impact of natural selection is only apparent in the changes in a population of organisms over time.

A **population** is a group of individuals of the same species that live in the same area and interbreed. We can measure evolution as a change in the prevalence of certain heritable traits in a population over a span of generations. The increasing proportion of resistant insects in areas sprayed with pesticide is one example. Natural selection favored insects with alleles for pesticide resistance; these insects left more offspring than nonresistant individuals, changing the genetic makeup of the population.

Different populations of the same species may be geographically isolated from each other to such an extent that an exchange of genetic material never or only rarely occurs. Such isolation is common in populations confined to different lakes (Figure 13.9) or islands. For example, each population of Galápagos tortoises is restricted to its own island. Not all populations have such sharp boundaries; however, members of a population typically breed with one another and are therefore more closely related to each other than they are to members of a different population.

In studying evolution at the population level, biologists focus on the **gene pool**, which consists of all copies of every type of allele at every locus in all members of the population. For many loci, there are two or more alleles in the gene pool. For example, in a mosquito population, there may be two alleles relating to DDT breakdown, one that codes for an enzyme that breaks down DDT and one for a version of the enzyme that does not. In populations living in fields sprayed with DDT, the allele for the enzyme conferring resistance will increase in frequency and the other allele will decrease in frequency. When the relative frequencies of alleles in a population change like this over a number of generations, evolution is occurring on its smallest scale. Such a change in a gene pool is often called **microevolution**.

In the next module, we'll explore how to test whether evolution is occurring in a population.

> **?** Why can't an individual evolve?

Evolution involves changes in the genetic makeup of a population over time. An individual's genetic makeup rarely changes during its lifetime.

▲ **Figure 13.9** Isolated lakes in Denali National Park, Alaska

13.10 The Hardy-Weinberg equation can test whether a population is evolving

To understand how microevolution works, let's first examine a simple population in which evolution is not occurring and thus the gene pool is not changing. Consider an imaginary population of iguanas with individuals that differ in foot webbing (Figure 13.10A). Let's assume that foot webbing is controlled by a single gene and that the allele for nonwebbed feet (W) is completely dominant to the allele for webbed feet (w). The term *dominant* (see Module 9.3) may seem to suggest that over many generations, the W allele will somehow come to "dominate," becoming more and more common at the expense of the

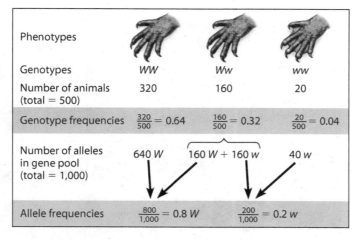

No webbing ⟋ Webbing

▲ Figure 13.10A   Imaginary iguanas, with and without foot webbing

recessive allele. In fact, this is not what happens. The shuffling of alleles that accompanies sexual reproduction does not alter the genetic makeup of the population. In other words, no matter how many times alleles are segregated into different gametes and united in different combinations by fertilization, the frequency of each allele in the gene pool will remain constant unless other factors are operating. This equilibrium is known as the **Hardy-Weinberg principle**, named for the two scientists who derived it independently in 1908.

To test the Hardy-Weinberg principle, let's look at two generations of our imaginary iguana population. Figure 13.10B shows the frequencies of alleles in the gene pool of the original population. We have a total of 500 animals; of these, 320 have the genotype WW (nonwebbed feet), 160 have the heterozygous genotype, Ww (also nonwebbed feet, because the nonwebbed allele W is dominant), and 20 have the genotype ww (webbed feet). The proportions or frequencies of the three genotypes are shown in the middle of Figure 13.10B: 0.64 for WW ($\frac{320}{500}$), 0.32 for Ww ($\frac{160}{500}$), and 0.04 for ww ($\frac{20}{500}$).

From these genotype frequencies, we can calculate the frequency of each allele in the population. Because these are diploid organisms, this population of 500 has a total of 1,000 alleles for foot type. To determine the number of W alleles,

we add the number in the WW iguanas, $2 \times 320 = 640$, to the number in the Ww iguanas, 160. The total number of W alleles is thus 800. The frequency of the W allele, which we will call p, is $\frac{800}{1,000}$, or 0.8. We can calculate the frequency of the w allele in a similar way; this frequency, called q, is 0.2. The letters p and q are often used to represent allele frequencies. Notice that $p + q = 1$. The combined frequencies of all alleles for a gene in a population must equal 1. If there are only two alleles and you know the frequency of one allele, you can calculate the frequency of the other.

What happens when the iguanas of this parent population form gametes? At the end of meiosis, each gamete has one allele for foot type, either W or w. The frequencies of the two alleles in the gametes will be the same as their frequencies in the gene pool of the parental population, 0.8 for W and 0.2 for w.

Figure 13.10C shows a Punnett square that uses these gamete allele frequencies and the rule of multiplication (see Module 9.7) to calculate the frequencies of the three genotypes in the next generation. The probability of producing a WW individual (by combining two W alleles from the pool of gametes) is $p \times p = p^2$, or $0.8 \times 0.8 = 0.64$. Thus, the frequency of WW iguanas in the next generation would be 0.64. Likewise, the frequency of ww individuals would be $q^2 = 0.04$. For heterozygous individuals, Ww, the genotype can form in two ways, depending on whether the sperm or egg supplies the dominant allele. In other words, the frequency of Ww would be $2pq = 2 \times 0.8 \times 0.2 = 0.32$. Do these frequencies look familiar? Notice that the three genotypes have the same frequencies in the next generation as they did in the parent generation.

Phenotypes			
Genotypes	WW	Ww	ww
Number of animals (total = 500)	320	160	20
Genotype frequencies	$\frac{320}{500} = 0.64$	$\frac{160}{500} = 0.32$	$\frac{20}{500} = 0.04$
Number of alleles in gene pool (total = 1,000)	640 W	160 W + 160 w	40 w
Allele frequencies	$\frac{800}{1,000} = 0.8\ W$		$\frac{200}{1,000} = 0.2\ w$

▲ Figure 13.10B   Gene pool of the original population of imaginary iguanas

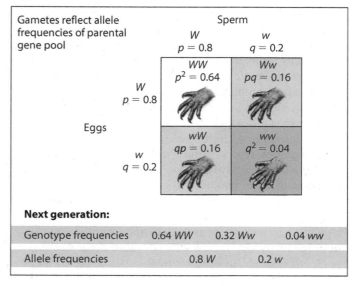

Gametes reflect allele frequencies of parental gene pool		Sperm	
		W $p = 0.8$	w $q = 0.2$
Eggs	W $p = 0.8$	WW $p^2 = 0.64$	Ww $pq = 0.16$
	w $q = 0.2$	wW $qp = 0.16$	ww $q^2 = 0.04$

Next generation:

Genotype frequencies	0.64 WW	0.32 Ww	0.04 ww
Allele frequencies		0.8 W	0.2 w

▲ Figure 13.10C   Gene pool of next generation of imaginary iguanas

Finally, what about the frequencies of the alleles in this new generation? Because the genotype frequencies are the same as in the parent population, the allele frequencies p and q are also the same. In fact, we could follow the frequencies of alleles and genotypes through many generations, and the results would continue to be the same. Thus, the gene pool of this population is in a state of equilibrium—Hardy-Weinberg equilibrium.

Now let's write a general formula for calculating the frequencies of genotypes in a population from the frequencies of alleles in the gene pool. In our imaginary iguana population, the frequency of the W allele (p) is 0.8, and the frequency of the w allele (q) is 0.2. Again note that $p + q = 1$. Also notice in Figures 13.10B and 13.10C that the frequencies of the three possible genotypes in the populations also add up to 1 (that is, $0.64 + 0.32 + 0.04 = 1$). We can represent these relationships symbolically with the Hardy-Weinberg equation:

$$\underset{\substack{\text{Frequency} \\ \text{of homozygous} \\ \text{dominants}}}{p^2} + \underset{\substack{\text{Frequency} \\ \text{of heterozygotes}}}{2pq} + \underset{\substack{\text{Frequency} \\ \text{of homozygous} \\ \text{recessives}}}{q^2} = 1$$

If a population is in Hardy-Weinberg equilibrium, allele and genotype frequencies will remain constant generation after generation. The Hardy-Weinberg principle tells us that something other than the reshuffling processes of sexual reproduction is required to change allele frequencies in a population. One way to find out what factors *can* change a gene pool is to identify the conditions that must be met if genetic equilibrium is to be maintained. For a population to be in Hardy-Weinberg equilibrium, it must satisfy five main conditions:

1. Very large population. The smaller the population, the more likely that allele frequencies will fluctuate by chance from one generation to the next.

2. No gene flow between populations. When individuals move into or out of populations, they add or remove alleles, altering the gene pool.

3. No mutations. By changing alleles or deleting or duplicating genes, mutations modify the gene pool.

4. Random mating. If individuals mate preferentially, such as with close relatives (inbreeding), random mixing of gametes does not occur, and genotype frequencies change.

5. No natural selection. The unequal survival and reproductive success of individuals (natural selection) can alter allele frequencies.

Rarely are all five conditions met in real populations; thus, allele and genotype frequencies often do change. The Hardy-Weinberg equation can be used to test whether evolution is occurring in a population. The equation also has medical applications, as we see next.

> **?** Which is *least* likely to alter allele and genotype frequencies in a few generations of a large, sexually reproducing population: gene flow, mutation, or natural selection? Explain.

13.11 The Hardy-Weinberg equation is useful in public health science

CONNECTION

Public health scientists use the Hardy-Weinberg equation to estimate how many people carry alleles for certain inherited diseases. Consider the case of phenylketonuria (PKU), an inherited inability to break down the amino acid phenylalanine that results in brain damage if untreated. Newborns are routinely screened for PKU, which occurs in about one out of 10,000 babies born in the United States. The health problems associated with PKU can be prevented by strict adherence to a diet that limits the intake of phenylalanine. Packaged foods with ingredients such as aspartame, a common artificial sweetener that contains phenylalanine, must be labeled clearly **(Figure 13.11)**.

PKU is due to a recessive allele, so the frequency of individuals born with PKU corresponds to the q^2 term in the Hardy-Weinberg equation. Given one PKU occurrence per 10,000 births, $q^2 = 0.0001$. Therefore, the frequency of the recessive allele for PKU in the population, q, equals the square root of 0.0001, or 0.01. And the frequency of the dominant allele, p, equals $1 - q$, or 0.99. The frequency of carriers, heterozygous people who do not have PKU but may pass the PKU allele on to offspring, is $2pq$, which equals $2 \times 0.99 \times 0.01$, or 0.0198. Thus, the equation tells us that about 2% (actually 1.98%) of the U.S. population are carriers of the

INGREDIENTS: SORBITOL, MAGNESIUM STEARATE, ARTIFICIAL FLAVOR, **ASPARTAME† (SWEETENER),** ARTIFICIAL COLOR (YELLOW 5 LAKE, BLUE 1 LAKE), ZINC GLUCONATE. **†PHENYLKETONURICS: CONTAINS PHENYLALANINE**

▲ **Figure 13.11** A warning to individuals with PKU

PKU allele. Estimating the frequency of a harmful allele is part of any public health program dealing with genetic diseases.

> **?** Which term in the Hardy-Weinberg equation—p^2, $2pq$, or q^2—corresponds to the frequency of individuals who have no alleles for the disease PKU?

13.12 Natural selection, genetic drift, and gene flow can cause microevolution

Deviations from the five conditions named in Module 13.10 for Hardy-Weinberg equilibrium can alter allele frequencies in a population (microevolution). Although new genes and new alleles originate by mutation, these random and rare events probably change allele frequencies little within a population of sexually reproducing organisms. Nonrandom mating can affect the frequencies of homozygous and heterozygous genotypes, but by itself usually does not affect allele frequencies. The three main causes of evolutionary change are natural selection, genetic drift, and gene flow.

Natural Selection The condition for Hardy-Weinberg equilibrium that there be no natural selection—that all individuals in a population be equal in ability to reproduce—is probably never met in nature. Populations consist of varied individuals, and some variants leave more offspring than others. In our imaginary iguana population, individuals with webbed feet (genotype *ww*) might survive better and produce more offspring because they are more efficient at swimming and catching food than individuals that lack webbed feet. Genetic equilibrium would be disturbed as the frequency of the *w* allele increased in the gene pool from one generation to the next.

Genetic Drift Flip a coin a thousand times, and a result of 700 heads and 300 tails would make you suspicious about that coin. But flip a coin 10 times, and an outcome of 7 heads and 3 tails would seem within reason. The smaller the sample, the more likely that chance alone will cause a deviation from an idealized result—in this case, an equal number of heads and tails. Let's apply that logic to a population's gene pool. The frequencies of alleles will be more stable from one generation to the next when a population is large. In a process called **genetic drift**, chance events can cause allele frequencies to fluctuate unpredictably from one generation to the next. The smaller the population, the more impact genetic drift is likely to have. In fact, an allele can be lost from a small population by such chance fluctuations. Two situations in which genetic drift can have a significant impact on a population are those that produce the bottleneck effect and the founder effect.

Catastrophes such as hurricanes, floods, or fires may kill large numbers of individuals, leaving a small surviving population that is unlikely to have the same genetic makeup as the original population. Such a drastic reduction in population size is called a **bottleneck effect**. Analogous to shaking just a few marbles through a bottleneck (Figure 13.12A), certain alleles (purple marbles) may be present at higher frequency in the surviving population than in the original population, others (green marbles) may be present at lower frequency, and some (orange marbles) may not be present at all. After a population is drastically reduced, genetic drift may continue for many generations until the population is again large enough for fluctuations due to chance to have less of an impact. Even if a population that has passed through a bottleneck ultimately recovers its size, it may have low levels of genetic

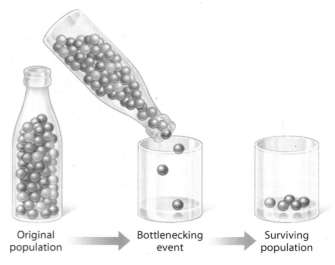

Original population → Bottlenecking event → Surviving population

▲ **Figure 13.12A** The bottleneck effect

variation—a legacy of the genetic drift that occurred when the population was small.

One reason it is important to understand the bottleneck effect is that human activities such as overhunting and habitat destruction may create severe bottlenecks for other species. Examples of species affected by bottlenecks include the endangered Florida panther, the African cheetah, and the greater prairie chicken (Figure 13.12B). Millions of these birds once lived on the prairies of Illinois. But as their habitat was converted to farmland and other uses during the 19th and 20th centuries, the number of greater prairie chickens plummeted. By 1993, only two Illinois populations remained, with a total of fewer than 50 birds. Less than 50% of the eggs of these birds hatched. Researchers compared the DNA of the 1993 population with DNA extracted from museum specimens dating back to the 1930s. They surveyed six gene loci and found that the modern birds had lost 30% of the alleles that were present

▲ **Figure 13.12B** Greater prairie chicken (*Tympanuchus cupido*)

in the museum specimens. Thus, genetic drift as a result of the bottleneck reduced the genetic variation of the population and may have increased the frequency of harmful alleles, leading to the low egg-hatching rate.

Genetic drift is also likely when a few individuals colonize an island or other new habitat, producing what is called the **founder effect**. The smaller the group, the less likely that the genetic makeup of the colonists will represent the gene pool of the larger population they left.

The founder effect explains the relatively high frequency of certain inherited disorders among some human populations established by small numbers of colonists. For example, in 1814, 15 people founded a colony on Tristan da Cunha, a group of small islands in the middle of the Atlantic Ocean. Apparently, one of the colonists carried a recessive allele for retinitis pigmentosa, a progressive form of blindness. Of the 240 descendants who still lived on the islands in the 1960s, four had retinitis pigmentosa, and at least nine others were known to be heterozygous carriers of the allele. The frequency of this allele is 10 times higher on Tristan da Cunha than in the British population from which the founders came.

Gene Flow Allele frequencies in a population can also change as a result of **gene flow**, by which a population may gain or lose alleles when fertile individuals move into or out of a population or when gametes (such as plant pollen) are transferred between populations. Gene flow tends to reduce differences between populations. For example, humans today move more freely about the world than in the past, and gene flow has become an important agent of evolutionary change in previously isolated human populations.

Let's return to the Illinois greater prairie chickens and see how gene flow improved their fate. To counteract the lack of genetic diversity, researchers added a total of 271 birds from neighboring states to the Illinois populations. This strategy worked. New alleles entered the population, and the egg-hatching rate improved to more than 90%.

> **?** How might gene flow between populations living in different habitats actually interfere with each population's adaptation to its local environment?

The introduction of alleles that may not be beneficial in a particular habitat prevents the population living there from becoming fully adapted to its local conditions.

13.13 Natural selection is the only mechanism that consistently leads to adaptive evolution

Genetic drift, gene flow, and even mutation can cause microevolution. But only by chance could these events result in improving a population's fit to its environment. In natural selection, on the other hand, only the events that produce genetic variation (mutation and sexual reproduction) are random. The process of natural selection, in which better-adapted individuals are more likely to survive and reproduce, is not random. Consequently, only natural selection consistently leads to adaptive evolution— evolution that results in a better fit between organisms and their environment.

The adaptations of organisms include many striking examples. Consider some of the features that make the blue-footed booby (Figure 13.13) suited to its home on the Galápagos Islands. The bird's body and bill are streamlined like a torpedo, minimizing friction as it dives from heights up to 24 m (over 75 feet) into the shallow water below. To pull out of this high-speed dive once it hits the water, the booby uses its large tail as a brake. Its large, webbed feet make great flippers, propelling the bird through the water at high speeds—a huge advantage when hunting fish.

Such adaptations are the result of natural selection. By consistently favoring some alleles over others, natural selection improves the match between organisms and their environment. However, the environment may change over time. As a result, what constitutes a "good match" between

▲ Figure 13.13 Blue-footed booby (*Sula nebouxii*)

an organism and its environment is a moving target, making adaptive evolution a continuous, dynamic process.

Let's take a closer look at natural selection. The commonly used phrases "struggle for existence" and "survival of the fittest" are misleading if we take them to mean direct competition between individuals. There *are* animal species in which individuals lock horns or otherwise do combat to determine mating privilege. But reproductive success is generally more subtle and passive. In a varying population of moths, certain individuals may produce more offspring than others because their wing colors hide them from predators better. Plants in a wildflower population may differ in reproductive success because some attract more pollinators, owing to slight variations in flower color, shape, or fragrance. In a given environment, such traits can lead to greater **relative fitness**: the contribution an individual makes to the gene pool of the next generation relative to the contributions of other individuals. The fittest individuals in the context of evolution are those that produce the largest number of viable, fertile offspring and thus pass on the most genes to the next generation.

> **?** Explain how the phrase "survival of the fittest" differs from the biological definition of relative fitness.

Surviving alone does not guarantee reproductive success. An organism's relative fitness is determined by its number of fertile offspring and thus its relative contribution to the gene pool of the next generation.

13.14 Natural selection can alter variation in a population in three ways

Evolutionary fitness is related to genes, but it is an organism's phenotype—its physical traits, metabolism, and behavior—that is directly exposed to the environment. Let's see how natural selection can affect the distribution of phenotypes using an imaginary mouse population that has a heritable variation in fur coloration. The bell-shaped curve in the top graph of Figure 13.14 depicts the frequencies of individuals in an initial population in which fur color varies along a continuum from very light (only a few individuals) through various intermediate shades (many individuals) to very dark (a few individuals). The bottom graphs show three ways in which natural selection can alter the phenotypic variation in the mouse population. The blue downward arrows symbolize the pressure of natural selection working against certain phenotypes.

Stabilizing selection favors intermediate phenotypes. In the mouse population depicted in the graph on the bottom left, stabilizing selection has eliminated the extremely light and dark individuals, and the population has a greater number of intermediate phenotypes, which may be best suited to an environment with medium gray rocks. Stabilizing selection typically reduces variation and maintains the status quo for a particular character. For example, this type of selection keeps the majority of human birth weights in the range of 3–4 kg (6.5–9 pounds). For babies a lot smaller or larger than this, infant mortality may be greater.

Directional selection shifts the overall makeup of the population by acting against individuals at *one* of the phenotypic extremes. For the mouse population in the bottom center graph, the trend is toward darker fur color, as might occur if a fire darkened the landscape so that darker fur would more readily camouflage the animal. Directional selection is most common during periods of environmental change or when members of a species migrate to some new habitat with different environmental conditions. The changes we described in populations of insects exposed to pesticides are an example of directional selection. Another example is the increase in beak depth in a population of Galápagos finches following a drought, when the birds that were better able to eat larger seeds were more likely to survive.

Disruptive selection typically occurs when environmental conditions vary in a way that favors individuals at *both* ends of a phenotypic range over individuals with intermediate phenotypes. For the mice in the graph on the bottom right, individuals with light and dark fur have increased numbers. Perhaps the mice colonized a patchy habitat where a background of light soil was studded with areas of dark rocks. Disruptive selection can lead to two or more contrasting phenotypes in the same population. For example, in a population of African black-bellied seedcracker finches, large-billed birds, which specialize in cracking hard seeds, and small-billed birds, which feed mainly on soft seeds, survive better than birds with intermediate-sized bills, which are fairly inefficient at cracking both types of seeds.

Next we consider a special case of selection, one that leads to phenotypic differences between males and females.

> **?** **What type of selection probably resulted in the color variations evident in the garter snakes in Figure 13.8?**
>
> Disruptive selection

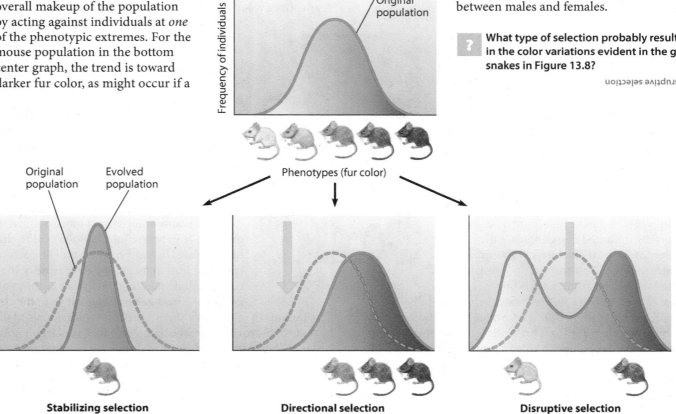

▲ **Figure 13.14** Three possible effects of natural selection on a phenotypic character

Try This Propose hypotheses to explain how natural selection on the original population resulted in each of the evolved populations.

13.15 Sexual selection may lead to phenotypic differences between males and females

Darwin was the first to examine **sexual selection**, a form of natural selection in which individuals with certain traits are more likely than other individuals to obtain mates. The males and females of an animal species obviously have different reproductive organs. But they may also have secondary sexual characteristics, noticeable differences not directly associated with reproduction or survival. This distinction in appearance, called **sexual dimorphism**, is often manifested in a size difference, but it can also include forms of adornment, such as manes on lions or colorful plumage on birds (Figure 13.15A). Males are usually the showier sex, at least among vertebrates.

In some species, individuals compete directly with members of the same sex for mates (Figure 13.15B). This type of sexual selection is called intrasexual selection (within the same sex, most often the males). Contests may involve physical combat, but are more often ritualized displays. Intrasexual selection is frequently found in species where the winning individual acquires a harem of mates.

In a more common type of sexual selection, called intersexual selection (between sexes) or mate choice, individuals of one sex (usually females) are choosy in selecting their mates. Males with the largest or most colorful adornments are often the most attractive to females. The extraordinary feathers of a peacock's tail are an example of this sort of "choose me" statement. What intrigued Darwin is that some of these mate-attracting features do not seem to be otherwise adaptive and may in fact pose some risks. For example, showy plumage may make male birds more visible to predators. But if such secondary sexual characteristics help a male gain a mate, then they will be reinforced over the generations for the most Darwinian of reasons—because they enhance reproductive success. Every time a female chooses a mate based on a certain appearance or behavior, she perpetuates the alleles that influenced her to make that choice and allows a male with that particular phenotype to perpetuate his alleles.

What is the advantage to females of being choosy? One hypothesis is that females prefer male traits that are correlated with "good genes." In several bird species, research has shown that traits preferred by females, such as bright beaks or long tails, are related to overall male health. The "good genes" hypothesis was also tested in gray tree frogs. Female frogs prefer to mate with males that give long mating calls (Figure 13.15C). Researchers collected eggs from wild gray tree frogs. Half of each female's eggs were fertilized with sperm from long-calling males, and the others with sperm from short-calling males. The offspring of long-calling male frogs grew bigger, grew faster, and survived better than their half-siblings fathered by short-calling males. The duration of a male's mating call was shown to be indicative of the male's overall genetic quality, supporting the hypothesis that female mate choice can be based on a trait that indicates whether the male has "good genes."

Next we return to the concept of directional selection, focusing on the evolution of drug resistance in microorganisms that cause disease.

▲ **Figure 13.15A** Extreme sexual dimorphism (peacock and peahen)

▲ **Figure 13.15B** A contest for access to mates between two male elks

▲ **Figure 13.15C** A male gray tree frog calling for mates

? Males with the most elaborate ornamentation may garner the most mates. How might choosing such a mate be advantageous to a female?

An elaborate display may signal good health and therefore good genes, which in turn could be passed along to the female's offspring.

13.16 The evolution of drug-resistant microorganisms is a serious public health concern

EVOLUTION CONNECTION

Antibiotics are drugs that kill infectious microorganisms. Penicillin, the first antibiotic to be developed, has been widely prescribed since the 1940s. A revolution in human health followed its introduction, rendering many previously fatal diseases easily curable. During the 1950s, some medical experts even thought the age of human infectious diseases would soon be over.

Why didn't that optimistic forecast come true? It did not take into account the force of evolution. In the same way that pesticides select for resistant insects, antibiotics select for resistant bacteria. A gene that codes for an enzyme that breaks down an antibiotic or a mutation that alters the site where an antibiotic binds can make a bacterium and its offspring resistant to that antibiotic. Again we see both the random and nonrandom aspects of natural selection—the random genetic mutations in bacteria and the nonrandom selective effects as the environment favors the antibiotic-resistant phenotype.

In what ways do we contribute to the problem of antibiotic resistance? Livestock producers add antibiotics to animal feed as a growth promoter and to prevent illness. These practices may select for bacteria that are resistant to standard antibiotics. Doctors may overprescribe antibiotics—for example, to patients with viral infections, which do not respond to antibiotic treatment. And patients may misuse prescribed antibiotics by prematurely stopping the medication because they feel better. This allows mutant bacteria that may be killed more slowly by the drug to survive and multiply. Subsequent mutations in such bacteria may lead to full-blown antibiotic resistance.

Difficulty in treating certain bacterial infections is a serious public health concern. Penicillin is virtually useless today in its original form. New drugs have been developed, but they are rendered ineffective as resistant bacteria evolve. Natural selection for antibiotic resistance is particularly strong in hospitals, where antibiotic use is extensive. A formidable "superbug" known as MRSA (methicillin-resistant *Staphylococcus aureus*) can cause "flesh-eating disease" **(Figure 13.16)** and

How does evolution hinder attempts to eradicate disease?

potentially fatal systemic (whole-body) infections. Incidents of MRSA infections in both hospital and community settings continue to increase.

MRSA is not the only antibiotic-resistant microorganism—medical and pharmaceutical researchers are engaged in a race against the powerful force of evolution on many fronts. In 2013, the Centers for Disease Control reported that drug-resistant microorganisms infect more than two million people in the United States each year, and 23,000 people die from their infections. At least a dozen bacterial infections are no longer treatable with standard antibiotics. The most recent "superbug" to emerge is a strain of the bacteria that causes gonorrhea, a sexually transmitted disease. Public health officials fear that as this strain spreads, gonorrhea will become an incurable disease. And, as you learned in the chapter introduction, the decreasing effectiveness of chloroquine against malaria also resulted from the evolution of drug resistance in populations of the parasite that causes the disease. Experts know that resistance to artemisinin, currently the most effective drug, is only a matter of time. Indeed, artemisinin-resistant malaria has already been detected in Southeast Asia.

? **Explain why the following statement is incorrect: "Antibiotics have created resistant bacteria."**

● The use of antibiotics did not cause bacteria to make new alleles. Rather, antibiotic use has increased the frequency of alleles for resistance that were already naturally present in bacterial populations.

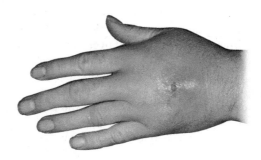

▲ **Figure 13.16** A MRSA skin infection

13.17 Diploidy and balancing selection preserve genetic variation

Natural selection acting on some variants within a population adapts that population to its environment. But what prevents natural selection from eliminating all variation as it selects against unfavorable genotypes? Why aren't less adaptive alleles eliminated as the "best" alleles are passed to the next generation? It turns out that the tendency for natural selection to reduce variation in a population is countered by mechanisms that maintain variation.

Most eukaryotes are diploid. Having two sets of chromosomes helps to prevent populations from becoming genetically uniform. As you know, natural selection acts on the phenotype, and recessive alleles only influence the phenotype of a homozygous recessive individual. In a heterozygote, a recessive allele is, in effect, protected from natural selection. The "hiding" of recessive alleles in heterozygotes can maintain a huge pool of alleles that may not be favored under present conditions but that could be advantageous if the environment changes.

In some cases, genetic variation is preserved rather than reduced by natural selection. **Balancing selection** occurs when natural selection maintains stable frequencies of two or more phenotypic forms in a population.

Heterozygote advantage is a type of balancing selection in which heterozygous individuals have greater reproductive success than either type of homozygote, with the result that two or more alleles for a gene are maintained in the population. An example of heterozygote advantage is the protection from malaria conferred by sickle hemoglobin (see Module 9.13). The frequency of the sickle-cell allele is generally highest in areas where malaria is a major cause of death, such as West Africa. Heterozygotes are protected from the most severe effects of malaria. Individuals who are homozygous for the normal hemoglobin allele are selected against by malaria. Individuals homozygous for the sickle-cell allele are selected against by sickle-cell disease. Thus, sickle hemoglobin is an evolutionary response to a fatal disease that first emerged in the environment of humans around 10,000 years ago. Notice that it is not an ideal solution—even heterozygotes may have health problems—but adaptations are often compromises.

Frequency-dependent selection is a type of balancing selection that maintains two different phenotypic forms in a population. In this case, selection acts against either phenotypic form if it becomes too common in the population. An example of frequency-dependent selection is a scale-eating fish in Lake Tanganyika, Africa, which attacks other fish from behind, darting in to remove a few scales from the side of its prey **(Figure 13.17)**. These fish are either "left-mouthed" or "right-mouthed," a heritable character. Because its mouth twists to the left, a left-mouthed fish always attacks its prey's

right side—try twisting your lower jaw and lips to the left and imagine which side of a fish you could take a bite from. Similarly, a right-mouthed fish attacks from the left. Prey fish guard more effectively against attack from whichever phenotype is most common. As a result, scale-eating fish with the less common phenotype have a feeding advantage that enhances survival and reproductive success. According to a recent study, frequency-dependent selection keeps each phenotype close to 50%.

Some of the genetic variation in a population probably has little or no impact on reproductive success. But even if only a fraction of the variation in a gene pool affects reproductive success, that is still an enormous resource of raw material for natural selection and the adaptive evolution it brings about.

> **?** Why would natural selection tend to reduce genetic variation more in populations of haploid organisms than in populations of diploid organisms?
>
> ● All alleles in a haploid organism are phenotypically expressed and are hence screened by natural selection.

"Left-mouthed"

"Right-mouthed"

▲ **Figure 13.17**　Left-mouthed and right-mouthed scale-eating fish (*Perissodus microlepis*)

13.18　Natural selection cannot fashion perfect organisms

Though natural selection leads to adaptation, there are several reasons why nature abounds with organisms that seem to be less than ideally "engineered" for their lifestyles.

1. *Selection can act only on existing variations.* Natural selection favors only the fittest variants from the phenotypes that are available, which may not be the ideal traits. New, advantageous alleles do not arise on demand.

2. *Evolution is limited by historical constraints.* Each species has a legacy of descent with modification from ancestral forms. Evolution does not scrap ancestral anatomy and build each new complex structure from scratch; it co-opts existing structures and adapts them to new situations. Thus, as birds and bats evolved from four-legged ancestors, their existing forelimbs took on new functions for flight and each lineage was left with only two limbs for walking.

3. *Adaptations are often compromises.* Each organism must do many different things. A blue-footed booby uses its webbed feet to swim after prey in the ocean, but these same feet make for clumsy travel on land.

4. *Chance, natural selection, and the environment interact.* Chance events often affect the genetic makeup of populations. When a storm blows insects over an ocean to an island, the wind does not necessarily transport the individuals that are best suited to the new environment. In small populations, genetic drift can result in the loss of beneficial alleles. In addition, the environment may change unpredictably from year to year, again limiting the extent to which adaptive evolution results in a close match between organisms and the environment.

With all these constraints, we cannot expect evolution to craft perfect organisms. Natural selection operates on a "better than" basis. Evidence for evolution is seen in the imperfections of the organisms it produces as well as in adaptations.

> **?** Humans owe much of their physical versatility and athleticism to their flexible limbs and joints. But we are prone to sprains, torn ligaments, and dislocations. Why?
>
> ● Adaptations are compromises: Structural reinforcement has been compromised as agility was selected for.

CHAPTER **13** REVIEW

For practice quizzes, BioFlix animations, MP3 tutorials, video tutors, and more study tools designed for this textbook, go to

MasteringBiology®

Reviewing the Concepts

Darwin's Theory of Evolution (13.1–13.7)

13.1 A sea voyage helped Darwin frame his theory of evolution. Darwin's theory differed greatly from the long-held notion of a young Earth inhabited by unchanging species. Darwin called his theory descent with modification, which explains that all of life is connected by common ancestry and that descendants have accumulated adaptations to changing environments over vast spans of time.

13.2 The study of fossils provides strong evidence for evolution. The fossil record reveals the historical sequence in which organisms have evolved.

13.3 Fossils of transitional forms support Darwin's theory of evolution.

13.4 Homologies provide strong evidence for evolution. Structural and molecular homologies reveal evolutionary relationships.

13.5 Homologies indicate patterns of descent that can be shown on an evolutionary tree.

13.6 Darwin proposed natural selection as the mechanism of evolution.

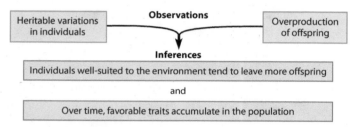

13.7 Scientists can observe natural selection in action.

The Evolution of Populations (13.8–13.11)

13.8 Mutation and sexual reproduction produce the genetic variation that makes evolution possible.

13.9 Evolution occurs within populations. Microevolution is a change in the frequencies of alleles in a population's gene pool.

13.10 The Hardy-Weinberg equation can test whether a population is evolving. The Hardy-Weinberg principle states that allele and genotype frequencies will remain constant if a population is large, mating is random, and there is no mutation, gene flow, or natural selection.

Allele frequencies	$p + q = 1$
Genotype frequencies	$p^2 + 2pq + q^2 = 1$

Dominant homozygotes — Heterozygotes — Recessive homozygotes

13.11 The Hardy-Weinberg equation is useful in public health science.

Mechanisms of Microevolution (13.12–13.18)

13.12 Natural selection, genetic drift, and gene flow can cause microevolution. The bottleneck effect and founder effect lead to genetic drift.

13.13 Natural selection is the only mechanism that consistently leads to adaptive evolution. Relative fitness is the relative contribution an individual makes to the gene pool of the next generation. As a result of natural selection, favorable traits increase in a population.

13.14 Natural selection can alter variation in a population in three ways.

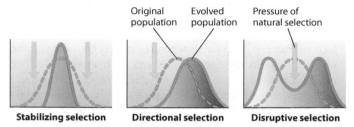

13.15 Sexual selection may lead to phenotypic differences between males and females. Secondary sex characteristics can give individuals an advantage in mating.

13.16 The evolution of drug-resistant microorganisms is a serious public health concern.

13.17 Diploidy and balancing selection preserve genetic variation. Diploidy preserves variation by "hiding" recessive alleles. Balancing selection may result from heterozygote advantage or frequency-dependent selection.

13.18 Natural selection cannot fashion perfect organisms. Natural selection can act only on available variation; anatomical structures result from modified ancestral forms; adaptations are often compromises; and chance, natural selection, and the environment interact.

Connecting the Concepts

1. Summarize the key points of Darwin's theory of descent with modification, including his proposed mechanism of evolution.
2. Complete this concept map describing potential causes of evolutionary change within populations.

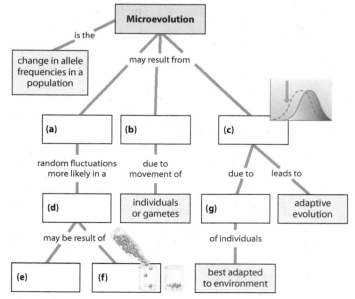

Testing Your Knowledge

Level 1: Knowledge/Comprehension

3. Which of the following did not influence Darwin as he synthesized the theory of evolution by natural selection?
   a. examples of artificial selection that produce large and relatively rapid changes in domesticated species
   b. Lyell's *Principles of Geology*, on gradual geologic changes
   c. comparisons of fossils with living organisms
   d. Mendel's paper describing the laws of inheritance

4. Natural selection is sometimes described as "survival of the fittest." Which of the following best measures an organism's fitness?
   a. how many fertile offspring it produces
   b. how strong it is when pitted against others of its species
   c. its ability to withstand environmental extremes
   d. how much food it is able to make or obtain

5. In an area of erratic rainfall, a biologist found that grass plants with alleles for curled leaves reproduced better in dry years, and plants with alleles for flat leaves reproduced better in wet years. This situation would tend to _____. (*Explain your answer.*)
   a. cause genetic drift in the grass population.
   b. preserve genetic variation in the grass population.
   c. lead to stabilizing selection in the grass population.
   d. lead to uniformity in the grass population.

6. If an allele is recessive and lethal in homozygotes before they reproduce,
   a. the allele will be removed from the population by natural selection in approximately 1,000 years.
   b. the allele will likely remain in the population at a low frequency because it cannot be selected against in heterozygotes.
   c. the fitness of the homozygous recessive genotype is 0.
   d. both b and c are correct.

7. In a population with two alleles, B and b, the allele frequency of b is 0.4. B is dominant to b. What is the frequency of individuals with the dominant phenotype if the population is in Hardy-Weinberg equilibrium?
   a. 0.16
   b. 0.36
   c. 0.48
   d. 0.84

8. Within a few weeks of treatment with the drug 3TC, a patient's HIV population consists entirely of 3TC-resistant viruses. How can this result best be explained?
   a. HIV can change its surface proteins and resist vaccines.
   b. The patient must have become reinfected with a resistant virus.
   c. A few drug-resistant viruses were present at the start of treatment, and natural selection increased their frequency.
   d. HIV began making drug-resistant versions of its enzymes in response to the drug.

Level 2: Application/Analysis

9. In the late 18th century, machines that could blast through rock to build roads and railways were invented, exposing deep layers of rocks. How would you expect this development to aid the science of paleontology?

10. Write a paragraph briefly describing the kinds of scientific evidence for evolution.

11. In the early 1800s, French naturalist Jean Baptiste Lamarck suggested that the best explanation for the relationship of fossils to current organisms is that life evolves. He proposed that by using or not using its body parts, an individual may change its traits and then pass those changes on to its offspring. He suggested, for instance, that the ancestors of the giraffe had lengthened their necks by stretching higher and higher into the trees to reach leaves. Evaluate Lamarck's hypotheses from the perspective of present-day scientific knowledge.

12. Sickle-cell disease is caused by a recessive allele. Roughly one out of every 400 African Americans (0.25%) is afflicted with sickle-cell disease. Use the Hardy-Weinberg equation to calculate the percentage of African Americans who are carriers of the sickle-cell allele. (*Hint*: $q^2 = 0.0025$.)

13. It seems logical that natural selection would work toward genetic uniformity; the genotypes that are most fit produce the most offspring, increasing the frequency of adaptive alleles and eliminating less adaptive alleles. Yet there remains a great deal of genetic variation within populations. Describe some of the factors that contribute to this variation.

Level 3: Synthesis/Evaluation

14. **SCIENTIFIC THINKING** Cetaceans are fully aquatic mammals that evolved from terrestrial ancestors. Gather information about the respiratory system of cetaceans and describe how it illustrates the statement made in Module 13.18 that "Evolution is limited by historical constraints."

15. A population of snails is preyed on by birds that break the snails open on rocks, eat the soft bodies, and leave the shells. The snails occur in both striped and unstriped forms. In one area, researchers counted both live snails and broken shells. Their data are summarized below:

	Striped	Unstriped	Total	Percent Striped
Living	264	296	560	47.1
Broken	486	377	863	56.3

Which snail form seems better adapted to this environment? Why? Predict how the frequencies of striped and unstriped snails might change in the future.

16. Advocates of "scientific creationism" and "intelligent design" lobby school districts for such things as a ban on teaching evolution, equal time in science classes to teach alternative versions of the origin and history of life, or disclaimers in textbooks stating that evolution is "just a theory." They argue that it is only fair to let students evaluate both evolution and the idea that all species were created by God as the Bible relates or that, because organisms are so complex and well adapted, they must have been created by an intelligent designer. Do you think that alternative views of evolution should be taught in science courses? Why or why not?

Answers to all questions can be found in Appendix 4.

14

The Origin of Species

Compared to many male birds that sport brilliant plumage—the shimmering eyes of the peacock's tail or the fire-engine red feathers of the cardinal, for example—the Vogelkop bowerbird (*Amblyornis inornata*) is a rather dull fellow. However, he does have a unique talent: He's a fabulous decorator. Bowerbirds, which are native to New Guinea and Australia, are named for the structure, called a bower, that the male weaves from twigs and grasses to attract females. The hut-style bower shown in the photo below, built by a Vogelkop bowerbird, is about two meters (6.5 feet) wide and one meter high.

After completing his elaborate construction project, the male bowerbird collects objects such as fruits, seeds, insect parts, rocks, flowers, and leaves and arranges them artfully by color and type. Individual males differ in their preferences for certain colors and arrangements of objects. Females tour the bowers of local males, inspecting each bower carefully while its owner courts her with a song and dance. A female may visit promising candidates multiple times before finally mating with one.

? *Can we observe speciation occurring?*

Not all Vogelkop bowerbirds construct displays like the one in the photo. The males of another population build a simpler structure consisting of sticks loosely woven around a central sapling. The objects ornamenting the display are all drab-colored. Researchers hypothesize that this divergence in display preferences has started the two populations on separate evolutionary paths, with each path leading to a new species, or speciation.

In this chapter, we explore how natural selection, which adapts a population to its environment, and other processes may lead to speciation—the origin of new species. Speciation is responsible for the amazing diversity of life on Earth. We begin with the biological definition of a species and describe the mechanisms through which new species may evolve. We also explore some of the evidence for speciation and how scientists study this evolutionary process.

BIG IDEAS

Defining Species
(14.1–14.3)

A species can be defined as a group of populations whose members can produce fertile offspring.

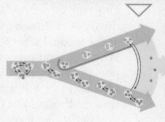

Mechanisms of Speciation
(14.4–14.11)

Speciation can take place with or without geographic isolation, as long as reproductive barriers evolve that keep species separate.

277

▷ Defining Species

14.1 The origin of species is the source of biological diversity

Darwin was eager to explore landforms newly emerged from the sea when he came to the Galápagos Islands. He noted that these volcanic islands, despite their geologic youth, were teeming with plants and animals found nowhere else in the world. He realized that these species, like the islands, were relatively new. He wrote in his diary: "Both in space and time, we seem to be brought somewhat near to that great fact—that mystery of mysteries—the first appearance of new beings on this Earth."

Even though Darwin titled his seminal work *On the Origin of Species by Means of Natural Selection*, most of his theory of evolution focused on the role of natural selection in the gradual adaptation of a population to its environment. We call this process microevolution—changes in the gene pool of a population from one generation to the next (see Module 13.9). But if microevolution were *all* that happened, then Earth would be inhabited only by a highly adapted version of the first form of life.

The "mystery of mysteries" that fascinated Darwin is **speciation**, the process by which one species splits into two or more species. He envisioned the history of life as a tree, with multiple branchings from a common trunk out to the tips of the youngest twigs (Figure 14.1).

Each time speciation occurs, the diversity of life increases. Over the course of 3.5 billion years, an ancestral species first gave rise to two or more different species, which then branched to new lineages, which branched again, until we arrive at the millions of species that live, or once lived, on Earth. This origin of species explains both the diversity and the unity of life. When one species splits into two, the new species share many characteristics because they are descended from a common ancestor.

? How does microevolution differ from speciation?

● Microevolution involves evolutionary changes within a population; speciation occurs when a population changes enough that it diverges from its parent species and becomes a new species.

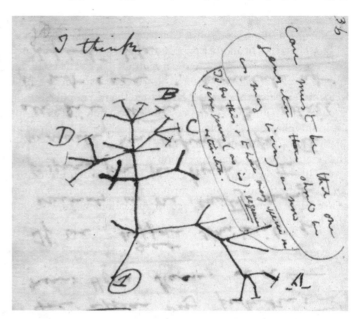

▲ **Figure 14.1** Sketch made by Darwin as he pondered the origin of species

14.2 There are several ways to define a species

The word *species* is from the Latin for "kind" or "appearance," and indeed, even young children learn to distinguish between kinds of plants and animals—between roses and dandelions or dogs and cats—from differences in their appearance. Although the basic idea of species as distinct life-forms seems intuitive, devising a more formal definition is not so easy.

In many cases, the differences between two species are obvious. In other cases, the differences between two species are not so obvious. Although the two birds in **Figure 14.2A** look much the same, they are different species—the one on the left is an eastern meadowlark (*Sturnella magna*); the bird on the right is a western meadowlark (*Sturnella neglecta*). They are distinct species because their songs and other behaviors are different enough that each type of meadowlark breeds only with individuals of its own species.

How similar are members of the same species? Whereas the individuals of many species exhibit fairly limited variation in physical appearance, certain other species—our own, for example—seem extremely varied. The physical diversity

▲ **Figure 14.2A** Similarity between two species: the eastern meadowlark (left) and western meadowlark (right)

within our species (partly illustrated in **Figure 14.2B**, on the facing page) might lead you to guess that there are several human species. Despite these outward appearances, however, humans all belong to the same species, *Homo sapiens*.

▲ **Figure 14.2B** Diversity within one species

The Biological Species Concept How then do biologists define a species? And what keeps one species distinct from others? The primary definition of species used in this book is called the **biological species concept**. It defines a **species** as a group of populations whose members have the potential to interbreed in nature and produce fertile offspring (offspring that themselves can reproduce). A businesswoman in Manhattan may be unlikely to meet a dairy farmer in Mongolia, but if the two should happen to meet and mate, they could have viable babies that develop into fertile adults. Thus, members of a biological species are united by being reproductively compatible, at least potentially.

Members of different species do not usually mate with each other. In effect, **reproductive isolation** prevents genetic exchange (gene flow) and maintains a boundary between species. But there are some pairs of clearly distinct species that do occasionally interbreed. The resulting offspring are called **hybrids**. An example is the grizzly bear (*Ursus arctos*) and the polar bear (*Ursus maritimus*), whose hybrid offspring have been called "grolar bears" **(Figure 14.2C)**. The two species have been known to interbreed in zoos, and DNA testing confirmed that a bear shot in 2006 in the Canadian Arctic was a wild polar bear–grizzly offspring. Another grolar bear was shot in 2010, and more sightings have been reported as melting polar sea ice brings the two species into contact more often. Hybridization is much more common in plants than animals and is a major factor in speciation. Clearly, identifying species solely on the basis of reproductive isolation can be more complex than it may seem.

There are other instances in which applying the biological species concept is problematic. For example, there is no way to determine whether organisms that are now known only through fossils were once able to interbreed. Also, this criterion is useless for organisms such as prokaryotes that reproduce asexually. Because of such limitations, alternative species concepts are useful in certain situations.

Other Definitions of Species For most organisms—sexual, asexual, and fossils

alike—classification is based mainly on physical traits such as shape, size, and other features of morphology (form). This **morphological species concept** has been used to identify most of the 1.8 million species that have been named to date. The advantages of this concept are that it can be applied to asexual organisms and fossils and does not require information on possible interbreeding. The disadvantage, however, is that this approach relies on subjective criteria, and researchers may disagree on which features distinguish a species.

Another species definition, the **ecological species concept**, identifies species in terms of their ecological niches, focusing on unique adaptations to particular roles in a biological community (see Module 37.3). For example, two species of fish may be similar in appearance but distinguishable based on what they eat or the depth of water in which they are usually found.

Finally, the **phylogenetic species concept** defines a species as the smallest group of individuals that share a common ancestor and thus form one branch on the tree of life. Biologists trace the phylogenetic history of such a species by comparing its characteristics, such as morphology, DNA sequences, or biochemical pathways, with those of other organisms. These sorts of analyses can distinguish groups that are generally similar yet different enough to be considered separate species. Of course, agreeing on the amount of difference required to establish separate species remains a challenge.

Each species definition is useful, depending on the situation and the questions being asked. The biological species concept, however, helps focus on how these discrete groups of organisms arise and are maintained by reproductive isolation. Because reproductive isolation is an essential factor in the evolution of many species, we look at it more closely next.

Grizzly bear

Polar bear

Hybrid "grolar" bear

▲ **Figure 14.2C** Hybridization between two species of bears

? **Which species concepts could you apply to both asexual and sexual species? Explain.**

The morphological, ecological, and phylogenetic species concepts could all be used because they do not rely on the criterion of reproductive isolation.

14.3 Reproductive barriers keep species separate

Clearly, a fly will not mate with a frog or a fern. But what prevents species that are closely related from interbreeding? Reproductive isolation depends on one or more types of reproductive barriers—biological features of the organism that prevent individuals of different species from interbreeding. The various types of reproductive barriers that isolate the gene pools of species can be categorized as either prezygotic or postzygotic, depending on whether they function before or after zygotes (fertilized eggs) form. **Prezygotic barriers** prevent mating or fertilization between species. **Postzygotic barriers** operate after hybrid zygotes have formed.

PREZYGOTIC BARRIERS

The garter snake *Thamnophis atratus* lives mainly in water.

The eastern spotted skunk (*Spilogale putorius*) breeds in late winter.

The blue-footed booby (*Sula nebouxii*) performs an elaborate courtship dance.

Heliconia pogonantha is pollinated by hummingbirds with long, curved bills.

Type of isolation	**Habitat** Lack of opportunities to encounter each other	**Temporal** Breeding at different times or seasons	**Behavioral** Failure to send or receive appropriate signals	**Mechanical** Physical incompatibility of reproductive parts

The garter snake *Thamnophis sirtalis* lives on land.

The western spotted skunk (*Spilogale gracilis*) breeds in the fall.

The masked booby (*Sula dactylatra*) performs a different courtship ritual.

Heliconia latispatha is pollinated by hummingbirds with short, straight bills.

Species are not necessarily separated by obvious physical barriers. These snakes occupy different habitats in the same area.

Temporal isolation also happens in plants that flower during different seasons or open flowers at different times during the day.

In another example, male fireflies signal to females of the same species by blinking their lights in the particular rhythm of their species. Females respond only to that rhythm.

Pollinators pick up pollen from the male parts of one flower and transfer it to the female parts of another flower. Floral characteristics determine the best fit between pollinator and flower.

POSTZYGOTIC BARRIERS

Reduced hybrid viability
Interaction of parental genes impairs the hybrid's development or survival.

Some species of salamander can hybridize, but their offspring do not develop fully or, like this one, are frail and will not survive long enough to reproduce.

Purple sea urchin (*Strongylocentrotus purpuratus*)

Gametic
Molecular incompatibility of eggs and sperm or pollen and stigma

Reduced hybrid fertility
Hybrids are vigorous but cannot produce viable offspring.

The hybrid offspring of a horse and a donkey is a mule, which is robust but sterile.

Red sea urchin (*Strongylocentrotus franciscanus*)

Hybrid breakdown
Hybrids are viable and fertile, but their offspring are feeble or sterile.

The rice hybrids on the left and right are fertile, but plants of the next generation (middle) are sterile.

Sea urchins release their gametes into the water. Surface proteins prevent the gametes of different species from binding to each other.

If chromosomes of the parent species differ in number or structure, meiosis in hybrids may fail to produce normal gametes.

? Two closely related fish live in the same lake, but one feeds along the shoreline and the other is a bottom feeder in deep water. This is an example of _____ isolation, which is a _____ reproductive barrier.

habitat . . . prezygotic

14.4 In allopatric speciation, geographic isolation leads to speciation

A key event in the origin of a new species is the separation of a population from other populations of the same species. With its gene pool isolated, the splinter population can follow its own evolutionary course. Changes in allele frequencies caused by natural selection, genetic drift, and mutation will not be diluted by alleles entering from other populations (gene flow). The initial block to gene flow may come from a geographic barrier that isolates a population. This mode of speciation is called **allopatric speciation** (from the Greek *allos*, other, and *patra*, fatherland). Populations separated by a geographic barrier are known as allopatric populations.

Geographic Barriers   Several geologic processes can isolate populations. A mountain range may emerge and gradually split a population of organisms that can inhabit only lowlands. A large lake may subside until there are several smaller lakes, isolating certain fish populations. On a larger scale, continents themselves can split and move apart (see Module 15.7). Allopatric speciation can also occur when individuals colonize a remote area and become geographically isolated from the parent population.

How large must a geographic barrier be to keep allopatric populations apart? The answer depends on the ability of the organisms to move. Birds, mountain lions, and coyotes can easily cross mountain ranges. The windblown pollen of trees is not hindered by such barriers, and the seeds of many plants may be carried back and forth by animals. In contrast, small rodents may find a canyon or a wide river a formidable barrier. The Grand Canyon and Colorado River (**Figure 14.4A**) separate two species of antelope squirrels. Harris's antelope squirrel (*Ammospermophilus harrisii*) inhabits the south rim. Just a few kilometers away on the north rim, but separated by the deep and wide canyon, lives the closely related white-tailed antelope squirrel (*Ammospermophilus leucurus*).

Evidence of Allopatric Speciation   Many studies provide evidence that speciation has occurred in allopatric populations. An interesting example is the 30 species of snapping shrimp in the genus *Alpheus* that live off the Isthmus of Panama, the land

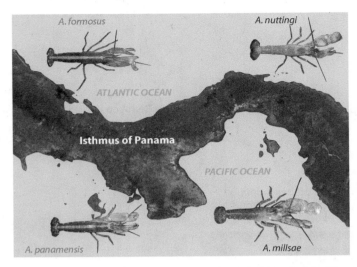

▲ Figure 14.4B   Allopatric speciation in snapping shrimp: 2 of the 15 pairs of shrimp species that are separated by the Isthmus of Panama

bridge that connects South and North America (**Figure 14.4B**). Snapping shrimp are named for the snapping together of their single oversized claw, which creates a high-pressure blast that stuns their prey. Morphological and genetic data group these shrimp into 15 pairs of species, with the members of each pair being each other's closest relative. In each case, one member of the pair lives on the Atlantic side of the isthmus, while the other lives on the Pacific side, strongly suggesting that geographic separation of the ancestral species of these snapping shrimp led to allopatric speciation.

> **?**   **Geologic evidence indicates that the Isthmus of Panama gradually closed about 3 million years ago. Genetic analyses indicate that the various species of snapping shrimp originated from 9 to 3 million years ago, with the species pairs that live in deepest water diverging first. How would you interpret these data?**
>
> ● The deeper species would have been separated into two isolated populations first, which enabled them to diverge into new species first.

▲ Figure 14.4A   Allopatric speciation of geographically isolated antelope squirrels

14.5 Reproductive barriers can evolve as populations diverge

Geographic isolation creates opportunities for speciation, but it does not necessarily lead to new species. Speciation occurs only when the gene pool undergoes changes that establish reproductive barriers such as those described in Module 14.3. What might cause such barriers to arise? The environment of an isolated population may include different food sources, different types of pollinators, and different predators. As a result of natural selection acting on preexisting variations (or as a result of genetic drift or mutation), a population's traits may change in ways that also establish reproductive barriers.

Researchers have successfully documented the evolution of reproductive isolation with laboratory experiments. While at Yale University, Diane Dodd tested the hypothesis that reproductive barriers can evolve as a by-product of changes in populations as they adapt to different environments. Dodd raised fruit flies on different food sources. Some populations were fed starch; others were fed maltose. After about 40 generations, populations raised on starch digested starch more efficiently, and those raised on maltose digested maltose more efficiently.

Dodd then combined flies from various populations in mating experiments. Figure 14.5A shows some of her results. When flies from "starch populations" were mixed with flies from "maltose populations," the flies mated more frequently with partners raised on the same food source (left grid), even when the partners came from different populations. In one of the control tests (right grid), flies taken from different populations adapted to starch were about as likely to mate with each other as with flies from their own populations. The mating preference shown in the experimental group is an example of a prezygotic barrier. The reproductive barrier was not absolute—some mating between maltose flies and starch flies did occur—but reproductive isolation was under way as these allopatric populations became adapted to different environments.

In plants, pollinator choice is often a reproductive barrier. Perhaps populations of an ancestral species became separated in environments that had either more hummingbirds than bees or vice versa. Flower color and shape would evolve through natural selection in ways that attracted the most common pollinator, and these changes would help separate the species should they later share the same region. For example, two closely related species of monkey flower are found in the same area of the Sierra Nevada, but they rarely interbreed. Bumblebees prefer the pink-flowered *Mimulus lewisii*, and hummingbirds prefer the red-flowered *Mimulus cardinalis*. Scientists experimentally exchanged the alleles for flower color between these two species. As a result, *M. lewisii* produced light orange flowers (Figure 14.5B) that received many more visits from hummingbirds than did the normal pink-flowered *M. lewisii*. *M. cardinalis* plants with the *M. lewisii* allele produced pinker flowers that received many more visits from bumblebees than the normal red-flowered plants. Thus, a change in flower color influenced pollinator preference, which normally provides a reproductive barrier between these two species.

Sometimes reproductive barriers can arise even when populations are not geographically separated, as we see next.

> **?** Females of the Galápagos finch *Geospiza difficilis* respond to the songs of males from their island but ignore songs of males from other islands. How would you interpret these findings?
>
> ● Behavioral barriers to reproduction have begun to develop in these allopatric (geographically separated) finch populations.

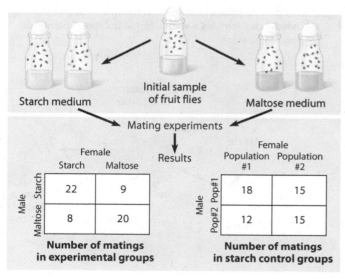

▲ **Figure 14.5A** Evolution of reproductive barriers in laboratory populations of fruit flies adapted to different food sources

Try This In your own words, explain how the experiment was performed and interpret the results.

Pollinator choice in typical monkey flowers

Typical *M. lewisii* (pink)

Typical *M. cardinalis* (red)

Pollinator choice after color allele transfer

M. lewisii with red-color allele

M. cardinalis with pink-color allele

▲ **Figure 14.5B** Effect of changing color of monkey flowers on pollinator choice

14.6 Sympatric speciation takes place without geographic isolation

In **sympatric speciation** (from the Greek *syn*, together, and *patra*, fatherland), a new species arises within the same geographic area as its parent species. How can reproductive isolation develop when members of sympatric populations remain in contact with each other? Sympatric speciation may occur when mating and the resulting gene flow between populations are reduced by factors such as polyploidy, habitat differentiation, and sexual selection.

Many plant species have originated from sympatric speciation that occurs when accidents during cell division result in extra sets of chromosomes. New species formed in this way are **polyploid**, meaning that their cells have more than two complete sets of chromosomes. Figure 14.6A shows one way in which a tetraploid plant (4*n*, with four sets of chromosomes) can arise from a parent species that is diploid. ❶ A failure of cell division after chromosome duplication could double a cell's chromosomes. ❷ If this 4*n* cell gives rise to a tetraploid branch, flowers produced on this branch would produce diploid gametes. ❸ If self-fertilization occurs, as it commonly does in plants, the resulting tetraploid zygotes would develop into plants that can produce fertile tetraploid offspring by self-pollination or by mating with other tetraploids.

A tetraploid cannot, however, produce fertile offspring by mating with a parent plant. The fusion of a diploid (2*n*) gamete from the tetraploid plant and a haploid (*n*) gamete from the diploid parent would produce triploid (3*n*) offspring. Triploid individuals are sterile; they cannot produce normal gametes because the odd number of chromosomes cannot form homologous pairs and separate normally during meiosis (see Module 8.13). Thus, the formation of a tetraploid (4*n*) plant is an instantaneous speciation event: A new species, reproductively isolated from its parent species, is produced in just one generation.

Most polyploid species, however, arise from hybridization of two different species. Figure 14.6B illustrates one way in which this can happen. ❶ When haploid gametes from two different species combine, the resulting hybrid is normally sterile because its chromosomes cannot pair during meiosis. ❷ However, the hybrid may reproduce asexually, as many plants can do. ❸ Subsequent errors in cell division may produce chromosome duplications that result in a diploid set of chromosomes (2*n* = 10). Now chromosomes *can* pair in meiosis, and haploid gametes will be produced; thus, a fertile polyploid species has formed. The new species has a chromosome number equal to the sum of the diploid chromosome numbers of its parent species. Again, this new species is reproductively isolated, this time from both parent species. Biologists have identified several plant species that originated through these mechanisms within the past 150 years—virtually instantaneously on an evolutionary time scale.

Does polyploid speciation occur in animals? It appears to happen occasionally. For example, the gray tree frog (see Figure 13.15C) is thought to have originated in this way. However, sympatric speciation in animals is

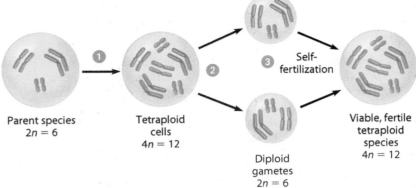

Parent species 2*n* = 6 | **Tetraploid cells** 4*n* = 12 | **Diploid gametes** 2*n* = 6 | Self-fertilization | **Viable, fertile tetraploid species** 4*n* = 12

▲ **Figure 14.6A** Sympatric speciation by polyploidy within a single species

more likely to happen through habitat differentiation or sexual selection than by polyploidy. Both habitat differentiation and sexual selection may have been involved in the origin of several hundred species of small fish called cichlids in Lake Victoria in East Africa. Adaptations for exploiting different food sources may have evolved in different subgroups of the original cichlid population. If those sources were in different habitats, mating between the populations would become rare, isolating their gene pools as each population becomes adapted to a different resource. As you will learn in Module 14.9, speciation in these brightly colored fish may also have been driven by the type of sexual selection in which females choose mates based on coloration. Such mate choice can contribute to reproductively isolating populations, keeping the gene pools of newly forming species separate. Of course, both habitat differentiation and sexual selection can also contribute to the formation of reproductive barriers between allopatric populations.

? Revisit the reproductive barriers in Module 14.3, and choose the barrier that isolates a viable, fertile polyploid plant from its parental species.

● Reduced hybrid fertility

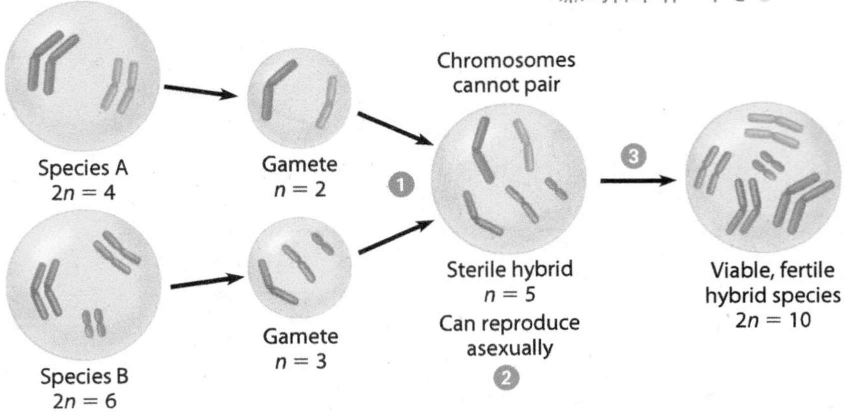

Species A 2*n* = 4 | **Gamete** *n* = 2 | Chromosomes cannot pair | **Sterile hybrid** *n* = 5 Can reproduce asexually | **Viable, fertile hybrid species** 2*n* = 10

Species B 2*n* = 6 | **Gamete** *n* = 3

▲ **Figure 14.6B** Sympatric speciation producing a hybrid polyploid from two different species

Try This Explain how a new species produced by the process shown in this figure differs from a new species produced by the process shown in Figure 14.6A.

14.7 The origin of most plant species can be traced to polyploid speciation

EVOLUTION CONNECTION

Plant biologists estimate that 80% of living plant species are descendants of ancestors that formed by polyploid speciation. Hybridization between two species accounts for most of these species, perhaps because of the adaptive advantage of the diverse genes a hybrid inherits from different parental species.

Many of the plants we grow for food are polyploids, including oats, potatoes, bananas, peanuts, barley, plums, apples, sugarcane, coffee, and wheat. Cotton, also a polyploid, provides one of the world's most popular clothing fibers.

Wheat, the most widely cultivated plant in the world, occurs as 20 different species of *Triticum*. We know that humans were cultivating wheat at least 10,000 years ago because wheat grains of *Triticum monococcum* ($2n = 14$) have been found in the remains of Middle Eastern farming villages from that time. This species has small seed heads and is not highly productive, but some varieties are still grown in the Middle East.

Our most important wheat species is bread wheat (*Triticum aestivum*), a polyploid with 42 chromosomes. **Figure 14.7** illustrates how this species may have evolved; the uppercase letters represent not genes but *sets of chromosomes* that have been traced through the lineage.

❶ The process may have begun with hybridization between two wheats, the cultivated species *T. monococcum* (AA) and one of several wild species that probably grew as weeds at the edges of fields (BB). Chromosome sets A and B of the two species would not have been able to pair at meiosis, making the AB hybrid sterile. ❷ However, an error in cell division and self-fertilization would have produced a new species (AABB) with 28 chromosomes. Today, we know this species as emmer wheat (*T. turgidum*), varieties of which are grown widely in Eurasia and western North America. Emmer wheat is used mainly for making macaroni and other noodle products because its proteins hold their shape better than bread-wheat proteins.

The final steps in the evolution of bread wheat are thought to have occurred in early farming villages on the shores of European lakes more than 8,000 years ago. ❸ The cultivated emmer wheat, with its 28 chromosomes, hybridized spontaneously with the closely related wild species *T. tauschii* (DD), which has 14 chromosomes. The hybrid (ABD, with 21 chromosomes) was sterile, ❹ but a cell division error in this hybrid and self-fertilization doubled the chromosome number to 42. The result was bread wheat, with two each of the three ancestral sets of chromosomes (AABBDD).

Today, plant geneticists generate new polyploids in the laboratory by using chemicals that induce meiotic and mitotic cell division errors. Researchers can produce new hybrids with special qualities, such as a hybrid combining the high yield of wheat with the hardiness of rye.

? **Why are errors in mitosis or meiosis a necessary part of speciation by hybridization between two species?**

If a hybrid has a single copy of the chromosomes from two species, homologous pairs cannot join and separate during meiosis to produce gametes. Errors in mitosis or meiosis must somehow duplicate chromosomes so that there is a diploid number of each set and normal gametes can form.

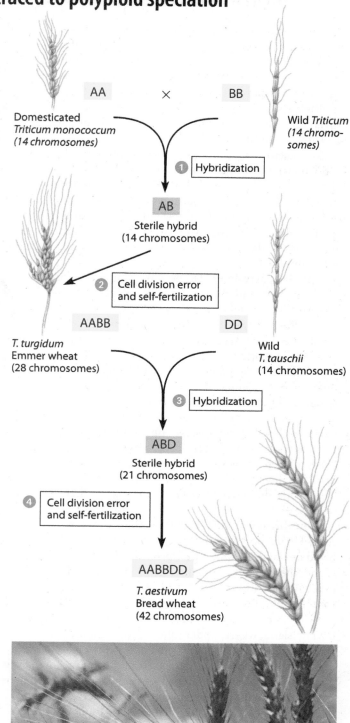

Domesticated *Triticum monococcum* (14 chromosomes)

AA × BB

Wild *Triticum* (14 chromosomes)

❶ Hybridization

AB
Sterile hybrid (14 chromosomes)

❷ Cell division error and self-fertilization

AABB

T. turgidum Emmer wheat (28 chromosomes)

DD

Wild *T. tauschii* (14 chromosomes)

❸ Hybridization

ABD
Sterile hybrid (21 chromosomes)

❹ Cell division error and self-fertilization

AABBDD

T. aestivum Bread wheat (42 chromosomes)

▲ Figure 14.7   The evolution of bread wheat, *Triticum aestivum*

14.8 Isolated islands are often showcases of speciation

Isolated island chains are often inhabited by unique collections of species. Islands that have physically diverse habitats and that are far enough apart to permit populations to evolve in isolation but close enough to allow occasional dispersions to occur are often the sites of multiple speciation events. The evolution of many diverse species from a common ancestor is known as **adaptive radiation**.

The Galápagos Archipelago, located about 900 km (560 miles) west of Ecuador, is one of the world's great showcases of adaptive radiation. Each island was born naked from underwater volcanoes from 5 million to 1 million years ago and was gradually covered by plants, animals, and microorganisms derived from strays that rode the ocean currents and winds from other islands and the South American mainland.

The Galápagos Islands today have numerous plants, snails, reptiles, and birds that are found nowhere else on Earth. For example, they have 14 species of closely related finches, which are often called Darwin's finches because Darwin collected them during his around-the-world voyage on the *Beagle* (see Module 13.1). These birds share many finch-like traits, but they differ in their feeding habits and their beaks, which are specialized for what they eat. Their various foods include insects, large or small seeds, cactus fruits, and even eggs of other species. The woodpecker finch uses cactus spines or twigs as tools to pry insects from trees. The "vampire" finch is noted for pecking wounds on the backs of seabirds and drinking their blood. Figure 14.8 shows some of these birds, with their distinctive beaks adapted for their specific diet.

How might Darwin's finch species have evolved from a small population of ancestral birds that colonized one of the islands? Completely isolated on the island, the founder population may have changed significantly as natural selection adapted it to the new environment, and thus it became a new species. Later, a few individuals of this species may have migrated to a neighboring island, where, under different conditions, this new founder population was changed enough through natural selection to become another new species. Some of these birds may then have recolonized the first island and coexisted there with the original ancestral species if reproductive barriers kept the species distinct. Multiple colonizations and speciations on the many separate islands of the Galápagos probably followed.

Today, each of the Galápagos Islands has several species of finches, with as many as 10 on some islands. The effects of the adaptive radiation of Darwin's finches are evident not just in their many types of beaks but also in their different habitats—some live in trees and others spend most of their time on the ground. Reproductive isolation due to species-specific songs helps keep the species separate. However, occasional interbreeding happens when a male sings the song

Cactus-seed-eater (cactus finch)

Tool-using insect-eater (woodpecker finch)

Seed-eater (large ground finch)

▲ Figure 14.8   Examples of differences in beak shape and size in Galápagos finches, each adapted for a specific diet

of a different species. For example, a cactus finch nestling whose father dies may learn a neighbor's song, even if the neighbor is not a cactus finch.

> **?** **Explain why isolated island chains provide opportunities for adaptive radiations.**

● The chance colonization of an island often presents a species with new resources and an absence of predators. Through natural selection acting on existing variation, the colonizing population becomes adapted to its new habitat and may evolve into a new species. Subsequent colonizations of nearby islands would provide additional opportunities for adaptation and genetic drift, which could lead to further speciations.

14.9 Lake Victoria is a living laboratory for studying speciation

SCIENTIFIC THINKING

In contrast to microevolutionary change, which may be apparent in a population within a few generations, the process of speciation is generally extremely slow. So you may be surprised to learn that we *can* see speciation occurring. Consider that life has been evolving over hundreds of millions of years and will continue to evolve. The species living today represent a snapshot, a brief instant in this vast span of time. The environment continues to change—sometimes rapidly due to human impact—and natural selection continues to act on affected populations. It is reasonable to assume that some of these populations are changing in ways that could eventually lead to speciation. Studying populations as they diverge gives biologists a window on the process of speciation. Researchers have documented at least two dozen cases in which populations are diverging as they exploit different food resources or breed in different habitats.

Can we observe speciation occurring?

The bowerbirds you read about in the chapter introduction provide an example of another means by which populations can diverge—sexual selection (see Module 13.15). Sexual selection is a form of natural selection in which individuals with certain traits are more likely to obtain mates. The authors of the bowerbird study hypothesized that the differences in male displays of the allopatric bowerbird populations resulted from changes in female preferences. Biologists have also identified several other animal populations that are diverging as a result of differences in how males attract females or how females choose mates. Because of its direct effect of reproductive success, sexual selection can interrupt gene flow within a population and may therefore be an important factor in sympatric speciation.

Biologists can also test hypotheses about the process of speciation by studying species that arose recently. Let's look at a series of investigations into the role of sexual selection in the adaptive radiation of cichlids in Lake Victoria (Figure 14.9A).

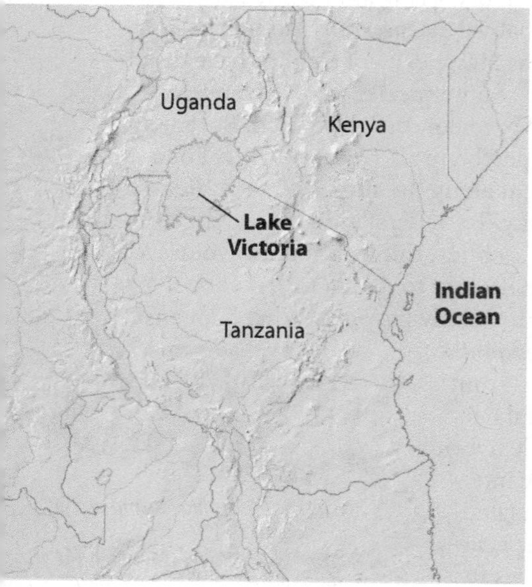

Cichlids are a family of fishes that live in tropical lakes and rivers. They come in all colors of the rainbow, making them favorites of the aquarium trade. Among evolutionary biologists, they are renowned for the spectacular adaptive radiations that stocked the large lakes of East Africa with more than a thousand species of cichlids in less than 100,000 years. In the largest of these lakes, Lake Victoria, roughly 500 species

evolved in about 15,000 years. For comparison, there are approximately 525 species of fish in all the lakes and rivers of Europe combined. How can a single body of water host such diversity? The answer lies partly in the heterogeneity of the environment. Various species have adaptations that suit them to inhabit the lake's rocky shores, muddy bottom, or open water. Specialized feeding adaptations abound. For example, there are algae-scrapers, snail-crushers, leaf-biters, insect-eaters, and fish-hunters. The visual environment, including predominant wavelengths of light and water clarity, is also heterogeneous, a fact that is crucial to speciation via sexual selection.

In Lake Victoria, there are pairs of closely related cichlid species that differ in color but nothing else. Breeding males of *Pundamilia nyererei* have a bright red back and dorsal fin, while *Pundamilia pundamilia* males are metallic blue-gray (Figure 14.9B). Researchers hypothesized that sexual selection—divergent female preference for red or blue mates—led to reproductive isolation. Let's examine the evidence for this hypothesis.

Pundamilia nyererei

Pundamilia females prefer brightly colored males. Mate-choice experiments performed in the laboratory showed that *P. nyererei* females prefer red males over blue males, and *P. pundamilia* females prefer blue males over red males. Furthermore, the vision of *P. nyererei* females is more sensitive to red light than blue light;

Pundamilia pundamilia

▲ **Figure 14.9B** Males of *Pundamilia nyererei* and *Pundamilia pundamilia*

P. pundamilia females are more sensitive to blue light. Researchers also demonstrated that this color sensitivity is heritable.

As mentioned above, the visual environment varies in Lake Victoria. As light travels through water, suspended particles selectively absorb and scatter the shorter (blue) wavelengths, so light becomes increasingly red with increasing depth. Thus, in deeper waters *P. nyererei* males are pleasingly apparent to females with red-sensitive vision but virtually invisible to *P. pundamilia* females. Accordingly, we would expect the two species to breed in different areas of the lake—and they do. When biologists sampled cichlid populations in Lake Victoria, they found that *P. nyererei* breeds in deep water, while *P. pundamilia* inhabits shallower habitats where the blue males shine brightly. As a consequence of their mating behavior, the two species encounter different environments that may result in further divergence.

In recent years, new environmental factors have had a dramatic impact on cichlids. Hybridization is rampant; a multitude of cichlid species have been genetically homogenized. You'll learn why in the next module.

? Why was it important for researchers to establish that cichlid color sensitivity is heritable?

Sensitivity to red is the phenotypic trait that allows *P. nyererei* females to choose *P. nyererei* males as mates, ensuring reproductive isolation.

▲ **Figure 14.9A** Map of East Africa showing Lake Victoria

Uganda
Kenya
Lake Victoria
Indian Ocean
Tanzania

14.10 Hybrid zones provide opportunities to study reproductive isolation

What happens when separated populations of closely related species come back into contact with one another? Will reproductive barriers be strong enough to keep the species separate? Or will the two species interbreed and become one? Biologists attempt to answer such questions by studying **hybrid zones**, regions in which members of different species meet and mate, producing at least some hybrid offspring.

Figure 14.10A illustrates the formation of a hybrid zone, starting with the ancestral species. ① Three populations are connected by gene flow. ② A barrier to gene flow separates one population. ③ Over time, this population diverges from the other two. ④ Later, gene flow is reestablished in the hybrid zone. Let's consider possible outcomes for this hybrid zone over time.

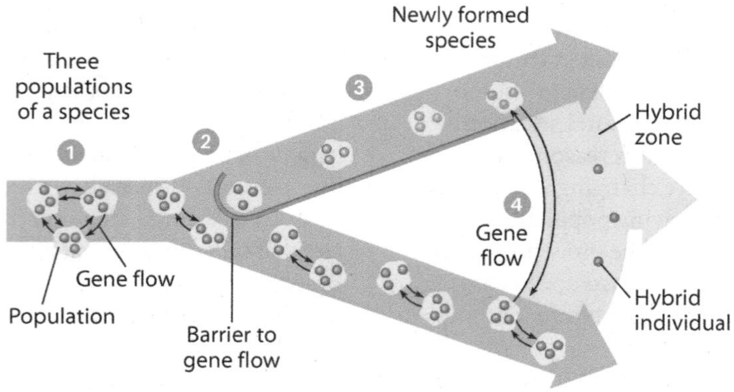

▲ Figure 14.10A Formation of a hybrid zone

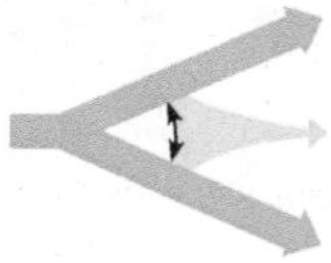

Reinforcement When hybrid offspring are less fit than members of both parent species, we might expect natural selection to strengthen, or *reinforce*, reproductive barriers, thus reducing the formation of unfit hybrids. And we would predict that barriers between species should be stronger where the species overlap (that is, where the species are sympatric).

As an example, consider the closely related collared flycatcher and pied flycatcher illustrated in Figure 14.10B.

When populations of these two species do not overlap (that is, when they are allopatric), males closely resemble each other, with similar black and white coloration (see left side of Figure 14.10B). However, when populations of the two species are sympatric, male collared flycatchers are still black but with enlarged patches of white, whereas male pied flycatchers are a dull brown (see right side of Figure 14.10B). The photographs at the bottom of the figure show two pied flycatchers, the one on the left from a population that has no overlap with collared flycatchers and the one on the right from a population in an area where both species coexist. When scientists performed mate choice experiments, they found that female flycatchers frequently made mistakes when presented with males from allopatric populations, which look similar. But females never selected mates from the other species when presented with males from sympatric populations, which look different. Thus, reproductive barriers are reinforced when populations of these two species overlap.

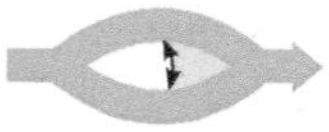

Fusion What happens when the reproductive barriers between species are not strong and the species come into contact in a hybrid zone? So much gene flow may occur that the speciation process reverses, causing the two hybridizing species to fuse into one.

Such a situation has been occurring among the cichlid species in Lake Victoria that we discussed in Module 14.9. Since the 1980s, as many as 200 species of cichlids have disappeared from Lake Victoria. Some species were driven to extinction by an introduced predator, the Nile perch. But many species not eaten by Nile perch are also disappearing. Pollution caused by development along the shores of Lake Victoria has turned the water murky. To understand how water clarity affects sexual selection in cichlids, think about how your eyes work in different lighting. It's easy to distinguish colors in bright light, but difficult in a dimly lit room. What happens when *P. nyererei* or *P. pundamilia* females can't tell red males from blue males? The behavioral barrier crumbles. Many viable hybrid offspring are produced by interbreeding, and the once isolated gene pools of the parent species are combining—two species fusing into a single hybrid species (Figure 14.10C).

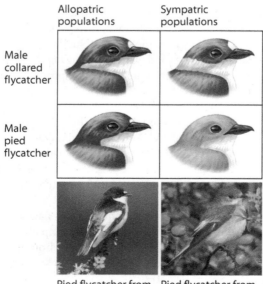

Pied flycatcher from allopatric population   Pied flycatcher from sympatric population

▲ Figure 14.10B   Reinforcement of reproductive barriers

Hybrid: *Pundamilia "turbid water"*

▲ Figure 14.10C   Fusion: hybrid of *Pundamilia nyererei* and *Pundamilia pundamilia* from an area with turbid water

Recently, pollution in Lake Victoria has been greatly reduced, and cichlid numbers—though not diversity—have rebounded. By mixing the unique alleles of separate species into a single gene pool, hybridization can increase a population's genetic variation, which in turn increases the phenotypic variation on which natural selection can act. If environmental conditions continue to improve, biologists may have an opportunity to study a new radiation of cichlid diversity.

 Stability   One might predict that either reinforcement of reproductive barriers or fusion of gene pools would occur in a hybrid zone. However, many hybrid zones are fairly stable, and hybrids continue to be produced. Although these hybrids allow for some gene flow between populations, each species maintains its own integrity. The island inhabited by two finch species that occasionally interbreed (see Module 14.8) is an example of a stable hybrid zone.

> ? **Why might hybrid zones be called "natural laboratories" in which to study speciation?**

● By studying the fate of hybrids over time, scientists can directly observe factors that cause (or fail to cause) reproductive isolation.

14.11 Speciation can occur rapidly or slowly

Biologists continue to make field observations and devise experiments to study evolution in progress. However, much of the evidence for evolution comes from the fossil record. What does this record say about the process of speciation?

Many fossil species appear suddenly in a layer of rock and persist essentially unchanged through several layers (strata) until disappearing just as suddenly. Paleontologists coined the term **punctuated equilibria** to describe these long periods of little apparent morphological change (equilibria) interrupted (punctuated) by relatively brief periods of sudden change. Figure 14.11 (top) illustrates the evolution of two lineages of butterflies in a punctuated pattern. Notice that the butterfly species change little, if at all, once they appear.

Other fossil species appear to have diverged gradually over long periods of time. As shown in Figure 14.11 (bottom), differences gradually accumulate, and new species (represented by the two butterflies at the far right) evolve gradually from the ancestral population.

Even when fossil evidence points to a punctuated pattern, species may not have originated as rapidly as it appears. Suppose that a species survived for 5 million years but that most of the changes in its features occurred during the first 50,000 years of its existence. Time periods this short often cannot be distinguished in fossil strata. And should a new species originate from a small, isolated population—as no doubt many species have—the chances of fossils being found are low.

But what about the total length of time between speciation events—between when a new species forms and when its populations diverge enough to produce another new species? In one survey of 84 groups of plants and animals, this time ranged from 4,000 to 40 million years. Overall, the time between speciation events averaged 6.5 million years. Such long time frames tell us that it has taken vast spans of time for life on Earth to evolve.

As you've seen, speciation may begin with small differences. However, as speciation occurs again and again, these differences accumulate and may eventually lead to new groups that differ greatly from their ancestors, as in the origin of cetaceans from four-legged land animals (see Module 13.3), The cumulative effects of multiple speciations, as well as extinctions, have shaped the dramatic changes documented in the fossil record. (Such macroevolutionary changes are the subject of our next chapter.)

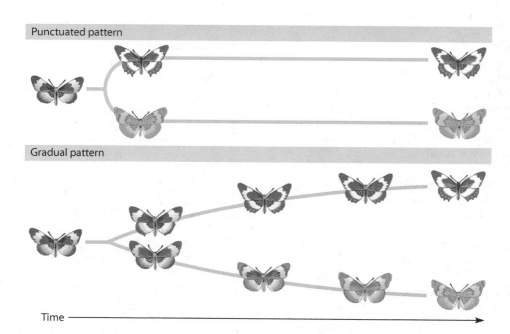

> ? **How does the punctuated equilibrium model account for the relative rarity of transitional fossils linking newer species to older ones?**

● If speciation takes place in a relatively short time or in a small isolated population, the transition of one species to another may be difficult to find in the fossil record.

▲ **Figure 14.11**   Two models for the tempo of speciation

CHAPTER **14** REVIEW

For practice quizzes, BioFlix animations, MP3 tutorials, video tutors, and more study tools designed for this textbook, go to

Mastering**Biology**®

Reviewing the Concepts

Defining Species (14.1–14.3)

14.1 The origin of species is the source of biological diversity. Speciation, the process by which one species splits into two or more species, accounts for both the unity and diversity of life.

14.2 There are several ways to define a species. The biological species concept holds that a species is a group of populations whose members can interbreed and produce fertile offspring with each other but not with members of other species. This concept emphasizes reproductive isolation. Most organisms are classified based on observable traits—the morphological species concept.

14.3 Reproductive barriers keep species separate. Such barriers isolate a species' gene pool and prevent interbreeding.

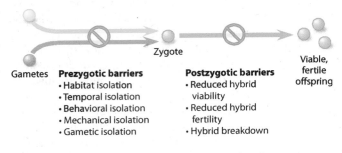

Gametes	**Prezygotic barriers**	**Postzygotic barriers**	Viable, fertile offspring
	• Habitat isolation	• Reduced hybrid viability	
	• Temporal isolation	• Reduced hybrid fertility	
	• Behavioral isolation	• Hybrid breakdown	
	• Mechanical isolation		
	• Gametic isolation		

Mechanisms of Speciation (14.4–14.11)

14.4 In allopatric speciation, geographic isolation leads to speciation. Geographically separated from other populations, a small population may become genetically unique as its gene pool is changed by natural selection, mutation, or genetic drift.

14.5 Reproductive barriers can evolve as populations diverge. Researchers have documented the beginning of reproductive isolation in fruit fly populations adapting to different food sources and have identified a gene for flower color involved in the pollinator choice that helps separate monkey flower species.

14.6 Sympatric speciation takes place without geographic isolation. Many plant species have evolved by polyploidy, duplication of the chromosome number due to errors in cell division. Habitat differentiation and sexual selection, usually involving mate choice, can lead to sympatric (and allopatric) speciation.

14.7 The origin of most plant species can be traced to polyploid speciation. Many plants, including food plants such as bread wheat, are the result of hybridization and polyploidy.

14.8 Isolated islands are often showcases of speciation. Repeated isolation, speciation, and recolonization events on isolated island chains have led to adaptive radiations of species, many of which are found nowhere else in the world.

14.9 Lake Victoria is a living laboratory for studying speciation. Through the rapid adaptive radiation of cichlids, researchers have gained insight into speciation via sexual selection.

14.10 Hybrid zones provide opportunities to study reproductive isolation. Hybrid zones are regions in which populations of different species overlap and produce at least some hybrid offspring. Over time, reinforcement may strengthen barriers to reproduction, or fusion may reverse the speciation process as gene flow

between species increases. In stable hybrid zones, a limited number of hybrid offspring continue to be produced.

14.11 Speciation can occur rapidly or slowly. The punctuated equilibria model, which states that species change most as they arise from an ancestral species and then change relatively little for the rest of their existence, draws on the fossil record. Other species appear to have evolved more gradually. The time interval between speciation events varies from a few thousand years to tens of millions of years.

Connecting the Concepts

1. Name the two types of speciation represented by this diagram. For each type, describe how reproductive barriers may develop between the new species.

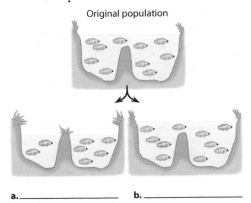

Original population

a. _____ b. _____

2. Fill in the blanks in the following concept map.

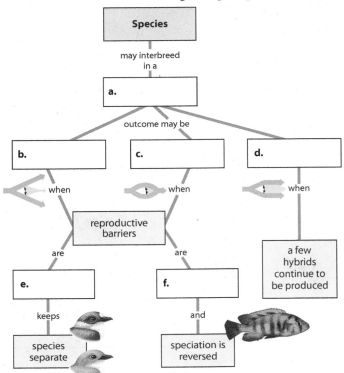

Testing Your Knowledge

Level 1: Knowledge/Comprehension

3. Which concept of species would be most useful to a field biologist identifying new plant species in a tropical forest?
   a. biological
   b. ecological
   c. morphological
   d. phylogenetic

4. The *largest* unit within which gene flow can readily occur is a
   a. population.
   b. species.
   c. genus.
   d. phylum.

5. Bird guides once listed the myrtle warbler and Audubon's warbler as distinct species that lived side by side in parts of their ranges. However, recent books show them as eastern and western forms of a single species, the yellow-rumped warbler. Most likely, it has been found that these two kinds of warblers
   a. live in similar habitats and eat similar foods.
   b. interbreed often in nature, and the offspring are viable and fertile.
   c. are almost identical in appearance.
   d. have many genes in common.

6. Which of the following is an example of a postzygotic reproductive barrier?
   a. One *Ceanothus* shrub lives on acid soil, another on alkaline soil.
   b. Mallard and pintail ducks mate at different times of year.
   c. Two species of leopard frogs have different mating calls.
   d. Hybrid offspring of two species of jimsonweeds always die before reproducing.

7. Biologists have found more than 500 species of fruit flies on the various Hawaiian Islands, all apparently descended from a single ancestor species. This example illustrates
   a. polyploidy.
   b. temporal isolation.
   c. adaptive radiation.
   d. sympatric speciation.

8. A new plant species C, which formed from hybridization of species A ($2n = 16$) with species B ($2n = 12$), would probably produce gametes with a chromosome number of
   a. 12.
   b. 14.
   c. 16.
   d. 28.

9. A horse ($2n = 64$) and a donkey ($2n = 62$) can mate and produce a mule. How many chromosomes would there be in a mule's body cells?
   a. 31
   b. 62
   c. 63
   d. 126

10. What prevents horses and donkeys from hybridizing to form a new species?
    a. limited hybrid fertility
    b. limited hybrid viability
    c. hybrid breakdown
    d. gametic isolation

11. When hybrids produced in a hybrid zone can breed with each other and with both parent species, and they survive and reproduce as well as members of the parent species, one would predict that
    a. the hybrid zone would be stable.
    b. sympatric speciation would occur.
    c. reinforcement of reproductive barriers would keep the parent species separate.
    d. reproductive barriers would lessen and the two parent species would fuse.

12. Which of the following factors would *not* contribute to allopatric speciation?
    a. A population becomes geographically isolated from the parent population.
    b. The separated population is small, and genetic drift occurs.
    c. The isolated population is exposed to different selection pressures than the parent population.
    d. Gene flow between the two populations continues to occur.

Level 2: Application/Analysis

13. Explain how each of the following makes it difficult to clearly define a species: variation within a species, geographically isolated populations, asexual species, fossil organisms.

14. Explain why allopatric speciation would be less likely on an island close to a mainland than on a more isolated island.

15. What does the term *punctuated equilibria* describe?

16. Can factors that cause sympatric speciation also cause allopatric speciation? Explain.

Level 3: Synthesis/Evaluation

17. Cultivated American cotton plants have a total of 52 chromosomes ($2n = 52$). In each cell, there are 13 pairs of large chromosomes and 13 pairs of smaller chromosomes. Old World cotton plants have 26 chromosomes ($2n = 26$), all large. Wild American cotton plants have 26 chromosomes, all small. Propose a testable hypothesis to explain how cultivated American cotton probably originated.

18. **SCIENTIFIC THINKING** Explain how the murky waters of Lake Victoria may be contributing to the decline in cichlid species. How might these polluted waters affect the formation of new species?

19. The red wolf, *Canis rufus,* which was once widespread in the southeastern and south central United States, was declared extinct in the wild by 1980. Saved by a captive breeding program, the red wolf has been reintroduced in areas of eastern North Carolina. The current wild population estimate is about 100 individuals. It is presently being threatened with extinction due to hybridization with coyotes, *Canis latrans*, which have become more numerous in the area. Red wolves and coyotes differ in terms of morphology, DNA, and behavior, although these differences may disappear if interbreeding continues. Although the red wolf has been designated as an endangered species under the Endangered Species Act, some people think that its endangered status should be withdrawn and resources should not be spent to protect what is not a "pure" species. Do you agree? Why or why not?

Answers to all questions can be found in Appendix 4.

15 Tracing Evolutionary History

How do brand-new structures arise by evolution?

The feathered flight of birds is a perfect marriage of structure and function. The skeleton, muscles, nervous system, internal organs, and especially feathers of birds, including those of the roseate spoonbill below, are marvelously adapted for life on the wing. Let's consider the evolution of feathers. Clearly, these structures are essential to avian aeronautics. In a flight feather, separate filaments called barbs emerge from a central shaft that runs from base to tip. Each barb is linked to the next by tiny hooks that act much like the teeth of a zipper. The result is a tightly connected sheet of barbs that is strong but flexible. In flight, the shapes and arrangements of various feathers produce lift, smooth airflow, and help with steering and balance. Layered like shingles over the bird's body, feathers also provide a waterproof, lightweight covering. How did such a beautifully intricate structure evolve? You'll learn the answer to this question later in this chapter, but here's a clue: Birds were not the first feathered animals on Earth—dinosaurs were.

The first feathered dinosaur to be discovered, a 130-million-year-old fossil found in northeastern China, was named *Sinosauropteryx* ("Chinese lizard-wing"). About the size of a turkey, it had short

arms and ran on its hind legs, using its long tail for balance. Its unimpressive plumage consisted of a downy covering of hairlike feathers. Since the discovery of *Sinosauropteryx*, thousands of fossils of feathered dinosaurs have been found and classified into more than 30 different species. Although none was unequivocally capable of flying, many of these species had elaborate feathers that would be the envy of any modern bird.

The evolution of birds is an example of macroevolution, the major changes recorded in the history of life over vast tracts of time. In this chapter, we turn our attention to macroevolution and explore some of the mechanisms responsible for such changes. Finally, we consider how scientists organize the amazing diversity of life according to evolutionary relationships. To approach these wide-ranging topics, we begin with the most basic of questions: How did life first arise on planet Earth?

BIG IDEAS

Early Earth and the Origin of Life
(15.1–15.3)

Scientific experiments can test the four-stage hypothesis of how life originated on early Earth.

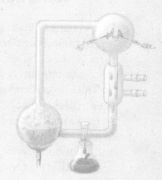

Major Events in the History of Life
(15.4–15.6)

The fossil record and radiometric dating establish a geologic record of key events in life's history.

Mechanisms of Macroevolution
(15.7–15.13)

Continental drift, mass extinctions, adaptive radiations, and changes in developmental genes have all contributed to macroevolution.

Phylogeny and the Tree of Life
(15.14–15.19)

The evolutionary history of a species is reconstructed using fossils, homologies, and molecular systematics.

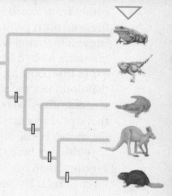

▷ Early Earth and the Origin of Life

15.1 Conditions on early Earth made the origin of life possible

Earth is one of eight planets orbiting the sun, and the sun is one of billions of stars in the Milky Way. The Milky Way, in turn, is one of billions of galaxies in the universe. The star closest to our sun is 40 trillion kilometers away.

The universe has not always been so spread out. Physicists have evidence that before the universe existed in its present form, all matter was concentrated in one mass. The mass seems to have blown apart with a "big bang" sometime between 12 and 14 billion years ago and has been expanding ever since.

Scientific evidence indicates that Earth formed about 4.6 billion years ago from a vast swirling cloud of dust that surrounded the young sun. As gases, dust, and rocks collided and stuck together, larger bodies formed, and the gravity of the larger bodies in turn attracted more matter, eventually forming Earth and other planets.

Conditions on Early Earth   Immense heat would have been generated by the impact of meteorites and compaction by gravity, and young planet Earth probably began as a molten mass. The mass then sorted into layers of varying densities, with the least dense material on the surface, solidifying into a thin crust.

As the bombardment of early Earth slowed about 3.9 billion years ago, conditions on the planet were extremely different from those of today. The first atmosphere was probably thick with water vapor, along with various compounds released by volcanic eruptions, including nitrogen and its oxides, carbon dioxide, methane, ammonia, hydrogen, and hydrogen sulfide. As Earth slowly cooled, the water vapor condensed into oceans. Not only was the atmosphere of young Earth very different from the atmosphere we know today, but lightning, volcanic activity, and ultraviolet radiation were much more intense.

When Did Life Begin?   The earliest evidence of life on Earth comes from fossils that are about 3.5 billion years old. One of these fossils is pictured in the inset in **Figure 15.1**; the larger illustration is an artist's rendition of what Earth may have looked like at that time. Life is already present in this painting, as shown by the "stepping stones" that dominate the shoreline. These rocks, called **stromatolites**, were built up by ancient photosynthetic prokaryotes. As evident in the fossil stromatolite shown in the inset, the rocks are layered. The prokaryotes that built them bound thin films of sediment together, then migrated to the surface and started the next layer. Similar layered mats are still being formed today by photosynthetic prokaryotes in a few shallow, salty bays, such as Shark Bay, in western Australia.

Photosynthesis is not a simple process, so it is likely that significant time had elapsed before life as complex as the organisms that formed the ancient stromatolites had evolved. The evidence that these prokaryotes lived 3.5 billion years ago is strong support for the hypothesis that life in a simpler form arose much earlier, perhaps as early as 3.9 billion years ago.

How Did Life Arise?   From the time of the ancient Greeks until well into the 1800s, it was commonly believed that nonliving matter could spontaneously generate living organisms. Many people believed, for instance, that flies come from rotting meat and fish from ocean mud. Experiments by the French scientist Louis Pasteur in 1862, however, confirmed that all life arises only by the reproduction of preexisting life.

Pasteur ended the argument over spontaneous generation of present-day organisms, but he did not address the question of how life arose in the first place. To attempt to answer that question, for which there is no fossil evidence available, scientists develop hypotheses and test their predictions.

Scientists hypothesize that chemical and physical processes on early Earth could have produced very simple cells through a sequence of four main stages:

1. The abiotic (nonliving) synthesis of small organic molecules, such as amino acids and nitrogenous bases

2. The joining of these small molecules into polymers, such as proteins and nucleic acids (see Module 3.3)

3. The packaging of these molecules into "protocells," droplets with membranes, maintained an internal chemistry different from that of their surroundings

4. The origin of self-replicating molecules that eventually made inheritance possible

In the next two modules, we examine some of the experimental evidence for each of these four stages.

> **?**   Why do 3.5-billion-year-old stromatolites suggest that life originated *before* 3.5 billion years ago?

> ● If photosynthetic prokaryotes existed by 3.5 billion years ago, a simpler, nonphotosynthetic cell probably originated well before that time.

▲ **Figure 15.1**   A depiction of Earth about 3 billion years ago (inset: photo of a cross section of a fossilized stromatolite)

15.2 Experiments show that the abiotic synthesis of organic molecules is possible

SCIENTIFIC THINKING

Organic molecules are essential to the structures and functions of life, but Earth and its atmosphere are made up of inorganic molecules. How did the first organic molecules arise?

In the 1920s, Russian chemist A. I. Oparin and British scientist J. B. S. Haldane independently proposed that conditions on early Earth could have generated organic molecules. They reasoned that present-day conditions on Earth do not allow the spontaneous synthesis of organic compounds simply because the atmosphere is now rich in oxygen. As a strong oxidizing agent, O_2 tends to disrupt chemical bonds. However, before the early photosynthetic prokaryotes added O_2 to the air, Earth may have had a reducing (electron-adding) atmosphere. The energy for this abiotic synthesis of organic compounds could have come from lightning and intense UV radiation.

In 1953, Stanley Miller, then a graduate student in the laboratory of Nobel laureate Harold Urey, tested the Oparin-Haldane hypothesis. Miller devised the apparatus shown in **Figure 15.2**. A flask of warmed water represented the primeval sea. ❶ The water was heated so that some vaporized and moved into a second, higher flask. ❷ The "atmosphere" in this higher flask consisted of water vapor, hydrogen gas (H_2), methane (CH_4), and ammonia (NH_3)—the gases that scientists at the time thought prevailed in the ancient world. Electrodes discharged sparks into the flask to mimic lightning. ❸ A condenser with circulating cold water cooled the atmosphere, raining water and any dissolved

compounds back down into the miniature sea. ❹ As material cycled through the apparatus, Miller periodically collected samples for chemical analysis.

Miller identified a variety of organic molecules that are common in organisms, including hydrocarbons (long chains of carbon and hydrogen) and some of the amino acids that make up proteins. His results—the first evidence that the molecules of life could have arisen spontaneously from inorganic precursors—attracted global attention. Many laboratories have since repeated Miller's classic experiment using various atmospheric mixtures and produced organic compounds.

Recent evidence indicates that the early atmosphere may not have been as strongly reducing as once assumed. However, results from experiments using such atmospheres have also produced organic molecules, corroborating Miller's results. And it is possible that small "pockets" of the early atmosphere—perhaps near volcanic openings—were reducing. In 2008, a former graduate student of Miller's discovered some samples from an experiment that Miller had designed to mimic volcanic conditions. Reanalyzing these samples using modern equipment, he identified additional organic compounds that had been synthesized. Indeed, 22 amino acids had been produced under Miller's simulated volcanic conditions, compared with the 11 produced with the atmosphere in his original 1953 experiment. (Miller had only found 5 amino acids using the analytical methods available to him at the time.)

Scientists continue to generate alternative hypotheses for the origin of organic molecules on Earth. Some researchers are exploring the hypothesis that life may have begun in submerged volcanoes or deep-sea hydrothermal vents, gaps in Earth's crust where hot water and minerals gush into deep oceans. These environments, among the most extreme environments in which life exists today, could have provided the initial chemical resources for life.

Another hypothesis proposes that meteorites were the source of Earth's first organic molecules. Fragments of a 4.5-billion-year-old meteorite that fell to Earth in Australia in 1969 contain more than 80 types of amino acids, some in large amounts. Recent studies have shown that this meteorite also contains other key organic molecules, including lipids, simple sugars, and nitrogenous bases such as uracil. Chemical analyses show that these organic compounds are not contaminants from Earth.

Research will continue on the possible origins of organic molecules on early Earth. We next turn our attention to the subsequent stages that scientists hypothesize gave rise to the earliest cells.

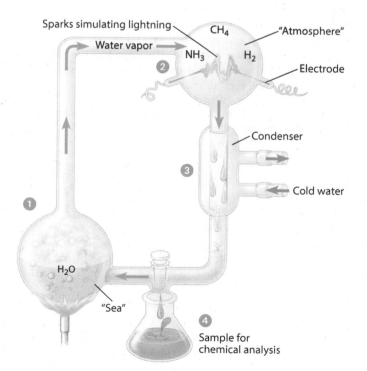

▲ **Figure 15.2** Diagram showing the synthesis of organic compounds in Miller's 1953 experiment

? **Which of the four stages in the hypothetical scenario of the origin of simple cells was Stanley Miller testing with his experiments?**

Stage 1: Conditions on early Earth favored abiotic synthesis of organic molecules important to life, such as amino acids, from simpler ingredients.

15.3 Stages in the origin of the first cells probably included the formation of polymers, protocells, and self-replicating RNA

The abiotic synthesis of small organic molecules would have been a first step in the origin of life. But what is the evidence that the next three stages—synthesis of polymers, formation of protocells, and self-replicating RNA—could have occurred on early Earth?

Abiotic Synthesis of Polymers   In a cell, enzymes catalyze the joining of monomers to build polymers. But could this happen without enzymes? Scientists have produced polymers in the laboratory by dripping dilute solutions of amino acids or RNA monomers onto hot sand, clay, or rock. The heat vaporizes the water and concentrates the monomers, some of which then spontaneously bond together in chains. A similar reaction might have happened on early Earth, when waves splashed organic monomers onto fresh lava or other hot rocks and then rinsed polypeptides and other polymers back into the sea.

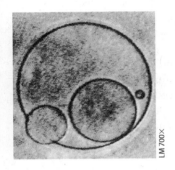

Formation of Protocells   A key step in the origin of life would have been the isolation of a collection of organic molecules within a membrane-enclosed compartment. Laboratory experiments demonstrate that small membrane-enclosed sacs or vesicles form when lipids are mixed with water (see Module 5.2). When researchers add to the mixture a type of clay thought to have been common on early Earth, such vesicles form at a faster rate. Organic molecules become concentrated on the surface of this clay and thus more easily inter-

▲ **Figure 15.3A**   Microscopic vesicle, with membranes made of lipids, "giving birth" to smaller vesicles

LM 700X

act. As shown by the smaller droplets forming in **Figure 15.3A**, these abiotically created vesicles are able to grow and divide (reproduce). Researchers have shown that these vesicles can absorb clay particles to which RNA and other molecules are attached. In a similar fashion, protocells on early Earth may have been able to form, reproduce, and create and maintain an internal environment different from their surroundings.

Self-Replicating RNA   Today's cells store their genetic information as DNA, transcribe the information into RNA, and then translate RNA messages into proteins. This DNA → RNA → protein assembly system is extremely intricate (as we saw in Chapter 10). Most likely, it emerged gradually through a series of refinements of much simpler processes.

What were the first genes like? One hypothesis is that they were short strands of self-replicating RNA. Laboratory experiments have shown that short RNA molecules can assemble spontaneously from

nucleotide monomers. Furthermore, when RNA is added to a solution containing a supply of RNA monomers, new RNA molecules complementary to parts of the starting RNA sometimes assemble. So we can imagine a scenario on early Earth like the one in **Figure 15.3B**: ❶ RNA monomers adhere to clay particles and become concentrated. ❷ Some monomers spontaneously join, which form the first small "genes." ❸ Then an RNA chain complementary to one of these genes assembles. If the new chain, in turn, serves as a template for another round of RNA assembly, the result is a replica of the original gene.

This replication process could have been aided by the RNA molecules themselves, acting as catalysts for their own replication. The discovery that some RNAs, which scientists call **ribozymes**, can carry out enzyme-like functions supports this hypothesis. Thus, the "chicken and egg" paradox of which came first, genes or enzymes, may be solved if the chicken and egg came together in the same RNA molecules. Scientists use the term "RNA world" for the hypothetical period in the evolution of life when RNA served as both rudimentary genes and catalytic molecules.

Once some protocells contained self-replicating RNA molecules, natural selection would have begun to shape their properties. Those that contained genetic information that helped them grow and reproduce more efficiently than others would have increased in number, passing their abilities on to subsequent generations. Mutations, errors in copying RNA "genes," would result in additional variation on which natural selection could work. At some point during millions of years of selection, DNA, a more stable molecule, replaced RNA as the repository of genetic information, and protocells passed a fuzzy border to become true cells. The stage was then set for the evolution of diverse life-forms, changes that we see documented in the fossil record.

> **?** **Why would the formation of protocells represent a key step in the evolution of life?**

● Segregating mixtures of molecules within compartments could concentrate organic molecules and facilitate chemical reactions. Natural selection could act on protocells once self-replicating "genes" evolved.

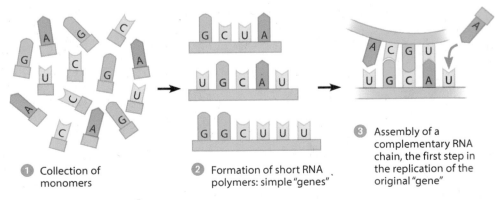

❶ Collection of monomers

❷ Formation of short RNA polymers: simple "genes"

❸ Assembly of a complementary RNA chain, the first step in the replication of the original "gene"

▲ **Figure 15.3B**   A hypothesis for the origin of the first genes

15.4 The origins of single-celled and multicellular organisms and the colonization of land were key events in life's history

We now begin our study of **macroevolution**, the broad pattern of changes in life on Earth. **Figure 15.4** shows a timeline from the origin of Earth 4.6 billion years ago to the present. Earth's history can be divided into four eons of geologic time. The Hadean, Archaean, and Proterozoic eons together lasted about 4 billion years. The Phanerozoic eon includes the last half billion years.

Origin of Prokaryotes   The earliest evidence of life comes from fossil stromatolites formed by ancient photosynthetic prokaryotes (see Figure 15.1). Prokaryotes (the gold band in Figure 15.4) were Earth's sole inhabitants from at least 3.5 billion years ago to about 2 billion years ago. During this time they transformed the biosphere. As a result of prokaryotic photosynthesis, oxygen saturated the seas and began to appear in the atmosphere 2.7 billion years ago (the green band). By 2.2 billion years ago, atmospheric O_2 began to increase rapidly, causing an "oxygen revolution." Many prokaryotes, unable to live in this aerobic environment, became extinct. Some species survived in anaerobic habitats, where their descendants live today. The evolution of cellular respiration, which uses O_2 in harvesting energy from organic molecules, allowed other prokaryotes to flourish.

Origin of Single-celled Eukaryotes   The oldest widely accepted fossils of eukaryotes are about 1.8 billion years old (the orange band). The more complex eukaryotic cell originated when small prokaryotic cells capable of aerobic respiration or photosynthesis took up life inside larger cells (as you learned in Module 4.15). After the first eukaryotes appeared, a great range of unicellular forms evolved, giving rise to the diversity of single-celled eukaryotes that continue to flourish today.

Origin of Multicellular Eukaryotes   Another wave of diversification followed: the origin of multicellular forms whose descendants include a variety of algae, plants, fungi, and animals. Molecular comparisons suggest that the common ancestor of multicellular eukaryotes arose about 1.5 billion years ago (the light blue band). The oldest known fossils of multicellular eukaryotes are of relatively small algae that lived 1.2 billion years ago.

Larger and more diverse multicellular organisms do not appear in the fossil record until about 600 million years ago. A great increase in the diversity of animal forms occurred 535–525 million years ago, in a period known as the Cambrian explosion. Animals are shown on the timeline by the bright blue band.

Colonization of Land   There is fossil evidence that photosynthetic prokaryotes coated damp terrestrial surfaces well over a billion years ago. However, larger forms of life did not begin to colonize land until about 500 million years ago (the purple band).

Plants colonized land in the company of fungi. Even today, the roots of most plants are associated with fungi that aid in absorption of water and minerals; the fungi receive nutrients in return.

The most widespread and diverse land animals are arthropods (particularly insects and spiders) and tetrapods (vertebrates with four appendages). Tetrapods include humans, but we are late arrivals on the scene—the human lineage diverged from other primates around 6 to 7 million years ago, and our own species originated about 195,000 years ago. If the clock of Earth's history were rescaled to represent an hour, humans appeared less than 0.2 second ago! In the next two modules, we see how scientists have determined when these key episodes in Earth's history have occurred in geologic time.

> ? **For how long did life on Earth consist solely of single-celled organisms?**

● More than 2 billion years: From the first fossils of prokaryotes (3.5 billion years old) until the oldest known fossils of multicellular eukaryotes (1.2 billion years old)

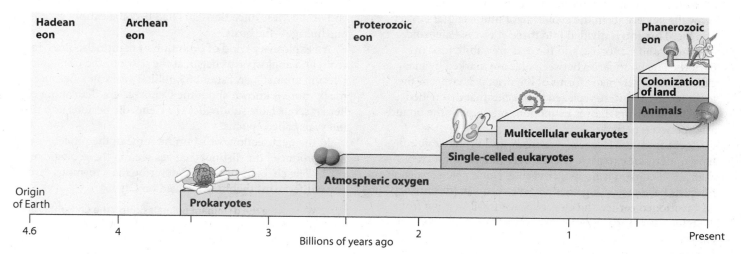

▲ **Figure 15.4**   Some key events in the history of life on Earth

15.5 The actual ages of rocks and fossils mark geologic time

Geologists use several techniques to determine the ages of rocks and the fossils they contain. The method most often used, called **radiometric dating**, is based on the decay of radioactive isotopes (unstable forms of an element; see Module 2.3). Fossils contain isotopes of elements that accumulated when the organisms were alive. For example, a living organism contains both the common isotope carbon-12 and the radioactive isotope carbon-14 in the same ratio as is present in the atmosphere. Once an organism dies, it stops accumulating carbon, and the stable carbon-12 in its tissues does not change. Its carbon-14, however, starts to decay to another element. The rate of decay is expressed as a half-life, the time required for 50% of the isotope in a sample to decay. Carbon-14 has a half-life of 5,730 years, so half the carbon-14 in a specimen decays in about 5,730 years, half the remaining carbon-14 decays in the next 5,730 years, and so on (Figure 15.5). Knowing both the half-life of a radioactive isotope and the ratio of radioactive to stable isotope in a fossil enables us to determine the age of the fossil.

Carbon-14 is useful for dating relatively young fossils—up to about 75,000 years old. Radioactive isotopes with longer half-lives are used to date older fossils.

There are indirect ways to estimate the age of much older fossils. For example, potassium-40, with a half-life of 1.3 billion years, can be used to date volcanic rocks hundreds of

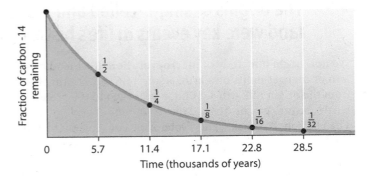

▲ Figure 15.5   Radiometric dating using carbon-14

millions of years old. A fossil's age can be inferred from the ages of the rock layers above and below the stratum in which it is found.

By dating rocks and fossils, scientists have established a geologic record of Earth's history.

> **?** Estimate the age of a fossil found in a sedimentary rock layer between two layers of volcanic rock that are determined to be 530 and 520 million years old.

● We can infer that the organism lived between 530 and 520 million years ago.

15.6 The fossil record documents the history of life

The fossil record, the sequence in which fossils appear in rock strata, is an archive of evolutionary history (see Module 13.2). Based on this sequence and the ages of rocks and fossils, geologists have established a **geologic record**, as shown in Table 15.6, on the facing page. As you saw in Figure 15.4, Earth's history is divided into four eons, the Hadean, Archaean, Proterozoic, and Phanerozoic. The timeline in Table 15.6 shows the lengths and ages (in millions of years ago) of these eons. Note that the Phanerozoic eon, which is only the last 542 million years, is expanded in the table to show the key events in the evolution of multicellular eukaryotic life. This eon is divided into three eras: the Paleozoic, Mesozoic, and Cenozoic, and the eras are subdivided into periods. The boundaries between eras are marked by mass extinctions, when many forms of life disappeared from the fossil record and were replaced by species that diversified from the survivors. Lesser extinctions often mark the boundaries between periods.

Rocks from the Hadean, Archaean, and Proterozoic eons have undergone extensive change over time, and much of their fossil content is no longer visible. Nonetheless, paleontologists have pieced together ancient events in life's history. As mentioned earlier, the oldest known fossils, dating from 3.5 billion years ago, are of prokaryotes; the oldest fossils of eukaryotic cells are from 1.8 billion years ago. Strata from the Ediacaran period (635–542 million years ago) bear diverse fossils of multicellular algae and soft-bodied animals.

Dating from about 542 million years ago, rocks of the Paleozoic ("ancient animal") era contain fossils of lineages that gave rise to present-day organisms, as well as many lineages that have become extinct. During the early Paleozoic, virtually all life was aquatic, but by about 400 million years ago, plants and animals were well established on land.

The Mesozoic ("middle animal") era is also known as the age of reptiles because of its abundance of reptilian fossils, including those of the dinosaurs. The Mesozoic era also saw the first mammals and flowering plants (angiosperms). By the end of the Mesozoic, dinosaurs had become extinct except for one lineage—the birds.

An explosive period of evolution of mammals, birds, insects, and angiosperms began at the dawn of the Cenozoic ("recent animal") era, about 65 million years ago. Because much more is known about the Cenozoic era than about earlier eras, our table subdivides the Cenozoic periods into finer intervals called epochs.

In the next section, we examine some of the processes that have produced the distinct changes seen in the geologic record. (The chapters in Unit IV describe the enormous diversity of life-forms that have evolved on Earth.)

> **?** What were the dominant animals during the Carboniferous period? When were gymnosperms the dominant plants? (*Hint:* Look at Table 15.6.)

● Amphibians. Gymnosperms were dominant during the Triassic and Jurassic periods (251–145.5 million years ago).

TABLE 15.6 | THE GEOLOGIC RECORD

Relative Duration of Eons	Era	Period	Epoch	Age (millions of years ago)	Important Events in the History of Life
Phanerozoic	Cenozoic	Quaternary	Holocene		Historical time
				0.01	
			Pleistocene		Ice ages; origin of genus *Homo*
				2.6	
			Pliocene		Appearance of bipedal human ancestors
				5.3	
			Miocene		Continued radiation of mammals and angiosperms; earliest direct human ancestors
				23	
		Tertiary	Oligocene		Origins of many primate groups
				33.9	
			Eocene		Angiosperm dominance increases; continued radiation of most present-day mammalian orders
				55.8	
			Paleocene		Major radiation of mammals, birds, and pollinating insects
				65.5	
Proterozoic	Mesozoic	Cretaceous			Flowering plants (angiosperms) appear and diversify; many groups of organisms, including most dinosaurs, become extinct at end of period
				145.5	
		Jurassic			Gymnosperms continue as dominant plants; dinosaurs abundant and diverse
				199.6	
		Triassic			Cone-bearing plants (gymnosperms) dominate landscape; dinosaurs evolve and radiate; origin of mammals
				251	
	Paleozoic	Permian			Radiation of reptiles; origin of most present-day groups of insects; extinction of many marine and terrestrial organisms at end of period
				299	
		Carboniferous			Extensive forests of vascular plants form; first seed plants appear; origin of reptiles; amphibians dominant
				359	
		Devonian			Diversification of bony fishes; first tetrapods and insects appear
				416	
		Silurian			Diversification of early vascular plants
				444	
Archaean		Ordovician			Marine algae abundant; colonization of land by diverse fungi, plants, and animals
				488	
		Cambrian			Sudden increase in diversity of many animal phyla (Cambrian explosion)
				542	
		Ediacaran			Diverse algae and soft-bodied invertebrate animals appear
				635	
				1,800	Oldest fossils of eukaryotic cells appear
				2,500	
				2,700	Concentration of atmospheric oxygen begins to increase
Hadean				3,500	Oldest fossils of cells (prokaryotes) appear
				3,850	Oldest known rocks on Earth's surface
				4,000	
				Approx. 4,600	Origin of Earth

15.7 Continental drift has played a major role in macroevolution

The fossil record documents macroevolution, the major events in the history of life on Earth. In this section, we explore some of the factors that helped shape these evolutionary changes, such as plate tectonics, mass extinctions, and adaptive radiations.

Plate Tectonics   If photographs of Earth were taken from space every 10,000 years and then spliced together, it would make a remarkable movie. The seemingly "rock solid" continents we live on move over time. Since the origin of multicellular eukaryotes roughly 1.5 billion years ago, there have been three occasions—1.1 billion, 600 million, and 250 million years ago—in which the landmasses of Earth came together to form a supercontinent, and later broke apart. Each time the landmasses split, they yielded a different configuration of continents. Geologists estimate that the continents will come together again and form a new supercontinent roughly 250 million years from now.

The continents and seafloors form a thin outer layer of planet Earth, called the crust, which covers a mass of hot, viscous material called the mantle. The outer core is liquid and the inner core is solid (Figure 15.7A). According to the theory of **plate tectonics**, Earth's crust is divided into giant, irregularly shaped plates (outlined in black in Figure 15.7B) that essentially float

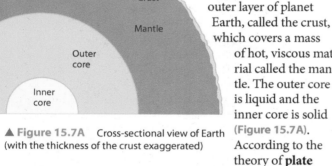

▲ **Figure 15.7A**   Cross-sectional view of Earth (with the thickness of the crust exaggerated)

on the underlying mantle. In a process called continental drift, movements in the mantle cause the plates to move (black arrows in the figure). In some cases, the plates are moving away from each other. North America and Europe, for example, are drifting apart at a rate of about 2 cm per year. In other cases, two plates are sliding past each other, forming regions where earthquakes are common. In still other cases, two plates are colliding. Massive upheavals may occur, forming mountains along the plate boundaries. The red dots in Figure 15.7B indicate zones of violent geologic activity, most of which are associated with plate boundaries.

Consequences of Continental Drift   Throughout Earth's history, continental drift has reshaped the physical features of the planet and altered the habitats in which organisms live. **Figure 15.7C**, on the facing page, shows continental movements that greatly influenced life during the Mesozoic and Cenozoic eras. ❶ About 250 million years ago, near the end of the Paleozoic era, plate movements brought all the previously separated landmasses together into a supercontinent we call **Pangaea**, meaning "all land." When the landmasses fused, ocean basins became deeper, lowering the sea level and draining the shallow coastal seas. Then, as now, most marine species inhabited shallow waters, and much of that habitat was destroyed. The interior of the vast continent was cold and dry. Overall, the formation of Pangaea had a tremendous impact on the physical environment and climate. As the fossil record documents, biological diversity was reshaped. Many species were driven to extinction, and new opportunities arose for organisms that survived the crisis.

During the Mesozoic era, Pangaea started to break apart, causing a geographic isolation of colossal proportions. As the continents drifted apart, each became a separate evolutionary arena—a huge island on which organisms evolved in isolation from their previous neighbors. ❷ At first, Pangaea split into northern and southern landmasses, which we call Laurasia and Gondwana, respectively. ❸ By the end of the Mesozoic era, some 65 million years ago, the modern continents were beginning to take shape. Note that at that time Madagascar became isolated and India was still a large island. Then, around 45 million years ago, the India plate collided with the Eurasian plate, and the slow, steady buckling at the plate boundary formed the Himalayas, the tallest and youngest of Earth's mountain ranges. ❹ The continents continue to drift today, and the Himalayas are still growing (about 1 cm per year).

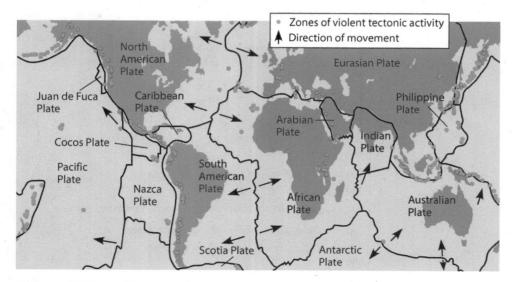

* Zones of violent tectonic activity
▲ Direction of movement

▲ **Figure 15.7B**   Earth's tectonic plates

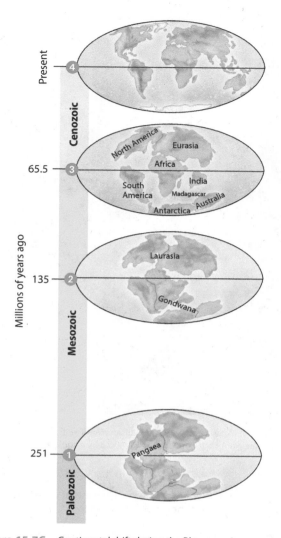

▲ **Figure 15.7C** Continental drift during the Phanerozoic eon

Try This Use Table 15.6 to identify important events in the history of life that occurred while the continents occupied the positions shown at 1, 2, and 3.

The history of continental mergers and separations explains many patterns of **biogeography**, the study of the past and present distribution of organisms. For example, almost all the animals and plants that live on the island of Madagascar are unique—they diversified from ancestral populations after Madagascar was isolated from Africa and India. As in the Galápagos Islands, adaptive radiations (see Module 14.8) occurred in many groups. The more than 50 species of lemurs that currently inhabit Madagascar, for instance, evolved from a common ancestor over the past 40 million years.

Continental drift solves the mystery of marsupials, mammals whose young complete their embryonic development in a pouch outside the mother's body, such as kangaroos, koalas, and wombats. Australia and its neighboring islands are home to more than 200 species of marsupials, most of which are found nowhere else in the world (Figure 15.7D).

What accounts for the predominance of marsupials in Australia, while the rest of the world is dominated by eutherian (placental) mammals, whose young complete their development in the mother's uterus? Looking at a current map of the world, you might hypothesize that marsupials evolved only on this island continent. But marsupials are not unique to Australia. More than a hundred species live in Central and South America (Figure 15.7E); North America is home to only a few, including the Virginia opossum (Figure 15.7F). The distribution of marsupials only makes sense in the context of continental drift—marsupials must have originated when the continents were joined. Fossil evidence suggests that marsupials originated in what is now Asia and later dispersed to the tip of South America while it was still connected to Antarctica. They made their way to Australia before continental drift separated Antarctica from Australia, setting it "afloat" like a great raft of marsupials. The few early eutherians that lived there became extinct, while on other continents, most marsupials became extinct. Isolated on Australia, marsupials evolved and diversified, filling ecological roles analogous to those filled by eutherians on other continents.

Continental drift solves puzzles about the geographic distribution of extinct organisms as well as living ones. For example, paleontologists have discovered fossils of the same species of Permian freshwater reptiles in West Africa and Brazil, regions now separated by 3,000 km of ocean.

In the next module, we consider some of the perils associated with the movements of Earth's crustal plates.

? If marsupials originated in Asia and reached Australia via South America, where else should paleontologists find fossil marsupials? (*Hint*: Look at Figure 15.7C.)

Antarctica

▲ **Figure 15.7D** Greater bilby (*Macrotis lagotis*), an Australian marsupial

▲ **Figure 15.7E** Mexican mouse opossum (*Marmosa mexicana*)

▲ **Figure 15.7F** Virginia opossum female with young (*Didelphis virginiana*)

15.8 Plate tectonics may imperil human life

CONNECTION

Not only do moving crustal plates cause continents to collide, pile up, and build mountain ranges; they also produce volcanoes and earthquakes. The boundaries of plates are hot spots of such geologic activity. California's frequent earthquakes are a result of movement along the infamous San Andreas Fault, part of the border where the Pacific and North American plates grind together and gradually slide past each other (Figure 15.8)—in what we can call a strike-slip fault. Two major earthquakes have occurred in the region in the past century: the San Francisco earthquake of 1906 and the 1989 Loma Prieta earthquake, also near San Francisco.

In such a strike-slip fault, the two plates do not slide smoothly past each other. They often stick in one spot until enough pressure builds along the fault that the landmasses suddenly jerk forward, releasing massive amounts of energy and causing the surrounding area to move or shake. A strike-slip fault runs under Haiti and is responsible for the devastating magnitude 7.0 earthquake of January 2010. In Haiti, the North American plate is moving west past the Caribbean plate (see Figure 15.7B). Undersea earthquakes can cause giant waves, such as the massive 2011 tsunami in Japan, a seismically active area where four tectonic plates meet.

A volcano is a rupture that allows hot, molten rock, ash, and gases to escape from beneath Earth's crust. Volcanoes are often found where tectonic plates are diverging or converging, as opposed to sliding past each other. Volcanoes can cause tremendous devastation, as when Mt. Vesuvius in southern Italy erupted in 79 AD, burying Pompeii in a layer of ash. But sometimes volcanoes imperil more than just local life, as we see in the next module.

▲ **Figure 15.8** An aerial view of the San Andreas Fault, a boundary between two crustal plates, about 100 miles northwest of Los Angeles

? Volcanoes usually destroy life. How might undersea volcanoes create new opportunities for life?

● By creating new landmasses on which life can evolve, such as the Galápagos and Hawaiian Islands

15.9 During mass extinctions, large numbers of species are lost

Extinction is inevitable in a changing world. Indeed, the fossil record shows that the vast majority of species that have ever lived are now extinct. A species may become extinct because its habitat has been destroyed, because of unfavorable climatic changes, or because of changes in its biological community, such as the evolution of new predators or competitors. Extinctions occur all the time, but extinction rates have not been steady.

Mass Extinctions The fossil record chronicles a number of occasions when global environmental changes were so rapid and disruptive that a majority of species were swept away in a relatively short amount of time. Five mass extinctions have occurred over the past 500 million years. In each of these events, 50% or more of Earth's species became extinct.

Of all the mass extinctions, the ones marking the ends of the Permian and Cretaceous periods have received the most attention. The Permian extinction, which occurred about 251 million years ago and defines the boundary between the Paleozoic and Mesozoic eras, claimed about 96% of marine animal species and took a tremendous toll on terrestrial life

as well. This mass extinction occurred in less than 500,000 years, and possibly in just a few thousand years—an instant in the context of geologic time.

At the end of the Cretaceous period, about 65 million years ago, the world again lost an enormous number of species—more than half of all marine species and many lineages of terrestrial plants and animals. At that point, dinosaurs had dominated the land and pterosaurs had ruled the air for some 150 million years. After the Cretaceous mass extinction, the pterosaurs and almost all the dinosaurs were gone, leaving behind only the descendants of one lineage, the birds.

Causes of Mass Extinctions The Permian mass extinction occurred at a time of enormous volcanic eruptions in what is now Siberia. Vast stretches of land were covered with lava hundreds to thousands of meters thick. Besides spewing lava and ash into the atmosphere, the eruptions may have produced enough carbon dioxide to warm the global climate by an estimated 6°C. Reduced temperature differences between the equator and the poles would have slowed the mixing of

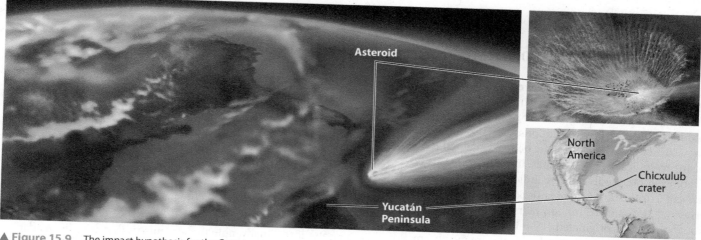

▲ Figure 15.9 The impact hypothesis for the Cretaceous mass extinction

ocean water, leading to a widespread drop in oxygen concentration in the water. This oxygen deficit would have killed many marine organisms and promoted the growth of anaerobic bacteria that emit a poisonous by-product, hydrogen sulfide. As this gas bubbled out of the water, it would have killed land plants and animals and initiated chemical reactions that would destroy the protective ozone layer. Thus, a cascade of factors may have contributed to the Permian extinction.

One clue to a possible cause of the Cretaceous mass extinction is a thin layer of clay enriched in iridium that separates sediments from the Mesozoic and Cenozoic eras. Iridium is an element very rare on Earth but common in meteorites and other extraterrestrial objects that occasionally fall to Earth. The rocks of the Cretaceous boundary layer have many times more iridium than normal Earth levels. Most paleontologists conclude that the iridium layer is the result of fallout from a huge cloud of dust that billowed into the atmosphere when an asteroid or large comet hit Earth. The cloud would have blocked light and severely disturbed the global climate for months.

Is there evidence of such an asteroid? A large crater, the 65-million-year-old Chicxulub impact crater, has been found in the Caribbean Sea near the Yucatán Peninsula of Mexico (Figure 15.9). About 180 km wide (about 112 miles), the crater is the right size to have been caused by an object with a diameter of 10 km (about 6 miles). The horseshoe shape of the crater and the pattern of debris in sedimentary rocks indicate that an asteroid or comet struck at a low angle from the southeast. The artist's interpretation in Figure 15.9 represents the impact and its immediate effect—a cloud of hot vapor and debris that could have killed most of the plants and animals in North America within hours. The collision is estimated to have released more than a billion times the energy of the nuclear bombs dropped in Japan during World War II.

In March 2010, an international team of scientists reviewed two decades' worth of research on the Cretaceous extinction and endorsed the asteroid hypothesis as the triggering event. Nevertheless, research will continue on other contributing causes and the multiple and interrelated effects of this major ecological disaster.

Consequences of Mass Extinctions Whatever their causes, mass extinctions affect biological diversity profoundly.

By removing large numbers of species, a mass extinction can decimate a thriving and complex ecological community. Mass extinctions are random events that act on species indiscriminately. They can permanently remove species with highly advantageous features and change the course of evolution forever. Consider what would have happened if our early primate ancestors living 65 million years ago had died out in the Cretaceous mass extinction—or if a few large, predatory dinosaurs had *not* become extinct!

How long does it take for life to recover after a mass extinction? The fossil record shows that it typically takes 5–10 million years for the diversity of life to return to previous levels. In some cases, it has taken much longer: It took about 100 million years for the number of marine families to recover after the Permian mass extinction.

Is a Sixth Mass Extinction Under Way? Human actions that result in habitat destruction and climate change are modifying the global environment to such an extent that many species are currently threatened with extinction. In the past 400 years, more than a thousand species are known to have become extinct. Scientists estimate that this rate is 100 to 1,000 times the normal rate seen in the fossil record. Does this represent the beginning of a sixth mass extinction?

This question is difficult to answer, partly because it is hard to document both the total number of species on Earth and the number of extinctions that are occurring. It is clear that losses have not reached the level of the other "big five" extinctions. Monitoring, however, does show that many species are declining at an alarming rate, suggesting that a sixth (human-caused) mass extinction could occur within the next few centuries or millennia. And as seen with prior mass extinctions, it may take millions of years for life on Earth to recover.

But the fossil record also shows a creative side to the destruction. Mass extinctions can pave the way for adaptive radiations in which new groups rise to prominence, as we see next.

> **?** The Permian and Cretaceous mass extinctions mark the ends of the _____ and _____ eras, respectively. (*Hint*: Refer to Table 15.6.)
>
> ◉ Paleozoic . . . Mesozoic

15.10 Adaptive radiations have increased the diversity of life

Adaptive radiations are periods of evolutionary change in which many new species evolve from a common ancestor, often following the colonization of new, unexploited areas (Module 14.8). Adaptive radiations have also followed each mass extinction, when survivors became adapted to the many vacant ecological roles, or niches, in their communities.

For example, fossil evidence indicates that mammals underwent a dramatic adaptive radiation after the extinction of terrestrial dinosaurs 65 million years ago (Figure 15.10). Although mammals originated 180 million years ago, fossils older than 65 million years indicate that they were mostly small and not very diverse. Early mammals may have been eaten or outcompeted by the larger and more diverse dinosaurs. With the disappearance of the dinosaurs (except for the bird lineage), mammals expanded greatly in both diversity and size, filling the ecological roles once occupied by dinosaurs.

The history of life has also been altered by radiations that followed the evolution of new adaptations. Major new adaptations facilitated the colonization of land by plants, insects, and tetrapods. The radiation of land plants, for example, was associated with features such as stems that supported the plant against gravity and a waxy coat that protected leaves from water loss. Finally, note that organisms that arise in an adaptive radiation can serve as a new source of food for still other organisms. In this way, the diversification of land plants stimulated a series of adaptive radiations in insects that ate or pollinated plants—helping to make insects the most diverse group of animals on Earth today.

Now that we've looked at geologic and environmental influences, let's consider how genes can affect macroevolution.

> **?** In addition to the new resources of plants, what other factors likely promoted the adaptive radiation of insects on land?

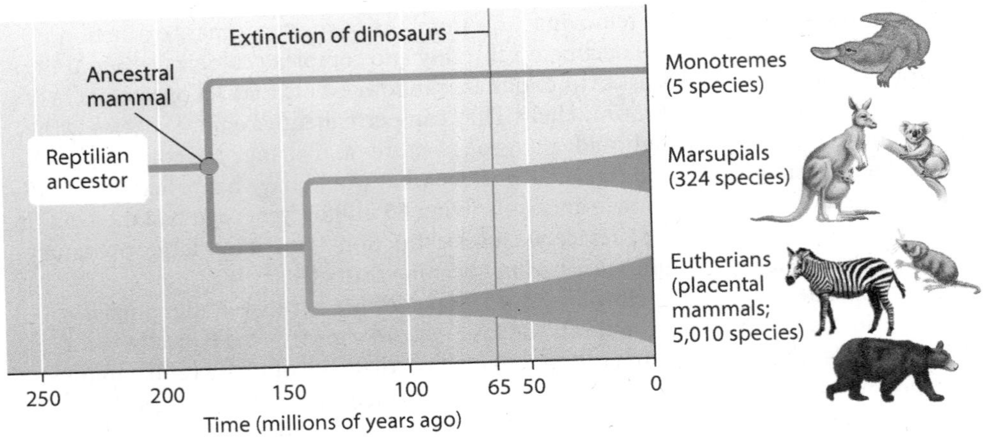

▲ Figure 15.10 Adaptive radiation of mammals (width of line reflects numbers of species).

● Many unfilled ecological roles on land and the evolution of wings and a supportive, protective, and waterproof exoskeleton

---

15.11 Genes that control development play a major role in evolution

The fossil record can tell us *what* the great events in the history of life have been and *when* they occurred. Continental drift, mass extinctions, and adaptive radiation provide a big-picture view of *how* those changes came about. But now we are increasingly able to understand the basic biological mechanisms that underlie the changes seen in the fossil record.

Scientists working at the interface of evolutionary biology and developmental biology—the research field abbreviated **"evo-devo"**—are studying how slight genetic changes can become magnified into major morphological differences between species. Genes that program development control the rate, timing, and spatial pattern of change in an organism's form as it develops from a zygote into an adult. A great many of these genes appear to have been conserved throughout evolutionary history: The same or very similar genes are involved in the development of form across multiple lineages.

Changes in Rate and Timing   Many striking evolutionary transformations are the result of a change in the rate or timing of developmental events. Figure 15.11A shows a photograph of an axolotl, a salamander that illustrates a phenomenon called **paedomorphosis** (from the Greek *paedos*, of a child, and *morphosis*, formation), the retention in the adult of body structures that were juvenile features in an ancestral species. Most salamander species have aquatic larvae (with gills) that undergo metamorphosis in becoming terrestrial adults (with lungs). The axolotl is a salamander that grows to a sexually mature adult while retaining gills and other larval features.

Slight changes in the relative growth of different body parts can change an adult form substantially. As the skulls and photo in Figure 15.11B on the next page show, humans and chimpanzees are much more alike as fetuses than they are as adults. As development proceeds, accelerated growth in the jaw produces the elongated skull, sloping forehead, and

▲ Figure 15.11A   An axolotl, a paedomorphic salamander

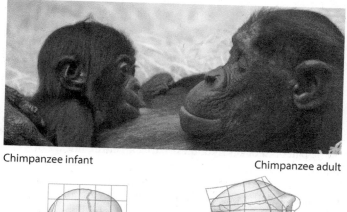

Chimpanzee infant

Chimpanzee adult

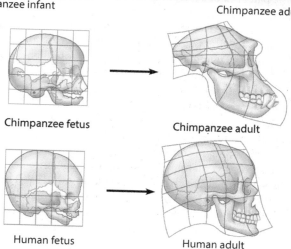

Chimpanzee fetus

Chimpanzee adult

Human fetus

Human adult

▲ **Figure 15.11B** Chimpanzee and human skull shapes compared

massive jaws of an adult chimpanzee. In the human lineage, genetic changes that slowed the growth of the jaw relative to other parts of the skull produced an adult whose head proportions still resembled that of a child (and that of a baby chimpanzee). Our large skull and complex brain are among our most distinctive features. Compared to the slow growth of a chimpanzee brain after birth, our brain continues to grow at the rapid rate of a fetal brain for the first year of life.

Changes in Spatial Pattern

Homeotic genes, the master control genes, determine such basic features as where a pair of wings or legs will develop on a fruit fly (see Module 11.8). Changes in homeotic genes or in how or where such genes are expressed can have a profound impact on body form. Consider, for example, the evolution of snakes from a four-limbed lizard-like ancestor. Researchers have found that one pattern of expression of two homeotic genes in tetrapods results in the formation of forelimbs and of vertebrae with ribs, whereas a different pattern of expression of these two genes results in the development of vertebrae with ribs but no limbs, as in snakes (see Figure 30.3C).

New Genes and Changes in Genes

New developmental genes that arose as a result of gene duplications may have facilitated the origin of new body forms. For example, a fruit fly (an invertebrate) has a single cluster of several homeotic genes that direct the development of major body parts. A mouse (a vertebrate) has four clusters of very similar genes that occur in the same linear order on chromosomes and direct the development of the same body regions as the fly genes (see Figure 27.14B). Two duplications of these gene

clusters appear to have occurred in the evolution of vertebrates from invertebrate animals. Mutations in these duplicated genes may then have led to the origin of novel vertebrate characters, such as a backbone, jaws, and limbs.

Changes in Gene Regulation

Researchers are finding that changes in the form of organisms often are caused by mutations that affect the regulation of developmental genes. As we just discussed, such a change in gene expression was shown to correlate with the lack of forelimbs in snakes.

Additional evidence for this type of change in gene regulation is seen in studies of the threespine stickleback fish. In western Canada, these fish live in the ocean and also in lakes that formed when the coastline receded during the past 12,000 years. Ocean populations have bony plates that make up a kind of body armor and a set of pelvic spines that help deter predatory fish. The body armor and pelvic spines are reduced or absent in threespine sticklebacks living in lakes that lack predatory fishes and that are also low in calcium. In the absence of predators, spineless sticklebacks may have a selective advantage because the limited calcium is needed for purposes other than constructing spines. **Figure 15.11C** shows specimens of an ocean and a lake stickleback, which have been stained to highlight their bony plates and spines.

Researchers have identified a key gene that influences the development of these spines. Was the reduction of spines in lake populations due to changes in the gene itself or to changes in how the gene is expressed? It turns out that the gene is identical in the two populations, and it is expressed in the mouth region and other tissues of embryos from both populations. Studies have shown, however, that while the gene is also expressed in the developing pelvic region of ocean sticklebacks, it is not turned on in the pelvic region in lake sticklebacks. This example shows how morphological change can be caused by altering the expression of a developmental gene in some parts of the body but not others.

> **?** **Research shows that many differences in body form are caused by changes in gene regulation and not changes in the nucleotide sequence of the developmental gene itself. Why might this be the case?**
>
> ● A change in sequence may affect a gene's function wherever that gene is expressed—with potentially harmful effects. Changes in the regulation of gene expression can be limited to specific areas in a developing embryo.

▲ **Figure 15.11C** Stickleback fish from ocean (top) and lake (bottom), stained to show bony plates and spines. (Arrow indicates the absence of the pelvic spine in the lake fish.)

15.12 Novel traits may arise in several ways

EVOLUTION CONNECTION

Let's see how the Darwinian theory of gradual change can account for the evolution of intricate structures such as eyes or of novel body structures such as wings (that is, new kinds of structures). Most complex structures have evolved in increments from simpler versions having the same basic function—a process of refinement.

Consider the amazing camera-like eyes of vertebrates and squids. Although these complex eyes evolved independently, the origin of both can be traced from a simple ancestral patch of photoreceptor cells through a series of incremental modifications that benefited their owners at each stage. Indeed, there appears to have been a single evolutionary origin of light-sensitive cells, and all animals with eyes—vertebrates and invertebrates alike—share the same master genes that regulate eye development.

Figure 15.12 illustrates the range of complexity in the structure of eyes among molluscs living today. Simple patches of pigmented cells enable limpets to distinguish light from dark, and they cling more tightly to their rock when a shadow falls on them—a behavioral adaptation that reduces the risk of being eaten. Other molluscs have eyecups that have no lenses or other means of focusing images but can indicate light direction. In those molluscs that do have complex eyes, the organs probably evolved in small steps of adaptation.

Although eyes have retained their basic function of vision throughout their evolutionary history, evolutionary novelty can also arise when structures that originally played one role gradually acquire a different one. Structures that evolve in one context but become co-opted for another function are called *exaptations*. However, exaptation does not mean that a structure evolves in anticipation of future use. Natural selection cannot predict the future; it can only improve an existing structure in the context of its current use. Novel features can arise gradually via a series of intermediate stages, each of which has some function in the organism's current situation.

The evolution of feathers is a good example of exaptation. Some paleontologists hypothesize that an entire lineage of dinosaurs—including the fearsome *Tyrannosaurus rex*—had feathers. But the feathers seen in these fossils could not have been used for flight, nor would their reptilian anatomy have been suited to flying. If feathers evolved before flight, what was their function? Their first utility may have been for insulation. It is possible that longer, wing-like forelimbs and feathers, which increased the surface area of these forelimbs, were co-opted for flight after functioning in some other capacity, such as mating displays, thermoregulation, or camouflage (all functions that feathers still serve today). The first flights may have been only short glides to the ground or from branch to branch in tree-dwelling species. Once flight itself became an advantage, natural selection would have gradually remodeled feathers and wings to fit their additional function.

How do brand-new structures arise by evolution?

The flippers of penguins are another example of the modification of existing structures for different functions. Penguins cannot fly, but their modified wings are powerful oars that make them strong, fast underwater swimmers.

? Explain why the concept of exaptation does not imply that a structure evolves in anticipation of some future environmental change.

● Although a structure is co-opted for new or additional functions in a new environment, the structure existed because it worked as an adaptation in the old environment.

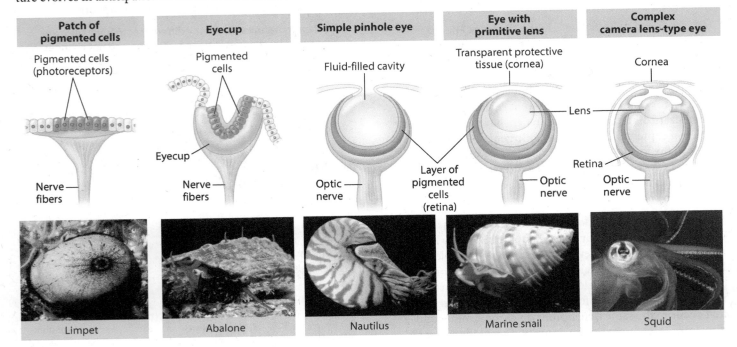

Patch of pigmented cells	Eyecup	Simple pinhole eye	Eye with primitive lens	Complex camera lens-type eye

Limpet | Abalone | Nautilus | Marine snail | Squid

▲ **Figure 15.12**   A range of eye complexity among molluscs

15.13 Evolutionary trends do not mean that evolution is goal directed

The fossil record seems to show trends in the evolution of many species, for example, toward larger or smaller body size. Let's look at apparent trends in the evolution of the modern horse (genus *Equus*), from an ancestor known as *Hyracotherium* that lived some 55 million years ago. *Hyracotherium*, which was about the size of a large dog, had four toes on its front feet and three toes on its hind feet. Its teeth were adapted to browsing on shrubs and trees. In contrast, the present-day horse has only one toe on each foot (the hoof) and teeth modified for grazing on grasses.

Did the horse lineage progress gradually toward larger size, reduced number of toes, and teeth adapted to grazing? Figure 15.13 shows the fossil record of horses, with the vertical bars representing the period of time each group persisted in the record. If you follow the fossil species highlighted in yellow from the bottom to the top of Figure 15.13, it appears that modern horses evolved linearly from *Hyracotherium* to *Equus* through a series of intermediate forms. However, if we consider *all* fossil horses known today, this apparent trend vanishes. The genus *Equus* actually descended through a series of speciation episodes, not all of which led to large, one-toed grazers. The present-day horse is the only surviving twig of an evolutionary tree with many divergent branches.

Branching evolution *can* lead to a real evolutionary trend, however. One model of long-term trends compares species to individuals: Speciation is their birth, extinction their death, and new species that diverge from them are their offspring. According to this model of species selection, unequal survival of species and unequal generation of new species play a role in macroevolution similar to the role of unequal reproduction in microevolution. In other words, the species that generate the greatest number of new species determine the direction of major evolutionary trends.

Evolutionary trends can also result directly from natural selection. For example, when horse ancestors invaded the grasslands that spread during the mid-Cenozoic, there was strong selection for grazers that could escape predators by

running faster. This trend would not have occurred without open grasslands.

Whatever its cause, it is important to recognize that an evolutionary trend does not imply that evolution progresses toward a particular goal. Evolution is the result of interactions between organisms and the current environment. If conditions change, an apparent trend may cease or even reverse itself.

In the final section, we explore how biologists arrange life's astounding diversity into an evolutionary tree of life.

? **A trend in the evolution of mammals was toward a larger brain size. Use the species selection model to explain how such a trend could occur.**

● Those species with larger brains persisted longer before extinction and gave rise to more "offspring" species than did species with smaller brains.

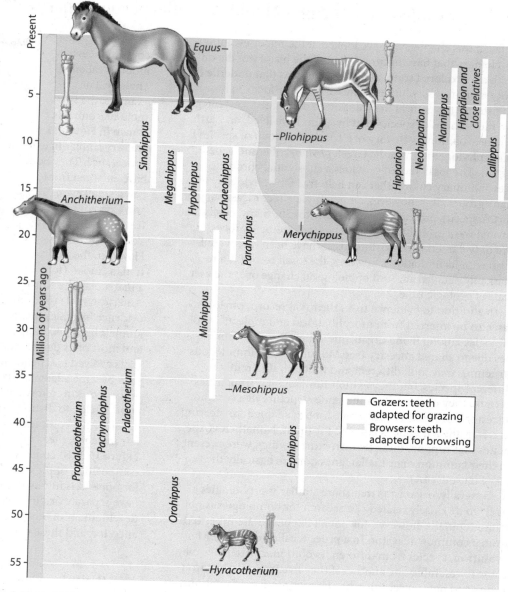

▲ Figure 15.13 The branched evolution of horses

Legend:
- Grazers: teeth adapted for grazing
- Browsers: teeth adapted for browsing

15.14 Phylogenies based on homologies reflect evolutionary history

So far in this chapter, we have looked at the major evolutionary changes that have occurred during the history of life on Earth and explored some of the mechanisms that underlie the process of macroevolution. Now we shift our focus to how biologists use the pattern of evolution to distinguish and categorize the millions of species that live, and have lived, on Earth.

The evolutionary history of a species or group of species is called **phylogeny** (from the Greek *phylon*, tribe, and *genesis*, origin). The fossil record provides a substantial chronicle of evolutionary change that can help trace the phylogeny of many groups. It is, however, an incomplete record, as many of Earth's species probably never left any fossils; many fossils that formed were probably destroyed by later geologic processes; and only a fraction of existing fossils have been discovered. Even with its limitations, however, the fossil record is a remarkably detailed account of biological change over the vast scale of geologic time.

In addition to evidence from the fossil record, phylogeny can also be inferred from morphological and molecular homologies among living organisms. Homologies are similarities due to shared ancestry (see Module 13.4). Homologous structures may look different and function differently in different species, but they exhibit fundamental similarities because they evolved from the same structure in a common ancestor. For instance, the whale limb is adapted for steering in water; the bat wing is adapted for flight. Nonetheless, the bones that support these two structures, which were present in their common mammalian ancestor, are basically the same (see Figure 13.4A).

Generally, organisms that share similar morphologies are likely to be closely related. The search for homologies is not without pitfalls, however, for not all likenesses are inherited from a common ancestor. In a process called **convergent evolution**, species from different evolutionary branches may come to resemble one another if they live in similar environments and natural selection has favored similar adaptations. In such cases, body structures and even whole organisms may resemble each other.

▲ Figure 15.14   Australian "mole" (top) and North American mole (bottom)

Similarity due to convergent evolution is called **analogy**. For example, the two mole-like animals shown in **Figure 15.14** are very similar in external appearance. They both have enlarged front paws, small eyes, and a pad of protective thickened skin on the nose. However, the Australian "mole" (top) is a marsupial; the North American mole (bottom) is a eutherian. Genetic and fossil evidence indicates that the last common ancestor of these two animals lived 140 million years ago. And in fact, that ancestor and most of its descendants were not mole-like. Analogous traits evolved independently in these two mole lineages as they each became adapted to burrowing lifestyles.

In addition to molecular comparisons and fossil evidence, another clue to distinguishing homology from analogy is to consider the complexity of the structure being compared. For instance, the skulls of a human and a chimpanzee (see Figure 15.11B) consist of many bones fused together, and the composition of these skulls matches almost perfectly, bone for bone. It is highly improbable that such complex structures have separate origins. More likely, the genes involved in the development of both skulls were inherited from a common ancestor, and these complex structures are homologous.

> **?**   Human forearms and a bat's wings are _____. A bat's wings and a bee's wings are _____.
>
> ● homologous . . . analogous

15.15 Systematics connects classification with evolutionary history

Systematics is a discipline of biology that focuses on classifying organisms and determining their evolutionary relationships. In the 18th century, Carolus Linnaeus introduced a system of naming and classifying species, a discipline we call **taxonomy**. Although Linnaeus's system was not based on evolutionary relationship, many of its features, such as the two-part Latin names for species, remain useful in systematics.

Common names such as squirrel and daisy may work well in everyday communication, but they can be ambiguous because there are many species of each of these kinds of organisms. In addition, people in different regions may use the same common name for different species. For example, the flowers called bluebells in Scotland, England, Texas, and the eastern United States are actually four unrelated species. And some common names are downright misleading. Consider these three "fishes": jellyfish (a cnidarian), crayfish (a crustacean), and silverfish (an insect).

To avoid such confusion, biologists assign each species a two-part scientific name, or **binomial**. The first part is the **genus** (plural, *genera*), a group of closely related species. For example, the genus of tree squirrels is *Sciurus*. The second part of the binomial, often called the specific epithet, is used to distinguish species within a genus. The scientific name for the Eastern gray squirrel is *Sciurus carolinensis*; the fox squirrel is *Sciurus niger*. The first part of the scientific name is analogous to a person's surname in that it is shared by close relatives. The specific epithet is analogous to a person's first name—unrelated people often have the same first name. For example, "*carolinensis*" is the second part of the binomial of diverse species: *Poecile carolinensis* is the Carolina chickadee and *Anolis carolinensis* is a type of lizard. Thus, both parts must be used together to name a species. Notice that the first letter of the genus name is capitalized and that the binomial is italicized and Latinized.

In addition to naming species, Linnaeus also grouped them into a hierarchy of categories. Beyond the grouping of species within genera, the Linnaean system extends to progressively broader categories of classification. It places related genera in the same **family**, puts families into **orders**, orders into **classes**, classes into **phyla** (singular, *phylum*), phyla into **kingdoms**, and kingdoms into **domains**.

Figure 15.15A uses the domestic cat (*Felis catus*) to illustrate this progressively more inclusive classification system. The genus *Felis* includes the domestic cat and several closely related species of small wild cats, represented by small yellow boxes in the figure. The genus *Felis* is placed in the cat family, Felidae, along with other genera of cats, such as the genus *Panthera*, which includes the tiger, leopard, jaguar, and African lion. Family Felidae belongs to the order Carnivora, which also includes the family Canidae (for example, the wolf and coyote) and several other families. Order Carnivora is grouped with many other orders in the class Mammalia, the mammals. Class Mammalia is one of the classes belonging to the phylum Chordata in the kingdom Animalia, which is one of several kingdoms in the domain Eukarya. Each taxonomic unit at any level—family Felidae or class Mammalia, for instance—is called a **taxon** (plural, *taxa*).

Grouping organisms into broader categories seems to come naturally to humans—it is a way to structure our world. Classifying species into higher (more inclusive) taxa, however, is ultimately arbitrary. Higher classification levels are generally defined by morphological characters chosen by taxonomists rather than by quantitative measurements that could apply to the same taxon level across all lineages.

Ever since Darwin, systematics has had a goal beyond simple organization: to have classification reflect evolutionary relationships. Biologists traditionally use **phylogenetic trees** to depict hypotheses about the evolutionary history of species. These branching diagrams reflect the hierarchical classification of groups nested within more inclusive groups. **Figure 15.15B** illustrates the connection between classification and phylogeny. This tree shows the classification of some of the taxa in the order Carnivora and the probable evolutionary relationships among these groups. Note that such a phylogenetic tree does not indicate when a particular species evolved but only the pattern of descent from the last common ancestors of the species shown.

 How much of the classification in Figure 15.15A do we share with the domestic cat?

⬤ We are classified the same from the domain to the class level: Both cats and humans are mammals. We do not belong to the same order.

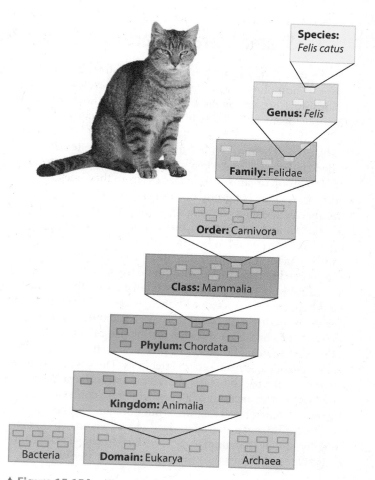

▲ **Figure 15.15A** Hierarchical classification of the domestic cat

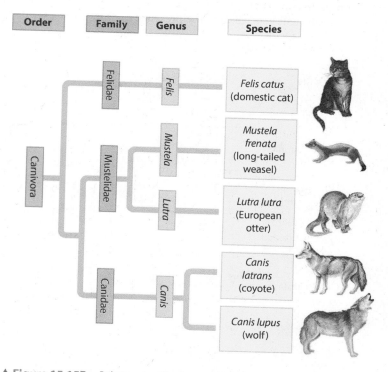

▲ **Figure 15.15B** Relating classification to phylogeny

Phylogeny and the Tree of Life 309

15.16 Shared characters are used to construct phylogenetic trees

In reconstructing a group's evolutionary history, biologists first sort homologous features, which reflect evolutionary relationship, from analogous features, which do not. They then infer phylogeny using these homologous characters.

Cladistics   The most widely used method in systematics is called **cladistics**. Common ancestry is the primary criterion used to group organisms into **clades** (from the Greek *clados*, branch). A clade is a group of species that includes an ancestral species and all its descendants. Such an inclusive group of ancestor and descendants, be it a genus, family, or some broader taxon, is said to be **monophyletic** (meaning "single tribe"). Clades reflect the branching pattern of evolution and can be used to construct phylogenetic trees.

Cladistics is based on the Darwinian concept that organisms both share characters with their ancestors and differ from them. For example, all mammals have backbones, but the presence of a backbone does not distinguish mammals from other vertebrates. The backbone predates the branching of the mammalian clade from other vertebrates. Thus, we say that for mammals, the backbone is a **shared ancestral character** that originated in an ancestor of all vertebrates. In contrast, hair, a character shared by all mammals but not found in their ancestors, is considered a **shared derived character**, an evolutionary novelty unique to mammals. Shared derived characters distinguish clades and thus the branch points in the tree of life.

Inferring Phylogenies Using Shared Characters   The simplified example in **Figure 15.16A** illustrates that the sequence in which shared derived characters appear can be used to construct a phylogenetic tree. The figure compares five animals according to the presence or absence of a set of characters. An important part of cladistics is a comparison between a so-called ingroup and an outgroup. The **outgroup** (in this example, the frog) is a species from a lineage that is known to have diverged before the lineage that includes the species we are studying, the **ingroup**.

In our example, the frog (representing amphibians, the outgroup) and the other four animals (collectively the ingroup) are all related in that they are tetrapods (vertebrates with limbs). By comparing members of the ingroup with each other and with the outgroup, we can determine which characters are the derived characters—evolutionary innovations—that define the sequence of branch points in the phylogeny of the ingroup.

In the character table in Figure 15.16A, 0 indicates that a particular character is not present in a group; 1 indicates that the character is present. Let's work through this example step by step. All the animals in the ingroup have an amnion, a membrane that encloses the embryo in a fluid-filled sac. The outgroup does not have this character. Now consider the next character—hair and mammary glands. This character is present in all three mammals (the duck-billed platypus, kangaroo, and beaver) but not the iguana or frog. The third character in the table is gestation, the carrying of developing offspring within the uterus of the female parent. Both the outgroup and iguanas do not exhibit gestation. Instead, frogs release their eggs into the water, and iguanas and most other reptiles lay eggs with a shell. One of the mammals, the duck-billed platypus, also lays eggs with a shell; and from this we might infer that the duck-billed platypus represents an early branch point in the mammalian clade. In fact, this hypothesis is strongly supported by structural, fossil, and molecular evidence. The final character is long gestation, in which an offspring completes its embryonic development within the uterus. This is

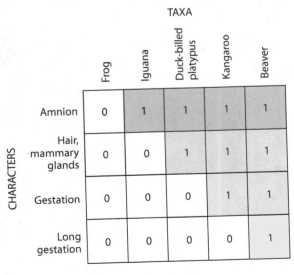

			TAXA		
CHARACTERS	Frog	Iguana	Duck-billed platypus	Kangaroo	Beaver
Amnion	0	1	1	1	1
Hair, mammary glands	0	0	1	1	1
Gestation	0	0	0	1	1
Long gestation	0	0	0	0	1

Character Table

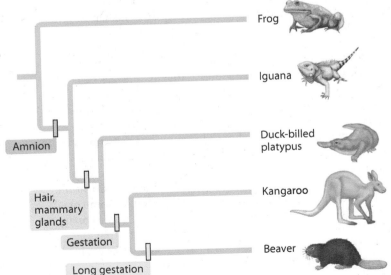

Phylogenetic Tree

▲ **Figure 15.16A**   Constructing a phylogenetic tree using cladistics

Try This   Label the outgroup and the ingroup. Circle the branch point that represents the most recent common ancestor of kangaroos and beavers, and name the derived character that defines this branch point.

the case for a beaver, but a kangaroo has a very short gestation period and completes its embryonic development while nursing in its mother's pouch.

We can now translate the data in our table of characters into a phylogenetic tree. Such a tree is constructed from a series of two-way branch points (see Module 13.5). Each branch point (also called a node) represents the divergence of two groups from a common ancestor and the emergence of a lineage possessing a new set of derived characters. By tracing the distribution of shared derived characters, you can see how we inferred the sequence of branching and the evolutionary relationships of this group of animals.

Parsimony   Useful in many areas of science, **parsimony** is the adoption of the simplest explanation for observed phenomena. Systematists use the principle of parsimony to construct phylogenetic trees that require the smallest number of evolutionary changes. For instance, parsimony leads to the hypothesis that a beaver is more closely related to a kangaroo than to a platypus, because in both the beaver and the kangaroo, embryos begin development within the female uterus. It is possible that gestation evolved twice, once in the kangaroo lineage and independently in the beaver lineage, but this explanation is more complicated and therefore less likely. Typical cladistic analyses involve much more complex data sets than that presented in Figure 15.16A (often including comparisons of DNA sequences) and are usually handled by computer programs designed to construct parsimonious trees.

Phylogenetic Trees as Hypotheses   Systematists use many kinds of evidence, such as structural and developmental features, molecular data, and behavioral traits, to reconstruct evolutionary histories. However, even the best tree represents only the most likely hypothesis based on available evidence. As new data accumulate, hypotheses may be revised and new trees drawn.

An example of a redrawn tree is shown in **Figure 15.16B**. In traditional vertebrate taxonomy, crocodiles, snakes, lizards, and other reptiles were classified in the class Reptilia, while birds were placed in the separate class Aves. However, such a reptilian clade is not monophyletic—in other words, it does not include an ancestral species and all of its descendants, one group of which includes the birds. Many lines of evidence support the tree shown in Figure 15.16B, showing that birds belong to the clade of reptiles.

Thinking of phylogenetic trees as hypotheses allows us to use them to make and test predictions. For example, if our phylogeny is correct, then features shared by two groups of closely related organisms should be present in their common ancestor. Using this reasoning, consider the novel predictions that can be made about dinosaurs. As seen in the tree in Figure 15.16B, the closest *living* relatives of birds are crocodiles. Birds and crocodiles share numerous features: They have four-chambered hearts, they "sing" to defend territories and attract mates (although a crocodile "song" is more like a bellow), and they build nests. Both birds and crocodiles care for and warm their eggs by brooding. Birds brood by sitting on their eggs, whereas crocodiles cover their eggs with their neck. Reasoning that any feature shared by birds and crocodiles is likely to have been present in their common ancestor (denoted by the red circle in Figure 15.16B) and all of its descendants, biologists hypothesize that dinosaurs had four-chambered hearts, sang, built nests, and exhibited brooding.

Internal organs such as hearts rarely fossilize, and it is, of course, difficult to determine whether dinosaurs sang. However, fossilized dinosaur nests have been found. **Figure 15.16C** shows a fossil of an *Oviraptor* dinosaur thought to have died in a sandstorm while incubating or protecting its eggs. The hypothesis that dinosaurs built nests and exhibited brooding has been further supported by additional fossils that show other species of dinosaurs caring for their eggs.

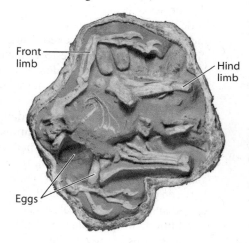

▲ **Figure 15.16C**   Fossil remains of *Oviraptor* and eggs (The orientation of the bones, which surround the eggs, suggests that the dinosaur died while incubating or protecting its eggs.)

The more we know about an organism and its relatives, the more accurately we can portray its phylogeny. In the next module, we consider how molecular biology is providing valuable data for tracing evolutionary history.

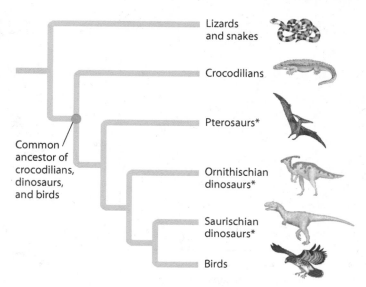

▲ **Figure 15.16B**   A phylogenetic tree of reptiles (* indicates extinct lineages)

? To distinguish a particular clade of mammals within the larger clade that corresponds to class Mammalia, why is hair not a useful character?

● Hair is a shared ancestral character common to all mammals and thus is not helpful in distinguishing different mammalian subgroups.

15.17 An organism's evolutionary history is documented in its genome

The more recently two species have branched from a common ancestor, the more similar their DNA sequences should be. The longer two species have been on separate evolutionary paths, the more their DNA is expected to have diverged.

Molecular Systematics   A method called **molecular systematics**, which uses DNA or other molecules to infer relatedness, is a valuable approach for tracing phylogeny. Scientists have sequenced more than 153 billion bases of DNA from thousands of species. This enormous database has fueled a boom in the study of phylogeny and clarified many evolutionary relationships. Consider the red panda, an endangered, Southeast Asian tree-dwelling mammal that feeds mostly on bamboo. It was initially classified as a close relative of the giant panda, and then as a member of the raccoon family. Recent molecular studies, however, suggest that the red panda represents a separate group, which diverged from the lineage that led to the raccoon and the weasel families. Molecular evidence has also begun to sort out the relationships among the species of bears. **Figure 15.17** presents a phylogenetic hypothesis for the lineages that include bears, raccoons, weasels, and the red panda. Notice that the phylogenetic tree in Figure 15.17 includes a timeline, which is based on fossil evidence and molecular data that can estimate when many of these divergences occurred. (Most of the phylogenetic trees we have seen so far indicate only the relative order in which lineages diverged; they do not show the timing of those events.)

Bears, raccoons, and the red panda are closely related mammals that diverged fairly recently. But biologists can also use DNA analyses to assess relationships between groups of organisms that are so phylogenetically distant that structural similarities are absent. In addition, it is possible to reconstruct phylogenies among groups of present-day prokaryotes and other microorganisms for which we have no fossil record at all. Molecular biology has helped to extend systematics to the extremes of evolutionary relationships far above and below the species level, ranging from major branches of the tree of life to its finest twigs.

The observation that different genes evolve at different rates allows scientists to use molecular systematics for constructing phylogenetic trees that encompass both long and short periods of time. The DNA specifying ribosomal RNA (rRNA) changes relatively slowly, so comparisons of DNA sequences in these genes are useful for investigating relationships between taxa that diverged hundreds of millions of years ago. Studies of the genes for rRNA have shown, for example, that fungi are more closely related to animals than to green plants—something that certainly could not have been deduced from morphological comparisons alone. In contrast, the DNA in mitochondria (mtDNA) evolves relatively rapidly and can be used

to investigate more recent evolutionary events. For example, researchers have used mtDNA sequences to study the relationships between Native American groups. Their studies support earlier evidence that the Pima of Arizona, the Maya of Mexico, and the Yanomami of Venezuela are closely related, probably descending from the first wave of immigrants to cross the Bering Land Bridge from Asia to the Americas about 15,000 years ago.

Genome Evolution   Now that we can compare entire genomes, including our own, some interesting facts have emerged. As you may have heard, the genomes of humans and chimpanzees are strikingly similar. An even more

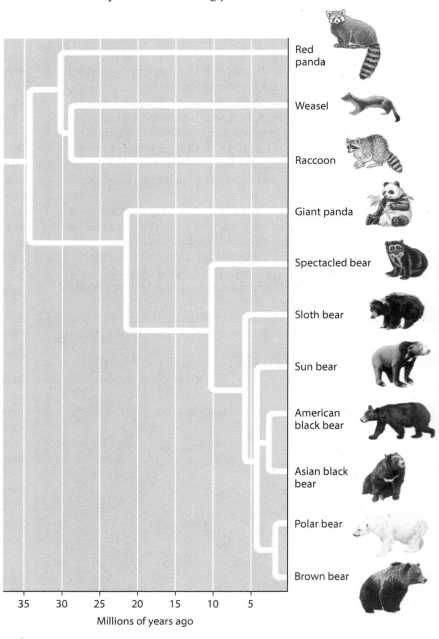

Red panda

Weasel

Raccoon

Giant panda

Spectacled bear

Sloth bear

Sun bear

American black bear

Asian black bear

Polar bear

Brown bear

| 35 | 30 | 25 | 20 | 15 | 10 | 5 |

Millions of years ago

▲ Figure 15.17   A phylogenetic tree based on molecular data remarkable fact is that homologous genes (similar genes that species share because of descent from a common ancestor) are widespread and can extend over huge evolutionary distances. While the genes of humans and mice are certainly not identical, 99% of them are detectably homologous. And 50% of human genes are homologous with those of yeast. This remarkable commonality demonstrates that all living organisms share many biochemical and developmental pathways and provides overwhelming support for Darwin's theory of "descent with modification."

Gene duplication has played a particularly important role in evolution because it increases the number of genes in the genome, providing additional opportunities for further evolutionary changes (see Module 15.11). Molecular techniques now allow scientists to trace the evolutionary history of such duplications—in which lineage they occurred and how the multiple copies of genes have diverged from each other over time.

Another interesting fact evident from genome comparisons is that the number of genes has not increased at the same rate as the complexity of organisms. Humans have only about four times as many genes as yeasts. Yeasts are simple, single-celled eukaryotes; humans have a complex brain and a body that contains more than 200 different types of tissues. Evidence is emerging that many human genes are more versatile than those of yeast, but explaining the mechanisms of such versatility remains an exciting scientific challenge.

> **?** What types of molecules should be compared to help determine whether fungi are more closely related to plants or to animals?

> ● Because these organisms diverged so long ago, scientists should compare molecules that change or evolve very slowly, such as the DNA that specifies rRNA.

15.18 Molecular clocks help track evolutionary time

The longer two groups have been separated, the greater the divergence of their genes. For example, sharks and tunas have been on separate evolutionary paths for more than 420 million years, whereas dolphins and bats diverged about 60 million years ago. Despite the obvious differences between dolphins and bats, their homologous genes are much more alike than are such genes in sharks and tuna. Indeed, molecular changes have kept better track of time than have changes in morphology. Biologists have found that some genes or other regions of genomes appear to accumulate changes at constant rates. Such observations form the basis for the concept of a **molecular clock**, a method that estimates the time required for a given amount of evolutionary change.

The molecular clock of a gene shown to have a reliable average rate of change can be calibrated in actual time by graphing the number of nucleotide differences against the dates of evolutionary branch points known from the fossil record. The graph line can then be used to estimate the dates of other evolutionary episodes not documented in the fossil record.

Molecular clocks have been used to date a wide variety of events. In one fascinating example published in 2011, researchers studied the divergence of human body lice (Figure 15.18) from head lice. Lice are tiny, blood-sucking insects that live in the fur of most mammal species. Early in human evolution, the loss of body hair restricted lice to the head—bare skin deprived the parasites of their refuge. When clothing offered a new habitat, populations diverged into two types, head lice and body lice, each with adaptations specific to its habitat. (Pubic lice have a different evolutionary history and are members of a different genus.) By comparing data from four different DNA sequences in head lice and body lice, the researchers estimated that people began to wear clothing between 83,000 and 170,000 years ago.

Some biologists are skeptical about the accuracy of molecular clocks because the rate of molecular change may vary at different times, in different genes, and in different groups

▲ Figure 15.18   Human body louse (*Pediculus humanus*)

of organisms. In some cases, problems may be avoided by calibrating molecular clocks with many genes rather than just one or a few genes. One group of researchers used sequence data from 658 genes to construct a molecular clock that covered almost 600 million years of vertebrate evolution. Their estimates of divergence times agreed closely with fossil-based estimates. An abundant fossil record extends back only about 550 million years, and molecular clocks have been used to date evolutionary divergences that occurred a billion or more years ago. But the estimates assume that the clocks have been constant for all that time. Thus, such estimates are highly uncertain.

Evolutionary theory holds that all of life has a common ancestor. Molecular systematics is helping to link all living organisms into a comprehensive tree of life, as we see next.

> **?** What is a molecular clock? What assumption underlies the use of such a clock?

> ● A molecular clock estimates the actual time of evolutionary events based on the number of DNA changes. It is based on the assumption that some regions of genomes evolve at constant rates.

15.19 Constructing the tree of life is a work in progress

Phylogenetic trees are hypotheses about evolutionary history. Like all hypotheses, they are revised, or in some cases rejected, in accordance with new evidence. As you have learned, molecular systematics and cladistics are remodeling some trees.

Over the years, many schemes have been proposed for classifying all of life. Historically, a two-kingdom system divided all organisms into plants and animals. But it was beset with problems. Where do bacteria fit? Or photosynthetic unicellular organisms that move? And what about the fungi?

By the late 1960s, many biologists recognized five kingdoms: Monera (prokaryotes), Protista (a diverse kingdom consisting mostly of unicellular eukaryotes), Plantae, Fungi, and Animalia. However, molecular studies highlighted fundamental flaws in the five-kingdom system. Biologists have since adopted a **three-domain system**, which recognizes three basic groups: two domains of prokaryotes, Bacteria and Archaea, and one domain of eukaryotes, called Eukarya. Kingdoms Fungi, Plantae, and Animalia are still recognized, but kingdoms Monera and Protista are obsolete because they are not monophyletic.

Molecular and cellular evidence indicates that the two lineages of prokaryotes (bacteria and archaea) diverged very early in the evolutionary history of life. Molecular evidence also suggests that archaea are more closely related to eukaryotes than to bacteria. **Figure 15.19A** is an evolutionary tree based largely on rRNA genes. As you just learned, rRNA genes have evolved so slowly that homologies between distantly related organisms can still be detected. This tree shows that ❶ the first major split in the history of life was the divergence of the bacteria from the other two domains, followed by the divergence of domains Archaea and Eukarya.

Comparisons of complete genomes from the three domains, however, show that, especially during the early history of life, there have been substantial interchanges of genes between organisms in the different domains. These took place through **horizontal gene transfer**, a process in which genes are transferred from one genome to another through mechanisms such as plasmid exchange and viral infection (see Modules 10.22 and 10.23) and even through the fusion of different organisms. Figure 15.19A shows two major episodes of horizontal gene transfer: ❷ gene transfer between a mitochondrial ancestor and the ancestor of eukaryotes and ❸ gene transfer between a chloroplast ancestor and the ancestor of green plants. (Module 4.15 describes the endosymbiont theory for the origin of mitochondria and chloroplasts.)

Some scientists have argued that horizontal gene transfers were so common that the early history of life should be represented as a tangled network of connected branches. Others have suggested that the early history of life is best represented by a ring, not a tree (**Figure 15.19B**). Based on an analysis of hundreds of genes, some researchers have hypothesized that the eukaryote lineage (gold in the figure) arose when an early archaean (blue-green) fused with an early bacterium (purple). In this model, eukaryotes are as closely related to bacteria as they are to archaea—an evolutionary relationship that can best be shown in a ring of life. As new data and new methods for analyzing that data emerge, constructing a comprehensive tree of life will continue to challenge and intrigue scientists.

In the next unit, we examine the enormous diversity of organisms that have populated Earth since life first arose more than 3.5 billion years ago.

> **?** **Why might the evolutionary history of the earliest organisms be best represented by a ring of life rather than a tree?**

● There appear to have been multiple horizontal gene transfers among the earliest organisms before the three domains of life eventually emerged from the ring and gave rise to Earth's diversity of life.

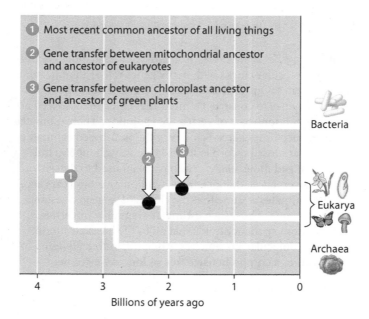

❶ Most recent common ancestor of all living things

❷ Gene transfer between mitochondrial ancestor and ancestor of eukaryotes

❸ Gene transfer between chloroplast ancestor and ancestor of green plants

Bacteria

Eukarya

Archaea

4 3 2 1 0
Billions of years ago

▲ **Figure 15.19A** Two major episodes of horizontal gene transfer in the history of life (dates are uncertain)

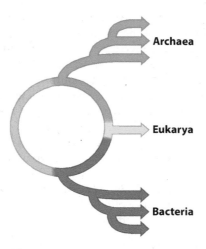

Archaea

Eukarya

Bacteria

▲ **Figure 15.19B** Is the tree of life really a ring of life? In this model, eukaryotes arose when an early archaean fused with an early bacterium.

CHAPTER **15** REVIEW

For practice quizzes, BioFlix animations, MP3 tutorials, video tutors, and more study tools designed for this textbook, go to

MasteringBiology®

Reviewing the Concepts

Early Earth and the Origin of Life (15.1–15.3)

15.1 Conditions on early Earth made the origin of life possible. Earth formed some 4.6 billion years ago. Fossil stromatolites formed by prokaryotes date back 3.5 billion years.

15.2 Experiments show that the abiotic synthesis of organic molecules is possible.

15.3 Stages in the origin of the first cells probably included the formation of polymers, protocells, and self-replicating RNA. Natural selection could have acted on protocells that contained self-replicating molecules.

Major Events in the History of Life (15.4–15.6)

15.4 The origins of single-celled and multicellular organisms and the colonization of land were key events in life's history.

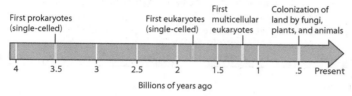

First prokaryotes (single-celled)

First eukaryotes (single-celled)

First multicellular eukaryotes

Colonization of land by fungi, plants, and animals

| 4 | 3.5 | 3 | 2.5 | 2 | 1.5 | 1 | .5 | Present |

Billions of years ago

15.5 The actual ages of rocks and fossils mark geologic time. Radiometric dating can date rocks and fossils.

15.6 The fossil record documents the history of life. In the geologic record, eras and periods are separated by major transitions in life-forms, often caused by extinctions.

Mechanisms of Macroevolution (15.7–15.13)

15.7 Continental drift has played a major role in macroevolution. The formation and split-up of Pangaea affected the distribution and diversification of organisms.

15.8 Plate tectonics may imperil human life. Volcanoes and earthquakes often occur at the boundaries of Earth's plates.

15.9 During mass extinctions, large numbers of species are lost. The Permian extinction is linked to the effects of extreme volcanic activity, and the Cretaceous extinction, which included most dinosaurs, may have been caused by the impact of an asteroid.

15.10 Adaptive radiations have increased the diversity of life. The origin of many new species often follows mass extinctions, colonization of new habitats, and the evolution of new adaptations.

15.11 Genes that control development play a major role in evolution. "Evo-devo" combines evolutionary and developmental biology. New forms can evolve by changes in the number, sequences, or regulation of developmental genes.

15.12 Novel traits may arise in several ways. Complex structures may evolve in stages from simpler versions with the same basic function or from the gradual adaptation of existing structures to new functions.

15.13 Evolutionary trends do not mean that evolution is goal directed. An evolutionary trend may be a result of species selection or natural selection in changing environments.

Phylogeny and the Tree of Life (15.14–15.19)

15.14 Phylogenies based on homologies reflect evolutionary history. Homologous structures and molecular sequences provide evidence of common ancestry.

15.15 Systematics connects classification with evolutionary history. Taxonomists assign each species a binomial—a genus and species name. Genera are grouped into progressively broader categories. A phylogenetic tree is a hypothesis of evolutionary relationships.

15.16 Shared characters are used to construct phylogenetic trees. Cladistics uses shared derived characters to define clades. A parsimonious tree requires the fewest evolutionary changes.

15.17 An organism's evolutionary history is documented in its genome. Molecular systematics uses molecular comparisons to build phylogenetic trees. Homologous genes are found across distantly related species.

15.18 Molecular clocks help track evolutionary time. Regions of DNA that change at a constant rate can provide estimated dates of past events.

15.19 Constructing the tree of life is a work in progress. Evidence of multiple horizontal gene transfers suggests that the early history of life may be best represented by a ring, from which domains Bacteria, Archaea, and Eukarya emerge.

Connecting the Concepts

1. Using the figure below, describe the stages that may have led to the origin of life.

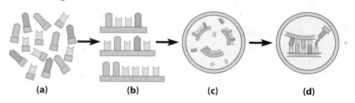

(a) (b) (c) (d)

2. Fill in this concept map about systematics.

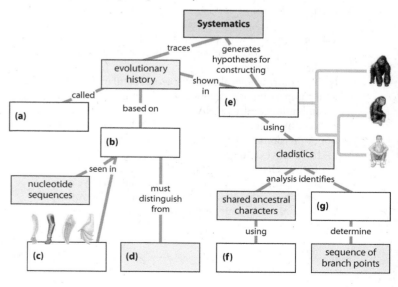

Systematics

traces

generates hypotheses for constructing

evolutionary history

shown in

(e)

called

based on

(a)

using

(b)

cladistics

seen in

nucleotide sequences

analysis identifies

must distinguish from

shared ancestral characters

(g)

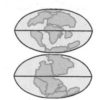

using

determine

(c)

(d)

(f)

sequence of branch points

Testing Your Knowledge

Level 1: Knowledge/Comprehension

3. You set your time machine for 3 billion years ago and push the start button. When the dust clears, you look out the window. Which of the following describes what you would probably see?
   a. a cloud of gas and dust in space
   b. green scum in the water
   c. land and water sterile and devoid of life
   d. an endless expanse of red-hot molten rock

4. Ancient photosynthetic prokaryotes were very important in the history of life because they
   a. produced the oxygen in the atmosphere.
   b. are the oldest known archaea.
   c. were the first multicellular organisms.
   d. showed that life could evolve around deep-sea vents.

5. The animals and plants of India are very different from the species in nearby Southeast Asia. Why might this be true?
   a. India was once covered by oceans and Asia was not.
   b. India is in the process of separating from the rest of Asia.
   c. Life in India was wiped out by ancient volcanic eruptions.
   d. India was a separate continent until about 45 million years ago.

6. Adaptive radiations may be promoted by all of the following *except* one. Which one?
   a. mass extinctions that result in vacant ecological niches
   b. colonization of an isolated region with few competitors
   c. a gradual change in climate
   d. a novel adaptation

7. A swim bladder is a gas-filled sac that helps fish maintain buoyancy. Evidence indicates that early fish gulped air into primitive lungs, helping them survive in stagnant waters. The evolution of the swim bladder from lungs of an ancestral fish is an example of
   a. an evolutionary trend.
   b. paedomorphosis.
   c. the gradual refinement of a structure with the same function.
   d. exaptation.

8. If you were using cladistics to build a phylogenetic tree of cats, which would be the best choice for an outgroup?
   a. kangaroo
   b. leopard
   c. domestic cat
   d. iguana

9. Which of the following could provide the best data for determining the phylogeny of very closely related species?
   a. the fossil record
   b. their morphological differences and similarities
   c. a comparison of nucleotide sequences in homologous genes and mitochondrial DNA
   d. a comparison of their ribosomal DNA sequences

10. Major divisions in the geologic record are marked by
    a. radioactive dating.
    b. distinct changes in the types of fossilized life.
    c. regular time intervals measured in millions of years.
    d. the appearance, in order, of prokaryotes, eukaryotes, protists, animals, plants, and fungi.

Level 2: Application/Analysis

11. Distinguish between microevolution and macroevolution.
12. Which are more likely to be closely related: two species with similar appearance but divergent gene sequences or two species with different appearances but nearly identical genes? Explain.
13. How can the Darwinian concept of descent with modification explain the evolution of such complex structures as an eye?
14. Explain why changes in the regulation of developmental genes may have played such a large role in the evolution of new forms.
15. What types of molecular comparisons are used to determine the very early branching of the tree of life? Explain.

Level 3: Synthesis/Evaluation

16. Measurements indicate that a fossilized skull you unearthed has a carbon-14/carbon-12 ratio about one-sixteenth that of the skulls of present-day animals. What is the approximate age of the fossil? (The half-life of carbon-14 is 5,730 years.)
17. A paleontologist compares fossils from three dinosaurs and *Archaeopteryx*, the earliest known bird. The following table shows the distribution of characters for each species, where 1 means that the character is present and 0 means it is not. The outgroup (not shown in the table) had none of the characters. Arrange these species on the phylogenetic tree below and indicate the derived character that defines each branch point.

Trait	Velociraptor	Coelophysis	Archaeopteryx	Allosaurus
Hollow bones	1	1	1	1
Three-fingered hand	1	0	1	1
Half-moon-shaped wrist bone	1	0	1	0
Reversed first toe	0	0	1	0

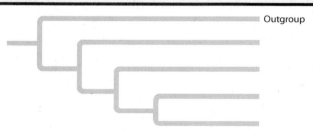

Outgroup

18. **SCIENTIFIC THINKING** When Stanley Miller's experiment was published in 1953, his results made global headlines. The general public thought Miller had answered the question of how life on Earth began by creating life in a test tube. However, scientists understood that Miller's experiment was neither a final answer nor a recipe for life. Rather, it was the first test of a long-standing hypothesis about the origin of life. Using the information in Module 15.2 (and additional research, if you wish) as an example, write an essay describing how the process of science progresses over time toward understanding how nature works. (You will find Module 1.8 helpful.)

Answers to all questions can be found in Appendix 4.

The Evolution of Biological Diversity

16 Microbial Life: *Prokaryotes and Protists*

? *Are antibiotics making us fat?*

You know that your body contains trillions of individual cells, but did you know that they aren't all "you"? In fact, microorganisms residing in and on your body outnumber your own cells 10 to 1—100 trillion bacteria (including *Helicobacter pylori,* shown below), archaea, and protists call your body home. Your skin, mouth, nasal passages, and digestive and urogenital tracts are prime real estate for these microorganisms. Although each individual is so tiny that it would have to be magnified hundreds of times for you to see it, the weight of your microbial residents totals two to five pounds.

We acquire our microbial communities during the first two years of life, and they remain fairly stable thereafter. However, modern life is taking a toll on that stability. We alter the makeup of these communities by taking antibiotics, purifying our water, sterilizing our food, attempting to germ-proof our surroundings, and scrubbing our skin and teeth. Scientists hypothesize that disrupting our microbial communities may increase our susceptibility to infectious diseases, predispose us to

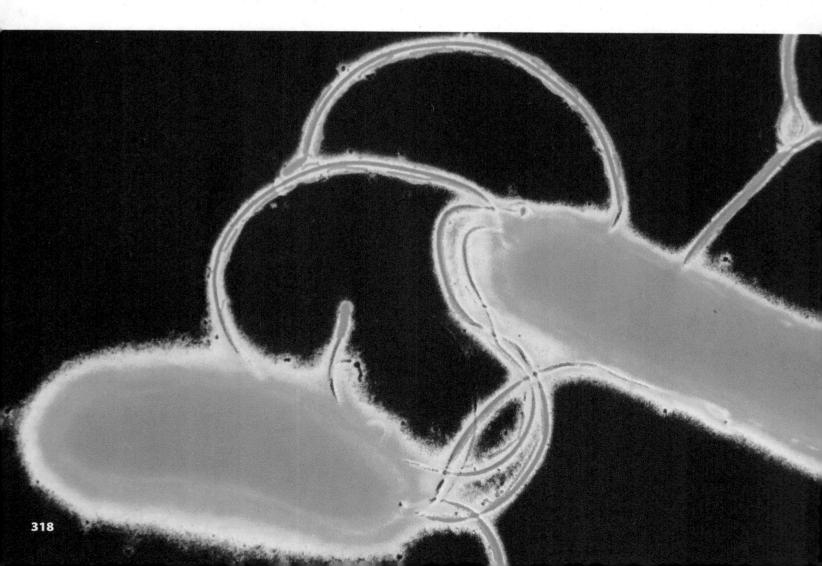

certain cancers, and contribute to conditions such as asthma and other allergies, irritable bowel syndrome, Crohn's disease, and autism. One of the most intriguing hypotheses, as you'll learn later in this chapter, is that obesity results from changes in the species composition of the stomach.

In this chapter, you will learn some of the benefits and drawbacks of human-microbe interactions. You will also sample a bit of the remarkable diversity of prokaryotes and protists.

Our exploration of the magnificent diversity of life begins with this chapter. And so it is fitting that we begin with the prokaryotes, Earth's first life-form, and the protists, the bridge between unicellular eukaryotes and multicellular plants, fungi, and animals.

BIG IDEAS

Prokaryotes
(16.1–16.11)

Prokaryotes, the smallest organisms known, are extraordinarily diverse.

Protists
(16.12–16.19)

Protists are eukaryotes. Though most are unicellular, microscopic organisms, some protists are multicellular.

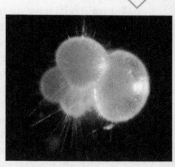

▷ Prokaryotes

16.1 Prokaryotes are diverse and widespread

In the first half of this chapter, you will learn about prokaryotes, organisms that have a cellular organization fundamentally different from that of eukaryotes (see Modules 4.3 and 4.4). Whereas eukaryotic cells have a membrane-enclosed nucleus and numerous other membrane-enclosed organelles, prokaryotic cells lack these structural features. Prokaryotes are also typically much smaller than eukaryotes. You can get an idea of the size of most prokaryotes from **Figure 16.1**, a colorized scanning electron micrograph of the point of a pin (purple) covered with numerous bacteria (orange). Most prokaryotic cells have diameters in the range of 1–5 μm, much smaller than most eukaryotic cells (typically 10–100 μm).

Despite their small size, prokaryotes have an immense impact on our world. They are found wherever there is life, including in and on the bodies of multicellular organisms. The collective biological mass (biomass) of prokaryotes is at least 10 times that of all eukaryotes! Prokaryotes also thrive in habitats too cold, too hot, too salty, too acidic, or too alkaline for any eukaryote. And scientists are just beginning to investigate the extensive prokaryotic diversity in the oceans.

Although prokaryotes are a constant presence in our environment, we hear most about the relatively few species that cause illnesses. We focus on bacterial **pathogens**, disease-causing agents, in Module 16.10. But harmless or beneficial prokaryotes are far more common than harmful prokaryotes. The chapter introduction introduced our **microbiota**, the community of microorganisms that live in and on our bodies. Each of us harbors several hundred different species and genetic strains of prokaryotes, including a few whose positive effects are well studied. For example, some of our intestinal inhabitants supply essential vitamins and enable us to extract nutrition from food molecules that we can't otherwise digest.

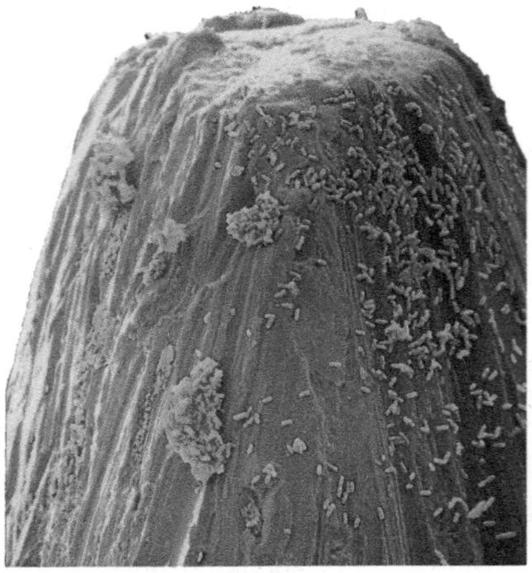

▶ **Figure 16.1** Bacteria on the point of a pin

Many of the bacteria that live on our skin perform helpful housekeeping functions such as decomposing dead skin cells. Prokaryotes also guard the body against pathogenic intruders.

Prokaryotes are also essential to the health of the environment. They help to decompose dead organisms and other organic waste material, returning vital chemical elements to the environment. They are indispensable components of the chemical cycle that makes nitrogen available to plants and other organisms. If prokaryotes were to disappear, the chemical cycles that sustain life would halt, and all forms of eukaryotic life would also be doomed. In contrast, prokaryotic life would undoubtedly persist in the absence of eukaryotes, as it once did for billions of years.

There are two very different kinds of prokaryotes, which are classified in the domains **Archaea** and **Bacteria** (Module 15.19). In the next several modules, we describe the features that have made prokaryotes so successful, followed by a look at the diversity of each domain.

> **?** The number of bacterial cells that live in and on our body is greater than the number of eukaryotic cells that make up the body. Why aren't we aware of these trillions of cells?

● We can't sense our own eukaryotic cells individually, and bacterial cells are much smaller than that. Also, our microbiota are adapted for coexisting with us.

16.2 External features contribute to the success of prokaryotes

Some of the diversity of prokaryotes is evident in their external features, including shape, cell walls, and projections such as flagella. These features are useful for identifying prokaryotes as well as helping the organisms survive in their environments.

Cell Shape   Determining cell shape by microscopic examination is an important step in identifying prokaryotes. The micrographs in **Figure 16.2A** show three of the most common prokaryotic cell shapes. Spherical prokaryotic cells are called **cocci** (singular, *coccus*). Cocci that occur in chains, like the ones in the left photo, are called streptococci (from the Greek *streptos*, twisted). The bacterium that causes strep throat in humans is a streptococcus. Other cocci occur in clusters; they are called staphylococci (from the Greek *staphyle*, cluster of grapes).

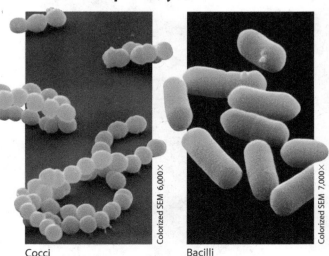

Cocci   Bacilli   Spirochete

▲ **Figure 16.2A**   Three common shapes of prokaryotes

Rod-shaped prokaryotes are called **bacilli** *(singular, bacillus)*. Most bacilli occur singly, like the *Escherichia coli* cells in the middle photo in Figure 16.2A. However, the cells of some species occur in pairs or chains of rods. Bacilli may also be threadlike, or filamentous.

A third prokaryotic cell shape is spiral, like a corkscrew. Spiral prokaryotes that are relatively short and rigid are called *spirilla*; those with longer, more flexible cells, like the one shown on the right in Figure 16.2A, which causes Lyme disease, are called *spirochetes*. The bacterium that causes syphilis is also a spirochete. Spirochetes include some giants by prokaryotic standards—cells 0.5 mm long (though very thin).

Cell Wall   Nearly all prokaryotes have a cell wall, a feature that enables them to live in a wide range of environments. The cell wall provides physical protection and prevents the cell from bursting in a hypotonic environment (see Module 5.5). The cell walls of bacteria fall into two general types, which scientists can identify with a technique called the **Gram stain** (Figure 16.2B). Gram-positive bacteria have simpler walls with a relatively thick layer of a unique material called **peptidoglycan**, a polymer of sugars cross-linked by short polypeptides. The walls of gram-negative bacteria stain differently. They have less peptidoglycan and are more complex, with an outer membrane that contains lipids bonded to carbohydrates. The cell walls of archaea do not contain peptidoglycan, but can also be gram-positive or gram-negative.

In medicine, Gram stains are often used to detect the presence of bacteria and indicate the type of antibiotic to prescribe. Among disease-causing bacteria, gram-negative species are generally more threatening than gram-positive species because lipid molecules of the outer membrane of gram-negative bacteria are often toxic. The membrane also protects the gram-negative bacteria against the body's defenses and hinders the entry of antibiotic drugs into the bacterium.

The cell wall of many prokaryotes is covered by a capsule, a sticky layer of polysaccharide or protein. The capsule enables prokaryotes to adhere to a surface or to other individuals in a colony. Capsules can also shield pathogenic prokaryotes from attacks by their host's immune system. The capsule surrounding the *Streptococcus* bacterium shown in Figure 16.2C enables it to attach to cells that line the human respiratory tract—in this image, a tonsil cell.

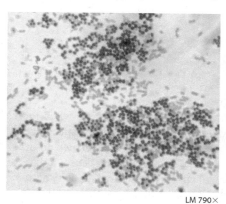

▲ **Figure 16.2B**   Gram-positive (purple) and gram-negative (pink) bacteria

LM 790×

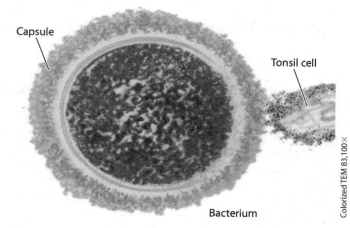

Capsule

Tonsil cell

Bacterium

Colorized TEM 83,100×

▲ **Figure 16.2C**   A capsule attaching a bacterium to a host cell

Projections   Some prokaryotes have external structures that extend beyond the cell wall. Many bacteria and archaea are equipped with flagella, adaptations that enable them to move about in response to chemical or physical signals in their environment. For example, prokaryotes can move toward nutrients or other members of their species or away from a toxic substance. Flagella may be scattered over the entire cell surface or concentrated at one or both ends of the cell. Unlike the flagellum of eukaryotic cells (described in Module 4.18), the prokaryotic flagellum is a naked protein structure that lacks microtubules. The flagellated bacterium in Figure 16.2D is *E. coli*, as seen in a TEM.

Figure 16.2D also illustrates the hairlike projections called **fimbriae** that enable some prokaryotes to stick to a surface or to one another. Fimbriae allow many pathogenic bacteria to latch onto the host cells they colonize. For example, *Neisseria gonorrhoeae*, which causes the sexually transmitted infection gonorrhea, uses fimbriae to attach to cells in the reproductive tract. During sexual intercourse, *N. gonorrhoeae* bacteria may also attach to sperm cells and travel to a woman's oviducts; an infection in these narrow tubes can impair fertility.

? **How could a microscope help you distinguish the cocci that cause "staph" infections from those that cause "strep" throat?**

It would show clusters of cells for staphylococcus and chains of cells for streptococcus.

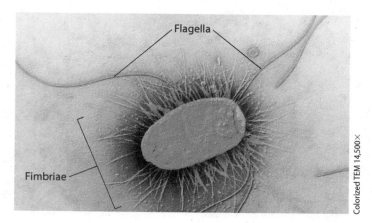

Flagella

Fimbriae

Colorized TEM 14,500×

▲ **Figure 16.2D**   Flagella and fimbriae

16.3 Populations of prokaryotes can adapt rapidly to changes in the environment

Certainly a large part of the success of prokaryotes is their potential to reproduce quickly in a favorable environment. Dividing by binary fission (see Module 8.2), a single prokaryotic cell becomes 2 cells, which then become 4, 8, 16, and so on. While many prokaryotes produce a new generation within 1–3 hours, some species can produce a new generation in only 20 minutes under optimal conditions. If reproduction continued unchecked at this rate, a single prokaryote could give rise to a colony outweighing Earth in only three days!

Salmonella bacteria, which cause food poisoning, are commonly found on raw poultry and eggs, but the bacterial population is often too small to cause symptoms. Refrigeration slows (but does not stop) bacterial reproduction. However, when raw poultry is left in the warm environment of the kitchen, bacteria multiply rapidly and can quickly reach a risky population size. Similarly, bacteria that remain on the counter, cutting board, or kitchen implements may continue to reproduce. So be sure to cook poultry thoroughly (an internal temperature of 165°F is considered safe), and clean anything that has come into contact with raw poultry with soap and hot water or an antimicrobial cleaner.

Each time DNA is replicated prior to binary fission, a few spontaneous mutations occur. As a result, rapid reproduction generates a great deal of genetic variation in a prokaryote population. If the environment changes, an individual that possesses a beneficial allele can quickly take advantage of the new conditions. For example, exposure to antibiotics may select for antibiotic resistance in a bacterial population (see Module 13.16).

The amount of DNA in a prokaryotic cell is on average only about one-thousandth as much as that in a eukaryotic cell. The genome of a typical prokaryote is one long, circular chromosome (Figure 16.3A). (In an intact cell, it is packed into a distinct region; see Figure 4.3.) Many prokaryotes also have additional small, circular DNA molecules called plasmids, which replicate independently of the chromosome (see Module 10.23). Some plasmids carry genes that enhance survival under certain conditions. For example, plasmids may provide resistance to antibiotics, direct the metabolism of rarely encountered nutrients, or have other "contingency" functions. The ability of many prokaryotes to transfer plasmids within and even between species provides another rapid means of adaptation to changes in the environment.

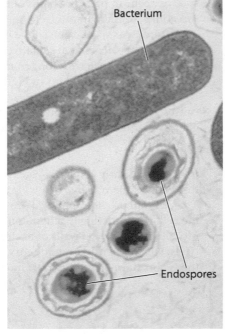

▲ Figure 16.3B   Endospores of anthrax bacteria

If environmental conditions become too harsh to sustain active metabolism—for example, when food or moisture is depleted—some prokaryotes form specialized resistant cells. Figure 16.3B shows an example of such an organism, *Bacillus anthracis*, the bacterium that causes a disease called anthrax in cattle, sheep, and humans. There are actually two cells here, one inside the other. The outer cell, which will later disintegrate, produced the specialized inner cell, called an **endospore**. The endospore, which has a thick, protective coat, dehydrates and becomes dormant. It can survive all sorts of trauma, including extreme heat or cold. When the endospore receives environmental cues that conditions have improved, it absorbs water and resumes growth.

Some endospores can remain dormant for centuries. Not even boiling water kills most of these resistant cells, making it difficult to get rid of spores in a contaminated area. An island off the coast of Scotland that was used for anthrax testing in 1942 was finally declared safe 48 years later, after tons of formaldehyde were applied and huge amounts of topsoil were removed. The food-canning industry kills endospores of dangerous bacteria such as *Clostridium botulinum*, the source of the potentially fatal disease botulism, by heating the food to a temperature of 110–150°C (230–300°F) with high-pressure steam.

Another feature that contributes to the success of prokaryotes is the diversity of ways in which they obtain their nourishment, which we consider in the next module.

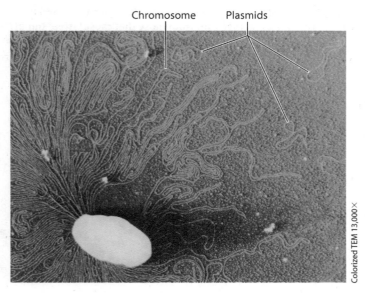

▲ Figure 16.3A   DNA released from a ruptured bacterial cell

? **Why does rapid reproduction produce high genetic variation in populations of prokaryotes?**

● Each time DNA replicates, spontaneous mutations may occur.

16.4 Prokaryotes have unparalleled nutritional diversity

One way to organize the vast diversity of prokaryotes is by their mode of nutrition—how they obtain energy for cellular work and carbon to build organic molecules. Prokaryotes exhibit much more nutritional diversity than eukaryotes. This allows them to inhabit almost every nook and cranny on Earth.

Source of Energy As shown in **Figure 16.4**, two sources of energy can be used by prokaryotes. Like plants, prokaryotic *phototrophs* capture energy from sunlight. Prokaryotic cells do not have chloroplasts, but some prokaryotes have thylakoid membranes where photosynthesis takes place.

Prokaryotes called *chemotrophs* harness the energy stored in chemicals, either organic molecules or inorganic chemicals such as hydrogen sulfide (H_2S), elemental sulfur (S), iron (Fe)-containing compounds, or ammonia (NH_3).

Source of Carbon Organisms that make their own organic compounds from inorganic sources are autotrophic (see Module 7.1). Autotrophs, including plants and some prokaryotes and protists, obtain their carbon atoms from carbon dioxide (CO_2). Most prokaryotes, as well as animals, fungi, and some protists, are heterotrophs, meaning they obtain their carbon atoms from the organic compounds of other organisms.

Mode of Nutrition The terms used to describe how an organism obtains energy and carbon are combined to describe its mode of nutrition (see Figure 16.4).

Photoautotrophs harness sunlight for energy and use CO_2 for carbon. Cyanobacteria, such as the *Oscillatoria* shown in Figure 16.4, are photoautotrophs. As in plants, photosynthesis in cyanobacteria uses chlorophyll *a* and produces O_2 as a by-product.

Photoheterotrophs obtain energy from sunlight but get their carbon atoms from organic sources. This unusual mode of nutrition is found in only a few types of bacteria called purple nonsulfur bacteria. Many of them, including *Rhodopseudomonas,* the example shown in Figure 16.4, are found in aquatic sediments.

Chemoautotrophs harvest energy from inorganic chemicals and use carbon from CO_2 to make organic molecules. Because they don't depend on sunlight, chemoautotrophs can thrive in conditions that seem totally inhospitable to life. Near hydrothermal vents, where scalding water and hot gases surge into the sea more than a mile below the surface, chemoautotrophic bacteria use sulfur compounds as a source of energy. The organic molecules they produce using CO_2 from the seawater support diverse animal communities. The chemoautotrophs shown in Figure 16.4 live between layers of rocks buried 100 m below Earth's surface. Chemoautotrophs are also found in more predictable habitats, such as the soil.

Chemoheterotrophs, which acquire both energy and carbon from organic molecules, are by far the largest and most diverse group of prokaryotes. Almost any organic molecule is food for some species of chemoheterotrophic prokaryote.

? **Which term would describe your mode of nutrition?**

● Chemoheterotrophy

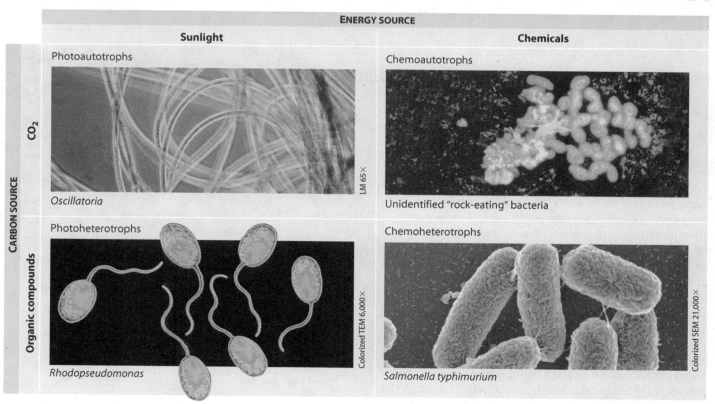

▲ **Figure 16.4** Sources of energy and carbon in prokaryotic modes of nutrition

16.5 Biofilms are complex associations of microbes

CONNECTION

In many natural environments, prokaryotes attach to surfaces in highly organized colonies called **biofilms**. A biofilm may consist of one or several species of prokaryotes, and it may include protists and fungi as well. Biofilms can form on almost any support, including rocks, soil, organic material (including living tissue), metal, and plastic. You have a biofilm on your teeth—dental plaque is a biofilm that can cause tooth decay. Biofilms can even form without a solid foundation, for example, on the surface of stagnant water.

Biofilm formation begins when prokaryotes secrete signaling molecules that attract nearby cells into a cluster. Once the cluster becomes sufficiently large, the cells produce a gooey coating that glues them to the support and to each other, making the biofilm extremely difficult to dislodge. For example, if you don't scrub your shower, you could find a biofilm growing around the drain—running water alone is not strong enough to wash it away. As the biofilm gets larger and more complex, it becomes a "city" of microbes. Communicating by chemical signals, members of the community coordinate the division of labor, defense against invaders, and other activities. Channels in the biofilm allow nutrients to reach cells in the interior and allow wastes to leave, and a variety of environments develop within it.

Biofilms are common among bacteria that cause disease in humans. For instance, ear infections and urinary tract infections are often the result of biofilm-forming bacteria. Cystic fibrosis patients are vulnerable to pneumonia caused by bacteria that form biofilms in their lungs. Biofilms of harmful bacteria can also form on implanted medical devices such as catheters, replacement joints, or pacemakers. The complexity of biofilms makes these infections especially difficult to defeat. Antibiotics may not be able to penetrate beyond the outer layer of cells, leaving much of the community intact. For example, some biofilm bacteria produce an enzyme that breaks down penicillin faster than it can diffuse inward.

Biofilms that form in the environment can be difficult to eradicate, too. A variety of industries spend billions of dollars every year trying to get rid of biofilms that clog and corrode pipes, gum up filters and drains, and coat the hulls of ships (Figure 16.5). Biofilms in water distribution pipes may survive chlorination, the most common method of ensuring that drinking water does not contain any harmful microorganisms. For example, biofilms of *Vibrio cholera*, the bacterium that causes cholera, found in water pipes were capable of withstanding levels of chlorine 10 to 20 times higher than the concentrations routinely used to chlorinate drinking water.

▲ Figure 16.5   A biofilm fouling the insides of a pipe

? **Why are biofilms difficult to eradicate?**

● The biofilm sticks to the surface it resides on, and the cells that make up the biofilm stick to each other; the outer layer of cells may prevent antimicrobial substances from penetrating into the interior of the biofilm.

16.6 Prokaryotes help clean up the environment

CONNECTION

The characteristics that have made prokaryotes so widespread and successful—their nutritional diversity, adaptability, and capacity for forming biofilms—also make them useful for cleaning up contaminants in the environment.

Bioremediation is the use of organisms to remove pollutants from soil, air, or water. Prokaryotic decomposers are the mainstays of sewage treatment facilities. Raw sewage is first passed through a series of screens and shredders, and solid matter settles out from the liquid waste. This solid matter, called sludge, is then gradually added to a culture of anaerobic prokaryotes, including both bacteria and archaea. The microbes decompose the organic matter in the sludge into material that can be placed in a landfill or used as fertilizer.

Liquid wastes are treated separately from the sludge. In Figure 16.6A, you can see a trickling filter system, one type of mechanism for treating liquid wastes. The long horizontal pipes rotate slowly, spraying liquid wastes through the air onto a thick bed of rocks, the filter. Biofilms of aerobic bacteria and fungi growing on the rocks remove much of the

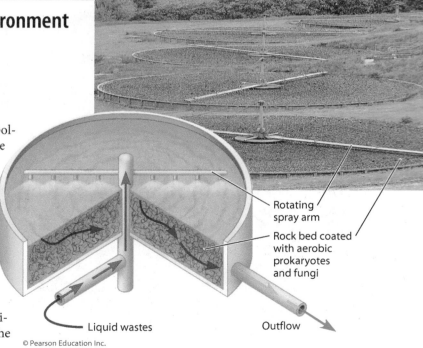

Rotating spray arm

Rock bed coated with aerobic prokaryotes and fungi

Liquid wastes

Outflow

© Pearson Education Inc.

▲ Figure 16.6A   The trickling filter system at a sewage treatment plant organic material dissolved in the waste. Outflow from the rock bed is sterilized and then released, usually into a river or ocean.

Bioremediation has also become a useful tool for cleaning up toxic chemicals released into the soil and water. Naturally occurring prokaryotes capable of degrading pollutants such as oil, solvents, and pesticides are often present in contaminated soil and water, but environmental workers may use methods of speeding up their activity. In **Figure 16.6B**, an airplane is spraying chemical dispersants on oil from the disastrous 2010 Deepwater Horizon spill in the Gulf of Mexico. Like detergents that help clean greasy dishes, these chemicals break oil into smaller droplets that offer more surface area for microbial attack.

? **What is bioremediation?**

ɴoᴉʇnๆๅod dn uɐǝๅɔ oʇ sɯsᴉuɐƃɹo ɟo ǝsn ǝɥ┴

▲ **Figure 16.6B** Spraying chemical dispersants on oil spill in the Gulf of Mexico, 2010

16.7 Bacteria and archaea are the two main branches of prokaryotic evolution

Researchers recently discovered that many prokaryotes once classified as bacteria are actually more closely related to eukaryotes and belong in a domain of their own (as you learned in Module 15.19). As a result, prokaryotes are now classified in two domains: Bacteria and Archaea (from the Greek *archaios*, ancient). Many bacterial and archaeal genomes have now been sequenced. When compared with each other and with the genomes of eukaryotes, these genome sequences strongly support the three-domain view of life. Some genes of archaea are similar to bacterial genes, others to eukaryotic genes, and still others seem to be unique to archaea.

Table 16.7 summarizes some of the main differences between the three domains. Differences between the ribosomal RNA (rRNA) sequences provided the first clues of a deep division among prokaryotes. Other differences in the cellular machinery for gene expression include differences in RNA polymerases (the enzymes that catalyze

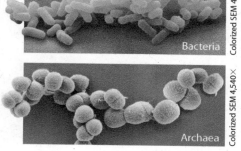

Bacteria Colorized SEM 4,290×

Archaea Colorized SEM 4,540×

the synthesis of RNA) and in the presence of introns within genes. The cell walls and membranes of bacteria and archaea are also distinctive. Bacterial cell walls contain peptidoglycan (see Module 16.2), while archaea do not. Furthermore, the lipids forming the backbone of plasma membranes differ between the two domains. Intriguingly, for most of the features listed in the table, archaea have at least as much in common with eukaryotes as they do with bacteria.

Now that you are familiar with the general characteristics of prokaryotes and the features underlying their spectacular success, let's take a look at prokaryotic diversity. We begin with domain Archaea.

? **As different as bacteria and archaea are, both groups are characterized by _____ cells, which lack nuclei and other membrane-enclosed organelles.**

ɔᴉʇoʎɹɐʞoɹd

TABLE 16.7 | DIFFERENCES BETWEEN THE DOMAINS BACTERIA, ARCHAEA, AND EUKARYA

Characteristic	Bacteria	Archaea	Eukarya
rRNA sequences	Some unique to bacteria	Some unique to archaea; some match eukaryotic sequences	Some unique to eukaryotes; some match archaeal sequences
RNA polymerase	One kind; relatively small and simple	Several kinds; complex	Several kinds; complex
Introns	Rare	In some genes	Present
Peptidoglycan in cell wall	Present	Absent	Absent
Histones associated with DNA	Absent	Present in some species	Present

16.8 Archaea thrive in extreme environments—and in other habitats

Archaea are abundant in many habitats, including places where few other organisms can survive. The archaeal inhabitants of extreme environments have unusual proteins and other molecular adaptations that enable them to metabolize and reproduce effectively. Scientists are only beginning to learn about these adaptations.

A group of archaea called the **extreme halophiles** ("salt lovers") thrive in very salty places, such as the Great Salt Lake in Utah, the Dead Sea, and seawater-evaporating ponds used to produce salt. Many species flourish when the salinity of the water is 15–30% and can tolerate even higher salt concentrations. Because seawater, with a salt concentration of about 3%, is hypertonic enough to shrivel most cells, these archaea have very little competition from other organisms. Extremely salty environments may turn red, purple, or yellow as a result of the dense growth and colorful pigments of halophilic archaea.

Another group of archaea, the **extreme thermophiles** ("heat lovers"), thrive in very hot water; some even live near deep-ocean vents, where temperatures are above 100°C, the boiling point of water at sea level! One such habitat is the Nevada geyser shown in Figure 16.8A. Other thermophiles thrive in acid. Many hot, acidic pools in Yellowstone National Park harbor such archaea, which give the pools a vivid greenish color. One of these organisms, *Sulfolobus*, can obtain energy by oxidizing sulfur or a compound of sulfur and iron; the mechanisms involved may be similar to those used billions of years ago by the first cells.

A third group of archaea, the **methanogens**, live in anaerobic (oxygen-lacking) environments and give off methane as a waste product. Many thrive in anaerobic mud at the bottom of lakes and swamps. You may have seen methane, also called marsh gas, bubbling up from a swamp. A large amount of methane is generated in solid waste landfills, where methanogens flourish in the anaerobic conditions. Many municipalities collect this methane and use it as a source of energy (Figure 16.8B). Great numbers of methanogens also inhabit the digestive tracts of cattle, deer, and other animals that depend heavily on cellulose for their nutrition. Because methane is a greenhouse gas, landfills and livestock contribute significantly to global warming.

Accustomed to thinking of archaea as inhabitants of extreme environments, scientists have been surprised to discover their abundance in more moderate conditions, especially in the oceans. Archaea live at all depths, making up a substantial fraction of the prokaryotes in waters more than 150 m beneath the surface and half of the prokaryotes that live below 1,000 m. Archaea are thus one of the most abundant cell types in Earth's largest habitat.

Because bacteria have been the subject of most prokaryotic research for over a century, much more is known about them than about archaea. Now that the evolutionary and ecological importance of archaea has come into focus, we can expect research on this domain to turn up many more surprises about the history of life and the roles of microbes in ecosystems.

▲ Figure 16.8A Orange and yellow colonies of heat-loving archaea growing in a Nevada geyser

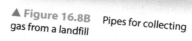

▲ Figure 16.8B Pipes for collecting gas from a landfill

 Some archaea are referred to as "extremophiles." Why?

● Because they can thrive in extreme environments that are too hot, too salty, or too acidic for other organisms

16.9 Bacteria include a diverse assemblage of prokaryotes

Domain Bacteria is currently divided into five groups based on comparisons of genetic sequences. In this module, we sample some of the diversity in each group.

Proteobacteria are all gram-negative and share a particular rRNA sequence. With regard to other characteristics, however, this large group encompasses enormous diversity. For example, all four modes of nutrition are represented.

Chemoheterotrophic proteobacteria include pathogens such as *Vibrio cholerae*, which causes cholera. *Escherichia coli* (see Figure 16.2A), which is a common resident of the intestines of humans and other mammals and a favorite research organism, is also a member of this group.

Thiomargarita namibiensis (Figure 16.9A), an example of a photoautotrophic species of proteobacteria, uses H_2S to generate organic molecules from CO_2. The small greenish globules you see in the photo are sulfur wastes. Other proteobacteria, including *Rhodopseudomonas* (see Figure 16.4), are photoheterotrophs; they cannot convert CO_2 to sugars.

Chemoautotrophic soil bacteria such as *Nitrosomonas* obtain energy by oxidizing inorganic nitrogen compounds. These and related species of proteobacteria are essential to the chemical cycle that makes nitrogen available to plants.

Proteobacteria also include *Rhizobium* species that live symbiotically in root nodules of legumes such as soybeans and peas (see Figure 32.13B). **Symbiosis** is a close association between organisms of two or more species, and *endo*symbiosis refers to one species, called the endosymbiont, living *within* another. *Rhizobium* endosymbionts convert atmospheric nitrogen gas to a form usable by their legume host.

A second major group of bacteria, **gram-positive bacteria**, rivals the proteobacteria in diversity. One subgroup, the actinomycetes (from the Greek *mykes*, fungus, for which these bacteria were once mistaken), forms colonies of branched chains of cells. Actinomycetes are very common in the soil, where they decompose organic matter. Soil-dwelling species in the genus *Streptomyces*, shown in Figure 16.9B, are cultured by pharmaceutical companies as a source of many antibiotics, including streptomycin. Gram-positive bacteria also include the pathogens *Staphylococcus* and *Streptococcus* as well as many solitary species, such as *Bacillus anthracis* (see Figure 16.3B).

The **cyanobacteria** are the only group of prokaryotes with plantlike, oxygen-generating photosynthesis. Ancient cyanobacteria generated the oxygen that changed Earth's atmosphere more than two billion years ago. Today, cyanobacteria provide an enormous amount of food for freshwater and marine ecosystems. Some species, such as the cyanobacterium *Anabaena* in Figure 16.9C, have specialized cells that fix nitrogen. Many species of cyanobacteria have symbiotic relationships with organisms such as fungi, mosses, and a variety of marine invertebrates.

The **chlamydias**, which live inside eukaryotic host cells, form a fourth bacterial group (Figure 16.9D). *Chlamydia trachomatis* is a common cause of blindness in developing countries and also causes nongonococcal urethritis, the most common sexually transmitted disease in the United States.

Spirochetes, the fifth group, are helical bacteria that spiral through their environment by means of rotating, internal filaments. Some spirochetes are notorious pathogens: *Treponema pallidum*, shown in Figure 16.9E, causes syphilis, and *Borrelia burgdorferi* (see Figure 16.2A) causes Lyme disease.

? How are *Thiomargarita namibiensis* similar to the cyanobacteria?

● They are both photoautotrophic.

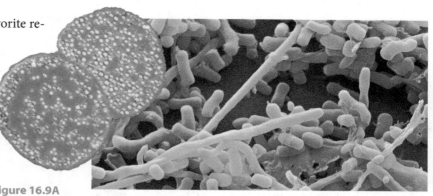

▲ Figure 16.9A *Thiomargarita namibiensis*

LM 20,000×

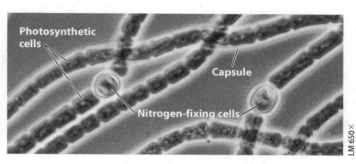

▲ Figure 16.9B *Streptomyces*, the source of many antibiotics

SEM 6,650×

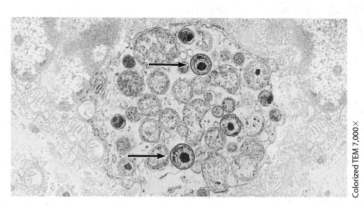

Photosynthetic cells

Capsule

Nitrogen-fixing cells

▲ Figure 16.9C *Anabaena*, a filamentous cyanobacterium

LM 650×

▲ Figure 16.9D *Chlamydia* cells (arrows) inside an animal cell

Colorized TEM 7,000×

▲ Figure 16.9E *Treponema pallidum*, the spirochete that causes syphilis

Colorized SEM 20,000×

16.10 Some bacteria cause disease

CONNECTION

All organisms, people included, are almost constantly exposed to pathogenic bacteria. Most often, our body's defenses prevent pathogens from affecting us. Occasionally, however, a pathogen establishes itself in the body and causes illness. Even some of the bacteria that are normal residents of the human body can make us ill when our immune system is compromised by poor nutrition or by a viral infection.

Most bacteria that cause illness do so by producing a poison—either an exotoxin or an endotoxin. **Exotoxins** are proteins that bacterial cells secrete into their environment. They include some of the most powerful poisons known. For example, *Staphylococcus aureus*, shown in **Figure 16.10A**, produces several exotoxins. Although *S. aureus* is commonly found on the skin and in the nasal passages, if it enters the body through a wound, it can cause serious disease. One of its exotoxins destroys the white blood cells that attack invading bacteria, resulting in the pus-filled skin bumps characteristic of methicillin-resistant *S. aureus* infections (MRSA; see Module 13.16). Food may also be contaminated with *S. aureus* exotoxins, which are so potent that less than a millionth of a gram causes vomiting and diarrhea.

Endotoxins are lipid components of the outer membrane of gram-negative bacteria that are released when the cell dies or is digested by a defensive cell. All endotoxins induce the same general symptoms: fever, aches, and sometimes a dangerous drop in blood pressure (septic shock). Septic shock triggered by an endotoxin of *Neisseria meningitidis*, which causes bacterial meningitis, can kill a healthy person in a matter of days or even hours. Because the bacteria are easily transmitted among people living in close contact, many colleges require students to be vaccinated against this disease. The species of *Salmonella* (shown in Figure 16.4) that causes food poisoning is another example of endotoxin-producing bacteria.

Because of their disease-causing potential, some bacteria have been used as biological weapons. *Bacillus anthracis*, the bacterium that causes anthrax, and the exotoxin of

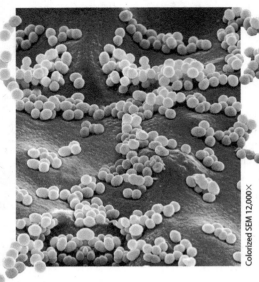

▲ **Figure 16.10A**   *Staphylococcus aureus*, an exotoxin producer

Clostridium botulinum are among the biological agents that are considered the highest-priority threats.

Bacillus anthracis forms hardy endospores (see Figure 16.3B) that are commonly found in the soil of agricultural regions. "Weaponizing" anthrax involves manufacturing a preparation of endospores that disperses easily in the air, where they will be inhaled by the target population. Endospores germinate in the lungs, and the bacteria multiply, producing an exotoxin that eventually accumulates to lethal levels in the blood. Although antibiotics can kill the bacteria, they can't eliminate the toxin already in the body. As a result, weaponized anthrax has a very high death rate.

The weapon form of *C. botulinum* is the exotoxin it produces, botulinum, rather than the living microbes. Botulinum is the deadliest poison known. Thirty grams of pure toxin, a bit more than an ounce, could kill every person in the United States. Botulinum blocks transmission of the nerve signals that cause muscle contraction, resulting in paralysis of the muscles required for breathing. This effect is also responsible for a more benign use of botulinum —relaxing facial muscles that cause wrinkles (**Figure 16.10B**).

?   Contrast exotoxins with endotoxins.

● Exotoxins are proteins secreted by pathogenic bacteria; endotoxins are components of the outer membranes of pathogenic bacteria.

▲ **Figure 16.10B**   Injecting Botox, which contains a minute amount of botulinum, to smooth wrinkles

16.11 Stomach microbiota affect health and disease

SCIENTIFIC THINKING

In the chapter introduction, you learned that each of us houses trillions of bacteria that are harmless, or even beneficial. In the previous module, you learned about bacteria that cause disease. How do scientists determine which is which?

To test the hypothesis that a certain bacterium is the cause of a disease, a researcher must satisfy four conditions. This method of hypothesis testing, formulated by microbiologist Robert Koch in the late 19th century, is known as *Koch's postulates*. For a human disease, the researcher must be able to (1) find the candidate bacterium in every case of the disease; (2) isolate the bacterium from a person who has the disease and grow it in pure culture; (3) show that the cultured bacterium causes the disease when transferred to a healthy subject (usually an animal); and (4) isolate the bacterium from the experimentally infected subject. So when Australian microbiologist Barry Marshall hypothesized that chronic gastritis (an inflammation of the stomach lining that can lead to ulcers) was caused by a bacterium called *Helicobacter pylori*, he knew he would need to fulfill these criteria.

Are antibiotics making us fat?

Over the course of several years, Marshall satisfied the first two requirements, but his efforts to infect animals failed to produce results. Although he continued to accumulate evidence supporting his hypothesis, the scientific community was skeptical of Marshall's idea and he had difficulty obtaining funding for his research. Frustrated by watching so many patients suffer life-threatening complications from peptic (stomach) ulcers when his research might yield a simple cure, Marshall decided to take a radical course of action—he would experiment on himself. He concocted a nasty brew of *H. pylori* and swallowed it. Several days later, he became ill from gastritis (step 3 of Koch's postulates). His stomach lining proved to be teeming with *H. pylori* (step 4). Marshall then cleared up his infection with antibiotics. He continued to make progress in his research, and other scientists followed up with further studies. Several years after Marshall's big gulp, antibiotics became a standard treatment for ulcer patients (**Figure 16.11A**).

Since Marshall's breakthrough work, scientists have learned that our relationship with *H. pylori* is ancient—at least 50,000 years old—and it's complicated. Only a particular genetic strain causes ulcers; other strains are harmless members of our microbiota. In fact, some scientists hypothesize that the *absence* of *H. pylori* can cause problems. Fifty years ago, *H. pylori* was present in most Americans, but its prevalence has been steadily declining. Researchers are investigating a possible connection between this decline and the high rate of obesity. *H. pylori* is thought to affect the stomach's production of a hormone called ghrelin that sends hunger signals to the brain (**Figure 16.11B**). Ghrelin output should decrease after a meal, ending the urge to eat. Studies have linked the

▲ **Figure 16.11A** Barry Marshall (left) and collaborator Robin Warren were awarded the 2005 Nobel Prize in Medicine for their discovery of *H. pylori* and its role in peptic ulcers

absence of *H. pylori* to continued ghrelin output after eating. In other words, the brain doesn't get the message that you've had dinner, which leads to overeating. Investigations have also suggested a correlation between an absence of *H. pylori* and increased body mass index.

Is a simple, microbe-based cure for obesity just around the corner? Probably not. *H. pylori* is just one member of a diverse microbial community within the complex ecosystem of the human body. While the results obtained so far are intriguing, they are characteristic of the early stages of scientific investigation—preliminary, tentative, and sometimes even contradictory.

? According to a study published in 2012, infants treated with antibiotics before the age of 6 months were more likely to be overweight at the age of 3. Do these results support the hypothesis that an absence of *H. pylori* is a factor in causing obesity?

● This evidence tentatively supports the hypothesis that disturbing the body's microbial community is a factor in causing obesity (other explanations for the results are possible), but the study did not look specifically at *H. pylori*.

▲ **Figure 16.11B** Effect of ghrelin on hunger

Try This Use the diagram to explain the hypothesis linking obesity to *H. pylori*.

Feel hungry

Ghrelin output rises

Stomach empty

Eat a meal

Stomach full

Hunger satisfied

Ghrelin output declines

16.12 Protists are an extremely diverse assortment of eukaryotes

Protists are a diverse collection of mostly unicellular eukaryotes. Biologists used to classify all protists in a kingdom called Protista, but now it is clear that these organisms constitute multiple kingdoms within domain Eukarya. While our knowledge of the evolutionary relationships among these diverse groups remains incomplete, *protist* is still useful as a convenient term to refer to eukaryotes that are not plants, animals, or fungi.

Protists obtain their nutrition in a variety of ways (**Figure 16.12A**). Some protists are autotrophs, producing their food by photosynthesis; these are called **algae** (another useful term that is not taxonomically meaningful). Many algae, including the one shown on the left in Figure 16.12A, are multicellular. Other protists, informally called **protozoans**, are heterotrophs, eating bacteria and other protists. Some heterotrophic protists are fungus-like and obtain organic molecules by absorption, and some are parasitic. **Parasites** derive their nutrition from a living host, which is harmed by the interaction. *Giardia*, shown in the middle of Figure 16.12A, is a human parasite. Still other protists are **mixotrophs**, capable of both photosynthesis and heterotrophy, depending on availability of light and nutrients. An example is *Euglena*, shown on the right in Figure 16.12A.

Protist habitats are also diverse. Most protists are aquatic, and they are found almost anywhere there is moisture, including terrestrial habitats such as damp soil and leaf litter. Others inhabit the bodies of various host organisms. For example, **Figure 16.12B** shows one of the protists that are endosymbionts in the intestinal tract of termites. Termite endosymbionts digest the tough cellulose in the wood eaten by their host. Some of these protists even have endosymbionts of their own—prokaryotes that metabolize the cellulose.

As eukaryotes, protists are more complicated than any prokaryotes. Their cells have a membrane-enclosed nucleus (containing multiple chromosomes) and other organelles

▼ **Figure 16.12B** A protist from a termite gut covered by thousands of flagella, viewed with scanning electron microscope (left) and light microscope (below)

SEM 560×

LM 325×

characteristic of eukaryotic cells. The flagella and cilia of protistan cells have a 9 + 2 pattern of microtubules, another typical eukaryotic trait (see Module 4.18).

Because most protists are unicellular, they are justifiably considered the simplest eukaryotes. However, the cells of many protists are among the most elaborate in the world. This level of cellular complexity is not really surprising, for each unicellular protist is a complete eukaryotic organism analogous to an entire animal or plant.

With their extreme diversity, protists are difficult to categorize. Recent molecular and cellular studies have shaken the foundations of protistan taxonomy as much as they have that of the prokaryotes. Intuitive groupings such as protozoans and algae are phylogenetically meaningless because the nutritional modes used to categorize them are spread across

▶ **Figure 16.12A** Protist modes of nutrition

Autotrophy

Caulerpa, a green alga

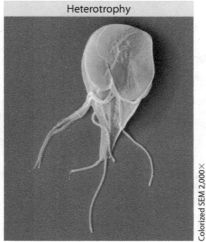
Heterotrophy

Colorized SEM 2,000×

Giardia, a parasite

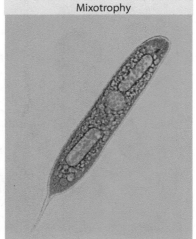
Mixotrophy

LM 700×

Euglena

many different lineages. It is now clear that there are multiple clades of protists, with some lineages more closely related to plants, fungi, or animals than they are to other protists. We have chosen to organize our brief survey of protist diversity using one current hypothesis of protist phylogeny, which proposes four monophyletic "supergroups." The largest and most diverse supergroup is "SAR," which contains three clades: Stramenopila, Alveolata, and Rhizaria. The other supergroups are Excavata, Unikonta, and Archaeplastida.

While there is general agreement on some of these groupings, others are hotly debated—the classification of protists is very much a work in progress. Before embarking on our tour of protists, however, let's consider how their extraordinary diversity originated.

? **What is a general definition for "protist"?**

● A eukaryote that is not an animal, fungus, or plant

16.13 Endosymbiosis of unicellular algae is the key to much of protist diversity

EVOLUTION CONNECTION

As Module 16.12 indicates, protists are bewilderingly diverse. What is the origin of this enormous diversity? To explain, let's first review the theory of endosymbiosis for the origin of mitochondria and chloroplasts in eukaryotes (see Module 4.15). According to this theory, oxygen-using prokaryotes established residence within other, larger cells. These endosymbionts evolved into mitochondria, giving rise to heterotrophic eukaryotes.

As shown in **Figure 16.13**, autotrophic eukaryotes also arose through endosymbiosis of a prokaryote by a eukaryote after ❶ a heterotrophic eukaryote engulfed an autotrophic cyanobacterium. If the cyanobacterium continued to function within its host cell, its photosynthesis would have provided a steady source of food for the heterotrophic host and thus given it a significant selective advantage. And because the cyanobacterium had its own DNA, it could reproduce to make multiple copies of itself within the host cell. In addition, cyanobacteria could be passed on when the host reproduced. Over time, ❷ the descendants of the original cyanobacterium evolved into chloroplasts. The chloroplast-bearing lineage of

eukaryotes later diversified into ❸ the autotrophs green algae and red algae (see Module 16.18).

On subsequent occasions during eukaryotic evolution ❹ green algae and red algae themselves became endosymbionts following ingestion by different heterotrophic eukaryotes. The heterotrophic host cells enclosed the algal cells in food vacuoles ❺ but the algae—or parts of them—survived and became cellular organelles. The presence of the endosymbionts, which also had the ability to replicate themselves, gave their hosts a selective advantage. Figure 16.13 shows how endosymbiosis of green algae could give rise to mixotrophs, such as the *Euglena* in Figure 16.12A. Endosymbiosis of red algae led to nutritional diversity in other groups of protists. Thus, endosymbiosis of unicellular algae appears to explain a large part of protist diversity.

? **How did the endosymbiosis that resulted in chloroplasts differ from the endosymbiosis that led to protist diversity?**

● Chloroplasts evolved from endosymbiosis of a photosynthetic prokaryote. Much of protist diversity resulted from endosymbiosis of photosynthetic eukaryotes.

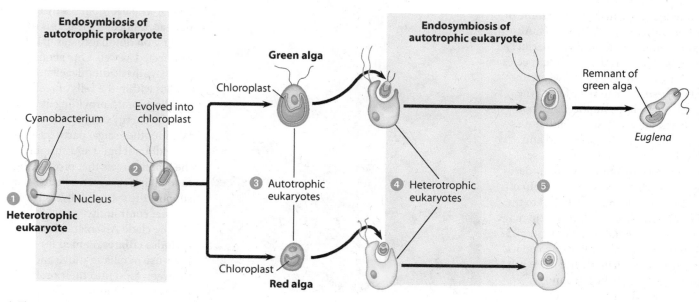

▲ **Figure 16.13** The theory of the origin of protistan diversity through endosymbiosis (mitochondria not shown)

Try This Trace the cyanobacterium from the left side of the figure to the protists at step 5.

16.14 The "SAR" supergroup represents the range of protist diversity

Our sample of protist diversity begins with **SAR**, recently proposed as a monophyletic supergroup on the basis of genomic studies. "SAR" stands for **Stramenopila**, **Alveolata**, and **Rhizaria**, the three clades that make up this huge, extremely diverse group.

Stramenopiles   Diatoms and brown algae are two examples of autotrophic stramenopiles. **Diatoms**, unicellular algae that are one of the most important photosynthetic organisms on Earth, have a unique glassy cell wall containing silica. The cell wall of a diatom consists of two halves that fit together like the bottom and lid of a shoe box (**Figure 16.14A**). Both freshwater and marine environments are rich in diatoms, and the organic molecules these microscopic algae produce are a key source of food in all aquatic environments. Some diatoms store food reserves in the form of lipid droplets as well as carbohydrates. In addition to being a rich source of energy, the lipids make the diatoms buoyant, which keeps them floating near the surface in the sunlight. Massive accumulations of fossilized diatoms make up thick sediments known as diatomaceous earth, which is mined for use as a filtering medium and as a grinding and polishing agent.

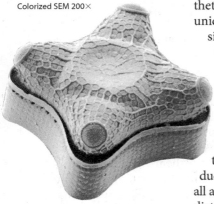

Colorized SEM 200×

▲ **Figure 16.14A**   Diatom, a unicellular alga

Brown algae are large, complex stramenopiles. Brown algae owe their characteristic brownish color to some of the pigments in their chloroplasts. All are multicellular, and most are marine. Brown algae include many of the species commonly called seaweeds. We use the word *seaweeds* here to refer to marine algae that have large multicellular bodies but lack the roots, stems, and leaves found in most plants. (Some red and green algae are also referred to as seaweeds.) **Figure 16.14B** shows an underwater bed of brown algae called **kelp** off the coast of California. Anchored to the seafloor by rootlike structures, kelp may grow to heights of 60 m, taller than a 15-story building. Fish, sea lions, sea otters, and gray whales regularly use these kelp "forests" as their feeding grounds.

Water molds are heterotrophic unicellular stramenopiles that typically decompose dead plants and animals in freshwater habitats. Because many species resemble fungi (**Figure 16.14C**), water molds were classified as fungi until molecular comparisons revealed their kinship to protists. Parasitic water molds sometimes grow on the skin or gills of fish. Water molds also include plant parasites called downy mildews. "Late blight" of potatoes, a disease caused by a downy mildew, led to a devastating famine in Ireland in the mid-1800s. A closely related pathogen has swept through tomato crops in the eastern United States, depriving fast-food burgers of a standard topping and home gardeners of a favorite summertime treat.

▲ **Figure 16.14C**   Water mold (white threads) decomposing a goldfish

Alveolates   **Dinoflagellates**, a diverse group that includes unicellular autotrophs, heterotrophs, and mixotrophs, are also very common components of marine and freshwater plankton (communities of microorganisms that live near the water's surface). Blooms—population explosions—of autotrophic dinoflagellates sometimes cause warm coastal waters to turn pinkish orange, a phenomenon known as "red tide" (**Figure 16.14D**, on the facing page). Toxins produced by some red-tide dinoflagellates have killed large numbers of fish. People who eat molluscs that have accumulated the toxins by feeding on dinoflagellates may be affected as well. One genus of photosynthetic dinoflagellates resides within the cells of reef-building corals, providing at least half the energy used by the corals. Without these algal partners, corals could not build and sustain the massive reefs that provide the food, living space, and shelter that support the splendid diversity of the reef community.

The clade Alveolata also includes **ciliates**, named for their use of cilia to move and to sweep food into their oral groove, or cell mouth. This group of unicellular protists includes

▲ **Figure 16.14B**   Brown algae: a kelp "forest"

▲ **Figure 16.14D** A red tide caused by *Gymnodinium*, a dinoflagellate

heterotrophs and mixotrophs. You may have seen the common freshwater protist *Paramecium* (**Figure 16.14E**) in a biology lab. Like many ciliates, *Paramecium* swims by beating its cilia in a wavelike motion. Other ciliates "crawl" over a surface using cilia that are arranged in bundles along the length of the cell.

Another subgroup of alveolates is made up of parasites, including some that cause serious diseases in humans. For example, *Plasmodium*, which causes malaria, kills nearly a million people a year. Some stages of *Plasmodium's* complex life cycle take place in certain species of mosquitoes, which transmit the parasite to humans.

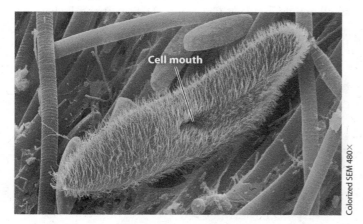

Cell mouth

Colorized SEM 480×

▲ **Figure 16.14E** A freshwater ciliate, *Paramecium*, showing cilia distributed over the cell surface (The photo also includes other unicellular organisms.)

Rhizaria The two largest groups in Rhizaria, foraminiferans and radiolarians, are among the organisms referred to as amoebas. **Amoebas** move and feed by means of **pseudopodia** (singular, *pseudopodium*), which are temporary extensions of the cell. Molecular systematics now indicates that many different taxonomic groups include organisms that share this means of movement and feeding. Most of the amoebas in Rhizaria are distinguished from other amoebas by their threadlike (rather than lobe-shaped) pseudopodia.

Foraminiferans (forams) (**Figure 16.14F**) are found both in the ocean and in fresh water. They have porous shells, called *tests,* composed of organic material hardened by calcium carbonate. The pseudopodia, which function in feeding and locomotion, extend through small pores in the test (see Figure 16.14F, inset). Ninety percent of forams that have been identified are fossils. The fossilized tests, which are a component of sedimentary rock, are excellent markers for correlating the ages of rocks in different parts of the world.

Like forams, **radiolarians** produce a mineralized support structure, in this case an internal skeleton made of silica (**Figure 16.14G**). The cell is also surrounded by a test composed of organic material. Most species of radiolarians are marine. When they die, their hard parts, like those of forams, settle to the bottom of the ocean and become part of the sediments. In some areas, radiolarians are so abundant that sediments, known as radiolarian ooze, are hundreds of meters thick.

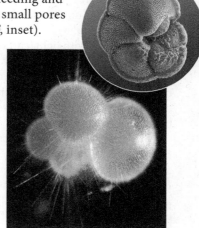

▲ **Figure 16.14F** A foraminiferan (inset SEM shows a foram test)

? **Which groups of Stramenopila, Alveolata, and Rhizaria include autotrophs?**

● Stramenopila: diatoms, brown algae; Alveolata: dinoflagellates; Rhizaria: none

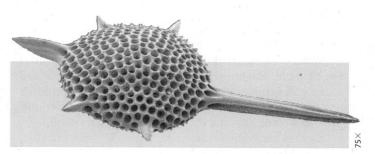

75×

▲ **Figure 16.14G** A radiolarian skeleton

16.15 Can algae provide a renewable source of energy?

CONNECTION

Have you ever wondered what the "fossils" are in fossil fuels? They are organic remains of organisms that lived hundreds of millions of years ago. Diatoms are thought to be the main source of oil, while coal was formed from primitive plants. However, rapid consumption is depleting the world's supply of readily accessible fossil fuels.

Entrepreneurs are now eying the lipid droplets in diatoms and other algae as a renewable source of energy. After all, the energy we extract from fossil fuels was originally stored in organisms through the process of photosynthesis. Why wait millions of years? If unicellular algae could be grown on a large scale, the oil could be harvested and processed into biodiesel. When supplied with light, carbon dioxide, and nutrients, unicellular algae reproduce rapidly. In one scenario, algae could be grown indoors in closed "bioreactor" vessels under tightly controlled environmental conditions (Figure 16.15). Outdoor systems using closed bioreactors or open-air ponds are also being developed.

There are numerous technical hurdles to overcome before the industrial-scale production of biofuel from algae becomes a reality. Investigators must identify the most productive of the hundreds of algal species and test whether they are suitable for mass culturing methods. With further research, scientists may be able to improve desirable characteristics such as growth rate or oil yield through genetic engineering. In addition, manufacturers need to develop cost-effective methods of harvesting the algae and extracting and processing the oil.

▲ Figure 16.15   Green algae in a bioreactor

Nevertheless, there might be an alga-powered vehicle in your future.

> **?** **What characteristics of unicellular algae make them attractive candidates for the production of biofuels?**

● Rapid reproduction; would not occupy farmland needed to grow food crops

---

16.16 Some excavates have modified mitochondria

Excavata, the second supergroup in our survey of protists, has recently been proposed as a clade on the basis of molecular and morphological similarities. The name refers to an "excavated" feeding groove possessed by some members of the group. Many excavates have modified mitochondria that lack functional electron transport chains and use anaerobic pathways such as glycolysis to extract energy. Heterotrophic excavates include the termite endosymbiont shown in Figure 16.12B. There are also autotrophic species and mixotrophs, such as *Euglena* (see Figure 16.12A).

Some excavates are parasites. *Giardia intestinalis* (see Figure 16.12A) is a common waterborne parasite that causes severe diarrhea. People most often pick up *Giardia* by drinking water contaminated with feces containing the parasite. For example, a swimmer in a lake or river might accidentally ingest water contaminated with feces from infected animals, or a hiker might drink contaminated water from a seemingly pristine stream. (Boiling the water first will kill *Giardia*.)

Another excavate, *Trichomonas vaginalis* (Figure 16.16A), is a common sexually transmitted parasite that causes an estimated 5 million new infections each year. The parasite travels through the reproductive tract by moving its flagella and undulating part of its membrane. In women, the protists feed on white blood cells and bacteria living on the cells lining the vagina. *T. vaginalis* also infects the cells lining the male reproductive tract, but limited availability of food results in very small population sizes. Consequently, males typically have no symptoms of infection, although they can repeatedly infect their female partners. The only treatment available is a drug

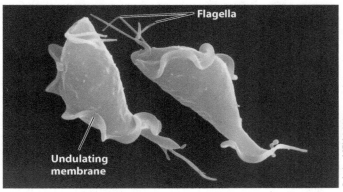

▲ Figure 16.16A   A parasitic excavate: *Trichomonas vaginalis*

called metronidazole. Disturbingly, drug resistance seems to be evolving in *T. vaginalis*, especially on college campuses.

Members of the excavate genus *Trypanosoma* are parasites that can be transmitted to humans by insects. For instance, the trypanosome shown in **Figure 16.16B** causes sleeping sickness, a potentially fatal disease spread by the African tsetse fly. The squiggly "worms" in the photo are cells of *Trypanosoma;* the circular cells are human red blood cells.

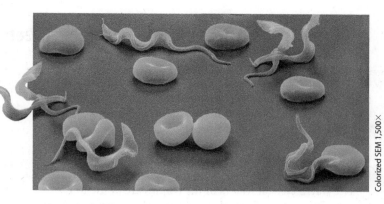

Colorized SEM 1,500×

> **?** How do the nutritional modes of *Euglena* and *Trichomonas* differ?

Euglena is mixotrophic; Trichomonas is strictly heterotrophic.

▲ **Figure 16.16B**   A parasitic excavate: *Trypanosoma* (with blood cells)

16.17 Unikonts include protists that are closely related to fungi and animals

Unikonta is a controversial grouping that joins two well-established clades: **amoebozoans**, which are protists, and a second clade that includes animals and fungi. You'll learn about the amoebozoans in this module, then return to the second clade in the last module of this chapter.

Amoebozoans, including many species of free-living amoebas, some parasitic amoebas, and the slime molds, have lobe-shaped pseudopodia. The amoeba in **Figure 16.17A** is poised to ingest an alga. Its pseudopodia arch around the prey and will enclose it in a food vacuole (see Figure 5.9). Free-living amoebas creep over rocks, sticks, or mud at the bottom of a pond or ocean. A parasitic species of amoeba causes amoebic dysentery, a potentially fatal diarrheal disease.

Colorized TEM 2,000×

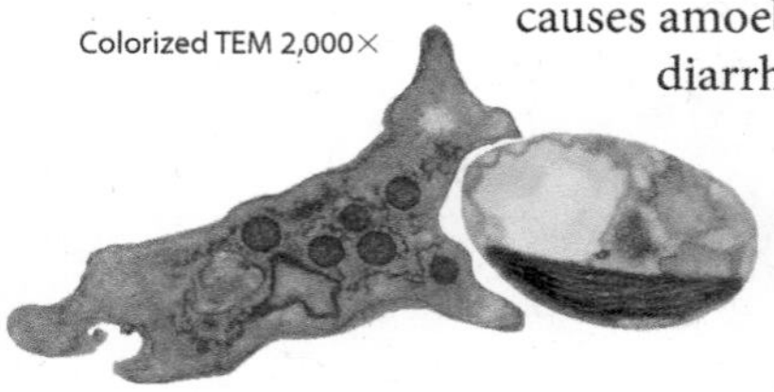

▲ **Figure 16.17A**
An amoeba beginning to ingest an algal cell

The yellow growth creeping over on the dead log in **Figure 16.17B** is an amoebozoan called a **plasmodial slime mold**. These protists are common where there is moist, decaying organic matter and are often brightly pigmented. Although it is large and has many extensions, the organism in Figure 16.17B is not multicellular. Rather, it is a **plasmodium**, a single, multinucleate mass of cytoplasm undivided by plasma membranes. (Don't confuse this word with the alveolate *Plasmodium*, which causes malaria.) Because most of the nuclei go through mitosis at the same time, plasmodial slime molds are used to study molecular details of the cell cycle.

The plasmodium extends pseudopodia through soil and rotting logs, engulfing food by phagocytosis as it grows. Within the fine channels of the plasmodium, cytoplasm streams first one way and then the other in pulsing flows that probably help distribute nutrients and oxygen. When food and water are in short supply, the plasmodium stops growing and differentiates into reproductive structures (shown in the inset in Figure 16.17B) that produce spores. When conditions become favorable, the spores release haploid cells that fuse to form a zygote, and the life cycle continues.

Cellular slime molds are also common on rotting logs and decaying organic matter. Most of the time, these organisms exist as solitary amoeboid cells. When food is scarce, the amoeboid cells swarm together, forming a slug-like aggregate that wanders around for a short time. Some of the cells then dry up and form a stalk supporting an asexual reproductive structure in which yet other cells develop into spores. The cellular slime mold *Dictyostelium*, shown in **Figure 16.17C**, is a useful model for researchers studying the genetic mechanisms and chemical changes underlying cellular differentiation.

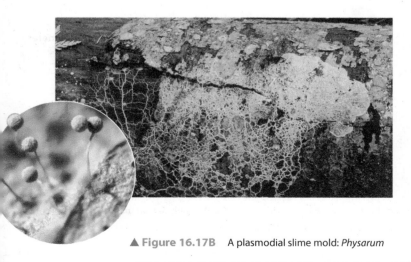

▲ **Figure 16.17B**   A plasmodial slime mold: *Physarum*

15×

▲ **Figure 16.17C**   An aggregate of amoeboid cells (left) and the reproductive structure of a cellular slime mold, *Dictyostelium*

> **?** Contrast the plasmodium of a plasmodial slime mold with the slug-like stage of a cellular slime mold.

A plasmodium is not multicellular, but is one cytoplasmic mass with many nuclei; the slug-like stage of a cellular slime mold consists of many cells.

16.18 Archaeplastids include red algae, green algae, and land plants

Almost all the members of the supergroup **Archaeplastida** are autotrophic. As you learned in Module 16.13, autotrophic eukaryotes are thought to have arisen by primary endosymbiosis of a cyanobacterium that evolved into chloroplasts. The descendants of this ancient protist evolved into red algae and green algae, which are key photosynthesizers in aquatic food webs. Archaeplastida also includes land plants, which evolved from a group of green algae.

The warm coastal waters of the tropics are home to the majority of species of **red algae**. Their red color comes from an accessory pigment that masks the green of chlorophyll. Although a few species are unicellular, most red algae are multicellular. Multicellular red algae are typically soft-bodied, but some have cell walls encrusted with hard, chalky deposits (Figure 16.18A). Encrusted species are common on coral reefs, and their hard parts are important in building and maintaining the reef. Other red algae are commercially important. Carrageenan, a gel that is used to stabilize many products, including ice cream, chocolate milk, and pudding, is derived from species of red algae. Sheets of a red alga, known as nori, are used to wrap sushi. Agar, a polysaccharide used as a substrate for growing bacteria, also comes from red algae.

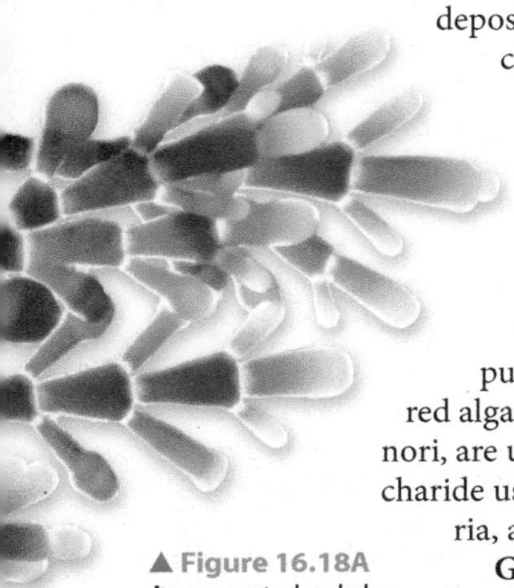

▲ Figure 16.18A
An encrusted red alga

Green algae, which are named for their grass-green chloroplasts, include unicellular and colonial species as well as multicellular seaweeds. The micrograph on the right in Figure 16.18B shows *Chlamydomonas,* a unicellular alga common in freshwater lakes and ponds. It is propelled through the water by two flagella. (Such cells are said to be biflagellated.) *Volvox*, shown on the left, is a colonial green alga. Each *Volvox* colony is a hollow ball composed of hundreds or thousands of biflagellated cells. As the flagella move, the colony tumbles slowly through the water. Some of the large colonies shown here contain small daughter colonies that will eventually be released.

Ulva, or sea lettuce, is a multicellular green alga. Like many multicellular algae and all land plants, *Ulva* has a complex life cycle that includes an **alternation of generations** (Figure 16.18C). In this type of life cycle, a multicellular diploid (2*n*) form alternates with a multicellular haploid (*n*) form. Notice in the figure that multicellular diploid forms are called **sporophytes**, because they produce spores. The sporophyte generation alternates with a haploid generation that features a multicellular haploid form called a **gametophyte**, which produces gametes. In *Ulva*, the gametophyte and sporophyte organisms are identical in appearance; both look like the one in the photograph, although they differ in chromosome number. The haploid gametophyte produces gametes by mitosis, and fusion of the gametes begins the sporophyte generation. In turn, cells in the sporophyte undergo meiosis and produce haploid, flagellated spores. The life cycle is completed when a spore settles to the bottom of the ocean and develops into a gametophyte.

? How does chromosome number differ in the gametophyte and sporophyte in the alternation of generations life cycle?

● The gametophyte is haploid (*n*); the sporophyte is diploid (2*n*).

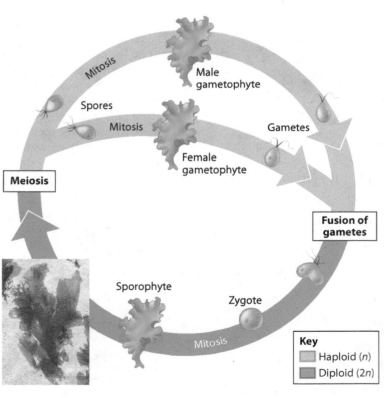

▲ Figure 16.18B   Green algae, colonial (left) and unicellular (right)

Volvox

Chlamydomonas

LM 29×

Colorized SEM 2,600×

▲ Figure 16.18C   The life cycle of *Ulva*, a multicellular green alga

Try This On a separate sheet of paper, make lists of the haploid and diploid structures in the life cycle.

Key
☐ Haploid (*n*)
■ Diploid (2*n*)

16.19 Multicellularity evolved several times in eukaryotes

EVOLUTION CONNECTION

Increased complexity often makes more variations possible. Thus, the origin of the eukaryotic cell led to an evolutionary radiation of new forms of life. As you have seen in this chapter, unicellular protists, which are structurally complex eukaryotic cells, are much more diverse in form than the simpler prokaryotes. The evolution of multicellular bodies broke through another threshold in structural organization.

Multicellular organisms—seaweeds, plants, animals, and most fungi—are fundamentally different from unicellular ones. In a unicellular organism, all of life's activities occur within a single cell. In contrast, a multicellular organism has various specialized cells that perform different functions and are dependent on one another. For example, some cells give the organism its shape, while others make or procure food, transport materials, enable movement, or reproduce.

As you have seen in this chapter, multicellular organisms have evolved in three different ancestral lineages: stramenopiles (brown algae), unikonts (fungi and animals), and archaeplastids (red algae and green algae). **Figure 16.19A** summarizes some current hypotheses for the early phylogeny of land plants and animals, which are all multicellular, and fungi, which are mostly multicellular.

According to one hypothesis, two separate unikont lineages led to fungi and animals. Based on molecular clock calculations (see Module 15.18), scientists estimate that the ancestors of animals and fungi diverged more than 1 billion years ago. A combination of morphological and molecular evidence suggests that a group of unikonts called *choanoflagellates* are the closest living protist relatives of animals. The bottom half of **Figure 16.19B** shows that the cells of

choanoflagellates strongly resemble the "collar cells" with which sponges, the group that is closest to the root of the animal tree, obtain food. Similar cells have been found in other animals, but not in fungi or plants. Some species of choanoflagellates live as colonies, federations of independent cells sticking loosely together. Scientists hypothesize that the common ancestor of living animals may have been a stationary colonial choanoflagellate similar to the one shown in Figure 16.19B.

A different group of unikont protists is thought to have given rise to the fungi. Molecular evidence suggests that a group of single-celled protists called *nucleariids*, amoebas that feed on algae and bacteria, are the closest living relatives of fungi (top of Figure 16.19B).

A group of green algae called *charophytes* are the closest living relatives of land plants. Around 500 million years ago, the move onto land began, probably as green algae living along the edges of lakes gave rise to primitive plants.

? **In what way do multicellular organisms differ fundamentally from unicellular ones?**

● In unicellular organisms, all the functions of life are carried out within a single cell. Multicellular organisms have specialized cells that perform different functions.

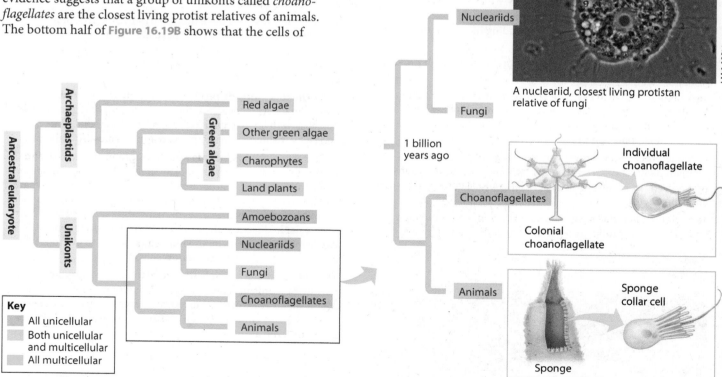

A nucleariid, closest living protistan relative of fungi

LM 1,100×

Individual choanoflagellate

Colonial choanoflagellate

Sponge collar cell

Sponge

Key
All unicellular
Both unicellular and multicellular
All multicellular

Red algae
Other green algae
Charophytes
Land plants
Amoebozoans
Nucleariids
Fungi
Choanoflagellates
Animals

Archaeplastids
Green algae
Ancestral eukaryote
Unikonts

Nucleariids
Fungi
1 billion years ago
Choanoflagellates
Animals

▲ **Figure 16.19A** A hypothesis for the phylogeny of plants, fungi, and animals

▲ **Figure 16.19B** The closest living protist relatives of fungi (top) and animals (bottom)

CHAPTER 16 REVIEW

For practice quizzes, BioFlix animations, MP3 tutorials, video tutors, and more study tools designed for this textbook, go to

MasteringBiology®

Reviewing the Concepts

Prokaryotes (16.1–16.11)

16.1 Prokaryotes are diverse and widespread. Prokaryotes are the most numerous organisms. Although small, they have an immense impact on the environment and on our own health.

16.2 External features contribute to the success of prokaryotes. Prokaryotes can be classified by shape and by reaction to a Gram stain. Almost all prokaryotes have a cell wall. Other features may include a sticky capsule, flagella, or fimbriae.

16.3 Populations of prokaryotes can adapt rapidly to changes in the environment. Rapid prokaryote population growth generates a great deal of genetic variation, increasing the likelihood that the population will persist in a changing environment. Some prokaryotes form endospores that remain dormant through harsh conditions.

16.4 Prokaryotes have unparalleled nutritional diversity.

Nutritional mode	Energy source	Carbon source
Photoautotroph	Sunlight	CO_2
Chemoautotroph	Inorganic chemicals	CO_2
Photoheterotroph	Sunlight	Organic compounds
Chemoheterotroph	Organic compounds	Organic compounds

16.5 Biofilms are complex associations of microbes. Prokaryotes attach to surfaces and form biofilm communities that are difficult to eradicate, causing both medical and environmental problems.

16.6 Prokaryotes help clean up the environment. Prokaryotes are often used for bioremediation, including in sewage treatment facilities.

16.7 Bacteria and archaea are the two main branches of prokaryotic evolution.

16.8 Archaea thrive in extreme environments—and in other habitats. Domain Archaea includes extreme halophiles ("salt lovers"), extreme thermophiles ("heat lovers"), and methanogens that thrive in anaerobic conditions.

16.9 Bacteria include a diverse assemblage of prokaryotes. Domain Bacteria is currently organized into five major groups: proteobacteria, gram-positive bacteria, cyanobacteria, chlamydias, and spirochetes.

16.10 Some bacteria cause disease. Pathogenic bacteria often cause disease by producing exotoxins or endotoxins. Certain

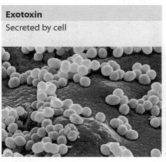

Exotoxin	Endotoxin
Secreted by cell	Component of gram-negative plasma membrane

Colorized SEM 12,400×
Colorized SEM 7,840×

Staphylococcus aureus   *Salmonella typhimurium*

bacteria, such as the species that causes anthrax, and bacterial toxins, such as botulinum, can be used as biological weapons.

16.11 Stomach microbiota affect health and disease. Barry Marshall used Koch's postulates to show that peptic ulcers are usually caused by a bacterium, *Helicobacter pylori*. Researchers are now beginning to learn that *H. pylori* may also have beneficial roles in the stomach microbiota.

Protists (16.12–16.19)

16.12 Protists are an extremely diverse assortment of eukaryotes. Protists are mostly unicellular eukaryotes that are found in a variety of aquatic or moist habitats. They may be autotrophic, heterotrophic, or mixotrophic. Molecular systematists are exploring protistan phylogeny, but at present it is highly tentative.

16.13 Endosymbiosis of unicellular algae is the key to much of protist diversity. Endosymbiosis of prokaryotic cells resulted in the evolution of eukaryotic cells containing mitochondria. By a similar process, heterotrophic eukaryotic cells engulfed cyanobacteria, which became chloroplasts. Endosymbiosis of red and green algae by eukaryotic cells gave rise to diverse lineages of protists.

16.14 The "SAR" supergroup represents the range of protist diversity. The three clades that make up this supergroup are Stramenopila (including diatoms, brown algae, and water molds), Alveolata (including dinoflagellates, ciliates, and certain parasites), and Rhizaria (including forams and radiolarians).

16.15 Can algae provide a renewable source of energy? Researchers are working on methods of growing diatoms and other algae as a source of biofuels.

16.16 Some excavates have modified mitochondria. Some excavates are anaerobic protists that have modified mitochondria; they include parasitic *Giardia*, *Trichomonas vaginalis*, and *Trypanosomas*. Other excavates include *Euglena*, a mixotroph, and termite endosymbionts.

16.17 Unikonts include protists that are closely related to fungi and animals. Amoebozoans, the protistan unikonts, include amoebas with lobe-shaped pseudopodia, plasmodial slime molds, and cellular slime molds. Fungi and animals are also unikonts.

16.18 Archaeplastids include red algae, green algae, and land plants. Red algae, which are mostly multicellular, include species that contribute to the structure of coral reefs and species that are commercially valuable. Green algae may be unicellular, colonial, or multicellular. The life cycles of many algae involve the alternation of haploid gametophyte and diploid sporophyte generations. Archaeplastida also includes land plants, which arose from a group of green algae called charophytes.

16.19 Multicellularity evolved several times in eukaryotes. Multicellular organisms have cells specialized for different functions. Multicellularity evolved in ancestral lineages of stramenopiles (brown algae), unikonts (fungi and animals), and archaeplastids (red and green algae).

Connecting the Concepts

1. Explain how each of the following characteristics contributes to the success of prokaryotes: cell wall, capsule, flagella, fimbriae, endospores.

2. Fill in the blanks on the phylogenetic tree to show current hypotheses for the origin of multicellular organisms.

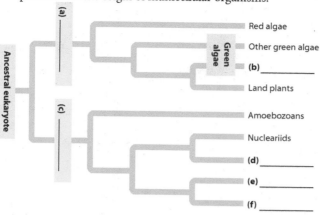

Testing Your Knowledge

Level 1: Knowledge/Comprehension

3. In terms of nutrition, autotrophs are to heterotrophs as
   a. kelp are to diatoms.
   b. archaea are to bacteria.
   c. slime molds are to algae.
   d. algae are to slime molds.

4. A new organism has been discovered. Tests have revealed that it is unicellular, is autotrophic, and has a cell wall that contains peptidoglycan. Based on this evidence, it should be classified as a(n)
   a. alga.
   b. archaean.
   c. protist.
   d. bacterium.

5. Which pair of protists has support structures composed of silica?
   a. dinoflagellates and diatoms
   b. diatoms and radiolarians
   c. radiolarians and forams
   d. forams and amoebozoans

6. Which of the following members of the SAR supergroup is incorrectly paired with its clade?
   a. stramenopiles—brown algae
   b. alveolates—parasites such as *Plasmodium*
   c. alveolates—dinoflagellates
   d. Rhizaria—diatoms

7. Which of the following prokaryotes is not pathogenic?
   a. *Chlamydia*
   b. *Rhizobium*
   c. *Streptococcus*
   d. *Salmonella*

8. Explain why prokaryote populations can adapt rapidly to changes in their environment.

9. What characteristic distinguishes true multicellularity from colonies of cells?

10. *Chlamydomonas* is a unicellular green alga. How does it differ from a photosynthetic bacterium, which is also single-celled? How does it differ from a protozoan, such as an amoeba? How does it differ from larger green algae, such as sea lettuce (*Ulva*)?

Level 2: Application/Analysis

11. The bacteria that cause tetanus can be killed only by prolonged heating at temperatures considerably above boiling. This suggests that tetanus bacteria
    a. have cell walls containing peptidoglycan.
    b. secrete endotoxins.
    c. are autotrophic.
    d. produce endospores.

12. Which of the following experiments could test the hypothesis that bacteria cause ulcers in humans? (Assume each experiment includes a control group.) Explain what evidence would be provided by the results of the experiment.
    a. Identify the microbes found in the stomachs of ulcer patients.
    b. Treat a group of ulcer patients with antibiotics.
    c. Place a group of ulcer patients on a strict low-acid diet.
    d. Obtain stomach fluid from ulcer patents and feed it to mice.

13. *Euglena* (an excavate) and *Gymnodinium* (an alveolate) are both capable of photosynthesis. However, researchers have identified differences in their chloroplasts. Use the theory of endosymbiosis to explain the reason for these differences. (*Hint*: Review Figure 16.13.)

Level 3: Synthesis/Evaluation

14. **SCIENTIFIC THINKING** Probiotics, foods and supplements that contain living microorganisms, are thought to cure problems of the digestive tract by restoring the natural balance of its microbial community. Sales of these products total billions of dollars a year. Explore the topic of probiotics and evaluate the scientific evidence for their beneficial effects. A good starting point is the website of the U.S. Food and Drug Administration, which regulates advertising claims of health benefits of dietary supplements (www.fda.gov/Food/DietarySupplements/default .htm. **Source** U.S. Food and Drug Administration website, 2013.).

15. Imagine you are on a team designing a moon base that will be self-contained and self-sustaining. Once supplied with building materials, equipment, and organisms from Earth, the base will be expected to function indefinitely. One of the team members has suggested that everything sent to the base be sterilized so that no bacteria of any kind are present. Do you think this is a good idea? Predict some of the consequences of eliminating all bacteria from an environment.

16. The buildup of CO_2 in the atmosphere resulting from the burning of fossil fuels is regarded as a major contributor to global warming. Diatoms and other microscopic algae in the oceans counter this buildup by using large quantities of atmospheric CO_2 in photosynthesis, which requires small quantities of iron. Experts suspect that a shortage of iron may limit algal growth in the oceans. Some scientists have suggested that one way to reduce CO_2 buildup might be to fertilize the oceans with iron. The iron would stimulate algal growth and thus the removal of more CO_2 from the air. A single supertanker of iron dust, spread over a wide enough area, might reduce the atmospheric CO_2 level significantly. Do you think this approach would be worth a try? Why or why not?

Answers to all questions can be found in Appendix 4.

Metric Conversion Table

Measurement	Unit and Abbreviation	Metric Equivalent	Approximate Metric-to-English Conversion Factor	Approximate English-to-Metric Conversion Factor
Length	1 kilometer (km)	$= 1,000 \ (10^3)$ meters	1 km = 0.6 mile	1 mile = 1.6 km
	1 meter (m)	$= 100 \ (10^2)$ centimeters	1 m = 1.1 yards	1 yard = 0.9 m
		$= 1,000$ millimeters	1 m = 3.3 feet	1 foot = 0.3 m
			1 m = 39.4 inches	
	1 centimeter (cm)	$= 0.01 \ (10^{-2})$ meter	1 cm = 0.4 inch	1 foot = 30.5 cm
				1 inch = 2.5 cm
	1 millimeter (mm)	$= 0.001 \ (10^{-3})$ meter	1 mm = 0.04 inch	
	1 micrometer (μm)	$= 10^{-6}$ meter $(10^{-3}$ mm$)$		
	1 nanometer (nm)	$= 10^{-9}$ meter $(10^{-3}$ μm$)$		
	1 angstrom (Å)	$= 10^{-10}$ meter $(10^{-4}$ μm$)$		
Area	1 hectare (ha)	$= 10,000$ square meters	1 ha = 2.5 acres	1 acre = 0.4 ha
	1 square meter (m²)	$= 10,000$ square centimeters	1 m² = 1.2 square yards	1 square yard = 0.8 m²
			1 m² = 10.8 square feet	1 square foot = 0.09 m²
	1 square centimeter (cm²)	$= 100$ square millimeters	1 cm² = 0.16 square inch	1 square inch = 6.5 cm²
Mass	1 metric ton (t)	$= 1,000$ kilograms	1 t = 1.1 tons	1 ton = 0.91 t
	1 kilogram (kg)	$= 1,000$ grams	1 kg = 2.2 pounds	1 pound = 0.45 kg
	1 gram (g)	$= 1,000$ milligrams	1 g = 0.04 ounce	1 ounce = 28.35 g
			1 g = 15.4 grains	
	1 milligram (mg)	$= 10^{-3}$ gram	1 mg = 0.02 grain	
	1 microgram (μg)	$= 10^{-6}$ gram		
Volume (Solids)	1 cubic meter (m³)	$= 1,000,000$ cubic centimeters	1 m³ = 1.3 cubic yards	1 cubic yard = 0.8 m³
			1 m³ = 35.3 cubic feet	1 cubic foot = 0.03 m³
	1 cubic centimeter (cm³ or cc)	$= 10^{-6}$ cubic meter	1 cm³ = 0.06 cubic inch	1 cubic inch = 16.4 cm³
	1 cubic millimeter (mm³)	$= 10^{-9}$ cubic meter $(10^{-3}$ cubic centimeter$)$		
Volume (Liquids and Gases)	1 kiloliter (kL or kl)	$= 1,000$ liters	1 kL = 264.2 gallons	
	1 liter (L or l)	$= 1,000$ milliliters	1 L = 0.26 gallon	1 gallon = 3.79 L
			1 L = 1.06 quarts	1 quart = 0.95 L
	1 milliliter (mL or ml)	$= 10^{-3}$ liter	1 mL = 0.03 fluid ounce	1 quart = 946 mL
		$= 1$ cubic centimeter	1 mL = ¼ teaspoon	1 pint = 473 mL
			1 mL = 15–16 drops	1 fluid ounce = 29.6 mL
				1 teaspoon = 5 mL
	1 microliter (μL or μl)	$= 10^{-6}$ liter $(10^{-3}$ milliliter$)$		
Time	1 second (s)	$= 1/60$ minute		
	1 millisecond (ms)	$= 10^{-3}$ second		
Temperature	Degrees Celsius (°C)		°F = 9/5 °C + 32	°C = 5/9 (°F − 32)

The Periodic Table

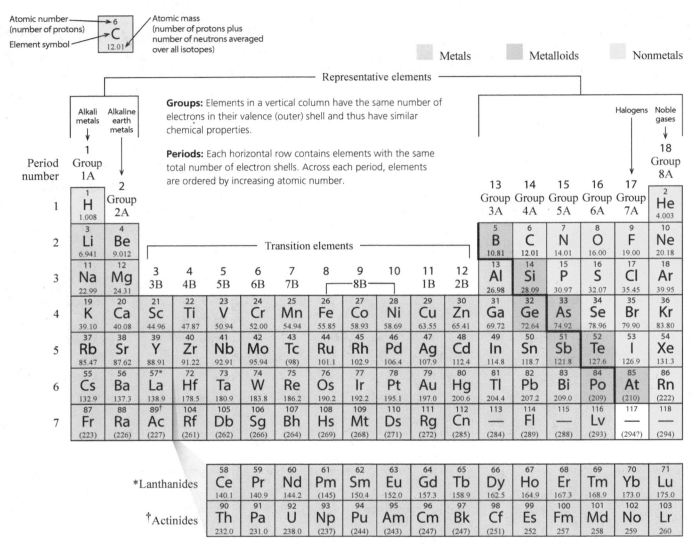

Atomic number (number of protons) → 6
Element symbol → C
Atomic mass (number of protons plus number of neutrons averaged over all isotopes) → 12.01

Metals   Metalloids   Nonmetals

Groups: Elements in a vertical column have the same number of electrons in their valence (outer) shell and thus have similar chemical properties.

Periods: Each horizontal row contains elements with the same total number of electron shells. Across each period, elements are ordered by increasing atomic number.

*Lanthanides

†Actinides

Name (Symbol)	Atomic Number	Name (Symbol)	Atomic Number	Name (Symbol)	Atomic Number	Name (Symbol)	Atomic Number	Name (Symbol)	Atomic Number
Actinium (Ac)	89	Copernicium (Cn)	112	Iodine (I)	53	Osmium (Os)	76	Silicon (Si)	14
Aluminum (Al)	13	Copper (Cu)	29	Iridium (Ir)	77	Oxygen (O)	8	Silver (Ag)	47
Americium (Am)	95	Curium (Cm)	96	Iron (Fe)	26	Palladium (Pd)	46	Sodium (Na)	11
Antimony (Sb)	51	Darmstadtium (Ds)	110	Krypton (Kr)	36	Phosphorus (P)	15	Strontium (Sr)	38
Argon (Ar)	18	Dubnium (Db)	105	Lanthanum (La)	57	Platinum (Pt)	78	Sulphur (S)	16
Arsenic (As)	33	Dysprosium (Dy)	66	Lawrencium (Lr)	103	Plutonium (Pu)	94	Tantalum (Ta)	73
Astatine (At)	85	Einsteinium (Es)	99	Lead (Pb)	82	Polonium (Po)	84	Technetium (Tc)	43
Barium (Ba)	56	Erbium (Er)	68	Lithium (Li)	3	Potassium (K)	19	Tellurium (Te)	52
Berkelium (Bk)	97	Europium (Eu)	63	Livermorium (Lv)	116	Praseodymium (Pr)	59	Terbium (Tb)	65
Beryllium (Be)	4	Fermium (Fm)	100	Lutetium (Lu)	71	Promethium (Pm)	61	Thallium (Tl)	81
Bismuth (Bi)	83	Flerovium (Fl)	114	Magnesium (Mg)	12	Protactinium (Pa)	91	Thorium (Th)	90
Bohrium (Bh)	107	Fluorine (F)	9	Manganese (Mn)	25	Radium (Ra)	88	Thulium (Tm)	69
Boron (B)	5	Francium (Fr)	87	Meitnerium (Mt)	109	Radon (Rn)	86	Tin (Sn)	50
Bromine (Br)	35	Gadolinium (Gd)	64	Mendelevium (Md)	101	Rhenium (Re)	75	Titanium (Ti)	22
Cadmium (Cd)	48	Gallium (Ga)	31	Mercury (Hg)	80	Rhodium (Rh)	45	Tungsten (W)	74
Calcium (Ca)	20	Germanium (Ge)	32	Molybdenum (Mo)	42	Roentgenium (Rg)	111	Uranium (U)	92
Californium (Cf)	98	Gold (Au)	79	Neodymium (Nd)	60	Rubidium (Rb)	37	Vanadium (V)	23
Carbon (C)	6	Hafnium (Hf)	72	Neon (Ne)	10	Ruthenium (Ru)	44	Xenon (Xe)	54
Cerium (Ce)	58	Hassium (Hs)	108	Neptunium (Np)	93	Rutherfordium (Rf)	104	Ytterbium (Yb)	70
Cesium (Cs)	55	Helium (He)	2	Nickel (Ni)	28	Samarium (Sm)	62	Yttrium (Y)	39
Chlorine (Cl)	17	Holmium (Ho)	67	Niobium (Nb)	41	Scandium (Sc)	21	Zinc (Zn)	30
Chromium (Cr)	24	Hydrogen (H)	1	Nitrogen (N)	7	Seaborgium (Sg)	106	Zirconium (Zr)	40
Cobalt (Co)	27	Indium (In)	49	Nobelium (No)	102	Selenium (Se)	34		

The Amino Acids of Proteins

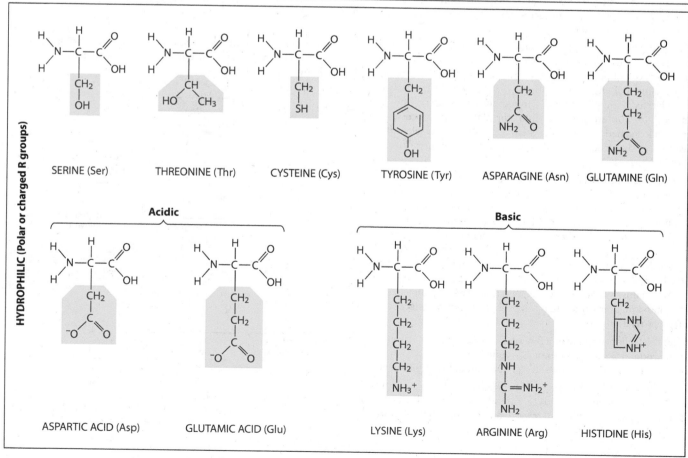

HYDROPHOBIC (Nonpolar R groups)

GLYCINE (Gly)

ALANINE (Ala)

VALINE (Val)

LEUCINE (Leu)

ISOLEUCINE (Ile)

METHIONINE (Met)

PHENYLALANINE (Phe)

TRYPTOPHAN (Trp)

PROLINE (Pro)

HYDROPHILIC (Polar or charged R groups)

SERINE (Ser)

THREONINE (Thr)

CYSTEINE (Cys)

TYROSINE (Tyr)

ASPARAGINE (Asn)

GLUTAMINE (Gln)

Acidic

Basic

ASPARTIC ACID (Asp)

GLUTAMIC ACID (Glu)

LYSINE (Lys)

ARGININE (Arg)

HISTIDINE (His)

Chapter Review Answers

Chapter 1

1. a. life; b. evolution; c. natural selection; d. unity of life; e. three domains (or numerous kingdoms; 1.8 million species)

2. b 3. c 4. b 5. b 6. d 7. a 8. d (You may have been tempted to choose b, the molecular level. However, protists may have chemical communication or interactions with other protists. No protists, however, have organs.) 9. d

10. Both energy and chemicals are passed through an ecosystem from producers to consumers to decomposers. But energy enters an ecosystem as sunlight and leaves as heat. Chemicals are recycled from the soil or atmosphere through plants, consumers, and decomposers and returned to the air, soil, and water.

11. Darwin described how natural selection operates in populations whose individuals have varied traits that are inherited. When natural selection favors the reproductive success of certain individuals in a population more than others, the proportions of heritable variations change over the generations, gradually adapting a population to its environment.

12. In pursuit of answers to questions about nature, a scientist uses a logical thought process involving these key elements: observations about natural phenomena, questions derived from observations, hypotheses posed as tentative explanations of observations, logical predictions of the outcome of tests if the hypotheses are correct, and actual tests of hypotheses. Scientific research is not a rigid method because a scientist must adapt these processes to the set of conditions particular to each study. Intuition, chance, and luck are also part of science.

13. Technology is the application of scientific knowledge. For example, the use of solar power to run a calculator or heat a home is an application of our knowledge, derived by the scientific process, of the nature of light as a type of energy and how light energy can be converted to other forms of energy. Another example is the use of DNA to insert new genes into crop plants. This process, often called genetic engineering, stems from decades of scientific research on the structure and function of DNA from many kinds of organisms.

14. The vertical scale of biology refers to the hierarchy of biological organization: from molecules to organelles, cells, tissues, organs, organ systems, organisms, populations, communities, ecosystems, and the biosphere. At each level, emergent properties arise from the interaction and organization of component parts. The horizontal scale of biology refers to the incredible diversity of living organisms, past and present, including the 1.8 million species that have been identified so far. Biologists divide these species into three domains—Bacteria, Archaea, and Eukarya—and organize them into kingdoms and other groups that attempt to reflect evolutionary relationships.

15. Natural selection screens (edits) heritable variations by favoring the reproductive success of some individuals over others. It can only select from the variations that are present in the population; it does not create new genes or variations.

16. a. Hypothesis: Giving rewards to mice will improve their learning. Prediction: If mice are rewarded with food, they will learn to run a maze faster.

b. The control group was the mice that were not rewarded. Without them, it would be impossible to know if the mice that were rewarded decreased their time running the maze only because of practice.

c. Both groups of mice should not have run the maze before and should be about the same age. Both experiments should be run at the same time of day and under the same conditions.

d. Yes, the results support the hypothesis because the data show that the rewarded mice began to run the maze faster by day 3 and improved their performance (ran faster than the control mice) each day thereafter.

17. The researcher needed to determine the percent of total attacks in each habitat that occurred on dark models. It may be that there were simply more predators in the inland habitat than in the beach habitat. The experiment needed proper data analysis.

18. If these cell division control genes are involved in producing the larger tomato, they may have similar effects if transferred to other fruits or vegetables. Cancer is a result of uncontrolled cell division. One could see if there are similarities between the tomato genes and any human genes that could be related to human development or disease. The control of cell division is a fundamental process in growth, repair, and asexual reproduction—all important topics in biology.

19. Virtually any news report or magazine contains stories that are about biology or at least have biological connections. How about biological connections in advertisements?

Chapter 2

1. a. protons; b. neutrons; c. electrons; d. different isotopes; e. covalent bonds; f. ionic bonds; g. polar covalent bonds; h. hydrogen bonding

2.

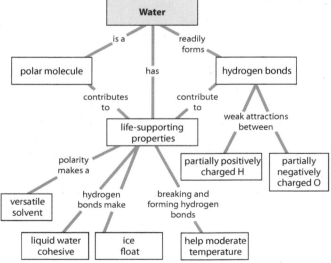

3. b 4. b 5. d 6. c 7. b (Sulfur has 6 electrons in its valence shell. It reaches a full outer shell of 8 by sharing one pair of electrons with each of two hydrogen atoms. Each H then has a full valence shell of 2.)

8. Iodine (part of a thyroid hormone) and iron (part of hemoglobin in blood) are both trace elements, required in minute quantities. Calcium and phosphorus (components of bones and teeth) are needed by the body in much greater quantities.

9. The atoms of each element have a characteristic number of protons in their nuclei, which is referred to as the atomic number and is 6 for carbon. The mass number is an indication of the approximate mass of an atom and is equal to the number of protons and neutrons in the nucleus. Carbon-12 has 6 neutrons (and 6 protons, of course), so its mass number is 12. The valence usually equals the number of electrons needed to fill an atom's outer shell (the number of unpaired electrons). Carbon's valence or bonding capacity of 4 indicates that it will form 4 covalent bonds. Thus, an atom's valence is most related to its chemical behavior.

10. In nonpolar covalent bonds, electrons are equally shared between two atoms. Polar covalent bonds form when a more electronegative atom pulls the shared electrons closer to it, producing a partial negative charge associated with that portion of the molecule and a partial positive charge associated with the atom from which the electrons are pulled. In the formation of ions, an electron is completely pulled away from one atom and transferred to another, creating negatively and positively charged ions. These oppositely charged ions may be attracted to each other in an ionic bond.

11. Fluorine needs 1 electron for a full outer shell of 8, and if potassium loses 1 electron, its outer shell will have 8. Potassium will lose an electron (becoming a + ion), and fluorine will pick it up (becoming a − ion). The ions can form an ionic bond.

12. The elements in a row all have the same number of electron shells. In a column, all the elements have the same number of electrons in their outer shell. Elements in the same column should have similar chemical properties because they have the same valence or bonding capacity and thus would make the same number of covalent bonds. Or if they have only 1 or 2 electrons, or if they have 7 electrons in their outer shell, atoms of these elements would tend to lose or gain electrons, forming ions and participating in ionic bonds.

13. The results indicate that both a lower pH and higher temperature negatively affected the growth of coral polyps and that the reduction in growth was much greater when both pH and temperature were varied at the same time. Because rising atmospheric levels of CO_2 are predicted to continue to acidify the oceans and raise ocean temperatures, it is beneficial to see how these two factors may interact.

14. When water is heated, much of the heat is absorbed in breaking hydrogen bonds before the water molecules increase their motion and the temperature increases. Conversely, when water is cooled, many hydrogen bonds are formed, which releases a significant amount of heat. This release of heat can provide some protection against freezing of the plants' leaves, thus protecting the cells from damage.

15. These extreme environments may be similar to those found on other planets. The fact that life may have evolved and continues to flourish in such extreme environments here on Earth suggests that some form of life may have evolved on other planets. In addition to seeking evidence for the past or current presence of water on Mars or other planets, scientists now know to search in environments that previously would have been thought incapable of supporting life.

Chapter 3

1. a. glucose; b. energy storage; c. cellulose; d. fats; e. cell membrane component; f. steroids; g. amino group; h. carboxyl group; i. R group; j. enzyme; k. structural protein; l. movement; m. membrane transport protein; n. defense; o. phosphate group; p. nitrogenous base; q. ribose or deoxyribose; r. DNA; s. code for proteins

2. d (The second kind of molecule is a polymer of the first.) 3. c 4. c 5. d 6. a 7. a 8. d 9. a

10. Circle NH_2, an amino group; COOH, a carboxyl group; and OH, a hydroxyl group on the R group. This is an amino acid, a monomer of proteins. The OH group makes it a polar amino acid.

11. Amino acids with hydrophobic R groups are most likely to be found clustered together in the interior of a protein, sheltered from the surrounding water.

12. This is a hydrolysis reaction, which consumes water. It is essentially the reverse of the diagram in Figure 3.5, except that fructose has a different shape than glucose.

13. Carbon forms four covalent bonds, either with other carbon atoms, producing chains or rings of various lengths and shapes, or with other atoms, such as characteristic chemical groups that confer specific properties on a molecule. This is the basis for the incredible diversity of organic compounds. Organisms can link a small number of monomers into different arrangements to produce a huge variety of polymers.

14. The 20 amino acids that are found in proteins can be arranged in many different sequences into chains of many different lengths. The sequences of DNA nucleotides in the genes of a cell dictate the amino acid sequences of its proteins.

15. A developing chick is growing rapidly, increasing its number of cells. To build new cells it needs large stores of cell membrane components, including cholesterol and lipids, and amino acids for building its proteins. It also requires energy to fuel all this construction, and that is available in the form of fats, as fat molecules can be broken down to yield a lot of energy.

16. a. A: at about 37°C; B: at about 78°C
    b. A: from humans (human body temperature is about 37°C); B: from thermophilic bacteria
    c. Above 40°C, the human enzyme denatures and loses its shape and thus its function. The increased thermal energy disrupts the weak bonds that maintain secondary and tertiary structure in an enzyme.

17. These results indicate that replacing either saturated or trans fats in the diet with unsaturated fats reduces the risk of coronary heart disease. The benefit is greater (risk reduced the most) when trans fats are replaced, even though the quantity of energy in the diet replaced was only 2% rather than the 5% of saturated fats replaced.

Chapter 4

1. a. rough ER; b. nucleus; c. nucleolus; d. ribosomes; e. peroxisome; f. centrosome; g. cytoskeleton; h. mitochondrion; i. plasma membrane; j. lysosome; k. Golgi apparatus; l. smooth ER. For functions, see Table 4.22. A centrosome is a microtubule-organizing center.

2. c 3. b (Small cells have a greater ratio of surface area to volume.) 4. b 5. a

6. DNA as genetic material, ribosomes, plasma membrane, and cytosol

7. Cilia may propel a cell through its environment or sweep a fluid environment past the cell.

8. d 9. b 10. a 11. c

12. Different conditions and conflicting processes can occur simultaneously within separate, membrane-enclosed compartments. Also, there is increased area for membrane-attached enzymes that carry out metabolic processes.

13. Part true, part false. All animal *and* plant cells have mitochondria; plant cells do have chloroplasts, but animal cells do not. Both organelles process energy. A mitochondrion converts chemical energy (such as sugar molecules) to another form of chemical energy (ATP). This process provides almost all eukaryotic cells with ATP needed for cellular work. A chloroplast converts light energy to chemical energy (sugar molecules). These sugar molecules may then provide a plant cell's mitochondria with a source of energy. Or they may be stored in the plant body and passed to animals that eat plants or each other.

14. The plasma membrane is a phospholipid bilayer with the hydrophilic heads facing the aqueous environment on both sides and the hydrophobic fatty acid tails mingling in the center of the membrane. Proteins are embedded in and attached to this membrane. Microfilaments form a three-dimensional network just inside the plasma membrane. The extracellular matrix outside the membrane is composed largely of glycoproteins, which may be attached to membrane proteins called integrins. Integrins can transmit information from the ECM to microfilaments on the other side of the membrane.

15. Cell 1: $S = 1{,}256 \ \mu m^2$; $V = 4{,}187 \ \mu m^3$; $S/V = 0.3$. Cell 2: $S = 5{,}024 \ \mu m^2$; $V = 33{,}493 \ \mu m^3$; $S/V = 0.15$. The smaller cell has a larger surface area relative to volume, facilitating the uptake of sufficient nutrients and oxygen and the excretion of waste.

16. An mRNA molecule is transcribed from the gene for insulin and moves into the cytosol. There it joins with a ribosome that becomes attached to the outside of the rough ER (a bound ribosome). The ribosome produces a polypeptide that is threaded into the ER compartment. The polypeptide folds up and may be modified within the ER. It is then packaged into a transport vesicle. The vesicle joins with a Golgi sac, and the protein may be further modified during its journey through the Golgi apparatus. A transport vesicle pinches off from the "shipping" face of the Golgi and fuses with the plasma membrane, secreting insulin from the cell.

17. According to the endosymbiotic theory, an ancestral eukaryotic cell engulfed (ingested) an aerobic bacterium but did not digest its potential food item. The prokaryote took up residence within the cell, and its aerobic metabolism probably contributed ATP to the host cell. Over many generations of cells, the host and endosymbiont became mutually dependent and unable to exist on their own—they became a single organism. A similar process may have occurred when one of these mitochondria-containing cells ingested but did not digest a photosynthetic prokaryote.

18. Individuals with PCD have nonfunctional cilia and flagella due to a lack of dynein motor proteins. This defect would also mean that the cilia involved in left-right pattern formation in the embryo would not be able to set up the fluid flow that initiates the normal arrangement of organs.

19. As the chromosomes moved poleward, the microtubule segments on the chromosome side of the mark shortened, while those on pole side stayed the same length. Thus chromosome movement toward the poles of this dividing cell is correlated with the shortening (depolymerizing) of the microtubules at the end where the chromosome is attached. The experiment would have to be repeated on different types of cells from different organisms to determine whether the location where a spindle fiber depolymerizes is always the same. Indeed, other experiments have shown that in some cells, the microtubules depolymerize from the pole end of the spindle fibers.

Chapter 5

1. a. active transport; b. concentration gradient; c. small nonpolar molecules; d. facilitated diffusion; e. transport proteins

2. a. enzyme; b. active site of enzyme; c. substrate; d. substrate in active site; induced fit strains substrate bonds; e. substrate converted to products; f. product molecules released

3. b 4. d 5. c (Only active transport can move solute against a concentration gradient.) 6. a 7. b

8. The work of cells falls into three main categories: chemical, transport, and mechanical. ATP provides the energy for cellular work by transferring a phosphate group to a substrate (chemical) or to a protein (transport and mechanical).

9. Energy is stored in the chemical bonds of a cell's organic molecules. The activation energy barrier prevents these molecules from spontaneously breaking down and releasing that energy. When a substrate fits into an enzyme's active site with an induced fit, its bonds may be strained and thus easier to break, or the active site may orient two substrates in such a way that facilitates the reaction.

10. Energy is neither created nor destroyed but can be transferred and transformed. Plants transform the energy of sunlight into chemical energy stored in organic molecules. Almost all organisms rely on the products of photosynthesis for the source of their energy. In every energy transfer or transformation, disorder increases as some energy is lost to the random motion of thermal energy and released as heat.

11. Cell membranes are composed of diverse proteins suspended in a fluid phospholipid bilayer. The hydrophilic heads of the phospholipids face the aqueous environment on both sides of the membrane and the fatty acid tails cluster in the hydrophobic center of the membrane The membrane forms a selectively permeable boundary between cells and their surroundings (or between organelles and the cytosol). The proteins perform the many functions of membranes, such as enzyme action, transport, attachment, and signaling.

12. Inhibitors that are toxins or poisons irreversibly inhibit key cellular enzymes. Inhibitors that are designed as drugs are beneficial, such as when they interfere with the enzymes of bacterial or viral invaders or cancer cells. Cells use feedback inhibition of enzymes in metabolic pathways as important mechanisms that conserve resources.

13. Aquaporins are water transport channels that allow for very rapid diffusion of water through a cell membrane. It would be most important for your body to reabsorb water from the urine, thus preventing dehydration, after a run on a hot day.

14. The aquaporin RNA-injected oocytes had a high rate of water permeability. (Remember from Module 5.7 that they swelled and ruptured in 3 minutes.) Treatment with mercury chloride inhibited the aquaporins, and the water permeability of the oocytes was reduced. As expected, the higher the concentration of mercury, the greater the inhibition and reduction in water permeability.

When that inhibition was reversed by treatment with the chemical ME, the channels once again functioned and water permeability increased to almost the level of the uninhibited oocytes. The control oocytes were not injected with aquaporin RNA and thus did not have aquaporins. Thus, their water permeability should be very low and not affected by the mercury treatment. Indeed, their water permeability was much lower than any of the RNA-injected oocytes.

15. a. The more enzyme present, the faster the rate of reaction, because it is more likely that enzyme and substrate molecules will meet.

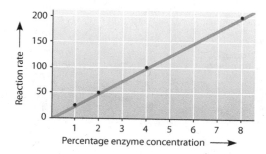

b. The more substrate present, the faster the reaction, for the same reason, but only up to a point. An enzyme molecule can work only so fast; once it is saturated (working at top speed), more substrate does not increase the rate.

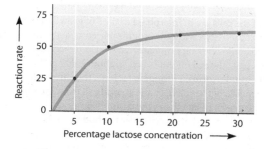

16. Some issues and questions to consider: Is improving crop yields of paramount importance in a world where many people can't get enough food? Does the fact that these compounds rapidly break down indicate that the risk to humans is low? How about the risks to people who work in agriculture or to other organisms, such as bees and other pollinating insects, birds, and small mammals? Might there be negative effects on ecosystems that are impossible to predict?

Chapter 6

1. a. glycolysis; b. pyruvate oxidation and citric acid cycle; c. oxidative phosphorylation; d. oxygen; e. electron transport chain; f. CO_2; g. H_2O

2. d 3. d 4. b 5. a 6. c (NAD^+ and FAD, which are recycled by electron transport, are in limited supply in a cell.) 7. b (at the same time NADH is oxidized to NAD^+)

8. Glycolysis is considered the most ancient because it occurs in all living cells and doesn't require oxygen or membrane-enclosed organelles.

9. In lactic acid fermentation (in muscle cells), pyruvate is reduced by NADH to form lactate, and NAD^+ is recycled. In alcohol fermentation, pyruvate is broken down to CO_2 and ethanol as NADH is oxidized to NAD^+. Both types of fermentation allow glycolysis to continue to produce 2 ATP per glucose by recycling NAD^+.

10. As carbohydrates are broken down in glycolysis and the oxidation of pyruvate, glycerol can be made from G3P and fatty acids can be made from acetyl CoA. Amino groups, containing N atoms, must be supplied to various intermediates of glycolysis and the citric acid cycle to produce amino acids.

11. 100 kcal per day is 700 kcal per week. According to Figure 6.4, walking 3 mph would require = about 2.8 hours; swimming, 1.7 hours; running, 0.7 hour.

12. NAD^+ and FAD are coenzymes that are not used up during the oxidation of glucose. NAD^+ and FAD are recycled when NADH and $FADH_2$ pass the electrons they are carrying to the electron transport chain. We need a small additional supply to replace those that are damaged.

13. a. No, this shows the blue color getting more intense. The reaction decolorizes the blue dye.
    b. No, this shows the dye being decolorized, but it also shows the three mixtures with different initial color intensities. The intensities should have started out the same, since all mixtures used the same concentration of dye.
    c. Correct. The mixtures all start out the same, and then the ones with more malate (reactant) decolorize faster.

14. The presence of ATP synthase enzymes in prokaryotic plasma membranes and the inner membrane of mitochondria provides support for the theory of endosymbiosis—that mitochondria evolved from an engulfed prokaryote that used aerobic respiration (see Module 4.15).

15. The percentage of body fat is the independent variable and is plotted on the x axis. The activity of brown fat is the dependent variable, and it is plotted on the y axis. Your graph should show a negative correlation between body fat percentage and activity of brown fat (the data points are higher for lower body fat percentage and decrease as the body fat percentage increases). One hypothesis is that thin individuals have more active brown fat and thus burn more calories, which contributes to their thinness (lower percentage of body fat). A second hypothesis is that the higher percentage of body fat insulated the bodies of the more overweight subjects, thus their brown fat did not have to be as active to maintain their body temperatures when exposed to cold.

16. In a person treated with uncoupling agents like DNP, the proton gradient established during electron transport is no longer tied to ATP synthesis. As a result, oxidation of glucose during cellular respiration yields very little ATP, since ATP is normally produced as H^+ ions flow back through ATP synthase in the inner mitochondrial membrane. Without large amounts of ATP available, biosynthesis cannot take place and new organic molecules cannot be synthesized. Low ATP levels would signal the body to continue breaking down its own molecules and feeding them into the cellular respiration pathway, leading to excessive weight loss and severe overheating, sweating, and dehydration. One or a combination of these factors can cause death.

17. The mitochondria of brown fat cells have protein channels that make the inner mitochondrial membrane leaky to H^+ ions, producing the same effect that the drug DNP has on mitochondria. When these channels are activated, brown fat burns fuel without producing ATP. Drugs that could activate brown fat would help a patient burn more calories. Thus, excess calories from the diet would not be converted to fat, and fat stores of the body could be reduced. If these drugs somehow affected the mitochondria of all body cells, however, the results could be as disastrous as they were with DNP.

1. a. light energy; b. light reactions; c. Calvin cycle; d. O_2 released; e. electron transport chain; f. NADPH; g. ATP; h. G3P (sugar)

2. c 3. b 4. a 5. c (NADPH and ATP from the light reactions are required by the Calvin cycle.) 6. d 7. b 8. c

9. CO_2 and H_2O are the products of respiration; they are the reactants in photosynthesis. In respiration, glucose is oxidized to CO_2 as electrons are passed through an electron transfer chain from glucose to O_2, producing H_2O. In photosynthesis, H_2O is the source of electrons, which are energized by light, temporarily stored in NADPH, and used to reduce CO_2 to carbohydrate.

10. The light reactions require ADP and $NADP^+$, neither of which are recycled from ATP and NADPH when the Calvin cycle stops.

11. Plants can break down the sugar for energy in cellular respiration or use the sugar as a raw material for making other organic molecules. Excess sugar is stored as starch.

12. a. electron transport chain; b. ATP synthase; c. thylakoid space; d. stroma; e. ATP. The higher H^+ concentration is found in the intermembrane space of the mitochondrion and in the thylakoid space of the chloroplast.

13. In mitochondria: a. Electrons come from food molecules.
b. Electrons have high potential energy in the bonds in organic molecules. c. Electrons are passed to oxygen, which picks up H^+ and forms water.
In chloroplasts: a. Electrons come from splitting of water.
b. Light energy excites the electrons to a higher energy level.
c. Electrons flow from water to the reaction-center chlorophyll in photosystem II to the reaction-center chlorophyll in photosystem I to $NADP^+$, reducing it to NADPH.
In both processes: d. Energy released by redox reactions in the electron transport chain is used to transport H^+ across a membrane. The flow of H^+ down its concentration gradient back through ATP synthase drives the phosphorylation of ADP to make ATP.

14. The hypothesis was that, because CO_2 is a raw material for photosynthesis, rising CO_2 levels would increase the growth and production of pollen by ragweed. Pollen production was positively correlated with CO_2 concentrations, and the results supported the hypothesis. Because rising CO_2 levels are associated with warmer temperatures, an experiment could also look at the effect of temperature on ragweed pollen production. One might also want to determine whether the growing season is getting longer, as this would expose hay fever sufferers to pollen for extended periods. It would also be interesting to measure whether ragweed pollen is more allergenic when grown in higher CO_2 levels, as poison ivy was shown to be. These types of experiments have been performed, and their results are as you would predict—the growing season for ragweed has gotten longer, and pollen that is more allergenic is produced in higher quantities under conditions of elevated CO_2.

15. Some issues and questions to consider: What are the risks that we take and costs we must pay if global climate change continues? How certain do we have to be that global warming is caused by human activities before we act? What can we do to reduce CO_2 emissions? Is it possible that the costs and sacrifices of reducing CO_2 emissions might actually improve our lifestyle?

Chapter 8

1.

	Mitosis	Meiosis
Number of chromosomal duplications	1	1
Number of cell divisions	1	2
Number of daughter cells produced	2	4
Number of chromosomes in the daughter cells	Diploid (2n)	Haploid (n)
How the chromosomes line up during metaphase	Singly	In tetrads (metaphase I), then singly (metaphase II)
Genetic relationship of the daughter cells to the parent cell	Genetically identical	Genetically unique
Functions performed in the human body	Growth, development, and repair	Production of gametes

2. b 3. c 4. b 5. b 6. b 7. a 8. b 9. d (A diploid cell would have an even number of chromosomes; the odd number suggests that meiosis I has been completed. Sister chromatids are together only in prophase and metaphase of meiosis II.) 10. c 11. d

12. Most of the cells are in interphase (a time of growth, DNA synthesis, metabolic activity), without recognizable compacted individual chromosomes. During prophase, chromosomes compact and thicken (e.g., the cell on the left edge, about halfway down) and the mitotic spindle forms. During metaphase, the chromosomes line up in the middle of the cell (e.g., the second cell from the top, near the top left corner). In anaphase, the chromosomes split into two groups (which you can see in two cells near the bottom right corner) as sister chromatids split. During telophase, the chromosomes reach opposite ends (e.g., at the very top, fifth cell from the right) as daughter nuclei form around the chromosomes and cytokinesis begins.

13. Mitosis without cytokinesis would result in a single cell with two nuclei. Multiple rounds of cell division like this could produce such a "megacell."

14. Various orientations of homologous chromosome pairs at metaphase I of meiosis lead to different combinations of chromosomes in gametes. Crossing over during prophase I results in an exchange of chromosome segments and new combinations of genes. Random fertilization of eggs by sperm further increases possibilities for variation in offspring.

15. In culture, normal cells usually divide only when they are in contact with a surface but not touching other cells on all sides (the cells usually grow to form only a single layer). The density-dependent inhibition of cell division apparently results from local depletion of substances called growth factors. Growth factors are proteins secreted by certain cells that stimulate other cells to divide; they act via signal transduction pathways to signal the cell cycle control system of the affected cell to proceed past its checkpoints. The cell cycle control systems of cancer cells do not function properly. Cancer cells generally do not require externally supplied growth factors to complete the cell cycle, and they divide indefinitely (in contrast to normal mammalian cells, which stop dividing after 20 to 50 generations)—two reasons why cancer cells

are relatively easy to grow in the lab. Furthermore, cancer cells can often grow without contacting a solid surface, making it possible to culture them in suspension in a liquid medium.

16. A ring of microfilaments pinches an animal cell in two, a process called cleavage. In a plant cell, membranous vesicles form a disk called the cell plate at the midline of the parent cell, cell plate membranes fuse with the plasma membrane, and a cell wall grows in the space, separating the daughter cells.

17. See Figure 8.18.

18. a. No. For this to happen, the chromosomes of the two gametes that fused would have to represent, together, a complete set of the donor's maternal chromosomes (the ones that originally came from the donor's mother) and a complete set of the donor's paternal chromosomes (from the donor's father). It is much more likely that the zygote would be missing one or more maternal chromosomes and would have an excess of paternal chromosomes, or vice versa.

   b. Correct. Consider what would have to happen to produce a zygote genetically identical to the gamete donor: The zygote would have to have a complete set of the donor's maternal chromosomes and a complete set of the donor's paternal chromosomes. The first gamete in this union could contain any mixture of maternal and paternal chromosomes, but once that first gamete was "chosen," the second one would have to have one particular combination of chromosomes—the combination that supplies whatever the first gamete did not supply. So, for example, if the first three chromosomes of the first gamete were maternal, maternal, and paternal, the first three of the second gamete would have to be paternal, paternal, and maternal. The chance that all 23 chromosome pairs would be complementary in this way is only one in 22^3 (that is, one in 8,388,608). Because of independent assortment, it is much more likely that the zygote would have an unpredictable combination of chromosomes from the donor's father and mother.

   c. No. First, the zygote could not be genetically identical to the gamete donor (see answer b). Second, the zygote could not be identical to either of the gamete donor's parents because the donor only has half the genetic material of each of his or her parents. For example, even if the zygote were formed by two gametes containing only paternal chromosomes, the combined set of chromosomes could not be identical to that of the donor's father because it would still be missing half of the father's chromosomes.

   d. No. See answer c.

19. Some possible hypotheses: The replication of the DNA of the bacterial chromosome takes less time than the replication of the DNA in a eukaryotic cell. The time required for a growing bacterium to roughly double its cytoplasm is much less than for a eukaryotic cell. Bacteria have a cell cycle control system much simpler than that of eukaryotes.

20. 1 cm^3 = 1,000 mm^3, so 5,000 mm^3 of blood contains 5,000 × 1,000 × 5,000,000 = 25,000,000,000,000, or 2.5 × 10^{13}, red blood cells. The number of cells replaced each day = 2.5 × 10^{13}/120 = 2.1 × 10^{11} cells. There are 24 × 60 × 60 = 86,400 seconds in a day. Therefore, the number of cells replaced each second = 2.1 × 10^{11}/86,400 = about 2 × 10^6, or 2 million. Thus, about 2 million cell divisions must occur each second to replace red blood cells that are lost.

21. Each chromosome is on its own in mitosis; chromosome replication and the separation of sister chromatids occur independently

for each horse or donkey chromosome. Therefore, mitotic divisions, starting with the zygote, are not impaired. In meiosis, however, homologous chromosomes must pair in prophase I. This process of synapsis cannot occur properly because horse and donkey chromosomes do not match in number or content.

22. There are two unusual cases presented in Table 8.10: the patient who did not have the mutation but responded to everolimus and the patient who had the mutation but did not respond to everolimus. These patients could be studied in a manner similar to the original patient by performing a genetic analysis of their tumor cells. Such an analysis might reveal other mutations that explain their results. Further experiments like the one presented in Table 8.10 might then be performed to see if these results can be generalized. Such an approach may allow refinement of the personalized cancer therapy.

Chapter 9

1. a. alleles; b. loci; c. homozygous; d. dominant; e. recessive; f. incomplete dominance

2. c 3. b 4. d (Neither parent is ruby-eyed, but some offspring are, so it is recessive. Different ratios among male and female offspring show that it is sex-linked.) 5. d

6. The trait of freckles is dominant, so Tim and Jan must both be heterozygous. There is a chance that they will produce a child with freckles and a chance that they will produce a child without freckles. The probability that the next two children will have freckles is 3/4 × 3/4 = 9/16.

7. As in problem 6, both Tim and Jan are heterozygous, and Mike is homozygous recessive. The probability of the next child having freckles is 3/4. The probability of the next child having a straight hairline is 1/4. The probability that the next child will have freckles and a straight hairline is 3/4 × 1/4 = 3/16.

8. The genotype of the black short-haired parent rabbit is *BBSS*. The genotype of the brown long-haired parent rabbit is *bbss*. The F$_1$ rabbits will all be black and short-haired, *BbSs*. The F$_2$ rabbits will be black short-haired, black long-haired, brown short-haired, and brown long-haired, in a proportion of 9:3:3:1.

9. If the genes are not linked, the proportions among the offspring will be 25% gray red, 25% gray purple, 25% black red, and 25% black purple. The actual percentages show that the genes are linked. The recombination frequency is 6%.

10. The recombination frequencies are black dumpy 36%, purple dumpy 41%, and black purple 6% (see problem 9). Because these recombination frequencies reflect distances between the genes, the sequence must be purple-black-dumpy (or dumpy-black-purple).

11. 1/4 will be boys suffering from hemophilia, and 1/4 will be female carriers. (The mother is a heterozygous carrier [X^{H}X^h], and the father is normal [X^{H}Y].)

12. Genes on the single X chromosome in males are always expressed because there are no corresponding genes on the Y chromosome to mask them. A male needs only one recessive colorblindness allele (from his mother) to show the trait; a female must inherit the allele from both parents, which is less likely.

13. The parental gametes are *WS* and *ws*. Recombinant gametes are *Ws* and *wS*, produced by crossing over.

14. Height appears to be a quantitative trait resulting from polygenic inheritance, like human skin color. See Module 9.14.

15. For a woman to be colorblind, she must inherit X chromosomes bearing the colorblindness allele from both parents. Her father has only one X chromosome, which he passes on to all his daughters, so he must be colorblind. A male need only inherit the colorblindness allele from a carrier mother; both his parents are usually phenotypically normal.

16. Start out by breeding the cat to get a population to work with. If the curl allele is recessive, two curl cats can have only curl kittens. If the allele is dominant, curl cats can have "normal" kittens. If the curl allele is sex-linked, ratios will differ in male and female offspring of some crosses. If the curl allele is autosomal, the same ratios will be seen among males and females. Once you have established that the curl allele is dominant and autosomal, you can determine if a particular curl cat is true-breeding (homozygous) by doing a testcross with a normal cat. If the curl cat is homozygous, all offspring of the testcross will be curl; if heterozygous, half of the offspring will be curl and half normal.

17. If the genes are unlinked, you expect puppies in a 9:3:3:1 ratio: 90 black normal vision, 30 black blind, 30 chocolate normal, and 10 chocolate blind. If the genes are linked, you would expect a 3:1 ratio of black normal to chocolate blind, with a small number of black blind and chocolate normal recombinant offspring.

·Chapter 10

1. a. nucleotides; b. transcription; c. RNA polymerase; d. mRNA; e. rRNA; f. tRNA; g. translation; h. ribosomes; i. amino acids

2. b

3. Ingredients: Original DNA, nucleotides, several enzymes and other proteins, including DNA polymerase and DNA ligase. Steps: Original DNA strands separate at a specific site (origin of replication), free nucleotides hydrogen-bond to each strand according to base-pairing rules, and DNA polymerase covalently bonds the nucleotides to form new strands. New nucleotides are added only to the 3′ end of a growing strand. One new strand is made in one continuous piece; the other new strand is made in a series of short pieces that are then joined by DNA ligase. Product: Two identical DNA molecules, each with one old strand and one new strand.

4. transcription; translation

5. d (Only the phage DNA enters a host cell; lambda DNA determines both DNA and protein.)

6. d

7. A gene is the polynucleotide sequence with information for making one polypeptide. Each codon—a triplet of bases in DNA or RNA—codes for one amino acid. Transcription occurs when RNA polymerase produces RNA using one strand of DNA as a template. In prokaryotic cells, the RNA transcript may immediately serve as mRNA. In eukaryotic cells, the RNA is processed: A cap and tail are added, and RNA splicing removes introns and links exons together to form a continuous coding sequence. A ribosome is the site of translation, or polypeptide synthesis, and tRNA molecules serve as interpreters of the genetic code. Each folded tRNA molecule has an amino acid attached at one end and a three-base anticodon at the other end. Beginning at the start codon, mRNA is moved relative to the ribosome a codon at a time. A tRNA with a complementary anticodon pairs with each codon, adding its amino acid to the polypeptide chain. The amino acids are linked by peptide bonds. Translation stops at a stop codon, and the finished polypeptide is released. The polypeptide folds to form a functional protein, sometimes in combination with other polypeptides.

8. c

9.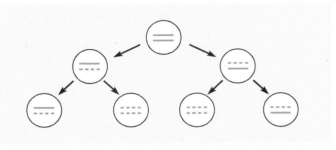

10. mRNA: GAUGCGAUCCGCUAACUGA; amino acids: Met-Arg-Ser-Ala-Asn

11. Some issues and questions to consider: Is it fair to issue a patent for a gene or gene product that occurs naturally in every human being? Or should a patent be issued only for something new that is invented rather than found? Suppose another scientist slightly modifies the gene or protein. How different does the gene or protein have to be to avoid patent infringement? Might patents encourage secrecy and interfere with the free flow of scientific information? What are the benefits to the holder of a patent? When research discoveries cannot be patented, what are the scientists' incentives for doing the research? What are the incentives for the institution or company that is providing financial support?

12. A bacteriophage is capable of easily infecting a host (bacterium) and therefore multiplying its genetic material. Most importantly, a bacteriophage has a very simple structure, allowing the outer structure (made entirely of protein) to be easily distinguished from the inner structure (made of DNA).

Chapter 11

1. a. proto-oncogene; b. repressor (or activator); c. cancer; d. operator; e. X inactivation; f. transcription factors; g. alternative RNA splicing

2. b 3. b 4. b 5. b (Different genes are active in different kinds of cells.) 6. c 7. d

8. They will be black, because the DNA of the cell was obtained from a black mouse.

9. a. If the mutated repressor could still bind to the operator on the DNA, it would continuously repress the operon; enzymes for lactose utilization would not be made, whether or not lactose was present.

   b. The *lac* genes would continue to be transcribed and the enzymes made, whether or not lactose was present.

   c. Same predicted result as for b.

   d. RNA polymerase would not be able to transcribe the genes; no proteins would be made, whether or not lactose was present.

10. A mutation in a single gene can influence the actions of many other genes if the mutated gene is a control gene, such as a homeotic gene. A single control gene may encode a protein that affects (activates or represses) the expression of a number of other genes. In addition, some of the affected genes may themselves be control genes that in turn affect other batteries of genes. Cascades of gene expression are common in embryonic development.

11. The protein to which dioxin binds in the cell is probably a transcription factor that regulates multiple genes (see Module 11.3). If the binding of dioxin influences the activity of this transcription factor—either activating or inactivating it—dioxin could thereby

affect multiple genes and thus have a variety of effects on the body. The differing effects in different animals might be explained by differing genetic details in the different species. It would be extremely difficult to demonstrate conclusively that dioxin exposure was the cause of illness in a particular individual, even if dioxin had been shown to be present in the person's tissues. However, if you had detailed information about how dioxin affects patterns of gene expression in humans and were able to show dioxin-specific abnormal patterns in the patient (perhaps using DNA microarrays; see Module 11.9), you might be able to establish a strong link between dioxin and the illness.

12. Wilmut was able to coordinate the cell cycle of the donor and host cells by depriving them of nutrients. When faced with starvation, both cells switched to the G_0 phase of the cell cycle. Wilmut could therefore be sure that, when placed in a growth medium with nutrients, the cell cycles within both the donor and host cell were synchronized. This allowed him to successfully clone a mammal from an adult cell for the first time.

Chapter 12

1. a. PCR; b. a restriction enzyme; c. gel electrophoresis; d. nucleic acid probe; e. cloning

2. d 3. b 4. b 5. c 6. c

7. Because it would be too expensive and time consuming to compare whole genomes. By choosing STR sites that vary considerably from person to person, investigators can get the necessary degree of specificity without sequencing the entire genome.

8. Medicine: Genes can be used to produce transgenic lab animals for AIDS research or for research related to human gene therapy. Proteins can be hormones, enzymes, blood-clotting factors, or the active ingredient of vaccines. Agriculture: Foreign genes can be inserted into plant cells or animal eggs to produce transgenic crop plants or farm animals. Animal growth hormones are examples of agriculturally useful proteins that can be made using recombinant DNA technology.

9. She could start with DNA isolated from liver cells (the entire genome) and carry out the procedure outlined in Module 12.1 to produce a collection of recombinant bacterial clones, each carrying a small piece of liver cell DNA. To find the clone with the desired gene, she could then make a probe of radioactive RNA with a nucleotide sequence complementary to part of the gene: GACCUGACUGU. This probe would bind to the gene, labeling it and identifying the clone that carries it. Alternatively, the biochemist could start with mRNA isolated from liver cells and use it as a template to make cDNA (using reverse transcriptase). Cloning this DNA rather than the entire genome would yield a smaller library of genes to be screened—only those active in liver cells. Furthermore, the genes would lack introns, making the desired gene easier to manipulate after isolation.

10. c (Bacteria lack the RNA-splicing machinery needed to delete eukaryotic introns.)

11. Isolate plasmids from a culture of *E. coli*. Cut the plasmids and the human DNA containing the HGH gene with the restriction enzyme to produce molecules with sticky ends. Join the plasmids and the fragments of human DNA with ligase. Allow *E. coli* to take up recombinant plasmids. Bacteria will then replicate plasmids and multiply, producing clones of bacterial cells. Identify a clone carrying and expressing the HGH gene using a nucleic acid probe. Grow large amounts of the bacteria and extract and purify HGH from the culture.

12. Determining the nucleotide sequences is just the first step. Once researchers have written out the DNA "book," they will have to try to figure out what it means—what the nucleotide sequences code for and how they work.

13. Some issues and questions to consider: What are some of the unknowns in recombinant DNA experiments? Do we know enough to anticipate and deal with possible unforeseen and negative consequences? Do we want this kind of power over evolution? Who should make these decisions? If scientists doing the research were to make the decisions about guidelines, what factors might shape their judgment? What might shape the judgment of business executives in the decision-making process? Does the public have a right to a voice in the direction of scientific research? Does the public know enough about biology to get involved in this decision-making process? Who represents "the public," anyway?

14. Some issues and questions to consider: What kinds of impact will gene therapy have on the individuals who are treated? On society? Who will decide what patients and diseases will be treated? What costs will be involved, and who will pay them? How do we draw the line between treating disorders and "improving" the human species?

15. Some issues and questions to consider: Should genetic testing be mandatory or voluntary? Under what circumstances? Why might employers and insurance companies be interested in genetic data? Since genetic characteristics differ among ethnic groups and between the sexes, might such information be used to discriminate? Which of these questions do you think is most important? Which issues are likely to be the most serious in the future?

16. Gather two groups of volunteers. Have one group ingest a standard amount of GMO corn in their diet and the other group ingest a standard amount of traditional corn. Monitor the health of the individuals in both groups, looking for differences. In real life, such a study would be problematic because it is difficult to control and monitor what people eat, it would require many years to search for long-term health effects, and it may run afoul of ethics standards for human testing.

Chapter 13

1. According to Darwin's theory of descent with modification, all life has descended from a common ancestral form as a result of natural selection. Individuals in a population have hereditary variations. The overproduction of offspring in the face of limited resources leads to a struggle for existence. Individuals that are well suited to their environment tend to leave more offspring than other individuals, leading to the gradual accumulation of adaptations to the local environment in the population.

2. a. genetic drift; b. gene flow; c. natural selection; d. small population; e. founder effect; f. bottleneck effect; g. unequal reproductive success

3. d 4. a 5. b (Erratic rainfall and unequal reproductive success would ensure that a mixture of both forms remained in the population.) 6. d 7. d 8. c

9. Exposing deep rock strata made it easier to obtain older fossils.

10. Your paragraph should include such evidence as fossils and the fossil record, homologous structures, molecular homologies, artificial selection, and examples of natural selection.

11. Evidence strongly supports Lamarck's hypothesis that life evolves. However, our understanding of genetics refutes his hypothesis for the mechanism of evolution.

12. If $q^2 = 0.0025$, $q = 0.05$. Since $p + q = 1$, $p = 1 - q = 0.95$. The proportion of heterozygotes is $2pq = 2 \times 0.95 \times 0.05 = 0.095$. About 9.5% of African Americans are carriers.

13. Genetic variation is retained in a population by diploidy and balanced selection. Recessive alleles are hidden from selection when in the heterozygote; thus, less adaptive or even harmful alleles are maintained in the gene pool and are available should environmental conditions change. Both heterozygote advantage and frequency-dependent selection tend to maintain alternate alleles in a population.

14. The terrestrial ancestors of cetaceans had lungs and breathed air. Evolution did not cause the invention of a new respiratory system for breathing underwater. Rather, the existing external structures were adapted. For example, the nostrils shifted position to the top of the head, where they form the blowhole, an opening to the trachea (windpipe), which leads to the lungs. The blowhole is closed while the cetacean is underwater. A cetacean must thrust its blowhole above the surface of the water periodically to obtain oxygen and expel carbon dioxide. Unlike other mammals, the cetacean respiratory system doesn't intersect with the digestive system, allowing the animal to take in food underwater.

15. The unstriped snails appear to be better adapted. Striped snails make up 47% of the living population but 56% of the broken shells. Assuming that all the broken shells result from the meals of birds, we would predict that bird predation would reduce the frequency of striped snails and the frequency of unstriped individuals would increase.

16. Some issues and questions to consider: Who should decide curriculum, scientific experts in a field or members of the community? Are these alternative versions scientific ideas? Who judges what is scientific? If it is fairer to consider alternatives, should the door be open to all alternatives? Are constitutional issues (separation of church and state) involved here? Can a teacher be compelled to teach an idea he or she disagrees with? Should a student be required to learn an idea he or she thinks is wrong?

Chapter 14

1. a. Allopatric speciation: Reproductive barriers may evolve between these two geographically separated populations as a by-product of the genetic changes associated with each population's adaptation to its own environment or as a result of genetic drift or mutation.
   b. Sympatric speciation: Some change, perhaps in resource use or female mate choice, may lead to a reproductive barrier that isolates the gene pools of these two populations, which are not separated geographically. Once the gene pools are separated, each species may go down its own evolutionary path. If speciation occurs by polyploidy—which is common in plants but unusual in animals—then the new species is instantly isolated from the parent species.

2. a. hybrid zone; b. reinforcement; c. fusion; d. stability;
   e. strengthened; f. weakened or eliminated

3. c 4. b 5. b 6. d 7. c 8. b 9. c 10. a 11. d 12. d

13. Different physical appearances may indicate that organisms belong in different species, but they may just be physical differences within a species. Isolated populations may or may not be able to interbreed; breeding experiments would need to be performed to determine this. Organisms that reproduce only asexually and fossil organisms do not have the potential to interbreed and produce fertile offspring; therefore, the biological species concept cannot apply to them.

14. There is more chance for gene flow between populations on a mainland and nearby island. This interbreeding would make it more difficult for reproductive isolation to develop and separate the two populations.

15. The term *punctuated equilibria* refers to a common pattern seen in the fossil record, in which most species diverge relatively quickly as they arise from an ancestral species and then remain fairly unchanged for the rest of their existence as a species.

16. Yes. Factors such as polyploidy, sexual selection, and habitat specialization can lead to reproductive barriers that would separate the gene pools of allopatric as well as sympatric populations.

17. A broad hypothesis would be that cultivated American cotton arose from a sequence of hybridization, mistakes in cell division, and self-fertilization. We can divide this broad statement into at least three hypotheses. *Hypothesis 1*: The first step in the origin of cultivated American cotton was hybridization between a wild American cotton plant (with 13 pairs of small chromosomes) and an Old World cotton plant (with 13 pairs of large chromosomes). If this hypothesis is correct, we would predict that the hybrid offspring would have had 13 small chromosomes and 13 large chromosomes. *Hypothesis 2*: The second step in the origin of cultivated American cotton was a failure of cell division in the hybrid offspring, such that all chromosomes were duplicated (now 26 small and 26 large). If this hypothesis is true, we would expect the resulting gametes to each have had 13 large chromosomes and 13 small chromosomes. *Hypothesis 3*: The third step in the origin of cultivated American cotton was self-fertilization of these gametes. If this hypothesis is true, we would expect the outcome of self-fertilization to be a hybrid plant with 52 chromosomes: 13 pairs of large ones and 13 pairs of small ones. Indeed, this is the genetic makeup of cultivated American cotton.

18. By decreasing the ability of females to distinguish males of their own species, the polluted turbid waters have increased the frequency of mating between members of species that had been reproductively isolated from one another. As the number of hybrid fish increase, the parent species' gene pools may fuse, resulting in a loss of the two separate parent species and the formation of a new hybrid species. Future speciation events in Lake Victoria cichlids are less likely to occur in turbid water because females are less able to base mate choice on male breeding color. Reducing the pollution in the lake may help reverse this trend.

19. Some issues and questions to consider: One could look at this question in two ways. If the biological species concept is followed strictly, one could argue that red wolves and coyotes are the same species, since they can interbreed. Because coyotes are not rare, this line of argument would suggest that red wolves should not be protected. On the other hand, because red wolves and coyotes differ in many ways, they can be viewed as distinct species by other species concepts. Protecting the remaining red wolves from hybridizing with coyotes can preserve their distinct species status. The rationale behind protecting all endangered groups is the desire to preserve genetic diversity. Questions for society in general include the following: What is the value of any particular species and its genetically distinct subgroups? And how far are we willing to go to preserve a rare and distinct group of organisms? How should the costs of preserving genetic diversity compare with the costs of other public projects?

Chapter 15

1. a. Abiotic synthesis of important molecules from simpler chemicals in the atmosphere, with lightning or UV radiation as the energy source
   b. Polymerization of monomers, perhaps on hot rocks
   c. Enclosure within a lipid membrane, which maintained a distinct internal environment
   d. Beginnings of heredity as RNA molecules replicated themselves. Natural selection could have acted on protocells that enclosed self-replicating RNA.

2. a. phylogeny; b. homologies; c. morphology; d. analogies; e. phylogenetic tree; f. outgroup; g. shared derived characters

3. b 4. a 5. d 6. c 7. d 8. a 9. c 10. b

11. Microevolution is the change in the gene pool of a population from one generation to the next. Macroevolution involves the pattern of evolutionary changes over large time spans and includes the origin of new groups and evolutionary novelties as well as mass extinctions.

12. The latter are more likely to be closely related, because even small genetic changes can produce divergent physical appearances. But if genes have diverged greatly, it implies that lineages have been separate for some time, and the similar appearances may be analogous, not homologous.

13. Complex structures can evolve by the gradual refinement of earlier versions of those structures, all of which served a useful function in each ancestor.

14. Where and when key developmental genes are expressed in a developing embryo can greatly affect the final form and arrangement of body parts. The regulation of gene expression allows these genes to continue to be expressed in some areas, turned off in other areas, and/or expressed at different times during development.

15. The ribosomal RNA genes, which specify the RNA parts of ribosomes, have evolved so slowly that homologies between even distantly related organisms can still be detected. Analysis of other homologous genes is also used.

16. 22,920 years old, a result of four half-life reductions

17.

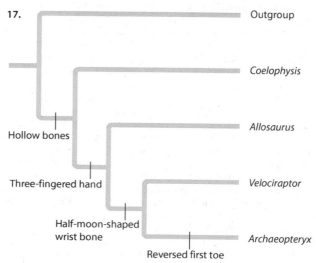

18. Your answer should include aspects of the process of science such as the following: how scientists develop hypotheses and test predictions; the importance of careful experimental design; generating and testing alternative hypotheses; using new technologies; and willingness to incorporate new evidence and revise hypotheses.

Chapter 16

1. Cell wall: maintains cell shape; provides physical protection; prevents cell from bursting in a hypotonic environment
   Capsule: enables cell to stick to substrate or to other individuals in a colony; shields pathogens from host's defensive cells
   Flagella: provide motility, enabling cell to respond to chemical or physical signals in the environment that lead to nutrients or other members of their species and away from toxic substances
   Fimbriae: allow cells to attach to surfaces, including host cells, or to each other
   Endospores: withstand harsh conditions

2. a. Archaeplastids; b. Charophytes; c. Unikonts; d. Fungi; e. Choanoflagellates; f. Animals

3. d (Algae are autotrophs; slime molds are heterotrophs.) 4. d
   5. b 6. c 7. b

8. Rapid rate of reproduction enables prokaryotes to colonize favorable habitats quickly. Mutations during the rapid production of large numbers of cells results in a great deal of genetic variation, making it more likely that some individuals will survive—and be able to recolonize the habitat—if the environment changes again.

9. Multicellular organisms have a greater extent of cellular specialization and more interdependence of cells. New organisms are produced from a single cell, either an egg or an asexual spore.

10. *Chlamydomonas* is a eukaryotic cell, much more complex than a prokaryotic bacterium. It is autotrophic, while amoebas are heterotrophic. It is unicellular, unlike multicellular sea lettuce.

11. d

12. b. Antibiotics kill bacteria. If ulcers are caused by bacteria, then ulcers patients should be cured by antibiotics. (Assume that the researchers have chosen an antibiotic that is effective against the bacteria they hypothesize to be the cause of ulcers.) If the ulcers persist, then the bacteria did not cause the ulcers.

13. According to the theory of secondary endosymbiosis, both organisms are descended from lineages of heterotrophic eukaryotes that engulfed autotrophic eukaryotes, which then evolved into chloroplasts. In the lineage that gave rise to *Euglena*, the autotrophic eukaryote was a green alga. In the lineage that gave rise to *Gymnodinium*, the chloroplast was derived from a different autotrophic eukaryote, a red alga.

14. Use the links on the FDA's main page on dietary supplements to learn how dietary supplements are—and are not—regulated. While manufacturers must prove to the FDA that medicinal products are effective before they can be marketed, there is no such approval process for dietary supplements. The manufacturer is responsible for ensuring that the product is safe and that any claims made on the label are true. This web page also provides links to help you find information about specific supplements and to help you make informed decisions about supplement use. Once you are familiar with these resources, select a specific probiotic product to evaluate.

15. This is not a good idea; all life depends on bacteria. You could predict that eliminating all bacteria from an environment would result in a buildup of toxic wastes and dead organisms (both of which bacteria decompose), a shutdown of all chemical cycling, and the consequent death of all organisms.

16. Some issues and questions to consider: Could we determine beforehand whether the iron would really have the desired effect? How? Would the "fertilization" need to be repeated? Could it be a cure for the problem, or would it merely treat the symptoms? Might the iron treatment have side effects? What might they be?

Credits

Photo Credits

COVER: Andy Rouse/Nature Picture Library

Detailed Table of Contents, pages xxiii–xxxvii

Uri Golman/Nature Picture Library; Herman Eisenbeiss/Science Source; Dieter Hopf/AGE Fotostock; M.I. Walker/Science Source; Peter B. Armstrong; R. Gino Santa Maria/Shutterstock; Graham Kent/Pearson Science; Dr. Yorgos Nikas/Science Source; akg-images/Newscom; NIBSC/Science Source; Eric Isselee/Shutterstock; Repligen Corporation; Peter Scoones/Science Source; David Kjaer/Nature Picture Library; Stephen Dalton/Science Source; Eric V. Grave/Science Source; Phil Dotson/Science Source; Reinhard Dirscherl/Getty Images; David Tlipling/Nature Picture Library; Eric Isselee/Shutterstock; Markus Varesvuo/Nature Picture Library; F Rauschenbach/F1 ONLINE/SuperStock; Ingram Publishing/Photolibrary Royalty Free; Chris Bjornberg/Science Source; Mike Wilkes/Nature Picture Library; Tier Images/Getty Images; D. Phillips/Science Source; Mike Kemp/RubberBall/Alamy; Dave Watts/NHPA/Science Source; Eric J. Simon; Carlyn Iverson/Science Source; MShieldsPhotos/Alamy; Eric Isselee/Shutterstock; Image Quest Marine; Roy Corral/Corbis; BERNARD CASTELEIN/Nature Picture Library; Roger Kirkpatrick/Image Quest Marine.

Unit Openers: Unit 1 SPL/Science Source. **Unit 2** Andrew Syred/Science Source. **Unit 3** Nick Garbutt/Nature Picture Library. **Unit 4** Vaughan Fleming/Science Source. **Unit 5** J & C Sohns/AGE Fotostock. **Unit 6** AVTG/Getty Images. **Unit 7** Paul Lawrence/AGE Fotostock America Inc.

Chapter 1: Chapter Opener Jared Hobbs/AGE Fotostock. **p. 1 top to bottom** ImageState Media Partners Limited; Sacha Vignieri; Sacha Vignieri; Pascal Goetgheluck/Science Source. **1.1.1** ImageState Media Partners Limited. **1.1.2** Werner Bollmann/AGE Fotostock. **1.1.3** WILDLIFE GmbH/Alamy. **1.1.4** ekawatchaow/Shutterstock. **1.1.5** Fabio Pupin/FLPA. **1.1.6** Kim Taylor and Jane Burton/DK Images. **1.1.7** Fabio Pupin/FLPA. **1.2 top to bottom** worker/Shutterstock; Universal Images Group/Super Stock; Tsolo T. Tsolo/RGB Ventures LLC dba SuperStock/Alamy; Bildagentur-online/McPhoto/Alamy. **1.3 left** Steve Gschmeissner/Science Source. **1.3 right** CNRI/Science Source. **1.4** Ron Erwin/AGE Fotostock. **1.6 top left** Eye of Science/Science Source. **1.6 top right** Eye of Science/Science Source. **1.6 center left** Dr. D. P. Wilson/Science Source. **1.6 center right** Florapix/Alamy. **1.6 bottom left** FLPA/Alamy. **1.6 bottom right** Michael & Patricia Fogden/CORBIS. **1.7A** Francois Gohier/Science Source/Science Source. **1.7B** Science Source. **1.7C top** zhaoyan/Shutterstock. **1.7C center** Uri Golman/Nature Picture Library. **1.7C bottom** Volodymyr Goinyk/Shutterstock. **1.9 left** Sacha Vignieri. **1.9 left inset** Sacha Vignieri. **1.9 right** Hopi Hoekstra, Harvard University. **1.9 right inset** Shawn P. Carey, Migration Productions. **1.10** Pascal Goetgheluck/Science Source. **p. 13** Ron Erwin/AGE Fotostock.

Chapter 2: Chapter Opener Mark Conlin/V&W/imagequestmarine.com. **2.1 left** Chip Clark. **2.1 center** Pearson Education/Pearson Science. **2.1 right** Pearson Education/Pearson Science. **2.2A** Alison Wright/Science Source. **2.2B** Anton Prado/Alamy. **2.4A** Will & Deni McIntyre/Science Source. **2.4B** Chester A. Mathis. **2.7B** Pearson Education/Pearson Science. **2.10** Herman Eisenbeiss/Science Source. **2.11** Joe Fox/Alamy. **2.12** thp73/istockphoto. **2.14 top to bottom** Jakub Semeniuk/istockphoto; VR Photos/Shutterstock; Beth Van Trees/Shutterstock. **2.15B** Reinhard Dirscherl/Alamy.

Chapter 3: Chapter Opener Kay Blaschke/Getty Images. **p. 33** Dougal Waters/Getty Images. **3.2 left** Miki Verebes/Shutterstock. **3.2 right** Herbert Kratky/istockphoto. **3.4A** Dougal Waters/Getty Images. **3.6** Kristin Piljay/Pearson Science. **3.7 clockwise from top left** Dougal Waters/Getty Images; Biophoto Associates/Science Source; Dr. Lloyd M. Beidler; Biophoto Associates/Science Source. **3.8C clockwise from top left** Stargazer/

Shutterstock; Angel Simon/Shutterstock; Alex Staroseltsev/Shutterstock; Thomas M Perkins/Shutterstock. **Table 3.9** Lilyana Vynogradova/Shutterstock. **p. 42** Anetta/Shutterstock. **3.12C** Dieter Hopf/AGE Fotostock. **3.17** Serge de Sazo/Science Source.

Chapter 4: Chapter Opener Dr. Torsten Wittmann/Science Source. **p. 51 top to bottom** M.I. Walker/Science Source; Dr. Mary Osborn. **4.1A** Michael Abbey/Science Source. **4.1B** Andrew Syred/Science Source. **4.1C** Dr. Klaus Boller/Science Source. **4.1D** M.I. Walker/Science Source. **4.3** Dr. Linda M. Stannard, University of Cape Town/Science Source. **4.5** David M. Phillips/Science Source. **4.6** Joseph F. Gennaro Jr./Science Source. **4.8A** Don W. Fawcett/Science Source. **4.9** Biophoto Associates/Science Source. **4.11A** Roland Birke/Getty Images. **4.11B** Biophoto Associates/Science Source. **4.13** Don W. Fawcett/Science Source. **4.16 left** Dr. Frank Solomon. **4.16 center** Mark Ladinsky. **4.16 right** Dr. Mary Osborn. **4.17** Dr. Alexey Khodjakov/Science Source. **4.18A** SPL/Science Source. **4.18B** Eye of Science/Science Source. **4.18C** Bjorn Afzelius.

Chapter 5: Chapter Opener B.L. de Groot. **5.2** Peter B. Armstrong. **5.16** Krista Kennell/Newscom.

Chapter 6: Chapter Opener Stephen Marks/Getty Images **p. 89 top to bottom** R. Gino Santa Maria/Shutterstock; StockLite/Shutterstock; GoodOlga/AGE Fotostock. **6.2** UpperCut Images/Alamy. **6.4** R. Gino Santa Maria/Shutterstock. **6.13C top** StockLite/Shutterstock. **6.13C bottom** Sean Lower/Marty Taylor. **6.15** Simon Smith/DK Images. **6.16** GoodOlga/AGE Fotostock.

Chapter 7: Chapter Opener John Burke/Getty Images. **p. 107 top to bottom** rodho/Shutterstock; ImageDJ/Jupiter Images. **7.1A** ODM/Shutterstock. **7.1B** Mark Conlin/Alamy. **7.1C** Susan M. Barns, Ph.D. **7.2 top to bottom** rodho/Shutterstock; Graham Kent/Pearson Science; Dr. Jeremy Burgess/Science Source. **7.3** Martin Shields/Alamy. **7.6B** llaszlo/Shutterstock. **7.7A** Christine Case. **7.11 bottom left** Dinodia/Pixtal/AGE Fotostock. **7.11 bottom right** ImageDJ/Jupiter Images. **7.13A** Prof. William H. Schlesinger. **7.14A** NASA. **7.14B** National Oceanic and Atmospheric Administration (NOAA).

Chapter 8: Chapter Opener Steve Gschmeissner/Science Source. **p. 125 top to bottom** Dr. Yorgos Nikas/Science Source; Michelle Gilders/Alamy. **8.1A** London School of Hygiene & Tropical Medicine/Science Source. **8.1B** Roger Steene/Image Quest Marine. **8.1C** Eric J. Simon. **8.1D** Bob Thomas/Getty Images. **8.1E** Dr. Yorgos Nikas/Science Source. **8.1F** Dr. Torsten Wittmann/Science Source. **8.2B** Lee D. Simon/Science Source. **8.3A** Dr. Andrew S. Bajer, University of Oregon. **8.3B** Biophoto Associates/Science Source. **8.5, p. 130 left** Conly L. Rieder, Ph.D. **8.5, p. 130 center** Conly L. Rieder, Ph.D. **8.5, p. 130 right** Conly L. Rieder, Ph.D. **8.5, p. 131 left** Conly L. Rieder, Ph.D. **8.5, p. 131 center** Conly L. Rieder, Ph.D. **8.5, p. 131 right** Conly L. Rieder, Ph.D. **8.6A** Don W. Fawcett/Science Source. **8.6B** Eldon H. Newcomb. **8.12A** Ron Chapple/Alamy. **p. 139** Ed Reschke/Getty Images. **8.16 top** F. Schussler/PhotoDisc/Getty Images, Inc. **8.16 bottom** Roxana Gonzalez/Shutterstock. **8.17A** Mark Petronczki. **8.19 left** Véronique Burger/Science Source. **8.19 right** CNRI/Science Source. **8.20A left** SPL/Science Source. **8.20A right** Lawrence Shear/Science Source. **8.22** Michelle Gilders/Alamy. **p. 151** J.L. Carson/Custom Medical Stock Photo.

Chapter 9: Chapter Opener David Pickford/Robert Harding. **p. 153 top to bottom** akg-images/Newscom; Eric J. Simon; Andrew Syred/Science Source. **9.1** bilwissedition Ltd. & Co. KG/Alamy. **9.2A** akg-images/Newscom. **9.8 left** PhotoDisc/Getty Images, Inc. **9.8 right** PhotoDisc/Getty Images, Inc. **9.9 top left** Liza McCorkle/iStockphoto. **9.9 top right** Westend61/Getty Images. **9.9 bottom left** Shell114/Shutterstock. **9.9 bottom right** David Terrazas Morales/Getty Images. **9.9C** Michael Ciesielski Photography. **9.10A** CNRI/Science Source. **9.10B top** Gusto/Science

Source. **9.10B bottom** Eric J. Simon. **9.13A** Eye of Science/Science Source. **9.13B** Eye of Science/Science Source. **9.15A** Eric J. Simon. **9.15B** Eric J. Simon. **9.18B** Graphic Science/Alamy. **9.20A** Andrew Syred/Science Source. **9.20B clockwise from top left** Jose Luis Pelaez, Inc./Getty Images; Yuri Arcurs/Shutterstock; Rubberball/Nicole Hill/Getty Images; Anatoliy Samara/Shutterstock. **Table 9.20 top** Tomasz Zachariasz/iStockphoto. **Table 9.20 center** kosam/Shutterstock. **Table 9.20 bottom** Tomasz Zachariasz/iStockphoto. **9.21A left** University of Texas MD Anderson Cancer Center. **9.21A right** University of Texas MD Anderson Cancer Center. **9.22** FPG/Getty Images.

Chapter 10: Chapter Opener Dr. Klaus Boller/Science Source. **10.1A** Biophoto Associates/Science Source. **10.3A left** Library of Congress. **10.3A right** Cold Spring Harbor Laboratory Archives. **10.3B** National Institutes of Health. **10.6B** Kevin McCluskey, PhD. **10.8C** Yonhap Choi Byung-kil/AP Images. **10.12** Joachim Frank. **p. 201** Hazel Appleton, Centre for Infections/Health Protection Agency/Science Source/Science Source. **10.19 left** NIBSC/Science Source. **10.19 right** Liu Siu Wai/Newscom. **10.23C left** Huntington Potter. **10.23C right** Huntington Potter.

Chapter 11: Chapter Opener dirtlight photography/Getty Images. **p. 209 top to bottom** Martin Oeggerli/Science Source; Robyn Mackenzie/Shutterstock. **11.1A** Martin Oeggerli/Science Source. **11.2A left** Don W. Fawcett/Science Source. **11.2A right** Biophoto Associates/Science Source. **11.2B** Eric Isselee/Shutterstock. **11.8A left** F. Rudolf Turner. **11.8A right** F. Rudolf Turner. **11.9** Alila Medical Images/Shutterstock. **11.12** Robyn Mackenzie/Shutterstock. **11.16A** GeoM/Shutterstock.

Chapter 12: Chapter Opener Efired/Shutterstock. **p. 231 top to bottom** Pichi Chuang/Thomson Reuters; Hank Morgan/Science Source; Steve Helber/AP Photo; Philippe Plailly & Atelier Daynes/Science Source. **12.1A** Pichi Chuang/Thomson Reuters. **12.1B top to bottom** Smileus/Dreamstime LLC; A.J. Sisco/UPI/Newscom; Kedrov/Shutterstock; Angel Hell/iStockphoto. **12.6A left** Brad DeCecco Photography. **12.6A right** Brad DeCecco Photography. **12.6B** Science Source. **12.7A** Eli Lilly and Company. **12.7B** Hank Morgan/Science Source. **12.8A** Vladimir Nikitin/Shutterstock. **12.8B** Patti McConville/Alamy. **12.9 left** Borys Shevchuk/Fotolia. **12.9 center** Kirill Kurashov/Shutterstock. **12.9 right** Dionisvera/Shutterstock. **12.10** Phil Date/Shutterstock. **12.13** Repligen Corporation. **12.15A** Steve Helber/AP Photo. **12.15B** Michael Stephens/Agence France Presse/Newscom. **Table 12.17 top to bottom** Olivia Meckes/Nicole Ottawa/Science Source/Science Source; Vaclav Volrab/Shutterstock; Andrew Burgess/Shutterstock; Gary Ombler/DK Images. **12.19** Rubberball/Getty Images, Inc. **12.21** Philippe Plailly & Atelier Daynes/Science Source.

Chapter 13: Chapter Opener GHANA-VACCINES/GAVI/Olivier Asselin/Handout/REUTERS. **p. 255 top to bottom** Archiv/Science Source; Steffen Foerster/Shutterstock. **13.1A left** Archiv/Science Source. **13.1A right** National Maritime Museum Picture Library. **13.1B** Peter Scoones/Science Source. **13.1C** Stefan Huwiler/Corbis. **13.2A** Colin Keates/DK Images. **13.2B** Chip Clark/Fundamental Photographs, NYC. **13.2C** John Henshall/Alamy. **13.3A** Miles Away Photography/Shutterstock. **13.4B left** Dr. Keith Wheeler/Science Source. **13.4B right** Scanpix Sweden AB. **13.6 top left** H Reinhard/Arco Images GmbH/Alamy. **13.6 top right** ZUMA Press, Inc./Alamy. **13.6 center** Luis César Tejo/Shutterstock. **13.6 bottom left** Kenneth W. Fink/Science Source. **13.6 bottom right** Juniors Bildarchiv/GmbH/Alamy. **13.7** Spirit/Corbis. **13.8** Edmund D. Brodie III. **13.9** Adam Jones/The Image Bank/Getty Images. **13.11** Anne Dowie/Pearson Education. **13.12B** William Ervin/Science Source. **13.13** Steffen Foerster/Shutterstock. **13.15A** Dave Blackey/Getty Images. **13.15B** George D. Lepp/Encyclopedia/Corbis. **13.15C** Barry Mansell/Nature Picture Library. **13.16** Scott Camazine/Science Source.

Chapter 14: Chapter Opener Tim Laman/Nature Picture Library. **p. 277** Jared Hobbs/All Canada Photos/SuperStock. **14.2A left** Malcom Schuyl/Alamy. **14.2A right** David Kjaer/Nature Picture Library **14.2B left to right** Robert Kneschke/iStockphoto; Justin Horrocks/iStockphoto; PhotoDisc/Getty Images, Inc.; Radius Images/Getty Images; Phil Date/Shutterstock; Masterfile Corporation. **14.2C top to bottom** Boris Karpinski/Alamy; janprchal/Shutterstock; Troy Maben/AP Photo. **14.3, p. 280 1st column** Joe McDonald/Photoshot Holdings Ltd.; Joe McDonald/Corbis. **14.3, p. 280 2nd column** USDA/APHIS Animal and Plant Health Inspection Service; Jared Hobbs/All Canada Photos/SuperStock. **14.3, p. 280 3rd column** J & C Sohns/AGE Fotostock America, Inc.; Tier und Naturfotografie/SuperStock. **14.3, p. 280 4th column** Philippe Clement/Nature Picture Library; Oyvind Martinsen/Alamy. **14.3, p. 281 1st column** SERDAR/Alamy; SERDAR/Alamy. **14.3, p. 281 2nd column** Charles W. Brown; DawnYL/Fotolia; Kazutoshi Okuno. **14.4A left** John Shaw/Photoshot. **14.4A center** Corbis. **14.4A right** Michael Fogden/Photoshot. **14.4B shrimp** Arthur Anker/Florida Museum of Natural History. **14.4B map** NASA Earth Observing System. **14.5B clockwise from top left** Douglas W. Schemske; Douglas W. Schemske; Douglas W. Schemske; Douglas W. Schemske. **14.7** photobank.kiev.ua/Shutterstock. **14.8 top to bottom** INTERFOTO/Alamy Images; INTERFOTO/Alamy Images; Mary Plage/Getty Images; Mary Plage/Getty Images; Ralph Lee Hopkins/Alamy; Ralph Lee Hopkins/Alamy. **14.9B top** Ole Seehausen. **14.9B bottom** Ole Seehausen. **14.10B left** Melvin Grey/Photoshot. **14.10B right** Juan Martin Simon. **14.10C** Seehausen, Ole. **p. 290** Seehausen, Ole.

Chapter 15: Chapter Opener Alfred & Annaliese Tr/AGE Fotostock America, Inc. **15.1 left** Francois Gohier/Science Source. **15.1 right** Peter Sawyer/Smithsonian Institution–Museum of Natural History. **15.3A** Fred M. Menger. **15.7D** Roland Seitre/Nature Picture Library. **15.7E** Phil Savoie/Nature Picture Library. **15.7F** Rick & Nora Bowers/Alamy. **15.8** David Parker/Science Source. **15.11A** Stephen Dalton/Science Source. **15.11B** Jean Kern. **15.11C top** Dr. William A. Cresko. **15.11C bottom** Dr. William A. Cresko. **15.12 left to right** Hal Beral/V & W/Image Quest Marine; Christophe Courteau/Science Source; Reinhard Dirscherl/Alamy; Jim Greenfield/Image Quest Marine; James Watt/ImageQuestMarine. **15.1A** Getty Images, Inc. **15.16C** American Museum of Natural History. **15.18** Frank Collins, Ph.D./CDC.

Chapter 16: Chapter Opener CAMR/A. Barry Dowsett/Science Source. **p. 319 top to bottom** SPL/Science Source; David Caron/Science Source. **16.1** SPL/Science Source. **16.2A left** Eye of Science/Science Source. **16.2A center** David McCarthy/Science Source. **16.2A right** Stem Jems/Science Source. **16.2B** ASM/Science Source. **16.2C** I. Rantala/Science Source. **16.2D** Eye of Science/Science Source. **16.3A** Huntington Potter. **16.3B** Scott Camazine/Science Source. **16.4 top left** Sinclair Stammers/Science Source. **16.4 top right** T. Stevens & P. McKinely, PNNL/Science Source. **16.4 bottom left** Pasieka/SPL/Science Source. **16.4 bottom right** Dr. Gary Gaugler/Science Source. **16.5** Garry Palmateer. **16.6A** Science Source. **16.6B** SIPA USA/SIPA Newscom. **16.7 top** Olive Meckes/Nicole Ottawa/Science Source/Science Source. **16.7 bottom** Eye of Science/Science Source/Science Source. **16.8A left** Jack Dykinga/Getty Images. **16.8A right** Jim West/Alamy. **16.9A** National Library of Medicine. **16.9B** Eye of Science/Science Source. **16.9C** Susan M. Barns, Ph.D. **16.9D** Moredon Animal Health/SPL/Science Source. **16.9E** Science Source. **16.10A** David M. Phillips/Science Source. **16.10B** STEVE LINDRIDGE/Alamy. **16.11A** Anders Wiklund/Reuters Limited. **16.12A left** Carol Buchanan/AGE Fotostock. **16.12A center** Eye of Science/Science Source. **16.12A right** Alex Rakosy/Custom Medical Stock Photo. **16.12B left** Patrick Keeling. **16.12B right** Eric V. Grave/Science Source. **16.14A** Steve Gschmeissner/Science Source. **16.14B** Georgie Holland/AGE Fotostock. **16.14C** Fred Rhoades. **16.14D** Miriam Godfrey/National Institute of Water and Atmospheric Research. **16.14E** Andrew Syred/Science Source. **16.14F** David Caron/Science Source. **16.14F inset** Dee Breger/Photo Researchers. **16.14G** Steve Gschmeissner/Science Source. **16.15** Photoshot/Newscom. **16.16A** David M. Phillips/Science Source. **16.16B** Oliver Meckes/Science Source. **16.17A** Biophoto Associates/Science Source. **16.17B** Dr. George L. Barron. **16.17B inset** Ray Simons/Science Source. **16.17C** Robert Kay. **16.18A** Alex Hyde/Nature Picture Library. **16.18B left** Manfred Kage/Science Source. **16.18B right** Aaron J. Bell/Science Source. **16.18C** D. P. Wilson/Eric and David Hosking/Science Source. **16.19B** David J. Patterson. **p. 338 left** David M. Phillips/Science Source. **p. 338 right** Dr. Gary Gaugler/Science Source.

Illustration and Text Credits

Chapter 2: 2.15A Adaptation of figure 5 from "Effect of Calcium Carbonate Saturation State on the Calcification Rate of an Experimental Coral

Reef" by C. Langdon, et al., from *Global Biogeochemical Cycles* (June 2000): 14(2). Copyright © 2000 by American Geophysical Union. Reprinted with permission of Wiley Inc.

Chapter 4: 4.2B Figure adapted from *The World of the Cell*, 3rd ed., by Wayne M. Becker, Jane B. Reece and Wayne F. Poenie. Copyright © 1996 by Pearson Education, Inc. Adapted and electronically reproduced by permission of Pearson Education, Inc., Upper Saddle River, New Jersey.

Chapter 5: 5.7 Adaptation of Figure 2A from "Appearance of Water Channels in *Xenopus* Oocytes Expressing Red Cell CHIP28 Protein" by Gregory Preston et al., from *Science* (April 1992): 256(5055). Copyright © 1992 by AAAS. Reprinted with permission.

Chapter 7: 7.13B Adaptation of Figure 1A from "Biomass and Toxicity Responses of Poison Ivy (*Toxicodendron radicans*) to Elevated Atmospheric CO_2" by Jacqueline E. Mohan, et al., from *PNAS* (June 2006): 103(24). Copyright © 2006 by National Academy of Sciences. Reprinted with permission.

Chapter 16: 16.6A Figure adapted from *Microbiology: An Introduction*, 9th ed., by Gerard J. Tortora, Berdell R. Funke, and Christine L. Case. Copyright © 2007 by Pearson Education, Inc. Adapted and electronically reproduced by permission of Pearson Education, Inc., Upper Saddle River, New Jersey. **p. 339** Source: U.S. Food and Drug Administration website, 2013.

APPENDIX 5

Glossary

A

A site One of two of a ribosome's binding sites for tRNA during translation. The A site holds the tRNA that carries the next amino acid in the polypeptide chain. (A stands for aminoacyl tRNA.)

abiotic factor (ā´-bī-ot´-ik) A nonliving component of an ecosystem, such as air, water, or temperature.

abiotic reservoir (ā´-bī-ot´-ik) The part of an ecosystem where a chemical, such as carbon or nitrogen, accumulates or is stockpiled outside of living organisms.

ABO blood groups Genetically determined classes of human blood that are based on the presence or absence of carbohydrates A and B on the surface of red blood cells. The ABO blood group phenotypes, also called blood types, are A, B, AB, and O.

abscisic acid (ABA) (ab-sis´-ik) A plant hormone that inhibits cell division, promotes dormancy, and interacts with gibberellins in regulating seed germination.

absorption The uptake of small nutrient molecules by an organism's own body; the third main stage of food processing, following digestion.

acetyl CoA (a-sē´-til kō´-ā´) (acetyl coenzyme A) The entry compound for the citric acid cycle in cellular respiration; formed from a two-carbon fragment of pyruvate attached to a coenzyme.

acetylcholine (a-sē´-til-kō´-lēn) A nitrogen-containing neurotransmitter. Among other effects, it slows the heart rate and makes skeletal muscles contract.

acid A substance that increases the hydrogen ion (H^+) concentration in a solution.

acrosome (ak´-ruh-som) A membrane-enclosed sac at the tip of a sperm. The acrosome contains enzymes that help the sperm penetrate an egg.

actin A globular protein that links into chains, two of which twist helically around each other, forming microfilaments in muscle cells.

action potential A change in membrane voltage that transmits a nerve signal along an axon.

activation energy The amount of energy that reactants must absorb before a chemical reaction will start.

activator A protein that switches on a gene or group of genes.

active immunity Immunity conferred by recovering from an infectious disease or by receiving a vaccine.

active site The part of an enzyme where a substrate molecule attaches; typically, a pocket or groove on the enzyme's surface.

active transport The movement of a substance across a biological membrane against its concentration gradient, aided by specific transport proteins and requiring an input of energy (often as ATP).

adaptation An inherited character that enhances an organism's ability to survive and reproduce in a particular environment.

adaptive immunity A vertebrate-specific defense that is activated only after exposure to an antigen and is mediated by lymphocytes. It exhibits specificity, memory, and self-nonself recognition. Also called acquired immunity.

adaptive radiation Period of evolutionary change in which groups of organisms form many new species whose adaptations allow them to fill new or vacant ecological roles in their communities.

adenine (A) (ad´-uh-nēn) A double-ring nitrogenous base found in DNA and RNA.

adhesion The attraction between different kinds of molecules.

adipose tissue A type of connective tissue whose cells contain fat.

adrenal cortex (uh-drē´-nul) The outer portion of an adrenal gland, controlled by ACTH from the anterior pituitary; secretes hormones called glucocorticoids and mineralocorticoids.

adrenal gland (uh-drē´-nul) One of a pair of endocrine glands, located atop each kidney in mammals, composed of an outer cortex and a central medulla.

adrenal medulla (uh-drē´-nul muh-dul´-uh) The central portion of an adrenal gland, controlled by nerve signals; secretes the fight-or-flight hormones epinephrine and norepinephrine.

adrenocorticotropic hormone (ACTH) (uh-drē´-nō-cōr´-ti-kō-trop´-ik) A protein hormone secreted by the anterior pituitary that stimulates the adrenal cortex to secrete corticosteroids.

adult stem cell A cell present in adult tissues that generates replacements for nondividing differentiated cells. Adult stem cells are capable of differentiating into multiple cell types, but they are not as developmentally flexible as embryonic stem cells.

age structure The relative number of individuals of each age in a population.

agonistic behavior (a´-gō-nis´-tik) Confrontational behavior involving a contest waged by threats, displays, or actual combat that settles disputes over limited resources, such as food or mates.

AIDS (acquired immunodeficiency syndrome) The late stages of HIV infection, characterized by a reduced number of T cells and the appearance of characteristic opportunistic infections.

alcohol fermentation Glycolysis followed by the reduction of pyruvate to ethyl alcohol, regenerating NAD^+ and releasing carbon dioxide.

alga (al´-guh) (plural, **algae**) A protist that produces its food by photosynthesis.

alimentary canal (al´-uh-men´-tuh-rē) A complete digestive tract consisting of a tube running between a mouth and an anus.

allantois (al´-an-tō´-is) In animals, an extraembryonic membrane that develops from the yolk sac. The allantois helps dispose of the embryo's nitrogenous wastes and forms part of the umbilical cord in mammals.

allele (uh-lē´-ul) An alternative version of a gene.

allergen (al´-er-jen) An antigen that causes an allergy.

allergy A disorder of the immune system caused by an abnormally high sensitivity to an antigen. Symptoms are triggered by histamines released from mast cells.

allopatric speciation The formation of new species in populations that are geographically isolated from one another.

alternation of generations A life cycle in which there is both a multicellular diploid form, the sporophyte, and a multicellular haploid form, the gametophyte; a characteristic of plants and multicellular green algae.

alternative RNA splicing A type of regulation at the RNA-processing level in which different mRNA molecules are produced from the same primary transcript, depending on which RNA segments are treated as exons and which as introns.

altruism (al´-trū-iz-um) Behavior that reduces an individual's fitness while increasing the fitness of another individual.

Alveolata (al-vē´-uh-let-uh) A clade of the SAR supergroup of protists that includes dinoflagellates, ciliates, and certain parasites.

alveolus (al-vē´-oh-lus) (plural, **alveoli**) One of the dead-end air sacs within the mammalian lung where gas exchange occurs.

Alzheimer's disease (AD) An age-related dementia (mental deterioration) characterized by confusion, memory loss, and other symptoms.

amino acid (uh-mēn´-ō) An organic molecule containing a carboxyl group and an amino group; serves as the monomer of proteins.

amino group (uh-mēn´-ō) A chemical group consisting of a nitrogen atom bonded to two hydrogen atoms.

ammonia NH_3; A small and very toxic nitrogenous waste produced by metabolism.

amniocentesis (am´-nē-ō-sen-tē´-sis) A technique for diagnosing genetic defects while a fetus is in the uterus. A sample of amniotic fluid, obtained by a needle inserted into the uterus, is analyzed for telltale chemicals and defective fetal cells.

amnion (am´-nē-on) In vertebrate animals, the extraembryonic membrane that encloses the fluid-filled amniotic sac containing the embryo.

amniote Member of a clade of tetrapods that have an amniotic egg containing specialized membranes that protect the embryo. Amniotes include mammals and birds and other reptiles.

amniotic egg (am´-nē-ot´-ik) A shelled egg in which an embryo develops within a fluid-filled amniotic sac and is nourished by yolk. Produced by reptiles (including birds) and egg-laying mammals, the amniotic egg enables them to complete their life cycles on dry land.

amoeba (uh-mē´-buh) A general term for a protist that moves and feeds by means of pseudopodia.

amoebocyte (uh-mē´-buh-sīt) An amoeba-like cell that moves by pseudopodia and is found in most animals; depending on the species, may digest and distribute food, dispose of wastes, form skeletal fibers, fight infections, and change into other cell types.

amoebozoan A member of a clade of protists in the supergroup Unikonta that includes amoebas and slime molds and is characterized by lobe-shaped pseudopodia.

amphibian Member of a clade of tetrapods that includes frogs, toads, salamanders, and caecilians.

amygdala (uh-mig´-duh-la) An integrative center of the cerebrum; functionally, the part of the limbic system that seems central in recognizing the emotional content of facial expressions and laying down emotional memories.

anabolic steroid (an´-uh-bol´-ik ster´-oyd) A synthetic variant of the male hormone testosterone that mimics some of its effects.

analogy The similarity between two species that is due to convergent evolution rather than to descent from a common ancestor with the same trait.

anaphase The fourth stage of mitosis, beginning when sister chromatids separate from each other and ending when a complete set of daughter chromosomes arrives at each of the two poles of the cell.

anatomy The study of the structures of an organism.

anchorage dependence The requirement that to divide, a cell must be attached to a solid surface.

androgen (an´-drō-jen) A steroid sex hormone secreted by the gonads that promotes the development and maintenance of the male reproductive system and male body features.

anemia (uh-nē´-me-ah) A condition in which an abnormally low amount of hemoglobin or a low number of red blood cells results in the body cells receiving too little oxygen.

angiosperm (an´-jē-ō-sperm) A flowering plant, which forms seeds inside a protective chamber called an ovary.

annelid (uh-nel´-id) A segmented worm. Annelids include earthworms, polychaetes, and leeches.

annual A plant that completes its life cycle in a single year or growing season.

antagonistic hormones Two hormones that have opposite effects.

anterior Pertaining to the front, or head, of a bilaterally symmetric animal.

anterior pituitary (puh-tū´-uh-tār-ē) An endocrine gland, adjacent to the hypothalamus and the posterior pituitary, that synthesizes several hormones, including some that control the activity of other endocrine glands.

anther A sac located at the tip of a flower's stamen; contains male sporangia in which meiosis occurs to produce spores that form the male gametophytes, or pollen grains.

anthropoid (an´-thruh-poyd) A member of a primate group made up of the apes (gibbons, orangutans, gorillas, chimpanzees, bonobos, and humans) and monkeys.

antibody (an´-tih-bod´-ē) A protein dissolved in blood plasma that attaches to a specific kind of antigen and helps counter its effects; secreted by plasma cells.

anticodon (an´-tī-kō´-don) On a tRNA molecule, a specific sequence of three nucleotides that is complementary to a codon triplet on mRNA.

antidiuretic hormone (ADH) (an´-tē-dī´-yū-ret´-ik) A hormone made by the hypothalamus and secreted by the posterior pituitary that promotes water retention by the kidneys.

antigen (an´-tuh-jen) A foreign (nonself) molecule that elicits an adaptive immune response.

antigen receptor (an´-tuh-jen) The general term for a surface protein, located on B cells and T cells, that binds to antigens and initiates the adaptive immune response.

antigen-binding site (an´-tuh-jen) A region of the antigen receptor or antibody that binds the antigenic determinant on the antigen.

antigenic determinant (an´-tuh-jen´-ik) A small region on the surface of an antigen molecule to which an antigen receptor or antibody binds; also called an epitope.

antigen-presenting cell (APC) (an´-tuh-jen) One of a family of white blood cells that ingests a foreign substance or a microbe and attaches antigenic portions of the ingested material to its own surface, thereby displaying the antigens to a helper T cell.

antihistamine (an´-tē-his´-tuh-mēn) A drug that interferes with the action of histamine, providing relief from an allergic reaction.

anus The opening through which undigested materials are expelled.

aorta (ā-or´-tuh) A large artery that conveys blood directly from the left ventricle of the heart to other arteries.

aphotic zone (ā-fō´-tik) The region of an aquatic ecosystem beneath the photic zone, where light does not penetrate enough for photosynthesis to take place.

apical dominance (ā´-pik-ul) In a plant, the hormonal inhibition of axillary buds by a terminal bud.

apical meristem (ā´-pik-ul mer´-uh-stem) A growth-producing region of cell division consisting of undifferentiated cells located at the tip of a plant root or in the terminal or axillary bud of a shoot.

apoptosis (ā-puh-tō´-sus) The timely and tidy suicide of cells; also called programmed cell death.

appendicular skeleton (ap´-en-dik´-yū-ler) Components of the skeletal system that support the fins of a fish or the arms and legs of a land vertebrate; in land vertebrates, the cartilage and bones of the shoulder girdle, pelvic girdle, forelimbs, and hind limbs. *See also* axial skeleton.

appendix (uh-pen´-dix) A small, finger-like extension of the vertebrate cecum; contains a mass of white blood cells that contribute to immunity.

aquaporin A transport protein in the plasma membrane of an animal, plant, or microorganism cell that facilitates the diffusion of water across the membrane (osmosis).

aqueous humor (ā´-kwē-us hyū´-mer) Plasma-like liquid in the space between the lens and the cornea in the vertebrate eye; helps maintain the shape of the eye, supplies nutrients and oxygen to its tissues, and disposes of its wastes.

aqueous solution (ā´-kwē-us) A solution in which water is the solvent.

arachnid A member of a major arthropod group (chelicerates) that includes spiders, scorpions, ticks, and mites.

Archaea (ar´-kē-uh) One of two prokaryotic domains of life, the other being Bacteria.

Archaeplastida One of four monophyletic supergroups proposed in a current hypothesis of the evolutionary history of eukaryotes. The other four supergroups are SAR (Stramenopila, Alveolata, and Rhizaria), Excavata, and Unikonta.

arteriole (ar-ter´-ē-ōl) A vessel that conveys blood between an artery and a capillary bed.

artery A vessel that carries blood away from the heart to other parts of the body.

arthropod (ar´-thrō-pod) A member of the most diverse phylum in the animal kingdom. Arthropods include the horseshoe crab, arachnids (for example, spiders, ticks, scorpions, and mites), crustaceans (for example, crayfish, lobsters, crabs, and barnacles), millipedes, centipedes, and insects. Arthropods are characterized by a chitinous exoskeleton, molting, jointed appendages, and a body formed of distinct groups of segments.

artificial selection The selective breeding of domesticated plants and animals to promote the occurrence of desirable traits.

ascomycete (as´-kuh-mī´-sēt) Member of a group of fungi characterized by saclike structures called asci that produce spores in sexual reproduction.

asexual reproduction The creation of genetically identical offspring by a single parent, without the participation of sperm and egg.

assisted reproductive technology Procedure that involves surgically removing eggs from a woman's ovaries, fertilizing them, and then returning them to the woman's body. *See also in vitro* fertilization.

association areas Sites of higher mental activities, making up most of the cerebral cortex.

associative learning The ability to associate one environmental feature with another. In one type of associative learning, the animal learns to link a particular stimulus with a particular outcome. Trial-and-error learning is also a type of associative learning.

astigmatism (uh-stig´-muh-tizm) Blurred vision caused by a misshapen lens or cornea.

atherosclerosis (ath´-uh-rō´-skluh-rō´-sis) A cardiovascular disease in which fatty deposits called plaques develop on the inner walls of the arteries, narrowing their inner diameters.

atom The smallest unit of matter that retains the properties of an element.

atomic mass The total mass of an atom; also called atomic weight. Given as a whole number, the atomic mass approximately equals the mass number.

atomic number The number of protons in each atom of a particular element.

ATP Adenosine triphosphate, the main energy source for cells. ATP releases energy when its phosphate bonds are hydrolyzed.

ATP synthase A cluster of several membrane proteins that function in chemiosmosis with adjacent electron transport chains, using the energy of a hydrogen ion concentration gradient to make ATP.

atrium (ā´-trē-um) (plural, **atria**) A heart chamber that receives blood from the veins.

auditory canal Part of the vertebrate outer ear that channels sound waves from the pinna or outer body surface to the eardrum.

autoimmune disorder An immunological disorder in which the immune system attacks the body's own molecules.

autonomic nervous system (ot´-ō-nom´-ik) The component of the vertebrate peripheral nervous system that regulates the internal environment; made up of sympathetic and parasympathetic subdivisions. Most actions of the autonomic nervous system are involuntary.

autosome A chromosome not directly involved in determining the sex of an organism; in mammals, for example, any chromosome other than X or Y.

autotroph (ot´-ō-trōf) An organism that makes its own food (often by photosynthesis), thereby sustaining itself without eating other organisms or their molecules. Plants, algae, and numerous bacteria are autotrophs.

auxin (ok´-sin) A plant hormone (indoleacetic acid or a related compound) that promotes seedling elongation.

AV (atrioventricular) node A region of specialized heart muscle tissue between the left and right atria where electrical impulses are delayed for about 0.1 second before spreading to both ventricles and causing them to contract.

axial skeleton (ak´-sē-ul) Components of the skeletal system that support the central trunk of the body: the skull, backbone, and rib cage in a vertebrate. *See also* appendicular skeleton.

axillary bud (ak´-sil-ār-ē) An embryonic shoot present in the angle formed by a leaf and stem.

axon (ak´-son) A neuron extension that conducts signals to another neuron or to an effector cell. A neuron has one long axon.

B

B cell A type of lymphocyte that completes its development in the bone marrow and is responsible for the humoral immune response. Effector B cells are also called plasma cells.

bacillus (buh-sil´-us) (plural, **bacilli**) A rod-shaped prokaryotic cell.

Bacteria One of two prokaryotic domains of life, the other being Archaea.

bacteriophage (bak-tēr´-ē-ō-fāj) A virus that infects bacteria; also called a phage.

balancing selection Natural selection that maintains stable frequencies of two or more phenotypic forms in a population.

ball-and-socket joint A joint that allows rotation and movement in several planes. Examples in humans are the hip and shoulder joints.

bark All the tissues external to the vascular cambium in a plant that is growing in thickness. Bark is made up of secondary phloem, cork cambium, and cork.

Barr body A dense body formed from a deactivated X chromosome found in the nuclei of female mammalian cells.

basal metabolic rate (BMR) The number of kilocalories a resting animal requires to fuel its essential body processes for a given time.

basal nuclei (bā´-sul nū´-klē-ī) Clusters of nerve cell bodies located deep within the cerebrum that are important in motor coordination.

base A substance that decreases the hydrogen ion (H^+) concentration in a solution.

basidiomycete (buh-sid´-ē-ō-mī´sēt) Member of a group of fungi characterized by club-shaped, spore-producing structures called basidia.

basilar membrane The floor of the middle canal of the inner ear.

behavior Individually, an action carried out by the muscles or glands under control of the nervous system in response to a stimulus; collectively, the sum of an animal's responses to external and internal stimuli.

behavioral ecology The study of behavior in an evolutionary context.

benign tumor An abnormal mass of cells that remains at its original site in the body.

benthic realm A seafloor or the bottom of a freshwater lake, pond, river, or stream.

biennial A plant that completes its life cycle in two years.

bilateral symmetry An arrangement of body parts such that an organism can be divided equally by a single cut passing longitudinally through it. A bilaterally symmetric organism has mirror-image right and left sides.

bilaterian Member of the clade Bilateria, animals exhibiting bilateral symmetry.

bile A mixture of substances that is produced by the liver and stored in the gallbladder. Bile emulsifies fats and aids in their digestion.

binary fission A means of asexual reproduction in which a parent organism, often a single cell, divides into two genetically identical individuals of about equal size.

binomial A two-part, latinized name of a species; for example, *Homo sapiens.*

biodiversity The variety of living things; includes genetic diversity, species diversity, and ecosystem diversity.

biodiversity hot spot A small geographic area with an exceptional concentration of endangered and threatened species, especially endemic species (those found nowhere else).

biofilm A surface-coating colony of prokaryotes that engage in metabolic cooperation.

biogeochemical cycle Any of the various chemical circuits that involve both biotic and abiotic components of an ecosystem.

biogeography The study of the past and present distribution of organisms.

biological clock An internal timekeeper that controls an organism's biological rhythms, marking time with or without environmental cues but often requiring signals from the environment to remain tuned to an appropriate period. *See also* circadian rhythm.

biological control The intentional release of a natural enemy to attack a pest population.

biological magnification The accumulation of harmful chemicals that are retained in the living tissues of consumers in food chains.

biological species concept Definition of a species as a group of populations whose members have the potential to interbreed in nature and produce viable, fertile offspring but do not produce viable, fertile offspring with members of other such populations.

biology The scientific study of life.

biomass The amount, or mass, of organic material in an ecosystem.

biome (bī´-ōm) A major type of ecological association that occupies a broad geographic region of land or water and is characterized by organisms adapted to the particular environment.

bioremediation The use of living organisms to detoxify and restore polluted and degraded ecosystems.

biosphere The entire portion of Earth inhabited by life; the sum of all the planet's ecosystems.

biotechnology The manipulation of living organisms or their components to make useful products.

biotic factor (bī-o´-tik) A living component of a biological community; an organism, or a factor pertaining to one or more organisms.

bipolar disorder Depressive mental illness characterized by extreme mood swings; also called manic-depressive disorder.

birds Members of a clade of reptiles that have feathers and adaptations for flight.

bivalve A member of a group of molluscs that includes clams, mussels, scallops, and oysters.

blastocoel (blas´-tuh-sēl) In a developing animal, a central, fluid-filled cavity in a blastula.

blastocyst (blas´-tō-sist) A mammalian embryo (equivalent to an amphibian blastula) made up of a hollow ball of cells that results from cleavage and that implants in the mother's endometrium.

blastula (blas´-tyū-luh) An embryonic stage that marks the end of cleavage during animal development; a hollow ball of cells in many species.

blood A type of connective tissue with a fluid matrix called plasma in which red blood cells, white blood cells, and platelets are suspended.

blood pressure The force that blood exerts against the walls of blood vessels.

blood-brain barrier A system of capillaries in the brain that restricts passage of most substances into the brain, thereby preventing large fluctuations in the brain's environment.

body cavity A fluid-containing space between the digestive tract and the body wall.

bolus A lubricated ball of chewed food.

bone A type of connective tissue consisting of living cells held in a rigid matrix of collagen fibers embedded in calcium salts.

bottleneck effect Genetic drift resulting from a drastic reduction in population size. Typically, the surviving population is no longer genetically representative of the original population.

Bowman's capsule A cup-shaped swelling at the receiving end of a nephron in the vertebrate kidney; collects the filtrate from the blood.

brain The master control center of the nervous system, involved in regulating and controlling body activity and interpreting information from the senses transmitted through the nervous system.

brainstem A functional unit of the vertebrate brain, composed of the midbrain, the medulla oblongata, and the pons; serves mainly as a sensory filter, selecting which information reaches higher brain centers.

brassinosteroids A class of plant steroid hormones that promote cell elongation and cell division in stems and seedlings.

breathing Ventilation of the lungs through alternating inhalation and exhalation of air.

breathing control center The part of the medulla in the brain that directs the activity of organs involved in breathing.

bronchiole (bron´-kē-ōl) A fine branch of the bronchi that transports air to alveoli.

bronchus (bron´-kus) (plural, **bronchi**) One of a pair of breathing tubes that branch from the trachea into the lungs.

brown alga One of a group of marine, multicellular, autotrophic protists belonging to the stramenopile clade of the SAR supergroup; the most common and largest type of seaweed. Brown algae include the kelps.

bryophyte (brī´-uh-fīt) A plant that lacks xylem and phloem; a seedless nonvascular plant. Bryophytes include mosses, liverworts, and hornworts.

budding A means of asexual reproduction whereby a new individual develops from an outgrowth of a parent. The new individual eventually splits off and lives independently.

buffer A chemical substance that resists changes in pH by accepting hydrogen ions from or donating hydrogen ions to solutions.

bulbourethral gland (bul´-bō-yū-rē´-thrul) One of a pair of glands near the base of the penis in the human male that secrete a clear alkaline mucus.

bulk feeder An animal that eats relatively large pieces of food.

C

C₃ plant A plant that uses the Calvin cycle for the initial steps that incorporate CO_2 into organic material, forming a three-carbon compound as the first stable intermediate.

C₄ plant A plant in which the Calvin cycle is preceded by reactions that incorporate CO_2 into a four-carbon compound, which then supplies CO_2 for the Calvin cycle.

Calvin cycle The second of two stages of photosynthesis; a cyclic series of chemical reactions that occur in the stroma of a chloroplast, using the carbon in CO_2 and the ATP and NADPH produced by the light reactions to make the energy-rich sugar molecule G3P.

CAM plant A plant that uses an adaptation for photosynthesis in arid conditions in which carbon dioxide entering open stomata during the night is converted to organic acids, which release CO_2 for the Calvin cycle during the day, when stomata are closed.

cancer A disease characterized by the presence of malignant tumors (rapidly growing and spreading masses of abnormal body cells) in the body.

capillary (kap´-il-er-ē) A microscopic blood vessel that conveys blood between an arteriole and a venule; enables the exchange of nutrients and dissolved gases between the blood and interstitial fluid.

capillary bed (kap´-il-er-ē) A network of capillaries in a tissue or organ.

capsid The protein shell that encloses a viral genome.

carbohydrate (kar´-bō-hī´-drāt) Member of the class of biological molecules consisting of single-monomer sugars (monosaccharides), two-monomer sugars (disaccharides), and polymers (polysaccharides).

carbon fixation The incorporation of carbon from atmospheric CO_2 into an organic compound. During photosynthesis in a C₃ plant, carbon is fixed into a three-carbon sugar as it enters the Calvin cycle. In C₄ and CAM plants, carbon is first fixed into a four-carbon sugar.

carbonyl group (kar´-buh-nēl´) A chemical group consisting of a carbon atom linked by a double bond to an oxygen atom.

carboxyl group (kar-bok´-sil) A chemical group consisting of a carbon atom double-bonded to an oxygen atom and also bonded to a hydroxyl group.

carcinogen (kar-sin´-uh-jin) A cancer-causing agent, either high-energy radiation (such as X-rays or UV light) or a chemical.

cardiac cycle (kar´-dē-ak) The alternating contractions and relaxations of the heart.

cardiac muscle (kar´-dē-ak) A type of striated muscle that forms the contractile wall of the heart.

cardiac output (kar´-dē-ak) The volume of blood pumped per minute by each ventricle of the heart.

cardiovascular disease (kar´-dē-ō-vas´-kyū-ler) Disorders of the heart and blood vessels.

cardiovascular system (kar´-dē-ō-vas´-kyū-ler) A closed circulatory system with a heart and a branching network of arteries, capillaries, and veins.

carnivore An animal that mainly eats other animals.

carpel (kar´-pul) The female part of a flower, consisting of a stalk with an ovary at the base and a stigma, which traps pollen, at the tip.

carrier An individual who is heterozygous for a recessively inherited disorder and who therefore does not show symptoms of that disorder but who may pass on the recessive allele to offspring.

carrying capacity In a population, the number of individuals that an environment can sustain.

cartilage (kar´-ti-lij) A flexible connective tissue consisting of living cells and collagenous fibers embedded in a rubbery matrix.

Casparian strip (kas-par´-ē-un) A waxy barrier in the walls of endodermal cells in a plant root that prevents water and ions from entering the xylem without crossing one or more cell membranes.

cation exchange A process in which positively charged minerals are made available to a plant when hydrogen ions in the soil displace mineral ions from the clay particles.

cecum (sē´-kum) (plural, **ceca**) A blind outpocket at the beginning of the large intestine.

cell A basic unit of living matter separated from its environment by a plasma membrane; the fundamental structural unit of life.

cell body The part of a cell, such as a neuron, that houses the nucleus.

cell cycle An ordered sequence of events (including interphase and the mitotic phase) that extends from the time a eukaryotic cell is first formed from a dividing parent cell until its own division into two cells.

cell cycle control system A cyclically operating set of proteins that triggers and coordinates events in the eukaryotic cell cycle.

cell division The reproduction of a cell through duplication of the genome and division of the cytoplasm.

cell plate A double membrane across the midline of a dividing plant cell, between which the new cell wall forms during cytokinesis.

cell theory The theory that all living things are composed of cells and that all cells come from other cells.

cell wall A protective layer external to the plasma membrane in plant cells, bacteria, fungi, and some protists; protects the cell and helps maintain its shape.

cell-mediated immune response The branch of adaptive immunity that involves the activation of cytotoxic T cells, which defend against infected cells.

cellular metabolism (muh-tab´-uh-lizm) All the chemical activities of a cell.

cellular respiration The aerobic harvesting of energy from food molecules; the energy-releasing chemical breakdown of food molecules, such as glucose, and the storage of potential energy in a form that cells can use to perform work; involves glycolysis, the citric acid cycle, and oxidative phosphorylation (the electron transport chain and chemiosmosis).

cellular slime mold A type of protist that has unicellular amoeboid cells and aggregated reproductive bodies in its life cycle; a member of the amoebozoan clade.

cellulose (sel´-yū-lōs) A structural polysaccharide of plant cell walls composed of glucose monomers. Cellulose molecules are linked by hydrogen bonds into cable-like fibrils.

centipede A carnivorous terrestrial arthropod that has one pair of long legs for each of its numerous body segments, with the front pair modified as poison claws.

central canal The narrow cavity in the center of the spinal cord that is continuous with the fluid-filled ventricles of the brain.

central nervous system (CNS) The integration and command center of the nervous system; the brain and, in vertebrates, the spinal cord.

central vacuole In a plant cell, a large membranous sac with diverse roles in growth and the storage of chemicals and wastes.

centralization The presence of a central nervous system (CNS) distinct from a peripheral nervous system.

centromere (sen´-trō-mēr) The region of a duplicated chromosome where two sister chromatids are joined (often appearing as a narrow "waist") and where spindle microtubules attach during mitosis and meiosis. The centromere divides at the onset of anaphase during mitosis and anaphase II during meiosis.

centrosome A structure found in animal cells from which microtubules originate and that is important during cell division. A centrosome has two centrioles.

cephalization (sef´-uh-luh-zā´-shun) An evolutionary trend toward concentration of the nervous system at the head end.

cephalopod A member of a group of molluscs that includes squids, cuttlefish, octopuses, and nautiluses.

cerebellum (sār´-ruh-bel´-um) Part of the vertebrate hindbrain; mainly a planning center that interacts closely with the cerebrum in coordinating body movement.

cerebral cortex (suh-rē´-brul kor´-teks) A folded sheet of gray matter forming the surface of the cerebrum. In humans, it contains integrating centers for higher brain functions such as reasoning, speech, language, and imagination.

cerebral hemisphere (suh-rē´-brul) The right or left half of the vertebrate cerebrum.

cerebrospinal fluid (suh-rē´-brō-spī´-nul) Blood-derived fluid that surrounds, nourishes, and cushions the brain and spinal cord.

cerebrum (suh-rē´-brum) The largest, most sophisticated, and most dominant part of the vertebrate forebrain, made up of right and left cerebral hemispheres.

cervix (ser´-viks) The neck of the uterus, which opens into the vagina.

chaparral (shap´-uh-ral´) A biome dominated by spiny evergreen shrubs adapted to periodic drought and fires; found where cold ocean currents circulate offshore, creating mild, rainy winters and long, hot, dry summers.

character A heritable feature that varies among individuals within a population, such as flower color in pea plants or eye color in humans.

chelicerate (kē-lih-suh´-rāte) A lineage of arthropods that includes horseshoe crabs, scorpions, ticks, and spiders.

chemical bond An attraction between two atoms resulting from a sharing of outer-shell electrons or the presence of opposite charges on the atoms. The bonded atoms gain complete outer electron shells.

chemical cycling The use and reuse of a chemical element, such as carbon, within an ecosystem.

chemical energy Energy available in molecules for release in a chemical reaction; a form of potential energy.

chemical reaction The making and breaking of chemical bonds, leading to changes in the composition of matter.

chemiosmosis (kem´-ē-oz-mō´-sis) An energy-coupling mechanism that uses the energy of hydrogen ion (H^+) gradients across membranes to drive cellular work, such as the phosphorylation of ADP; powers most ATP synthesis in cells.

chemoautotroph An organism that obtains both energy and carbon from inorganic chemicals. A chemoautotroph makes its own organic compounds from CO_2 without using light energy.

chemoheterotroph An organism that obtains both energy and carbon from organic compounds.

chemoreceptor (kē´-mō-rē-sep´-ter) A sensory receptor that detects chemical changes within the body or a specific kind of molecule in the external environment.

chiasma (kī-az´-muh) (plural, **chiasmata**) The microscopically visible site where crossing over has occurred between chromatids of homologous chromosomes during prophase I of meiosis.

chitin (kī-tin) A structural polysaccharide found in many fungal cell walls and in the exoskeletons of arthropods.

chlamydia A member of a group of bacteria that live inside eukaryotic host cells; a common sexually transmitted disease caused by the bacterium *Chlamydia trachomatis*.

chlorophyll A green pigment located within the chloroplasts of plants and algae and in the membranes of certain prokaryotes. Chlorophyll *a* participates directly in the light reactions, which convert solar energy to chemical energy.

chloroplast (klō´-rō-plast) An organelle found in plants and algae that absorbs sunlight and uses it to drive the synthesis of organic compounds (sugars) from carbon dioxide and water.

choanocyte (kō-an´-uh-sīt) A flagellated feeding cell found in sponges. Also called a collar cell, it has a collar-like ring that traps food particles around the base of its flagellum.

cholesterol (kō-les´-tuh-rol) A steroid that is an important component of animal cell membranes and that acts as a precursor molecule for the synthesis of other steroids, such as hormones.

chondrichthyan (kon-drik´-thē-an) Cartilaginous fish; member of a clade of jawed vertebrates with skeletons made mostly of cartilage, such as sharks and rays.

chorion (kō´r-ē-on) In animals, the outermost extraembryonic membrane, which becomes the mammalian embryo's part of the placenta.

chorionic villus (kor´-ē-on´-ik vil´-us) Outgrowth of the chorion, containing embryonic blood vessels. As part of the placenta, chorionic villi absorb nutrients and oxygen from, and pass wastes into, the mother's bloodstream.

chorionic villus sampling (CVS) A technique for diagnosing genetic defects while the fetus is in an early development stage within the uterus. A small sample of the fetal portion of the placenta is removed and analyzed.

choroid (kor´-oyd) A thin, pigmented layer in the vertebrate eye, surrounded by the sclera. The iris is part of the choroid.

chromatin (krō´-muh-tin) The complex of DNA and proteins that makes up eukaryotic chromosomes; often used to refer to the diffuse, very extended form taken by chromosomes when a cell is not dividing.

chromosome (krō´-muh-sōm) A gene-carrying structure found in the nucleus of a eukaryotic cell and most visible during mitosis and meiosis; also, the main gene-carrying structure of a prokaryotic cell. A chromosome consists of one very long DNA molecule and associated proteins.

chromosome theory of inheritance (krō´-muh-sōm) A basic principle in biology stating that genes are located on chromosomes and that the behavior of chromosomes during meiosis accounts for inheritance patterns.

chronic traumatic encephalopathy A dementia (mental deterioration) caused by brain trauma such as sports concussions and characterized by depression, memory loss, and other symptoms.

chyme (kīm) The mixture of partially digested food and digestive juices formed in the stomach.

chytrid (kī-trid) Member of a group of fungi that are mostly aquatic and have flagellated spores. They probably represent the most primitive fungal lineage.

ciliate (sil´-ē-it) A type of protist that moves and feeds by means of cilia. Ciliates belong to the alveolate clade of the SAR supergroup.

cilium (plural, **cilia**) A short cellular appendage specialized for locomotion or moving fluid past the cell, formed from a core of nine outer doublet microtubules and two single microtubules (the "9 + 2" arrangement) covered by the cell's plasma membrane.

circadian rhythm (ser-kā´-dē-un) In an organism, a biological cycle of about 24 hours that is controlled by a biological clock, usually under the influence of environmental cues; a pattern of activity that is repeated daily. *See also* biological clock.

circulatory system The organ system that transports materials such as nutrients, O_2, and hormones to body cells and transports CO_2 and other wastes from body cells.

citric acid cycle The chemical cycle that completes the metabolic breakdown of glucose molecules begun in glycolysis by oxidizing acetyl CoA (derived from pyruvate) to carbon dioxide. The cycle occurs in the matrix of mitochondria and supplies most of the NADH molecules that carry electrons to the electron transport chains. Together with pyruvate oxidation, the second major stage of cellular respiration.

clade A group of species that includes an ancestral species and all its descendants.

cladistics (kluh-dis´-tiks) An approach to systematics in which common descent is the primary criterion used to classify organisms by placing them into groups called clades.

class In Linnaean classification, the taxonomic category above order.

cleavage (klē´-vij) (1) Cytokinesis in animal cells and in some protists, characterized by pinching in of the plasma membrane. (2) In animal development, the first major phase of embryonic development, in which rapid cell divisions without cell growth transforms the animal zygote into a ball of cells.

cleavage furrow (klē´-vij) The first sign of cytokinesis during cell division in an animal cell; a shallow groove in the cell surface near the old metaphase plate.

clitoris An organ in the female that engorges with blood and becomes erect during sexual arousal.

clonal selection (klōn´-ul) The process by which an antigen selectively binds to and activates only those lymphocytes bearing receptors specific for the antigen. The selected lymphocytes proliferate and differentiate into a clone of effector cells and a clone of memory cells specific for the stimulating antigen.

clone As a verb, to produce genetically identical copies of a cell, organism, or DNA molecule. As a noun, the collection of cells, organisms, or molecules resulting from cloning; colloquially, a single organism that is genetically identical to another because it arose from the cloning of a somatic cell.

closed circulatory system A circulatory system in which blood is confined to vessels and is kept separate from the interstitial fluid.

club fungus *See* basidiomycete.

clumped dispersion pattern A pattern in which the individuals of a population are aggregated in patches.

cnidarian (nī-dār´-ē-un) An animal characterized by cnidocytes, radial symmetry, a gastrovascular cavity, and a polyp and medusa body form. Cnidarians include the hydras, jellies, sea anemones, corals, and related animals.

cnidocyte (nī´-duh-sīt) A specialized cell for which the phylum Cnidaria is named; consists of a capsule containing a fine coiled thread, which, when discharged, functions in defense and prey capture.

coccus (kok´-us) (plural, **cocci**) A spherical prokaryotic cell.

cochlea (kok´-lē-uh) A coiled tube in the inner ear of birds and mammals that contains the hearing organ, the organ of Corti.

codominant Inheritance pattern in which a heterozygote expresses the distinct trait of both alleles.

codon (kō´-don) A three-nucleotide sequence in mRNA that specifies a particular amino acid or polypeptide termination signal; the basic unit of the genetic code.

coelom (sē´-lom) A body cavity completely lined with mesoderm.

coenzyme An organic molecule serving as a cofactor. Most vitamins function as coenzymes in important metabolic reactions.

coevolution Evolutionary change in which adaptations in one species act as a selective force on a second species, inducing adaptations that in turn act as a selective force on the first species; a series of reciprocal evolutionary adaptations in two interacting species.

cofactor A nonprotein molecule or ion that is required for the proper functioning of an enzyme. *See also* coenzyme.

cognition The process carried out by an animal's nervous system to perceive, store, integrate, and use information obtained by the animal's sensory receptors.

cohesion (kō-hē´-zhun) The sticking together of molecules of the same kind, often by hydrogen bonds.

collecting duct A tube in the vertebrate kidney that concentrates urine while conveying it to the renal pelvis.

collenchyma cell (kō-len´-kim-uh) In plants, a cell with a thick primary wall and no secondary wall, functioning mainly in supporting growing parts.

colon (kō´-lun) The largest section of the large intestine.

communication Animal behavior including transmission of, reception of, and response to signals.

community An assemblage of all the populations of organisms living close enough together for potential interactions.

companion cell In a plant, a cell connected to a sieve-tube element whose nucleus and ribosomes provide proteins for the sieve-tube element.

competitive inhibitor A substance that reduces the activity of an enzyme by entering the active site in place of the substrate. A competitive inhibitor's structure mimics that of the enzyme's substrate.

complement system A family of innate defensive blood proteins that cooperate with other components of the vertebrate defense system to protect against microbes; can enhance phagocytosis, directly lyse pathogens, and amplify the inflammatory response.

complementary DNA (cDNA) A DNA molecule made *in vitro* using mRNA as a template and the enzyme reverse transcriptase. A cDNA molecule therefore corresponds to a gene but lacks the introns present in the DNA of the genome.

complete digestive tract A digestive tube with two openings, a mouth and an anus.

complete dominance A type of inheritance in which the phenotypes of the heterozygote and dominant homozygote are indistinguishable.

complete metamorphosis (met´-uh-mōr´-fuh-sis) A type of development in certain insects in which development from larva to adult is achieved by multiple molts that are followed by a pupal stage. While encased in its pupa, the body rebuilds from clusters of embryonic cells that have been held in reserve. The adult emerges from the pupa.

compost Decomposing organic material that can be used to add nutrients to soil.

compound A substance containing two or more elements in a fixed ratio. For example, table salt (NaCl) consists of one atom of the element sodium (Na) for every atom of chlorine (Cl).

compound eye The photoreceptor in many invertebrates; made up of many tiny light detectors, each of which detects light from a tiny portion of the field of view.

concentration gradient A region along which the density of a chemical substance increases or decreases. Cells often maintain concentration gradients of ions across their membranes. When a concentration gradient exists, substances tend to move from where they are more concentrated to where they are less concentrated.

conception The fertilization of the egg by a sperm cell in humans.

condom A form of contraception; a sheath that fits over the penis to prevent the transfer of sperm to the vagina.

cone (1) In vertebrates, a photoreceptor cell in the retina stimulated by bright light and enabling color vision. (2) In conifers, a reproductive structure bearing pollen or ovules.

coniferous forest A biome characterized by conifers, cone-bearing evergreen trees.

conjugation The union (mating) of two bacterial cells or protist cells and the transfer of DNA between the two cells.

conjunctiva A thin mucous membrane that lines the inner surface of vertebrate eyelids.

connective tissue Animal tissue that functions mainly to bind and support other tissues, having a sparse population of cells scattered through an extracellular matrix, which they produce.

conservation biology A goal-oriented science that endeavors to sustain biological diversity.

continental shelf The submerged part of a continent.

contraception The deliberate prevention of pregnancy.

controlled experiment An experiment in which an experimental group is compared with a control group that varies only in the factor being tested.

convergent evolution The evolution of similar features in different evolutionary lineages, which can result from living in very similar environments.

copulation Sexual intercourse, usually necessary for internal fertilization to occur.

cork The outermost protective layer of a plant's bark, produced by the cork cambium.

cork cambium Meristematic tissue that produces cork cells during secondary growth of a plant.

cornea (kor´-nē-uh) The transparent frontal portion of the sclera, which admits light into the vertebrate eye.

corpus callosum (kor´-pus kuh-lō´-sum) The thick band of nerve fibers that connect the right and left cerebral hemispheres in placental mammals, enabling the hemispheres to process information together.

corpus luteum (kor´-pus lū´-tē-um) A small body of endocrine tissue that develops from an ovarian follicle after ovulation and secretes progesterone and estrogen during pregnancy.

cortex In plants, the ground tissue system of a root, made up mostly of parenchyma cells, which store food and absorb minerals that have passed through the epidermis.

corticosteroid A hormone synthesized and secreted by the adrenal cortex. The corticosteroids include the mineralocorticoids and glucocorticoids.

cotyledon (kot´-uh-lē´-don) The first leaf that appears on an embryo of a flowering plant; a seed leaf. Monocot embryos have one cotyledon; dicot embryos have two.

countercurrent exchange The transfer of a substance or heat between two fluids flowing in opposite directions.

countercurrent heat exchange A circulatory adaptation in which parallel blood vessels convey warm and cold blood in opposite directions, maximizing heat transfer to the cold blood.

covalent bond (ko-vā´-lent) A type of strong chemical bond in which two atoms share one or more pairs of valence electrons.

craniate A chordate with a head.

crista (kris´-tuh) (plural, **cristae**) An infolding of the inner mitochondrial membrane.

crop A pouch-like organ in a digestive tract where food is softened and may be stored temporarily.

cross A mating of two sexually reproducing individuals; often used to describe a genetics experiment involving a controlled mating (a "genetic cross").

crossing over The exchange of segments between chromatids of homologous chromosomes during synapsis in prophase I of meiosis; also, the exchange of segments between DNA molecules in prokaryotes.

crustacean A member of a major arthropod group that includes lobsters, crayfish, crabs, shrimps, and barnacles.

cuticle (kyū´-tuh-kul) (1) In animals, a tough, nonliving outer layer of the skin. (2) In plants, a waxy coating on the surface of stems and leaves that helps retain water.

cyanobacteria (sī-an´-ō-bak-tēr´-ē-uh) Photoautotrophic prokaryotes with plantlike, oxygen-generating photosynthesis.

cytokinesis (sī´-tō-kuh-nē´-sis) The division of the cytoplasm to form two separate daughter cells. Cytokinesis usually occurs in conjunction with telophase of mitosis. Mitosis and cytokinesis make up the mitotic (M) phase of the cell cycle.

cytokinin (sī´-tō-kī´-nin) One of a family of plant hormones that promotes cell division, retards aging in flowers and fruits, and may interact antagonistically with auxins in regulating plant growth and development.

cytoplasm (si´-tō-plaz´-um) The contents of a eukaryotic cell between the plasma membrane and the nucleus; consists of a semifluid medium and organelles; can also refer to the interior of a prokaryotic cell.

cytosine (C) (sī´-tuh-sin) A single-ring nitrogenous base found in DNA and RNA.

cytoskeleton A network of protein fibers in the cytoplasm of a eukaryotic cell; includes microfilaments, intermediate filaments, and microtubules.

cytosol The semifluid portion of the cytoplasm.

cytotoxic T cell (sī-tō-tok´-sik) A type of lymphocyte that attacks body cells infected with pathogens.

D

decomposer A prokaryote or fungus that secretes enzymes that digest molecules in organic material and convert them to inorganic forms.

decomposition The breakdown of organic materials into inorganic ones.

dehydration reaction (dē-hī-drā´-shun) A chemical reaction in which two molecules become covalently bonded to each other with the removal of a water molecule.

deletion The loss of one or more nucleotides from a gene by mutation; the loss of a fragment of a chromosome.

demographic transition A shift from zero population growth in which birth rates and death rates are high to zero population growth characterized by low birth and death rates.

denaturation (dē-nā´-chur-ā´-shun) A process in which a protein unravels, losing its specific structure and hence function; can be caused by changes in pH or salt concentration or by high temperature; also refers to the separation of the two strands of the DNA double helix, caused by similar factors.

dendrite (den´-drīt) A neuron fiber that conveys signals from its tip inward, toward the rest of the neuron. A neuron typically has many short dendrites.

density-dependent factor A population-limiting factor whose intensity is linked to population density. For example, there may be a decline in birth rates or a rise in death rates in response to an increase in the number of individuals living in a designated area.

density-dependent inhibition The ceasing of cell division that occurs when cells touch one another.

density-independent factor A population-limiting factor whose intensity is unrelated to population density.

deoxyribonucleic acid (DNA) (dē-ok´-sē-rī´-bō-nū-klā´-ik) A double-stranded helical nucleic acid molecule consisting of nucleotide monomers with deoxyribose sugar and the nitrogenous bases adenine (A), cytosine (C), guanine (G), and thymine (T). Capable of replicating, DNA is an organism's genetic material. *See also* gene.

dermal tissue system The outer protective covering of plants.

desert A biome characterized by organisms adapted to sparse rainfall (less than 30 cm per year) and rapid evaporation.

desertification The conversion of semi-arid regions to desert.

determinate growth Termination of growth after reaching a certain size, as in most animals. *See also* indeterminate growth.

detritivore (duh-trī´-tuh-vor) An organism that consumes decaying organic material.

detritus (duh-trī´-tus) Dead organic matter, including animal wastes, plant litter, and the bodies of dead organisms.

deuterostome (dū-ter´-ō-stōm) A mode of animal development in which the opening formed during gastrulation becomes the anus. Animals with the deuterostome pattern of development include the echinoderms and the chordates.

diabetes mellitus (dī´-uh-bē´-tis me-lī´-tis) A human hormonal disease in which body cells cannot absorb enough glucose from the blood and become energy starved; body fats and proteins are then consumed for their energy. Type 1 (insulin-dependent) diabetes results when the pancreas does not produce insulin; type 2 (non-insulin-dependent) diabetes results when body cells fail to respond to insulin.

dialysis (dī-al´-uh-sis) Separation and disposal of metabolic wastes from the blood by mechanical means; an artificial method of performing the functions of the kidneys that can be life sustaining in the event of kidney failure.

diaphragm (dī´-uh-fram) The sheet of muscle separating the chest cavity from the abdominal cavity in mammals. Its contraction expands the chest cavity, and its relaxation reduces it.

diastole (dȳ´-as´-tō-lē) The stage of the heart cycle in which the heart muscle is relaxed, allowing the chambers to fill with blood. *See also* systole.

diatom (dī´-uh-tom) A unicellular, autotrophic protist that belongs to the stramenopile clade of the SAR supergroup. Diatoms possess a unique glassy cell wall containing silica.

dicot (dī´-kot) A term traditionally used to refer to flowering plants that have two embryonic seed leaves, or cotyledons.

differentiation The specialization in the structure and function of cells that occurs during the development of an organism; results from selective activation and deactivation of the cells' genes.

diffusion The random movement of particles that results in the net movement of a substance down its concentration gradient from a region where it is more concentrated to a region where it is less concentrated.

digestion The mechanical and chemical breakdown of food into molecules small enough for the body to absorb; the second stage of food processing in animals.

digestive system The organ system involved in ingestion and digestion of food, absorption of nutrients, and elimination of wastes.

dihybrid cross (dī-hī´-brid) An experimental mating of individuals that are each heterozygous for both of two characters (or the self-pollination of a plant that is heterozygous for both characters).

dinoflagellate (dī-nō-flaj´-uh-let) A member of a group of protists belonging to the alveolate clade of the SAR supergroup. Dinoflagellates are common components of marine and freshwater phytoplankton.

diploid In an organism that reproduces sexually, a cell containing two homologous sets of chromosomes, one set inherited from each parent; a $2n$ cell.

directional selection Natural selection in which individuals at one end of the phenotypic range survive and reproduce more successfully than do other individuals.

disaccharide (dī-sak´-uh-rīd) A sugar molecule consisting of two monosaccharides linked by a dehydration reaction.

dispersion pattern The manner in which individuals in a population are spaced within their area. Three types of dispersion patterns are clumped (individuals are aggregated in patches), uniform (individuals are evenly distributed), and random (unpredictable distribution).

disruptive selection Natural selection in which individuals on both extremes of a phenotypic range are favored over intermediate phenotypes.

distal tubule In the vertebrate kidney, the portion of a nephron after the loop of Henle that helps refine filtrate and empties it into a collecting duct.

disturbance In ecology, an event that changes a biological community by removing organisms from it or altering the availability of resources.

DNA *See* deoxyribonucleic acid (DNA).

DNA ligase (lī´-gās) An enzyme, essential for DNA replication, that catalyzes the covalent bonding of adjacent DNA polynucleotide strands. DNA ligase is used in genetic engineering to paste a specific piece of DNA containing a gene of interest into a bacterial plasmid or other vector.

DNA microarray A glass slide carrying thousands of different kinds of single-stranded DNA fragments arranged in an array (grid). A DNA microarray is used to detect and measure the expression of thousands of genes at one time. Tiny amounts of a large number of single-stranded DNA fragments representing different genes are fixed to the glass slide. These fragments, ideally representing all the genes of an organism, are tested for hybridization with various samples of cDNA molecules.

DNA polymerase (puh-lim´-er-ās) A large molecular complex that assembles DNA nucleotides into polynucleotides using a preexisting strand of DNA as a template.

DNA profiling A procedure that analyzes DNA samples to determine if they came from the same individual.

DNA technology Methods used to study and/or manipulate DNA, including recombinant DNA technology.

doldrums (dol´-drums) An area of calm or very light winds near the equator, caused by rising warm air.

domain A taxonomic category above the kingdom level. The three domains of life are Archaea, Bacteria, and Eukarya.

dominance hierarchy The ranking of individuals within a group, based on social interactions and usually maintained by agonistic behavior.

dominant allele (uh-lē´-ul) The allele that determines the phenotype of a gene when the individual is heterozygous for that gene.

dorsal Pertaining to the back of a bilaterally symmetric animal.

dorsal, hollow nerve cord One of the four hallmarks of chordates, a tube that forms on the dorsal side of the body, above the notochord.

double circulation A circulatory system with separate pulmonary and systemic circuits, in which blood passes through the heart after completing each circuit; ensures vigorous blood flow to all organs.

double fertilization In flowering plants, the formation of both a zygote and a cell with a triploid nucleus, which develops into the endosperm.

double helix The form of native DNA, referring to its two adjacent polynucleotide strands interwound into a spiral shape.

Down syndrome *See* trisomy 21.

duodenum (dū-ō-dē´-num) The first portion of the vertebrate small intestine after the stomach, where chyme from the stomach mixes with bile and digestive enzymes.

duplication Repetition of part of a chromosome resulting from fusion with a fragment from a homologous chromosome; can result from an error in meiosis or from mutagenesis.

E

eardrum A sheet of connective tissue separating the outer ear from the middle ear that vibrates when stimulated by sound waves and passes the waves to the middle ear.

echinoderm (uh-ki´-nō-derm) Member of a phylum of slow-moving or sessile marine animals characterized by a rough or spiny skin, a water vascular system, an endoskeleton, and radial symmetry in adults. Echinoderms include sea stars, sea urchins, and sand dollars.

ecological footprint An estimate of the amount of land and water area required to provide the resources an individual or nation consumes and to absorb the waste it generates.

ecological niche (nich) The role of a species in its community; the sum total of a species' use of the biotic and abiotic resources of its environment.

ecological species concept A definition of species in terms of ecological niche, the sum of how members of the species interact with the nonliving and living parts of their environment.

ecological succession The process of biological community change resulting from disturbance; transition in the species composition of a biological community. *See also* primary succession; secondary succession.

ecology The scientific study of how organisms interact with their environment.

ecosystem (ē´-kō-sis-tem) All the organisms in a given area, along with the nonliving (abiotic) factors with which they interact; a biological community and its physical environment.

ecotourism Travel to natural areas for tourism and recreation.

ectoderm (ek´-tō-derm) The outer layer of three embryonic cell layers in a gastrula. The ectoderm forms the skin of the gastrula and gives rise to the epidermis and nervous system in the adult.

ectopic pregnancy (ek-top´-ik) The implantation and development of an embryo outside the uterus.

ectothermic (ek´-tō-therm-ik) Referring to organisms that do not produce enough metabolic heat to have much effect on body temperature.

effector cell (1) A muscle cell or gland cell that performs the body's response to stimuli, responding to signals from the brain or other processing center of the nervous system. (2) A lymphocyte that has undergone clonal selection and is capable of mediating an acquired immune response.

egg A female gamete.

ejaculation (ih-jak´-yū-lā´-shun) Expulsion of semen from the penis.

ejaculatory duct The short section of the ejaculatory route in mammals formed by the convergence of the vas deferens and a duct from the seminal vesicle. The ejaculatory duct transports sperm from the vas deferens to the urethra.

electromagnetic receptor A sensory receptor that detects energy of different wavelengths, such as electricity, magnetism, and light.

electromagnetic spectrum The entire spectrum of electromagnetic radiation ranging in wavelength from less than a nanometer to more than a kilometer.

electron A subatomic particle with a single negative electrical charge. One or more electrons move around the nucleus of an atom.

electron microscope (EM) A microscope that uses magnets to focus an electron beam through, or onto the surface of, a specimen. An electron microscope achieves a hundredfold greater resolution than a light microscope.

electron shell A level of electrons at a characteristic average distance from the nucleus of an atom.

electron transport chain A series of electron carrier molecules that shuttle electrons during a series of redox reactions that release energy used to make ATP; located in the inner membrane of mitochondria, the thylakoid membranes of chloroplasts, and the plasma membranes of prokaryotes.

electronegativity The attraction of a given atom for the electrons of a covalent bond.

element A substance that cannot be broken down to other substances by chemical means.

elimination The passing of undigested material out of the digestive compartment; the fourth and final stage of food processing in animals.

embryo (em´-brē-ō) A developing stage of a multicellular organism. In humans, the stage in the development of offspring from the first division of the zygote until body structures begin to appear, about the 9th week of gestation.

embryo sac (em´-brē-ō) The female gametophyte contained in the ovule of a flowering plant.

embryonic stem cell (ES cell) Cell in the early animal embryo that differentiates during development to give rise to all the different kinds of specialized cells in the body.

embryophyte Another name for land plants, recognizing that land plants share the common derived trait of multicellular, dependent embryos.

emergent properties New properties that arise with each step upward in the hierarchy of life, owing to the arrangement and interactions of parts as complexity increases.

emerging virus A virus that has appeared suddenly or has recently come to the attention of medical scientists.

endemic species A species whose distribution is limited to a specific geographic area.

endergonic reaction (en´-der-gon´-ik) An energy-requiring chemical reaction, which yields products with more potential energy than the reactants.

endocrine gland (en´-dō-krin) A ductless gland that synthesizes hormone molecules and secretes them directly into the bloodstream.

endocrine system (en´-dō-krin) The organ system consisting of ductless glands that secrete hormones and the molecular receptors on or in target cells that respond to the hormones. The endocrine system cooperates with the nervous system in regulating body functions and maintaining homeostasis.

endocytosis (en´-dō-sī-tō´-sis) Cellular uptake of molecules or particles via formation of new vesicles from the plasma membrane.

endoderm (en´-dō-derm) The innermost of three embryonic cell layers in a gastrula; gives rise to the innermost linings of the digestive tract and other hollow organs in the adult.

endodermis The innermost layer (a one-cell-thick cylinder) of the cortex of a plant root; forms a selective barrier determining which substances pass from the cortex into the vascular tissue.

endomembrane system A network of membranes inside and surrounding a eukaryotic cell, related either through direct physical contact or by the transfer of membranous vesicles.

endometrium (en´-dō-mē´-trē-um) The inner lining of the uterus in mammals, richly supplied with blood vessels that provide the maternal part of the placenta and nourish the developing embryo.

endoplasmic reticulum (ER) An extensive membranous network in a eukaryotic cell, continuous with the outer nuclear membrane and composed of ribosome-studded (rough) and ribosome-free (smooth) regions. *See also* rough ER; smooth ER.

endoskeleton A hard skeleton located within the soft tissues of an animal; includes spicules of sponges, the hard plates of echinoderms, and the cartilage and bony skeletons of vertebrates.

endosperm In flowering plants, a nutrient-rich mass formed by the union of a sperm cell with two polar nuclei during double fertilization; provides nourishment to the developing embryo in the seed.

endospore A thick-coated, protective cell produced within a bacterial cell. The endospore becomes dormant and is able to survive harsh environmental conditions.

endosymbiont theory (en´-dō-sim´-bī-ont) The theory that mitochondria and chloroplasts originated as prokaryotic cells engulfed by an ancestral eukaryotic cell. The engulfed cell and its host cell then evolved into a single organism.

endothermic Referring to organisms that use heat generated by their own metabolism to maintain a warm, steady body temperature.

endotoxin A poisonous component of the outer membrane of gram-negative bacteria that is released only when the bacteria die.

energy The capacity to cause change, especially to perform work.

energy coupling In cellular metabolism, the use of energy released from an exergonic reaction to drive an endergonic reaction.

energy flow The passage of energy through the components of an ecosystem.

enhancer A eukaryotic DNA sequence that helps stimulate the transcription of a gene at some distance from it. An enhancer functions by means of a transcription factor called an activator, which binds to it and then to the rest of the transcription apparatus.

enteric division Part of the autonomic nervous system consisting of complex networks of neurons in the digestive tract, pancreas, and gallbladder.

entropy (en´-truh-pē) A measure of disorder, or randomness. *See also* second law of thermodynamics.

enzyme (en´-zīm) A macromolecule, usually a protein, that serves as a biological catalyst, changing the rate of a chemical reaction without being consumed by the reaction.

epidermis (ep´-uh-der´-mis) (1) In animals, one or more living layers of cells forming the protective covering, or outer skin. (2) In plants, the tissue system forming the protective outer covering of leaves, young stems, and young roots.

epididymis (ep´-uh-did´-uh-mus) A long coiled tube into which sperm pass from the testis and are stored until mature and ejaculated.

epigenetic inheritance The inheritance of traits transmitted by mechanisms not directly involving the nucleotide sequence of a genome, such as the chemical modification of histone proteins or DNA bases.

epiglottis A flap of elastic cartilage that protects the entrance to the trachea. Normally, the epiglottis is positioned to allow air to enter the trachea; it changes position when food is swallowed, allowing food to enter the esophagus and preventing food from entering the trachea.

epinephrine (ep´-uh-nef´-rin) An amine hormone (also called adrenaline) secreted by the adrenal medulla that prepares body organs for action (fight or flight); also serves as a neurotransmitter.

epithelial tissue (ep´-uh-thē´-lē-ul) A sheet of tightly packed cells lining organs, body cavities, and external surfaces; also called epithelium.

erythrocyte (eh-rith´-rō-sīt´) A blood cell containing hemoglobin, which transports oxygen; also called a red blood cell.

erythropoietin (EPO) (eh-rith´rō-poy´uh-tin) A hormone that stimulates the production of erythrocytes. It is secreted by the kidney when tissues of the body do not receive enough oxygen.

esophagus (eh-sof´-uh-gus) A muscular tube that conducts food by peristalsis, usually from the pharynx to the stomach.

essential amino acid An amino acid that an animal cannot synthesize itself and must obtain from food. Eight amino acids are essential for the human adult.

essential element In plants, a chemical element required for the plant to complete its life cycle (to grow from a seed and produce another generation of seeds).

essential fatty acid An unsaturated fatty acid that an animal needs but cannot make.

essential nutrient A substance that an organism must absorb in preassembled form because it cannot synthesize it from any other material. In humans, there are essential vitamins, minerals, amino acids, and fatty acids.

estrogen (es´-trō-jen) One of several chemically similar steroid hormones secreted by the gonads; maintains the female reproductive system and promotes the development of female body features.

estuary (es´-chū-ār-ē) The area where a freshwater stream or river merges with the ocean.

ethylene A gas that functions as a hormone in plants, triggering aging responses such as fruit ripening and leaf drop.

eudicot (yūdī´-kot) Member of a group that consists of the vast majority of flowering plants that have two embryonic seed leaves, or cotyledons.

Eukarya (yū-kar´-ē-uh) Domain of life that includes all eukaryotic organisms.

eukaryotic cell (yū-kar-ē-ot´-ik) A type of cell that has a membrane-enclosed nucleus and membrane-enclosed organelles. All organisms except bacteria and archaea are composed of eukaryotic cells.

eumetazoan (yū-met-uh-zō´-un) Member of the clade of "true animals," the animals with true tissues (all animals except sponges).

Eustachian tube (yū-stā´-shun) An air passage between the middle ear and throat of vertebrates that equalizes air pressure on either side of the eardrum.

eutherian (yū-thēr´-ē-un) Placental mammal; mammal whose young complete their embryonic development within the uterus, joined to the mother by the placenta.

evaporative cooling The process in which the surface of an object becomes cooler during evaporation.

evo-devo Evolutionary developmental biology; the field of biology that combines evolutionary biology with developmental biology.

evolution Descent with modification; the idea that living species are descendants of ancestral species that were different from present-day ones; also, the genetic changes in a population from generation to generation.

evolutionary tree A branching diagram that reflects a hypothesis about evolutionary relationships among groups of organisms.

Excavata One of four monophyletic supergroups proposed in a current hypothesis of the evolutionary history of eukaryotes. The other three supergroups are SAR (Stramenopila, Alveolata, and Rhizaria), Unikonta, and Archaeplastida.

excretion (ek-skrē´-shun) The disposal of nitrogen-containing metabolic wastes.

exergonic reaction (ek´-ser-gon´-ik) An energy-releasing chemical reaction in which the reactants contain more potential energy than the products.

exocytosis (ek´-sō-sī-tō´-sis) The movement of materials out of a cell by the fusion of vesicles with the plasma membrane.

exon The part of a gene that becomes part of the final messenger RNA and is therefore expressed.

exoskeleton A hard external skeleton that protects an animal and provides points of attachment for muscles.

exotoxin A poisonous protein secreted by certain bacteria.

exponential growth model A mathematical description of idealized, unregulated population growth.

external fertilization The fusion of gametes that parents have discharged into the environment.

extinction The irrevocable loss of a species.

extirpation The loss of a single population of a species.

extracellular matrix (ECM) The meshwork surrounding animal cells; consists of glycoproteins and polysaccharides synthesized and secreted by cells.

extraembryonic membranes Four membranes (the yolk sac, amnion, chorion, and allantois) that form a life-support system for the developing embryo of a reptile, bird, or mammal.

extreme halophile A microorganism that lives in a highly saline environment, such as the Great Salt Lake or the Dead Sea.

extreme thermophile A microorganism that thrives in a hot environment (often 60–80°C).

eyecup The simplest type of photoreceptor, a cluster of photoreceptor cells shaded by a cuplike cluster of pigmented cells; detects light intensity and direction.

F

F factor A piece of DNA that can exist as a bacterial plasmid. The F factor carries genes for making sex pili and other structures needed for conjugation, as well as a site where DNA replication can start. F stands for fertility.

F_1 generation The offspring of two parental (P generation) individuals; F_1 stands for first filial.

F_2 generation The offspring of the F_1 generation; F_2 stands for second filial.

facilitated diffusion The passage of a substance through a specific transport protein across a biological membrane down its concentration gradient.

family In Linnaean classification, the taxonomic category above genus.

farsightedness An inability to focus on close objects; occurs when the eyeball is shorter than normal and the focal point of the lens is behind the retina; also called hyperopia.

fat A lipid composed of three fatty acids linked to one glycerol molecule; a triglyceride. Most fats function as energy-storage molecules.

feces The wastes of the digestive tract.

feedback inhibition A method of metabolic control in which a product of a metabolic pathway acts as an inhibitor of an enzyme within that pathway.

fertility rate In a human population, the average number of children produced by a woman over her lifetime.

fertilization The union of the nucleus of a sperm cell with the nucleus of an egg cell, producing a zygote.

fertilizer A compound given to plants to promote their growth.

fetus (fē´-tus) A developing human from the 9th week of gestation until birth. The fetus has all the major structures of an adult.

fiber (1) In animals, an elongate, supportive thread in the matrix of connective tissue; an extension of a neuron; a muscle cell. (2) In plants, a long, slender sclerenchyma cell that usually occurs in a bundle.

fibrin (fī-brin) The activated form of the blood-clotting protein fibrinogen, which aggregates into threads that form the fabric of a blood clot.

fibrinogen (fī´-brin´-uh-jen) The plasma protein that is activated to form a clot when a blood vessel is injured.

fibrous connective tissue A dense tissue with large numbers of collagenous fibers organized into parallel bundles. This is the dominant tissue in tendons and ligaments.

filter feeder An aquatic animal that strains small food particles from the water as it is pumped through a sieve-like structure; a type of suspension feeder.

filtrate Fluid extracted by the excretory system from the blood or body cavity. The excretory system produces urine from the filtrate after removing valuable solutes from it and concentrating it.

filtration In the vertebrate kidney, the extraction of water and small solutes, including metabolic wastes, from the blood by the nephrons.

fimbria (plural, **fimbriae**) One of the short, hairlike projections on some prokaryotic cells that help attach the cells to their substrate or to other cells.

first law of thermodynamics The principle of conservation of energy. Energy can be transferred and transformed, but it cannot be created or destroyed.

fission A means of asexual reproduction whereby a parent separates into two or more genetically identical individuals of about equal size.

fixed action pattern (FAP) A genetically programmed, virtually unchangeable behavioral sequence performed in response to a certain stimulus.

flagellum (fluh-jel´-um) (plural, **flagella**) A long cellular appendage specialized for locomotion. The flagella of prokaryotes and eukaryotes differ in both structure and function. Like cilia, eukaryotic flagella have a "9 + 2" arrangement of microtubules covered by the cell's plasma membrane.

flatworm A member of the phylum Platyhelminthes.

fluid feeder An animal that lives by sucking nutrient-rich fluids from another living organism.

fluid mosaic model The currently accepted model of cell membrane structure, depicting the membrane as a mosaic of diverse protein molecules embedded in a fluid bilayer of phospholipid molecules.

fluke One of a group of parasitic flatworms.

follicle (fol´-uh-kul) A cluster of cells that surround, protect, and nourish a developing egg cell in the ovary. Follicles secrete the hormone estrogen.

food chain A sequence of food transfers from producers through one to four levels of consumers in an ecosystem.

food web A network of interconnecting food chains.

foot In an invertebrate animal, a structure used for locomotion or attachment, such as the muscular organ extending from the ventral side of a mollusc.

foraging Behavior used in recognizing, searching for, capturing, and consuming food.

foraminiferan A protist that moves and feeds by means of threadlike pseudopodia and has porous shells composed of calcium carbonate. Forams belong to the Rhizaria clade of the SAR supergroup.

forebrain One of three ancestral and embryonic regions of the vertebrate brain; develops into the thalamus, hypothalamus, and cerebrum.

forensics The scientific analysis of evidence for crime scene and other legal proceedings. Also referred to as forensic science.

fossil A preserved remnant or impression of an organism.

fossil fuel An energy-containing deposit of organic material formed from the remains of ancient organisms.

fossil record The chronicle of evolution over millions of years of geologic time engraved in the order in which fossils appear in rock strata.

founder effect Genetic drift that occurs when a few individuals become isolated from a larger population and form a new population whose gene pool is not reflective of that of the original population.

fovea (fō´-vē-uh) An eye's center of focus and the place on the retina where photoreceptors are highly concentrated.

fragmentation A means of asexual reproduction whereby a single parent breaks into parts that regenerate into whole new individuals.

frameshift mutation A change in the genetic material that involves the insertion or deletion of one or more nucleotides in a gene, resulting in a change in the triplet grouping of nucleotides.

free-living flatworm A nonparasitic flatworm.

frequency-dependent selection Selection in which the fitness of a phenotype depends on how common the phenotype is in a population.

fruit A ripened, thickened ovary of a flower, which protects developing seeds and aids in their dispersal.

functional group A specific configuration of atoms commonly attached to the carbon skeletons of organic molecules and involved in chemical reactions.

Fungi (fun´-ji) The kingdom that contains the fungi.

G

gallbladder An organ that stores bile and releases it as needed into the small intestine.

gametangium (gam´-uh-tan´-jē-um) (plural, **gametangia**) A reproductive organ that houses and protects the gametes of a plant.

gamete (gam´-ēt) A sex cell; a haploid egg or sperm. The union of two gametes of opposite sex (fertilization) produces a zygote.

gametogenesis The creation of gametes within the gonads.

gametophyte (guh-mē´-tō-fīt) The multicellular haploid form in the life cycle of organisms undergoing alternation of generations; mitotically produces haploid gametes that unite and grow into the sporophyte generation.

ganglion (gang´-glē-un) (plural, **ganglia**) A cluster of neuron cell bodies in a peripheral nervous system.

gas exchange The exchange of O_2 and CO_2 between an organism and its environment.

gastric juice The collection of fluids (mucus, enzymes, and acid) secreted by the stomach.

gastrin A digestive hormone that stimulates the secretion of gastric juice.

gastropod A member of the largest group of molluscs, including snails and slugs.

gastrovascular cavity A central compartment with a single opening, the mouth; functions in both digestion and nutrient distribution and may also function in circulation, body support, waste disposal, and gas exchange.

gastrula (gas´-trū-luh) The embryonic stage resulting from gastrulation in animal development. Most animals have a gastrula made up of three layers of cells: ectoderm, endoderm, and mesoderm.

gastrulation (gas´-trū-lā´-shun) The second major phase of embryonic development, which transforms the blastula into a gastrula. Gastrulation adds more cells to the embryo and sorts the cells into distinct cell layers.

gel electrophoresis (jel´ ē-lek´-trō-fōr-ē´-sis) A technique for separating and purifying macromolecules, either DNA or proteins. A mixture of the macromolecules is placed on a gel between a positively charged electrode and a negatively charged one. Negative charges on the molecules are attracted to the positive electrode, and the molecules migrate toward that electrode. The molecules separate in the gel according to their rates of migration, which is mostly determined by their size: Smaller molecules generally move faster through the gel, while larger molecules generally move more slowly.

gene A discrete unit of hereditary information consisting of a specific nucleotide sequence in DNA (or RNA, in some viruses). Most of the genes of a eukaryote are located in its chromosomal DNA; a few are carried by the DNA of mitochondria and chloroplasts.

gene cloning The production of multiple copies of a gene.

gene expression The process whereby genetic information flows from genes to proteins; the flow of genetic information from the genotype to the phenotype.

gene flow The transfer of alleles from one population to another as a result of the movement of individuals or their gametes.

gene pool All copies of every type of allele at every locus in all members of the population.

gene regulation The turning on and off of genes within a cell in response to environmental stimuli or other factors (such as developmental stage).

gene therapy A treatment for a disease in which the patient's defective gene is supplemented or altered.

genetic code The set of rules that dictates the amino acid translations of each mRNA nucleotide triplet.

genetic drift A change in the gene pool of a population due to chance. Effects of genetic drift are most pronounced in small populations.

genetic engineering The direct manipulation of genes for practical purposes.

genetic recombination The production, by crossing over and/ or independent assortment of chromosomes during meiosis, of offspring with allele combinations different from those in the parents. The term may also be used more specifically to mean the production by crossing over of eukaryotic or prokaryotic chromosomes with gene combinations different from those in the original chromosomes.

genetically modified organism (GMO) An organism that has acquired one or more genes by artificial means. If the gene is from another species, the organism is also known as a transgenic organism.

genetics The scientific study of heredity. Modern genetics began with the work of Gregor Mendel in the 19th century.

genital herpes A sexually transmitted disease caused by the herpes simplex virus type 2.

genome The complete set of genetic material of an organism or virus.

genomic library (juh-nō´-mik) A collection of cloned DNA fragments that includes an organism's entire genome. Each segment is usually carried by a plasmid or phage.

genomics The study of complete sets of genes and their interactions.

genotype (jē´-nō-tīp) The genetic makeup of an organism.

genus (jē´-nus) (plural, **genera**) In classification, the taxonomic category above species; the first part of a species' binomial; for example, *Homo*.

geologic record A time scale established by geologists that divides Earth's history into four eons—Hadean, Archaean, Proterozoic, and Phanerozoic—and further subdivides it into eras, periods, and epochs.

germinate To start developing or growing.

gestation (jes-tā´-shun) Pregnancy; the state of carrying developing young within the female reproductive tract.

gibberellin (jib´-uh-rel´-in) One of a family of plant hormones that triggers the germination of seeds and interacts with auxins in regulating growth and fruit development.

gill An extension of the body surface of an aquatic animal, specialized for gas exchange and/or suspension feeding.

gizzard A pouch-like organ in a digestive tract where food is mechanically ground.

glans The rounded, highly sensitive head of the clitoris in females and penis in males.

glia A network of supporting cells that is essential for the structural integrity and for the normal functioning of the nervous system.

global climate change Increase in temperature and change in weather patterns all around the planet, due mostly to increasing atmospheric CO_2 levels from the burning of fossil fuels. The increase in temperature, called global warming, is a major aspect of global climate change.

glomeromycete (glō´-mer-ō-mī´-sēt) Member of a group of fungi characterized by a distinct branching form of mycorrhizae (symbiotic relationships with plant roots) called arbuscules.

glomerulus (glō-mer´-ū-lus) (plural, **glomeruli**) In the vertebrate kidney, the part of a nephron consisting of the capillaries that are surrounded by Bowman's capsule; together, a glomerulus and Bowman's capsule produce the filtrate from the blood.

glucagon (glū´-kuh-gon) A peptide hormone, secreted by the islets of Langerhaus in the pancreas, that raises the level of glucose in the blood. It is antagonistic with insulin.

glucocorticoid (glū´-kuh-kor´-tih-koyd) A corticosteroid hormone secreted by the adrenal cortex that increases the blood glucose level and helps maintain the body's response to long-term stress.

glucose A six-carbon monosaccharide that serves as a building block for many polysaccharides and whose oxidation in cellular respiration is a major source of ATP for cells.

glycogen (glī´-kō-jen) An extensively branched glucose storage polysaccharide found in liver and muscle cells; the animal equivalent of starch.

glycolysis (glī-kol´-uh-sis) A series of reactions that ultimately splits glucose into two molecules of pyruvate; the first stage of cellular respiration in all organisms; occurs in the cytosol.

glycoprotein (glī´-kō-prō´-tēn) A protein with one or more short chains of sugars attached to it.

goiter An enlargement of the thyroid gland resulting from a dietary iodine deficiency.

Golgi apparatus (gol´-jē) An organelle in eukaryotic cells consisting of stacks of membranous sacs that modify, store, and ship products of the endoplasmic reticulum.

gonad A sex organ in an animal; an ovary or testis.

Gram stain Microbiological technique to identify the cell wall composition of bacteria. Results categorize bacteria as gram-positive or gram-negative.

gram-positive bacteria Diverse group of bacteria with a cell wall that is structurally less complex and contains more peptidoglycan than that of gram-negative bacteria. Gram-positive bacteria are usually less toxic than gram-negative bacteria.

granum (gran´-um) (plural, **grana**) A stack of membrane-bounded thylakoids in a chloroplast. Grana are the sites where light energy is trapped by chlorophyll and converted to chemical energy during the light reactions of photosynthesis.

gravitropism (grav´-uh-trō´-pizm) A plant's directional growth in response to gravity.

gray matter Regions within the central nervous system composed mainly of nerve cell bodies and dendrites.

green alga A member of a group of photosynthetic protists that includes chlorophytes and charophyceans, the closest living relatives of land plants. Green algae include unicellular, colonial, and multicellular species and belong to the supergroup Archaeplastida.

greenhouse effect The warming of Earth due to the atmospheric accumulation of CO_2 and certain other gases, which absorb infrared radiation and reradiate some of it back toward Earth.

ground tissue system A tissue of mostly parenchyma cells that makes up the bulk of a young plant and is continuous throughout its body. The ground tissue system fills the space between the epidermis and the vascular tissue system.

growth factor A protein secreted by certain body cells that stimulates other cells to divide.

growth hormone (GH) A protein hormone secreted by the anterior pituitary that promotes development and growth and stimulates metabolism.

guanine (G) (gwa´-nēn) A double-ring nitrogenous base found in DNA and RNA.

guard cell A specialized epidermal cell in plants that regulates the size of a stoma, allowing gas exchange between the surrounding air and the photosynthetic cells in the leaf.

gymnosperm (jim´-nō-sperm) A naked-seed plant. Its seed is said to be naked because it is not enclosed in an ovary.

H

habitat A place where an organism lives; the environment in which an organism lives.

habituation Learning not to respond to a repeated stimulus that conveys little or no information.

hair cell A type of mechanoreceptor that detects sound waves and other forms of movement in air or water.

haploid In the life cycle of an organism that reproduces sexually, a cell containing a single set of chromosomes; an *n* cell.

Hardy-Weinberg principle The principle that frequencies of alleles and genotypes in a population remain constant from generation to generation, provided that only Mendelian segregation and recombination of alleles are at work.

heart A muscular pump that propels a circulatory fluid (blood) through vessels to the body.

heart attack The damage or death of cardiac muscle cells and the resulting failure of the heart to deliver enough blood to the body.

heart rate The frequency of heart contraction, usually expressed in number of beats per minute.

heartwood In the center of trees, the darkened, older layers of secondary xylem made up of cells that no longer transport water and are clogged with resins. *See also* sapwood.

heat Thermal energy in transfer from one body of matter to another.

helper T cell A type of lymphocyte that, when activated, secretes stimulatory signals that promote the response of B cells (humoral response) and cytotoxic T cells (cell-mediated response) to antigens.

hemoglobin (hē´-mō-glō-bin) An iron-containing protein in red blood cells that reversibly binds O_2.

hepatic portal vein A blood vessel that conveys nutrient-laden blood from capillaries surrounding the intestine directly to the liver.

herbivore An animal that mainly eats plants or algae. *See also* carnivore; omnivore.

herbivory Consumption of plant parts or algae by an animal.

heredity The transmission of traits (inherited features) from one generation to the next.

hermaphroditism (her-maf´-rō-dī-tizm) A condition in which an individual has both female and male gonads and functions as both a male and female in sexual reproduction by producing both sperm and eggs.

heterokaryotic stage (het´-er-ō-ker-ē-ot´-ik) A fungal life cycle stage that contains two genetically different haploid nuclei in the same cell.

heterotroph (het´-er-ō-trōf) An organism that obtains organic food molecules by eating other organisms or substances derived from them; a consumer or a decomposer in a food chain.

heterozygote advantage (het´-er-ō-zī´-gōt) Greater reproductive success of heterozygous individuals compared to homozygotes; tends to preserve variation in gene pools.

heterozygous (het´-er-ō-zī´-gus) Having two different alleles for a given gene.

high-density lipoprotein (HDL) A cholesterol-carrying particle in the blood, made up of thousands of cholesterol molecules and other lipids bound to a protein. HDL scavenges excess cholesterol.

hindbrain One of three ancestral and embryonic regions of the vertebrate brain; develops into the medulla oblongata, pons, and cerebellum.

hinge joint A joint that allows movement in only one plane. In humans, examples include the elbow and knee.

hippocampus (hip´-uh-kam´-pus) An integrative center of the cerebrum; functionally, the part of the limbic system that plays a central role in the formation of memories and their recall.

histamine (his´-tuh-mēn) A chemical alarm signal released by mast cells that causes blood vessels to dilate and become more permeable in inflammatory and allergic responses.

histone (his´-tōn) A small protein molecule associated with DNA and important in DNA packing in the eukaryotic chromosome.

Eukaryotic chromatin consists of roughly equal parts of DNA and histone protein.

HIV (human immunodeficiency virus) The retrovirus that attacks the human immune system and causes AIDS.

homeobox (hō´-mē-ō-boks´) A 180-nucleotide sequence within a homeotic gene and some other developmental genes.

homeostasis (hō´-mē-ō-stā´-sis) The steady state of body functioning; a state of equilibrium characterized by a dynamic interplay between outside forces that tend to change an organism's internal environment and the internal control mechanisms that oppose such changes.

homeotic gene (hō´-mē-ot´-ik) A master control gene that determines the identity of a body structure of a developing organism, presumably by controlling the developmental fate of groups of cells.

hominin (hah´-mi-nin) Member of a species on the human branch of the evolutionary tree; a species more closely related to humans than to chimpanzees.

homologous chromosomes (hō-mol´-uh-gus) The two chromosomes that make up a matched pair in a diploid cell. Homologous chromosomes are of the same length, centromere position, and staining pattern and possess genes for the same characters at corresponding loci. One homologous chromosome is inherited from the organism's father, the other from the mother.

homologous structures (hō-mol´-uh-gus) Structures in different species that are similar because of common ancestry.

homology (hō-mol´-uh-jē) Similarity in characters resulting from a shared ancestry.

homozygous (hō´-mō-zī´-gus) Having two identical alleles for a given gene.

horizontal gene transfer The transfer of genes from one genome to another through mechanisms such as transposable elements, plasmid exchange, viral activity, and perhaps fusions of different organisms.

hormone (1) In animals, a regulatory chemical that travels in the blood from its production site, usually an endocrine gland, to other sites, where target cells respond to the regulatory signal. (2) In plants, a chemical that is produced in one part of the plant and travels to another part, where it acts on target cells to change their functioning.

human chorionic gonadotropin (hCG) (kōr´-ē-on´-ik gō-na´-dō-trō´-pin) A hormone secreted by the chorion that maintains the production of estrogen and progesterone by the corpus luteum of the ovary during the first few months of pregnancy. hCG secreted in the urine is the target of many home pregnancy tests.

Human Genome Project (hGP) An international collaborative effort to map and sequence the DNA of the entire human genome. The project was begun in 1990 and completed in 2004.

humoral immune response The branch of adaptive immunity that involves the activation of B cells and that leads to the production of antibodies, which defend against bacteria and viruses in body fluids.

humus (hyū´-mus) Decomposing organic material found in topsoil.

Huntington's disease A human genetic disease caused by a single dominant allele; characterized by uncontrollable body movements and degeneration of the nervous system; usually fatal 10 to 20 years after the onset of symptoms.

hybrid An offspring of parents of two different species or of two different varieties of one species; an offspring of two parents that differ in one or more inherited traits; an individual that is heterozygous for one or more pairs of genes.

hybrid zone A geographic region in which members of different species meet and mate, producing at least some hybrid offspring.

hydrocarbon An organic compound composed only of the elements carbon and hydrogen.

hydrogen bond A type of weak chemical bond formed when the slightly positive hydrogen atom of a polar covalent bond in one molecule is attracted to the slightly negative atom of a polar

covalent bond in another molecule (or in another region of the same molecule).

hydrolysis (hī-drol´-uh-sis) A chemical reaction that breaks bonds between two molecules by the addition of water; process by which polymers are broken down and an essential part of digestion.

hydrophilic (hī´-drō-fil´-ik) "Water-loving"; pertaining to polar or charged molecules (or parts of molecules) that are soluble in water.

hydrophobic (hī´-drō-fō´-bik) "Water-fearing"; pertaining to nonpolar molecules (or parts of molecules) that do not dissolve in water.

hydrostatic skeleton A skeletal system composed of fluid held under pressure in a closed body compartment; the main skeleton of most cnidarians, flatworms, nematodes, and annelids.

hydroxyl group (hī-drok´-sil) A chemical group consisting of an oxygen atom bonded to a hydrogen atom.

hyperglycemia An abnormally high level of glucose in the blood that results when the pancreas does not secrete enough insulin or cells do not respond to insulin. Hyperglycemia is a characteristic of diabetes.

hypertension A disorder in which blood pressure remains abnormally high.

hypertonic Referring to a solution that, when surrounding a cell, will cause the cell to lose water.

hypha (hī´-fuh) (plural, **hyphae**) One of many filaments making up the body of a fungus.

hypoglycemia (hī´-pō-glī-sē´-mē-uh) An abnormally low level of glucose in the blood that results when the pancreas secretes too much insulin into the blood.

hypothalamus (hī-pō-thal´-uh-mus) The master control center of the endocrine system, located in the ventral portion of the vertebrate forebrain. The hypothalamus functions in maintaining homeostasis, especially in coordinating the endocrine and nervous systems; secretes hormones of the posterior pituitary and releasing hormones that regulate the anterior pituitary.

hypothesis (hī-poth´-uh-sis) (plural, **hypotheses**) A testable explanation for a set of observations based on the available data and guided by inductive reasoning.

hypotonic Referring to a solution that, when surrounding a cell, will cause the cell to take up water.

I

immune system An animal body's system of defenses against agents that cause disease.

immunodeficiency disorder An immunological disorder in which the immune system lacks one or more components, making the body susceptible to infectious agents that would ordinarily not be pathogenic.

imperfect fungus A fungus with no known sexual stage.

impotence The inability to maintain an erection; also called erectile dysfunction.

imprinting Learning that is limited to a specific critical period in an animal's life and that is generally irreversible.

in vitro **fertilization (IVF)** (vē´-tro) Uniting sperm and egg in a laboratory container, followed by the placement of a resulting early embryo in the mother's uterus.

inclusive fitness An individual's success at perpetuating its genes by producing its own offspring and by helping close relatives to produce offspring.

incomplete dominance A type of inheritance in which the phenotype of a heterozygote (*Aa*) is intermediate between the phenotypes of the two types of homozygotes (*AA* and *aa*).

incomplete metamorphosis A type of development in certain insects in which development from larva to adult is achieved by multiple molts, but without forming a pupa.

indeterminate growth Growth that continues throughout life, as in most plants. *See also* determinate growth.

induced fit The change in shape of the active site of an enzyme, caused by entry of the substrate so that it binds the substrate snugly.

induction During embryonic development, the influence of one group of cells on an adjacent group of cells.

inferior vena cava (vē´-nuh kā´-vuh) A large vein that returns oxygen-poor blood to the heart from the lower, or posterior, part of the body. *See also* superior vena cava.

infertility The inability to conceive after one year of regular, unprotected intercourse.

inflammatory response An innate body defense in vertebrates caused by a release of histamine and other chemical alarm signals that trigger increased blood flow, a local increase in white blood cells, and fluid leakage from the blood. The resulting inflammatory response includes redness, heat, and swelling in the affected tissues.

ingestion The act of eating; the first main stage of food processing in animals.

ingroup In a cladistic study of evolutionary relationships, the group of taxa whose evolutionary relationships are being determined. *See also* outgroup.

inhibiting hormone A kind of hormone released from the hypothalamus that prompts the anterior pituitary to stop secreting hormone.

innate behavior Behavior that is under strong genetic control and is performed in virtually the same way by all members of a species.

innate immunity The kind of immunity that is present in an animal before exposure to pathogens and is effective from birth. Innate immune defenses include barriers, phagocytic cells, antimicrobial proteins, the inflammatory response, and natural killer cells.

inner ear One of three main regions of the vertebrate ear; includes the cochlea, organ of Corti, and semicircular canals.

insulin A protein hormone, secreted by the islets of Langerhans in the pancreas, that lowers the level of glucose in the blood. It is antagonistic with glucagon.

integration The analysis and interpretation of sensory signals within neural processing centers of the central nervous system.

integrin A transmembrane protein that interconnects the extracellular matrix and the cytoskeleton in animal cells.

integumentary system (in-teg´-yū-ment-ter-ē) The organ system consisting of the skin and its derivatives, such as hair and nails in mammals. The integumentary system helps protect the body from drying out, mechanical injury, and infection.

interferon (in´-ter-fer´-on) An innate defensive protein produced by virus-infected vertebrate cells and capable of helping other cells resist viruses.

intermediate One of the compounds that form between the initial reactant and the final product in a metabolic pathway, such as between glucose and pyruvate in glycolysis.

intermediate filament An intermediate-sized protein fiber that is one of the three main kinds of fibers making up the cytoskeleton of eukaryotic cells. Intermediate filaments are ropelike, made of fibrous proteins.

internal fertilization Reproduction in which sperm are typically deposited in or near the female reproductive tract and fertilization occurs within the tract.

interneuron (in´-ter-nūr´-on) A nerve cell, located entirely within the central nervous system, that integrates sensory signals and relays signals to other interneurons and to motor neurons.

internode The portion of a plant stem between two nodes.

interphase The period in the eukaryotic cell cycle when the cell is not actually dividing. Interphase constitutes the majority of the time spent in the cell cycle. *See also* mitotic phase (M phase).

interspecific competition Competition between individuals or populations of two or more species that require the same limited resource.

interspecific interactions Relationships between individuals of different species in a community.

interstitial fluid (in´-ter-stish´-ul) An aqueous solution that surrounds body cells and through which materials pass back and forth between the blood and the body tissues.

intertidal zone (in´-ter-tīd´-ul) A shallow zone where the waters of an estuary or ocean meet land.

intestine The region of a digestive tract located between the gizzard or stomach and the anus and where chemical digestion and nutrient absorption usually occur.

intraspecific competition Competition between members of a population for a limited resource.

intrauterine device (IUD) A T-shaped device that, when placed within the uterus, acts as female contraception.

intron (in´-tron) An internal, noncoding region of a gene that does not become part of the final messenger RNA molecule and is therefore not expressed.

invasive species A non-native species that spreads beyond its original point of introduction and causes environmental or economic damage.

inversion A change in a chromosome resulting from reattachment of a chromosome fragment to the original chromosome, but in the reverse direction. Mutagens and errors during meiosis can cause inversions.

invertebrate An animal that lacks a backbone.

ion (ī-on) An atom or group of atoms that has gained or lost one or more electrons, thus acquiring a charge.

ionic bond (ī-on´-ik) A chemical bond resulting from the attraction between oppositely charged ions.

iris The colored part of the vertebrate eye, formed by the anterior portion of the choroid.

isomers (ī´-sō-mers) Organic compounds with the same molecular formula but different structures and, therefore, different properties.

isotonic (ī-sō-ton´-ik) Referring to a solution that, when surrounding a cell, causes no net movement of water into or out of the cell.

isotope (ī´-sō-tōp) One of several atomic forms of an element, each with the same number of protons but a different number of neutrons.

K

karyotype (kār´-ē-ō-tīp) A display of micrographs of the metaphase chromosomes of a cell, arranged by size and centromere position. Karyotypes may be used to identify certain chromosomal abnormalities.

kelp Large, multicellular brown algae that form undersea "forests."

keystone species A species whose impact on the community is much larger than its biomass or abundance would indicate.

kilocalorie (kcal) A quantity of heat equal to 1,000 calories. Used to measure the energy content of food, it is usually called a "Calorie."

kin selection The natural selection that favors altruistic behavior by enhancing reproductive success of relatives.

kinesis (kuh-nē´-sis) (plural, **kineses**) Random movement in response to a stimulus.

kinetic energy (kuh-net´-ik) The energy associated with the motion of objects. Moving matter does work by imparting motion to other matter.

kingdom In classification, the broad taxonomic category above phylum.

K-selection The concept that in certain (*K*-selected) populations, life history is centered on producing relatively few offspring that have a good chance of survival.

L

labia majora (lā´-bē-uh muh-jor´-uh) A pair of outer thickened folds of skin that protect the female genital region.

labia minora (lā´-bē-uh mi-nor´-uh) A pair of inner folds of skin, bordering and protecting the female genital region.

labor The series of events that expel the infant from the uterus.

lactic acid fermentation Glycolysis followed by the reduction of pyruvate to lactate, regenerating NAD^+.

lancelet One of a group of small, bladelike, invertebrate chordates.

landscape Several different ecosystems linked by exchanges of energy, materials, and organisms.

landscape ecology The application of ecological principles to the study of the structure and dynamics of a collection of ecosystems; the scientific study of the biodiversity of interacting ecosystems.

large intestine The portion of the alimentary canal between the small intestine and the anus; functions mainly in water absorption and the formation of feces.

larva (lar´-vuh) (plural, **larvae**) A free-living, sexually immature form in some animal life cycles that may differ from the adult in morphology, nutrition, and habitat.

larynx (lār´-inks) The upper portion of the respiratory tract containing the vocal cords; also called the voice box.

lateral line system A row of sensory organs along each side of a fish's body that is sensitive to changes in water pressure. It enables a fish to detect minor vibrations in the water.

lateral meristem Plant tissue made up of undifferentiated cells that enable roots and shoots of woody plants to thicken. The vascular cambium and cork cambium are lateral meristems.

lateralization The phenomenon in which the two hemispheres of the brain become specialized for different functions during infant and child brain development.

law of independent assortment A general rule of inheritance (originally formulated by Gregor Mendel) that when gametes form during meiosis, each pair of alleles for a particular character segregates independently of other pairs; also known as Mendel's second law of inheritance.

law of segregation A general rule in inheritance (originally formulated by Gregor Mendel) that individuals have two alleles for each gene and that when gametes form by meiosis, the two alleles separate, each resulting gamete ending up with only one allele of each gene; also known as Mendel's first law of inheritance.

leaf The main site of photosynthesis in a plant; typically consists of a flattened blade and a stalk (petiole) that joins the leaf to the stem.

learning Modification of behavior as a result of specific experiences.

leech A member of one of the three large groups of annelids, known for its bloodsucking ability. *See also* annelid.

lens The structure in an eye that focuses light rays onto the retina.

leukemia (lū-kē´-mē-ah) A type of cancer of the blood-forming tissues, characterized by an excessive production of white blood cells and an abnormally high number of them in the blood; cancer of the bone marrow cells that produce leukocytes.

leukocyte (lū´-kō-sȳt´) A blood cell that functions in fighting infections; also called a white blood cell.

lichen (lī´-ken) A close association between a fungus and an alga or between a fungus and a cyanobacterium, some of which are known to be beneficial to both partners.

life cycle The entire sequence of stages in the life of an organism, from the adults of one generation to the adults of the next.

life history The traits that affect an organism's schedule of reproduction and death, including age at first reproduction, frequency of reproduction, number of offspring, and amount of parental care.

life table A listing of survivals and deaths in a population in a particular time period and predictions of how long, on average, an individual of a given age will live.

ligament A type of fibrous connective tissue that joins bones together at joints.

light microscope (LM) An optical instrument with lenses that refract (bend) visible light to magnify images and project them into a viewer's eye or onto photographic film.

light reactions The first of two stages in photosynthesis; the steps in which solar energy is absorbed and converted to the chemical energy of ATP and NADPH, releasing oxygen in the process.

lignin A chemical that hardens the cell walls of plants.

limbic system (lim´-bik) A functional unit of several integrating and relay centers located deep in the human forebrain; interacts with the cerebral cortex in creating emotions and storing memories.

limiting factor An environmental factor that restricts population growth.

linkage map A listing of the relative locations of genes along a chromosome, as determined by recombination frequencies.

linked genes Genes located near each other on the same chromosome that tend to be inherited together.

lipid An organic compound consisting mainly of carbon and hydrogen atoms linked by nonpolar covalent bonds, making the compound mostly hydrophobic. Lipids include fats, phospholipids, and steroids and are insoluble in water.

liver The largest organ in the vertebrate body. The liver performs diverse functions, such as producing bile, preparing nitrogenous wastes for disposal, and detoxifying poisonous chemicals in the blood.

lobe-fin A bony fish with strong, muscular fins supported by bones.

locomotion Active movement from place to place.

locus (plural, **loci**) The particular site where a gene is found on a chromosome. Homologous chromosomes have corresponding gene loci.

logistic growth model A mathematical description of idealized population growth that is restricted by limiting factors.

long-day plant A plant that flowers in late spring or early summer, when day length is long. Long-day plants actually flower in response to short nights.

long-term memory The ability to hold, associate, and recall information over one's lifetime.

loop of Henle (hen´-lē) In the vertebrate kidney, the portion of a nephron that helps concentrate the filtrate while conveying it between a proximal tubule and a distal tubule.

loose connective tissue The most widespread connective tissue in the vertebrate body. It binds epithelia to underlying tissues and functions as packing material, holding organs in place.

low-density lipoprotein (LDL) A cholesterol-carrying particle in the blood, made up of thousands of cholesterol molecules and other lipids bound to a protein. An LDL particle transports cholesterol from the liver for incorporation into cell membranes.

lung An infolded respiratory surface of terrestrial vertebrates that connects to the atmosphere by narrow tubes.

lymph A colorless fluid, derived from interstitial fluid, that circulates in the lymphatic system.

lymph node An organ of the immune system located along a lymph vessel. Lymph nodes filter lymph and contain cells that attack viruses and bacteria.

lymphatic system (lim-fat´-ik) The vertebrate organ system through which lymph circulates; includes lymph vessels, lymph nodes, and the spleen. The lymphatic system helps remove toxins and pathogens from the blood and interstitial fluid and returns fluid and solutes from the interstitial fluid to the circulatory system.

lymphocyte (lim´-fuh-sīt) A type of white blood cell that is chiefly responsible for the adaptive immune response and is found mostly in the lymphatic system. *See also* B cell; T cell.

lysogenic cycle (lī´-sō-jen´-ik) A type of bacteriophage replication cycle in which the viral genome is incorporated into the bacterial host chromosome as a prophage. New phages are not produced, and the host cell is not killed or lysed unless the viral genome leaves the host chromosome.

lysosome (lī-sō-sōm) A digestive organelle in eukaryotic cells; contains hydrolytic enzymes that digest engulfed food or damaged organelles.

lytic cycle (lit´-ik) A type of viral replication cycle resulting in the release of new viruses by lysis (breaking open) of the host cell.

M

macroevolution Evolutionary change above the species level, encompassing the origin of new taxonomic groups, adaptive radiation, and mass extinction.

macromolecule A giant molecule formed by the joining of smaller molecules, usually by a dehydration reaction: a protein, carbohydrate, or nucleic acid.

macronutrient A chemical substance that an organism must obtain in relatively large amounts. *See also* micronutrient.

macrophage (mak´-rō-fāj) A large, amoeboid, phagocytic white blood cell that functions in innate immunity by destroying microbes and in adaptive immunity as an antigen-presenting cell.

major histocompatibility complex (MHC) molecule *See* self protein.

malignant tumor An abnormal tissue mass that can spread into neighboring tissue and to other parts of the body; a cancerous tumor.

malnutrition Health problems caused by a diet that contains insufficient calories or nutrients.

mammal Member of a clade of amniotes that possess mammary glands and hair.

mantle In a mollusc, the outgrowth of the body surface that drapes over the animal. The mantle produces the shell and forms the mantle cavity.

marsupial (mar-sū´-pē-ul) A pouched mammal, such as a kangaroo, opossum, or koala. Marsupials give birth to embryonic offspring that complete development while housed in a pouch and attached to nipples on the mother's abdomen.

mass number The sum of the number of protons and neutrons in an atom's nucleus.

matter Anything that occupies space and has mass.

mechanoreceptor (mek´-uh-nō-ri-sep´-ter) A sensory receptor that detects changes in the environment associated with pressure, touch, stretch, motion, or sound.

medulla oblongata (meh-duh´-luh ob´-long-got´-uh) Part of the vertebrate hindbrain, continuous with the spinal cord; passes data between the spinal cord and forebrain and controls autonomic, homeostatic functions, including breathing, heart rate, swallowing, and digestion.

medusa (med-ū´-suh) (plural, **medusae**) One of two types of cnidarian body forms; an umbrella-like body form.

meiosis (mī-ō´-sis) In a sexually reproducing organism, the division of a single diploid nucleus into four haploid daughter nuclei. Meiosis and cytokinesis produce haploid gametes from diploid cells in the reproductive organs of the parents.

membrane potential The charge difference between a cell's cytoplasm and extracellular fluid due to the differential distribution of ions.

memory The ability to store and retrieve information. *See also* long-term memory; short-term memory.

memory cell A clone of long-lived lymphocytes formed during the primary adaptive immune response. Memory cells remain in lymph nodes until activated by exposure to the same antigen that triggered their formation. When activated, a memory cell forms a large clone that mounts the secondary immune response.

meninges (muh-nin´-jēz) Layers of connective tissue that enwrap and protect the brain and spinal cord.

menstrual cycle (men´-strū-ul) The hormonally synchronized cyclic buildup and breakdown of the endometrium of some primates, including humans.

menstruation (men´-strū-ā´-shun) Uterine bleeding resulting from shedding of the endometrium during a menstrual cycle.

meristem (mer´-eh-stem) Plant tissue consisting of undifferentiated cells that divide and generate new cells and tissues.

mesoderm (mez´-ō-derm) The middle layer of the three embryonic cell layers in a gastrula. The mesoderm gives rise to muscles, bones, the dermis of the skin, and most other organs in the adult.

mesophyll (mes´-ō-fil) Leaf cells specialized for photosynthesis; a leaf's ground tissue system.

messenger RNA (mRNA) The type of ribonucleic acid that encodes genetic information from DNA and conveys it to ribosomes, where the information is translated into amino acid sequences.

metabolic pathway A series of chemical reactions that either builds a complex molecule or breaks down a complex molecule into simpler compounds.

metabolic rate The total amount of energy an animal uses in a unit of time.

metabolism The totality of an organism's chemical reactions.

metamorphosis (met´-uh-mōr´-fuh-sis) The transformation of a larva into an adult. *See also* complete metamorphosis; incomplete metamorphosis.

metaphase (met´-eh-fāz) The third stage of mitosis, during which all the cell's duplicated chromosomes are lined up at an imaginary plane equidistant between the poles of the mitotic spindle.

metastasis (muh-tas´-tuh-sis) The spread of cancer cells beyond their original site.

methanogen (meth-an´-ō-jen) An archaean that produces methane as a metabolic waste product.

methyl group A chemical group consisting of a carbon atom bonded to three hydrogen atoms.

microbiota The community of microorganisms that live in and on the body of an animal.

microevolution A change in a population's gene pool over generations.

microfilament The thinnest of the three main kinds of protein fibers making up the cytoskeleton of a eukaryotic cell; a solid, helical rod composed of the globular protein actin.

micronutrient An element that an organism needs in very small amounts and that functions as a component or cofactor of enzymes. *See also* macronutrient.

microRNA (miRNA) A small, single-stranded RNA molecule that associates with one or more proteins in a complex that can degrade or prevent translation of an mRNA with a complementary sequence.

microtubule The thickest of the three main kinds of fibers making up the cytoskeleton of a eukaryotic cell; a hollow tube made of globular proteins called tubulins; found in cilia and flagella.

microvillus (plural, **microvilli**) One of many microscopic projections on the epithelial cells in the lumen of the small intestine. Microvilli increase the surface area of the small intestine.

midbrain One of three ancestral and embryonic regions of the vertebrate brain; develops into sensory integrating and relay centers that send sensory information to the cerebrum.

middle ear One of three main regions of the vertebrate ear; a chamber containing three small bones (the hammer, anvil, and stirrup) that convey vibrations from the eardrum to the oval window.

migration The regular back-and-forth movement of animals between two geographic areas at particular times of the year.

millipede A terrestrial arthropod that has two pairs of short legs for each of its numerous body segments and that eats decaying plant matter.

mineral In nutrition, a simple inorganic nutrient that an organism requires in small amounts for proper body functioning.

mineralocorticoid (min´-er-uh-lō-kort´-uh-koyd) A corticosteroid hormone secreted by the adrenal cortex that helps maintain salt and water homeostasis and may increase blood pressure in response to long-term stress.

missense mutation A change in the nucleotide sequence of a gene that alters the amino acid sequence of the resulting polypeptide. In a missense mutation, a codon is changed from encoding one amino acid to encoding a different amino acid.

mitochondrial matrix (mī´-tō-kon´-drē-ul) The compartment of the mitochondrion enclosed by the inner membrane and containing enzymes and substrates for the citric acid cycle.

mitochondrion (mī´-tō-kon´-drē-on) (plural, **mitochondria**) An organelle in eukaryotic cells where cellular respiration occurs. Enclosed by two membranes, it is where most of the cell's ATP is made.

mitosis (mī´-tō-sis) The division of a single nucleus into two genetically identical nuclei. Mitosis and cytokinesis make up the mitotic (M) phase of the cell cycle.

mitotic phase (M phase) The part of the cell cycle when the nucleus divides (via mitosis), its chromosomes are distributed to the daughter nuclei, and the cytoplasm divides (via cytokinesis), producing two daughter cells.

mitotic spindle A football-shaped structure formed of microtubules and associated proteins that is involved in the movement of chromosomes during mitosis and meiosis.

mixotroph A protist that is capable of both autotrophy and heterotrophy.

mold A rapidly growing fungus that reproduces asexually by producing spores.

molecular biology The study of biological structures, functions, and heredity at the molecular level.

molecular clock A method for estimating the time required for a given amount of evolutionary change, based on the observation that some regions of genomes evolve at constant rates.

molecular systematics A scientific discipline that uses nucleic acids or other molecules in different species to infer evolutionary relationships.

molecule Two or more atoms held together by covalent bonds.

mollusc (mol´-lusk) A soft-bodied animal characterized by a muscular foot, mantle, mantle cavity, and visceral mass. Molluscs include gastropods (snails and slugs), bivalves (clams, oysters, and scallops), and cephalopods (squids and octopuses).

molting The process of shedding an old exoskeleton or cuticle and secreting a new, larger one.

monoclonal antibody (mAb) (mon´-ō-klōn´-ul) An antibody secreted by a clone of cells and therefore specific for the one antigen that triggered the development of the clone.

monocot (mon´-ō-kot) A flowering plant whose embryos have a single seed leaf, or cotyledon.

monogamous Referring to a type of relationship in which a male and a female mate exclusively with each other, and both parents care for the offspring.

monohybrid cross An experimental mating of individuals that are heterozygous for the character being followed (or the self-pollination of a heterozygous plant).

monomer (mon´-uh-mer) The subunit that serves as a building block of a polymer.

monophyletic (mon´-ō-fī-let´-ik) Pertaining to a group of taxa that consists of a common ancestor and all its descendants, equivalent to a clade.

monosaccharide (mon´-ō-sak´-uh-rīd) The simplest carbohydrate; a simple sugar with a molecular formula that is generally some multiple of CH_2O. Monosaccharides are the monomers of disaccharides and polysaccharides.

monotreme (mon´-uh-trēm) An egg-laying mammal, such as the duck-billed platypus.

morning after pill (MAP) A birth control pill taken within three days of unprotected intercourse to prevent fertilization or implantation.

morphological species concept A definition of species in terms of measurable anatomical criteria.

motor neuron A nerve cell that conveys command signals from the central nervous system to effector cells, such as muscle cells or gland cells.

motor output The conduction of signals from a processing center in the central nervous system to effector cells.

motor system The component of the vertebrate peripheral nervous system that carries signals to and from skeletal muscles, mainly in response to external stimuli. Most actions of the motor system are voluntary.

motor unit A motor neuron and all the muscle fibers it controls.

movement corridor A series of small clumps or a narrow strip of quality habitat (usable by organisms) that connects otherwise isolated patches of quality habitat.

muscle fiber Muscle cell.

muscle tissue Tissue consisting of long muscle cells that can contract, either on its own or when stimulated by nerve impulses; the most abundant tissue in a typical animal. *See* skeletal muscle; cardiac muscle; smooth muscle.

muscular system The organ system that includes all the skeletal muscles in the body. (Cardiac muscle and smooth muscle are components of other organ systems.)

mutagen (myū´-tuh-jen) A chemical or physical agent that interacts with DNA and causes a mutation.

mutagenesis (myū´-tuh-jen´-uh-sis) The creation of a change in the nucleotide sequence of an organism's DNA.

mutation A change in the genetic information of a cell; the ultimate source of genetic diversity. A mutation also can occur in the DNA or RNA of a virus.

mutualism An interspecific relationship in which both partners benefit.

mycelium (mī-sē´-lē-um) (plural, **mycelia**) The densely branched network of hyphae in a fungus.

mycorrhiza (mī-kō-rī´-zuh) (plural, **mycorrhizae**) A close association of plant roots and fungi that is beneficial to both partners.

myelin sheath (mī´-uh-lin) A series of cells, each wound around, and thus insulating, the axon of a nerve cell in vertebrates. Each pair of cells in the sheath is separated by a space called a node of Ranvier.

myofibril (mī´-ō-fī´-bril) A contractile strand in a muscle cell (fiber), made up of many sarcomeres. Longitudinal bundles of myofibrils make up a muscle fiber.

myosin A type of protein filament that interacts with actin filaments to cause cell contraction.

N

NAD⁺ Nicotinamide adenine dinucleotide; a coenzyme that can accept electrons during the redox reactions of cellular metabolism. It cycles between oxidized (NAD^+) and reduced (NADH) states.

NADP⁺ Nicotinamide adenine dinucleotide phosphate, an electron acceptor that, as NADPH, temporarily stores energized electrons produced during the light reactions.

natural killer (NK) cell A cell type that provides an innate immune response by attacking cancer cells and infected body cells, especially those harboring viruses.

natural selection A process in which individuals with certain inherited traits are more likely to survive and reproduce than are individuals that do not have those traits.

nearsightedness An inability to focus on distant objects; occurs when the eyeball is longer than normal and the lens focuses distant objects in front of the retina; also called myopia.

negative feedback A primary mechanism of homeostasis, whereby a change in a physiological variable triggers a response that counteracts the initial change. Negative feedback is a common control mechanism in which a chemical reaction, metabolic pathway, or hormone-secreting gland is inhibited by the products of the reaction, pathway, or gland. As the concentration of the products builds up, the product molecules themselves inhibit the process that produced them.

negative pressure breathing A breathing system in which air is pulled into the lungs.

nematode (nem´-uh-tōd) A roundworm, characterized by a pseudocoelom, a cylindrical, wormlike body form, and a tough cuticle that is molted to permit growth.

nephron The tubular excretory unit and associated blood vessels of the vertebrate kidney; extracts filtrate from the blood and refines it into urine. The nephron is the functional unit of the urinary system.

nerve A cable-like bundle of neurons tightly wrapped in connective tissue.

nerve cord An elongated bundle of neurons, usually extending longitudinally from the brain or anterior ganglia. One or more nerve cords and the brain make up the central nervous system in many animals.

nerve net A weblike system of interconnected neurons, characteristic of radially symmetric animals such as a hydra.

nervous system The organ system that forms a communication and coordination network between all parts of an animal's body.

nervous tissue Tissue made up of neurons and supportive cells called glia.

neural tube (nyūr´-ul) An embryonic cylinder that develops from the ectoderm after gastrulation and gives rise to the brain and spinal cord.

neuron (nyūr´-on) A nerve cell; the fundamental structural and functional unit of the nervous system, specialized for carrying signals from one location in the body to another.

neurosecretory cell A nerve cell that synthesizes hormones and secretes them into the blood and also conducts nerve signals.

neurotransmitter A chemical messenger that carries information from a transmitting neuron to a receiving cell, either another neuron or an effector cell.

neutron A subatomic particle having no electrical charge, found in the nucleus of an atom.

neutrophil (nyū´-truh-fil) The most abundant type of white blood cell; functions in innate immunity as a type of phagocytic cell that tends to self-destruct as it destroys foreign invaders.

nitrogen fixation The conversion of atmospheric nitrogen (N_2) to nitrogen compounds (NH_4^+, NO_3^-) that plants can absorb and use.

node The point of attachment of a leaf on a stem.

node of Ranvier (ron´-vē-ā) An unmyelinated region on a myelinated axon of a nerve cell, where nerve signals are regenerated.

noncompetitive inhibitor A substance that reduces the activity of an enzyme without entering an active site. By binding elsewhere on the enzyme, a noncompetitive inhibitor changes the shape of the enzyme so that the active site no longer effectively catalyzes the conversion of substrate to product.

nondisjunction An accident of meiosis or mitosis in which a pair of homologous chromosomes or a pair of sister chromatids fail to separate at anaphase.

nonpolar covalent bond A type of covalent bond in which electrons are shared equally between two atoms of similar electronegativity.

nonself molecule A foreign antigen; a protein or other macromolecule that is not part of an organism's body. *See also* self protein.

nonsense mutation A change in the nucleotide sequence of a gene that converts an amino-acid-encoding codon to a stop codon. A nonsense mutation results in a shortened polypeptide.

norepinephrine (nor´-ep-uh-nef´-rin) An amine hormone (also called noradrenaline) secreted by the adrenal medulla that prepares body organs for action (fight or flight); also serves as a neurotransmitter.

notochord (nō´-tuh-kord) A flexible, cartilage-like, longitudinal rod located between the digestive tract and nerve cord in chordate animals; present only in embryos in many species.

nuclear envelope A double membrane that encloses the nucleus, perforated with pores that regulate traffic with the cytoplasm.

nuclear transplantation A technique in which the nucleus of one cell is placed into another cell that already has a nucleus or in which the nucleus has been previously destroyed.

nucleic acid (nū-klā´-ik) A polymer consisting of many nucleotide monomers; serves as a blueprint for proteins and, through the actions of proteins, for all cellular structures and activities. The two types of nucleic acids are DNA and RNA.

nucleic acid probe (nū-klā´-ik) In DNA technology, a radioactively or fluorescently labeled single-stranded nucleic acid molecule used to find a specific gene or other nucleotide sequence within a mass of DNA. The probe hydrogen-bonds to the complementary sequence in the targeted DNA.

nucleoid (nū´-klē-oyd) A non–membrane-bounded region in a prokaryotic cell where the DNA is concentrated.

nucleolus (nū-klē´-ō-lus) A structure within the nucleus where ribosomal RNA is made and assembled with proteins imported from the cytoplasm to make ribosomal subunits.

nucleosome (nū´-klē-ō-sōm) The bead-like unit of DNA packing in a eukaryotic cell; consists of DNA wound around a protein core made up of eight histone molecules.

nucleotide (nū´-klē-ō-tīd) A building block of nucleic acids, consisting of a five-carbon sugar covalently bonded to a nitrogenous base and one or more phosphate groups.

nucleus (plural, **nuclei**) (1) An atom's central core, containing protons and neutrons. (2) The organelle of a eukaryotic cell that contains the genetic material in the form of chromosomes, made of chromatin.

O

obesity The excessive accumulation of fat in the body.

ocean acidification Decreasing pH of ocean waters due to absorption of excess atmospheric CO_2 from the burning of fossil fuels.

ocean current One of the river-like flow patterns in the oceans.

omnivore An animal that eats animals as well as plants or algae.

oncogene (on´-kō-jēn) A cancer-causing gene; usually contributes to malignancy by abnormally enhancing the amount or activity of a growth factor made by the cell.

oogenesis (ō´-uh-jen´-uh-sis) The development of mature egg cells.

open circulatory system A circulatory system in which blood is pumped through open-ended vessels and bathes the tissues and organs directly. In an animal with an open circulatory system, blood and interstitial fluid are the same.

operator In prokaryotic DNA, a sequence of nucleotides near the start of an operon to which an active repressor protein can attach. The binding of a repressor prevents RNA polymerase from attaching to the promoter and transcribing the genes of the operon. The operator sequence thereby acts as a "genetic switch" that can turn all the genes in an operon on or off as a single functional unit.

operculum (ō-per´-kyuh-lum) (plural, **opercula**) A protective flap on each side of a fish's head that covers a chamber housing the gills. Movement of the operculum increases the flow of oxygen-bearing water over the gills.

operon (op´-er-on) A unit of genetic regulation common in prokaryotes; a cluster of genes with related functions, along with the promoter and operator that control their transcription.

opportunistic infection An infection that can be controlled by a normally functioning immune system but that causes illness in a person with an immunodeficiency.

opposable thumb An arrangement of the fingers such that the thumb can touch the fingertips of all four fingers.

optimal foraging theory The basis for analyzing behavior as a compromise between feeding costs and feeding benefits.

oral cavity The mouth of an animal.

oral contraceptive A chemical contraceptive that contains synthetic estrogen and/or progesterone (or a synthetic progesterone-like hormone called progestin) and prevents the release of eggs. Also called a birth control pill.

order In Linnaean classification, the taxonomic category above family.

organ A specialized structure composed of several different types of tissues that together perform specific functions.

organ of Corti (kor´-tē) The hearing organ in birds and mammals, located within the cochlea.

organ system A group of organs that work together in performing vital body functions.

organelle (ōr-guh-nel´) A membrane-enclosed structure with a specialized function within a cell.

organic compound A chemical compound containing the element carbon and usually the element hydrogen.

organic farming A set of agricultural principles that are intended to promote biological diversity and ecological sustainability. The use of the term *organic* on food labels is regulated by the U.S. Department of Agriculture.

organism An individual living thing, such as a bacterium, fungus, protist, plant, or animal.

orgasm A series of rhythmic, involuntary contractions of the reproductive structures.

osmoconformer (oz´-mō-con-form´-er) An organism whose body fluids have a solute concentration equal to that of its surroundings.

Osmoconformers do not have a net gain or loss of water by osmosis. Examples include most marine invertebrates.

osmoregulation The homeostatic maintenance of solute concentrations and water balance by a cell or organism.

osmoregulator An organism whose body fluids have a solute concentration different from that of its environment and that must use energy in controlling water loss or gain. Examples include most land-dwelling and freshwater animals.

osmosis (oz-mō´-sis) The diffusion of free water across a selectively permeable membrane.

osteoporosis (os´-tē-ō-puh-rō´-sis) A skeletal disorder characterized by thinning, porous, and easily broken bones.

outer ear One of three main regions of the ear in reptiles (including birds) and mammals; made up of the auditory canal and, in many birds and mammals, the pinna.

outgroup In a cladistic study, a taxon or group of taxa known to have diverged before the lineage that contains the group of species being studied. *See also* ingroup.

ovarian cycle (ō-vār´-ē-un) Hormonally synchronized cyclic events in the mammalian ovary, culminating in ovulation.

ovary (1) In animals, the female gonad, which produces egg cells and reproductive hormones. (2) In flowering plants, the basal portion of a carpel in which the egg-containing ovules develop.

oviduct (ō´-vuh-dukt) The tube that conveys egg cells away from an ovary; also called a fallopian tube. In humans, the oviduct is the normal site of fertilization.

ovulation (ah´-vyū-lā´-shun) The release of an egg cell from an ovarian follicle.

ovule (ō-vyūl) seed plants, a structure that develops within the female cone (in gymnosperms) or ovary (in angiosperms) that contains the female gametophyte.

ovum (plural, *ova*) A mature reproductive egg.

oxidation The loss of electrons from a substance involved in a redox reaction; always accompanies reduction.

oxidative phosphorylation (fos´-fōr-uh-lā´-shun) The production of ATP using energy derived from the redox reactions of an electron transport chain; the third major stage of cellular respiration.

ozone layer The layer of ozone (O_3) in the upper atmosphere that protects life on Earth from the harmful ultraviolet rays in sunlight.

P

P generation The parent individuals from which offspring are derived in studies of inheritance; P stands for parental.

P site One of two of a ribosome's binding sites for tRNA during translation. The P site holds the tRNA carrying the growing polypeptide chain. (P stands for peptidyl tRNA.)

paedomorphosis (pē´-duh-mōr´-fuh-sis) The retention in an adult of juvenile features of its evolutionary ancestors.

pain receptor A sensory receptor that detects pain.

paleoanthropology (pā´-lē-ō-an´-thruh-pol´-uh-jē) The study of human origins and evolution.

paleontologist (pa´-lē-on-tol´-uh-jist) A scientist who studies fossils.

pancreas (pan´-krē-us) A gland with dual functions: The digestive portion secretes digestive enzymes and an alkaline solution into the small intestine via a duct. The endocrine portion secretes the hormones insulin and glucagon into the blood.

Pangaea (pan-jē´-uh) The supercontinent that formed near the end of the Paleozoic era, when plate movements brought all the landmasses of Earth together.

parasite Organism that derives its nutrition from a living host, which is harmed by the interaction.

parasympathetic division The component of the autonomic nervous system that generally promotes body activities that gain and conserve energy, such as digestion and reduced heart rate. *See also* sympathetic division.

parenchyma cell (puh-ren´-kim-uh) In plants, a relatively unspecialized cell with a thin primary wall and no secondary wall; functions in photosynthesis, food storage, and aerobic respiration and may differentiate into other cell types.

Parkinson's disease A motor disorder caused by a progressive brain disease and characterized by difficulty in initiating movements, slowness of movement, and rigidity.

parsimony (par´-suh-mō´-nē) In scientific studies, the search for the least complex explanation for an observed phenomenon.

partial pressure The pressure exerted by a particular gas in a mixture of gases; a measure of the relative amount of a gas.

passive immunity Temporary immunity obtained by acquiring ready-made antibodies, as occurs in the transfer of maternal antibodies to a fetus or nursing infant. Passive immunity lasts only a few weeks or months.

passive transport The diffusion of a substance across a biological membrane, with no expenditure of energy.

pathogen An agent, such as a virus, bacteria, or fungus, that causes disease.

pattern formation During embryonic development, the emergence of a body form with specialized organs and tissues in the right places.

PCR *See* polymerase chain reaction (PCR).

pedigree A family genetic tree representing the occurrence of heritable traits in parents and offspring across a number of generations. A pedigree can be used to determine genotypes of matings that have already occurred.

pelagic realm (puh-laj´-ik) The region of an ocean occupied by seawater.

penis The copulatory structure of male mammals.

peptide bond The covalent bond between two amino acid units in a polypeptide, formed by a dehydration reaction.

peptidoglycan (pep´-tid-ō-glī´-kan) A polymer of complex sugars cross-linked by short polypeptides; a material unique to bacterial cell walls.

per capita rate of increase The average contribution of each individual in a population to population growth.

perennial (puh-ren´-ē-ul) A plant that lives for many years.

peripheral nervous system (PNS) The network of nerves and ganglia carrying signals into and out of the central nervous system.

peristalsis (per´-uh-stal´-sis) Rhythmic waves of contraction of smooth muscles. Peristalsis propels food through a digestive tract and also enables many animals, such as earthworms, to crawl.

permafrost Continuously frozen ground found in the arctic tundra.

peroxisome An organelle containing enzymes that transfer hydrogen atoms from various substrates to oxygen, producing and then degrading hydrogen peroxide.

petal A modified leaf of a flowering plant. Petals are the often colorful parts of a flower that advertise it to pollinators.

pH scale A measure of the acidity of a solution, ranging in value from 0 (most acidic) to 14 (most basic). The letters pH stand for potential hydrogen and refer to the concentration of hydrogen ions (H^+).

phage (fāj) *See* bacteriophage.

phagocyte (fag´-ō-sīt´) A white blood cell (for example, a neutrophil or macrophage) that engulfs bacteria, foreign proteins, and the remains of dead body cells.

phagocytosis (fag´-ō-sī-tō´-sis) Cellular "eating"; a type of endocytosis in which a cell engulfs macromolecules, other cells, or particles into its cytoplasm.

pharyngeal slit (fā-rin´-jē-ul) A gill structure in the pharynx; found in chordate embryos and some adult chordates.

pharynx (fār´-inks) The organ in a digestive tract that receives food from the oral cavity; in terrestrial vertebrates, the region of the throat that is a common passageway for air and food.

phenotype (fē´-nō-tīp) The expressed traits of an organism.

phenotypic plasticity An individual's ability to change phenotype in response to local environmental conditions.

phloem (flō´-um) The portion of a plant's vascular tissue system that transports sugars and other organic nutrients from leaves or storage tissues to other parts of the plant.

phloem sap (flō´-um) The solution of sugars, other nutrients, and hormones conveyed throughout a plant via phloem tissue.

phosphate group (fos´-fāt) A chemical group consisting of a phosphorus atom bonded to four oxygen atoms.

phospholipid (fos´-fō-lip´-id) A lipid made up of glycerol joined to two fatty acids and a phosphate group, giving the molecule two nonpolar hydrophobic tails and a polar hydrophilic head. Phospholipids form bilayers that function as biological membranes.

phosphorylation (fos´-fōr-uh-lā´-shun) The transfer of a phosphate group, usually from ATP, to a molecule. Nearly all cellular work depends on ATP energizing other molecules by phosphorylation.

photic zone (fō´-tik) The region of an aquatic ecosystem into which light penetrates and where photosynthesis occurs.

photoautotroph An organism that obtains energy from sunlight and carbon from CO_2 by photosynthesis.

photoheterotroph An organism that obtains energy from sunlight and carbon from organic sources.

photon (fō´-ton) A fixed quantity of light energy. The shorter the wavelength of light, the greater the energy of a photon.

photoperiod The relative lengths of day and night; an environmental stimulus that plants use to detect the time of year.

photophosphorylation (fō´-tō-fos´-fōr-uh-lā´-shun) The production of ATP by chemiosmosis during the light reactions of photosynthesis.

photopsin (fō-top´-sin) One of a family of visual pigments in the cones of the vertebrate eye that absorb bright, colored light.

photoreceptor A type of electromagnetic sensory receptor that detects light.

photorespiration In a plant cell, a metabolic pathway that consumes oxygen, releases CO_2, and decreases photosynthetic output. Photorespiration generally occurs on hot, dry days, when stomata close, O_2 accumulates in the leaf, and rubisco fixes O_2 rather than CO_2. Photorespiration produces no sugar molecules or ATP.

photosynthesis (fō´-tō-sin´-thuh-sis) The process by which plants, algae, and some protists and prokaryotes convert light energy to chemical energy that is stored in sugars made from carbon dioxide and water.

photosystem A light-capturing unit of a chloroplast's thylakoid membrane, consisting of a reaction-center complex surrounded by numerous light-harvesting complexes.

phototropism (fō´-tō-trō´-pizm) The growth of a plant shoot toward light (positive phototropism) or away from light (negative phototropism).

phylogenetic species concept (fī´-lō-juh-net´-ik) A definition of species as the smallest group of individuals that shares a common ancestor, forming one branch on the tree of life.

phylogenetic tree (fī´-lō-juh-net´-ik) A branching diagram that represents a hypothesis about the evolutionary history of a group of organisms.

phylogeny (fi-loj´-uh-nē) The evolutionary history of a species or group of related species.

phylum (fī´-lum) (plural, **phyla**) In Linnaean classification, the taxonomic category above class.

physiology (fi´-zē-ol´-uh-ji) The study of the functions of an organism's structures.

phytochrome (fī´-tuh-krōm) A plant protein that has a light-absorbing component.

phytoplankton (fī´-tō-plank´-ton) Algae and photosynthetic bacteria that drift passively in aquatic environments.

pineal gland (pin´-ē-ul) An outgrowth of the vertebrate brain that secretes the hormone melatonin, which coordinates daily and seasonal body activities such as the sleep/wake circadian rhythm with environmental light conditions.

pinna (pin´-uh) The flap-like part of the outer ear, projecting from the body surface of many birds and mammals; collects sound waves and channels them to the auditory canal.

pistil Part of the reproductive organ of an angiosperm, a single carpel or a group of fused carpels.

pith Part of the ground tissue system of a dicot plant. Pith fills the center of a stem and may store food.

pituitary gland An endocrine gland at the base of the hypothalamus; consists of a posterior lobe, which stores and releases two hormones produced by the hypothalamus, and an anterior lobe, which produces and secretes many hormones that regulate diverse body functions.

pivot joint A joint that allows precise rotations in multiple planes. An example in humans is the joint that rotates the forearm at the elbow.

placenta (pluh-sen´-tuh) In most mammals, the organ that provides nutrients and oxygen to the embryo and helps dispose of its metabolic wastes; formed of the embryo's chorion and the mother's endometrial blood vessels.

placental mammal (pluh-sen´-tul) Mammal whose young complete their embryonic development in the uterus, nourished via the mother's blood vessels in the placenta; also called a eutherian.

plasma The liquid matrix of the blood in which the blood cells are suspended.

plasma cell An antibody-secreting B cell; the effector cell of the humoral immune response.

plasma membrane The membrane at the boundary of every cell that acts as a selective barrier to the passage of ions and molecules into and out of the cell; consists of a phospholipid bilayer with embedded proteins.

plasmid A small ring of independently replicating DNA separate from the main chromosome(s). Plasmids are found in prokaryotes and yeasts.

plasmodesma (plaz´-mō-dez´-muh) (plural, **plasmodesmata**) An open channel in a plant cell wall that connects the cytoplasm of adjacent cells.

plasmodial slime mold (plaz-mō´-dē-ul) A type of protist that has amoeboid cells, flagellated cells, and an amoeboid plasmodial feeding stage in its life cycle; a member of the amoebozoan clade.

plasmodium (1) A single mass of cytoplasm containing many nuclei. (2) The amoeboid feeding stage in the life cycle of a plasmodial slime mold.

plate tectonics (tek-tän´-iks) The theory that the continents are part of great plates of Earth's crust that float on the hot, underlying portion of the mantle. Movements in the mantle cause the continents to move slowly over time.

platelet A pinched-off cytoplasmic fragment of a bone marrow cell. Platelets circulate in the blood and are important in blood clotting.

pleiotropy (plī´-uh-trō-pē) The control of more than one phenotypic character by a single gene.

polar covalent bond A covalent bond between atoms that differ in electronegativity. The shared electrons are pulled closer to the more electronegative atom, making it slightly negative and the other atom slightly positive.

polar ice A terrestrial biome that includes regions of extremely cold temperature and low precipitation located at high latitudes north of the arctic tundra and in Antarctica.

polar molecule A molecule containing polar covalent bonds and having an unequal distribution of charges in different regions of the molecule.

pollen grain The structure that will produce the sperm in seed plants; the male gametophyte.

pollination In seed plants, the delivery by wind or animals of pollen from the pollen-producing parts of a plant to a female cone (in gymnosperms) or the stigma of a carpel (in angiosperms).

polychaete (pol´-ē-kēt) A member of the largest group of annelids. See also annelid.

polygamous Referring to a type of relationship in which an individual of one sex mates with more than one of the other sex.

polygenic inheritance (pol´-ē-jen´-ik) The additive effects of two or more gene loci on a single phenotypic character.

polymer (pol´-uh-mer) A large molecule consisting of many identical or similar monomers linked together by covalent bonds.

polymerase chain reaction (PCR) (puh-lim´-uh-rās) A technique used to obtain many copies of a DNA molecule or a specific part of a DNA molecule. In the procedure, the starting DNA is mixed with a heat-resistant DNA polymerase, DNA nucleotides, and a few other ingredients. Specific nucleotide primers flanking the region to be copied ensure that it, and not other regions of the DNA, is replicated during the PCR procedure.

polynucleotide (pol´-ē-nū´-klē-ō-tīd) A polymer made up of many nucleotide monomers covalently bonded together.

polyp (pol´-ip) One of two types of cnidarian body forms; a columnar, hydra-like body.

polypeptide A polymer (chain) of amino acids linked by peptide bonds.

polyploid An organism that has more than two complete sets of chromosomes as a result of an accident of cell division.

polysaccharide (pol´-ē-sak´-uh-rīd) A carbohydrate polymer of many monosaccharides (sugars) linked by dehydration reactions.

pons (pahnz) Part of the vertebrate hindbrain that functions with the medulla oblongata in passing data between the spinal cord and forebrain and in controlling autonomic, homeostatic functions.

population A group of individuals belonging to one species and living in the same geographic area.

population density The number of individuals of a species per unit area or volume.

population ecology The study of how members of a population interact with their environment, focusing on factors that influence population density and growth.

population momentum In a population in which $r = 0$, the continuation of population growth as girls in the prereproductive age group reach their reproductive years.

positive feedback A type of control in which a change triggers mechanisms that amplify that change.

post-anal tail A tail posterior to the anus; found in chordate embryos and most adult chordates.

posterior Pertaining to the rear, or tail, of a bilaterally symmetric animal.

posterior pituitary An extension of the hypothalamus composed of nervous tissue that secretes hormones made in the hypothalamus; a temporary storage site for hypothalamic hormones.

postzygotic barrier A reproductive barrier that prevents hybrid zygotes produced by two different species from developing into viable, fertile adults. Includes reduced hybrid viability, reduced hybrid fertility, and hybrid breakdown.

potential energy The energy that matter possesses because of its location or spatial arrangement. Water behind a dam possesses potential energy, and so do chemical bonds.

predation An interaction between species in which one species, the predator, kills and eats the other, the prey.

prepuce (prē´-pyūs) A fold of skin covering the head of the clitoris or penis.

pressure flow mechanism The method by which phloem sap is transported through a plant from a sugar source, where sugars are produced, to a sugar sink, where sugars are used.

prevailing winds Winds that result from the combined effects of Earth's rotation and the rising and falling of air masses.

prezygotic barrier A reproductive barrier that impedes mating between species or hinders fertilization if mating between two species is attempted. Includes temporal, habitat, behavioral, mechanical, and gametic isolation.

primary consumer In the trophic structure of an ecosystem, an organism that eats plants or algae.

primary growth Growth in the length of a plant root or shoot, produced by an apical meristem.

primary immune response The initial adaptive immune response to an antigen, which appears after a lag of about 10 days.

primary production The amount of solar energy converted to chemical energy (in organic compounds) by autotrophs in an ecosystem during a given time period.

primary structure The first level of protein structure; the specific sequence of amino acids making up a polypeptide chain.

primary succession A type of ecological succession in which a biological community arises in an area without soil. See also secondary succession.

primers Short, artificially created, single-stranded DNA molecules that bind to each end of a target sequence during a PCR procedure.

prion An infectious form of protein that may multiply by converting related proteins to more prions. Prions cause several related diseases in different animals, including scrapie in sheep and mad cow disease.

problem solving Applying past experiences to overcome obstacles in novel situations.

producer An organism that makes organic food molecules from CO_2, H_2O, and other inorganic raw materials: a plant, alga, or autotrophic prokaryote.

product An ending material in a chemical reaction.

progestin (prō-jes´-tin) One of a family of steroid hormones, including progesterone, produced by the mammalian ovary. Progestins prepare the uterus for pregnancy.

programmed cell death The timely and tidy suicide (and disposal of the remains) of certain cells, triggered by certain genes; an essential process in normal development; also called apoptosis.

prokaryotic cell (prō-kār´-ē-ot´-ik) A type of cell lacking a membrane-enclosed nucleus and other membrane-enclosed organelles; found only in the domains Bacteria and Archaea.

prolactin (PRL) (prō-lak´-tin) A protein hormone secreted by the anterior pituitary that stimulates human mammary glands to produce and release milk and produces other responses in different animals.

prometaphase The second stage of mitosis, during which the nuclear envelope fragments and the spindle microtubules attach to the kinetochores of the sister chromatids.

promiscuous Referring to a type of relationship in which mating occurs with no strong pair-bonds or lasting relationships.

promoter A specific nucleotide sequence in DNA located near the start of a gene that is the binding site for RNA polymerase and the place where transcription begins.

prophage (prō´-fāj) Phage DNA that has inserted by genetic recombination into the DNA of a bacterial chromosome.

prophase The first stage of mitosis, during which the chromatin condenses to form structures (sister chromatids) visible with a light microscope and the mitotic spindle begins to form, but the nucleus is still intact.

prostate gland (pros´-tāt) A gland in human males that secretes a thin fluid that nourishes the sperm.

protein A functional biological molecule consisting of one or more polypeptides folded into a specific three-dimensional structure.

proteobacteria A clade of gram-negative bacteria that encompasses enormous diversity, including all four modes of nutrition.

proteomics The study of whole sets of proteins and their interactions.

protist A member of a diverse collection of eukaryotes. Most protists are unicellular, but some are colonial or multicellular.

proton A subatomic particle with a single positive electrical charge, found in the nucleus of an atom.

proto-oncogene (prō´-tō-on´-kō-jēn) A normal gene that, through mutation, can be converted to a cancer-causing gene.

protostome A mode of animal development in which the opening formed during gastrulation becomes the mouth. Animals with the protostome pattern of development include the flatworms, molluscs, annelids, nematodes, and arthropods.

protozoan (prō´-tō-zō´-un) (plural, **protozoans**) A protist that lives primarily by ingesting food; a heterotrophic, "animal-like" protist.

proximal tubule In the vertebrate kidney, the portion of a nephron immediately downstream from Bowman's capsule that conveys and helps refine filtrate.

proximate cause In animal behavior, a condition in an animal's internal or external environment that is the immediate reason or mechanism for a behavior.

proximate question In animal behavior, a question that concerns the immediate reason for a behavior.

pseudocoelom (sū´-dō-sē´-lōm) A body cavity that is not lined with mesoderm and is in direct contact with the wall of the digestive tract.

pseudopodium (sū´-dō-pō´-dē-um) (plural, **pseudopodia**) A temporary extension of an amoeboid cell. Pseudopodia function in moving cells and engulfing food.

pulmonary artery A large blood vessel that conveys blood from the heart to a lung.

pulmonary circuit The branch of the circulatory system that supplies the lungs. *See also* systemic circuit.

pulmonary vein A blood vessel that conveys blood from a lung to the heart.

pulse The rhythmic stretching of the arteries caused by the pressure of blood during contraction of ventricles in systole.

punctuated equilibria In the fossil record, long periods in which a species undergoes little or no morphological change (equilibria), interrupted (punctuated) by relatively brief periods of sudden change.

Punnett square A diagram used in the study of inheritance to show the results of random fertilization.

pupil The opening in the iris that admits light into the interior of the vertebrate eye. Muscles in the iris regulate the pupil's size.

Q

quaternary consumer (kwot´-er-ner-ē) An organism that eats tertiary consumers.

quaternary structure (kwot´-er-ner-ē) The fourth level of protein structure; the shape resulting from the association of two or more polypeptide subunits.

R

R plasmid A bacterial plasmid that carries genes for enzymes that destroy particular antibiotics, thus making the bacterium resistant to the antibiotics.

radial symmetry An arrangement of the body parts of an organism like pieces of a pie around an imaginary central axis. Any slice passing longitudinally through a radially symmetric organism's central axis divides the organism into mirror-image halves.

radioactive isotope An isotope whose nucleus decays spontaneously, giving off particles and energy.

radiolarian A protist that moves and feeds by means of threadlike pseudopodia and has a mineralized support structure composed of silica. Radiolarians belong to the Rhizaria clade of the SAR supergroup.

radiometric dating A method for determining the absolute ages of fossils and rocks, based on the half-life of radioactive isotopes.

radula (rad´-yū-luh) A toothed, rasping organ used to scrape up or shred food; found in many molluscs.

random dispersion pattern A pattern in which the individuals of a population are spaced in an unpredictable way.

ray-finned fish Bony fish; member of a clade of jawed vertebrates having fins supported by thin, flexible skeletal rays.

reabsorption In the vertebrate kidney, the reclaiming of water and valuable solutes from the filtrate.

reactant A starting material in a chemical reaction.

receptor potential The electrical signal produced by sensory transduction.

receptor-mediated endocytosis (en´-dō-sī-tō´-sis) The movement of specific molecules into a cell by the infolding of vesicles containing proteins with receptor sites specific to the molecules being taken in.

recessive allele An allele that has no noticeable effect on the phenotype of a gene when the individual is heterozygous for that gene.

recombinant DNA A DNA molecule that has been manipulated in the laboratory to carry nucleotide sequences derived from two sources, often different species.

recombination frequency With respect to two given genes, the number of recombinant progeny from a mating divided by the total number of progeny. Recombinant progeny carry combinations of alleles different from those in either of the parents as a result of crossing over during meiosis.

Recommended Dietary Allowance (RDA) A recommendation for daily nutrient intake established by a national scientific panel.

rectum The terminal portion of the large intestine where the feces are stored until they are eliminated.

red alga A member of a group of marine, mostly multicellular, autotrophic protists, which includes the reef-building coralline algae. Red algae belong to the supergroup Archaeplastida.

red blood cell *See* erythrocyte.

red bone marrow A specialized tissue that is found in the cavities at the ends of bones and that produces blood cells.

redox reaction Short for **red**uction-**ox**idation reaction; a chemical reaction in which electrons are lost from one substance (oxidation) and added to another (reduction).

reduction The gain of electrons by a substance involved in a redox reaction; always accompanies oxidation.

reflex An automatic reaction to a stimulus, mediated by the spinal cord or lower brain.

regeneration The regrowth of body parts from pieces of an organism.

regulatory gene A gene that codes for a protein, such as a repressor, that controls the transcription of another gene or group of genes.

relative fitness The contribution an individual makes to the gene pool of the next generation, relative to the contributions of other individuals in the population.

releasing hormone A kind of hormone secreted by the hypothalamus that promotes the release of hormones from the anterior pituitary.

renal cortex The outer portion of the vertebrate kidney, above the renal medulla.

renal medulla The inner portion of the vertebrate kidney, beneath the renal cortex.

repetitive DNA Nucleotide sequences that are present in many copies in the DNA of a genome. The repeated sequences may be long or short and may be located next to each other (tandomly) or dispersed in the DNA.

repressor A protein that blocks the transcription of a gene or operon.

reproduction The creation of new individuals from existing ones.

reproductive cloning Using a somatic cell from a multicellular organism to make one or more genetically identical individuals.

reproductive cycle A recurring sequence of events that produces eggs, makes them available for fertilization, and prepares the female body for pregnancy.

reproductive isolation The existence of biological factors (barriers) that impede members of two species from producing viable, fertile hybrids.

reproductive system The organ system responsible for reproduction.

reptile Member of the clade of amniotes that includes snakes, lizards, turtles, crocodilians, and birds, along with a number of extinct groups, such as dinosaurs.

respiratory system The organ system that functions in exchanging gases with the environment. It supplies the blood with O_2 and disposes of CO_2.

resting potential The voltage across the plasma membrane of a resting neuron. The resting potential in a vertebrate neuron is typically around −70 millivolts, with the inside of the cell negatively charged relative to the outside.

restoration ecology The use of ecological principles to develop ways to return degraded ecosystems to conditions as similar as possible to their natural, predegraded state.

restriction enzyme A bacterial enzyme that cuts up foreign DNA (at specific DNA sequences called *restriction sites*), thus protecting bacteria against intruding DNA from phages and other organisms. Restriction enzymes are used in DNA technology to cut DNA molecules in reproducible ways. The pieces of cut DNA are called restriction fragments.

restriction fragment length polymorphism (RFLP) (rif´-lip) Variation in the length of a restriction fragment. RFLPs are produced when homologous DNA sequences containing SNPs are cut up with restriction enzymes.

restriction fragments Molecules of DNA produced from a longer DNA molecule cut up by a restriction enzyme. Restriction fragments are used in genome mapping and other applications.

restriction site A specific sequence on a DNA strand that is recognized as a "cut site" by a restriction enzyme.

retina (ret´-uh-nuh) The light-sensitive layer in an eye, made up of photoreceptor cells and sensory neurons.

retrovirus An RNA virus that reproduces by means of a DNA molecule. It reverse-transcribes its RNA into DNA, inserts the DNA into a cellular chromosome, and then transcribes more copies of the RNA from the viral DNA. HIV and a number of cancer-causing viruses are retroviruses.

reverse transcriptase (tran-skrip´-tās) An enzyme encoded and used by retroviruses that catalyzes the synthesis of DNA on an RNA template.

RFLP *See* restriction fragment length polymorphism (RFLP).

Rhizaria A clade of the SAR supergroup of protists that includes foraminiferans and radiolarians.

rhizome (rī´-zōm) A horizontal stem of a plant that grows below the ground.

rhodopsin (ro-dop´-sin) A visual pigment that is located in the rods of the vertebrate eye and that absorbs dim light.

rhythm method A form of contraception that relies on refraining from sexual intercourse when conception is most likely to occur; also called natural family planning.

ribonucleic acid (RNA) (rī-bō-nū-klā´-ik) A type of nucleic acid consisting of nucleotide monomers with a ribose sugar and the nitrogenous bases adenine (A), cytosine (C), guanine (G), and uracil (U); usually single-stranded; functions in protein synthesis, gene regulation, and as the genome of some viruses.

ribosomal RNA (rRNA) (rī´-buh-sōm´-ul) The type of ribonucleic acid that, together with proteins, makes up ribosomes; the most abundant type of RNA in most cells.

ribosome (rī´-buh-sōm) A cell structure consisting of RNA and protein organized into two subunits and functioning as the site of protein synthesis in the cytoplasm. In eukaryotic cells, the ribosomal subunits are constructed in the nucleolus.

ribozyme (rī´-bō-zīm) An RNA molecule that functions as an enzyme.

RNA interference (RNAi) A biotechnology technique used to silence the expression of specific genes. Synthetic RNA molecules with sequences that correspond to particular genes trigger the breakdown of the gene's mRNA.

RNA polymerase (puh-lim´-uh-rās) A large molecular complex that links together the growing chain of RNA nucleotides during transcription, using a DNA strand as a template.

RNA splicing The removal of introns and joining of exons in eukaryotic RNA, forming an mRNA molecule with a continuous coding sequence; occurs before mRNA leaves the nucleus.

rod A photoreceptor cell in the vertebrate retina enabling vision in dim light.

root cap A cone of cells at the tip of a plant root that protects the root's apical meristem.

root hair An outgrowth of an epidermal cell on a root, which increases the root's absorptive surface area.

root system All of a plant's roots, which anchor it in the soil, absorb and transport minerals and water, and store food.

rough endoplasmic reticulum (reh-tik´-yuh-lum) That portion of the endoplasmic reticulum with ribosomes attached that make membrane proteins and secretory proteins.

r-selection The concept that in certain (*r*-selected) populations, a high reproductive rate is the chief determinant of life history.

rule of addition A rule stating that the probability that an event can occur in two or more alternative ways is the sum of the separate probabilities of the different ways.

rule of multiplication A rule stating that the probability of a compound event is the product of the separate probabilities of the independent events.

ruminant (rū´-min-ent) An animal, such as a cow or sheep, with multiple stomach compartments housing microorganisms that can digest cellulose.

S

SA (sinoatrial) node (sȳ´-nō´-ā´-trē-ul) The pacemaker of the heart, located in the wall of the right atrium, that sets the rate and timing at which all cardiac muscle cells contract.

sac fungus *See* ascomycete.

salivary glands Glands associated with the oral cavity that secrete substances to lubricate food and begin the process of chemical digestion.

salt A compound resulting from the formation of an ionic bond.

sapwood Light-colored, water-conducting secondary xylem in a tree. *See also* heartwood.

SAR (Stramenopila, Alveolata, and Rhizaria) One of four monophyletic supergroups proposed in a current hypothesis of the evolutionary history of eukaryotes. The other three supergroups are Excavata, Unikonta, and Archaeplastida.

sarcomere (sar´-kō-mēr) The fundamental unit of muscle contraction, composed of thin filaments of actin and thick filaments of myosin; in electron micrographs, the region between two narrow, dark lines, called Z lines, in a myofibril.

saturated fatty acid A fatty acid in which all carbons in the hydrocarbon tail are connected by single bonds and the maximum number of hydrogen atoms are attached to the carbon skeleton. Saturated fats and fatty acids solidify at room temperature.

savanna A biome dominated by grasses and scattered trees.

scanning electron microscope (SEM) A microscope that uses an electron beam to study the surface details of a cell or other specimens.

scavenger An animal that feeds on the carcasses of dead animals.

schizophrenia Severe mental disturbance characterized by psychotic episodes in which patients have a distorted perception of reality.

sclera (sklār´-uh) A layer of connective tissue forming the outer surface of the vertebrate eye. The cornea is the frontal part of the sclera.

sclereid (sklār´-ē-id) In plants, a very hard sclerenchyma cell found in nutshells and seed coats.

sclerenchyma cell (skluh-ren´-kē-muh) In plants, a supportive cell with rigid secondary walls hardened with lignin.

scrotum A pouch of skin outside the abdomen that houses a testis and functions in cooling sperm, keeping them viable.

search image The mechanism that enables an animal to find a particular kind of food efficiently.

second law of thermodynamics The principle stating that every energy conversion reduces the order of the universe, increasing its entropy. Ordered forms of energy are at least partly converted to heat.

secondary consumer An organism that eats primary consumers.

secondary growth An increase in a plant's diameter, involving cell division in the vascular cambium and cork cambium.

secondary immune response The adaptive immune response elicited when an animal encounters the same antigen at some later time. The secondary immune response is more rapid, of greater magnitude, and of longer duration than the primary immune response.

secondary phloem A type of phloem plant tissue produced by the vascular cambium during secondary growth.

secondary structure The second level of protein structure; the regular local patterns of coils or folds of a polypeptide chain.

secondary succession A type of ecological succession that occurs where a disturbance has destroyed an existing biological community but left the soil intact. *See also* primary succession.

secondary xylem A type of xylem plant tissue produced by the vascular cambium during secondary growth.

secretion (1) The discharge of molecules synthesized by a cell. (2) In the vertebrate kidney, the discharge of wastes from the blood into the filtrate from the nephron tubules.

seed A plant embryo packaged with a food supply within a protective covering.

seed coat A tough outer covering of a seed, formed from the tissue surrounding an ovule. The seed coat encloses and protects the embryo and its food supply.

seedless vascular plants The informal collective name for lycophytes (club mosses and their relatives) and monilophytes (ferns and their relatives).

segmentation Subdivision along the length of an animal body into a series of repeated parts called segments; allows for greater flexibility and mobility.

selective permeability (per´-mē-uh-bil´-uh-tē) A property of biological membranes that allows some substances to cross more easily than others and blocks the passage of other substances altogether.

self protein A protein on the surface of an antigen-presenting cell that can hold a foreign antigen and display it to T cells. Each individual has a unique set of self proteins that serve as molecular markers for the body. The technical name for self proteins is *major histocompatibility complex (MHC) proteins. See also* nonself molecule.

semen (sē´-mun) The sperm-containing fluid that is ejaculated by the male during orgasm.

semicircular canals Fluid-filled channels in the inner ear that detect changes in the head's rate of rotation or angular movement.

semiconservative model Type of DNA replication in which the replicated double helix consists of one old strand, derived from the old molecule, and one newly made strand.

seminal vesicle (sem´-uh-nul ves´-uh-kul) A gland in males that secretes a thick fluid that contains fructose, which provides most of the sperm's energy.

seminiferous tubule (sem´-uh-nif´-uh-rus) A coiled sperm-producing tube in a testis.

sensitive period A limited phase in an individual animal's development when learning of particular behaviors can take place.

sensory adaptation The tendency of sensory neurons to become less sensitive when they are stimulated repeatedly. For example, a prominent smell becomes unnoticeable over time.

sensory input The conduction of signals from sensory receptors to processing centers in the central nervous system.

sensory neuron A nerve cell that receives information from sensory receptors and conveys signals into the central nervous system.

sensory receptor A specialized cell or neuron that detects specific stimuli from an organism's external or internal environment and sends information to the central nervous system.

sensory transduction The conversion of a stimulus signal to an electrical signal by a sensory receptor.

sepal (sē´-pul) A modified leaf of a flowering plant. A circle of sepals encloses and protects the flower bud before it opens.

sessile An organism that is anchored to its substrate.

sex chromosome A chromosome that determines whether an individual is male or female.

sex-linked gene A gene located on a sex chromosome. In humans, the vast majority of sex-linked genes are located on the X chromosome.

sexual dimorphism (dī-mōr´-fizm) Marked differences between the secondary sex characteristics of males and females.

sexual reproduction The creation of genetically unique offspring by the fusion of two haploid sex cells (gametes), forming a diploid zygote.

sexual selection A form of natural selection in which individuals with certain inherited traits are more likely than other individuals to obtain mates.

sexually transmitted disease (STD) A contagious disease spread by sexual contact.

shared ancestral character A character shared by members of a particular clade that originated in an ancestor that is not a member of that clade.

shared derived character An evolutionary novelty that is unique to a particular clade.

shoot system All of a plant's stems, leaves, and reproductive structures.

short tandem repeat (STR) A series of short DNA sequences that are repeated many times in a row in the genome.

short-day plant A plant that flowers in late summer, fall, or winter, when day length is short. Short-day plants actually flower in response to long nights.

short-term memory The ability to hold information, anticipations, or goals for a time and then release them if they become irrelevant.

sickle-cell disease A genetic condition caused by a mutation in the gene for hemoglobin. The mutation causes the protein to crystallize, which deforms red blood cells into a curved shape. Such blood cells produce a cascade of symptoms that can be life-threatening.

sieve plate An end wall in a sieve-tube element that facilitates the flow of phloem sap.

sieve-tube element A food-conducting cell in a plant; also called a sieve-tube member. Chains of sieve-tube elements make up phloem tissue.

signal In behavioral ecology, a stimulus transmitted by one animal to another animal.

signal transduction pathway In cell biology, a series of molecular changes that converts a signal on a target cell's surface to a specific response inside the cell.

silent mutation A mutation in a gene that changes a codon to one that codes for the same amino acid as the original codon. The amino acid sequence of the resulting polypeptide is thus unchanged.

single circulation A circulatory system with a single pump and circuit, in which blood passes from the sites of gas exchange to the rest of the body before returning to the heart.

single nucleotide polymorphism (SNP) A one-nucleotide variation in DNA sequence found within the genomes of at least 1% of a population.

single-lens eye The camera-like eye found in some jellies, polychaetes, spiders, many molluscs, and vertebrates.

sister chromatid (krō´-muh-tid) One of the two identical parts of a duplicated chromosome in a eukaryotic cell. Prior to mitosis, sister chromatids remain attached to each another at the centromere.

skeletal muscle A type of striated muscle attached to the skeleton; generally responsible for voluntary movements of the body.

skeletal system The organ system that provides body support and protects body organs, such as the brain, heart, and lungs.

small intestine The longest section of the alimentary canal. It is the principal site of the enzymatic hydrolysis of food macromolecules and the absorption of nutrients.

smooth endoplasmic reticulum That portion of the endoplasmic reticulum that lacks ribosomes.

smooth muscle A type of muscle lacking striations; responsible for involuntary body activities.

SNP *See* single nucleotide polymorphism (SNP).

social behavior Any kind of interaction between two or more animals, usually of the same species.

social learning Learning by observing the behavior of other individuals.

sociobiology The study of the evolutionary basis of social behavior.

sodium-potassium (Na-K) pump A membrane protein that transports sodium ions out of, and potassium ions into, a cell against their concentration gradients. The process is powered by ATP.

solute (sol´-yūt) A substance that is dissolved in a solution.

solution A liquid that is a homogeneous mixture of two or more substances.

solvent The dissolving agent of a solution. Water is the most versatile solvent known.

somatic cell (sō-mat´-ik) Any cell in a multicellular organism except a sperm or egg cell or a cell that develops into a sperm or egg.

spatial learning Modification of behavior based on experience of the spatial structure of the environment.

speciation The evolution of a new species.

species A group whose members possess similar anatomical characteristics and have the ability to interbreed and produce viable, fertile offspring. *See also* biological species concept.

species diversity The variety of species that make up a community. Species diversity includes both species richness (the total number of different species) and the relative abundance of the different species in the community.

sperm A male gamete.

spermatogenesis (sper-mat´-ō-jen´-uh-sis) The formation of sperm cells.

spermicide A sperm-killing chemical (cream, jelly, or foam) that works with a barrier device as a method of contraception.

sphincter (sfink´-ter) A ringlike band of muscle fibers that regulates passage between some compartments of the alimentary canal.

spinal cord A bundle of nervous tissue that runs lengthwise inside the spine in vertebrates and integrates simple responses to certain stimuli.

spirochete (spī´-ruh-kēt) A member of a group of helical bacteria that spiral through the environment by means of rotating, internal filaments.

sponge An aquatic animal characterized by a highly porous body.

sporangium (spuh-ranj´-ē-um´) (plural, **sporangia**) A structure in fungi and plants in which meiosis occurs and haploid spores develop.

spore (1) In plants and algae, a haploid cell that can develop into a multicellular individual without fusing with another cell. (2) In prokaryotes, protists, and fungi, any of a variety of thick-walled life cycle stages capable of surviving unfavorable environmental conditions.

sporophyte (spōr´-uh-fīt) The multicellular diploid form in the life cycle of organisms undergoing alternation of generations; results from a union of gametes and meiotically produces haploid spores that grow into the gametophyte generation.

stabilizing selection Natural selection that favors intermediate variants by acting against extreme phenotypes.

stamen (stā´-men) A pollen-producing male reproductive part of a flower, consisting an anther supported by a filament (stalk).

starch A storage polysaccharide in plants; a polymer of glucose.

start codon (kō´-don) On mRNA, the specific three-nucleotide sequence (AUG) to which an initiator tRNA molecule binds, starting translation of genetic information.

stem The part of a plant's shoot system that supports the leaves and reproductive structures.

stem cell An unspecialized cell that can divide to produce an identical daughter cell and a more specialized daughter cell, which undergoes differentiation.

steroid (ster´-oyd) A type of lipid whose carbon skeleton is in the form of four fused rings with various chemical groups attached. Examples are cholesterol, testosterone, and estrogen.

steroid hormone (ster´-oyd) A lipid made from cholesterol that acts as a regulatory chemical, entering a target cell and activating the transcription of specific genes.

stigma (stig´-muh) (plural, **stigmata**) The sticky tip of a flower's carpel, which traps pollen grains.

stimulus (plural, **stimuli**) (1) In the context of a nervous system, any factor that causes a nerve signal to be generated. (2) In behavioral biology, an environmental cue that triggers a specific response.

stoma (stō´-muh) (plural, **stomata**) A microscopic pore surrounded by guard cells in the epidermis of a leaf. When stomata are open, CO_2 enters a leaf, and H_2O and O_2 exit. A plant conserves water when its stomata are closed.

stomach An organ in a digestive tract that stores food and performs preliminary steps of digestion.

stop codon In mRNA, one of three triplets (UAG, UAA, UGA) that signal gene translation to stop.

STR *See* short tandem repeat (STR).

Stramenopila A clade of the SAR supergroup of protists that includes diatoms, brown algae, and water molds.

STR analysis Short tandem repeat analysis; a method of DNA profiling that compares the lengths of short tandem repeats (STRs) selected from specific sites within the genome.

stratum (plural, **strata**) Rock layer formed when a new layer of sediment covers an older one and compresses it.

stretch receptor A type of mechanoreceptor sensitive to changes in muscle length; detects the position of body parts.

stroke The death of nervous tissue in the brain, usually resulting from rupture or blockage of arteries in the head.

stroma (strō´-muh) The dense fluid within the chloroplast that surrounds the thylakoid membrane and is involved in the synthesis of organic molecules from carbon dioxide and water. Sugars are made in the stroma by the enzymes of the Calvin cycle.

stromatolite (strō-mat´-uh-līt) Layered rock that results from the activities of prokaryotes that bind thin films of sediment together.

substrate (1) A specific substance (reactant) on which an enzyme acts. Each enzyme recognizes only the specific substrate or substrates of the reaction it catalyzes. (2) A surface in or on which an organism lives.

substrate feeder An organism that lives in or on its food source, eating its way through the food.

substrate-level phosphorylation The formation of ATP by an enzyme directly transferring a phosphate group to ADP from an organic molecule (for example, one of the intermediates in glycolysis or the citric acid cycle).

sugar sink A plant organ that is a net consumer or storer of sugar. Growing roots, shoot tips, stems, and fruits are sugar sinks supplied by phloem.

sugar source A plant organ in which sugar is being produced by either photosynthesis or the breakdown of starch. Mature leaves are the primary sugar sources of plants.

sugar-phosphate backbone In a polynucleotide (DNA or RNA strand), the alternating chain of sugar and phosphate to which nitrogenous bases are attached.

superior vena cava (vē´-nuh kā´-vuh) A large vein that returns oxygen-poor blood to the heart from the upper body and head. *See also* inferior vena cava.

surface tension A measure of how difficult it is to stretch or break the surface of a liquid. Water has a high surface tension because of the hydrogen bonding of surface molecules.

surfactant A substance secreted by alveoli that decreases surface tension in the fluid that coats the alveoli.

survivorship curve A plot of the number of members of a cohort that are still alive at each age; one way to represent age-specific mortality.

suspension feeder An aquatic animal that collects small food particles from the water; includes filter feeders.

sustainability The goal of developing, managing, and conserving Earth's resources in ways that meet the needs of people today without compromising the ability of future generations to meet theirs.

sustainable agriculture Long-term productive farming methods that are environmentally safe.

sustainable resource management Management practices that allow use of a natural resource without damaging it.

swim bladder A gas-filled internal sac that helps bony fishes maintain buoyancy.

symbiosis (sim´-bē-ō-sis) A physically close association between organisms of two or more species.

sympathetic division A set of neurons in the autonomic nervous system that generally prepares the body for energy-consuming activities, such as fleeing or fighting. *See also* parasympathetic division.

sympatric speciation The formation of new species in populations that live in the same geographic area.

synapse (sin´-aps) A junction between two neurons, or between a neuron and an effector cell. Electrical or chemical signals are relayed from one cell to another at a synapse.

synaptic cleft (sin-ap´-tik) In a chemical synapse, a narrow gap separating the synaptic terminal of a transmitting neuron from a receiving neuron or an effector cell.

synaptic terminal (sin-ap´-tik) The tip of a transmitting neuron's axon, where signals are sent to another neuron or to an effector cell.

synaptic vesicle (sin-ap´-tik) A membrane-enclosed sac containing neurotransmitter molecules at the tip of the sending neuron's axon.

systematics A scientific discipline focused on classifying organisms and determining their evolutionary relationships.

systemic acquired resistance A defensive response in plants infected with a pathogenic microbe; helps protect healthy tissue from the microbe.

systemic circuit The branch of the circulatory system that supplies oxygen-rich blood to, and carries oxygen-poor blood away from, organs and tissues in the body. *See also* pulmonary circuit.

systems biology An approach to studying biology that aims to model the dynamic behavior of whole biological systems based on a study of the interactions among the system's parts.

systole (sis´-tō-lē) The contraction stage of the heart cycle, when the heart chambers actively pump blood. *See also* diastole.

T

T cell A type of lymphocyte that matures in the thymus; T cells include both effector cells for the cell-mediated immune response and helper cells required for both the humoral and cell-mediated adaptive responses.

taiga (tī´-guh) The northern coniferous forest, characterized by long, snowy winters and short, wet summers, extending across North America and Eurasia to the southern border of the arctic tundra; also found just below alpine tundra on mountainsides in temperate zones.

tapeworm A parasitic flatworm characterized by the absence of a digestive tract.

target cell A cell that responds to a regulatory signal, such as a hormone.

taxis (tak´-sis) (plural, **taxes**) Virtually automatic orientation toward or away from a stimulus.

taxon A named taxonomic unit at any given level of classification.

taxonomy The scientific discipline concerned with naming and classifying the diverse forms of life.

technology The application of scientific knowledge for a specific purpose, often involving industry or commerce but also including uses in basic research.

telomere (tel´-uh-mēr) The repetitive DNA at each end of a eukaryotic chromosome.

telophase The fifth and final stage of mitosis, during which daughter nuclei form at the two poles of a cell. Telophase usually occurs together with cytokinesis.

temperate broadleaf forest A biome located throughout midlatitude regions, where there is sufficient moisture to support the growth of large, broadleaf deciduous trees.

temperate grassland A grassland region maintained by seasonal drought, occasional fires, and grazing by large mammals.

temperate rain forest Coniferous forests of coastal North America (from Alaska to Oregon) supported by warm, moist air from the Pacific Ocean.

temperate zones Latitudes between the tropics and the Arctic Circle in the north and the Antarctic Circle in the south; regions with milder climates than the tropics or polar regions.

temperature A measure in degrees of the average thermal energy of the atoms and molecules in a body of matter.

tendon Fibrous connective tissue connecting a muscle to a bone.

tendril A modified leaf used by some plants to climb around a fixed structure.

terminal bud Embryonic tissue at the tip of a shoot, made up of developing leaves and a compact series of nodes and internodes.

terminator A special sequence of nucleotides in DNA that marks the end of a gene. It signals RNA polymerase to release the newly made RNA molecule and then to depart from the gene.

territory An area that one or more individuals defend and from which other members of the same species are usually excluded.

tertiary consumer (ter´-shē-ār-ē) An organism that eats secondary consumers.

tertiary structure (ter´-shē-ār-ē) The third level of protein structure; the overall three-dimensional shape of a polypeptide due to interactions of the R groups of the amino acids making up the chain.

testcross The mating between an individual of unknown genotype for a particular character and an individual that is homozygous recessive for that same character. The testcross can be used to determine the unknown genotype (homozygous dominant versus heterozygous).

testicle A testis and scrotum together.

testis (plural, **testes**) The male gonad in an animal. The testis produces sperm and, in many species, reproductive hormones.

testosterone (tes-tos´-tuh-rōn) An androgen hormone that stimulates an embryo to develop into a male and promotes male body features.

tetrapod A vertebrate with two pairs of limbs. Tetrapods include mammals, amphibians, and birds and other reptiles.

thalamus (thal´-uh-mus) An integrating and relay center of the vertebrate forebrain; sorts and relays selected information to specific areas in the cerebral cortex.

theory A widely accepted explanatory idea that is broader in scope than a hypothesis, generates new hypotheses, and is supported by a large body of evidence.

therapeutic cloning The cloning of human cells by nuclear transplantation for therapeutic purposes, such as the generation of embryonic stem cells. *See also* nuclear transplantation; reproductive cloning.

thermal energy Kinetic energy due to the random motion of atoms and molecules; energy in its most random form.

thermodynamics The study of energy transformation that occurs in a collection of matter. *See also* first law of thermodynamics; second law of thermodynamics.

thermoreceptor A sensory receptor that detects heat or cold.

thermoregulation The homeostatic maintenance of an organism's internal body temperature within a range that allows cells to function efficiently.

thick filament The thicker of the two protein filaments in muscle fibers, consisting of staggered arrays of myosin molecules.

thigmotropism (thig´-mō-trō´-pizm) A plant's directional growth movement in response to touch.

thin filament The thinner of the two protein filaments in muscle fibers, consisting of two strands of actin and two strands of regulatory protein coiled around each other.

three-domain system A system of taxonomic classification based on three basic groups: Bacteria, Archaea, and Eukarya.

thylakoid (thī´-luh-koyd) A flattened membranous sac inside a chloroplast. Thylakoid membranes contain chlorophyll and the molecular complexes of the light reactions of photosynthesis. A stack of thylakoids is called a granum.

thymine (T) (thī´-min) A single-ring nitrogenous base found in DNA.

thymus gland (thī´-mus) An endocrine gland in the neck region of mammals that is active in establishing the immune system; secretes several hormones that promote the development and differentiation of T cells.

thyroid gland (thī´-royd) An endocrine gland located in the neck that secretes thyroxine (T_4), triiodothyronine (T_3), and calcitonin.

thyroid-stimulating hormone (TSH) (thī´-royd) A protein hormone secreted by the anterior pituitary that stimulates the thyroid gland to secrete its hormones.

thyroxine (T_4) (thī-rok´-sin) An amine hormone secreted by the thyroid that stimulates metabolism in virtually all body tissues. Each molecule of this hormone contains four atoms of iodine.

tissue An integrated group of cells with a common function, structure, or both.

tonicity The ability of a solution surrounding a cell to cause that cell to gain or lose water.

topsoil The uppermost soil layer, consisting of a mixture of particles derived from rock, living organisms, and humus.

trace element An element that is essential for life but required in extremely minute amounts.

trachea (trā´-kē-uh) (plural, **tracheae**) The windpipe; the portion of the respiratory tube that passes from the larynx to the two bronchi.

tracheal system A system of branched, air-filled tubes in insects that extends throughout the body and carries oxygen directly to cells.

tracheid (trā´-kē-id) A tapered, porous, water-conducting and supportive cell in plants. Chains of tracheids or vessel elements make up the water-conducting, supportive tubes in xylem.

trade winds The movement of air in the tropics (those regions that lie between 23.5° north latitude and 23.5° south latitude).

trait A variant of a character found within a population, such as purple or white flowers in pea plants.

trans fat An unsaturated fat linked to health risks that is formed artificially during hydrogenation of vegetable oils.

transcription The synthesis of RNA on a DNA template.

transcription factor In the eukaryotic cell, a protein that functions in initiating or regulating transcription. Transcription factors bind to DNA or to other proteins that bind to DNA.

transduction (1) The transfer of bacterial genes from one bacterial cell to another by a phage. (2) *See* sensory transduction. (3) *See* signal transduction pathway.

transfer RNA (tRNA) A type of ribonucleic acid that functions as an interpreter in translation. Each tRNA molecule has a specific anticodon, picks up a specific amino acid, and conveys the amino acid to the appropriate codon on mRNA.

transformation The incorporation of new genes into a cell from DNA that the cell takes up from the surrounding environment.

transgenic organism An organism that contains genes from another species.

translation The synthesis of a polypeptide using the genetic information encoded in an mRNA molecule. There is a change of "language" from nucleotides to amino acids.

translocation (1) During protein synthesis, the movement of a tRNA molecule carrying a growing polypeptide chain from the A site to the P site on a ribosome. (The mRNA travels with it.) (2) A change in a chromosome resulting from a chromosomal fragment attaching to a nonhomologous chromosome; can occur as a result of an error in meiosis or from mutagenesis.

transmission electron microscope (TEM) A microscope that uses an electron beam to study the internal structure of thinly sectioned specimens.

transpiration The evaporative loss of water from a plant.

transport vesicle A small membranous sac in a eukaryotic cell's cytoplasm carrying molecules produced by the cell. The vesicle buds from the endoplasmic reticulum or Golgi and eventually fuses with another organelle or the plasma membrane, releasing its contents.

transposable element A transposable genetic element, or "jumping gene"; a segment of DNA that can move from one site to another within a cell and serve as an agent of genetic change.

TRH (TSH-releasing hormone) A peptide hormone that triggers the release of TSH (thyroid-stimulating hormone), which in turn stimulates the thyroid gland.

trial-and-error learning Type of associative learning in which an animal learns to associate one of its own behaviors with a positive or negative effect.

triiodothyronine (T_3) (trī-ī-ō-dō-thī´-rō-nīn) An amine hormone secreted by the thyroid gland that stimulates metabolism in virtually all body tissues. Each molecule of this hormone contains four atoms of iodine.

triplet code A set of three-nucleotide-long "words" that specify the amino acids for polypeptide chains. *See also* genetic code.

trisomy 21 A human genetic disorder resulting from the presence of an extra chromosome 21; characterized by heart and respiratory defects and varying degrees of mental retardation.

trophic structure The pattern of feeding relationships in a community.

trophoblast (trōf´-ō-blast) In mammalian development, the outer portion of a blastocyst. Cells of the trophoblast secrete enzymes that enable the blastocyst to implant in the endometrium of the mother's uterus.

tropical forest A terrestrial biome characterized by high levels of precipitation and warm temperatures year-round.

tropics Latitudes between 23.5° north and south.

tropism (trō´-pizm) A growth response that makes a plant grow toward or away from a stimulus.

true-breeding Referring to organisms for which sexual reproduction produces offspring with inherited traits identical to those of the parents. The organisms are homozygous for the characters under consideration.

tubal ligation A means of sterilization in which a segment of each of a woman's two oviducts (fallopian tubes) is removed. The ends of the tubes are then tied closed to prevent eggs from reaching the uterus (commonly referred to as having the "tubes tied").

tuber An enlargement at the end of a rhizome in which food is stored.

tumor An abnormal mass of rapidly growing cells that forms within otherwise normal tissue.

tumor-suppressor gene A gene whose product inhibits cell division, thereby preventing uncontrolled cell growth. A mutation that deactivates a tumor-suppressor gene may lead to cancer.

tundra A biome at the northernmost limits of plant growth and at high altitudes, characterized by dwarf woody shrubs, grasses, mosses, and lichens.

tunicate One of a group of invertebrate chordates, also known as sea squirts.

U

ultimate cause In animal behavior, the evolutionary reason for a behavior.

ultimate question In animal behavior, a question that addresses the evolutionary basis for behavior.

ultrasound imaging A technique for examining a fetus in the uterus. High-frequency sound waves echoing off the fetus are used to produce an image of the fetus.

uniform dispersion pattern A pattern in which the individuals of a population are evenly distributed over an area.

Unikonta One of four monophyletic supergroups proposed in a current hypothesis of the evolutionary history of eukaryotes. The other three supergroups are SAR (Stramenopila, Alveolata, and Rhizaria), Excavata, and Archaeplastida.

unsaturated fatty acid A fatty acid that has one or more double bonds between carbons in the hydrocarbon tail and thus lacks the maximum number of hydrogen atoms. Unsaturated fats and fatty acids do not solidify at room temperature.

uracil (U) (yū´-ruh-sil) A single-ring nitrogenous base found in RNA.

urea (yū-rē´-ah) A soluble form of nitrogenous waste excreted by mammals and most adult amphibians.

ureter (yū-rē´-ter or yū´-reh-ter) A duct that conveys urine from the kidney to the urinary bladder.

urethra (yū-rē´-thruh) A duct that conveys urine from the urinary bladder to the outside. In the male, the urethra also conveys semen out of the body during ejaculation.

uric acid (yū´-rik) An insoluble precipitate of nitrogenous waste excreted by land snails, insects, birds, and some reptiles.

urinary bladder The pouch where urine is stored prior to elimination.

urinary system The organ system that forms and excretes urine while regulating the amount of water and ions in the body fluids.

urine Concentrated filtrate produced by the kidneys and excreted by the bladder.

uterus (yū´-ter-us) In the reproductive system of a mammalian female, the organ where the development of young occurs; the womb.

V

vaccination (vak´-suh-nā´-shun) A procedure that presents the immune system with a harmless variant or derivative of a pathogen, thereby stimulating the adaptive immune system to mount a long-term defense against the pathogen.

vaccine (vak-sēn´) A harmless variant or derivative of a pathogen used to stimulate a host organism's immune system to mount a long-term adaptive response against the pathogen.

vacuole (vak´-ū-ōl) A membrane-enclosed sac that is part of the endomembrane system of a eukaryotic cell and has diverse functions in different kinds of cells.

vagina (vuh-jī´-nuh) Part of the female reproductive system between the uterus and the outside opening; the birth canal in mammals; also accommodates the male's penis and receives sperm during copulation.

vas deferens (vas def´-er-enz) (plural, **vasa deferentia**) Part of the male reproductive system that conveys sperm away from the testis; the sperm duct; in humans, the tube that conveys sperm between the epididymis and the common duct that leads to the urethra.

vascular bundle (vas´-kyū-ler) A strand of vascular tissues (both xylem and phloem) in a plant stem.

vascular cambium (vas´-kyū-ler kam´-bē-um) During secondary growth of a plant, the cylinder of meristematic cells, surrounding the xylem and pith, that produces secondary xylem and phloem.

vascular cylinder The central cylinder of vascular tissue in a plant root.

vascular plant A plant with xylem and phloem, including club mosses, ferns, gymnosperms, and angiosperms.

vascular tissue Plant tissue consisting of cells joined into tubes that transport water and nutrients throughout the plant body.

vascular tissue system A transport system formed by xylem and phloem throughout the plant. Xylem transports water and minerals, while phloem transports sugars and other organic nutrients.

vasectomy (vuh-sek´-tuh-mē) Surgical removal of a section of the two sperm ducts (vasa deferentia) to prevent sperm from reaching the urethra; a means of sterilization in males.

vector In molecular biology, a piece of DNA, usually a plasmid or a viral genome, that is used to move genes from one cell to another.

vein (1) In animals, a vessel that returns blood to the heart. (2) In plants, a vascular bundle in a leaf, composed of xylem and phloem.

ventilation The flow of air or water over a respiratory surface.

ventral Pertaining to the underside, or bottom, of a bilaterally symmetric animal.

ventricle (ven´-truh-kul) (1) A heart chamber that pumps blood out of the heart. (2) A space in the vertebrate brain filled with cerebrospinal fluid.

venule (ven´-yūl) A vessel that conveys blood between a capillary bed and a vein.

vertebra (ver´-tuh-bruh) (plural, **vertebrae**) One of a series of segmented skeletal units that enclose the nerve cord, making up the backbone of a vertebrate animal.

vertebral column Backbone, composed of a series of segmented units called vertebrae.

vertebrate (ver´-tuh-brāt) A chordate animal with a backbone, including lampreys, chondrichthyans, ray-finned fishes, lobe-finned fishes, amphibians, reptiles (including birds), and mammals.

vesicle (ves´-i-kul) A sac made of membrane in the cytoplasm of a eukaryotic cell.

vessel element A short, open-ended, water-conducting and supportive cell in plants. Chains of vessel elements or tracheids make up the water-conducting, supportive tubes in xylem.

vestigial structure A feature of an organism that is a historical remnant of a structure that served a function in the organism's ancestors.

villus (vil´-us) (plural, **villi**) (1) A finger-like projection of the inner surface of the small intestine. (2) A finger-like projection of the chorion of the mammalian placenta. Large numbers of villi increase the surface areas of these organs.

viroid (vī´-royd) A plant pathogen composed of molecules of naked, circular RNA several hundred nucleotides long.

virus A microscopic particle capable of infecting cells of living organisms and inserting its genetic material. Viruses are generally not considered to be alive because they do not display all of the characteristics associated with life.

visceral mass (vis´-uh-rul) One of the three main parts of a mollusc, containing most of the internal organs.

visual acuity The ability of the eyes to distinguish fine detail. Normal visual acuity in humans is usually reported as "20/20 vision."

vital capacity The maximum volume of air that a mammal can inhale and exhale with each breath.

vitamin An organic nutrient that an organism requires in small quantities. Many vitamins serve as coenzymes or parts of coenzymes.

vitreous humor (vit´-rē-us hyū´-mer) A jellylike substance filling the space behind the lens in the vertebrate eye; helps maintain the shape of the eye.

vocal cord A band of elastic tissue in the larynx. Air rushing past the tensed vocal cords makes them vibrate, producing sounds.

vulva The collective term for the external female genitalia.

W

water mold A fungus-like protist in the stramenopile clade of the SAR supergroup.

water vascular system In echinoderms, a radially arranged system of water-filled canals that branch into extensions called tube feet. The system provides movement and circulates water, facilitating gas exchange and waste disposal.

wavelength The distance between crests of adjacent waves, such as those of the electromagnetic spectrum.

westerlies Winds that blow from west to east.

wetland An ecosystem intermediate between an aquatic ecosystem and a terrestrial ecosystem, where soil is saturated with water permanently or periodically.

white blood cell *See* leukocyte.

white matter Regions within the central nervous system composed mainly of axons, with their whitish myelin sheaths.

whole-genome shotgun method A method for determining the DNA sequence of an entire genome. After a genome is cut into small fragments, each fragment is sequenced and then placed in the proper order.

wild-type trait The version of a character that most commonly occurs in nature.

wood Secondary xylem of a plant. *See also* heartwood; sapwood.

wood ray A column of parenchyma cells that radiates from the center of a log and transports water to its outer living tissues.

X

X chromosome inactivation In female mammals, the inactivation of one X chromosome in each somatic cell.

xylem (zī´-lum) The nonliving portion of a plant's vascular system that provides support and conveys xylem sap from the roots to the rest of the plant. Xylem is made up of vessel elements and/or tracheids, water-conducting cells. Primary xylem is derived from the procambium. Secondary xylem is derived from the vascular cambium in plants exhibiting secondary growth.

Y

yeast A single-celled fungus that inhabits liquid or moist habitats and reproduces asexually by simple cell division or by the pinching of small buds off a parent cell.

yellow bone marrow A tissue found within the central cavities of long bones, consisting mostly of stored fat.

yolk sac An extraembryonic membrane that develops from the endoderm. The yolk sac produces the embryo's first blood cells and germ cells and gives rise to the allantois.

Z

zoned reserve An extensive region of land that includes one or more areas that are undisturbed by humans. The undisturbed areas are surrounded by lands that have been altered by human activity.

zooplankton (zō´-ō-plank´-tun) Animals that drift in aquatic environments.

zygomycete (zī´-guh-mī-sēt) Member of a group of fungi characterized by a sturdy structure called a zygosporangium, in which meiosis produces haploid spores.

zygote (zī´-gōt) The diploid fertilized egg, which results from the union of a sperm cell nucleus and an egg cell nucleus.

GLOSSARY

Index

Page numbers with *f* indicate figure, *t* indicate table, and those in bold indicate page where listed as a key term.

2,4-D herbicide, 669
3' end, DNA, 189
3-phosphoglyceric acid (3-PGA), 116
5' end, DNA, 189

A

a and α mating types, 220–221
Abdomen, arthropod, 378, 380
Abiotic factors, **680**, 682–685, 688, 728–729
Abiotic reservoirs, 752–755
Abiotic synthesis of organic molecules, 294–296
Abnormal behavior, 714
ABO blood groups, **167**
Abortion, 545
Abscisic acid (ABA), 664*t*, **667**
Abscission, leaf, 667–669
Absorption, **355**, **431**, 439
Abstinence, 545
Abundance, relative species, 746
Acanthostega, 395
Accommodation, visual, 596
Acetylcholine, **570**, 575, 614
Acetyl CoA, **96**–97, 102–103
Achondroplasia, 162*t*–163
Acid precipitation, 695, 755
Acid reflux, 437
Acids, **28**–29
Acids, nucleic. *See* Nucleic acids
Acids, stomach, 433, 436–437
Acne studies, 423
Acquired traits, 262
Acrosome, **546**
Actin, 66, 132, **612**–613
Actinomycetes, 327
Action potentials, **566**
    in hearing, 592–593
    in magnetoreception, 586–589, 591
    nerve signals as, 566–568
    in sensory reception, 588–589
    in skeletal muscle contraction, 614–615
Activation, humoral immune response, 494–495*f*
Activation energy, **83**
Activators, **211**, 214
Active immunity, **488**, 493
Active sites, **84**
Active transport, 74*f*, **78**–79, 566–568
ACTN3 genetic test, 616
Adam's apple, 434
Adaptations, **257**. *See also* Evolution
    to abiotic and biotic factors, 683
        animal, for exchange with environments, 424–425
    animal behavioral. *See* Behavior
    in animal thermoregulation, 506–507
    chemical digestion of food, 432
    correlation of structure and function in, 412–414
    in evolution by natural selection, 8–9, 257, 262–263, 269, 273
    flight, of birds, 398
    of gills for gas exchange in aquatic environments, 455–456*f*
    to global climate change, 769
    human skin colors as, to sunlight, 407
    lungs as tetrapod, for gas exchange, 458
    of plants to herbivory, 742–743
    of plants to obtain water and nutrients, 643
    of prey species to predation, 742
    prokaryotic, to environmental changes, 322
    as property of life, 2

of snowy owls in Arctic tundra, 1
    terrestrial. *See* Terrestrial adaptations
    of vertebrate digestive systems to diets, 441
Adaptive immunity, **488**
    as acquired response to specific invaders, 488
    antibodies of, as tools in laboratories and clinics, 495
    antigen binding by B cells and antibodies in, 491
    clonal selection in, 492
    dependence of, on molecular fingerprints of self proteins, 500
    destruction of infected body cells by cytotoxic T cells in, 498
    effects of HIV destruction of helper T cells on, 498–499
    helper T-cell stimulation of humoral and cell-mediated responses in, 497
    human papillomavirus (HPV) vaccination and, 484–485, 496, 544
    humoral and cell-mediated immune responses of B and T cells in, 490–491
    innate immunity vs., 485
    lymphatic system response to infection in, 489
    primary and secondary immune responses in, 493
    rapid HIV evolution as complication in AIDS treatment and, 499
    structure-function correlation of antigen-antibody complexes in, 494–495*f*
Adaptive radiations, **286**
    of cichlids in Lake Victoria, 284, 287–288
    on Galápagos Islands, 286
    in macroevolution, 297–299*t*, 304
    mammalian, 399
Adderall, 571
Addiction, 577
Addition, rule of, **160**
Adelie penguins, 768
Adenine, 46–47, 184–**185**, 186–187, 191–192
Adenoid, 489*f*
Adhesion, **26**, 646*f*
ADP (adenosine diphosphate), 82, 94–97
Adrenal cortex, **521***f*, **528**–529
Adrenal glands, **521***f*, **528**–529
Adrenal medulla, **521***f*, **528**–529
Adrenocorticotropic hormone (ACTH), 522–523, 528–**529**
Adult stem cells, **223**
Aerobic respiration, 297, 615–616
Aerosols, 120
Africa, 405–406
African violets, 126*f*
Agar, 336
Agarose, 243
Agent Orange, 665
Age structures, **733**–734
Agglutination, humoral immune response, 494–495*f*
Aggression, 715–716
Aging, plant, 640, 668–669
Agonistic behavior, **716**, 718
Agre, Peter, 78
Agriculture. *See also* Crops, agricultural
    abnormal behaviors caused by chemicals of, 714
    animal cloning in, 222
    artificial selection in, 262
    C_3 crop plants in, 117
    degradation of aquatic ecosystems by, 756

ecosystem services in, 757
    fungal parasites and pathogens in, 361
    genetically modified organisms in, 230–231, 239–240, 653, 654–655
    habitat loss and, 764
    history of, 620–622
    integrated pest management in, 731
    monocultures in, 639
    in nitrogen cycle, 755
    organic farming and sustainable, 642–643, 654
    origins of, 620–622
    pesticide resistance in, 263
    phosphorus cycle and, 754
    plant cloning in, 221
    plant diversity and, 354
    soil conservation in, 653
    species diversity and monocultures in, 746
    uses of plant hormones in, 669
Agrobacterium, 239, 360
AIDS (acquired immunodeficiency syndrome), 199, **202**–203, **498**–499, 532, 544. *See also* HIV (human immunodeficiency virus)
Ain, Michael C., 163*f*
Air
    breathing of, 396, 457
    lichens and pollution of, 359
    nitrogen in, 754–755
    plant acquisition of nutrients from, 342–343*f*, 644
    pollution of, 459, 695
Air pressure waves, hearing and, 592–593
Air sacs, 378
Alarm calls
    kin selection and, 717
    social learning and, 708–709
Albatrosses, 398
Albinism, 162
Albumen, 397
Alcohol consumption, 440, 555, 571
Alcohol fermentation, **101**
Alcohols, 35, 37
Aldehydes, 35, 37
Alertness, 580
Algae, **330**
    biofuel production from, 334
    brown, 332
    endosymbiosis of, 331
    eutrophication and blooms of, 756
    in freshwater biomes, 688
    land plants vs., 342–343*f*
    lichens as symbiotic associations of fungi and, 359
    photosynthesis by, 330
    red and green, as archaeplastids, 336
Alimentary canals, **432**–433, 441
Alkaline solutions, 28
Alkaptonuria, 190
Allantois, 397, 399, **555**
Alleles, **156**
    as alternative versions of genes, 156–157. *See also* Gene(s)
    complete and incomplete dominance of, 166–167
    diploidy and recessive, 272–273
    genes with multiple, 167
    Hardy-Weinberg principle and, 266–267
    origination of, by mutations, 264–265
    production of new combinations of, by crossing over, 172–173
Allergens, **501**
Allergies, **501**

Alligators, 3*f*, 397
Allopatric speciation, **282**, 286
α-actinin-3 protein, 616
Alpha animals, 716, 718
Alpha cells, 526*f*
Alpha-fetoprotein (AFP), 165
Alpha helix, protein, 45*f*
Alternation of generations, **336**, 343, **346***f*–**347***f*, 635
Alternative RNA splicing, 214–**215**
Altruism, 699, **717**
Alveolates, **332**–333
Alveoli, **459**
Alzheimer's disease, 21, 43, 248, **582**–583
Amazon rain forest, 354*f*
Ambulocetus, 259
American Cancer Society (ACS), 449
American pikas, 760–762
Amines, 35, 571
Amino acids, **44**. *See also* Polypeptides; Proteins
  abiotic synthesis of, 295
  adding of, to polypeptide chains during translation, 197
  in cellular respiration and biosynthesis, 102–103
  deficiencies of, 446
  essential, for animal and human diet, 443
  in food processing, 431
  genetic triplet code of codons for, 191–192
  in hormone signaling mechanisms, 519
  as neurotransmitters, 570–571
  proteins as polymers of, 36, 44
Amino group, **35**
Ammonia, 294–295, **509**, 754–755
Ammonifying bacteria, 655–656
Ammonites, 258
Ammonium, 754–755
Ammonium ions, 651, 655–656
Amnesia, 581
Amniocentesis, **164**
Amnion, 310, 397, 399, **554**–555
Amniotes, **390**, 397, 399. *See also* Mammals; Reptiles
Amniotic eggs, **397**
Amniotic fluid, 463
Amoebas, **333**
Amoebic dysentery, 335
Amoebocytes, **370**
Amoeboid movement, 65
Amoebozoans, **335**
Amphetamines, 571, 577
Amphibians, **396**
  cardiovascular systems of, 469
  endangered species of, 763*f*
  endocrine disruptors and, 516–517, 520
  fungal diseases of, 356
  gas exchange by, 458
  prolactin in, 529
  waste disposal by, 509
Amplexus, 520
Amygdala, **581**
Amylase, 434
Amyloplasts, 622
Anabaena, 327
Anabolic steroids, **42**
Anabolism, 42
Anaerobes, 101
Anal cancer, 484
Analogies, **308**
Anaphase, **130**–131*f*, 140*f*
Anaphase I, 138*f*, 140*f*
Anaphase II, 139*f*
Anaphylactic shock, 501
Anatomy, **415**
Ancestral characters, 310–311
Anchorage dependence, **133**
Anchoring junctions, 68

Androgen insensitivity syndrome, 525
Androgens, **521***f*, **525**, 539, 714
Anemia, 168, **480**
Angiosperms, **345**. *See also* Plant(s)
  in agriculture, 621
  annual, biennial, and perennial, and primary growth of, 630–631
  bodies of, 624–629
  flowers in life cycle of, 350–351
  fruits in seed dispersal by, 352
  as human food source, 352, 354
  monocots and eudicots of, 623
  pollination by animals in evolution of, 353
  reproduction of, 634–639. *See also* Plant reproduction
Angler fish, 687*f*
Animals. *See also* Invertebrates; Vertebrates
  adaptive radiations of, 286–287
  behavioral adaptations of. *See* Behavior
  birds, 8
  body plans of, 8, 368*f*–369. *See also* Animal bodies
  building phylogenetic trees for, 369
  cell cycle for, 130–132. *See also* Cell cycle; Cell division
  cells of, 56–57, 63–64, 67–69*t*. *See also* Eukaryotic cells
  cellular respiration by. *See* Cellular respiration
  characteristics of, 365
  circulatory systems of. *See* Circulatory systems
  cloning of, 208–209, 222–223
  as consumers in ecosystems, 5
  determinate growth of, 630
  discovery and naming of new species of, 408
  DNA profiling to determine origins of species of, 245
  effects of DDT on, 254, 263–265, 681
  effects of global climate change on, 768–769
  embryonic development of. *See* Animal embryonic development
  endangered species of, 761, 763*f*
  endocrine system of. *See* Endocrine system
  as eukaryotes, 7. *See also* Eukaryotes
  evolutionary diversification of, 367
  evolution of eyes among, 595. *See also* Vision
  external exchange and internal regulation in, 424–426
  fungal parasites of, 355, 361
  gas exchange mechanisms. *See* Gas exchange mechanisms
  genetically modified and transgenic, 230–231, 237, 239–240. *See also* Genetically modified organisms (GMOs); Transgenic organisms
  geographic distribution of, 301
  hibernating, 89
  homeotic genes and gene regulation in development of, 218
  hormonal regulation by. *See* Animal hormones; Hormonal regulation
  immune system of. *See* Immune system
  movement and locomotion as characteristic of, 604. *See also* Animal movement; Locomotion
  multiple functions of prolactin in, 529
  mutation rates of, 265
  nervous systems of. *See* Nervous systems
  nutrition for. *See* Animal nutrition
  organs and organ systems of, 419–423, 425, 426
  origin and macroevolution of, 297–299*t*
  osmoregulation by, 77, 508–513
  plant recruitment of predatory, 674
  pollination by, 351, 353, 635
  polysaccharides of, 39*f*
  prions as pathogens of, 203
  regeneration in, 221
  reproduction of. *See* Animal reproduction

seed dispersal by, 352, 637
senses of. *See* Senses
sex determination of, 174–175
sympatric speciation in, 284
terrestrial, 689
thermoregulation by, 504–507
viral diseases of, 201
Animal bodies
  body plans for. *See* Body plans
  changes in, in macroevolution, 305
  circulatory systems of. *See* Circulatory systems
  elements in human, 18*t*
  embryonic development of. *See* Animal embryonic development
  energy requirements of, for diets, 442
  evolution of nervous systems and symmetry of, 573
  external exchange and internal regulation of, 424–426
  gas exchange in. *See* Gas exchange mechanisms
  hierarchical organization of, 415
  homeostatic regulation of, 425–426. *See also* Endocrine system; Hormonal regulation
  integumentary systems, 422–423
  organs and organ systems of, 419–423
  osmoregulation by, 508–513
  sexual dimorphism of, 271
  skeletal muscle of, 611–616
  skeletons of, 606–611
  somatic cells of, 136
  structure-function correlation in, 412–415
  thermoregulation by, 505–507
  tissues of, 414–418
Animal embryonic development. *See also* Animal reproduction; Human development
  cellular processes of embryo formation in, 552
  cleavage and blastula formation in, 548
  control of pattern formation in, by homeotic genes, 552–553
  fertilization and zygote formation as start of, 546–547
  gastrulation and embryo formation in, 549
  homeotic genes and gene regulation in, 218, 608–609
  organ formation in, 550–551
  vertebrate brains in, 576
  vertebrate embryonic development, laryngeal nerve, 414
Animal fats, 40–41
Animal hormones, **518**. *See also* Endocrine system; Hormonal regulation
  antagonistic, 526*f*
  DNA technology and therapeutic, 238
  endocrine disruptors as mimics of, 516–517, 520
  endocrine glands and, 521*f*
  evolution of multiple functions for prolactin, 529
  in hormonal regulation by endocrine and nervous systems, 518
  human behavior and, 719
  human female, 537
  human female reproductive cycles and, 542–543
  human male, 539
  oxytocin in social bonding, 530
  regulation of urinary system by, 513
  signaling mechanisms of water-soluble and lipid-soluble, 519
  similarity of plant hormones to, 660–661
Animalia kingdom, 7
Animal movement
  locomotion as, 604. *See also* Locomotion
  migratory. *See* Migration
  penguin huddling as thermoregulation, 504–505, 507
  as pump for open circulatory systems, 468
  and spatial learning, 706*f*

Animal nutrition. *See also* Human nutrition
  digestion in specialized compartments in, 432
  energy requirements of diets in, 442
  essential fatty acids and essential amino acids
    in, 443
  evolutionary adaptations of vertebrate digestive
    systems to diets in, 441
  four stages of food processing in, 431
  nutritional modes and feeding mechanisms
    in, 430
Animal reproduction, **534**. *See also* Human
    reproduction
  asexual vs. sexual, 534–535
  endocrine disruptors and, 516–517, 520
  fish parental care in, 722–723
  life cycles of, 366
  life histories and, 730
  mating behavior in. *See* Mating
  sexual selection in, 271
  waste disposal and, 509
Animal reproductive systems, **421***f*
Animal responses
  animal movement as, to stimuli, 706*f*
  associative learning and, 708
  coupling of stimuli and, by central nervous
    system, 600
  in hormonal regulation, 518
  hormone signaling, 519
  peripheral nervous system, 575
Anions, 652
Ankle bones, 259
Annelids, **376**–377
Annual growth rings, 632–633*f*
Annuals, **630**, 748
Anomalocaris, 367
Anorexia nervosa, 446
Antacids, 437
Antagonistic hormones, **526***f*
Antagonistic skeletal muscles, 611
Antarctica, 120, 408, 504, 507, 694, 766, 768
Antelope, 683
Antelope squirrels, 282
Anterior ends, **368***f*
Anterior pituitary, **521***f*, **522**–523, 525, 529
Anterior-posterior axis, 553
Anthers, **350**, **634**
Anthrax, 322, 328
Anthropoids, **400***f*–405. *See also* Hominins
Antibiotics, 318, 321, 327, 328
  for digestive ailments, 329, 437
  as enzyme inhibitors, 85
  fungi in production of, 358
  resistance to, 12, 205, 272, 322, 324
  sponges in production of, 370
  targeting of prokaryotic ribosomes by, to
    combat bacterial infections, 55, 196
Antibodies, **488**
  in adaptive immunity, 488
  in antigen-antibody complex of humoral
    immune response, 494–495*f*
  binding of, to antigen determinants, 491
  in blood, 479
  in clonal selection, 492*f*
  human papillomavirus (HPV), 496
  as powerful tools in laboratories and clinics,
    496
  as proteins, 43
Anticancer drugs, 124–125, 133, 135–136
Anticoagulant drugs, 377, 481
Anticodons, **195**
Antidepressants, 562–563, 571–572
Antidiuretic hormone (ADH), **513**, **521***f*, 522
Antigen-antibody complex, 494–495*f*
Antigen-binding sites, **491**, 494
Antigen determinants, **491**
Antigen-presenting cells, **497**
Antigen receptors, **490**–491

Antigens, **488**
  adaptive immune response to specific, 488
  allergies as hypersensitive reactions to
    environmental, 501
  in antigen-antibody complex of humoral
    immune response, 494–495*f*
  binding of antigen receptors and antibodies
    to, 491
  clonal selection and specific, 492*f*
  primary and secondary responses to, 493
Antihistamines, **501**
Anti-inflammatory drugs, 487
Antismoking therapies, 460
Antithrombin, 237
Anus, **432**
Anvil, ear, 592–593
Aorta, 414, **470***f*, 475
Apes, **400***f*–401*f*
Aphids, 430, 649, 728*f*–729
Aphotic zone, **687**–688
Apical dominance, **624**, 666
Apical meristems, **342**, **630**
Apical surface, 416–417
Apolipoprotein E (APOE), 583
Apoptosis, **552**
Appendages, arthropod, 378, 380
Appendicular skeletons, **608**
Appendix, **440**, 489*f*
Appetite regulators, 447
Aquaporins, 72*f*–73, **77**–78
  abiotic factors for life in, 682
  degradation of, by nutrient inflow, 756
  fishes in, 392–393
  food chains in, 744
  freshwater, 688
  gills as adaptation for gas exchange in, 455–
    456*f*
  global water cycle as connection of terrestrial
    biomes and, 695
  loss of biodiversity in, 762
  marine, 686–687
  osmoregulation in, 508
  pollution of, 765
  search for new species in, 408
Aqueous humor, **596**
Aqueous solutions, **27**–28. *See also* Water
Arabidopsis thaliana, 247, 664–665
Arachnids, **378**–379
Arboreal primates, **400***f*–402
Arbuscular fungi, 360
Arbuscules, 357
Archaea
  differences between bacteria, eukaryotes, and,
    325*t*
  domain of, 7, 314, **320**, 325*t*
  extreme environments and habitats of, 326
  as prokaryotic, 320, 325. *See also* Prokaryotes
  prokaryotic cells of, 4, 55, 320–321. *See also*
    Prokaryotic cells
Archaea domain, 7, 314, **320**, 325*t*. *See also*
    Archaea
Archaean eon, 297–299*t*
Archaeobotanists, 622
Archaeopteryx, 398
Archaeplastids, **336**
Arctic terns, 605
Arctic tundra, 1, 694, 777
Ardipithecus ramidus, 402–403
Aristotle, 256, 644
Armstrong, Lance, 237, 480
Arousal, alertness and, 580
Arousal, sexual, 537, 539, 571
Arrhythmias, 472
Artemisinin, 255, 272
Arteries, **468**, 474, 476, 510
Arterioles, **468**, 474, 477*f*
Arthritis, 500

Arthropods, 297, **378**–382, 468, 606–607
Artificial hips, 610
Artificial incubation, 705
Artificial lenses, 597
Artificial pacemakers, 472
Artificial selection, **12**, 232, **262**–263
Asci, 357
Ascomycetes, **357**
Asexual reproduction, **126**, **534**
  binary fission as, 204
  cell division and, 126–127, 140*f*
  fungal, 356
  plant cloning as, 221, 638–639
  sexual reproduction vs., 534–535
A site, **197**
A soil horizon, 652
Aspartame, 267
Aspartic acid, 44
Aspens, 639
Aspirin, 473, 481, 487, 591, 675, 738
Assisted reproductive technologies, **559**
Association areas, cerebral cortex, **578**
Associative learning, 703*t*, **708**
Asteroids. *See* Meteorites
Asthma, 738
Astigmatism, **597**
Astrobiologists, 29
Astronauts, 594
Atherosclerosis, 79, 166, **473**
Athletes. *See also* Sports
  blood doping by, 237, 480
  brain trauma of, 583
  genetic testing of, for fast-twitch muscle fibers,
    602–603, 616
Athlete's foot, 361
Atlantic cod fishery collapse, 731
Atlantic salmon, 239
Atmospheric nitrogen, 754–755
Atmospheric pollution, 359, 459, 695
Atomic mass, **20**
Atomic number, **20**
Atoms, 3, **20**, 22–23
ATP (adenosine triphosphate), **82**
  in active transport, 78–79
  anaerobic synthesis of, in fermentation,
    100–102
  animal energy from, 442
  brown fat and, 88–89, 99
  in Calvin cycle, 116
  in cellular respiration, 90
  conversion of food energy to, by mitochondria,
    63–64
  in energy coupling of exergonic and endergonic
    reactions, 81–82
  in photosynthesis, 111, 114–115*f*, 118
  in skeletal muscle contraction, 612–613,
    615–616
  in transcription, 195
ATP synthase, **98**–99, 114–115*f*
Atrazine, 516–517, 520
Atria, heart, **468**–469
Attachment proteins, 74*f*
Attention deficit hyperactivity disorder (ADHD),
    571
Auditory canal, **592**–593
Auditory nerve, 593
Auditory signals, 711
Australia, 301, 735*f*, 749
Australian moles, 308
Australopiths, 403*f*, 404
Autism, 719
Autoimmune disorders, **500**, 527
Automatic external defibrillators (AEDs), 472
Autonomic nervous system, **575**
Autosomal human disorders, 162–163
Autosomes, **137**
Autotrophs, **108**, 323, 330, 336, 744

INDEX

Human papillomavirus (HPV), 484–485, 488, 496, 498, 532, 544
Human population
  age structures of, 733–734
  demographic transition of, 732–733
  ecological footprints of, as measures of resource consumption, 734–735
  in energy flow, 752
Human reproduction. *See also* Animal embryonic development; Animal reproduction
  cell division in, 126–127. *See also* Cell division
  childbirth in, 558–559
  contraception in, 545
  female reproductive system in, 536–537
  formation of sperm and eggs by meiosis in, 540–541
  hormonal regulation of female reproductive cycles in, 542–543
  male reproductive system in, 538–539
  population growth and, 732–734
  pregnancy in, 554–557f
  reproductive technologies in, 559
  sexually transmitted diseases (STDs) in, 532–533, 544–545
Human respiratory system
  automatic control of breathing in, 461
  as branching tubes conveying air to lungs, 458–459
  effects of cigarette smoking on, 452–453, 460, 463
  gas exchange by, 454
  gas transport system and, 462–463
  respiratory problems of, 459
  ventilation of lungs by negative pressure breathing in, 460–461
Hummingbirds, 280f
Humoral immune response, 490–491, 497
Humpback whales, 259f, 430
Humulin, 238
Humus, **652**
Hunger, human deaths from, 654
Huntington's disease, 162t–**163**, 164, 246
Hybrid breakdown, 281f
Hybridization, 284–285, 287, 288–289
Hybrids, **155**, **279**, 281f, 288–289
Hybrid zones, **288**–289
Hydras, 371, 424, 432, 534, 573, 606
Hydrocarbons, **34**
Hydrochloric acid, 28, 436–437
Hydrogen
  in cellular respiration, 92
  molecules of, 23f
  in origin of life, 294–295
  water as compound of oxygen and, 18
Hydrogenated vegetable oils, 40–41, 449
Hydrogenation, 40–41
Hydrogen bonds, **24**–27, 39–41, 186–187
Hydrogen ions, 28
Hydrogen peroxide, 57, 63
Hydrolysis, **36**, 82
Hydrophilic molecules, **35**, 44f, 54
Hydrophobic molecules, **40**, 44f, 54
Hydroponic culture, 650
Hydrostatic skeletons, **606**
Hydrothermal vents, 295, 323, 682, 750
Hydroxide ions, 28
Hydroxyl group, **35**
Hypercholesterolemia, 162t, 166–167
Hyperglycemia, **527**
Hyperopia, 597
Hypertension, **476**–477
Hyperthyroidism, 524
Hypertonic cells, 508
Hypertonic solutions, **76**
Hyphae, **355**–356
Hypodermis, 422

Hypoglycemia, **527**
Hypothalamus, **521**f, **522**–523, 525, 539, 542–543, 576–577, 580–581, 671
Hypotheses, **10**
  G. Mendel's, 156–157
  phylogenetic trees as, 311, 314
  in science, 10–11, 328–329
Hypothyroidism, 524
Hypotonic cells, 508
Hypotonic solutions, **76**
Hyracotherium, 307

I

Ibuprofen, 85, 487, 591
Ice, 27
Ice, polar, 694
Ichthyostega, 394–395
Identical twins, 548, 582, 719
Iguanas, 257
Imaging technologies, 580, 582
Imitation, social learning and, 708–709
Immigration, 724, 726
Immune system, **421**f, **486**
  adaptive immunity in, 488–500. *See also* Adaptive immunity
  diabetes and, 527
  disorders of, 500–501
  functions of, 421f
  gene therapy for diseases of, 241
  immunoglobulins and leukocytes in, 479
  innate immunity in, 486–487
  innate vs. adaptive immunity in, 485
  stem cells in, 481
Immunodeficiency disorders, **500**–501
Immunofluorescence microscopy, 66
Immunoglobulins, 479
Imperfect fungi, **356**
Imperfection, evolution of, 413–414
Implants, penile, 559
Impotence, **559**
Imprinting, 703t, **704**–705
Inbreeding, 163
Incisors, 434
Inclusive fitness, **717**
Incomplete dominance, **166**–167
Incomplete metamorphosis, **380**
Incus, 592–593
Independent assortment, law of, **158**–160, 171
Independent orientation, chromosome, 141, 265
Indeterminate growth, **630**
India, 752
Indigo buntings, 707
Individual variation, 8–9, 262–265
Indoleacetic acid (IAA), 664. *See also* Auxins
Induced fit, **84**
Induction, **552**
Inductive reasoning, 10
Infant diarrhea, 239
Infants, passive immunity of, 488
Infections, 489, 499
Inferior vena cava, 470f
Infertility, 544, **559**
Inflammation, 85, 473, 476, 487–488, 494, 500
Inflammatory response, **487**, 529
Influenza viruses, 180–181, 202
Information processing, limbic system, 581
Ingestion, 7, **366**, 430–**431**
Ingredients, food, 446
Ingroups, **310**
Inhalation, 460–461
Inheritance
  artificial selection, natural selection, and, 262–263
  cell division and. *See* Cell division
  chromosomal basis of, 170–174

DNA as molecule of, 3, 6. *See also* Chromosomes; DNA (deoxyribonucleic acid); Gene(s)
  epigenetic, 212–213
  of genetic mutations by Tibetan people, 152–153
  genetics as study of, 154. *See also* Genetics
  of human disorders, 162–165, 177
  G. Mendel's laws on. *See* Mendelian genetics
  in microevolution of populations. *See* Microevolution
  obesity and, 447
Inhibiting hormones, **522**–523
Inhibition
  abscisic acid in, of plant processes, 667
  density-dependent, 133
  by enzymes, 85
  by nerve signals, 570
Initiation stage, transcription, 193f
Initiation stage, translation, 196–198, 216
Injuries
  bone, 610
  brain, 579, 583
Innate behaviors, **700**–701, 704
Innate immunity, **486**
  adaptive immunity vs., 485
  antigen-antibody complex in, 494–495f
  inflammatory response in, 487
  invertebrate and vertebrate, 486
Inner ear, **592**–594
Innocence Project, 245
Inorganic fertilizers, 651, 653
Inorganic nutrients, 644, 650–651, 682
Inquiry, scientific, 10. *See also* Science; Scientific Thinking modules
Insecticides, 654, 742
Insectivores, 744
Insects
  characteristics of, as most successful animals, 380–381
  compound eyes of, 595
  digestion of, by plants, 657
  diversity of, 364–365
  evolution of pesticide resistance in, 12, 254–255, 263
  fossils of, in amber, 258
  gas exchange by tracheal systems of, 455, 457
  limiting factors for population growth of, 728f–729
  nervous systems of, 573
  osmoregulation by, 508–509
  pollination by, 353, 635
  sex determination in, 175
Insoluble fiber, 39
Insulation, animal, 422, 506
Insulin, 6, 60, 216, 238, **521**f, **526**f–527
Integrated pest management (IPM), 731
Integration, **564**
Integrins, **67**
Integumentary systems, **420**f, 422–423
Interaction theme, 5
Interbreeding, 279
Intercellular communication function, eukaryotic cell, 56–57, 69
Interferons, **486**
Intergovernmental Panel on Climate Change (IPCC), 766
Intermediate compounds, **94**–95f, 103
Intermediate filaments, **65**
Internal clocks, plant, 671–673. *See also* Biological clocks
Internal fertilization, **535**, 713
International Union for Conservation of Nature (IUCN), 763
Interneurons, **564**, 588–589f
Internodes, **624**

INDEX

INDEX

plant acquisition of nutrients from, 342–343f, 644

plant essential inorganic nutrients in, 650

preventing nutrient deficiencies in, with fertilizers, 651

secondary succession and, 748

support of plant growth with fertile, 652

Solar energy

as biosphere energy source, 682

climate and seasons from uneven distribution of, 684–685

conversion of, to chemical energy by photosynthesis, 64, 111–115f, 118. *See also* Photosynthesis

in ecosystem energy flow, 750–751

in energy flow and chemical cycling in ecosystems, 5

sunlight as electromagnetic, 112. *See also* Sunlight

Solid matter, 18

Solomon, Susan, 120

Solutes, **27**

animal osmoregulation of, 508–513

plant uptake and transport of, 645–649

transport of, across plasma membranes, 75–79

Solutions, **27–28**

Solvents, **27**

Somatic cells, **136**

Somatosensory cortex, 578

Somites, 551, 608–609

Songbirds, 286, 704

Sonoran desert community, 745f

Sound

communication signals as, 711

conversion of air pressure waves to action potentials by ears in hearing, 592–593

detection of, by mechanoreceptors, 590–591f

Sour tastes, 599

Southeast Asia, 408

Sow bugs, 706f

Soybeans, 239, 660f–661f

Space, territorial behavior and, 715

Space-filling models, 23f

Spatial learning, 703t, **706f**

Speciation, 276–277, **278**. *See also* Evolution

allopatric, from geographic isolation, 282

in bowerbirds, 276–277, 287

definitions of species, 278–279

from errors in cell division, 147

evolution of reproductive barriers as populations diverge in, 283

on isolated islands, 286

Lake Victoria as laboratory for studying, 287

mechanisms of, 282–289

natural selection as mechanism for, 8–9

origin of plant species in polyploid, 285

punctuated equilibrium and rates of, 289

reproductive barriers between species in, 280f–281f

reproductive isolation and, in hybrid zones, 288–289

as source of biological diversity, 278

sympatric, in absence of geographic isolation, 284

Species, **279**

binomial names for, 308–309

classification of, 6–7

cloning of endangered, 208–209, 222

coexisting, in hominin evolution, 403

communities of, 740. *See also* Communities

definitions of, 278–279

discovery and naming of new animal, 408

diversity of. *See* Species diversity; Species richness

emerging viruses and contact between, 202

genomics and comparisons of, 248, 250

geographic distribution of, 301

human impacts on extinctions of, 12

insect, 365

invasive, 749, 764

keystone, 747, 763, 775

mass extinctions of. *See* Mass extinctions

natural selection in evolution of, 8–9. *See also* Evolution; Natural selection

phylogenies as evolutionary histories of, 308. *See also* Phylogenies

sequenced genomes of, 6

species selection in macroevolution of, 307

Species diversity, **746–747**, 756, 762–763

Species richness, 746

Species selection, 307

Speech, 250

Sperm, **534**

in fertilization, 546–547

formation of human, by meiosis, 540–541

as gametes, 137

infertility and, 559

in male reproductive system, 538–539

plant, 343

in sexual reproduction, 534

Spermatogenesis, **540–541**

Spermicides, **545**

Sperry, Roger, 579

S phase, 129

Sphincters, **433**, 441

Spices, 352

Spiders, 378–379

Spina bifida, 550–551

Spinal cords, 564–565, **574**, 575–577, 608

Spinal nerves, 574

Spines, 625, 742

Spiny shrubs, chaparral, 692

Spirilla, 321

Spirochetes, 320f–321, **327**

Spleen, 489f

Splicing, RNA, 194, 214–215

Sponges (Porifera), **370**, 430

Spontaneous generation theory, 294

Spontaneous mutations, 199

Sporangia, **343**, 346f–347f

Spores, 335, **343**, 356, 635

Sporophytes, **336**, 346f–347f, 350–351, **635**

Sports, 602–603, 616. *See also* Athletes

Spyhopping, 707

Squamous epithelium, 416–417

Squids, 375, 573f

Squirrels, 282

SRY gene, 175

S-shaped population growth curve, 727

SSRIs (selective serotonin reuptake inhibitors), 562–563, 571–572

Stability, hybrid zone reproductive barriers and, 289

Stabilizing selection, **270**

Stable isotopes, 20

Staghorn ferns, 657

Staining techniques, 66

Stamens, 155, **350, 634**

Standing water, 688

Stapes, 592–593

Staphylococcus, 327–328

Starch, 39

Start codons, 192, **196**–197

Starvation, 446

Stem cells, 223, **481**, 490, 548

Stems, **624**. *See also* Shoots

gibberellins in elongation of, 666–667

modified, 625

of monocots and eudicots, 623f

as plant organs, 342, 624

primary growth of, 630–631

secondary growth of, 632–633

Sterilization, contraceptive, 545

Steroid hormones, 519, 528–529

Steroids, **42**

Stethoscope, 476

Stickleback fish, 305, 714

Sticky ends, DNA, 234f

Stigma, 350, **634**

Stimuli (stimulus), **566, 700**

animal movement as response to, 706f

associative learning and, 708

behavior and, 700

conversion of, to action potentials by sensory receptors, 588–589

coupling of response and, by central nervous system, 600

generation and propagation of action potentials from nerve signal, 566–568

in hormonal regulation, 518

responses of plants to environmental. *See* Plant responses

sensory receptor detection of five categories of, 590–591

Stinging cells, cnidarian, 371

Stingrays, 392

Stirrup, ear, 592–593

Stolon, 625

Stomachs, 328–329, **432–437**

Stomata, **109**, 117, 342, **626–627f**, 647

Stop codons, 192, **197**

Storage, energy, 81

Storage proteins, 43

Stramenopiles, **332**

STR analysis, **244**

Strata, **258**

Stratified epithelium, 416–417

Strawberries, 625

Streams, 688

Streptococcus, 321, 327

Streptomyces, 327

Streptomycin, 55

Stress

adrenal response to, 528–529

blood pressure and, 475

bones and, 610

effects of, on immunity, 501

maternal behavior and, 702–703f

plant response to, 668

Stress fractures, 610

Stretch receptors, **590–591f**

Striated muscle, 612. *See also* Skeletal muscle

Strike-slip faults, 302

Strokes, **473**, 583

Stroma, **64, 109**, 111, 114–115f, 118

Stromatolites, **294**

Structural formulas, 23f

Structural proteins, 43

Structure, anatomy as study of, 415

Structure-function correlation

in animal bodies, 412–418

in human blood vessels, 474, 478

in skeletal muscles, 612

Strychnine, 742

Sturtevant, Alfred H., 174

Style, 350

Subatomic particles, 20

Substrate, enzyme, **84**

Substrate, marine biome, 686–687

Substrate feeders, **430**

Substrate-level phosphorylation, **94–95f**

Succulent plants, 117

Sucrase, 84, 438t

Sucrose, 38

Sugar-phosphate backbone, DNA, 46–47, **184–185**, 189

Sugars

photosynthesis of, 111, 116–118. *See also* Carbohydrates

plant transport of, by phloem, 644, 648–649

Sugar sinks, **648–649**

INDEX

17 Study Skills: *The Proper Care and Feeding of a Human Brain*

When you complete this chapter, you should be able to:

- Understand your preferred learning style and study strategies that emphasize it.

- Utilize skills that will help you get the most benefit from lectures, labs, and readings.

- Draft a written schedule that includes adequate study time.

- Know how to prepare well for an exam.

- Take responsibility, realizing that you are ultimately accountable for your own success or failure.

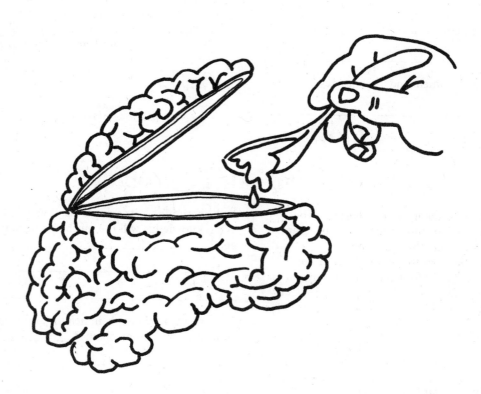

▷ Your Starting Point

Answer the following questions to assess your study habits.

1. How often do you read a course textbook?

   _____

2. How many days of the week do you study for one course?

   _____

3. Do you study hard the day before an exam, but rarely between exams? _____

   _____

4. Where do you study? _____

5. How long should you spend studying outside of class?

   _____

6. Do you schedule your study time and stick to it?

   _____

7. Do you study hard or hardly study? _____

   _____

8. Do you mostly memorize when studying for a test?

   _____

9. Do you have a good support group of family and friends who encourage you? _____

   _____

10. Do you quiz yourself when studying? _____

   _____

Welcome to the exciting and sometimes challenging world of anatomy and physiology! You will quickly discover how amazing the human machine truly is—a curious marvel of complexity that is simultaneously surprisingly simple. I hope you will be fascinated by learning how your own body is built (anatomy) and how it works (physiology). Interest in your subject matter always makes it much easier to learn.

Still, no matter how exciting your anatomical explorations may be, your course may, at times, seem rigorous and demanding. You've taken a great first step by turning to this book to jump-start your studies. This book is meant to help you enter the course with a well-planned strategy for success and with confidence in your basic science knowledge. The purpose of this chapter is to help you "train your brain" to make your learning process easier and more efficient.

● **Answers:** Answers will be individualized, except for #5—you should spend 2–3 hours studying for each hour of class time.

▷ Why Should I Study Anatomy and Physiology?

Most students take anatomy and physiology because it is required for their educational programs. Sometimes when something is required, we do it only because we have to without considering what benefits the task might hold for us. Unfortunately, some students use that approach for anatomy and physiology. Certainly it is easier to study something if you understand why it matters, and this course is no exception.

Picture This

Until recently your car has run perfectly, but now the engine occasionally quits running and is difficult to restart. Assuming you have little knowledge of auto mechanics, you are not likely to solve the mystery or make repairs yourself. You take it to an auto mechanic, who will consider how your car is

malfunctioning—its symptoms, if you will—and then fix it. What knowledge will the mechanic need to accomplish that goal? _____

   _____

   _____

In what ways are people in health- and medical-related fields similar to the auto mechanic? _____

   _____

   _____

Why do they need to fully understand anatomy and physiology?

   _____

   _____

Now consider your own future—what is your planned career?

_____

_____

Why will you need to know anatomy and physiology?

_____

_____

Many anatomy and physiology students plan careers in a medical or health field. Others may be heading into kinesiology, athletic or personal training, perhaps biomechanics or bioengineering, and many other fields. These career areas share a common thread—anatomy and physiology form the foundation on which they are all built. Now, back to our example. To understand your malfunctioning car, the mechanic must first fully understand the parts of your car—how they fit together and how they normally function, just as you will need to understand the parts of the human body and their normal functions. Finally, there is a simpler reason why you should care about learning anatomy and physiology. The human body is an amazing machine, and you own one. Anatomy and physiology are your owner's manual.

▷ To Thine Own Self Be True: Learning Styles

What *is* the best way to learn these subjects? A tremendous amount of research has explored how people learn, and there are many opinions. One common and simple approach considers which of the senses a learner relies on the most—sight, sound, or touch:

■ *Visual learners* learn best by *seeing*.
■ *Auditory learners* learn best by *hearing*.
■ *Tactile (kinesthetic) learners* learn best by *doing*.

Time to Try

Let's uncover your learning style. Look at **Table 17.1**.

1. Read an activity in the first column, then read each of the three responses to the right of that activity. Mark the response that seems most characteristic of you.
2. Do this for each row. Then add the marks in each column and write the total in the bottom row.
3. You will likely have a higher total in one column. That's your primary learning style. The second highest number is your secondary style.

My primary learning style is: _____

My secondary learning style is: _____

Now that you know your primary and secondary learning styles, you can design your study approach accordingly, emphasizing activities that use your preferred senses. Look closely at your scores, though. If two scores are rather close, you already use two learning styles well and will benefit from using both of them when studying. If your high score is much higher than your other scores, you have a strong preference and should particularly emphasize that style. Most people use a combination of learning styles.

In addition, information coming in through different senses reaches different parts of your brain, activating more neural pathways that allow you to learn. The more of your brain that is engaged in the learning process, the more effective your learning will be, so try strategies for all three styles and merely emphasize your preferred style over the others. You'll know which strategies work best for you. We'll consider some strategies that you might try for each style; these ideas are summarized for you in **Table 17.2**.

Visual Learners

If you are a **visual learner,** you rely heavily on visual cues. You notice your teacher's mannerisms, expressions, gestures, and body language. Seeing these cues is especially helpful, so sit at the front of the classroom, close to the teacher. You tend to think in pictures and learn well from visual aids such as diagrams, illustrations, tables, videos, and hand-outs. Here are some strategies for you.

■ In class, take detailed notes and make sketches.
■ When studying on your own, draw pictures that relate to the information, make flow charts and concept maps, use flash cards, focus on illustrations and tables in your textbook, and read the captions that accompany them.
■ Use anatomy and physiology coloring books and picture atlases.
■ Mentally visualize the material you are studying and imagine yourself acting out processes. For example, to learn major blood vessels, you might imagine yourself swimming through them.

TABLE 17.1 | ASSESSING YOUR LEARNING STYLE.

Activity	Column 1	Column 2	Column 3
1. While I try to **concentrate** . . .	I grow distracted by clutter or movement, and I notice things in my visual field that other people don't.	I get distracted by sounds, and I prefer to control the amount and type of noise around me.	I become distracted by commotion, and I tend to retreat inside myself.
2. While I am **visualizing** . . .	I see vivid, detailed pictures in my thoughts.	I think in voices and sounds.	I see images in my thoughts that involve movement.
3. When I talk to **someone** . . .	I dislike listening for very long.	I enjoy listening, or I may get impatient to talk.	I gesture and use expressive movements.
4. When I **contact people** . . .	I prefer face-to-face meetings.	I prefer speaking by telephone for intense conversations.	I prefer to interact while walking or participating in some activity.
5. When I **see an acquaintance** . . .	I tend to forget names but usually remember faces, and I can usually remember where we met.	I tend to remember people's names and can usually remember what we discussed.	I tend to remember what we did together and may almost "feel" our time together.
6. When I am **relaxing** . . .	I prefer to watch TV, see a play, or go to a movie.	I prefer to listen to the radio, play music, read, or talk with a friend.	I prefer to play sports, make crafts, or build something with my hands.
7. While I am **reading** . . .	I like descriptive scenes and may pause to imagine the action.	I enjoy the dialogue most and can "hear" the characters talking.	I prefer action stories, but I rarely read for pleasure.
8. When I am **spelling** . . .	I try to see the word in my mind or imagine what it would look like on paper.	I sound out the word, sometimes aloud, and tend to recall rules about letter order.	I get a feel for the word by writing it out or pretending to type it.
9. When I **do something new** . . .	I seek out demonstrations, pictures or diagrams.	I like verbal and written instructions, and talking it over with someone else.	I prefer to jump right in to try it, and I will keep trying and try different ways.
10. When I **assemble something** . . .	I look at the picture first and then, maybe, read the directions.	I like to read the directions, or I talk aloud as I work.	I usually ignore the directions and figure it out as I go along.
11. When I **am interpreting someone's mood** . . .	I mostly look at his or her facial expressions.	I listen to the tone of the voice.	I watch body language.
12. When I **teach others how to do something** . . .	I prefer to show them how to do it.	I prefer to tell them or write out how to do it.	I demonstrate how it is done and ask them to try.
TOTAL:	**Visual:** _____	**Auditory:** _____	**Tactile/Kinesthetic:** _____

Source: Courtesy of Marcia L. Conner, www.agelesslearner.com

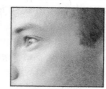
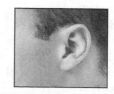

	Visual	Auditory	Tactile
Techniques to use	❑ Sit close to the teacher.	❑ Listen carefully to your teacher's voice.	❑ Highlight while reading.
	❑ Take detailed notes.	❑ Read the textbook and your notes out loud.	❑ Write your own notes in class and while reading.
	❑ Draw pictures.		❑ Transfer your notes to another tablet or type into your computer.
	❑ Make flow charts.	❑ Tape record lectures and listen to them later.	❑ Doodle and draw as you read.
	❑ Use flash cards.	❑ Listen during class instead of writing notes.	❑ Build models.
	❑ Focus on the figures, tables, and their captions.	❑ Work in a study group.	❑ Create and conduct your own experiments.
	❑ Try coloring books and picture atlases.	❑ Discuss the material with others.	❑ Walk or stand to read.
	❑ Use visualization.		❑ Use A&P coloring books.
			❑ Use flash cards.

Auditory Learners

If you are an **auditory learner**, you learn well from traditional lectures and discussion. You listen carefully to your teacher's vocal pitch, tone, speed, and mannerisms. Material that you struggle with while reading becomes clearer when you hear it. Here are some strategies for you.

▪ Read the textbook and your notes out loud.

▪ Tape record the lectures so you can listen to them later. Taping lectures also allows you to listen during class instead of focusing on writing, which is less beneficial for you.

▪ Work in a study group, and discuss material with your teacher, lab group, and friends.

Tactile Learners

If you are a **tactile learner**, you learn best by actively participating and doing hands-on activities. You may become bored easily in class from sitting still too long and start fidgeting or doodling. You need to do something physical while studying and learning. Here are some ideas for you.

▪ Try using a marker to highlight important information while you are reading.

▪ Write out your own notes in class and while reading the textbook. Later, transfer your notes to another tablet or type them into your computer.

▪ Draw pictures of appropriate material as you read.

▪ Build models of anatomical structures using clay or other materials.

▪ Create and conduct your own experiments.

▪ Hold your book and walk while reading.

▪ Use anatomy coloring books.

▪ Make and use your own flash cards.

▪ Keep your hands and your mind busy together.

We've considered only one set of learning styles, but there are many other systems. The VARK system, for example, recognizes four styles: visual, aural, read/write, and kinesthetic. Another system, called Memletics ("*memory athletics*") identifies seven learning styles. Many other systems, such as the Kolb Learning Style Inventory and the Myers-Briggs Type Indicator are also available, some for free and online. To gain more insight into your preferences, you can explore other systems by doing a web search for "learning styles." Whether or not you seek additional information, it's good to at least have a general idea of your learning preferences. Matching your study approach to your learning preference can help you gain the most from your study sessions. Find out what works for you.

Understanding your own learning style allows you to develop more effective and efficient study techniques that take advantage of your sensory preferences. By emphasizing your preferred learning style, the material will be easier to learn and will stay with you longer.

✔ QUICK CHECK

Homemade flash cards would be most beneficial to which two learning styles? _____ and _____.

How could they be used to benefit a learner of the third style?

_____

Answer: They would benefit visual and tactile learners. Reading them out loud would benefit auditory learners.

▷ Putting on Your Best Face: Getting Ready

Many students mistakenly wait until the first lecture to start thinking about class. The key to starting your semester well is to be organized and ready when you enter the classroom. This takes advance planning, but the time invested will save you tremendous time while the semester is underway.

Putting It in Writing

As the semester begins—preferably before—you should get organized, and that begins with making a commitment to yourself. Too often we begin a project without setting goals in advance. If you set a goal, you enter with a purpose and a direction. If you do not set a goal, it's too easy to just go along and see where you end. Take time to think about your goals for the semester.

Your goals should be **SMART**, which stands for the characteristics to incorporate into your goals:

- *Specific.* Instead of trying to "do well," perhaps strive for a specific grade.
- *Measurable.* How will you know if you achieve your goals? For example, a goal of studying for two hours a day is measurable.
- *Accountable and attainable.* Set goals for yourself that you can achieve through your own effort and accountability. Start your goals with "I will . . . ," and be sure they are attainable. Having the top grade in class might not be possible, but you can get an "A."
- *Realistic.* If you are a single mother with youngsters at home, it may not be realistic to set a goal of studying two hours each evening when your children need your attention.
- *Time-based.* Set a time frame for achieving your goals and be realistic about how much time to allow. Let's say you plan to enter a nursing program. If you must take several prerequisite courses before admission, you'll not likely get in after a year if you attend school part time.

Take time to set appropriate goals for yourself. Many students underestimate how important these goals are. They will help you stay motivated by keeping you focused on why you are in school and where you are going in your life.

After you've decided on your goals, write them down to give them more importance. Once you've written them, be firmly committed to them. To reinforce these goals, write them on an index card or type them into your computer, print the sheet, and place it in a prominent location in your study area so you'll see your goals every day.

Set three main goals for yourself that relate to this class, and write them below. Explain why achieving each goal is important to you.

Goal 1: _____

It is important to me because: _____

_____

Goal 2: _____

It is important to me because: _____

_____

Goal 3: _____

It is important to me because: _____

_____

Pulling It All Together

I'm amazed when students show up for a test with no writing utensils! Don't let that happen to you. The more organized you are, the more efficient you will be, so let's organize what you will need for class. Categorize the items by what you take to class every day, what remains at home in your study spot, and optional items that are nice, but nonessential, additions.

Use the checklist provided for you in **Table 17.3**. Search your house and you'll likely find that you have many of these items already. Most items can be bought at your college bookstore, but many are available at discount stores. We will discuss some of these items specifically.

TABLE 17.3 | ORGANIZER'S CHECKLIST.

Item	✎X
To take to class each day:	
Book bag/backpack/rolling carrier	
Textbook/lab manual	
Pocket-sized day planner	
To Do List	
Separate notebooks for each course	
Copy of class schedule with buildings and room numbers	
Several blue or black ink pens	
Several #2 pencils	
Small pencil sharpener	
2–3 colored highlighter pens	
Small stapler	
Grade record sheet for each course	
Calculator	
At home:	
Master calendar	
Separate file or folder for each course	
Loose notebook paper	
Index cards for making flash cards	
Computer paper (if I have a computer)	
More writing utensils (pens and pencils)	
Stapler	
Calculator	
Scissors	
Paper clips	
Optional:	
Personal organizer	
Anatomy and Physiology coloring book(s)	
Colored markers/pencils	
Small digital recorder to record lectures/readings	
Extra batteries for recorder	
Anatomy atlas	
Medical dictionary	

You'll be going back and forth to class a lot, so it is most efficient to keep all the items you might need for class in one place. To haul them, most students use a book bag, backpack, or briefcase. An advantage to using one of these is that you can load it up with the essentials so that they are always ready to walk out the door with you. Let's discuss some of the items to pack.

You need a pocket-sized day planner that has plenty of room for writing and that you can keep with you at all times. Or you may opt for a personal organizer portfolio or an electronic organizer. You can probably find a good phone app for this, but be sure your instructor will allow you to have your phone on in class before relying on only this option. Select one you like, because you'll use it every day. In it, write all important dates you already know—when classes begin, holidays, last day to withdraw from a class, when finals begin. Enter all class times, your work schedule, and any other known time commitments. Try to keep your day planner current so you always know how your time is being spent and can plan ahead.

If it's not part of your day planner, you need a separate To Do List. You will write all assignments and due dates on this list. You want one single To Do List for all of your classes as well as non-school activities, because they must all be done from the same pool of time. Writing them down allows you to view the entire list and review the deadlines for each item so you can easily prioritize, doing the assignments in the order in which they are due.

Maintain a record of all grades you receive (**Figure 17.1**). For each graded item, list what it is, when you turned it in, when you got it back, how many points you received, how many points were possible, and any additional notes. Once you know how your grade will be determined for the course, you can use this to keep track as you go along. It also provides a backup in case there is any confusion later about your grade or your work. You should also maintain a separate folder for all graded items that are returned to you.

Check with your instructor to see which books you should bring to class. Typically, you may not need your textbook in lecture, but you may need it in lab. If your course uses a lab manual, always take it to lab, but you may not need it in lecture.

And for both lecture and lab, always carry the basics. You need a notebook for note-taking. If you come to my class without a writing utensil, it says you do not think that what I am saying is important enough for notes. If you ask me for a stapler before turning in an assignment, it says you threw it together with little thought. Pens, pencils, erasers, staples, paper, highlighters, colored pencils, index cards, paper clips—these are just some items you may find useful. Replenish your supply as needed.

Set up your home study space like a home office. Be sure to have all the essential office supplies on hand—plenty of writing utensils, paper, a stapler, and so on. A critical part of the home study area is the master calendar. There are large desktop versions and wall charts, for example. You could use a calendar feature on your computer or phone, but the more visible the calendar is, the more often you will look at it. This calendar should be large enough to accommodate plenty of writing, so think BIG! Each day, you should add anything that you put in your day planner or on your To Do List to this master calendar. All time commitments should be entered, so also add all personal appointments and vacations. This is how you will schedule your life while in school, and the practice will likely stick with you far beyond that.

You may have already started your class before using this book. If so, you certainly cannot do all these things before class at this point, but it is never too late to get organized. So, go get it together!

✔ **QUICK CHECK**

To be successful in class, your effort should start before class begins. What are some tasks you should do before the first day of class?

_____

_____

● **Answers:** Set and write down your goals, organize the items you will need for class and at home, pack your carrier, start your day planner and master calendar, and organize your study space.

Graded item	Date turned in	Date returned	My score	Possible points	Notes
Lab 1	9/6	9/13	10	10	Worked with Emily, Mike, Tom
Quiz 1	9/7	9/9	18	20	Study terms again
Lab 2	9/13	9/16	6	10	Messed up the math!
Pop Quiz	9/14	9/16	5	5	From yesterday's lecture.
					I was ready!
Quiz 2	9/21	9/25	19	20	Forgot to answer one question!

▲ **Figure 17.1** A sample grade record for keeping track of your progress.

▷ I Hate to Lecture on this, but Can You Hear Me Now?

Welcome to class! Imagine that it is the first day. You walk into class.

Where do you sit? _____

Why do you sit there? _____

The best seat in the house is front and center. Obviously not everyone can sit there, but you should arrive early enough to sit within the first few rows and as near to the middle as possible. You want an unobstructed view of the instructor and anything he or she might show, because anatomy is often a very visual course. People sitting on the sides or in the back often do not want to be called on, or they want to be in their own space. They often are not very engaged in the class. Don't let that be you. To succeed, you need to focus all of your attention on your instructor, minimize distractions, and actively participate. Instructors tend to teach to the middle of the room. In fact, if your instructor is right-handed and uses equipment, such as an overhead projector, that is positioned on the right, the instructor's focus shifts to his or her right. You want to see your instructor and you want your instructor to see that you are present, actively listening, and engaged.

Some instructors provide lecture notes so you can sit back and really think about what is being said. Notes or not, you need to get all the information you can from each lecture. Remember your learning style and use techniques that enhance it. We will discuss note-taking momentarily, but consider recording the lectures. That way you miss nothing, and you can listen to the recording repeatedly, rewinding as needed. Another good technique is to write out your own notes while listening to the recording, then listen again while reading your notes and making corrections. This combination strongly reinforces the material.

Always try to preview the material that will be covered before going to class. This is as simple as lightly reading the corresponding sections in the textbook. You may not understand all that you read, but it will sound familiar and be easier to comprehend as your instructor covers it in class. This preview also helps you identify new vocabulary words.

While your instructor is lecturing, don't hesitate to raise your hand to ask a question or get clarification. Many students are shy and reluctant to speak in class—you may be doing them a favor! Avoid discussing personal issues in front of the whole class—that is better done alone with the instructor, outside the classroom.

Note your instructor's gestures, facial expressions, and voice tone for clues about what your instructor finds most important. That material is likely to show up on a quiz or test. Write down any material that is particularly emphasized, or mark it in your notes. Listen carefully for assignments and write them down immediately on your To Do List. If you are not clear about the expectations of the assignment or when it is due, seek immediate clarification. Don't ever try to second-guess your instructor's expectations.

✔ QUICK CHECK

Why is it best to sit front and center in class?

_____

_____

● Answer: You will be more engaged in the class, have the best view and fewer distractions, and be within your instructor's focal area.

▷ Passing Notes

Anybody can take notes in class, but will the notes be good enough to help them succeed in the class? There are many strategies and models for how to take notes, and none of them is necessarily the best. Find what works for you, then use it consistently. Let's review one easy-to-use system (Figure 17.2).

Start with a full-sized (8.5" x 11") notebook that you will use just for this class. Take your notes on only the front side of the paper and leave about a 2" margin on the left. The margin will be used for marking key words and concepts later. At the beginning of class, date the top of the page so you know when the material was covered. During lecture, use an outline format to get as much information down as you can. Use the main concept as a major heading then, under it, indent the information discussed on that topic. When that section ends, either draw a horizontal line to mark its end or leave a couple of blank lines before you write the next major heading. Don't try to write every word—just the main ideas—and put them in your own words. Instead of writing out every example, give a brief summary or a one- or two-word reminder. Use abbreviations when possible, and develop your own shorthand. You can often drop most of the vowels in a word and still be able to sound it out later when reading it. Write legibly or your efforts will be useless later. Underline new or stressed terms and place a star or an arrow

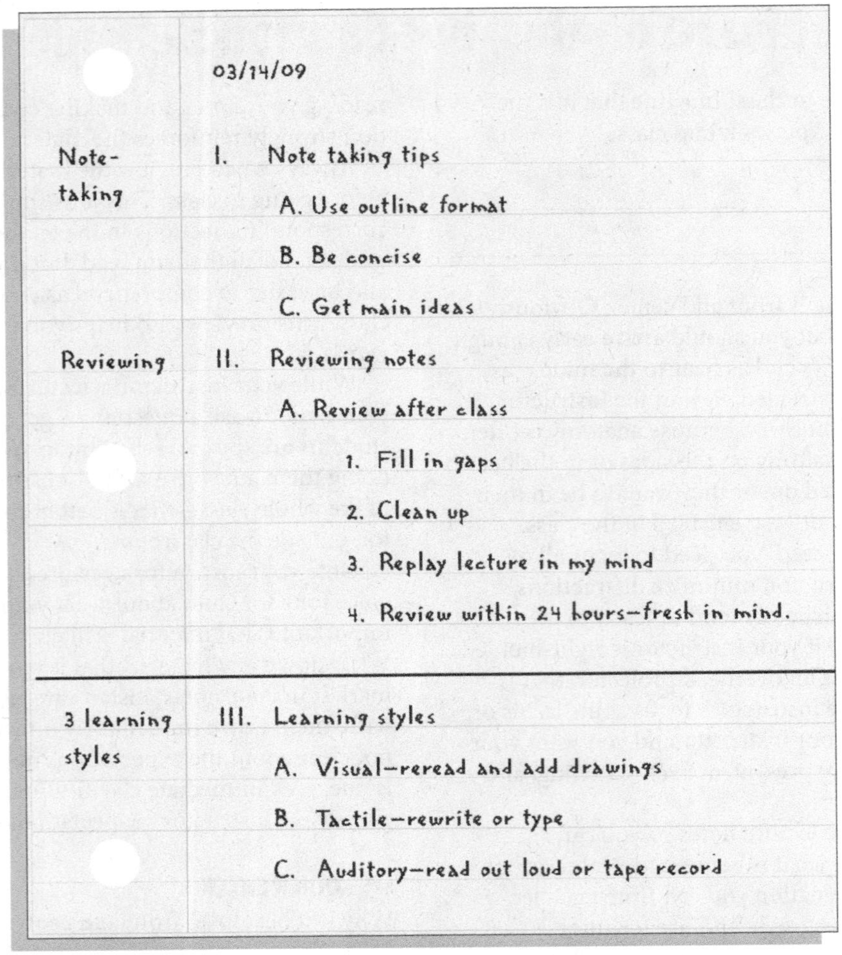

```
                    03/14/09

Note-        I.    Note taking tips
taking
                   A. Use outline format

                   B. Be concise

                   C. Get main ideas

Reviewing    II.   Reviewing notes

                   A. Review after class

                       1. Fill in gaps

                       2. Clean up

                       3. Replay lecture in my mind

                       4. Review within 24 hours—fresh in mind.

3 learning   III.  Learning styles
styles
                   A.  Visual—reread and add drawings

                   B.  Tactile—rewrite or type

                   C.  Auditory—read out loud or tape record
```

▲ **Figure 17.2**   Sample of lecture notes using the outline style and leaving room in the left margin.

by anything that is emphasized. Be as thorough as you can, but you will need to write very quickly. The instructor will not wait for you to catch up, so both speed and accuracy are essential.

As soon as possible after class, read your notes and improve them as necessary. Add anything that's missing. Make them clearer and cleaner. Put the concepts in your own words. Next, use the left margin to summarize each section—the main concept, subtopics, and key terms. The latter column will be your "Recall" column. Once you are sure all of the key ideas are in the left column, you can cover the right side of the page—the meat of your notes—and quiz yourself on the main points listed in the left column. It makes an easy way to review.

But you are not finished—if you are a tactile learner, rewrite your notes in another notebook or type them into your computer. Visual learners might type and reorganize the notes. Auditory learners can read the notes out loud or record them. You can make flash cards from the key points and terms by writing the term on one side of an index card and its definition or use on the other side. You can add drawings. Review your notes as much as you can

during the next 24 hours while the lecture is still fresh in your mind.

Go through your notes several times and think about related questions that might be asked on tests. Find creative ways to quiz yourself on what was covered.

As mentioned earlier, your instructor may provide lecture notes for the class. This allows you to listen carefully and think about what the instructor is saying rather than focusing on writing. Even so, always be ready to take additional notes, noting what your teacher emphasizes or adds that's not already in the lecture notes. And you can and certainly should continue to employ the study techniques we've discussed here even if you did not take the original notes.

Time to Try

 Look at the sample notes in Figure 17.2. Now practice: Take notes using this style while listening to a 1-hour TV show. Capture the conversations and action in words. You can't get every word down, so paraphrase—put it in your own words so the meaning still comes across. When you're finished, assess how you did.

Can you tell who was talking? _____

Do your notes make sense? _____

Did you capture the main ideas? _____

Did you keep up or fall behind? _____

Do you have breaks to separate main conversations and action? _____

What can you do better while taking notes in class?
_____

✔ **QUICK CHECK**

What should you do with your notes after class?
_____
_____

● **Answer: Review them within 24 hours, fill in anything missing, clean them up, put them into your own words, add key concepts and terms to the Recall column, add drawings, make flash cards, record them, rewrite or type them.**

▷ Looking for Some-Body Special In the Lab

Your anatomy and physiology class comes in two parts: lecture and lab. Many students put most of their effort into the lecture material and disregard the lab component. Avoid this. Lab is the hands-on part of the course, and most people learn better by seeing demonstrations and actually doing the work themselves. Also, part of your grade comes from your performance in lab. Always go to lab prepared to take notes, equipped with your lab manual, if required, and your textbook if it will be needed.

When in lab, you may work with a lab partner or group. You will be expected to contribute equally to the team effort, so it is important that you arrive prepared for lab. If you have a prelab assignment, complete it before you go to class. If you know in advance what the lab will be, read through it and think about what you will be doing. Pay attention to the instructions and especially note any safety precautions. At times you will be working with very expensive equipment and specimens, and perhaps potentially dangerous materials, so always use great care.

Some students try to take shortcuts in lab so they can leave a bit early. You should value lab as a time to further explore the material covered in lectures. You get to hold the

bones, microscopically examine various tissues, use models and charts, test physiological processes, and perhaps see real organs or cadavers. It is a unique aspect of your education that reinforces everything else that you are learning. You will spend much time learning structures, and the more you go over them, the better you will recall them. The more time you spend in lab, the more you learn. Remember that lecture and lab are both part of the same class and try to see how they fit together. Never leave lab early—there's always more to learn.

✔ **QUICK CHECK**

What are some of the learning advantages gained from attending lab sessions? _____
_____
_____
_____

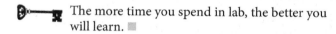 The more time you spend in lab, the better you will learn. ■

● **Answer: Lab is time for exploration, hands-on learning, collaboration, and discussion.**

▷ Your Secret Life Outside of Class

Reality Check

Answer True or False to each of the following statements:

1. I study the day before a test but rarely study on a daily basis. **T F**

2. I mostly review my notes and don't read the textbook. **T F**

3. I am too busy to study each day. **T F**

4. When I finally get around to it, I study hard for a long time. **T F**

5. I get by fine with cramming. **T F**

Just for Fun

 Let's see how good a studier you REALLY are! Take a few moments to learn these terms. We will come back to this exercise a bit later.

1. **Frizzled greep.** This is a member of the *Teroplicanis domesticus* family with girdish jugwumps and white frizzles.

2. **Gleendoggled frinlap.** This is a relatively large fernmeiker blib found only in sproingy sugnipers.

3. **Borky-globed dungwinger.** This groobler has gallerific phroonts and is the size of a pygmy wernocked frit.

Stay tuned!

You made it through lecture or lab, and are ready to head home. Finally! School is done for the day, right? Not if you plan to be successful! The real work begins after class, because most of your learning occurs outside the classroom on your own.

This is often the hardest part, for many reasons. We schedule many activities and set aside time for them, but studying tends to get crammed into the cracks. Too often, studying becomes what you do when you "get around to it." It is an obligation that often gets crowded out by other daily activities, and studying is often the first item dropped from the To Do List.

Too many students only study when they have to—before a quiz or exam. A successful student studies every day. The goal is to learn the material as you go rather than frantically try to memorize a large amount at the last minute. Here is something you need to know and really take to heart.

 You should study for at least two to three hours for every hour spent in class.

Simple math shows you that if you have three lectures on Monday, for example, you should plan to spend from six to nine hours studying before the next lectures. YIKES!

Schedule Your Study Time

Writing assignments on your To Do List makes them seem more urgent, but that does not cover the daily work that must be done. You must take charge of your time and studying. In addition to specific assignments, each day you should:

- go over that day's notes,
- read the corresponding sections in the textbook,
- quiz yourself,
- review your notes again, and
- preview the next day's material.

All of this takes time. You must build study time into your schedule or you either will not get around to it or you will put it off until you are too tired to study effectively. The first thing to do is to write your study time into your day planner and master calendar, and regard that time as sacred—don't borrow from it to do something else. Be sure to allow break time during study sessions as well—if you study too long, your brain gets weary and starts to wander, and it takes much longer to do even simple tasks. Plan a 10- to 15-minute break for every hour of studying.

Chunk It

If a job seems too large, we put it off, but if we have many small tasks, each alone seems manageable. Break your workload into small chunks. Write them down, partly so you do not forget any, but especially because you will get a great feeling of accomplishment when you complete a task and cross it off your To Do List! Completing a task is also

a convenient time to take a mini-break to keep your mind fresh. Many students try to read a whole chapter or cover a few weeks of notes in one sitting. The brain really dislikes that. When studying a large amount of material, divide it into subcategories, then study one until you really understand it before moving to the next.

Study Actively

Merely reading your notes or the book is not learning. You must think about the material and become an **active learner**. Constantly ask yourself, "What is most important in this section?" While reading, take notes or underline key terms

and major concepts. Make flash cards. Consider how what you are studying relates to something with which you are already familiar. If you can put the information in a familiar context, you will retain it better.

The best preparation for quizzes and tests is practice. Develop and answer questions as you read. Try to anticipate all the ways your instructor might quiz you about that material. Recall which specific items your instructor stressed. Outline the material in each section and be sure to understand how the different concepts are related. Check yourself on the meanings and usage of the key terms. Say the key words out loud and look carefully at them. Do they remind you of anything? Have you heard them before? Can you spell them?

Move Past Memorizing

This is one of the hardest study traps to avoid. In anatomy and physiology, it may at times seem like there is so much to learn and so little time. Most students at first attempt to just memorize. If you only read your notes and the book, you are using this approach without realizing it.

At the beginning of this section, I gave you three items to learn. Without turning back, write the names I asked you to learn a few pages ago:

1. _____

2. _____

3. _____

Did you remember them? Now, also without looking back, can you explain each of them to me?

_____

_____

(I am betting not)

These three "things" are fictitious, but my point is that you may, indeed, have memorized the names—it doesn't take much to memorize words—but it takes a lot more to understand them, especially if the words are unfamiliar, as they often will be in this course. If you find that you study hard but the wording of the quiz or test confuses you, I can almost guarantee that you are memorizing. The question is worded a bit differently than what you memorized, so you don't realize that you know the answer. You must get past memorizing by looking for relationships between the concepts and terms, and really strive for full understanding. Reading often produces memorization. Active studying produces understanding.

The Concept Map

A very useful technique for learning relationships is drawing a **concept map**. This is somewhat like brainstorming. Here is the general process:

1. Start with a blank piece of (preferably) unlined paper.

2. Near the center, draw a circle and, inside it, list the main concept you will explore.

3. Around that circle, and allowing some space, draw more circles and list in each anything that pops into your mind related to your main concept. Do this quickly and don't think about the relationships yet. Just get your ideas down.

4. Once you've added all your secondary concepts, look at them and think about how they are related, not just to the main concept but to each other as well.

5. As relationships occur to you, draw arrows connecting related concepts and add a brief description of the relationships between them.

6. Examine the relationships and you will start to understand how these concepts fit together.

You can also use concept maps to learn terminology. On blank paper, randomly write new terms from lecture or from a section of your textbook. Then think about the terms. What does each term mean? Which are related to each other? How are they related ? Next, draw lines to connect related terms, adding brief explanations of the relationships between them. Try this with flash cards, with the term on one side and its definition on the other. Scatter the cards in front of you. Look at each term and quiz yourself on its meaning, then flip the card to check the definition. Flip the cards back over so the terms are facing up, then think about how the terms are related. As relationships emerge, move the cards around and place other cards between them on which you note the relationships. You might start by placing the cards with the definitions visible—sometimes it's easier to see relationships by comparing the meanings. Once you complete this step, turn the cards so you see the terms that are related, and then restudy their definitions and relationships.

Time to Try

 Construct a concept map around the main concept of *energy* by adding arrows to show relationships between the following concepts: cell activity, food, plants, the sun, and work.

When you are finished, look at Figure 17.3.

First draw a circle or "node" for each concept, keeping the main concept, if there is one, near the middle.

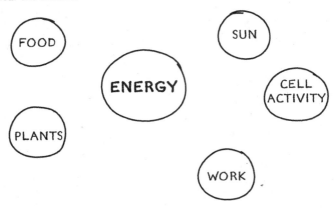

Next, add arrows linking the different concepts to each other, then add brief descriptions of how they are linked.

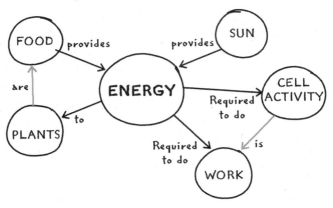

▲ Figure 17.3   **Drawing a concept map.** In this example, the arrows show that the sun provides energy to the plants, and plants are food that provide energy required to do cell activity, which is a type of work.

Review

OK, you've been at this study thing for awhile and you think you're starting to get the material. You did all of the tasks above. Can you quit now? Almost, but once you think you have the material under control, review it one more time. Repetition is the key to your long-term memory—the more you go over the material, the longer it will stay with you. There is actually a physiological basis for this—you are stimulating and reinforcing neural pathways in your brain. I always recommend a minimum of three passes, even for easy stuff—read your notes, read the text, re-read your notes—and that assumes you are understanding the material. Always slow down and go through it more if you are struggling with a certain section. Use **active learning** with each pass, then finish with one more review. If you are alert enough to review right before you go to bed, once you are

asleep your brain often continues going over the material without bothering you too much (although one of my students reported a dream in which she was chased by a herd of giant bones!).

The website for your textbook also provides a good way to review. The address is in your book. Most book websites offer a wide variety of activity options, perhaps including online animations, flashcards, puzzles, objectives, vocabulary lists, and quizzes. When taking online quizzes, be sure to do so without looking in your book or your notes—after all, you do not use them for quizzes in class. Not using them provides a better simulation of the classroom experience. And, if you do well on the online quizzes without using your notes, you will have confidence in the classroom knowing you have already passed one quiz!

No Cramming allowed!

I have a very busy life, so my house occasionally gets a bit cluttered. If company drops by and it is a "bad house day," I might quickly grab some of the clutter and cram it into a spare closet. After the guests leave, perhaps I open the closet door to pull out a quilt. What happens?

_____

_____

Now imagine what you do to your brain when you cram for an exam. You are essentially opening the closet door and cramming stuff in, then slamming the door. When you are taking the test, you open the door to pull out the answer you need, but anything might tumble out and land on your paper. Cramming at best allows partial memorization. At worst, it causes the information to get mixed up and you fail. It is a desperate act of superficial studying guaranteed to NOT get you through anatomy and physiology. If you study on a daily basis instead of doing a panicky cram session, before a test you will be calmly reviewing what you already learned well and smiling at the crammers in class.

No Vampires Allowed!

Do you think you can pull an all-nighter and really do well?

_____

What do you think are some of the reasons this will not work?

_____

If you normally live your life by day, you can't suddenly override your natural biological clock and expect your brain to stay alert and focused late at night when it knows it should be asleep. Sleep deprivation impairs focus and attention. Your eyes may skim the page but you'll struggle to comprehend the words and retain very little of the small amount you do manage to absorb. Caffeine may temporarily keep your eyes open, but you'll only be a tad more alert while you still mentally drift away from the task at hand. Caffeine may also prevent sleeping later on.

Much of what we try to learn is solidified in our brains (moved to long-term memory) while we sleep, so without adequate sleep you won't retain what you tried to learn. And the next day, you won't be mentally alert while taking your test; you won't be able to focus or think things through. Your exhausted neurons won't be able to coordinate the information you tried to learn, you'll be less able to recall what you covered, it will be hard to understand exam questions, and your judgment will be impaired—doesn't sound like a good situation for testing, does it? Even sleep deprivation of as little as one hour can impair mental function the next day, so forget the all-nighter. Give your brain what it wants and needs—a good night of sleep.

An all-nighter is basically a marathon cram session held at the worst possible time. It simultaneously robs your brain and body of what they need—restoration before the next day. You may be able to stay awake all night, but if you doze off you may oversleep and miss your exam. Or, if you do arrive (I hope you weren't driving with no sleep!), you'll likely get part way into the test only to have your brain bail on you. If you are prone to "test anxiety," your defenses will be down and you will quite likely freeze and fail. Ah, if only you had been studying all along . . .

 For your brain to be kind to you, you have to be kind to its home. You must take care of yourself physically—eat, sleep, exercise, and RELAX. ■

✔ QUICK CHECK

Why should you study every day if the test is not for two weeks?

_____

_____

● Answer: Studying on a regular basis breaks the material into smaller, more manageable pieces that you can master; the material is fresh in your mind and you will only need to review it before the test.

▷ Strength in Numbers: The Study Group

One of the best ways to learn anything is to teach it to someone else, so form a study group. Although this may not be the best option for everyone, it is highly effective for many students. In fact, many instructors view study groups as essential for success in A&P. As soon as possible, start asking your classmates who wants to be in a study group—you *will* get people to join. You can quiz each other, discuss the material, help each other, and quite importantly, support each other. If you study solo, you may not be aware of your weaknesses. Your study partners can help you identify them and overcome them. A good way to work in a study group is to split up the material and assign different sections to different members, who then master the material and teach it to the group. Each member should also be studying it all on his or her own—that ensures better effort from everyone and allows other members to correct any errors in a presentation.

Scheduling joint study sessions can be challenging. Many students find that scheduling group sessions before or after class works best. You may want to establish some ground rules, including agreeing to use the time for studying and not for gossiping or just socializing. And although it may be tempting to meet over a pizza, you do want a quiet location where you can freely discuss the material with few distractions. Check with your instructor to see if there are any open lab times that might work for this. Some areas on campus may be available for study groups.

▷ SQRHuh? How to Read a Textbook

Science textbooks do not read like novels, so you need to approach them differently. The name may sound odd, but **SQR3** is an effective method for studying your textbook. This method also works well for reviewing your notes. It stands for *Su*rvey, *Q*uestion, *R*ead, *R*ecite, *R*eview.

During the **survey phase**, you basically skim the chapter. Read the chapter title, the chapter introduction, any other items at the beginning of the chapter, and all of the headings. This gives you the road map of where you will be going in the chapter. As you skim the chapter, also read all items in bold or italic. Next, read the summary at the end of the chapter.

During the **question phase**, look at the heading of each section and form as many questions as you can that you think may be covered in that section. Write them down. Try to be comprehensive in this step. By having these questions in mind, you will automatically search for answers as you read. You may also come up with some of the questions on which you will later be tested.

Now **read** the chapter for details. Take your time. Adjust your reading speed with the difficulty of the material. Also, keep in mind the questions you developed and try to answer them.

The next phase is to **recite**. You are now working on your ability to recall information. After reading each section, think about your questions and try to answer them from recall. If you cannot, reread the section and try again. Continue this cycle until you can recite the answers.

Finally, you want to **review**. This helps reinforce your memory. After you complete the previous steps for all sections you're studying, go back to each heading and see if you can still answer all of your questions. Repeat the recite phase until you can. When you are done, be sure you can also answer the questions at the end of the chapter.

SQR3 is one way to read a textbook, but there are many others. A similar method is called **PORPE**. With this method, after reading a section you:

- *Predict* possible essay questions.
- *Organize*, summarize, and synthesize the major points in your own words.

- *Rehearse* by reciting the information and quizzing yourself.
- *Practice* your answers to the essay questions you identified.
- *Evaluate* your work for accuracy and completeness.

Another method suggests a three-column note-taking system:

What I know	What I want to know	What I learned

In the first column, list what you already know before you read the topic. In the second column, write questions about the content that you want to answer. To do this, preview the section by reading titles and headings and examining tables and figures. Finally, read the material thoroughly and use the third column to answer your questions from column 2.

Each method is effective, but the best method for you is what *works* for you. Try each method and modify them to suit your needs. Incorporate your learning style preferences. Visit *Get Ready's* companion website at www.aw-bc.com/getready for some specific activities to try. The more of them you incorporate, the better you'll reinforce what you read. This approach may feel strange at first, but you'll quickly discover how effective active reading is for truly learning the material.

As mentioned earlier, a science textbook isn't written like a novel, so you won't learn by reading it like one—straight through once. Also, the writing style is different. Scientific writing can be rather tedious and challenging. Break the reading into sections, and do at least three passes for each: prereading, in-depth reading, and final review. Here are some final tips:

- Read within 24 hours of the lecture while the lecture is fresh in your mind.
- Read slowly—comprehension and retention matter, not speed. If you don't understand something, take a deep breath, slow down, and reread it until you do.
- Don't skip unfamiliar words—look them up and jot them down. You must know the language to understand the concepts.

- If you're stuck or your mind is wandering, do a quick review of what you've covered and then take a break. This lets you process what you've learned and allows you to return later, ready again to focus on new material.

- Don't underestimate the importance of reading assignments—they are a major component of your course and, with an effective reading method, they can be the key to mastering course content and succeeding in your course.

▷ A Place to Call My Own: The Study Environment

Briefly describe the location where you plan to do most of your studying. _____

_____

_____

Now you know how to study effectively, but we often overlook WHERE to study. Your options may be limited, so you need to make the best of what you have. Ideally your study spot is somewhat isolated and free of distractions like TV, music, and people. At the least, you should minimize distractions.

Do you study in front of a TV that is on? Even if you try hard to ignore it, you will be drawn to it, especially if the material you are studying is tough. Music can be tricky—songs that you know, especially peppy ones, may get you tapping and singing along with them while you think your mind is actively engaged in learning. However, soft or classical music may keep you calm and more focused, unless you really dislike that kind of music.

Thinking about the study site you listed above, what distractions might you face? _____

_____

_____

How can you minimize them? _____

_____

_____

_____

_____

If you cannot, what might make a better study spot?

_____

_____

For studying, you really need a space that is your own. A desk is a good place (unless it is also the computer desk shared by other members of your household or at which you spend hours playing computer games for fun!). Ideally it will be a place where you do nothing but study, so that when you are seated there you know exactly what your purpose is. If you are having trouble staying on task in your work spot, get up and walk away briefly. The mental and physical break may help you "come back" to work, and you won't begin associating the spot with struggling. Your study spot should be quiet and it should have good lighting to avoid eye strain, a comfortable chair, good ventilation and temperature, and a work surface on which you can spread out.

You will spend a lot of time studying here, so take time initially to set up your study space. The area should be uncluttered and well organized. It should also be inspiring and motivational. Perhaps frame a sign that says *"I WILL be a _____(your career)_____ by ___(your goal date)___."* Try this same approach for the goals you set at the beginning of this chapter, and display them boldly and prominently. Consider displaying a photo of your hero, or of someone in the family who inspires you or whom you want to make proud. Parents, you might display a photo of your children with a caption saying something like "You are my reason," or "I will teach by example." Realize that you are their role model—your children's attitudes toward education will be formed by what you do now. This also applies for those of you who have brothers or sisters. You may be *their* inspiration. With these treasures surrounding you, you're a mere glance away from being reinvigorated if a study session starts to fizzle.

Why Should I Care?

Most of your learning is done outside of class. The more efficiently you study, the better you will learn. Your study spot affects your attitude and concentration. The more seriously you take your study location, the more seriously you will study there.

If you live with family or a roommate, you absolutely must stress to them the importance of respecting your study time and study space. Be sure they know your career goals and why they are important to you, and ask them to help by giving you the time and space you need to succeed. Ask them not to disturb you when you are in your space. If you have small children who want time with mommy or daddy while you are studying, assuming they have adequate supervision, try getting them to play or study on their own until "the clock hands are in these positions," then do something fun with them at that time. They will learn to anticipate your time together and to leave you alone if the reward is worthwhile. This will also provide you with a relaxing study break. If you have too many distractions at home, the solution is to study elsewhere. Whether on campus, in the local library, or at a

friend's house, you need a distraction-free setting, and if you can't get it at home, remove yourself instead of trying to cope with a poor study space.

✔ **QUICK CHECK**

What are some of the main considerations in selecting your study spot?

_____

_____

● Answer: Few distractions, own space just for studying, comfortable, good lighting/ventilation, sufficient work space, and welcoming.

▷ My, How Time Flies!

You know you need to study and that it takes a lot of time, but how will you fit it in? Let's discuss a few ways to budget time for studying. First, be consistent. Consider your schedule to see if you can study at the same time each day. Studying will become a habit more easily if you always do it at the same time. Some students adhere to one schedule on weekdays and a different one on weekends. When scheduling study time, consider your other obligations and how distracted you might be by other people's activities at those times. Don't overlook free hours you might have while on campus and even consider building some into your schedule. Head to the library, study room, or a quiet corner. This is the ideal time to preview for the next class or to review what was just covered.

Time to Try

This is a two-part exercise designed to help you find your study time.

Part A: Each week has a total of 168 hours. How do you spend *yours*? **Table 17.4** on the facing page allows you to quickly approximate how you spend your time each week.

1. Complete the assessment in Table 17.4 to see how many hours are left each week for you to study.

2. Enter that number here. _____ hours

Part B: Next, turn your attention to **Table 17.5** on page 360.

1. Enter your class schedule, work schedule, and any other activities in which you regularly participate.

2. Now look for times when you can schedule study sessions and write them in.

3. Are you able to schedule 2 to 3 hours of study time per hour of class time? _____

It can be difficult, but it is essential to make the time. Writing it into your schedule makes it more likely to happen.

Don't overbook! Be sure to build in break time during and between your study sessions, especially the longer ones. Allow for flexibility—realize that unexpected events occur, so be sure you have some extra time available. Also, be sure you plan for and schedule recreation, too. You cannot and should not study all the time, but these other activities do take time and need to be in your schedule as well so that you do not double-book yourself.

▷ Putting It to The Test

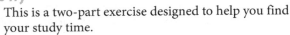

If I had a nickel for every student who said they have test anxiety . . .

Some people really do suffer from true test anxiety, but the majority of students who claim to have this condition believe it to be true not because of an actual diagnosis, but rather because they get very nervous and may go blank during tests. If I ask a class who amongst them suffers from test anxiety, most hands go up. By the end of the semester, with some coaching, the number is far less.

Why? They have learned how to take tests and how to stay calm. If you do suffer from true test anxiety, consult with your counselor right away so he or she can put you in contact with the support services you need to understand your condition and to learn how to conquer it. **Table 17.6** offers some tips on ways to reduce your anxiety about tests.

Most people dread taking tests and experience some anxiety when taking them. Not surprisingly, the better prepared you are for an exam, the less worried you will be. The best

TABLE 17.4 | **ASSESSING HOW YOUR TIME IS SPENT**. FOR EACH ITEM IN THIS INVENTORY, REALLY THINK BEFORE ANSWERING AND BE AS HONEST AS POSSIBLE. ITEMS THAT ARE DONE EACH DAY MUST BE MULTIPLIED BY 7 TO GET YOUR WEEKLY TOTAL. ONE ITEM MAY BE DONE ANY NUMBER OF TIMES A WEEK, SO YOU'LL NEED TO MULTIPLY THAT ITEM BY THE NUMBER OF TIMES EACH WEEK YOU DO IT. AFTER YOU HAVE RESPONDED TO ALL THE QUESTIONS, YOU'LL HAVE AN OPPORTUNITY TO SEE HOW MANY HOURS REMAIN DURING THE WEEK FOR STUDYING.

Where Does Your Time Go? Record the number of hours you spend:	How many hours per day?	How many days per week?	Total hours per week: (hours × days)
1. **Grooming,** including showering, shaving, dressing, makeup, and so on.			
2. **Dining,** including preparing food, eating, and cleaning up.			
3. **Commuting** to and from class and work, from door to door.			
4. **Working** at your place of employment.			
5. **Attending class.**			
6. **Doing chores** at home, including housework, mowing, laundry, and so on.			
7. **Caring** for family, a loved one, or a pet.			
8. On **extracurricular activities** such as clubs, church, volunteering.			
9. **Doing errands.**			
10. On **solo recreation,** including time spent online or watching TV, reading, games, working out, and so on.			
11. **Socializing,** including parties, phone calls, hanging out, dating, and so on.			
12. **Sleeping** (don't forget those naps!)			
Now add all numbers in the far column to get the total time you spend on all these activities.			
		Hours/week	168
		Total hours spent on other activities −	
		Left for studying =	

remedy for the stress you associate with taking tests is to be very well prepared. If you know you understand the material, what is left to worry about?

Some people get very anxious before tests because they fear they will not do well. This may be because they know they are not prepared. Again, the remedy is simple: Study well. But anxiety can also arise from a bad past experience. If you have done poorly on tests in the past, your self-confidence may be shot, so you anticipate doing poorly. That may lead to cramming and memorizing instead of truly learning, and may cause you to become excessively nervous during the test, which can cause poor performance. All you need is a couple of good grades on tests to get your confidence back! And effective studying will help you get those grades.

If you are a nervous test taker, stop studying for at least an hour immediately before your exam. Most of my students who complain of test anxiety are frantically reviewing their notes right up to the moment I give them the test. They have been trying to quickly glance back over everything while racing against the clock. No wonder they are stressed when they begin the test! Remember that your brain needs time to process the information. When you cram information into the "closet," who knows what will fall out when you open the door during the test.

If you have studied well in advance and don't get very nervous at exam time, you might want to glance quickly through your notes beforehand, but only if you have time to do so and still allow *at least* a half-hour to relax and mentally prepare for your test. The half-hour off allows your brain to process the information while you relax. Try getting a light snack so you are alert—a heavy meal could make you drowsy during the test. Walk around to release nervous energy. Listen to music that makes you happy and relaxed. Sit comfortably,

TABLE 17.5 | MY STUDY SCHEDULE.

Time	Monday	Tuesday	Wednesday	Thursday	Friday	Saturday
6:00 AM						
7:00 AM						
8:00 AM						
9:00 AM						
10:00 AM						
11:00 AM						
Noon						
1:00 PM						
2:00 PM						
3:00 PM						
4:00 PM						
5:00 PM						
6:00 PM						
7:00 PM						
8:00 PM						
9:00 PM						
10:00 PM						
11:00 PM						
Midnight						

close your eyes, and breathe deeply and slowly while you picture yourself in a very relaxing setting—maybe on a tropical beach, curled up on your couch with a good book, or out on a boat fishing. Focus on how relaxed you feel and try to hold that feeling. Now, staying in that mood, concentrate on how well you have studied and keep reminding yourself that:

- I have prepared very well for this test.
- I know this material very well and I answered all questions correctly while studying.
- I can and *will* do well on this test.

- I refuse to get nervous over one silly test and one grade, especially because I know I am ready.
- I am ready and relaxed. Let's get it done!

Test-Taking Tips

There are also strategies you can use while taking the test. Let's explore your current strategies. Complete the survey in Table 17.7, then we will discuss specific strategies.

During an exam, be careful—read each question thoroughly before you answer. This is especially true of multiple choice and true/false questions. We know the answer is there,

TABLE 17.6 | WAYS TO MINIMIZE YOUR TEST STRESS.

When	Actions
While preparing for the test	❑ Study daily to avoid last-minute cramming.
	❑ Start reviewing several days before big tests.
	❑ Quiz yourself on terms.
	❑ Review concept maps.
	❑ Review the questions you developed while reading the material.
	❑ Read your notes for anything the instructor emphasized.
	❑ Consider possible essay questions and write out thorough answers.
	❑ Review materials and practice quizzes on your textbook's website.
	❑ Meet more often with your study group; focus on reviewing and quizzing.
	❑ Counter negative thoughts ("There's too much!") with positives ("I've studied hard and I know this stuff!").
	❑ Remind yourself this is just one grade—it won't determine your worth or your future.
	❑ Take adequate study breaks.
	❑ Eat well and exercise (a great stress reliever).
	❑ Avoid sleep deprivation, especially the night before the exam.
On the day of the test	❑ Eat moderately; don't skip meals; don't eat anything too heavy that might make you groggy.
	❑ Avoid excessive caffeine—it increases anxiety and makes you jittery.
	❑ Stop studying at least an hour before exam time and do something to relax.
	❑ Stretch out somewhere comfortable. Focus on fully relaxing your muscles—from your head to your toes—savoring the feeling of relaxation.
	❑ Listen to calming music before arriving in class.
	❑ Arrive early to get your seat and organize your thoughts (do NOT look at your notes!); put your head down and relax until test time.
	❑ Avoid discussing course content or listening to classmates before the exam.
During the test	❑ Take five slow, deep breaths just before you begin.
	❑ Browse the whole test so you know its layout and length.
	❑ Budget your time, allowing more time for harder sections.
	❑ Carefully read all directions twice.
	❑ Start with the easiest part of the test.
	❑ Check the clock regularly to assess your progress and adjust your speed as needed.
	❑ If you start to feel anxious, close your eyes, focus on relaxing as you take slow, deep breaths, and remind yourself how well you prepared.
	❑ Focus on one question at a time—read it carefully, underline key words, and think before answering.
	❑ Ignore students who finish before you—often the first people to leave had little to write. Take your time and be thorough and careful.
	❑ If you run short on time, answer what you can quickly and just leave the rest.
After the test	❑ Reward yourself regardless of how you feel you did.
	❑ Don't obsess over how you think you did—you'll know when the test is returned, and your "second" guesses are likely not accurate.
	❑ Review any material that you still feel unsure about.
	❑ Once returned, record your score and how many points the test was worth.
	❑ Examine your test. Note what you missed and why, and ask for clarification if you're not sure. Review that material again.
	❑ Let it go—it's finished and you can't change it now. Move on.

TABLE 17.7 | **SELF-EVALUATION OF TEST-TAKING SKILLS.** THINK ABOUT HOW YOU HAVE PREPARED FOR TESTS IN YOUR PREVIOUS COURSES. FOR EACH OF THE FOLLOWING VALUABLE TEST-TAKING SKILLS, MARK IF YOU DO EACH ONE ALWAYS, SOMETIMES, OR NEVER. HIGHLIGHT ANY THAT YOU DO NOT CURRENTLY USE THAT YOU THINK MIGHT HELP YOU BE MORE SUCCESSFUL.

Test-Taking skill	Always	Sometimes	Never
1. While studying my notes and the book, I think of and answer possible test questions.			
2. I use online practice quizzes when they are available.			
3. I avoid last-minute cramming to avoid confusing myself.			
4. I scan the whole test before starting to see how long it is and what type of questions it contains.			
5. I do the questions I am sure of first.			
6. I budget my time during a test so I can complete it.			
7. I answer questions with the highest point values first.			
8. I read all answer options on multiple choice questions before marking my answer.			
9. I know what key words to look for in a multiple choice question.			
10. I use the process of elimination during multiple choice or matching tests.			
11. I know what key words to look for in essay questions.			
12. I look for key words like *always, never,* and *sometimes.*			
13. When I am unsure of an answer, I go with my first answer and fight the urge to change it later.			
14. I try to answer everything even if I am uncertain, instead of leaving some questions blank.			
15. I check my answers before turning in a test.			

so our eyes tend to get ahead of our brains. We skim the question and jump down to the answers before even trying to mentally answer the question. Slow down and think before moving to the answers. Otherwise you may grab an answer that sounds familiar but is incorrect. An easy way to slow down and focus on the question is to underline key words as you read it. If you have trouble keeping your eyes off the answers, cover them with your hand until you finish reading the question, think of the answer on your own, then read all the answers to see if yours is there.

If you do not know the answer initially, take a deep breath and think of all you do know about the words in the question. Often this is all you need to recall the answer. This is when those concept maps you made will really come through for you.

Use the process of elimination. If you are not sure which answer is correct, can you eliminate any you know are incorrect? Narrow down your choices. Avoid making a guess unless the process of elimination fails you; however, guessing is usually better than leaving a question unanswered. On short-answer questions, fill-in-the-blank questions, and essays, always write something. Whatever you write just may be correct, but an empty space is always wrong.

After you answer a question, read your answer to be sure it says what you want it to, then leave it alone. Once you move on, avoid the temptation to go back and change your answers, even those of which you were unsure. Often we have a gut instinct to write the correct answer; perhaps we are recalling it at some subconscious level. But the very act of going back is a conscious reminder of uncertainty, and we often choose something different only because we doubt ourselves.

When answering multiple choice or true/false questions, ignore any advice that suggests you should select one answer consistently over others. Also, don't worry if you choose the same answer several times in a row, thinking the instructor would not structure a test that way. I can't speak for all instructors, but I do not personally know any who give much thought to the pattern the answers will make on the answer sheet, so neither should you.

Here are a few more pointers:

- Glance over the exam as soon as you receive it, so you know what to expect, then budget your time accordingly.
- Look for questions on the backs of pages so you don't miss them.

- Note the wording on questions. Key words to look for that can change an answer are *always, sometimes, never, most, some, all, none, is,* and *is not.*
- Tackle easy questions first. They may provide hints to the tougher ones.
- Be aware of point values and be sure the questions with the greatest point values are done well. Often essay questions—which usually are worth more points—are at the end, and some students run out of time before reaching them, losing significant points and seriously hurting their grades.
- If you have trouble writing essay answers, recall all you know about the topic, organize in your mind how you would explain it to someone, then write down your thoughts as if you are writing yourself a script on what to say.
- If a question has multiple parts, be sure to answer each part. This is especially true for essays.
- For true/false questions, mark true only if the *entire* statement is true. If any part is false, mark it as false.
- For multiple choice questions, read the directions carefully—you may have to choose more than one answer.
- If you are asked to choose only one answer, choose the *best* answer. Although more than one answer may be correct, the most inclusive is the best answer.
- Look for answers elsewhere in the test.
- If the instructions say "...include in your answer...," then DO!

- If you are asked for a definition, give a book explanation of what the term or concept means. If you are asked for an example, list an example and explain why it is an example of the concept. If you are asked to explain a concept or term, approach it as if you are trying to teach it to a 12-year-old. Assume the grader has no prior knowledge.
- Be very thorough and specific in your answers. The grader cannot get inside your head to decide if you knew it or not, so your words must very literally convey your meaning.

When a test is returned, record your grade. Be sure to review the test to see which questions you missed and why you missed them, and make notes to go back and review that material. Remember—it may come back to haunt you on a bigger test or on the final exam, and you should know it anyway.

✔ QUICK CHECK

How can you slow yourself down when taking a multiple choice or true/false test?

_____

_____

_____

● **Answer: Cover the answers with your hand while you read the question, and don't look at them until you think of the answer.**

▷ Through the Looking Glass: Individual Accountability

I hope you have gained insight into the learning process and developed new strategies to improve your success, not just in anatomy and physiology, but in all of your classes. One area remains for us to discuss, though, and that is your responsibility and attitude. When we get frustrated, we often look elsewhere for the cause, even when it may be right on top of our own shoulders. I have watched poorly prepared students transform into honors students and I have seen honors students drop out as they start getting really bad grades. Many factors can contribute to these changes, but a common thread is always attitude and accountability. Here are three facts you need to firmly implant in your mind:

1. **You**, and nobody else, chose to pursue this academic and career path.
2. **You**, and nobody else, are responsible for attaining the success you desire.
3. **You**, and nobody else, earn the grades you get.

You must do everything you can to guarantee your success—nobody will do it for you. That means always

accepting responsibility for your own actions and effort. No excuses. To stay on track, you must know exactly where you are at all times. You must always know precisely what your grade is and remember that you always get the grade that *you earn* through your hard work (or lack of it). You must always be very clear about exactly what you want and always stay focused on where you are going. At times, you may not feel like you can keep up, but instead of quitting or slacking off, you need to refocus on where you are going and why it matters to you. Always set short-term and long-term goals. Write them down and post them where you will see them often. You are responsible for keeping yourself motivated. Learn to visualize your success—see yourself in your future career. Think about how your life will be and how that will benefit those around you. Dream big. Then go after that dream with all you have.

An important part of any journey is to anticipate roadblocks before you hit them. Carefully think of any possible obstacles to your success, then plan around them. You have an unreliable car? Find someone you can ride with in emergencies or look into public transportation. You have small children at home? Have daycare lined up and a backup plan for when your child is too ill to go to daycare. You have a learning disability? Immediately contact student support services or your counselor to find out what services are available to assist you. Make a list of anything that might get between you and your success, then write down at least two solutions so you have a main strategy and a backup plan.

Finally, consider those around you. Family and friends must know your goals and understand how important they are. But do they support you? I have had women whose husbands burned their books because the men felt threatened that their wives might no longer need them once a degree was attained. And there are certainly more subtle means of sabotage. Perhaps your friends needle you because you don't go out as much, or they say you're no fun anymore. Your significant other whines that you don't get enough time together. Relatives accuse you of thinking you are better than them

because you are getting some education. Realize that when you change, whether through education or something else, those who know you may feel excluded, threatened, left behind, or even envious. You can try to assure these people how much you still value and need them in your life, but don't let them distract you from your mission.

You must surround yourself with supportive people who are happy and proud of you, who celebrate your victories, and who want for you what you want. They will help you succeed. It may be your study group or others around you who will help you study. Perhaps they will watch your children so you get some quiet time. On the other hand, anyone who ridicules you or is upset by your new schedule and goals is really not a friend you want around. Make new friends in class who share your goals and guard yourself from those who would derail you. Stay on track, and, if you *choose* to, you will soon be living your dream. Good luck!

▷ Final Stretch!

 Now that you have finished reading this chapter, it's time to stretch your brain a bit and check how much you learned. For online tests, tutorials, animations, activities, web links, and an ebook, visit the *Get Ready for A&P* companion website.

Running Words

At the end of each chapter, be sure you have learned the language. Here are the terms introduced in this chapter with which you should be familiar. Write them in a notebook or enter them in your computer. Define them in your own words, then go back through the chapter to check your meaning, correcting as needed. Also try to list examples when appropriate.

- Visual learner
- Auditory learner
- Tactile learner
- SMART
- Active learner
- Concept map
- Active learning
- SQR3
- PORPE

What Did You Learn...

Part A: In the left-hand column below, write your approach before reading this chapter. In the right-hand column, list any changes you plan to make to ensure your success in this class.

What I have done before this chapter	What I will do to improve
During lectures:	
Note-taking:	
Study habits:	
Textbook reading:	
My study place:	
Time management:	
Test-taking:	

Part B: List the three areas in which you think your study skills are the weakest, and ways in which you plan to improve them.

1.

2.

3.

18 Chemistry: *The Science of Stuff*

When you complete this chapter, you should be able to:

- Explain the different states of matter.
- Describe atomic structure.
- Read and understand the Periodic Table of Elements.
- Explain ionic, covalent, and hydrogen bonding.
- Describe polar molecules and their unique characteristics.
- Discuss basic inorganic and organic molecules.
- Explain how we use chemicals for building and for energy.

▷ Your Starting Point

Answer the following questions to assess your chemistry knowledge.

1. The most basic unit of a chemical substance is the

   _____

2. Matter is defined as anything that _____

   _____

3. What are the three most common subatomic particles?

   _____

4. Which subatomic particles interact during chemical reactions? _____

   _____

5. What is the molecular formula for water? _____

   _____

6. What are three common types of chemical bonds?

   _____

7. What happens in anabolic reactions? _____

   _____

8. What is meant by *organic* molecule? _____

   _____

9. Are proteins organic or inorganic? _____

   _____

10. What is ATP? _____

   _____

Yes, we are going to tackle some basic chemistry, but relax—it is really not that difficult. Why do you have to learn chemistry? Anatomy is the study of all of the parts and materials in the body—all of the "stuff" that you're made of. And chemistry is the science that covers all of that stuff. Physiology is the study of how the body works, and all of the work done in the body involves chemical reactions. Chemistry is very much a part of our everyday lives. Some of you may have previously taken a chemistry class, but others will be new to this discipline. In this chapter, we'll explore basic chemistry concepts to give you a head start in A&P class.

Recall our discussion of the Biological Hierarchy of Organization. It is organized from the simplest level of organization to the most complex.

The first three levels are part of chemistry so, as you see, chemistry forms the very foundation of anatomy and physiology (**Figure 18.1**).

Learning chemistry may seem tough at times because the terminology can be challenging. To see what I mean, just read the ingredient list on almost any packaged food product. *Do we really eat all that stuff?* But don't let the words interfere with your understanding—much of chemistry is quite simple, even though it may not seem so at first. Here's an example. What do you know about a chemical compound called *dihydrogen oxide*? You probably know more than you realize—that is the technical name for something we usually call *water*!

▷ What's the Matter?

Let's start with something you already know about: **matter**. All the "stuff" of which you are made is matter, and matter is defined as anything that

- has mass (or weight), and
- takes up space (has volume).

The terms **mass** and **weight** are often used interchangeably, but there is a difference. Mass refers to the actual

physical amount of a substance. Weight takes into account the force of gravity acting on that mass. Consider astronauts. Each has a certain mass—the actual amount of material his or her body contains. Each astronaut is weightless during space travel when there is no gravity, but his or her individual mass does not change. For the sake of our discussion, matter can be defined using mass or weight, but mass is more precise. The second part of the definition of matter is that it takes up space. The space it occupies is called **volume**.

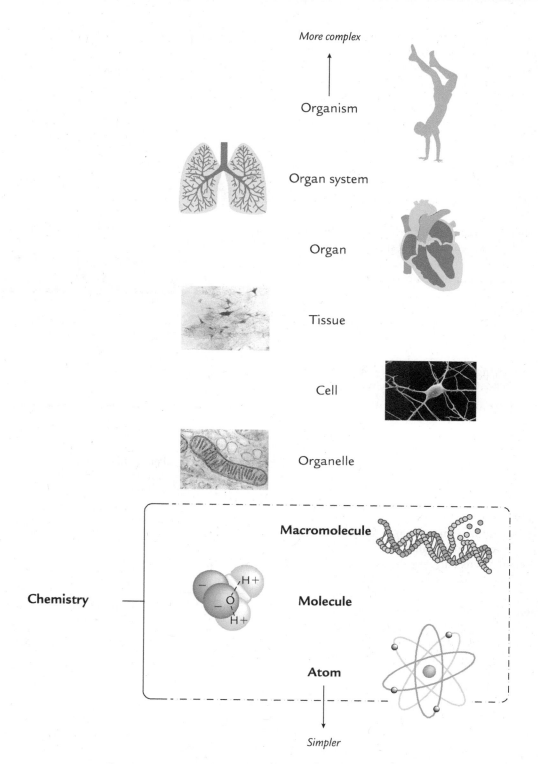

More complex

Organism

Organ system

Organ

Tissue

Cell

Organelle

Chemistry

Macromolecule

Molecule

H+
O
H+

Atom

Simpler

▲ **Figure 18.1** **The Biological Hierarchy of Organization for anatomy and physiology.** The simplest level of organization is the atom. The first three levels of this hierarchy are part of the discipline of chemistry: the science of matter. All of the other levels of organization are built upon this chemistry foundation.

Matter typically exists in any of three physical states: solid, liquid, or gas. Once again let's consider water. What do we call the three states of water?

Solid: _____ Liquid: _____ Gas: _____

I hope you got those! Solid water is ice, liquid water is water (duh!), and its gas form is vapor, or steam. See—you already know chemistry! Now, how can you change solid water to its gas form? _____

_____

When you add heat, which is a type of energy, ice melts to become a liquid. With enough heat, the liquid eventually boils to become vapor. If you collect the vapor and cool it, it will condense back to liquid. If you cool it enough, it will become ice (solid). As you can see, the three forms of matter are interchangeable.

✔ **QUICK CHECK**
What are the three states of matter?

_____

_____

● Answer: Solid, liquid, gas.

▷ It's Element-ary, My Dear Watson!

All matter is composed of **elements**, which are the most basic chemical substances. Over 110 elements are recognized, and around 90 of these occur naturally on Earth. Some elements you likely know are iron, copper, silver, gold, aluminum, carbon, oxygen, nitrogen, and hydrogen. Some exist in pure form, such as helium and neon, but most occur combined with other elements.

For the most part, living organisms require only about 20 elements. By weight, 95% of the human body is composed of just four of these:

- carbon,
- hydrogen,
- oxygen, and
- nitrogen.

Each chemical is represented by a symbol, typically the first one or two letters of the element's name. If more than one element name begins with the same letter, the most common of these elements usually gets the single-letter symbol. Hydrogen, for example, is represented by H, and the less common helium is represented by He. The symbols for some of the elements, such as the four listed above, are quite logical. Others are less obvious. For example, the symbol for silver is *Ag*, but that is because it comes from the Latin word *argentum,* meaning *silver.* **Table 18.1** lists the names and symbols of some of the elements that are most important for life.

TABLE 18.1 | SOME OF THE IMPORTANT ELEMENTS IN LIVING ORGANISMS.

Element Name	Chemical Symbol	Element Name	Chemical Symbol
Hydrogen	H	Phosphorus	P
Carbon	C	Sulfur	S
Nitrogen	N	Chlorine	Cl
Oxygen	O	Potassium	K
Sodium	Na	Calcium	Ca
Magnesium	Mg	Iron	Fe

Time to Try

Several elements have names that begin with the letter C, so most of them use a two-letter chemical symbol. Try to match each of the chemical names on the next page with their symbols. (*Hint: Recall that one of these is very common and is a major component of all living organisms, including the human body.*)

Your Choices	Names	Symbols
_____	Calcium	Cu
_____	Chromium	C
_____	Cobalt	Ca
_____	Copper (*Latin = cuprum*)	Co
_____	Carbon	Cr

● Answers: Calcium = Ca; Chromium = Cr; Cobalt = Co; Copper = Cu; Carbon = C.

▷ Chemical Carpentry: Atomic Structure

All chemical elements are composed of tiny particles called **atoms**. An atom is the smallest complete unit of an element—one atom of carbon, for example, is the smallest unit, or piece, of carbon that can exist. Two or more atoms can combine together to form larger structures called **molecules**. And simple molecules can join together to form more complex chemical structures called **macromolecules**. Macromolecules include things like proteins, carbohydrates,

DNA, and fats—many of the substances we associate with living organisms. But they all begin the same way—with atoms.

Atoms vary in size, weight, and how they interact with other atoms, but they all share some common characteristics. All are made of smaller units called **subatomic particles** that are arranged in a very precise manner. Although many subatomic particles are now recognized, the main ones of interest to us are **protons, neutrons,** and **electrons**.

The Nucleus

The **nucleus** of an atom is not a physical structure. Instead, think of the nucleus as the area in the middle of an atom where some of the subatomic particles hang out. This can be confusing because the nucleus of an atom is often referred to as if it is a structure. You should merely think of it as the atom's central region.

An atom's nucleus is where we find two types of relatively large subatomic particles called **protons** and **neutrons**.

Protons and neutrons have a similar size and about the same mass. Protons are positively charged particles and may be designated as **p⁺**. Neutrons carry no electrical charge and they are, as their name suggests, neutral. Neutrons may be designated by **n⁰**, indicating they lack any electrical charge, or simply by **n**. All of the protons and neutrons in an atom are located in the nucleus.

Electrons

Orbiting around the nucleus are the other major subatomic particles—the **electrons**—that are in constant motion. Electrons are very small and have almost no weight. They also carry a negative charge and are often designated as **e⁻**. Because the protons are inside the nucleus, the nucleus always has a positive charge. However, the number of negative-charged electrons orbiting the nucleus always equals the number of positive-charged protons at the nucleus. Thus the negative charges of the electrons exactly balance the positive charges of the protons. That means that any atom is, overall, neutral.

 An atom is electrically neutral. The number of e⁻ = the number of p⁺. ■

Electrons are never in the nucleus. Let's start with a simple image to get our bearings. Think of the rings of the planet Saturn. The rings never touch the planet itself. These rings can represent the paths of the electrons around the nucleus. Unlike Saturn's rings, however, the electrons do not travel in a nice, even, straight line along a single plane. Rather, they buzz about quite rapidly in multiple paths called **orbitals** that have different shapes and different orientations. For this reason it is more accurate to envision a cloud of electrons that constantly circle the entire nucleus. A picture of an electron cloud does not show actual electrons. Instead, it is more like a map that shows the probability of where the electrons are at any moment.

Pcture This

You arrive home late one evening, well after the sun has set. Your front light is on so you can see to put your key in the lock. You glance overhead and see a large cloud of insects swarming around the light. This is the basic image you should have of the electrons orbiting the nucleus of an atom (**Figure 18.2**). They are constantly in motion around the nucleus, but their individual paths vary.

Now that your skin is crawling from thinking about insects swarming overhead, let's get more specific. The movement of electrons around the nucleus is not as random as the movement of the insects around the light. It is actually a bit complicated, but for our purposes a simplified version will do. Electrons circle around the nucleus at different energy levels, each of which is called a **shell** or **orbital**, and these each have their own paths around the nucleus. Each orbital has its own range of distance from the nucleus and its own

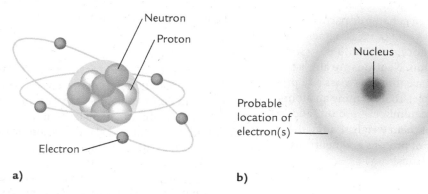

▲ Figure 18.2   **Electron orbitals. a)** Electrons orbiting the nucleus of an atom of boron. **b)** An electron cloud shows the probable location of the electron(s) at any given time.

path shape, so you can think of each orbital as being a specific part of the electron cloud. The first orbital is closest to the nucleus. Electrons try to stay as close to the nucleus as they can, but the first orbital can only accommodate two electrons. If an atom has more than two electrons, it must have more than one orbital. Each additional orbital is located a bit further from the nucleus. Electrons always fill the orbitals (shells) from the nucleus outward.

✔ **QUICK CHECK**

What are the three subatomic particles, and where is each located in an atom? _____

_____

_____

Answer: Protons and neutrons are always in the nucleus; electrons are always orbiting around the nucleus.

Atomic Number

Each element has its own **atomic number**. It is, by definition, the number of protons in an individual atom of that element. Each element has a specific number of protons, and all atoms of that element have the same number. For example, hydrogen has an atomic number of 1. If you gave hydrogen another proton, it would no longer be hydrogen—it would now become a different element—helium, with an atomic number of 2. So, in order for atoms to be of the same element, they must all have the same number of protons.

 Atomic number = number of protons in an atom.

Now, recall that an atom is electrically neutral overall. This means that the number of positive charges from protons must be counterbalanced with an equal number of negative charges from electrons. In other words, the number of protons in an atom always equals the number of electrons. Because of this, if you know an atom's atomic number, you know not only

how many protons it has, but also how many electrons it has—they are the same numbers! Let's try this.

Time to Try

 Nitrogen's atomic number is 7.

1. How many protons does an atom of nitrogen have? _____

2. How many electrons does an atom of nitrogen have? _____

If nitrogen's atomic number is 7, that tells you it has 7 protons. You know the number of protons must equal the number of electrons, so an atom of nitrogen will also have 7 electrons. The seven positive charges from the protons are balanced by the seven negative charges from the electrons, so the atom is electrically neutral.

 The number of protons = the number of electrons in an atom.

Mass Number and Atomic Weight

An atom's **mass number** refers to its total mass. Electrons are so tiny that they have almost no mass, so the mass number merely ignores them. Almost all of an atom's mass comes from the combined masses of its protons and neutrons. But what is the mass of a single proton or neutron?

Obviously atoms are too tiny to be weighed in pounds or ounces, so imagine trying to weigh a subatomic particle! Conveniently, scientists developed a unit of measurement called the **atomic mass unit** (amu or u), and 1 amu is, to simplify it, about the mass of one proton. Neutrons are almost the same size so we assume they have the same mass as a proton. This becomes amazingly simple! To determine an atom's mass number, all you do is add the number of protons and neutrons together. Because each of them weighs 1 amu, the total mass is just the total number of protons and neutrons. Simply ignore those tiny little electrons!

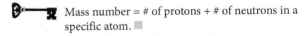 Mass number = # of protons + # of neutrons in a specific atom.

For atoms of the same element, although the number of protons is constant, the number of neutrons can vary, and for

this reason atoms of the same element can have different mass numbers. For example, carbon (atomic number 6) has 6 protons and usually 6 neutrons, so its mass number is usually 12. But some atoms of carbon have 7 neutrons, giving them a mass number of 13, and some have 8, giving them a mass number of 14. Atoms of the same element that have different mass numbers are called **isotopes**.

Why Should I Care?

 Some isotopes are radioactive, meaning they emit certain types of energy. For this reason, some radioactive isotopes are used in medicine. The energy they emit can often be seen with special equipment. For example, the thyroid gland uses iodine to make certain hormones. If a patient might have a thyroid problem, a radioactive isotope of iodine (^{131}I) can be injected into the blood, then the clinician can use an imaging technique to monitor how well the thyroid is working. In another use, cobalt (^{60}Co) can be injected into an area where there is cancer to irradiate the tumor cells.

When discussing elements, the term atomic mass refers to the *average* mass number of atoms of that element. Recall our earlier discussion, though, about mass and weight—the terms **atomic mass** and **atomic weight** are often used interchangeably. Because you are likely more familiar with weight than mass, we will stick with *atomic weight*. You need to recognize, though, that either of these terms might be used, atomic mass is the more precise term, and they have almost the same meaning. More importantly, be sure you realize that mass number refers to the mass of one specific atom, whereas atomic mass/weight is an average of several atoms. Here is a hint that may help—mass number will always be a whole number and used when discussing a single atom, but atomic mass or atomic weight is often a decimal value because it is an average of several atoms.

▷ Is That an Eye Chart or a Periodic Table of Elements?

 Look at **Figure 18.3**. YIKES! It may look a bit scary at first, but that's only because you don't know how to read it. This is the **Periodic Table of Elements.** All chemical elements that are currently known are listed in this table, and more are added as they are discovered. The table is arranged in a specific manner that is quite useful, so we will take some time to explore it.

Look at **Figure 18.4a.** From the Periodic Table, we know that hydrogen's atomic number is 1, meaning it has 1 proton, which is shown in the center of the atom at the nucleus. This means it also has 1 electron, which is shown orbiting the proton, in the first shell. It rarely has any neutrons. Helium's atomic number is 2. The helium atom in **Figure 18.4b** has 2 protons and also 2 neutrons (so what is its mass number? _____). Helium also has 2 electrons, as shown. Next, look at lithium (**Figure 18.4c**), which has atomic number 3. You see it has 3 protons and 3 neutrons in its nucleus, and 3 electrons in orbit. The first shell can only hold two electrons, so a second shell is added to hold the third electron.

Time to Try

In the illustrations below, assume that the gray sphere in the middle represents the nucleus and all of the neutrons and protons in it. Add the shells (orbitals) and electrons for each of the elements below. Boron is done as an example. Don't worry about the positions of the electrons; just draw the right number in the right shell.

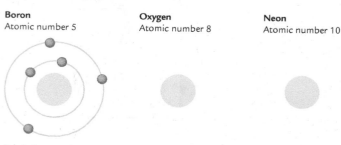

Boron
Atomic number 5

Oxygen
Atomic number 8

Neon
Atomic number 10

Needs 5 e⁻ total.
2 e⁻ are in the inner shell,
the other 3 in the outer shell.

1A																	8A
1 **H** 1.008	2A											3A	4A	5A	6A	7A	2 **He** 4.003
3 **Li** 6.941	4 **Be** 9.012											5 **B** 10.81	6 **C** 12.01	7 **N** 14.01	8 **O** 16.00	9 **F** 19.00	10 **Ne** 20.18
11 **Na** 22.99	12 **Mg** 24.31	3B	4B	5B	6B	7B		8B		1B	2B	13 **Al** 26.98	14 **Si** 28.09	15 **P** 30.97	16 **S** 32.07	17 **Cl** 35.45	18 **Ar** 39.95
19 **K** 39.10	20 **Ca** 40.08	21 **Sc** 44.96	22 **Ti** 47.87	23 **V** 50.94	24 **Cr** 52.00	25 **Mn** 54.94	26 **Fe** 55.85	27 **Co** 58.93	28 **Ni** 58.69	29 **Cu** 63.55	30 **Zn** 65.41	31 **Ga** 69.72	32 **Ge** 72.64	33 **As** 74.92	34 **Se** 78.96	35 **Br** 79.90	36 **Kr** 83.80
37 **Rb** 85.47	38 **Sr** 87.62	39 **Y** 88.91	40 **Zr** 91.22	41 **Nb** 92.91	42 **Mo** 95.94	43 **Tc** (98)	44 **Ru** 101.1	45 **Rh** 102.9	46 **Pd** 106.4	47 **Ag** 107.9	48 **Cd** 112.4	49 **In** 114.8	50 **Sn** 118.7	51 **Sb** 121.8	52 **Te** 127.6	53 **I** 126.9	54 **Xe** 131.3
55 **Cs** 132.9	56 **Ba** 137.3	57* **La** 138.9	72 **Hf** 178.5	73 **Ta** 180.9	74 **W** 183.8	75 **Re** 186.2	76 **Os** 190.2	77 **Ir** 192.2	78 **Pt** 195.1	79 **Au** 197.0	80 **Hg** 200.6	81 **Tl** 204.4	82 **Pb** 207.2	83 **Bi** 209.0	84 **Po** (209)	85 **At** (210)	86 **Rn** (222)
87 **Fr** (223)	88 **Ra** (226)	89† **Ac** (227)	104 **Rf** (261)	105 **Db** (262)	106 **Sg** (266)	107 **Bh** (264)	108 **Hs** (269)	109 **Mt** (268)	110 **Ds** (271)	111 **Rg** (272)	112 — (285)	113 — (284)	114 — (289)	115 — (288)			

58 **Ce** 140.1	59 **Pr** 140.9	60 **Nd** 144.2	61 **Pm** (145)	62 **Sm** 150.4	63 **Eu** 152.0	64 **Gd** 157.3	65 **Tb** 158.9	66 **Dy** 162.5	67 **Ho** 164.9	68 **Er** 167.3	69 **Tm** 168.9	70 **Yb** 173.0	71 **Lu** 175.0
90 **Th** 232.0	91 **Pa** 231.0	92 **U** 238.0	93 **Np** (237)	94 **Pu** (244)	95 **Am** (243)	96 **Cm** (247)	97 **Bk** (247)	98 **Cf** (251)	99 **Es** 252	100 **Fm** 257	101 **Md** 258	102 **No** 259	103 **Lr** 260

▲ **Figure 18.3   The Periodic Table of Elements.**

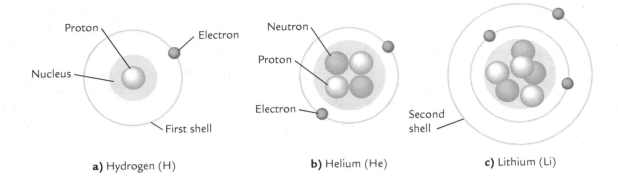

a) Hydrogen (H)   b) Helium (He)   c) Lithium (Li)

▲ **Figure 18.4** **Illustrations of atoms of a)** hydrogen, **b)** helium, and **c)** lithium show the placement of the electrons around the nucleus. The first shell (orbital) fills first and can hold only 2 electrons.

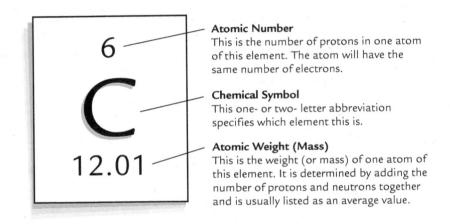

Atomic Number
This is the number of protons in one atom of this element. The atom will have the same number of electrons.

Chemical Symbol
This one- or two- letter abbreviation specifies which element this is.

Atomic Weight (Mass)
This is the weight (or mass) of one atom of this element. It is determined by adding the number of protons and neutrons together and is usually listed as an average value.

▲ **Figure 18.5** **Information contained in the Periodic Table.**

In your drawings, oxygen should have 2 electrons in its inner shell and 6 in its outer shell. Neon should have 2 electrons in its inner shell and 8 in its outer shell, giving it a full outer shell.

Now look at **Figure 18.5**. This is the square from the Periodic Table that represents carbon. You can see that each square of the Table tells you an element's chemical symbol, its atomic number, and its atomic weight. What do those three items tell you? _____

_____

_____

Remember, if you know an element's atomic number, you know how many protons are in its atoms. Once you know that, you also know how many electrons it has, because the number of protons and electrons is the same. But look at the atomic weight. Carbon's atomic weight is 12.01. Atomic weight equals the number of protons plus the number of neutrons. How can you have 0.01 (1/100th) of a proton or a neutron? You can't. Remember isotopes? The atomic weights shown in the Periodic Table are averages of samples that contain isotopes. You can round up or down to a whole number to figure out the typical number of neutrons.

How would you do that? If carbon has an atomic number of 6 and an atomic weight of 12.01, how many neutrons does it typically have? _____

The correct answer is 6, because the atomic weight is closest to 12, of which 6 are protons. The rest are neutrons.

Time to Try

Use the Periodic Table (**Figure 18.3**) to answer the following questions.

1. How many protons are there in an atom of calcium (Ca)? _____

2. How many electrons are there? _____

3. How many neutrons does a typical atom of calcium have?

   _____

4. How many neutrons does a typical atom of phosphorus (P) have? _____

You should see that calcium's atomic number is 20, so it has 20 protons and thus also 20 electrons. Its average atomic weight is 40.08, which rounds down to 40. Of that, 20 are protons, which leaves 20 neutrons. Phosphorus has an atomic number of 15, meaning it has 15 protons. Its average atomic weight is 30.97, closer to 31. So,

$$31 - 15 \text{ protons} = 16 \text{ neutrons.}$$

See—this is just simple math!

Now look again at the Periodic Table. Starting at the top, read it across, left to right, row by row. How is it organized?

_____

_____

_____

Next, look at the atomic numbers for the first four elements in Column 1— 1 (H), 3 (Li), 11 (Na), and 19 (K). Remember that in any atom the first shell holds only 2 electrons, and each of the next two shells can initially hold up to 8 more. Fill in the missing information:

Element: H   Li   Na   K
Electrons in
its outer shell: _____   _____   _____   _____

You should see that all elements in Column 1 have a lone electron in their outermost shell. Hydrogen has only 1 electron. Lithium has 2 electrons in the first shell and 1 in the outermost shell. Sodium has 2 in the first shell, 8 in the second, and 1 in the outermost shell. Potassium has 2, 8, 8, and 1. If you do the same for the second column, you'll find that each element has 2 electrons in its outermost shell. And you'll find that all the elements in the last column have 8

electrons in their outermost shells, except for helium, which has only 2 electrons.

The Periodic Table is organized by atomic number. The atomic number—the number of protons—increases from the left to the right, and from the top to the bottom. The Table is also organized into rows, called **periods**, and columns, called **groups**. Each row, or period, represents a shell (orbital) of electrons. The first row has one shell, the second row has two shells, and so on. Each column, or group, represents how many electrons are in the outermost shell. This organizational approach is very simple to use for the first three rows of the Periodic Table, but becomes more complicated below that. Those complexities, however, are beyond the scope of our current discussion.

✔ QUICK CHECK

What information do you know from the period in which an element is found in the Periodic Table?

_____

_____

What information do you know from the group in which an element is found in the Periodic Table?

_____

_____

● **Answers: 1.** The period tells you how many shells of electrons there are. **2.** The group tells you how many electrons are in the outermost shell.

▷ Bumper Cars and Chemical Interactions

Have you ever tried bumper cars? If not, you really should—it's a great way to release tension. Atoms interact with each other rather like bumper cars do (**Figure 18.6**). The first part of a bumper car that makes contact with another car is the outer rubber bumper. When two atoms come together, the first parts to make contact are always the electrons in the outermost shells. The protons and neutrons are safely tucked away in the middle of the atoms at their nuclei. So, the electrons in the outermost shell act as the "bumper" and determine how atoms interact with each other. We will discuss specifically how they interact shortly.

In bumper cars, the outer rubber bumpers of the cars make contact first. The riders inside the cars should never contact each other.

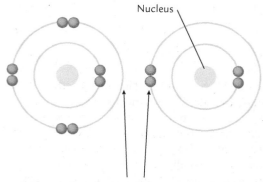

Nucleus

In atoms, the outer shell electrons make contact first. The protons and neutrons inside the nuclei never contact each other.

▲ **Figure 18.6** **Chemicals interact somewhat like bumper cars.** The electrons in the outermost shells become the atoms' "bumpers" and determine the chemical's reactivity.

Remember these two points:

1. The number of protons in all atoms of a particular element is constant.

2. The number of protons in an atom = the number of electrons in that atom.

From this, we see that all atoms of a particular element have the same number of electrons. Because the electrons determine their chemical activity, all atoms of a particular element will react the same way.

Time to Try

Consider carbon in the Periodic Table.

What is its atomic number? _____

How many protons does it have? _____
How many electrons? _____

Once you see that carbon's atomic number is 6, you know that it has 6 protons, and so it also has 6 electrons. Now draw the electrons for carbon around its nucleus.

You should see that carbon has 4 electrons in its second (outermost) shell, and these are the electrons that will interact with other electrons.

The electrons in an atom's outermost shell determine its chemical reactivity. ■

The Union: Chemical Bonding

As mentioned earlier, two or more atoms can join together through **chemical bonding** to form a molecule. Recall that the atom's electrons are arranged around the nucleus in one or more shells. These shells can have multiple subshells. The outermost of these subshells is called the **valence shell**. For simplicity, we will refer to this as the outermost shell. It can contain at most 2 electrons for helium, or 8 electrons for all other elements. The electrons in the outermost shell are called **valence electrons** and they alone determine the atom's reactivity. If this outermost shell contains the maximum number of electrons, or is full, the atom is amazingly stable. It is said to be chemically **inert**—it will not easily react with other atoms. It is "happy," so to speak. All of the elements in the last column of the Periodic Table are inert.

On the other hand, atoms of elements in all of the other columns lack a full outermost shell. That means they are unstable and want to become stable. If it helps you remember this, think about life. When we are ful**filled**, we feel happy. If we are not happy, perhaps we feel something is missing

from our lives, or maybe we feel we have lots of good to give and nobody to give it to. Now don't you feel sorry for those unfulfilled atoms?

An atom that does not have a full outermost shell of electrons is not stable, and it will react with other atoms to try to become stable. Unstable atoms can gain, lose, or share electrons with other unstable atoms until they become stable. That's how atoms interact. Let's explore this more deeply.

✔ **QUICK CHECK**

Under what circumstances is an atom stable?

_____

_____

_____

● **Answer:** An atom is stable when its outermost, or valence, shell is full, meaning it has 2 electrons for helium or 8 electrons for all other elements.

Ionic Bonding

When atoms become stable by losing and gaining electrons, electrons actually leave one atom's outermost shell and join the outermost shell of another atom. The atoms are now stable, meaning they each have a full outermost shell. However, gaining or losing electrons also changes the atoms in another way. Recall that atoms are normally electrically neutral—they have the same number of protons (+) and electrons (−). Once the electrons move, though, the atoms are no longer neutral because the protons and electrons are no longer balanced. An atom that gains an electron has one extra negative charge, and

an atom that loses an electron is short one negative charge, making it positive.

All atoms that have gained or lost electrons carry an electrical charge and are called **ions**. These are designated with a $^+$ or $^-$ sign. For example, sodium tends to lose an electron and become a sodium ion, Na^+. Chlorine tends to gain an electron, becoming a chloride ion, Cl^-. Ions of opposite charges attract each other (*"Opposites attract"*). Whenever ions are formed, oppositely charged ions will join to form a compound that is electrically neutral. When they join, they form a strong **ionic bond**—ions form ionic bonds.

 Atoms that gain or lose electrons form ions, and ions of opposite charges form ionic bonds. ■

Time to Try

 Let's see how ionic bonding works, using sodium and chlorine. Look at the Periodic Table and fill in the following information:

	Sodium (Na)	Chlorine (Cl)
Atomic number:	_____	_____
Number of protons:	_____	_____
Number of electrons:	_____	_____

You know from the Periodic Table that neither of these elements is stable—they are not in the last column of the Table, so their outermost shells are not full. How can they become stable?

_____

_____

Draw the electrons around the nuclei of each of these atoms (the shells are drawn for you):

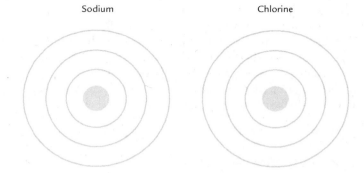

Sodium, with atomic number 11, should have 2 electrons in its inner shell, 8 in the second, and a single electron in its outermost shell. Chlorine, atomic number 17, should have 2 electrons in its inner shell, 8 in its second shell, and 7 in its outermost shell. That is pretty convenient—sodium has one too many and chlorine is short one. Sodium will lose its electron to chlorine, producing two ions, Na^+ and Cl^-. Once

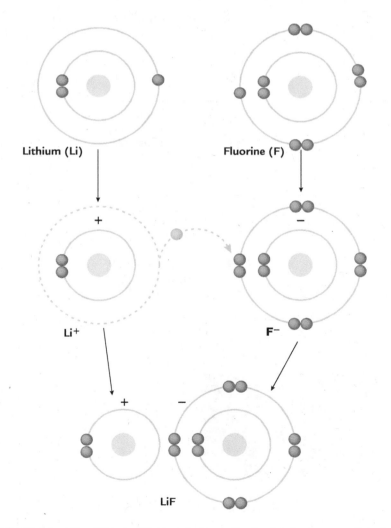

1. Lithium and fluorine both have unstable outer shells.

2. Lithium loses an electron to become stable, forming the ion Li^+.

   Fluorine gains that electron to become stable, forming the ion F^-.

3. The ions are strongly attracted to each other because of their opposite charges. They join through a stable ionic bond, forming the compound lithium flouride.

▲ Figure 18.7 **Ionic bonding.** Lithium will lose an electron to fluorine, forming two oppositely charged ions. These ions are then attracted to each other and form an ionic bond, producing the compound called lithium fluoride.

the ions are formed, their opposite electrical charges will draw them together and they will form a strong ionic bond, creating a compound called *sodium chloride*. You know it better as table salt!

Now remember that magic from the Periodic Table: Sodium is in the first column, so it has 1 extra electron it wants to lose. As we saw earlier, all elements in that column have one electron in their outermost shell. Chlorine is in the next to last (stable) column. All of the elements in that column need only 1 electron to have a full outermost shell and be stable.

What would you predict about calcium? _____

What about oxygen? _____

Calcium is in the second column, so it has 2 electrons in an outermost shell that wants 8. It is not stable. Oxygen is two

columns short of being stable, so it needs 2 more electrons to fill its outermost shell and be stable.

For review, **Figure 18.7** shows how an ionic bond forms between lithium and fluorine. These elements are in the same columns as sodium and chlorine, so the process is the same except these new elements have only two shells of electrons. But, as you now know, in chemical interactions, only the electrons in the outermost shells are important.

✔ QUICK CHECK

How does an ionic bond form? _____

_____

_____

Covalent Bonding

I have an older brother. Growing up there were times, of course, when we, um, shall we say, disagreed? This often revolved around possession of some toy or other item. If you have siblings, you know how these squabbles usually ended—a parental voice from somewhere in the distance yelling for us to . . . *share*.

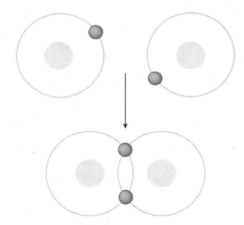

1. Each hydrogen atom has a single electron in its outer shell, so each is unstable.

2. Instead of gaining or losing electrons, the atoms share their single electrons, forming a covalent bond that makes a stable molecule. The two electrons then orbit around both atoms' nuclei.

Everyone is happy when they share.

▲ **Figure 18.8** **Covalent bonding.** In covalent bonding, instead of engaging in a tug of war, two atoms share the electrons in their outermost shells to become stable. Here a covalent bond between two hydrogen atoms is shown.

Apparently some atoms have learned that lesson as well. Let's consider two hydrogen atoms, each of which has a single electron. To form an ionic bond, one hydrogen atom would have to give up its electron and another atom would have to gain it. But which will gain and which will lose? (From my childhood I remember many long standoffs in which neither I nor my brother had any intention of giving up anything!) Neither; instead, both hydrogen atoms can share their electrons. By combining them, the electrons will orbit around both nuclei together, and both atoms will be stable as long as they stay together. This type of bond is called a **covalent bond**. Recall that the outermost shell is called the valence shell and it contains the valence electrons that are interacting. The atoms that are sharing electrons in order to have full valence shells are said to be covalent (*co-* as in together

or cooperating; the electrons share a common valence shell). Figure 18.8 illustrates the formation of a covalent bond. In general, elements that are closer to the right or left side of the Periodic Table are more likely to form ionic bonds, and those closer to the middle of the Table are more likely to form covalent bonds.

✔ **QUICK CHECK**

How does a covalent bond form? _____

_____

POLAR AND NONPOLAR COVALENT BONDS

We just saw that in covalent bonds the valence electrons are shared between two atoms. However, the electrons may or may not be shared equally. The negative electrons are attracted to the positive protons in the two atoms' nuclei. When the nuclei equally attract the valence electrons, the electrons are shared equally (Figure 18.9a). However,

sometimes one atom's protons attract the electrons more strongly than the other. When this occurs, the electrons spend more time around the atom with the greater attraction, causing a slight imbalance in the electrical charge (Figure 18.9b). The atom that holds onto the electrons the most has a slight negative charge, and the other atom that is often missing its

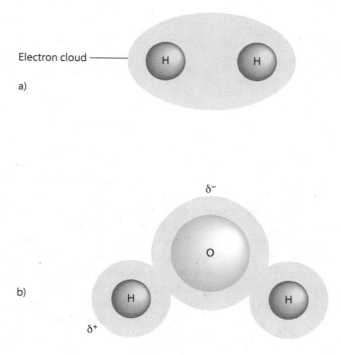

Electron cloud

a)

b)

δ^-

O

H   H

δ^+

▲ Figure 18.9   **A)** In nonpolar covalent bonds, such as this one between two hydrogen atoms, the electrons are shared equally between the two atoms. **B)** In polar covalent bonds, such as these between two hydrogen atoms and an oxygen atom, the electrons are shared unequally, spending more time around the oxygen and resulting in a slight imbalance in the charge—the oxygen becomes slightly negative and the hydrogen atoms become slightly positive.

electrons has a slight positive charge. This slight imbalance in electrical charge is called **polarity**. Covalent bonds in which the valence electrons are shared unequally, producing polarity, are called **polar covalent bonds**. Covalent bonds in which the valence electrons are shared equally are called **nonpolar covalent bonds**.

Picture This

With polar covalent bonds, electrons spend more time around the atom with the strongest attraction. Prove that to yourself with Figure 18.9b. Moving your finger at a steady pace, trace the path around one hydrogen and move from there to the oxygen and go around it. Notice that your finger is near the oxygen longer.

Substances that contain polar covalent bonds and have that slight electrical imbalance are called polar, and substances that lack this imbalance are called nonpolar. When it comes to combining these substances, polar substances are compatible with each other, but not with nonpolar substances. Shown in Figure 18.9b, water is a classic polar molecule. Polar substances will easily dissolve in water, but nonpolar substances will not—they will form a separate layer.

Time to Try

Let's examine the compatibility of polar and nonpolar substances.

1. Take any clear container, preferably one that can be closed. A plastic baggie will work. Fill it about a third full with water.

2. Add to that about half as much cooking oil. Try to get them to mix and observe what happens. _____ _____ (*Water is polar and the oil is nonpolar—they will not mix well.*)

3. Add a few drops of food coloring to the container and shake it well to mix.

4. Is the food coloring polar or nonpolar (*Hint: into which layer does it settle?*) _____

5. Now find any three harmless liquids and try to mix each of them, individually, with water. Avoid household cleaners which may be strong and may react with each other if mixed.

Liquid tested: **Polar or nonpolar?**

_____   _____

_____   _____

_____   _____

You likely found that your liquids, unless they were other oils, were polar because they mixed with the polar water layer. Water is often used to make solutions because so many substances will dissolve in it. In a solution, one substance, the solute, dissolves in another, the solvent. Water is considered a universal solvent, and most chemical reactions in the human body occur in water. Water readily dissolves polar molecules, but it causes nonpolar molecules to bunch together.

✔ QUICK CHECK

Explain what is meant by polar molecule. _____

_____

_____

● Answer: A polar molecule is one in which there is an uneven charge distribution across the molecule, resulting in slightly positive and slightly negative charges.

Hydrogen Bonds

We have discussed ionic and covalent bonds, which form between individual atoms. Although there are other types of chemical bonds, we will look at just one more—the **hydrogen bond**. Unlike the first two types that form between atoms to make molecules, hydrogen bonds instead can form both within molecules and also between separate molecules. A hydrogen bond is a weak bond that can form between a hydrogen atom in one molecule and another atom in the same or a different molecule. A classic example of this is in water. Look at Figure 18.10.

Polar molecules can form weak hydrogen bonds, as shown in Figure 18.10b. The slightly more positive hydrogen is attracted to the slightly more negative oxygen in an adjacent water molecule, so they form a weak bond that holds the two atoms together. This is the hydrogen bond. It is kind of like striking up a conversation with a stranger in the checkout line at the grocery store. You happen to be standing close, so perhaps you chat briefly, but you are not going to become lifelong buddies from that short and superficial exchange. Although they are weak, hydrogen bonds are important. They help shape many important molecules, such as the proteins in your individual hairs (straight vs. curly), and your DNA.

Water has lots of hydrogen bonds, as shown in Figure 18.10c, giving it many unique characteristics. Ice floats because the hydrogen bonds cause the water molecules to spread out more in the solid form than they do in the liquid form. Water also has a high boiling point because it is slightly resistant to temperature changes. Water has high adhesion, meaning it sticks to surfaces very well, and high cohesion, meaning its molecules stick to each other. These unique characteristics make it well suited to life processes. It plays a critical role in maintaining proper body temperature and the water in our blood plasma easily dissolves many substances and transports them rapidly through the widest artery and the narrowest capillary. Let's demonstrate a couple of water's characteristics.

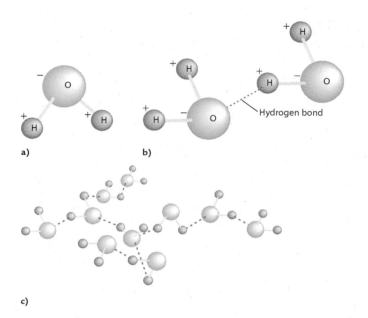

▲ Figure 18.10   Hydrogen bonding. a) A water molecule is polarized—the hydrogen atoms tend to be slightly more positive than the oxygen. **b)** A hydrogen bond forms between a slightly positive hydrogen atom and a slightly negative oxygen atom. **c)** Hydrogen bonds between water molecules give water many unique properties.

Time to Try

You need two pennies, alcohol, water, a dropper (or carefully use your finger), and a paper towel.

1. Place the pennies on a paper towel and examine them. Estimate how many drops of liquid you can put on a penny before it will spill over: _____ drops

2. Start with the alcohol. Using the dropper or your finger, carefully add the alcohol, counting each drop, until it overflows. How many drops of alcohol did you get on the penny? _____

3. Now repeat this on the other penny using water. How many drops of water did you get on this penny? _____

If you did it correctly, you should have been able to pile far more drops of water than alcohol on a penny because the water molecules stick to the penny (adhesion) and to each other (cohesion) much more than the alcohol molecules do. Because most beverages have a high water content, this property also allows you to fill a beverage glass higher than the rim—just don't try to put a lid on it or pick it up! These characteristics are important for how our blood moves through our vessels.

Molecules and Compounds

When two or more atoms bind together by covalent bonds, they form a **molecule**. A molecule of water, for example, is composed of two atoms of hydrogen covalently bonded to an oxygen atom. When atoms join by ionic bonds, they form **compounds**, which always contain atoms of different elements. Sodium chloride, for example, is a compound. Even with ionic compounds, though, we often refer to a single unit as a molecule. Whenever you hear the term molecule, as you know from the Biological Hierarchy of Organization, you should realize that it is one structure composed of more than one atom joined together by chemical bonds. But how are molecules named and described?

A molecule is described by a **molecular formula** that tells you what the molecule is made of. This formula includes the letter symbols for the elements and the number of atoms of each element that are present in the molecule. The numbers are always in the subscript position. For example,

H_2O = water CO_2 = carbon dioxide

O_2 = oxygen   CO = carbon monoxide

Note that the only difference between carbon dioxide and carbon monoxide is one atom of oxygen. We make carbon dioxide in our body and exhale it with every breath, whereas carbon monoxide is a deadly poison.

The molecular formula gives us limited information. It tells us how many pieces are in a molecule, but not how they

are hooked together. For that, we can consult the **structural formula**, which is a simplified drawing of how the molecule is built. Lines in a structural formula represent chemical bonds (see Figure 18.10). Now look at **Figure 18.11**. This shows the structural formulae for three sugars: glucose, galactose, and fructose. Glucose and galactose are quite similar, so the differences are highlighted. Fructose, also called fruit sugar, has an obviously different appearance.

Time to Try

Look carefully at Figure 18.11 and fill in the following information.

	Glucose	Galactose	Fructose
Number of carbon atoms:	_____	_____	_____
Number of hydrogen atoms:	_____	_____	_____
Number of oxygen atoms:	_____	_____	_____
Molecular formula:	C _ H _ O _	C _ H _ O _	C _ H _ O _

(*Hint: Use the numbers you wrote for each element above.*)

You can see that all three of these sugars have the same molecular formula: $C_6H_{12}O_6$. The structural formula provides more detailed information and is often more useful than the molecular formula. However, the molecular formula is the most common method of describing molecules and compounds.

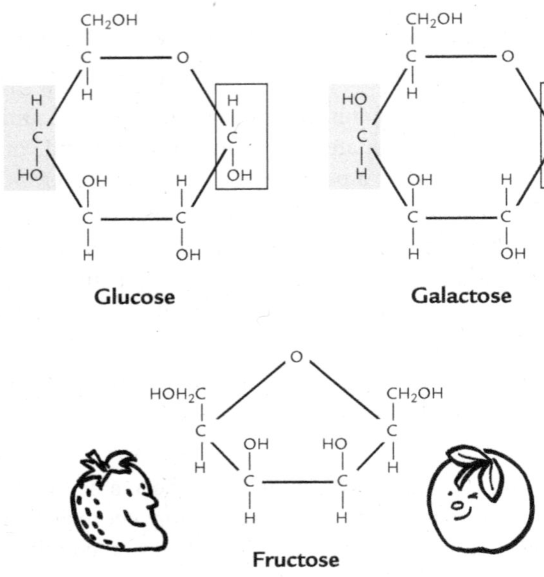

Glucose

Galactose

Fructose

▲ Figure 18.11   The structural formulae for glucose, galactose, and fructose. Although they all have the same molecular formula, the highlighted areas show the differences between glucose and galactose, and fructose is more obviously different.

▷ Double Bubble, Toil and Trouble: Solutions, Electrolytes and pH

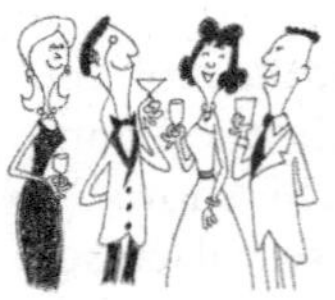

Molecules are often found in solutions. In a **solution**, one substance, the **solute**, dissolves in another, the **solvent**. Water is often used to make solutions because so many substances will dissolve in it. Water is considered a universal solvent, and most chemical reactions in the human body occur in water. Water readily dissolves polar molecules, but it causes nonpolar molecules to bunch together.

Molecules can be categorized in ways other than by their polarity. Let's explore a group called **electrolytes**. Recall that ions are atoms with electrical charges. Water molecules, which are polar, have slight positive charges and slight negative charges, and these slight charges attract the negative and positive ions. This pull on the ions causes them to separate, or dissociate, in water. An electrolyte is any compound that releases ions in water. Because ions are released within the solution, electrolyte solutions can

conduct electricity—hence the term electrolyte. Strong electrolytes dissociate, or separate, completely in water, whereas weak electrolytes only partially dissociate. In other words, for weak electrolytes only some of the ions are released in water; the others remain bonded together.

There are three types of *electrolytes*:

■ **Acids** release H^+ in water. Examples include the strong acid, hydrochloric acid (HCl), and the weak carbonic acid (H_2CO_3).

■ **Bases** form ions that can bind with H^+. Examples include the strong base, sodium hydroxide ($NaOH$), and the weak base, sodium bicarbonate ($NaHCO_3$).

■ **Salts** release ions other than hydrogen, and are produced when acids and bases combine with each other. For example, HCl and $NaOH$ react together to form the salt sodium chloride ($NaCl$) and water.

Acids

Let's start by looking at acids. How does hydrogen become the ion H^+? _____

_____

Recall that positive ions form when electrons are lost. H^+ is an atom of hydrogen minus its electron—it is primarily a

proton. Thus, acids are called *proton donors*. Acids in the home might include vinegar (acetic acid), carbonated soft drinks (phosphoric and citric acids), and citrus fruit (citric acid). Acids in your body include hydrochloric acid (HCl) in your stomach and lactic acid that can accumulate in your muscles.

Bases

Bases form ions that bind H^+, so they are *proton acceptors*. Bases in the home include ammonia and bleach. Bases in your body include compounds that release bicarbonate ions, such as sodium bicarbonate (also in baking soda).

Bases minimize the damaging effects of acids in your body. For example, the hydrochloric acid from your stomach is tamed by bicarbonate in your intestine.

Salts

When acids and bases react together, they produce salts and water. As electrolytes, salts release ions in water, providing many important ions, such as calcium, potassium, sodium, magnesium, and chloride. Salts also help maintain our water balance, which in turn affects our blood volume, blood pressure, and normal cell functions.

term "electrolyte" is often used to refer to the ions themselves, rather than the compounds that produce them. Maintaining proper amounts of these ions is essential for normal body functions. Calcium, for example, is required for nerve communication, muscle contraction, and strong bones and teeth. Maintaining the proper *fluid-electrolyte balance* is essential for homeostasis.

Why Should I Care?

 Ions from electrolytes play such critical roles in keeping us alive that in the medical field the

Acid-Base Balance and pH

Many physiological processes depend on certain amounts of acids and bases—the *acid-base balance.* Like the fluid-electrolyte balance, acid-base balance is essential for our survival. Acids release H^+, and the more H^+ that is present, the more acidic the solution is. Bases bind H^+, so the more base that is present, the less H^+ there is. The amount of acid and base in a solution is measured in pH units. The **pH** refers to how much H^+ is present. The **pH scale** ranges from 0 to 14 (Figure 18.12). Pure water has equal amounts of H^+ and OH^- (hydroxide ion, which acts as a base). Because of this, pure water has a neutral pH of 7.0. A pH below 7.0 is *acidic*; a value above 7.0 is basic or *alkaline*. Each one-unit change in pH is actually a ten-fold change because each pH unit represents a power of 10. The difference between a pH of 1 and a pH of 2 is 10^1 (10) and the difference between a pH of 1 and a pH of 3 is 10^2 (100). H^+ concentration and pH are inversely related—as

H^+ concentration goes up, pH drops, and vice versa. In other words, the stronger the acid, the lower the pH, and the stronger the base, the higher the pH.

✔ **QUICK CHECK**

Gastric juice—the liquid in your stomach—has a pH around 1.5. Coffee's pH is about 5.0, and most colas are around 3.0.

Which of these is the most acidic, and which is the least?

_____

_____

● **Answer:** Gastric juice is the most acidic; colas are next; and coffee is the least acidic.

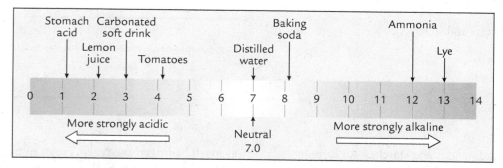

▲ **Figure 18.12** **The pH scale measures the H^+ concentration in solutions.** The scale has values from 0 to 14; 7.0 is neutral, with equal amounts of acid and base. The pH values of some familiar solutions are shown.

▷ I'm In with the In Crowd: Inorganic Compounds

Chemical compounds are classified as organic or inorganic. **Organic compounds** contain both carbon and hydrogen. All others are classified as **inorganic compounds,** which may contain C or H, neither of them, but not both.

Water (H_2O) is our most abundant inorganic compound. It's the major component of all body fluids. It both bathes and fills our cells, and transports substances to and from them. Water is considered the universal solvent and, as we just saw, it frees ions from electrolytes. Most chemical reactions occur in water, and it allows us to lose excess heat through sweating. Water is, arguably, our most important nutrient.

We take in *oxygen* (O_2) by breathing, and it enters our blood through our lungs. Most oxygen travels in our blood and is released where it is needed. Oxygen allows us to get the most energy from foods we eat by freeing the energy in food molecules. This energy fuels our cells' activities. While using oxygen to extract energy, cells produce *carbon dioxide* (CO_2) as a waste product. This CO_2 moves through your blood to your lungs where it is exhaled.

Time to Try

The pigments in red cabbage can act as a pH indicator. Let's try it. You need red cabbage, boiling water, a clear glass container, a drinking straw, and baking soda.

1. Chop 1 cup of red cabbage into enough boiling water to cover it. Let this stand for 15 minutes.

2. Put about 1/4 cup of the water—the indicator—in your clear container. Its current color indicates a near-neutral pH of 7.0. *What color is the indicator for a neutral pH?* _____ With an acidic pH, the indicator turns more red; with a basic pH, it turns more bluish-green.

3. Use the straw to blow bubbles in the indicator. Blow until the color changes. (Get comfortable—this could take awhile.) *What color is it turning?* _____ *What does this say about the pH?* _____

4. Now add baking soda to the indicator and stir it. Repeat this until the indicator returns to the neutral color.

5. Add double the amount of baking soda you first put in and stir. *What color is the solution now?* _____ *Is baking soda an acid or a base?* _____

Blowing bubbles (CO_2) into the water creates carbonic acid, and the indicator should turn redder. Baking soda is a base, binding the H^+ from the carbonic acid, and the indicator should return to the neutral color, then move into the basic range as you add more. The main reason we exhale is to clear CO_2 from the body. If we don't clear enough CO_2, too much carbonic acid forms and our pH drops. Fortunately, our bodies also produce bicarbonate ion to help neutralize the H^+ from the carbonic acid.

▷ Is it Organic?

The term *organic* is used today to describe artwork, home décor, and how food is grown, among other things. In chemistry, though, it has a very precise meaning. By definition, organic compounds contain both carbon and hydrogen. They must have these two elements, and they usually have others as well, especially oxygen. Most of your body is made of organic molecules. That, Earthling, is what is meant by saying we are a carbon-based life form. The main categories of organic compounds are

▪ carbohydrates (sugars and starches),
▪ proteins,

▪ lipids (which include fats and steroids), and
▪ nucleic acids (DNA, which is your genetic material, and RNA, which assists DNA).

✔ QUICK CHECK

What is the difference between organic and inorganic molecules?

_____

_____

● **Answer: Organics contain both carbon and hydrogen; inorganics do not.**

Carbohydrates

Carbohydrates include sugars and starches. All carbohydrates contain C, H, and O, with hydrogen and oxygen present in a 2:1 ratio. That means carbohydrates contain twice as much hydrogen as oxygen. For example, the molecular formula for glucose is $C_6H_{12}O_6$. Sucrose (table sugar) is $C_{12}H_{22}O_{11}$. Notice that the 2:1 rule does not involve carbon.

▲ **Figure 18.13** **Monomers are like children's pop beads.** Each bead is one unit, or a monomer. Monomers can be linked together to form larger structures called polymers.

What common small molecule can you think of that also has this ratio? _____

_____

Hopefully you got that: it's good ol' H_2O—water.

Picture This

It's a hot summer day. You've been sweating heavily and feel overheated and weak. You go inside to cool off and quench your thirst. Heavy sweating caused you to lose more water than you should.

What term do we use for that situation? We would say that you are de __ __ __ __ __ __ __ __ .

You drink some water and feel refreshed because you are re __ __ __ __ __ __ __ __ .

The term "hydrate" refers to water. Now look again at the name of this category of compounds—*carbohydrate*. It literally means carbon that is hydrated—carbon with water. That is why we expect carbohydrates to have the 2:1 ratio of hydrogen to oxygen—H_2O.

Many organic compounds are organized from small units called **monomers** (*mono* means *one*). Monomers are the simplest form of each category of compounds, and they can link together into larger, more complex compounds called **polymers** (*poly* means *many*). To understand this, consider children's pop beads (**Figure 18.13**). Each "bead" is like a monomer, and when monomers join they form a polymer. Our foods contain polymers, but digestion breaks them down to monomers so they can enter our blood for delivery to our cells. Once in the cells, monomers are used directly or formed into various polymers for your body's needs.

The major carbohydrate monomer is $C_6H_{12}O_6$ (**Figure 18.14**), which is a sugar. Another term for sugar is *saccharide*. Because this is a sugar monomer, $C_6H_{12}O_6$ is also called a **monosaccharide**—it is a single sugar unit. Our most common monosaccharide is *glucose*. Two monosaccharides linked together make a **disaccharide,** such as table sugar, or *sucrose*. If more monosaccharides join, the product is a **polysaccharide,** also known as a complex carbohydrate. *Starch* is a polysaccharide, as is *glycogen*, the form in which our cells store glucose. Carbohydrates provide energy and building materials. Dietary sources of carbohydrates include sweets and starches and food groups like fruits, vegetables, and grains.

✔ **QUICK CHECK**

What are the monomers of carbohydrates?

_____

_____

Answer: Monosaccharides.

Lipids

Lipids, which include fats and steroids, among others, don't dissolve in water. Our most familiar lipid is **fat**. Like carbohydrates, fats contain C, H, and O, but the ratio of hydrogen to oxygen is much higher in fat. Consider the formula for one fat: $C_{57}H_{110}O_6$. It has 110 hydrogens and only 6 oxygens! A single molecule of fat is also called a **triglyceride,** and

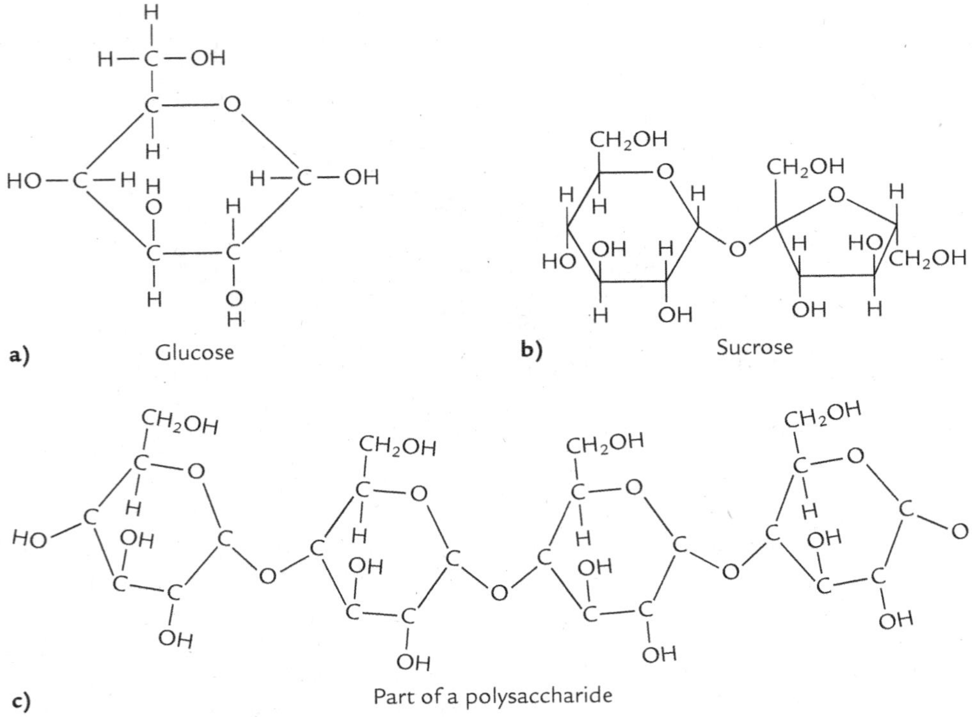

▲ Figure 18.14 **Carbohydrates. a)** A monosaccharide, such as glucose, is a carbohydrate monomer. **b)** Two monosaccharides linked together form a disaccharide, such as sucrose. **c)** More than two monosaccharides unite to form a polysaccharide. Part of a polysaccharide is shown here—note the repeating monomer units.

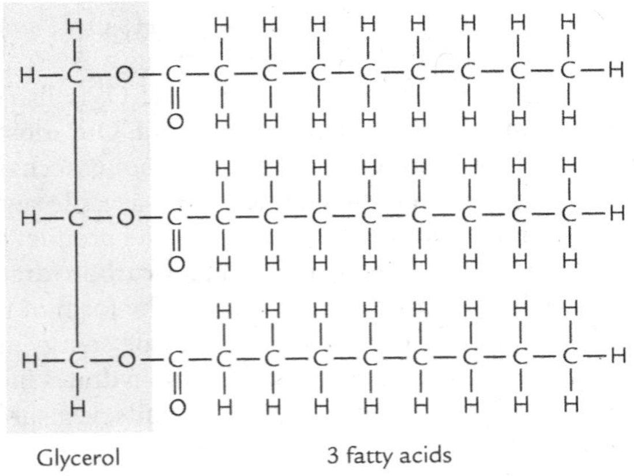

▲ Figure 18.15 **A triglyceride (fat) has three fatty acids linked together by glycerol.**

it contains three carbon chains called *fatty acids* linked together by a small compound called glycerol (Figure 18.15). These compounds are the monomers. Dietary sources of fat include many meats, cheese, whole milk, oils, and butter. Much of our pleasure from food comes from the smooth texture, or "mouth feel," that fats contribute.

In our bodies, fat is a major energy source; in fact, we store extra energy (Calories) as fat. It insulates us (Ask any walrus how important blubber is in frigid water!), cushions our organs, and some of our vitamins need fat to enter our bodies. Fat is not the only type of lipid, though. *Phospholipids* are the main component of cell membranes. *Steroids* include cholesterol, which is an essential part of our cell membranes, and some hormones, like testosterone and estrogen.

Proteins

Like carbohydrates and fats, **protein** contains C, H, and O, but it also has nitrogen (N). Protein's monomers are **amino acids** (Figure 18.16). Each amino acid has an *amine* group ($^-NH_2$) and another part called a *carboxyl* group (^-COOH), both attached to a central carbon. The carboxyl group allows the compound to act as an acid—hence the name amino acid. Another part, the *R group,* makes each amino acid distinct.

Each protein contains amino acids linked together in a specific sequence, called the *primary structure.* Think of it as a string of assorted beads making a necklace—if you change any bead or their order, you make a different necklace. Similarly, the specific order of amino acids determines what the protein is and how it functions. A protein's primary structure is determined by genes—your DNA. The chain of amino

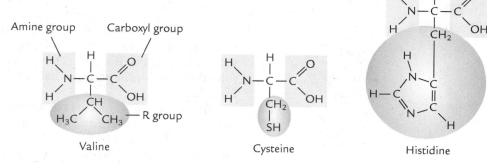

▲ **Figure 18.16** **Amino acid.** An amino acid contains an amine group, a carboxyl group, and a variable area called "R." Compare these amino acids and you will see that the R area is the only place that they differ.

acids is usually twisted and folded into a unique three-dimensional shape by chemical bonds, and some proteins even contain more than one chain twisted and folded together. This sounds complicated, but it is very important—the protein's specific 3-D shape determines how it works, and any change in that shape can make it nonfunctional.

Time to Try

Time to head to the kitchen for a snack. Crack an egg into a pan and describe the egg white. _____
_____ Now turn on the heat, cook the egg until it is "done," and describe the egg white after cooking. _____

Oops! You changed your mind and don't want an egg after all. Put it back in the refrigerator to cool. Does it go back to its original state after cooling? _____

_____

Egg white contains a protein called *albumin*. It comes out of the shell as a clear, thick liquid, but when heated it becomes a white, rubbery solid. A protein's shape is maintained by hydrogen bonds cross-linking parts of the amino acid chain to each other. These bonds can be broken by heat. If that happens, the protein is *denatured*—it becomes disorganized and loses its unique shape and thus its special

properties. Denaturation can't be reversed—you can't uncook an egg white. In cells, if proteins are denatured they may be nonfunctional.

Dietary sources of protein include meat, fish, poultry, dairy products, nuts, and legumes. Proteins provide structural materials for growth and repair. Many hormones are built from proteins, as are cell receptors that allow materials to enter, antibodies that keep us healthy, and enzymes. **Enzymes** are especially important for body processes—they allow chemical reactions to occur. All enzymes are proteins, and most chemical reactions in the body require specific enzymes. They assist other chemicals, acting a bit like tour guides ensuring that the chemicals get where they need to be and do what they are supposed to. They make it easier for reactions to occur. Without enzymes, very little work could occur in our cells—almost no energy production, synthesis, or repair. Our metabolic processes, and our existence, would grind to a halt.

✔ **QUICK CHECK**

How is the term amino acid related to proteins?

_____

_____

● **Answer:** Amino acids are the monomers that form proteins; their name reflects that they contain an amine group and an acidic carboxyl group.

Nucleic Acids

The last organic compounds to explore are **nucleic acids—DNA and RNA.** Each nucleic acid contains C, H, O, N, and phosphorus (P). Nucleic acids are large, complex compounds, and **nucleotides** are their monomers. Each nucleotide contains a sugar, a phosphate group, and an organic base. Nucleic acids are named for the sugar they contain.

Picture This

Imagine a ladder. The uprights (hand rails) represent alternating sugars and phosphates, with

the "steps" attached to the sugars. These steps are paired organic bases—adenine (A), thymine (T), guanine (G), and cytosine (C). They match up specifically—adenine and thymine are always together, and guanine is always on a step with cytosine. Now, imagine twisting your ladder into a spiral staircase. You just made a double helix, the classical shape of DNA.

Deoxyribonucleic acid (DNA) contains the sugar deoxyribose; *ribonucleic acid (RNA)* instead contains ribose. Nucleic acids consist of many nucleotides linked together in a long chain and folded into special shapes.

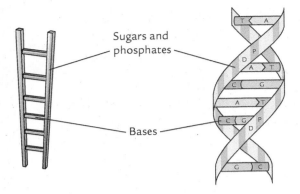

▲ **Figure 18.17** **Structure of DNA.** The chemical structure of DNA is like a ladder, with sugars (D) and phosphates (P) forming the uprights and organic bases (A, T, C, and G) forming the steps.

DNA is your genetic material, and it is organized into chromosomes (**Figure 18.17**). DNA contains stacked pairs of nucleotides. The organic bases store information in the form of a molecular code that provides instructions for building your proteins. A span of DNA with instructions for a single polypeptide is a *gene*. These instructions are what you inherit from your parents—half from mom and half from dad.

RNA's three major types are *messenger RNA (mRNA)*, *ribosomal RNA (rRNA)*, and *tRNA (transfer RNA)*. RNA's job is to carry out the DNA's instructions. Think of DNA as the blueprints for building a protein. RNA, then, is like the workers that do the building. We'll discuss the specific roles of nucleic acids more in Chapter 19.

▷ Love is Just a Chemical Reaction

All activities that occur within our bodies, including the functioning of our brains and affairs of our hearts, start with chemical reactions. When chemicals react with each other, bonds are formed or broken to produce new chemical combinations or to release ions. Energy is stored, energy is released, and energy is used in chemical reactions. Many aspects of physiology involve amazingly complex reactions that are meticulously controlled, whereas others are quite simple.

Chemical reactions are written in the form of **chemical equations**, but instead of using an equals sign, we use an arrow. The substances to the left of the arrow are the **reactants**—the things that react together. The items to the right of the arrow are the **products**—the end result of the reaction. The arrow means "produces" or "yields." For example, $Na^+ + Cl^- \rightarrow NaCl$ would be read "sodium ion plus chloride ion produces sodium chloride." Many reactions are **reversible**, meaning they can go in either direction. You can combine the ions we just mentioned to make salt, but salt can also break down to produce the ions. Reversible reactions are often indicated with a special double arrow symbol: $\rightleftharpoons$. Let's examine three basic types of reactions: synthesis, decomposition, and exchange.

Synthesis reactions are reactions that build. Another term for these is **anabolic reactions**. With that in mind, think

about why athletes sometimes engage in illicit use of *anabolic* steroids—to *build* their muscles and strength. In synthesis reactions, two or more atoms or molecules combine to make a larger molecule. For example, proteins combine to build muscles. Small sugars combine to build large molecules of starch. This is done by forming new chemical bonds to hold the pieces together. Synthesis reactions are especially important in humans for growth and repair processes.

The most common type of synthesis reaction is **dehydration synthesis.** Think about that term. What does "dehydration" mean? _____

_____

In dehydration synthesis, adjacent monomers are connected by removing water and linking them together at the removal sites. Specifically, a hydrogen atom is removed from one monomer, and both a hydrogen and an oxygen are removed from an adjacent momomer (**Figure 18.18**). A quick glance shows us that the removed atoms make water. The monomers then join where these atoms were removed. Dehydration synthesis is how most organic monomers form polymers.

Decomposition reactions are the opposite of synthesis reactions. During decomposition reactions, larger structures

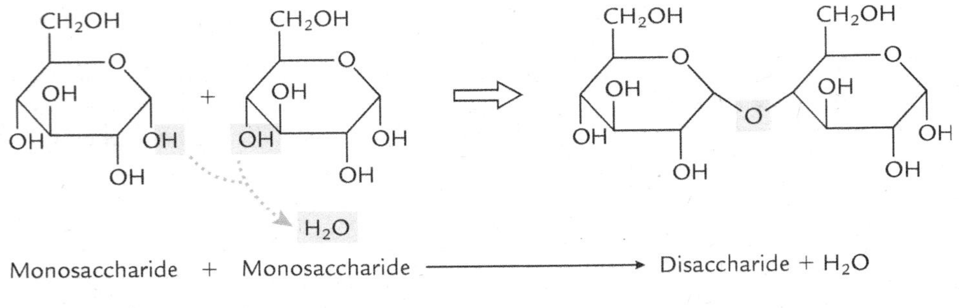

Monosaccharide + Monosaccharide ⟶ Disaccharide + H_2O

▲ **Figure 18.18** **Two monosaccharides can join by dehydration synthesis.** In this process, a hydrogen is removed from one monosaccharide, and an oxygen and a hydrogen are removed from the other one. Once removed, they form water and the monosaccharides attach at the removal site, forming a disaccharide.

are broken down into smaller parts. These are also called **catabolic reactions**. For example, starch is broken down into smaller sugars. These reactions are done by breaking chemical bonds. Decomposition reactions are especially important in humans for digesting food and getting energy.

For organic molecules, the most common type of decomposition is **hydrolysis**. Think about that term and refer to the word root and suffix tables.

What does hydro mean? _____

What does lysis mean? _____

Hydro means water; *lysis* means destroy or rupture. Decomposition is the opposite of synthesis, thus hydrolysisis is the opposite of dehydration synthesis. Hydrolysis uses water to *break* bonds. Bonds are split and water is put back in at the same places where it was removed during dehydration synthesis—one hydrogen from the water joins the already present oxygen, and the other hydrogen and oxygen from the water join the other broken bond. This is the basic process that breaks down food into usable units.

Exchange reactions involve swapping pieces. Two or more molecules split apart and then recombine in a new way; for example, AB and CD separate, then recombine to form AC and BD. Exchange reactions allow the body to receive and store chemicals in one form and then reuse them for multiple purposes. Here is an example of an exchange reaction:

$$HCl + NaOH \rightarrow NaCl + H_2O$$

Notice that both of the original compounds separate and swap parts. The final products have the same atoms, but they are rearranged.

Physiology is the study of how the body and all of its parts work. Although it may be hard to realize it, all of the work done by the body—collectively referred to as *metabolism*—involves chemical reactions. We eat and breathe to bring in the necessary chemicals, then the body uses those molecules in an amazing array of chemical reactions that allow us to do virtually everything we do. All body processes rely on synthesis, decomposition, and exchange reactions. When you begin studying specific chemical processes in the body, it may help to understand them if you think of what the outcome should be—are the reactions building, breaking down, or swapping? If you know the goal, you can more easily understand the reactions.

✔ QUICK CHECK

What are the three basic types of chemical reactions?

_____

_____

● Answer: The three basic chemical reactions are synthesis, decomposition, and exchange.

▷ The Big Bang: Chemistry and Energy

We briefly discussed the importance of energy, which is the ability to do work. Because our energy comes from what we eat (chemicals) it's appropriate to end with this topic. Energy comes in many forms, such as mechanical, electric, solar, and nuclear. All types can be categorized as either kinetic or potential. **Kinetic energy** is energy that's in use—it's the energy of action, or the energy used to do work. **Potential energy** is energy waiting to be used—it's not doing work at the moment but has the *potential* to do work. It's like stored energy.

We previously defined *metabolism* as all the work going on in your body. Even when you're asleep, your body is very busy—your heart beats, you breathe, your brain controls the processes that keep you alive, for example. Such activities require energy, and you need a supply available at all times. Energy can't be created or destroyed—it can only change from one form to another. That means we have to get our energy from somewhere, but we can use only **chemical energy**. Recall that we rely on plants to change solar energy (sunlight) to chemical energy through photosynthesis, creating carbohydrates that store this energy. We eat the plants, or

animals that ate them, to get chemical energy. All foods store energy in the chemical bonds that hold them together.

To use energy from our foods, we extract it from our foods then store it in a molecule called **adenosine triphosphate, or ATP.** All living organisms rely on ATP for their energy needs—it's universal. ATP is often referred to as our energy currency—to do work, we have to "spend" ATP. We do this by breaking a bond in the ATP and releasing the energy we stored there. We need a lot of ATP at all times, and we need to constantly make more to keep going. We do this primarily through a complex series of chemical reactions collectively called *cellular respiration.*

It's appropriate that chemistry occupies the first three levels of the biological hierarchy of organization. Chemistry is the foundation of all living organisms.

Our existence requires both organic and inorganic substances. These chemicals are constantly reacting, forming new bonds and breaking old ones, and they account for virtually everything you do and you are. Atoms and molecules are the very stuff of life, and the reactions between them are the processes of life. I hope now you can see that to achieve success in anatomy and physiology, chemistry truly does matter.

▷ Final Stretch!

Now that you have finished reading this chapter, it is time to stretch your brain a bit and check how much you learned. For online tests, tutorials, animations, activities, web links, and an ebook, visit the *Get Ready for A&P* companion website.

Running Words

At the end of each chapter, be sure you have learned the language. Here are the terms introduced in this chapter with which you should be familiar. Write them in a notebook or enter them in your computer. Define them in your own words, then go back through the chapter to check your meaning, correcting as needed. Also try to list examples when appropriate.

- Matter
- Mass
- Weight
- Volume
- Element
- Atom
- Molecule
- Macromolecule
- Subatomic particle
- Proton
- Neutron
- Electron
- Nucleus
- Orbital
- Shell
- Atomic number
- Mass Number
- Atomic Mass Unit
- Isotope
- Atomic Mass
- Atomic Weight
- Periodic Table of Elements
- Period
- Group
- Chemical bonding
- Valence shell
- Inert
- Ion
- Ionic bond
- Covalent bond
- Polarity
- Polar Covalent Bond
- Nonpolar Covalent Bond
- Hydrogen bond

- Molecule
- Compound
- Molecular formula
- Structural formula
- Solution
- Solute
- Solvent
- Electrolyte
- Acid
- Base
- Salt
- pH
- pH scale
- Organic compound
- Inorganic compound
- Carbohydrate
- Monomer
- Polymer
- Monosaccharide
- Disaccharide
- Polysaccharide
- Lipid
- Fat
- Triglyceride
- Protein
- Amino acid
- Enzyme
- Nucleic acid
- DNA
- RNA
- Nucleotide
- Chemical equation
- Reactant
- Product

- Reversible reaction
- Synthesis reaction
- Anabolic reaction
- Dehydration synthesis
- Decomposition reaction
- Catabolic reaction
- Hydrolysis
- Exchange reaction
- Kinetic energy
- Potential energy
- Adenosine triphosphate (ATP)

What Did You Learn?

Part A: Provide the missing information. Consult the Periodic Table, Figure 18.3.

	Potassium	Iodine	Oxygen	Neon
Chemical symbol	_____	_____	_____	_____
Atomic number	_____	_____	_____	_____
Atomic weight	_____	_____	_____	_____
Number of protons	_____	_____	_____	_____
Number of electrons	_____	_____	_____	_____
Number of neutrons	_____	_____	_____	_____
Number of electrons in outermost shell	_____	_____	_____	_____

Part B: Answer the following questions.

1. Which subatomic particles are always in the nucleus?

   _____

2. Which subatomic particles are not included in the atomic weight?

   _____

3. What are the four main elements that make up most of the human body?

   _____

   _____

4. In the Periodic Table, what does the row (period) in which an element is positioned tell you about that element?

   _____

5. What does the element's column in the Periodic Table tell you?

   _____

   _____

6. A calcium ion has a +2 electrical charge. How did this ion form to give it that charge?

   _____

7. What is the basic difference between an ionic bond and a covalent bond?

   _____

8. Which gives you the most information: a molecular formula or a structural formula?

   _____

9. When you eat, the food is converted into small, simple molecules that can be absorbed into your blood. What type of chemical reactions does that involve?

   _____

10. If you get a paper cut, what type of chemical reactions will allow your skin to repair itself?

    _____

11. What elements are always found in organic molecules?

    _____

12. For each of the following, is the compound organic (O) or inorganic (I)?

    $C_6H_{12}O_6$ _____ CO_2 _____

    CH_4 _____ CO _____

    HCl _____ H_2O _____

13. What are the monomers of carbohydrates and of proteins?

    _____

14. Enzymes are examples of which type of organic compound?

    _____

15. What molecule do we use directly to supply energy for our cells' work?

    _____

19 Cell Biology: *Life's Little Factories*

When you complete this chapter, you should be able to:

- Explain the Cell Theory.

- Distinguish between prokaryotic and eukaryotic cells.

- Describe the structures and functions of the cell membrane and cell organelles.

- Explain various movement processes that occur in cells.

- Describe the complete cell cycle and the basics of cell reproduction.

▷ Your Starting Point

Answer the following questions to assess your knowledge about cells.

1. Give an example of a prokaryotic cell.

    _____

2. The liquid located between a cell's membrane and its nucleus is called

    _____

3. Another word for *single-celled* is _____.

    _____

4. What types of molecules make up the cell membrane?

    _____

5. What is the function of a ribosome? _____

    _____

6. Where in a cell would you find the genes that determine your eye color? _____

7. What kind of molecules can easily pass through a cell membrane?_____

8. What is *diffusion*? _____

    _____

9. What moves during *osmosis*? _____

    _____

10. What happens during *mitosis*? _____

    _____

● Answers: 1. Bacteria. 2. Cytoplasm or cytosol. 3. Unicellular. 4. Phospholipids, proteins, cholesterol, and some carbohydrates. 5. Build proteins. 6. In the DNA in the nucleus. 7. Lipid-soluble molecules. 8. Movement of molecules from an area of higher concentration to an area of lower concentration. 9. Water. 10. The nuclear contents divide.

▷ Good Things Come in Small Packages: Cell Theory

In the last chapter, we explored chemistry and the first few levels of the Biological Hierarchy of Organization: atoms, molecules, and macromolecules. In this chapter, we continue our climb up the ladder (**Figure 19.1**) as we explore the next two levels: organelles and cells, which are where most of the chemistry occurs in our bodies. This chapter's focus is **cytology**, which is the study of cells (*cyto-* = cell, *-ology* = study of).

In the 1600s, while examining slices of cork with a microscope, English naturalist Robert Hooke noticed that the cork was made of tiny chambers that reminded him of the cells in which monks lived in a monastery. From this observation, he coined the term **cell,** from the Latin word *cella,* meaning "storeroom" or "small container." Since then, vast amounts of cellular research have led to and continue to support a set of conclusions that are collectively referred to as the **Cell Theory**. Most sources acknowledge at least three major parts to this theory and some list as many as seven, so don't be surprised to see variation—all of these ideas are closely related. We shall consider the following five main principles:

1. All organisms are composed of one or more cells.
2. Cells are the basic structural and functional units of life.
3. All vital functions of an organism occur within cells.
4. All cells come from preexisting cells.
5. Cells contain hereditary information that regulates cell functions and is passed from generation to generation.

All organisms are composed of one or more cells. Some organisms are merely a single cell and are called **unicellular** organisms (*uni* = one). Organisms made of two or more cells are called **multicellular**. Whether the organism is a bacterium, fungus, plant, or animal (like you), it is made of cells, and the cells of all these organisms show tremendous diversity. Cells come in many different shapes, sizes, and types. In fact, we humans have over 200 different types of cells in our bodies (**Figure 19.2**). Red blood cells, or erythrocytes, are among our tiniest cells, measuring only about 2 μm thick and 7 μm in diameter. (Recall that a micrometer is only 1/1000 of a millimeter.) At the other end of the spectrum, a single neuron (nerve cell) may be up to a meter long! Sperm are minute compared to the ova that they fertilize. Yet, all of the diverse cells found in all organisms share striking similarities.

Cells are the basic structural and functional units of life. Cells are certainly the basic structural units—all organisms are built from them. But cells are also the functional units of life. Housed within its single cell, a unicellular organism has all of the structures and the processes necessary to keep itself alive. Similarly, each cell in a multicellular organism, such as you or me, is an independent living unit capable of maintaining itself. It takes in nutrients, uses them to make the molecules it needs to function, and harnesses energy for doing its work. While going about its daily business, the cell generates and also rids itself of waste. And, in most cases, it reproduces.

All vital functions of an organism occur within cells. Because each individual cell is alive and carries on all of its

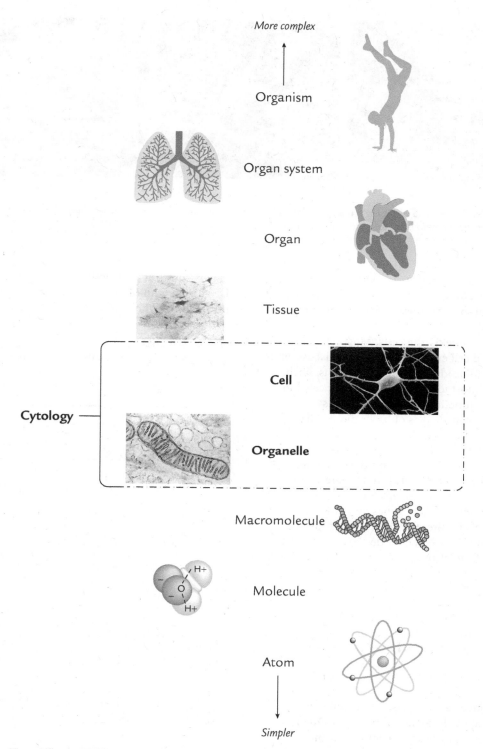

More complex

Organism

Organ system

Organ

Tissue

Cytology

Cell

Organelle

Macromolecule

Molecule

Atom

Simpler

▲ **Figure 19.1** **Moving up the Biological Hierarchy of Organization,** we explore the organelle and cell, both covered in the discipline of cytology.

own life processes, it is no surprise that these same vital functions carried out at the higher levels of organization are still done by the cells. As you move up the ladder of complexity, life processes are performed within and around the cells. But as more cells are added, more organization is required to meet their collective demands. As organisms increase in size and complexity, cells become more specialized and join together to share functions, forming tissues and eventually organs. For example, your digestive system brings in adequate nutrients for all of your cells, and your circulatory system ensures that all of your cells are well-serviced and able to communicate with each other. While your cells perform their highly specialized functions in complex organ systems, your nervous system carefully choreographs them. All the specializations in

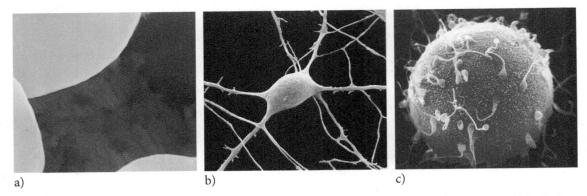

▲ **Figure 19.2** **Human cells come in a variety of types and sizes. a)** This scanning electron micrograph clearly shows that red blood cells are biconcave disks. **b)** A nerve cell (neuron) has numerous cell extensions that can be quite long, as shown in this scanning electron micrograph. **c)** A human ovum (egg cell) is covered by very tiny sperm cells at fertilization.

structure and organization keep your individual cells alive and functioning in a highly efficient and synchronized manner, while the cells go about their business of life, maintaining not only themselves, but also you.

All cells come from preexisting cells. Most cells can reproduce. The normal cell cycle, which we will discuss, ends with the cell dividing to produce two daughter cells. Each of the daughter cells is almost identical to the parent cell and will quickly take on its function. So our body parts are constantly being replenished as old cells die. Similarly, cells divide to replace other cells that may be lost during an injury.

Cells contain hereditary information that regulates cell functions and is passed from generation to generation. Inside each of your cells is the blueprint for life—the DNA that houses your cells' genes. These genes determine what work your cells will do, and these instructions for life are passed on with reproduction. Not only do the cells divide, but the organism itself can also reproduce through combining special cells. Gametes—ova in females and sperm in

males—unite at fertilization, yielding a new combination of DNA from both Mom and Dad, and producing a new offspring in which the whole process of life begins anew at many levels.

✔ **QUICK CHECK**

What are five principles that make up the Cell Theory?

_____

_____

_____

_____

_____

● **Answer:** All organisms are composed of one or more cells. Cells are the basic structural and functional units of life. All vital functions of an organism occur within cells. All cells come from preexisting cells. Cells contain the hereditary information needed to regulate cell functions and it is passed on to the next generation of cells.

▷ A Cell by Any Other Name . . . Prokaryotes and Eukaryotes

As mentioned earlier, cells can be quite diverse. Even within the human body we see tremendous variation in cell form, so imagine how much variety there is if we consider all living organisms! For example, plant cells have rigid cell walls and green chloroplasts, neither of which is found in humans. Despite this tremendous variation, all cells share at least three common characteristics:

1. They are enclosed in an outer **cell membrane,** which separates their internal environment from the external environment.

2. They are filled with **cytoplasm,** which is a mixture of substances and structures in a liquid (cytosol).

3. They contain deoxyribonucleic acid (**DNA**), which is the cell's genetic material.

Because cells come in many forms, there are many ways to classify them. One classification considers the basic organization of a cell's internal structure. All cells are either **prokaryotes** or **eukaryotes** (**Figure 19.3**). *Pro-* means before and *karyo-* means "*nucleus,*" so the term prokaryote means "before the nucleus." Prokaryotic cells lack internal membranes so, indeed, they don't have an enclosed nucleus. Instead, their DNA exists mostly in a loop and the area in which it tends to be located (but not enclosed) is referred to as the **nucleoid**. Additional DNA may be present in small loops, called **plasmids**, that can be transferred to other cells.

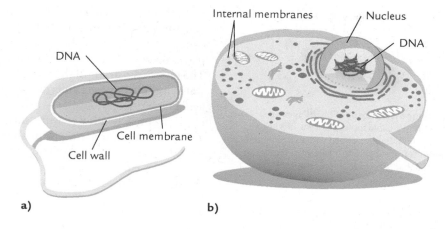

▲ **Figure 19.3   Cells are classified as either prokaryotic or eukaryotic. a)** Prokaryotes lack internal membranes and have no nucleus. **b)** Eukaryotes have both.

Prokaryotes also lack most other internal cellular structures found in eukaryotes. Although these cells appear primitive, they remain all around us—all bacteria are prokaryotes.

Why Should I Care?

Although the human body is composed entirely of eukaryotic cells, prokaryotes are also important. Some bacteria enter our bodies through the foods we eat and take up residence in our colons (large intestines), where they live off our dietary leftovers. While consuming these materials, the bacteria actually produce vitamins that we use. They also, unfortunately, release methane gas in our guts that can cause us to be uncomfortable or, if it escapes, perhaps a bit embarrassed! Other bacteria can cause infection and illness if they enter our systems.

The cells of the human body are all eukaryotic cells, or eukaryotes. The name comes from Latin: *eu-* means "true" and these cells have a true nucleus. The nucleus is a membrane-bound structure that houses the cell's DNA,

keeping it localized. The cytoplasm in eukaryotes also has other structures with specialized jobs. Collectively these structures—the functional parts inside the cell—are called **organelles**. Some of these organelles are built from membranes; others are not. All eukaryotes contain some of the same organelles, but specialized cells often have unique features as well.

All human cells are eukaryotic cells. ■

✔ QUICK CHECK

In which type of cell would you find a nucleoid, and how is it different from what would be present in the other type of cell?

_____

_____

_____

that encloses their DNA.
DNA loop is located. Eukaryotic cells, instead, have a membrane-bound nucleus
Answer: A nucleoid is found only in prokaryotic cells and it is where the
● **Answer:** A nucleoid is found only in prokaryotic cells and it is where the DNA loop is located. Eukaryotic cells, instead, have a membrane-bound nucleus that encloses their DNA.

▷ Paper or Plastic, Ma'am? The Cell Membrane

Your cells have certain requirements that must be met for them to give their peak performance. For example, they need the right amount of fluid, nutrients, water, and oxygen. Recall that **homeostasis** means maintaining a relatively constant internal environment (which you can think of as optimal working conditions). Doing so is not always easy.

One feature that helps achieve the goal of homeostasis is the cell membrane, also called the **plasma membrane**. It is simultaneously a container that holds a cell together and a physical partition that separates the cell's inside world from the outside, making it easier to maintain constancy inside.

The heading of this section, "Paper or Plastic," conjures up the image of a grocery sack. That image works for the concept of the cell membrane as a physical separation between the cell's inside and outside worlds. Clearly, this separation makes it easier to maintain homeostasis inside the cell even if conditions outside the cell vary.

But if the membrane was truly like an actual sack and formed a complete barrier, nutrients could not enter your cells, nor could wastes and products manufactured by your cells leave. Thus, the cell membrane must have unique characteristics that allow some materials to pass through while blocking others.

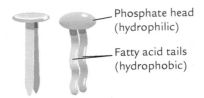

Phosphate head
(hydrophilic)

Fatty acid tails
(hydrophobic)

▲ **Figure 19.4** **The cell membrane is a phospholipid bilayer.** To understand the organization of a phospholipid molecule, think of a brass brad that is used to hold paper together. There is a head with two long parts hanging off of it. The head represents the phosphate "head" of our molecule, which is hydrophilic. The prongs that hang down represent the lipid "tails," which are hydrophobic.

The cell membrane is made primarily of **phospholipid** molecules. These molecules have phosphorous and other atoms at one end, forming what is called the **phosphate head**. This portion of the molecule is polar, or **hydrophilic**. Look back to the word root and suffix tables. What does hydrophilic mean? _____

_____

Attached to one side of the phosphate head are two longer molecules called **fatty acid tails**. These tails are the main reason that the molecule is a lipid, and you should recall from the last chapter that lipids are nonpolar, or **hydrophobic**. What does that mean? _____

_____

To envision how a phospholipid molecule is organized, think about a brass brad—an old-fashioned paper fastener you likely used in school when you were young or that may even be built into some of your folders now (**Figure 19.4**).

Time to Try

Let's figure out how phospholipid molecules arrange in a cell membrane.

1. What happens when a lipid comes into contact with water? Fill a clear container about 2/3 full of water. Watching closely, add 1/2 teaspoon of cooking oil. Describe what happens when the oil first enters the water, and where it ends.

_____

2. Cover half of a slice of bread with a thick layer of peanut butter, which has a very high fat (lipid) content. Gently place a drop of water on the bare bread. What happens? _____

_____

Place a drop of water on the peanut butter. What happens?

_____

How do these observations relate to the organization of phospholipids in a cell membrane? _____

Realize that a cell has an inside and an outside, and both contain water. In humans, the space outside of your cells contains extracellular fluid that is mostly water. The cytoplasm inside your cells also contains large amounts of water. The phosphate heads of the phospholipids interact fine with water, but the opposite ends of the molecules—the fatty acid tails—do not. As you saw when you placed oil in water, lipids in contact with water first form a ball, then settle into a single layer at the surface with one side in contact with the air, not water. In a cell, though, both surfaces are in contact with water. How can the phospholipid molecules arrange themselves so the fatty acid tails don't contact water?

_____

Think about that partial peanut butter sandwich you made earlier. You should have seen the water readily enter the bare part of the bread, but ball up on the peanut butter. How could you organize bread and peanut butter in such a way that there are two major surfaces, or sides, and water will not be repelled from either one? _____

_____

I hope you guessed it—you have likely eaten it plenty of times. Consider the basic peanut butter sandwich. Assume you made it with two slices of bread, each smeared with a thick layer of peanut butter, then sandwiched together. You would have bread on both sides of the sandwich and peanut butter in the middle—two layers of it facing each other. This is the basic structure of the **phospholipid bilayer** (*bilayer* = two layers). The hydrophilic phosphate heads (bread) are arranged in two layers so that they face the water in the extracellular fluid and in the cytoplasm. The hydrophobic tails (peanut butter) are sandwiched in the middle, out of contact with the water. This is how the cell membrane is organized (**Figure 19.5**).

But cell membranes don't contain only phospholipids—there are other molecules as well. Cell membranes contain cholesterol molecules, for example, which help stabilize the membrane. Some carbohydrate molecules act as labels that allow your cells to recognize other cells, such as when sperm are trying to locate an ovum for fertilization or when your immune system is destroying foreign invaders to keep you healthy. These are but a few examples.

Cell membranes also contain assorted proteins. Some of these proteins form channels that act like tunnels that allow certain molecules to pass through the membrane. Other proteins might be carriers that pull various molecules through the membrane. The combination of phospholipid molecules and specialized protein channels and carriers determines what can and cannot pass through the cell membrane. Because not everything can pass through, the cell membrane is said to be **selectively permeable**—its chemical composition restricts the movement of some substances, so it is selective about what can pass through.

All of these assorted molecules are positioned throughout the cell membrane in what can be thought of as a sea of phospholipid molecules (see Figure 19.5). Imagine a child's pool filled with water, and floating in it are toy boats,

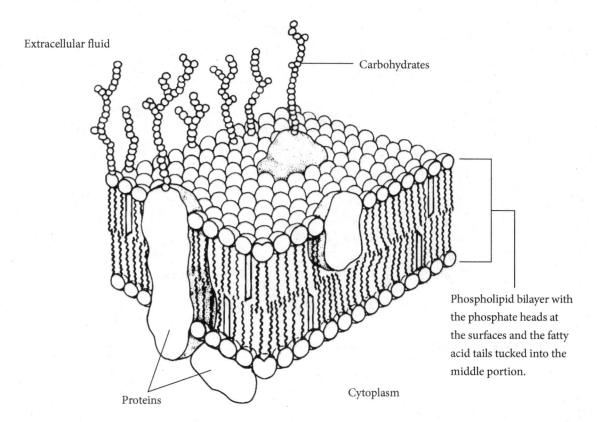

Extracellular fluid

Carbohydrates

Phospholipid bilayer with the phosphate heads at the surfaces and the fatty acid tails tucked into the middle portion.

Proteins

Cytoplasm

▲ Figure 19.5   **Organization of the cell membrane.** The phospholipid molecules are organized into a bilayer in which other molecules are embedded.

inflatable toys, and a few children. The objects are free to move around in the water, and in fact they do. This is the nature of the cell membrane. This model, known as the **fluid mosaic model**, reveals a cell membrane that is very dynamic, moving, changing, and fluid in nature.

 The cell membrane is composed of a phospholipid bilayer but also contains other molecules, and it is a very active structure. ■

Just for Fun

 Borrow a child's bottle of bubbles or, if no child is available, fashion your own wand by making a loop

out of a large paperclip or a length of wire—those twisty ties for garbage bags work well. Make your own bubble solution by mixing some liquid dishwashing soap in a bowl or cup of water. Now, blow! Be sure there is plenty of overhead light as you observe the bubbles. Notice how the colors on the wall of a bubble constantly swirl around and change. This is the way the cell membrane is—constantly in motion and changing. See why it is wrong to think of it as just a sack?

▷ What Department Are You With? Cell Organelles

 Eukaryotic cells contain cytoplasm and a nucleus. The cytoplasm fills the space between the cell membrane and the nucleus. The liquid part of the cytoplasm is called **cytosol**, and it contains many dissolved substances, such as nutrients. It is a rather thick fluid in which numerous cell structures are suspended.

Recall that a typical cell has all the structures and does all the work needed to maintain life. Eukaryotic cells divide the

labor among different specialized structures called organelles, each with a particular job. To understand this, think about a factory in which some product is manufactured. Inside this factory are many different departments, all involved in some way to make sure the factory is working properly and that the product is made and delivered. In a cell, the departments are the organelles. Although each has its own particular task, all organelles are coordinated and work together. Figure 19.6 illustrates the main structures of a cell.

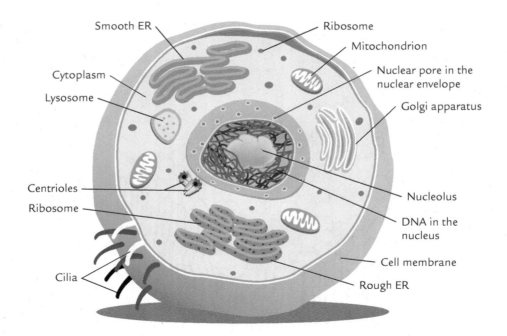

Smooth ER
Cytoplasm
Lysosome
Centrioles
Ribosome
Cilia

Ribosome
Mitochondrion
Nuclear pore in the nuclear envelope
Golgi apparatus
Nucleolus
DNA in the nucleus
Cell membrane
Rough ER

▲ Figure 19.6   **A composite eukaryotic cell showing the major organelles.**

The Nucleus

The **nucleus** is the largest organelle and it really has one specific task: it houses the DNA that contains your genes. Each gene is essentially the instructions for how to make a specific protein. All cells in your body contain two copies of each of your genes—one from Mom and one from Dad. The only exceptions to this are your sex cells—ova or sperm—which contain only one copy of each of your genes. This copy will combine with a second copy from your partner if conception occurs. Your DNA is organized into threadlike strands, called **chromatin**, that condense into rodlike structures called **chromosomes** when the cell reproduces (more about this later).

Your DNA determines what proteins can be made in your body, but only certain proteins are made by each of your cells. For example, the cells on your elbow don't usually grow moustaches, but those on your face might! The genes are activated and deactivated within the nucleus based on many different factors, and the activation determines the cell's productivity. Thus, in your cell "factory," the office is the nucleus where the boss—your DNA—determines what needs to be done.

The nucleus is enclosed in a **nuclear envelope** made of a double membrane, each of which is similar to the cell membrane. This envelope is pierced periodically by holes called **nuclear pores** that make it more permeable than the cell membrane, allowing larger molecules to pass through. This is important because the instructions—the genes—never leave the nucleus. To get the daily work assignment, a memo is sent out to the workers—the boss does not come to them. Inside the nuclear membrane is a jellylike liquid called the **nucleoplasm**, which is similar to the cytoplasm.

✔ QUICK CHECK

What is the main function of the nucleus? _____

_____

 DNA is your genetic material and it determines what proteins your cells can make. ■

◉ Answer: The nucleus houses the DNA.

The Ribosome and Protein Synthesis

The DNA in the cell's nucleus has the instructions for all proteins that will be made in the cell, but the proteins are not manufactured in the boss's office. A separate cellular department—a tiny organelle called the **ribosome**—is responsible for assembling the protein during a process called **protein synthesis**. You can think of a ribosome as

being the work bench on which the protein is built, rather similar to an assembly line. The workers who build the proteins there are called **RNA**, which stands for **ribonucleic acid**.

The instructions or work assignments from the boss—the DNA in the nucleus—are carried to the ribosome by a special worker, a molecule called **messenger RNA (mRNA)**. The mRNA carries the work assignment *to* the assembly line. Another worker, a type of RNA called **ribosomal RNA (rRNA)**, is always *at* the assembly line—it is part of the ribosome. This RNA is actually made inside the nucleus at a structure called the **nucleolus**, and it leaves the nucleus through those large nuclear pores.

Once the mRNA delivers the work order from the DNA to the ribosome, the specific proteins are made at the ribosome by linking together small molecules called amino acids, which you should recall from Chapter 18. The amino acids are carried to the ribosomal assembly line by other workers called **transfer RNA (tRNA)**, then assembled according to the DNA's instructions. RNA's job is to build the protein the DNA tells it to make. One type of RNA carries DNA's instructions to the ribosome, and the other two types of RNA are directly involved in building the protein according to those specifications.

The Endoplasmic Reticulum

Some ribosomes are free to float around the cytoplasm; others are attached to yet another organelle called the **endoplasmic reticulum**, or **ER**. The ER is an extensive network of membranous tubes and channels inside the cell. Ribosomes look like tiny dots, so when they are attached to the ER they give it a rough appearance; thus it is called rough ER. The presence of ribosomes tells you that at least part of rough ER's job is protein synthesis. Smooth ER lacks ribosomes. Instead of making proteins, it is involved in making other materials (like lipids), detoxifying potentially harmful substances, and transporting materials around the cell.

You can think of the ER partly as being like a system of workers who are always passing through various hallways, moving materials from one work station to another, and throughout the factory. Because the ER connects different parts of the cell, it also provides a communication network within the cell. Materials are brought into this system, moved around, changed, and turned into raw, rough product here.

Golgi Apparatus

The **Golgi apparatus** looks like a stack of flattened membranous sacs. This is the processing, packaging, and shipping department in our cells. Products that have been made elsewhere in the cell, such as at the ribosomes or in the ER, are sent here to be finished. They are modified and put into their final forms. They are slapped with a molecular "shipping label"—a chemical tag that determines where they will go. They are packaged in some membrane that pinches off of the Golgi and surrounds the product, forming a saclike structure called a **vesicle**. Finally the products are shipped, some to other parts of the cell, some to the cell membrane, and some out to the great extracellular world beyond.

✔ **QUICK CHECK**

1. Where in a eukaryotic cell would you find ribosomes?

_____

2. What is the functional relationship between the nucleus, nucleolus, ribosome, rough endoplasmic reticulum, and Golgi apparatus? _____

_____

_____

_____

● Answers: 1. Free-floating in the cytoplasm or attached to endoplasmic reticulum. 2. The nucleus houses DNA that has instructions for how to build proteins. Proteins are built at the ribosome, part of which is made in the nucleolus inside the nucleus. Many ribosomes are located on the rough ER. Proteins made at the ribosomes move into the Golgi apparatus to be processed, packaged, and shipped to their final destinations.

The Mitochondrion

If your factory is to do its work 24/7, it needs a good power source. The **mitochondrion** is your cell's powerhouse. It provides a constant supply of energy to drive the work being done throughout the cell. As discussed in Chapter 18, cellular energy comes from the foods we eat, where it is stored in the chemical bonds that hold the food's atoms together. Specialized chemical reactions in the mitochondria harness that energy and store it in a molecule called **ATP**— denosine rihosphate (see why we call it ATP?). All cells, in any organism, use ATP directly for energy. Think of it as the electricity that powers our cells. The more work a cell is doing, the more ATP it needs, and the more mitochondria it will have.

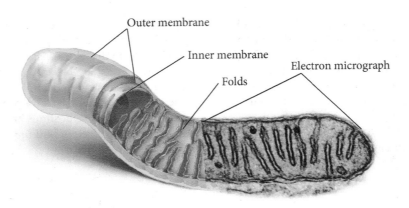

Outer membrane

Inner membrane

Electron micrograph

Folds

▲ Figure 19.7   **A mitochondrion.** This illustration includes a drawing (left) blended into an actual electron micrograph (right).

Mitochondria are unique organelles (Figure 19.7). They contain their own genetic information and can reproduce. These elongated organelles are enclosed by a double membrane, similar to the nuclear membrane. The outer membrane is smooth, but the inner membrane is highly folded. In general, such folding occurs to increase the surface area of the membrane, and increasing the surface area is the same as increasing the workspace. It is rather like expanding a department.

Lysosomes

While the organelles are doing all this hard work in your cellular factories, they need some assistance in keeping their workplace tidy. **Lysosomes** are your cell's janitorial staff. A lysosome is a small membranous bag containing strong digestive enzymes. Its main job is to break down materials. Some materials are brought into your cell and digested to provide basic building materials for your cell to use in its work. Other materials may be old, worn out cell parts or foreign material that invades your cells. Lysosomes destroy these items so they neither harm nor clutter your cell's interior. A lysosome's job is to recycle what it can and get rid of the remaining garbage.

Peroxisomes

If lysosomes are your cell's janitorial staff, **peroxisomes** are its hazardous waste disposal team. Peroxisomes break down organic compounds, such as fatty acids, whose breakdown produces hydrogen peroxide (H_2O_2). You're probably familiar with the bubbling that H_2O_2 causes when you use it to disinfect a wound. That demonstrates its high reactivity—it could do a lot of damage to your cells. Instead, the peroxisome conducts its work inside its own membrane and, conveniently, contains enzymes that break down the H_2O_2, rendering it and other chemicals harmless to your cell. How's that for service?

The Cytoskeleton

Remember that all of this work is going on inside your cells, in a liquid environment. The "building" needs a frame to hold it up. We discussed the outer partition—the cell membrane. But we need something inside to hold the membrane out so the cell does not collapse on itself. The **cytoskeleton** is composed mostly of tiny tubes (**microtubules**) and filaments (**microfilaments**). These structures form a type of scaffolding that supports the cell and to which various organelles are attached. Although the name sounds like this structure is made of bone, the cytoskeleton is actually made of proteins. You can think of them as being the struts and beams that hold up the building, or cell.

Cell Movement: Centrioles, Cilia, and Flagella

We have discussed how materials can move through a cell. But there are other movements associated with a cell, too. An area of the cell called the **centrosome** ("central body") is composed of paired cylindrical structures made of microtubules. These structures are called **centrioles**. They direct the movement of the chromosomes when a cell reproduces, as we will discuss shortly, but they also form part of two other structures involved in cell movement: cilia and flagella.

Cilia look like fringe on a cell. Not all cells have cilia, but the ones that do have several. They are extensions of the cell and they are mobile. Cilia are coordinated so that they tend to move in a wavelike manner. Cilia sweep materials over the outer surface of a cell, moving materials past the cell. For example, cilia in your respiratory tract help clear debris so it doesn't clog the air sacs where oxygen enters your blood.

Why Should I Care?

Cigarette smoke paralyzes the respiratory cilia for about an hour per cigarette. During that time, they cannot prevent the particulate material that we breathe in from reaching the lungs. Over time, more of this material clogs the small air sacs and begins to damage them. People who experience this must cough, especially upon arising in the morning, to try to clear the material that has accumulated in their lungs. This is the basis of *smoker's cough*.

Picture This

Imagine you are at the "big game" and the crowd is tossing a beach ball around. As this is going on, off in the distance you see the crowd start a "wave," where they stand and wave their arms overhead, then sit, group by group, all around the stadium. The wave approaches you just as the beach ball is heading your way. The wave passes you and so does the beach ball. It was carried away on the wave and you see it now making its way around the stadium, riding the wave. This is how cilia move materials across the surface of the cell—they beat in a coordinated manner, sweeping materials along.

In contrast to the cilia, a **flagellum** is a single, long, tail-like extension of the cell. In humans, these are found only on sperm cells. A flagellum whips back and forth to propel the sperm through the male reproductive tract and up into the female's tract in search of an ovum to fertilize.

We have reviewed the organelles of a typical eukaryotic cell, like our human cells. You will learn more detailed descriptions of these structures and their jobs as you proceed in your A & P course. For now, you should have a general understanding that will give you a knowledge base from which to work. Table 19.1 summarizes the organelles we have discussed and provides a quick review.

TABLE 19.1   SUMMARY OF CELL ORGANELLES AND STRUCTURES.

Organelle	Description	Function
Nucleus	Rounded larger membranous sac with pores.	Houses the DNA that directs cellular activities.
Chromatin	Relaxed strands of DNA in the nucleus.	Contain genes that determine what proteins can be made in the cell.
Ribosome	Small nonmembranous structure free in the cytoplasm or attached to ER.	Protein synthesis.
Nucleolus	Small body located in the nucleus.	Makes part of a ribosome.
Endoplasmic reticulum (ER)	Extensive network of membranous tubes and channels.	Protein synthesis (rough ER); lipid synthesis (smooth ER); detoxification; communication and transport system.
Golgi apparatus	Flattened stack of membranous sacs.	Processing, packaging, and shipping of cellular products.
Mitochondrion	Elongated membranous structure with highly folded internal membrane.	Powerhouse; harnesses energy from food molecules and stores it in ATP.
Lysosome	Small membranous sac.	Breakdown of unwanted materials; recycling of molecules.
Peroxisome	Small membranous sac.	Breaks down organic compounds and neutralizes H_2O_2 created in the process.
Cytoskeleton	Meshwork of microtubules and microfilaments.	Provides support and structure to the cell interior; anchors organelles.
Centrioles	Cylindrical structures made of microtubules.	Direct movement of chromosomes during cell reproduction; form part of cilia and flagella.
Cilia	Small, numerous, hairlike processes that beat in a wave.	Sweep materials over the surface of the cell membrane.
Flagellum	A single whiplike tail.	Propels the cell forward.
Vesicle	Small membranous sac.	Contains materials entering or leaving a cell.

1. Flagella use tremendous amounts of energy to propel the cell forward. Which organelle would you expect to see in large numbers near the very busy flagellum? _____

_____

2. How do the movements of cilia and flagella differ? _____

_____

_____

▷ Tunnels and Doorways: Movement Processes

Atoms and molecules are always moving, both inside and outside the cell. Cell products packaged at the Golgi apparatus are shipped out of the cell to travel elsewhere in the body. Nutrients and building blocks are moved in from the outside. Waste products must leave. Let's examine how some of these movements occur.

Brownian Motion

Atoms and molecules constantly move in a random manner called **Brownian motion**. This is a rather nondirectional, jiggling movement. Remember those bumper cars we had fun with before? If you're in a car and someone hits you, their car bounces off in a new direction, while your car careens off in yet another. This is similar to how atoms and molecules move. Because they are constantly in motion, you can imagine how particles bump into each other and ricochet away.

Concentration Gradients and Equilibrium

Although Brownian motion is random, other movement processes are not. Before we discuss these movements, though, we need to understand the concepts of concentration gradients and equilibrium. You can think of concentration as referring to how crowded together molecules are—the more crowded they are, the more concentrated they are. A **concentration gradient** exists whenever there is a difference between the concentrations of the molecules in two areas (**Figure 19.8a**). Perhaps your vehicle has gradient glass in its windshield—it is tinted with more color at the top than at the bottom, which means there is a *gradient* in the color.

If, instead, there is about equal space between all of the molecules, we say they are at **equilibrium** (**Figure 19.8b**). Think about standing in an elevator. If there are only two of you on the elevator, you likely stand at opposite sides. Add two more people and you likely stand one in each corner with about equal distance between yourselves. As you add more and more people to the elevator, you become more closely crowded and are more likely to bump into each other. And if you do collide, you respond by moving away, always trying to maximize your personal space. That is how atoms and molecules move, but not by conscious decision. They move by basic laws of science. Let's explore how.

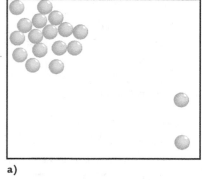 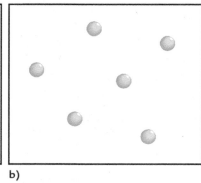

a) b)

▲ **Figure 19.8** **a)** A concentration gradient exists when there is a difference in the concentration, or spacing, around molecules in two different areas. **b)** Equilibrium exists when the molecules are spaced about evenly.

Simple Diffusion

One basic type of molecular movement is **simple diffusion**. This is how oxygen enters your cells and carbon dioxide leaves them, for example, and it is critical for sustaining life. Simple diffusion occurs when molecules move from an area of higher concentration to an area of lower concentration. In other words, they move from where they are more crowded to where they have more room. Think of it simply as the molecules spreading out. Whenever there is a concentration gradient, molecules will spontaneously move *down the concentration gradient*—that means they move from where they are most concentrated, or crowded, to where they are least crowded. You are already familiar with diffusion. Consider, for example, baking brownies. The molecules that produce the yummy smell quickly diffuse through the air in your house so that any visitors know you have a treat to share!

With individual molecules the motion is random but, like people in an elevator, the more molecules that are present in an area, the more likely it is that they will bump into each other and bounce away. There will be more collisions in an area where the molecules are more crowded, sending them skidding off. They will ricochet less as they move into areas where there are fewer molecules to bounce off of. In time the molecules, like the people on the elevator, will have moved around enough to have almost equal distance between them. This is equilibrium. However, unlike the people on the elevator carefully maintaining their positions, molecules at equilibrium do not stop. They continue moving, but all molecules experience about the same number of collisions and they maintain a fairly even spacing.

Molecules diffuse at different rates under different conditions. Molecules diffuse faster when there is a greater concentration gradient between the two areas. Molecules in high concentrations diffuse faster than those in lower concentrations. Smaller molecules also move faster than larger molecules, and temperature alters the diffusion rate as well.

Time to Try

 Let's see how temperature affects diffusion. Get three clear glass containers of about the same size. Fill one halfway with very hot water, another with room temperature water, and the third with very cold water. Wait until the water stops moving, then gently add a drop of food coloring to each container. Or you could instead use a tea bag. Now just observe. You should see evidence that the molecules are diffusing—the color should spread out from where it is most concentrated. Eventually you should see the equilibrium state—all of the water should be of uniform color, meaning that the molecules have spread out equally, even though they continue to move.

How did the diffusion rates differ, and why? _____

_____

You should see that increased temperature also increases the diffusion rate. This is because heat makes molecules move faster.

Facilitated Diffusion

Simple diffusion is only one mechanism that allows materials to enter and leave a cell. Only lipid-soluble nonpolar molecules can diffuse directly through the cell membrane. Larger polar molecules, such as glucose (one type of sugar) cannot diffuse through the membrane as easily. Instead, they are moved by a special protein carrier molecule in the cell membrane. The molecules still move from an area of high concentration to one of low concentration, trying to reach

equilibrium. The carrier molecule merely helps, or facilitates, the molecules' movements through the cell membrane. It acts like a special door through which they can pass. This type of diffusion is called **facilitated diffusion**.

 Diffusion is a passive process by which molecules spontaneously move from where they are in high concentration to where they are in low concentration. ▪

Osmosis

Osmosis is a special type of diffusion that is also critical to our survival. It is the diffusion of water through a selectively permeable membrane, such as the cell membrane. We've discussed the lipid nature of the cell membrane, so it seems surprising to

discover that water actually passes through it fairly well. This is partly due to the fluid nature of the molecules in the membrane, but for our purposes the specifics aren't critical. Before proceeding, though, let's recall the basics of solutions.

Let's head to the kitchen. Get a clear drinking glass or measuring cup and fill it about 2/3 full with warm water.

Describe what you see. (Humor me, OK?) _____

_____

Next, get a spoonful of sugar. Describe what you see. _____

_____

Finally, add the sugar to the water and mix it thoroughly. What do you see? _____

This exercise may have seemed silly, but you just made a solution by combining a solute and a solvent. The sugar is the **solute**—the material that gets dissolved. As in our bodies, water is the **solvent**—the material that dissolves the solute. The end result is a **solution**, which is a homogeneous mixture—it should look uniformly clear throughout, because you cannot see the dissolved solute.

To understand the relationship between water and solute molecules, recall that matter is anything that has mass and occupies space, so no two molecules can occupy the same space at the same time. Let's think about that sugar solution you just made. If you started by first putting a half-cup of sugar in the container, there would have been less room left to fill with water. The opposite would also be true—less sugar would allow more water. And it doesn't matter what the solute molecules are—they each take up their own space (**Figure 19.9**). That is why I have adopted, in my own classes, a highly technical term for the various solutes: *stuff*. When we are talking about osmosis through a cell membrane, we must look at the water and the other stuff for a simple reason—the more stuff you have, the less water there can be because the stuff (solute) takes up space that water can no longer occupy.

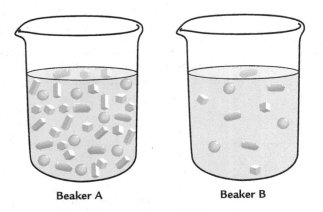

Beaker A   Beaker B

▲ **Figure 19.9** **A solution contains both a solvent, such as water, and solute molecules.** In this illustration, the beakers contain the same amount of solution. The geometric shapes in each solution represent various solute molecules. The remaining shaded space represents the water. Clearly, beaker A, which contains more solute molecules, has less space left for water, but beaker B, with fewer solute molecules, contains more water.

Prove to yourself that when there are more solute molecules in a given space, there must be less solvent, and vice versa. In other words, the more concentrated the solute, the less concentrated the solvent (water). Get a glass measuring cup, then grab a handful of household items—paper clips, coins, marbles, and so on. The only rules are that the objects cannot float and they cannot dissolve (most food items are not good for this reason). We had better add one more rule—they should be waterproof! These objects represent the solute molecules—the stuff—and the water, of course, is the solvent. Drop all of the objects into the cup, then fill it with water to the one-cup mark. Look at the layers of water and objects and note the sizes of each layer. Carefully pour the water into a second container and put it aside. Place the objects on some paper towels, then pour the water back into the cup to measure it. How much water was in the solution? _____

Repeat this procedure, but this time place only about half of the items in the cup before filling it with water to the one-cup mark. Again, pour the water into your second container, remove the objects, then pour the water back into the cup to measure it. How much water did your mock "solution" contain this time?

_____

In which trial did you use more "solute molecules" (objects)?

_____

In which trial did you have the least water? _____

_____

Explain the relationship between the amount of solute molecules and the amount of solvent present in a solution.

_____

_____

Recall that molecules never stop moving, even after reaching equilibrium. Each of your cells has two solutions separated by a selectively permeable membrane—the extracellular fluid outside of the cell and the intracellular fluid inside the cell. These solutions have different compositions. If your cell membranes were fully permeable, all molecules could pass through and move down their concentration gradients until reaching equilibrium, and we would have simple diffusion. But the cell membrane is semipermeable. We know water can pass through the cell membrane rather easily, but many solute molecules can't because of their size or their chemical composition. You also know from your previous activity that there is a higher concentration of water (solvent) wherever there is a lower concentration of other stuff (solute molecules).

Look at **Figure 19.10**. There is a higher concentration of solute molecules inside the cell than there is outside. Assume the solute molecules can't pass through the cell membrane. Now answer these questions:

1. Which fluid contains the lowest concentration of solute molecules?

_____

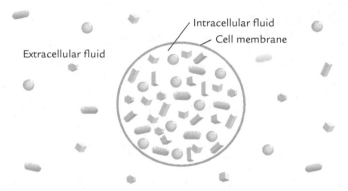

Extracellular fluid

Intracellular fluid

Cell membrane

▲ **Figure 19.10** **The cell membrane separates the extracellular fluid from the intracellular fluid.** In this figure, a situation is shown in which there are more solute molecules inside the cell than there are outside of it. Assume the shaded shapes are solute molecules and the remaining space is filled with water.

2. Which fluid has the highest concentration of water? (Recall that when water is high, solute is low, and vice versa.)

_____

By osmosis, water diffuses—it moves down its concentration gradient—from where it is in higher concentration to where it is in lower concentration. You should see clearly from Figure 19.10 that, in this example, there is a greater concentration of water in the extracellular fluid than there is in the intracellular fluid, so water will enter the cell.

For osmosis, you just need to know where the highest concentration of water is, because it will always move from that area to the area with less concentration. The only reason to consider the other stuff (solute) is because it tells you where the water is—the area with the lower solute concentration has the higher water concentration, so the water will move away from that area.

 Osmosis is diffusion of water through a selectively permeable membrane. ■

What happens to cells when water moves across the cell membrane? **Figure 19.11** shows three views of red blood cells. Figure 19.11a shows a normal red blood cell, shaped like a

biconcave disk. If water leaves a cell, the cell will shrink and the cell won't function efficiently. This is shown in Figure 19.11b. If water moves into a cell, the cell will swell. This is shown in Figure 19.11c. This swelling increases the pressure inside the cell and impedes normal function. In fact, if enough water enters, some cells may rupture.

Picture This

 You are already familiar with water moving into and out of cells and changing their shapes and sizes. Unlike our cells, plant cells are surrounded by a rigid cell wall that helps maintain their shape. Have you ever had a houseplant or a plant in your yard that was a bit wilted and droopy? When the plant cells lose water, they shrink and cannot support the weight of the plant parts above them, so they droop. When they receive water, the cells enlarge, exerting pressure against the rigid cell wall, and this pressure helps support the rest of the plant—it stands back up.

Why Should I Care?

Animal cells lack a cell wall, so they are more likely than plant cells to rupture if they take in too much water. In health care, IV (intravenous) fluids must have the appropriate amount of water—if there is more water in the IV fluid than in the patient's intracellular fluid, his or her cells will swell. If there is less water in the IV fluid, the patient's cells will shrink. Unless the patient is being treated for a fluid imbalance, IV fluids should have the same water concentration as intracellular fluids so the water will be at equilibrium. Such fluids are called *isotonic*. The wrong amount of water in an IV fluid can be fatal.

When comparing solutions, we often look at their concentrations, meaning their solute content. Two solutions with the same concentration are said to be **isotonic** to each other. But if their concentrations differ, the one whose solute concentration is highest is **hypertonic**, and the one with the lower solute concentration is **hypotonic**. (*hyper* means *over* or *above*, and *hypo*, then, means *under* or *below*.) Beware,

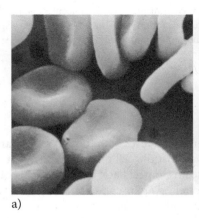

a)

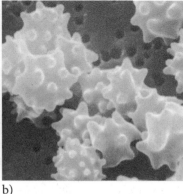

b)

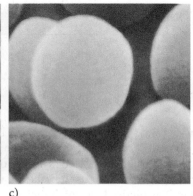

c)

▲ **Figure 19.11** **Red blood cells showing the effects of osmosis. a)** Normal red blood cells. **b)** Red blood cells that have lost water through osmosis. **c)** Red blood cells swollen from taking in too much water by osmosis, and at risk of rupturing.

though—when considering osmosis, you must focus on the water. A hypertonic solution has more solute, but that means it has *less* water. By osmosis, water moves from a hypotonic area to a hypertonic area. Perhaps it is easier to think of it this way—hypotonic solutions are weaker or more dilute, meaning they have more . . . *water*!

Active Transport

It took awhile to get through osmosis, so let's regroup and review what we have done. We discussed simple diffusion, facilitated diffusion, and osmosis. These are all types of diffusion, so the molecules being examined will move from an area where they are more concentrated to an area where they are less concentrated. Diffusion is a spontaneous process—it happens automatically. These types of diffusion do not require energy, so they are referred to as **passive transport**.

Sometimes, instead, cells need to move molecules against their concentration gradients. For example, for a nerve cell to transmit a signal, sodium ions must enter the cell. Special channels in the cell membrane open and sodium ions diffuse into the cell because there are more sodium ions outside than inside. This is simple diffusion. After that nerve signal is sent, though, the sodium ions must leave so the cell is ready for the next signal. But there are still more sodium ions outside than there are inside. The ones inside can't merely diffuse out—they would be moving up their concentration gradient.

Picture This

 Assume you are a dedicated anatomy and physiology student and you've been studying much more than you've been cleaning house. You hear a van pull up outside and you see that it is the *Prize Patrol* from a major sweepstakes sponsor, with a camera crew. They are broadcasting live and they are quickly approaching your door. You grab an armfull of clutter and all your books and open your closet door to stash them on the overhead shelf, but the shelf is full because it has already been jammed with previous clutter.

1. What likely happens if you just open the closet door and stand back? _____

2. Is it easy or difficult to cram more clutter onto the closet shelf?

_____

3. Does the clutter spontaneously head onto the shelf on its own, or do you have to really work at getting it to go and stay there?

_____

In the situation with the closet, when you open the door there is more clutter inside than there is outside, so the clutter inside will spontaneously fall out. This represents diffusion—molecules moving from where they are more concentrated to where they are less concentrated. You likely have to use your arm or somehow exert effort to prevent the clutter from falling out. At the same time, you have to force the additional clutter in your arms into the closet, and you have to work hard to do it. Work requires energy, so you must use energy to do it.

With cells, molecules will not spontaneously move against their concentration gradients. Work must be done, so energy must be used. For this reason, this type of movement—moving molecules up, or against, their concentration gradient—is called **active transport**. This type of movement also requires special one-way "doorways" in the cell membrane, called **pumps**, that ensure the molecules can only move in one direction. Otherwise molecules on the opposite side would spontaneously diffuse out, which is not our goal.

 Active transport moves molecules against their concentration gradient, which requires a special molecular pump and energy. ■

Exocytosis

We have discussed ways for moving molecules, but now it is time to think bigger! Recall that cells may make proteins and other molecules that will be exported. These products are usually wrapped in a membranous sac, called a **vesicle**, at the Golgi apparatus. The method by which they are expelled is called **exocytosis** (*exo-* = outside, *cyto-* = cell). The method is rather simple. The vesicle makes its way to the edge of the cell and its membrane fuses with the cell membrane. As the vesicle pushes against the cell membrane, its own membrane ruptures and seems to peel back, becoming part of the cell membrane and releasing its contents. Figure 19.12 shows a cell secreting a product via exocytosis. Notice the contents spewing out of the cell.

Endocytosis

Endocytosis (*endo-* = inside) is the reverse of exocytosis. It is a way for cells to take in larger objects or even liquid that contains dissolved materials, such as nutrients. There are three major types of endocytosis:

- phagocytosis,
- receptor-mediated endocytosis, and
- pinocytosis.

Phagocytosis is the process by which solids are moved into your cells, and is sometimes referred to as "cell eating." This process demonstrates the active nature of the cell membrane. Extensions of the cell membrane, called **pseudopodia** ("false feet"), seem to reach out from the cell surface, rather like tiny arms, on each side of the object to be taken in. Then the extensions fuse and form a membranous sac, like a vesicle, around the object. This saclike structure is called a **phagosome**, and it moves inward, pinching off from the cell membrane on the inside of the cell. The object is now inside your cell. Soon, several lysosomes typically fuse with the phagosome. Some cells in your immune system are specialized for phagocytosis and use this process to rid your body of foreign material, such as bacteria, that might make you ill.

✔ QUICK CHECK

Why do lysosomes fuse with the phagosome? _____

_____

ǝsnǝɹ ɹoɟ llǝɔ ǝɥʇ oʇ ǝlqɐlᴉɐʌɐ ǝpɐɯ uǝɥʇ ǝɹɐ
ʇɐɥʇ slɐᴉɹǝʇɐɯ ɓuᴉlɔʎɔǝɹ puɐ ssǝlɯɹɐɥ sʇɐǝɹɥʇ lɐᴉʇuǝʇod ɓuᴉɹǝpuǝɹ 'ǝɯosoɓɐɥd
ǝɥʇ ɟo sʇuǝʇuoɔ ǝɥʇ uʍop ʞɐǝɹq llᴉʍ ʇɐɥʇ sǝɯʎzuǝ uᴉɐʇuoɔ sǝɯososʎ˥ :ɹǝʍsu∀ ●

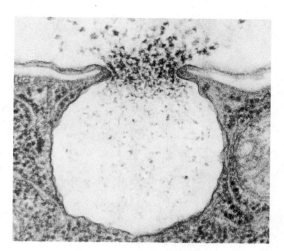

▲ Figure 19.12   **A cell performing exocytosis.**

In **receptor-mediated endocytosis,** before the cell can take the materials in, the objects to be moved must bind to special receptors on the surface of your cell membrane. This binding triggers the cell membrane to form a pocket that will enclose the materials and bring them into your cell. From this point on, the process is very much like phagocytosis.

Pinocytosis is a way your cells can bring in liquids and is sometimes referred to as "cell drinking." In this process, part of your cell membrane puckers inward, forming a pouch at the surface that contains extracellular fluid. In that fluid are a variety of dissolved substances that are now surrounded by cell membrane, which pinches off to form a vesicle-like structure called an **endosome**. The contents are then released inside the cell and are available for its use.

▷ Ashes to Ashes, Cells to Cells: The Cell Cycle

We have discussed many processes that occur in a cell, but a very important one remains: the cell life cycle. Remember from the Cell Theory that cells come from preexisting cells. Each cell goes through the **cell cycle** (Figure 19.13), and the duration of this cycle varies with the cell type. The cell cycle is divided into multiple phases. Simply, though, it can be viewed as having two main parts: **interphase** and **cell reproduction**.

Most cells spend the majority of their life cycle in interphase, which is when they are doing their normal living activities. This makes sense—we spend most of our time living our life, and only a fraction, if any, in reproductive behavior. During interphase, cells go about their normal business, growing, maturing, and doing all the activities we have discussed and more. This is when the cell makes its contribution to the overall function of the whole organism.

During this phase, it also prepares for the reproduction to come. The DNA—your genetic material—replicates. That

means it reproduces. Cells reproduce by dividing, but each daughter cell needs to have a complete set of all the DNA. So, during interphase, the complete set of DNA is copied in a process called **DNA replication.**

DNA replication occurs in the nucleus during interphase. During this process, all of your genetic code is reproduced exactly. The coiled strands of DNA are held together by hydrogen bonds. When it is time to replicate, an enzyme breaks these bonds, allowing the strands to "unzip" (Figure 19.14a), which exposes their bases. Also in the nucleus are free nucleotides, which are the building blocks of your nucleic acids—each containing a sugar, a phosphate group, and a base. Once the DNA bases are exposed, the free nucleotides move in and search for partners. They are picky—adenine (A) only partners with thymine (T), and cytosine (C) always pairs with guanine (G). This type of match-up is called *complementary base pairing*.

When the DNA bases have the correct new nucleotides next to them, the sugars and phosphates of the free

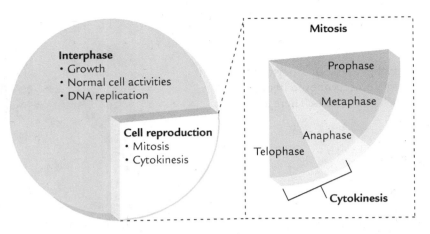

▲ Figure 19.13 **The cell cycle.**

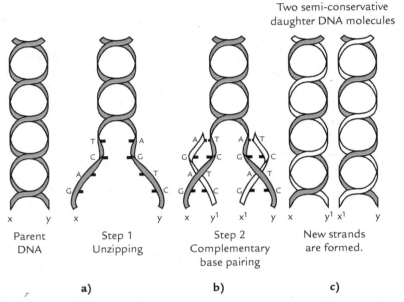

Two semi-conservative daughter DNA molecules

Parent DNA	Step 1 Unzipping	Step 2 Complementary base pairing	New strands are formed.
	a)	b)	c)

▲ Figure 19.14 **DNA replication doubles our DNA before our cells divide. a)** In the first step, an enzyme unzips the strands of the original DNA, exposing their bases. **b)** Next, free nucleotides move in and align with the original bases through complementary base pairing (A with T, C with G). **c)** Finally, the free nucleotides are joined together to make a new strand of DNA that is identical to the original strand that it is replacing.

nucleotides are joined together by another enzyme. The result is an exact copy of the DNA strand that was previously there. Each original DNA strand is now mated with an exact copy of the other. Notice in **Figure 19.14c** that we now have twice as much DNA as when we started. That's the purpose of DNA replication—we double the DNA so that when the cell divides, each new cell gets a complete set of genetic instructions.

Once the DNA has replicated, cell reproduction may begin. Cell division, or reproduction, includes two processes:

■ **mitosis**, which is nuclear division, and

■ **cytokinesis**, which is cytoplasmic division.

 Students (and instructors!) sometimes forget that cell reproduction is actually both mitosis and cytokinesis and instead refer to mitosis as meaning cell

reproduction or division. To help you see why this is incorrect, think about the basic egg. The yolk represents the cell nucleus and the white represents the cytoplasm. If you were trying to split an egg into two eggs, just splitting the yolk would not achieve your goal—you would need to split both the egg yolk (nucleus, by mitosis) and the egg white (cytoplasm, by cytokinesis). Let's try one more image. Change the egg in your mind to a balloon filled with water. Imagine placing your hand around the center of the balloon and pinching in. That will cause the middle to narrow and the two sides to bulge. This is similar to what happens in cytokinesis to divide the cytoplasm—the cell membrane pinches in along the midline.

The DNA is important to your cells—it controls all of their functions. Because of this, division of the nucleus is a separate process, called **mitosis**. This is a very precise event designed to ensure that the DNA is equally divided into the daughter cells.

Mitosis includes four phases:

- prophase
- metaphase
- anaphase, and
- telophase.

Before mitosis, during interphase, the DNA is stretched out in thin strands called chromatin. During **prophase**, the first phase of mitosis, the chromatin condenses into rodlike structures—the chromosomes (Table 19.2). The nuclear membrane also disappears so that the chromosomes can move more freely and the nucleolus is disassembled. The next phase is **metaphase**. *Meta-* means *middle*, and during metaphase the chromosomes align very precisely, in duplicated pairs, along the midline, or equator, of the cell. This ensures that they will separate precisely. The next phase is **anaphase**. *Ana-* means *away*, and the duplicated chromosomes separate during this phase—one complete set goes to each side, or pole, of the cell. Movement of the chromosomes is directed

TABLE 19.2 **THE STAGES OF THE CELL CYCLE INCLUDE INTERPHASE AND CELL REPRODUCTION**. CELL REPRODUCTION INCLUDES THE FOUR PHASES OF MITOSIS DURING WHICH THE NUCLEAR CONTENTS DIVIDE, AND CYTOKINESIS DURING WHICH THE REMAINDER OF THE CELL DIVIDES. CYTOKINESIS OVERLAPS THE LATTER PHASES OF MITOSIS.

Picture	Stage	Events
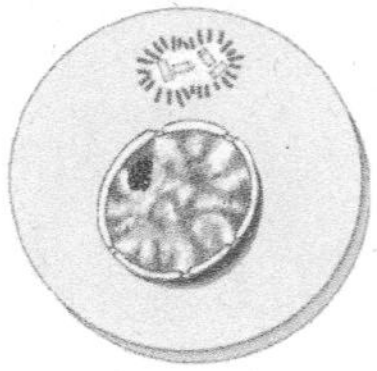	Interphase	Normal cell activities, growth, DNA replication. DNA is visible as thin strands called chromatin.
	Prophase	Chromatin condenses into rodlike structures called chromosomes that are clearly visible, and the nuclear membrane disappears.
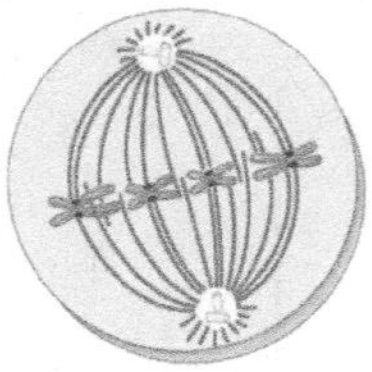	Metaphase	Chromosomes align very precisely along the midline.
	Anaphase	Chromosomes separate and are pulled to opposite poles of the cell. Cytokinesis begins once the chromosomes separate (visible here where the edge of the cell is just beginning to pinch in).
	Telophase	Chromosomes are in opposite poles and cytokinesis continues. This stage ends when the cells completely separate, forming two daughter cells.

by the centrioles and delicate structures that form from them, called spindle fibers, which pull the chromosomes in opposite directions. The final phase of mitosis is **telophase**, during which the chromosomes complete their journey to the opposite poles. This phase is like a reverse prophase. The nuclear membrane reappears and the chromosomes relax back into the stretched-out chromatin strands.

Time to Try

In the spaces provided, list the phases of mitosis in the correct order, then sketch what the cell would look like during that phase if it contained three pairs of chromosomes.

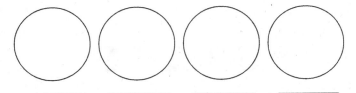

Mitosis just divides the nucleus or, more specifically, the chromosomes. Once the chromosomes have carefully separated, the rest of the cell can be divided. This process, by which the cytoplasm divides, is called **cytokinesis**. It begins during anaphase of mitosis, after the chromosomes have separated, and ends at the end of telophase. At the end of cytokinesis, the original cell is gone and in its wake are two new daughter cells, almost identical and each with a complete set of DNA. These daughter cells are in interphase, and the whole cell cycle begins anew. Congratulations! Your cell just had babies.

 Cell reproduction includes mitosis, which is division of the nuclear contents, and cytokinesis, which is division of the cytoplasm. ▪

▷ Here's Looking at You, Kid! Meiosis

At the end of the normal cell life cycle, we get two daughter cells, each containing all 46 chromosomes—23 pairs. But when we make a baby, each parent contributes only half of the baby's genetic makeup. Our reproductive cells—sperm and ova—undergo a unique type of nuclear division called **meiosis,** which produces cells with only one chromosome from each pair. The division occurs in two cycles—meiosis I and meiosis II. The phases are the same as those of mitosis, but are also numbered according to the cycle. The key difference between mitosis and meiosis happens during metaphase. In mitosis, all 46 chromosomes line up individually, with their replicated copies, along the midline. When they separate during anaphase, the original separates from its copy, so each cell gets either an original or a copy of all 46 chromosomes.

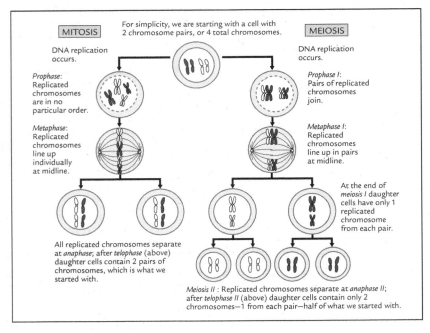

▲ **Figure 19.15** **Comparison of mitosis (left) and meiosis (right).**

In meiosis, though, during metaphase I, chromosome pairs, not individual chromosomes, line up together at the midline, along with their replicated pairs. Then, in anaphase I, the pairs separate into different cells—each cell getting only one chromosome (and its copy) from each pair. At the end of telophase I, there are two daughter cells, each with only 23 chromosomes—one from each pair—still attached to its replicated copy (Figure 19.15). Because meiosis I cuts the chromosome count from 46 to 23, it is referred to as the *reduction division*. Meiosis II is similar to mitosis: Single chromosomes

and their copies align along the midline, then separate during anaphase. Each daughter cell gets either an original or a copy of the 23 chromosomes. At the end of mitosis, there were only two daughter cells, but division occurs twice in meiosis, so there are four cells total. In males, that means four functional sperm, but in females only one of the daughter cells becomes a functioning ovum. Also, the daughter cells of mitosis are identical, but the cells produced by meiosis have unique combinations, allowing for genetic diversity and sometimes surprises when Baby arrives!

▷ Final Stretch!

 Now that you have finished reading this chapter, it is time to stretch your brain a bit and check how much you learned. For online tests, tutorials, animations, activities, web links, and an ebook, visit the *Get Ready for A&P* companion website.

Running Words

At the end of each chapter, be sure you have learned the language. Here are the terms introduced in this chapter with which you should be familiar. Write them in a notebook or enter them into your computer. Define them in your own words, then go back through the chapter to check your meaning, correcting as needed. Also try to list examples when appropriate.

- Cytology
- Cell
- Cell Theory
- Unicellular
- Multicellular
- Cell membrane
- Cytoplasm
- DNA
- Prokaryote
- Eukaryote
- Nucleoid
- Plasmid
- Organelle
- Homeostasis
- Plasma membrane
- Phospholipid
- Phosphate head
- Hydrophilic
- Fatty acid tail
- Hydrophobic
- Phospholipid bilayer
- Selectively permeable
- Fluid mosaic model

- Cytosol
- Nucleus
- Chromatin
- Chromosome
- Nuclear envelope
- Nuclear pore
- Nucleoplasm
- Ribosome
- Protein synthesis
- RNA (ribonucleic acid)
- Messenger RNA (mRNA)
- Ribosomal RNA (rRNA)
- Nucleolus
- Transfer RNA (tRNA)
- Endoplasmic reticulum (ER)
- Golgi apparatus
- Vesicle
- Mitochondrion
- ATP
- Lysosome
- Peroxisome
- Cytoskeleton
- Microtubule

- Microfilament
- Centrosome
- Centriole
- Cilia
- Flagellum
- Brownian motion
- Concentration gradient
- Equilibrium
- Simple diffusion
- Facilitated diffusion
- Osmosis
- Solute
- Solvent
- Solution
- Isotonic
- Passive transport
- Active transport
- Pump
- Exocytosis

- Endocytosis
- Phagocytosis
- Pseudopodia
- Phagosome
- Receptor-mediated endocytosis
- Pinocytosis
- Endosome
- Cell cycle
- Interphase
- Cell reproduction
- DNA replication
- Mitosis
- Prophase
- Metaphase
- Anaphase
- Telophase
- Cytokinesis
- Meiosis

What Did You Learn?

PART A: ANSWER THE FOLLOWING QUESTIONS.

1. List the five principles of the Cell Theory.

_____

_____

_____

_____

_____

2. What is the basic difference between prokaryotic cells and eukaryotic cells?

_____

_____

3. Describe the organization of the cell membrane. _____

   _____

4. Design a concept map for the following terms: protein, DNA, nucleus, nucleolus, ribosome, rough ER, Golgi apparatus, and exocytosis.

5. Differentiate between passive and active movement processes. _____

   _____

   _____

6. In terms of movement processes, explain how making a cup of hot tea with a tea bag involves both osmosis and simple diffusion. _____

   _____

   _____

7. Assume you have limp carrot sticks in your refrigerator. To get them plump and crisp again, would you soak them in pure water or in a strong salt solution?

   _____

   _____

8. Differentiate between phagocytosis and pinocytosis. _____

   _____

   _____

9. List in order the four phases of mitosis:

   _____

10. Explain the complete cell cycle. _____

   _____

   _____

   _____

   _____

PART B: FOR EACH OF THE FOLLOWING ITEMS, MATCH THE TERM WITH ITS DESCRIPTION.

1. mitochondrion _____

2. lysosome _____

3. ribosome _____

4. Golgi apparatus _____

5. nucleolus _____

6. pinocytosis _____

7. exocytosis _____

8. osmosis _____

9. active transport _____

10. simple diffusion _____

a) Diffusion of water through a selectively permeable membrane.

b) Expelling materials out of the cell.

c) Site where ribosomes are made.

d) Process that uses energy to move molecules against their concentration gradients.

e) Spontaneous movement of molecules down their concentration gradient.

f) "Garbage disposal" containing digestive enzymes.

g) Site where proteins are made.

h) Site where cellular products are packaged.

i) Cell drinking.

j) Site where ATP (energy) is made.

20 Biology of Cancer

▷ Cancer

Richard is 60 years old. For the past few months he has been feeling a little under the weather. He has chronic indigestion and his stomach is somewhat sore. He is more tired than usual, and when he eats his indigestion flares up. He goes to the doctor, who prescribes an antacid but it doesn't really help. A few weeks later, he wakes up itching all over. His wife takes one look at him and is shocked to see that his skin and the whites of his eyes are yellow. His doctor is worried about his sudden jaundice and orders a CAT scan. The image of Richard's pancreas reveals a mass. The doctor gives Richard the bad news: He probably has pancreatic cancer and the prognosis is not good.

Richard undergoes surgery but the tumor has spread into tissues around the pancreas and cannot be removed. The surgeon sees the signs of malignancy from the shape, color, texture, and spreading nature of the tumor. He removes a sample of the tumor for laboratory analysis. The surgeon also corrects the blockage of his bile duct that lead to jaundice and marks the tumor with metal clips. These clips will be used in Richard's subsequent therapy to focus a beam of radiation directly at the tumor.

In the lab, the sample of Richard's tumor is stained and examined under the microscope. The pathologist also recognizes the cells as cancerous. Compared to the surrounding healthy cells, the tumor cells are more round and not well organized into layers (Figure 20.1). The nuclei in the tumor cells are enlarged and many of the cells are visibly undergoing mitosis. Further tests reveal that the cells are secreting unusually high levels of proteins normally produced by pancreas cells.

Richard undergoes months of chemotherapy and radiation treatments. These treatments help, and Richard feels better for several months. When additional CAT scans are performed, they show that the tumor has shrunk. But as the months pass, Richard's condition worsens. His stomach hurts more and he starts losing weight. The tumor has started to grow again despite continued chemotherapy. After a few short months, the cancer is growing out of control. Not only is the tumor in the pancreas growing, but the cancer is spreading. Richard develops new tumors in his liver, bones and lungs. His condition rapidly deteriorates and his weight loss accelerates. When Richard finally dies, he has lost over 100 pounds.

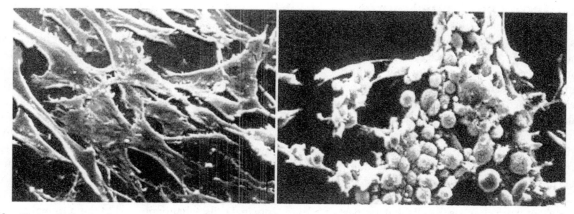

▲ Figure 20.1. Photographs taken by a scanning electron microscope of normal cells and cancer cells. Note that the normal cells are fairly flat, have complex shapes and have many attachments to each other and the underlying growth surface. In contrast, the cancer cells are round, have lost their complex shapes and are poorly attached to each other, or anything else. Source: Judith Kimball's web site, http://www.ultranet.com/~jkimball/BiologyPages/C/Cancer-CellsInCulture.html. Photographs: G. Steven Martin.

Males			Females		
Type	New Cases	Deaths	Type	New Cases	Deaths
Prostate	198,100	31,500	Breast	192,200	40,200
Lung & Bronchus	90,700	90,100	Lung & Bronchus	78,800	67,300
Colon & Rectum	67,300	27,700	Colon & Rectum	68,100	29,000
Bladder	39,200	8,300	Uterus	38,300	6,600
NH Lymphoma	31,100	13,800	NH Lymphóma	25,100	12,500
Melanoma	29,000	5,000	Ovary	23,400	13,900
Oral	20,200	5,100	Melanoma	22,400	2,800
Kidney	18,700	7,500	Bladder	15,100	4,100
Leukemia	17,700	12,000	Pancreas	15,000	14,800
Pancreas	14,200	14,100	Thyroid	14,900	800

Source: "Cancer Facts and Figures 2001." American Cancer Society. http://www.cancer.org/eprise/main/docroot/STT/stt_0_2001?site area+STT&level+1.

This kind of diagnosis, treatment, and death from cancer is replayed all too often. Over 1.2 million cases of cancer will be diagnosed this year in the United States alone, and over half a million cancer deaths will occur. Pancreatic cancer will make up only 5% of those deaths, but is one of the most difficult to treat, and kills over 95% of its victims within five years of diagnosis. Cancer of the lung, breast, prostate, and colon account for the majority of the other cancer cases.

As this example shows, cancer results from the loss of control over several key cellular properties. Cells that should not divide, divide. Cells that should not be invading surrounding tissue, invade surrounding tissue. Cells that should remain in specific tissues or organs, migrate to new locations in the body and continue to grow. Cancer cells that leave their original location for a new location in the body and begin to divide in the new location are said to have metastasized.

These three traits—dividing when they should not divide, having the capacity to invade surrounding tissue, and having the capacity to metastasize—separate cancer cells from normal cells.

Extensive scientific and medical resources have been mobilized to understand the basic biology of cancer and treat those afflicted by the disease. More than $50 billion will be spent this year for cancer healthcare, and nearly $15 billion for research. It is relatively easy to understand how the money is spent on cancer treatment. Healthcare is expensive, and the array of medicines, physicians, nurses, facilities, and sophisticated medical equipment account for this expense. But what about the research money? What do scientists do when they are studying cancer? What have they discovered about how the biology of cancer cells is different from normal cells? How will those discoveries be translated into treatments to help patients like Richard?

Where Do Cancer Cells Come From?

In some ways, cancer behaves like an infection. It starts at a specific place, and then spreads to other places in the body. In bacterial infections, bacterial cells come in contact with the body and start to grow. Bacteria grow by dividing, and as they divide a cluster of cells is formed, called a colony. Colonies of bacterial cells can break up and the cells that are released can spread and start to grow at new sites and form new colonies. Some cells from a bacterial colony can travel in the blood or other body fluids and grow at sites distant from the initial infection.

There is a critical difference between bacterial infections and cancer. Cancer is produced not from cells that originate outside the body, but from changes in cells that are part of the body itself. Richard had pancreatic cancer. Other patients

may have lung cancer or colon cancer or breast cancer. The assignment of these different types of cancer reflects the cells types or organs in which the cancer started. When cancer spreads, it is these abnormal body cells, produced from rapid cell division, that break free and spread through the body fluids to distant sites where they lodge in healthy tissues and continue to divide. Because these cells are actually the body's own cells, they are not recognized as foreign, infectious agents and are not aggressively attacked and removed by the immune system.

If cancer cells are not foreign cells, but are derived from normal cells, what happened to them to make them change? Why are they abnormal? What do they do "wrong"?

▷ Cancer Cells Have Profound Genetic Defects

To start this discussion, it is important to look more closely at cancer cells and their defects. When Richard's tumor cells were sent to the lab, they were subjected to several tests, one of which was to determine their karyotype. This is a microscopic analysis of the cells to determine how many chromosomes they have and whether the chromosomes are normal or have defects that can be seen under the microscope. Richard's tumor cells had striking changes in their chromosomes (Figure 20.2). Many of the chromosome were broken or had parts missing. Others had extra parts attached that came from other chromosomes. Several extra copies of some chromosomes were present. Other chromosomes were nearly missing, with only a part of a single copy remaining. These are startling defects. No normal cell ever has such problems. How do cancer cells develop these problems? How are these genetic changes related to the abnormal behavior of cancer cells? How do cancer cells survive despite having such problems?

Damage Control

To understand how cancer cells accumulate such high levels of genetic and cellular damage, we need to understand what normal cells do in the face of significant damage to their chromosomes. Normal cells have a robust system for damage control that can do four things: (1) Detect cellular damage, especially DNA damage; (2) arrest cell division and prevent the replication of damaged cells; (3) activate damage repair systems; and (4) activate cell death if damage cannot be repaired. This system of damage control functions routinely in normal cells. For example, when you get sunburned, your skin cells activate damage control, stop dividing and activate damage repair. Skin cells mildly damaged by solar radiation can be repaired and when repair is complete, the cells start dividing again. However, some cells may be damaged so severely that the damage cannot be repaired, and a system in the damaged cell is activated that causes cellular suicide. This process, called apoptosis or programmed cell death, is a critical part of damage control. Cells damaged beyond repair normally remove themselves by activating cell death systems. You might think that cells so badly damaged would just die anyway. The problem is that cells that die directly from damage or injury, called necrotic cell death, are not effectively removed from surrounding tissue. Necrotic cell death triggers inflammation and the leftover cell debris can be a target for bacterial infection. In apoptotic cell death, the cell is efficiently disassembled and the parts are readily engulfed by healthy cells and recycled.

To think through the logic of damage control in another way, let's think of cells as automobiles. When our car is damaged, we quit driving it and take it to the repair shop. The mechanics then fix the car or decide the damage is too extensive to fix, and have the "totaled" car hauled off to the junkyard. Most damage to cars hinders their performance. A fender may be dented and rub against a wheel or the radiator may leak and cause the engine to overheat and not run well. Most damage to cells is similar. It prevents normal cellular function and needs to be repaired for cells to start working properly again.

What is the damage in cancer cells like? Cancer cells divide out of control and can spread throughout the body. Our automobile model of damage and repair makes sense if we consider the idea that damage to cancer cells is more complex than a dented fender is to a car. Let's propose that cancer is to cells what driving out of control is to cars. What sorts of damage could cause cars to go out of control and careen around corners and crash into things? Well, what if there is damage to the brakes? What if the steering doesn't work or the accelerator gets stuck? These kinds of damage affect the

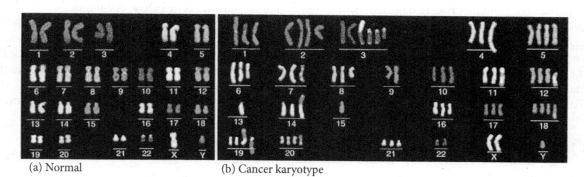

(a) Normal   (b) Cancer karyotype

▲ **Figure 20.2.** Karyotypes of a normal cell and a cancer cell. Note that there are two copies of each of the 22 chromosomes and an X and Y. The staining technique used to obtain these karyotypes allows each different chromosome to be reocognized because it stains a different color. Note that in the cancer karyotype, there are many extra chromosomes present. Some of the chromosomes also have extra DNA attached such as the right most copy of chromosome 4.

Source: http://www.nature.com/genomics/human/slide-show/4.html.

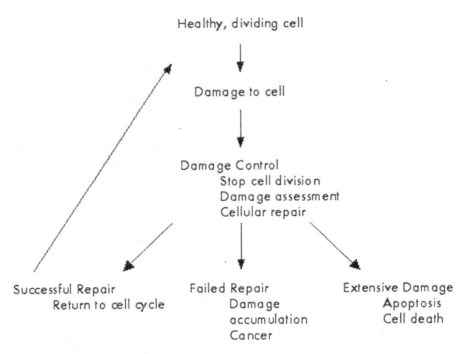

Healthy, dividing cell

↓

Damage to cell

↓

Damage Control
Stop cell division
Damage assessment
Cellular repair

Successful Repair
Return to cell cycle

Failed Repair
Damage
accumulation
Cancer

Extensive Damage
Apoptosis
Cell death

▲ **Figure 20.3.** Normal cells divide under proper control but can be damaged from toxins or radiation. When damage occurs, the damage control systems are activated. First, damage is detected by several proteins that become active when damage to DNA or other cellular components occurs. These damage detectors then activate damage control genes such as p53 that stop the cell cycle and activate repair. If the damage is mild, it is repaired properly and the cell becomes a normal dividing cell again. If the damage is very severe it triggers the programmed cell death system and causes cell death, called apoptosis. Finally, the damage repair systems may fail, and damage may accumulate without either being repaired properly or triggering cell death. In this case the accumulation of damage to genes can lead to cancer.

car's control systems and are especially dangerous. Damage to these systems must be recognized by the driver and fixed by a mechanic or the car will go out of control when driven. If the problem is too extensive to be repaired, the car should be taken to the junkyard.

Let us take this analogy and apply it back to damage control systems in cells (**Figure 20.3**). To activate damage controls systems, the damage must be detected and a decision must be made by the cell to stop dividing and initiate repair. Several genes that encode proteins that function in these systems have been identified, but the details of many parts of this system are still unresolved. Damage to DNA is detected by proteins that bind to chemically altered nucleotides or broken DNA molecules. Damage to membranes and proteins can also be detected by several enzymes normally present in cells. These damage detectors function much like a driver sensing something is wrong with a car, feeling the brakes not work correctly or the engine running improperly.

When damage is detected, a coordinator of damage repair is activated. This job is similar to the manager of a repair shop. This individual has to assess the extent of the damage

and make sure the repairs are completed properly. If the damage is too extensive, this manager must call the junkyard and have the car hauled away. In cells, the job of damage control manager is performed in part by a key protein in the cell called p53. The p53 protein has many functions including arresting cell division, activating repair enzymes, and, if necessary, triggering cell death.

The gene encoding p53 is mutant in over half of all cancers. When this mutation occurs, damage responses are much more likely to fail. When p53 does not function correctly, repair systems are not properly activated, and most importantly, cell death is not triggered when cells have severe damage and should be destroyed. If the management of damage control is defective, cellular defects go unrepaired. This failed repair is especially dangerous if the defects in the cell lead to increases in cell division rates, increased ability of cells to penetrate tissues by invasive growth, or the ability of cells to break free and spread to distant sites in the body. When these defects are present and not repaired, the result is an aggressive cancer that is rapidly growing and likely to spread.

Tumor Suppressors

The genes that function in the damage control systems fix cells when they are broken. In cancer cells, these genes are

mutant, and cannot properly perform their tasks. The defects in these genes reduce their expression or block their ability to do their jobs, and are called loss of function mutations. Genes that contribute to cancer formation when they experience loss of function mutations are called tumor suppressor genes. They encode proteins whose normal job is to suppress the changes in cells that lead to cancerous growth. Some tumor suppressor genes encode proteins that detect DNA damage; others encode proteins that function in the repair of damage to DNA or other cellular components such as proteins or lipids. Still other tumor suppressor genes, such as TP53 that encodes the p53 protein, function as coordinators of repair systems. They stop cell division when damage is detected and activate repair systems. Finally, a group of tumor suppressor genes function in programmed cell death by helping cells commit suicide when the cells have severe damage that cannot be properly repaired.

It is not hard to see how loss of tumor suppressor functions could contribute to cancer. Cells with mutations in tumor suppressor genes accumulate damage that is not repaired. If the damage affects key control systems, it could lead to cancer formation. As mutations build up in cells, they would lose their mature shapes and physiology. This process, called dedifferentiation, is characteristic of cancer cells, and was observed in Richard's tumor cells. His cancer cells didn't look normal to the surgeon, nor the pathologist in the lab. They had lost their shape and the tissues they formed had lost normal organization and structure. In normal circumstances, these cells die from apoptosis and are lost from the body, but cancer cells are frequently incapable of apoptosis and persist and spread despite their damage and malfunctions.

Growth Rates and Rapid Cell Division

We have discussed how cancer cells are defective and have defective damage control systems, but what about their growth? Why do tumors made of cancer cells get bigger? What changes occur that cause increased growth rate? Normal tissues and organs have controls that regulate their growth. When they achieve proper size, their growth stops. These controls on growth are ignored or lost in tumor cells.

To start our discussion of cancer cell growth, we have to distinguish between two basic possibilities of tissue growth. One possibility is that cells increase in size and content, and bigger cells make bigger tissues. The other possibility is that growth results from an increase in cell numbers. In cancer more cells are formed, but the cells are not appreciably larger than normal cells.

Microscopic analysis of tumors allows us to distinguish between these possibilities. When Richard's tumor was examined, the cancer cells were visibly different from surrounding healthy cells, and there were clearly many of them. In fact, the cancer cells themselves tended to be somewhat smaller than normal cells. The cancer cells had dedifferentiated, and lost their mature characteristics and their complex shapes had been lost. Richard's cancer resulted in the growth of tumors and increased amount of tumor tissue, but the cells that made up the tumors were smaller than normal cells. This occurred because tumor growth was due to excess cell division and increased cell numbers rather than an increase in cell size. Even though the cancer cells within the tumor were smaller than normal cells, the very large number of the cancer cells accounted for the increase in tumor size.

To understand the reasons for increased rates of cell division in cancer we must think about how cell division is regulated in normal cells. We have to look for special kinds of defects that could make cells divide too fast. To bring up our car analogy, most damage to a car will make it run very poorly. However, having a stuck accelerator is a specific defect in a key control system that would make the car go too fast. Many of the defects in cancer cells are in key control systems that accelerate cell division.

▷ The Cell Cycle

Many conditions must be met before a cell can divide normally. Some of these are internal conditions having to do with cell growth and metabolism. A cell must grow in size and content before it divides (**Figure 20.4** on page 420). It must produce enough protein, membrane, organelles, and carbohydrates so that when those materials are divided in half in cell division, there is enough to support each of the two daughter cells formed. A cell must also fully replicate its DNA, so a complete genome can be provided to each daughter cell. The status of these aspects of internal growth are monitored by regulatory systems that block cell division unless proper growth has occurred.

Other conditions are external and involve signals from other cells. External conditions required for proper cell division are more easily understood if a cell is viewed in a "social" context, where it is part of a community of cells that must cooperate to form an organism. For cells to contribute to tissues or organs, they must be in contact with the appropriate neighboring cells and be properly anchored in place within the tissue. Cells have a complex array of signaling systems that relay information about contact with other cells and the strength of the anchors that hold the cell in place. Cells must also receive signals from distant parts of the body that coordinate the function of different organs. These signals are transmitted by hormones and

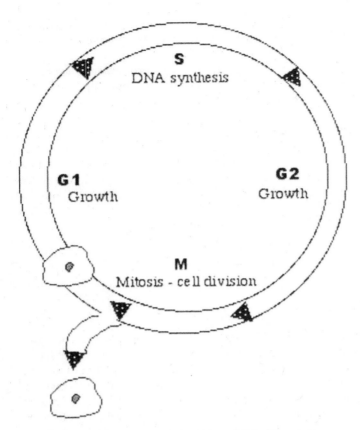

▲ **Figure 20.4.** The cell cycle. Cells go through four different stages each time they divide. Cells start with a growth phase, called G1, in which they synthesize proteins, lipids, and carbohydrates and perform important metabolic functions. Once they grow properly and receive signals that stimulate cell division, they move to S phase, in which they replicate their DNA. After DNA replication, further growth and metabolism occurs. Finally, the cells undergoes mitosis, or M phase, in which it divides its chromosomes evenly and splits into two genetically identical cells. Each of those cells can then cycle, or go through the process again.

important part of growth control. Most cells in the body are not dividing much at all and many cell types have undergone terminal differentiation and matured, never to divide again. The signals these mature cells receive from neighboring cells, hormonal control systems, and internal triggers prevent them from returning to a cycling state of division.

The signals controlling growth, both positive and negative, are integrated in a basic control system regulating the cell cycle. The cell cycle refers to the sequence of events that are repeated each time a cell grows and divides to form two daughter cells. As the cycle proceeds, the cells goes through a growth phase called G1, a DNA synthesis phase called S, another growth phase, called G2, and finally into mitosis, or M phase when the cell divides.

The transitions from each phase of the cell cycle to the next are tightly regulated by a system that combines signals about both internal and external cellular cues into a single control switch for cell division. This system involves a series of proteins called cyclins that act as triggers for progression through the cell cycle (Figure 20.5). At the start of the cell cycle, the concentration of cyclins is very low. As signals are received to stimulate cell division, cyclins accumulate to high concentrations within the cell. When cyclin concentration increases, they combine with a second class of proteins called cyclin-dependent kinases. The dimers of cyclins and their corresponding cyclin-dependent kinases become active enzymes that stimulate additional proteins. These target proteins function to actually move the cell from one phase of the cell cycle to the next. For example, many of the targets of cyclin-dependent kinases activated at the end of the G1 phase are enzymes required for DNA synthesis. Thus, the DNA replication machinery used in S phase is engaged actively only after all of the signals from G1 phase cues have combined to produce high G1 cyclin levels. These integrated signals are combined into a unified activation event triggered by the G1 cyclin-cyclin-dependent kinase enzyme complexes.

Each of the transition steps of the cell cycle, from G1 to S phase, from G2 to M phase, and the final completion of mitosis are regulated and triggered by specific sets of cyclins and their corresponding kinases. The production of cyclins at each stage are stimulated by positive growth signals and inhibited by negative signals. Through this give-and-take, the cell cycle can be either stimulated to allow the cell to divide, or stalled, arresting the cell in its existing growth phase.

growth factors released by other cells and endocrine glands. These signals allow coordination of growth among different tissues. Regulatory systems sense these external signals and coordinate the information to regulate cell division.

It is important to understand that these growth signals can be either positive or negative. Many signals stimulate division and are required for growth of tissues. However, many of the signals cells inhibit or block cell division and are an

Oncogenes—Cell Division Stimulants

Early in the study of genetic changes in cancer cells, it was found that some viral infections could transform normal cells into cancer cells. This transformation was traced back to specific genes carried into the cells on the viral DNA. The src oncogene (pronounced "sark") represents one of the first of these transforming genes discovered by Harold Varmus and Michael Bishop. These researchers were eventually awarded the Nobel Prize for the discovery of this gene in a virus, and

the identification of a corresponding gene normally present in the genome of healthy cells. They proposed that oncogenes, genes that can transform normal cells into cancer cells, were just mutant forms of genes normally present in cells. The normal counterparts, called proto-oncogenes, function in regulating the cell cycle. When those genes become overactive, they accelerate the cell cycle by stimulating cyclin production and produce rapidly dividing cells. The functions of

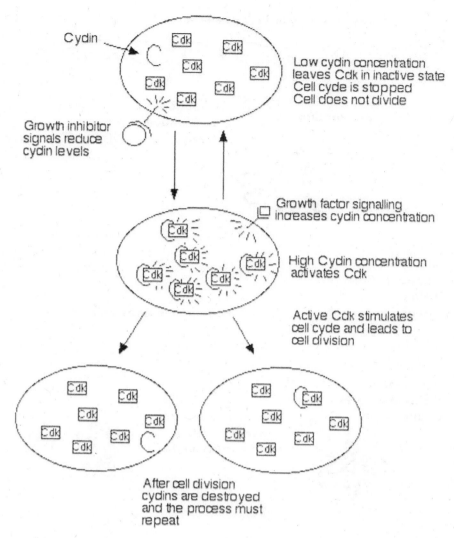

Cydin

Cdk Cdk
Cdk
Cdk
Cdk Cdk
Cdk

Low cydin concentration
leaves Cdk in inactive state
Cell cyde is stopped
Cell does not divide

Growth inhibitor
signals reduce
cydin levels

Growth factor signalling
increases cydin concentration

Cdk
Cdk
Cdk Cdk
Cdk Cdk

High Cydin concentration
activates Cdk

Active Cdk stimulates
cell cyde and leads to
cell division

Cdk Cdk
Cdk
Cdk Cdk
Cdk

Cdk Cdk
Cdk
Cdk Cdk
Cdk

After cell division
cydins are destroyed
and the process must
repeat

▲ **Figure 20.5.** Early in the cell cycle, cyclins are at very low concentrations in the cell. When growth factors signal the cell, it stimulates cyclin production. When the cyclins are present in high concentration, they bind with the cdk's, or cyclin-dependent kinases. These two-molecule combinations, or dimers, then signal other molecules that allow the cell cycle to proceed. Once the cell cycle proceeds, the cyclins that were at high concentrations are uncoupled from the cyclin-dependent kinases are destroyed, and the cyclin-dependent kinases are deactivated.

many proto-oncogenes are now reasonably well understood. Many proto-oncogenes function in the signaling systems from internal or external growth cues. For example, the src proto-oncogene functions to provide information about how well cells are anchored in place, and provides positive growth signals when anchors are intact.

Most oncogenes are caused by gain of function mutations in proto-oncogenes (Figure 20.6). This kind of mutation does what it sounds like it does. It causes genes to gain functions, such as being expressed too much, or in cells where it is normally turned off. Many of these mutations affect proteins that function to transmit signals from growth factors and cause them to be turned on constantly. In this case, the cell thinks that there are growth factors present even when there are not. The cell responds by building up its cyclins and speeding up the cell cycle, even though the signals to do so are not actually present.

Now let us imagine the worst-case scenario and consider a cell that has oncogene mutations and tumor suppressor

mutations. Such a cell would have abnormal function in both genes that control the cell cycle and the rate of cell division, and genes that regulate damage control. What would result? First, the loss of damage control would lead to the accumulation of cellular damage, especially genetic mutations. When these mutations occur in proto-oncogenes, they generate oncogenes that speed up the cell cycle. Further mutations, again still not repaired by damage control, might increase cell motility. Now the rapidly dividing cells would be able to move more rapidly and spread from their original site. As more mutations accumulate, more oncogenes are created and the cells would divide more and more rapidly. In addition, further mutations can occur in the damage control system and make it even worse. It is this disastrous downward spiral caused by the combination of tumor suppressor mutations that block proper damage control, and oncogene accumulation that speeds up cell division and increases the cell's invasive properties that is characteristic of advanced cancer.

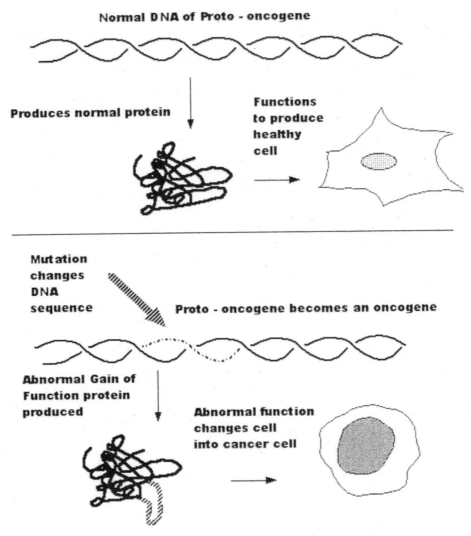

Figure 20.6. Proto-oncogenes are normal genes that perform regular functions within the cell. When proto-oncogenes function, they contribute to the normal growth and regulation of cellular functions. Mutations can occur in the DNA sequence of proto-oncogenes to turn them into oncogenes. When this occurs, the protein they produce does not function normally, and gains new functions. In turn, it leads to changes in cell growth and metabolism that contribute to cancer.

▷ The Six Hallmarks of Cancer Cells

Douglas Hanahan and Robert Weinberg recently wrote a review of cancer research in which they outlined six features common to all types of cancer cells. This review and the ideas it contains are an excellent synthesis of many complex and diverse discoveries in cancer research. The six features of cancer cells Hanahan and Weinberg (2000) consider are:

1. self-sufficiency in growth signals or response
2. insensitivity to growth inhibitory (antigrowth) signals
3. evasion of programmed cell death (apoptosis)
4. limitless replicative potential

5. sustained angiogenesis [stimulation of blood vessel growth]
6. tissue invasion and metastasis.

These specific features of cancer cells are the result of changes in cell physiology produced by mutation and genomic alteration characteristic of cancer cells. The specific genes involved and the manner in which they function are only partially understood. Understanding what these genes do and how their malfunction contributes to cancer is the subject of a wide array of intense research efforts. Given the general outlines of the cancer process already discussed, we will now explore some of the important concepts underlying each of these "hallmarks of cancer."

Self Sufficiency in Growth Signals

Let us start with external signals controlling growth. Several tumors overactivate receptor systems that sense growth factors and regulate cell division. Some cancer cells achieve this by increasing the number of growth factor receptors on their surface so that even small amounts of growth factor produce a strong signal response inside the cell and activate cell division. Other cancer cells have mutant receptors that transmit their signals even without growth factor present. In a similar way some cancers have mutations in the proteins inside the cell that are activated by the receptor and transduce or transmit the signal into the cell. These mutant oncogenes activate cell division and are common in many cancer cells. An example is a gene called ras, which encodes a protein that functions as a signal transduction molecule. The mutant ras protein becomes overactive in cancer cells and delivers a growth signal even when none is actually being transmitted from outside the cell.

Among the most devious of the systems that lead to the mistaken signaling of growth factor systems are cancers that co-opt neighboring healthy cells to overexpress growth factors. This effectively represents a hijacking of healthy cells by cancer cells to support their rapid growth. Cancer cells that thrive on extra growth signals get their "fix" by releasing molecules that affect nearby cells and fool them into expressing high levels of growth factors. With this in mind, the complexity of cell types within tumors can make sense. Many tumors are a mixture of cancer cells that are capable of rapid growth, invasive growth and metastasis, and noncancer cells that may function to "support" the rapid growth of the cancer cells.

Insensitivity to Growth inhibitory Signals

Just as cancer cells can become overly sensitive to growth factors, cancer cells can also become selectively deaf to signals that normally slow cell division. Most of these changes involve mutations that block receptors for growth inhibitory signals. An interesting example is found in the growth inhibiting signals transmitted when cells are properly anchored in place. The anchors that attach cells to each other are formed by special cell adhesion molecules (CAMs), which are imbedded in the membranes of adjacent cells and stick to each other. When such contact is made, the internal parts of these molecules activate a signaling system that reduces cyclin levels and slows or stops cell division. A key pair of players in this system are molecules called cadherins, which are the transmembrane anchoring molecules, and catenins, which are the internal signaling partners of cadherins. Defects in these systems can lead to the loss of the stop signals associated with cell anchors and cause unregulated cell growth.

Evasion of Programmed Cell Death

Many of the strategies cancer cells use to sustain rapid growth and spread throughout the body cause cellular damage and would be suicidal for normal cells. First of all, most changes in cancer cells result from some kind of mutation. Mutational damage to DNA is detected by normal cells and frequently triggers cell death. Cancer cells accumulate an impressive array of mutational defects but fail to trigger cell death when the mutations occur. In addition, the metabolic stresses of rapid cell division, including oxygen deprivation, normally trigger cell death, except in cancer cells. Finally, cell death is triggered when cells lose contact with other cells and their anchors are disrupted, except in cancer cells. The biochemical pathways that trigger apoptosis or cell death are becoming more clearly understood and are quite complex. There are several mutations, including in the p53 encoding gene as described earlier, that can disrupt this process and allow cancer cells to survive despite the presence of several apoptosis-triggering signals.

The loss of apoptotic capacity in cancer cells has important implications for cancer treatment. Many cancer treatments in wide use today, including radiation and chemotherapy, are designed to cause DNA damage to rapidly dividing cells. The logic of these treatments is that targeting DNA synthesis will focus the treatment on cells undergoing rapid division. Therefore, cancer cells will be selectively affected, and slower growing healthy cells will experience less damage. The catch is that even though the rapidly dividing cancer cells accumulate damage from the treatment, they frequently fail to react to that damage by triggering cell death. Therefore, the very design of the treatment is often defeated by one of the properties that comprise the hallmarks of cancer.

The good news is that research reveals the mechanisms of apoptosis are quite complex and can be triggered many different ways. Though some cancers may have mutations that block apoptosis from damage to DNA, they may still activate cell death from loss of cellular anchors. A number of cancer treatments are in development target the apoptosis pathways that are still intact in cancer cells, to activate cell death to eliminate cancer cells.

Limitless Replicative Potential

Almost all normal cells can divide only a limited number of times. For many years it has been known that cells removed from the body and grown in cell culture survive for a limited number of cell divisions. Once human cells have divided 60–70 times, they become incapable of further division and die. In contrast, cancer cells never stop dividing. They can be cultured in the laboratory indefinitely. This raises the question, what exactly wears out in normal cells that stops their ability to divide?

Much of the answer is found in the special structures at the ends of chromosomes, called telomeres. These are special repeating DNA sequences that serve two critical functions. First, they help protect the free ends of chromosomes. Double-stranded ends of DNA molecules are viewed by cells with deep suspicion. Except for telomeres, the only source of double-stranded DNA ends in cells would be from broken chromosomes, or DNA introduced by viruses—both clear signs of trouble. When double-stranded DNA ends do occur in cells, several proteins bind to them and check them for matching sequences elsewhere in the genome. If such matches are found, the ends are joined in DNA repair. If there is no match, enzymes are employed to degrade the DNA or even kill the cell. Telomere sequences are protected by special telomere specific proteins that bind to their repetitive DNA sequences. This combination of repetitive sequence and protective proteins allow the normal ends of chromosomes to exist in cells without triggering repair.

A second important function of telomere sequences is to accommodate problems with DNA replication at double-stranded DNA ends. DNA polymerase, the enzyme that functions in DNA synthesis, can add new DNA sub-units only to the ends of an existing DNA strand. DNA molecules are double stranded, and the strands run in opposite directions. During DNA replication, one strand can be synthesized to the end of a chromosome because the DNA strand is oriented so that DNA polymerase can move out toward the end as it functions. In contrast, the other strand of the DNA molecule is oriented the opposite way, and DNA polymerase moves in from the end (**Figure 20.7**). The DNA bases right at the end cannot be properly replicated on that strand. Consequently, at each cell division the ends of DNA molecules are not completely replicated, and some sequence is lost. During each cell division, some of the repeated telomere DNA sequences are lost from chromosomes ends. The repetitive nature of telomeres accommodates this under-replication problem. At birth, our telomeres are quite long, and there are plenty of repeats to lose. However, as we age and cells continue to divide, the sequences are progressively lost until all of the repeats are gone. These "worn out" telomeres then lose their ability to bind to the protective proteins and are attacked by the repair functions that frequently attempt join them together. This creates a long string of connected chromosomes that cannot separate properly in mitosis. When these form, the cells enters a crisis phase and ultimately dies.

Cancer cells avoid this problem. They activate a special enzyme, called telomerase, that can rebuild telomere sequences and prevent the cell from ever entering crisis. The expression of telomerase is normally limited to very few cells in the body, primarily stem cells and germ line cells in the gonads. These special cells are the rare examples of healthy cells in the body that have limitless replicative potential. Cancer cells use the strategy of these cell types and activate telomerase to continuously rebuild their telomeres and avoid the crisis and death caused by telomere loss. Indeed, nearly 90% of cancers

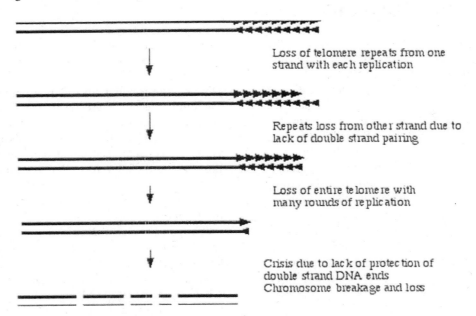

▲ Figure 20.7. Normal chromosome ends, called telomeres, have repeated sequences. At each round of replication, a few of these repeated sequences are not properly replicated and are lost. After many cell divisions, each with a round of DNA replication, all the telomere repeats can be lost. When this occurs, the DNA ends are not protected, the chromosome enters a crisis of joining to other chromosomes, fails to separate properly in mitosis, and ultimately dies.

have activated telomerase as one of the genetic changes that have led to their cancerous state.

The telomerase activity present in cancer cells has recently become the target of new experimental cancer therapies. The strategy is to block the activity of telomerase and prevent the rebuilding of telomeres. Because of their rapid rates of DNA replication, cancer cells without telomerase would quickly exhaust their supply of telomere sequences and enter crisis phase.

These therapies have some promise, but also some concerns. Most healthy cells do not have active telomerase, while most cancer cells do. This provides a mechanism for specificity of treatment. If telomerase is inhibited by some drug or genetic therapy, most healthy cells wouldn't be affected, while cancer cells would. However, the healthy cells that do express telomerase are very important. For example, the stem cells in bone marrow that divide continuously to produce blood cells have active telomerase. The potential to negatively affect stem cells with telomerase therapy has led to careful consideration of this approach and efforts to target the telomerase treatment away from such sensitive cells.

Sustained Angiogenesis and Nutrient Supply

As tumors grow and their cell division rate increases, their metabolic needs increase as well. Not only are nutrients required that build cellular structures, but oxygen is required for cellular respiration. To meet these demands, cancer cells develop the ability to stimulate the growth of blood vessels, called angiogenesis. Cancer cells release factors that activate signaling systems that cause blood vessels to branch and grow. An example is the overproduction by some cancer cells of vascular epithelial growth factor (VEGF), a secreted molecule that is released by cancer cells and interacts with receptors on the epithelial cells of blood vessels. This interaction causes the cells to grow and divide. In addition, these activated blood vessel cells become motile, and can grow into new tissues. As they do, they form new blood vessels that supply nutrients and oxygen. These functions are characteristic of normal blood vessel growth, where the cells of small vessels or capillaries divide and grow into new tissue, ultimately organizing into the tubes that are connected to existing blood vessels and extending the supply of blood. The difference with tumors is that the signals that stimulate this growth are expressed at very high levels and lead to the hypervascularization of tumors and rich supplies of blood and nutrients. Not only does this supply the cancer cells with nutrients and oxygen they require for their rapid growth, but in advanced cancers, these tumors can rob surrounding healthy tissue of adequate nutrients and oxygen and contribute significantly to the pathology of cancer.

Researchers are developing therapies to block angiogenesis stimulated by tumors and to rob them of their blood supply. For example, a therapy that would interfere with VEGF signaling by pancreatic tumor cells has been successful in mouse model systems and is currently being developed as a human therapy. Pancreatic cancers are particularly angiogenic, and it accounts in part for their aggressive growth, spread, and ability to affect overall metabolism.

Tissue Invasion and Metastasis

Careful analysis shows that the spread of cancer not only involves the release from anchors or attachments cells normally have, but also requires the activation of cell motility systems. Many cells can crawl or move from place to place by rearranging their cytoskeleton. Motility is characteristic of many cells early in development. Mesenchymal cells are a key example. These cells have very active cytoskeletal systems and can send out projections, called filopodia, to explore their surroundings and ruffle their edges, forming broad protrusions called lamellipodia. Active filopodia and lamellipodia are characteristic of motile cells that can crawl or move from place to place. Some normal cells, like white blood cells, have this mobile nature as well, but most mature cells do not, and stay anchored in place. Key genes involved in mobilizing filopodia and lamellipodia are rac, rho, and cdc42. Misregulation of these genes is common in cancer cells capable of invasive growth and metastasis (**Figure 20.8**). Cancer cells shift from their role as stationary cells within organs to motile cells that can crawl to new locations and penetrate other tissues by changing the dynamics of their internal structural supports.

▷ Evolution of Tumor Cells

Many genetic changes occur during the transition normal cells make to become cancer cells. The receptor systems involved in growth signaling are disrupted, cell death pathways are blocked, cell motility proteins are altered, the ability to induce changes in other cells, especially blood vessels, is acquired, and immortality is achieved by protecting chromosome ends. Each of these changes requires mutations to alter the genes that function in these central aspects of cell physiology. By the

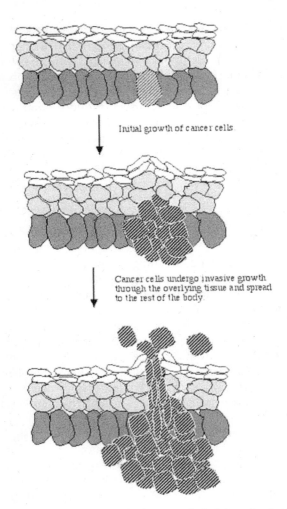

Initial growth of cancer cells.

Cancer cells undergo invasive growth through the overlying tissue and spread to the rest of the body.

Figure 20.8. Invasive growth of cancer cells. Early in tumor development, cancer cells grow, but remain in place in the tissue. As cancer progresses, the cells develop the ability to change shape, secrete enzymes that break down surrounding tissues, and grow through adjacent cell layers. This invasive growth allows cancer cells to metastasize, or spread, to new locations in the body where they can attach and form new tumors.

time cancer has progressed to a lethal level, an entire array of mutations has occurred to produce the hallmarks of cancer that appear in the ultimate tumor cells. But how does this progression occur? Is there an inevitable deterioration of cancer cells that lead them to this life-threatening state?

It is helpful to compare the development of cancer to the process of evolution by natural selection. In natural selection, genetic mutations that increase reproductive success become more frequent in a population over time. When this logic is applied to populations of cancer cells, it can explain the progression of small, slow-growing, localized tumors to large, rapidly growing tumors with rich blood supplies and the capacity to spread throughout the body.

A critical requirement for the selection process is a source of genetic variation. In the body, cells all start out with the same genetic makeup, and therefore no genetic variation exists. Cells become genetically different when mutations occur in some cells but not others. When mutations occur at a high enough rate, it can create genetic variation among cells to allow selection to operate. Through the process of selection, cells that can

divide more rapidly than others become more frequent than their slow-growing counterparts. Importantly, because mutations that occur in a cell are passed to both daughter cells at each cell division, mutations that cause rapid cell division accumulate in rapidly growing cells. As mutations occur that cause some cells to divide and grow more rapidly than others, those mutant cells would become more prevalent in a tissue. Further mutation may occur, and again this causes some of those more rapidly growing cells to divide even faster. As this process recurs, the most common cells in the tissue would be the cells that have accumulated mutations that allow them to divide the fastest. Ultimately, mutations accumulate and selection occurs until cancer cells have acquired the six hallmarks of cancer previously described. It is clear that agents that cause mutation, such as radiation and some toxins, increase cancer rates, and that the likelihood of developing cancer from these sources is correlated with their mutagenic strength.

If we follow a cell lineage from its healthy start to its final fate as a part of a fully developed tumor we might observe the following mutation sequence. Initially, a cell might acquire a mutation in growth factor receptors that would increase the balance of growth stimulating signals and decrease growth inhibiting signals. The descendants of this cell would now divide faster than neighbors and form a small benign tumor. Next, a cell within this tumor might develop an additional mutation that blocks apoptosis so that the stress of increased growth rates would not trigger cell death. Cells derived from this mutant cell would now not only be dividing faster, but would not undergo apoptosis and disappear from the tumor. Within this cell-death-resistant population of tumor cells, a mutation might occur that stimulates the release of VEGF and cause the formation of blood vessels that would supply the tumor with nutrients. Again, further mutations could occur in a cell within the tumor that activate cell motility and allow that cell and its descendants to lose anchors and move from the original site. When these cells move to new sites in the body, they would retain all of these mutations: They would be capable of growing rapidly, resistant to cell death, and able to induce the formation of new blood vessels. Finally, cells in this population could mutate further to activate telomerase and become immortal, unconstrained by the limits on DNA replication imposed by telomere shortening.

It should be noted that each mutation did not occur in every cell within the tumor. The cell in which it did occur, however, had a growth advantage, and because all of its descendants also carried the mutation, they too shared this advantage. Over time, this higher rate of growth in this population of mutant cells allowed them to outnumber other cells within the tumor that did not have the mutation. Also, a series of mutations is required. There are two logical outcomes of this. First, if mutations are rare, then the accumulation of multiple mutations must take time. This is consistent with the observation that cancer is largely a disease of old age. Data on almost all types of cancer suggest that time is required for mutations to accumulate and full-blown cancer to develop (Figure 20.9). But age is not the only factor. Agents such as radiation or chemical mutagens that increase the rate at which mutations occur will also accelerate the appearance of cancer in the body.

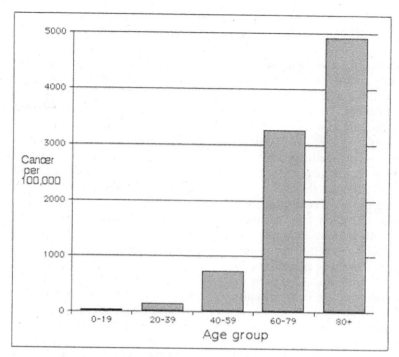

Figure 20.9. The incidence of cancer in different age groups in the United States. Cancer is quite rare prior to age 40, before a sufficient number of mutations have accumulated in cells of the body. However, as we age, the mutations accumulate and the incidence of cancer increases dramatically.

Source: "Cancer Facts and Figures 2001." American Cancer Society. http://www.cancer.org/eprise/main/docroot/STT/stt_0_2001?sitearea +STT&level+1.

Side Effects and Dirty Tricks—Drug Resistance

As cancer cells accumulate mutations, some of the changes they cause contribute to the severity of the disease and the difficulty in its treatment. For example, Richard's cancer ultimately became resistant to chemotherapy, and spread in the face of aggressive treatment. This kind of drug resistance has been shown to result from mutations that occur in tumor cells. There are several kinds of mutation that can confer resistance to drugs, but two examples are especially instructive. The first is P-glycoprotein, a transmembrane protein that can function as a pump to eject cancer drugs from the cell before the drug can have therapeutic effects. As expression of the P-glycoprotein gene increases in cancer cells, they increase their capacity to pump chemotherapy drugs out, and this dramatically decreases treatment effectiveness.

The second drug resistance feature shared by many cancer cell centers around the anti-apoptotic characteristic of cancer. Many chemotherapy agents use the strategy of damaging DNA, and rely on the DNA damage detection system in cells to activate apoptosis. However, many cancer cells experience mutations in these very systems during their development. They may no longer be able to detect DNA damage or use signals from DNA damage detection to activate apoptosis.

This represents a central paradox of cancer therapy, that the very characteristics that are defined as hallmarks of cancer cells also defeat the treatment strategies commonly used in cancer therapy.

Cachexia. One of the life-threatening side effects of many kinds of cancer is uncontrollable weight loss, specifically marked by the wasting away of muscle and other lean tissue. This condition, termed cachexia, is the direct cause of 10–20% of cancer deaths. The causes of cachexia are complex and not fully understood. It is clear, however, that the metabolism of healthy cells is affected by signals released by cancer cells. Some of these signals include protein and lipids that affect appetite control centers in the brain. Other signals can directly induce metabolic changes within healthy cells. These metabolic changes then lead to loss of healthy cells, and the wasting of healthy tissue. Tumor-derived signals released in the bloodstream are received by muscle and change the rate of protein degradation within muscle cells. This capacity of tumor cells to not only elude intrinsic damage-monitoring systems, avoid cell death, hijack the blood supply, resist drug therapy, and cause the deterioration of healthy tissue, points out the severity of the disease and the imposing challenges of developing treatments.

▷ Hereditary vs. Sporadic Cancer

We have seen that there is a close link between mutations and the development of cancer. In fact our current understanding of cancer suggests that all cancers arise as a result of cell mutations. When a cancer cell divides, it passes its mutations on to the two new cancer cells that are formed. However, saying that all cancers arise as a result of mutations in cells is not the same as saying that all cancers are hereditary. Mutations that arise in pancreatic cells may cause pancreatic cancer in that individual. But those mutations are in the cells of the pancreas; they are not in the egg or sperm cells that supply genetic information to the next generation. Egg and sperm cells are germ-line cells. Pancreatic cells are among the cells known as somatic, or body, cells. The genetic information from somatic cells is never passed to a new generation. So mutations in somatic cells may lead to cancer but these mutations cannot be inherited or cause cancer in the patient's children.

We do know that some forms of cancer can be inherited. A good example would be some forms of breast cancer. Breast cancer sometimes will "run in families" and the affected families will have a very high incidence of breast cancer. But even in these high-risk families not every woman is certain to develop breast cancer. What is inherited is a predisposition, or increased likelihood, of developing breast cancer. In light of what we know about cancer, what can explain this inherited predisposition to develop breast cancer? Well, we know that no type of cancer is the result of a single mutation. Each is the result of some series of mutations. Let us assume that we know that a certain series of mutations can lead to breast cancer. If an individual was to inherit from either parent, either through the egg or sperm, one of the mutations in the series, there would be one less mutation that would have to occur within the breast cells of that individual for cancer to arise. The mutation that they inherited from the parent would be present in all of the individual's cells, including the breast cells. Having inherited one of the mutations in the series increases the likelihood that breast cancer will develop, but does not make it inevitable.

Recently, much attention has been given to the discovery of "the genes for breast cancer." In fact what was discovered were two genes, BRCA1 and BRCA2. These are not the only two genes involved in the development of breast cancer.

However, inheriting a mutated form of either of these two genes greatly increases a person's risk of developing breast cancer. It makes the most sense to refer to BRCA1 and BRCA2 as breast cancer susceptibility genes. In the United States approximately 1 in 12 women develops breast cancer. However, only between 5 and 10% of breast cancers are hereditary. Another way of saying this is that between 90 and 95% of breast cancer patients do not carry germ-line mutations that predispose them to developing the disease. In these patients, all of the mutations necessary to develop breast cancer occurred sporadically within breast cells some time during their lifetime. In the other 5 to 10% of brest cancer patients, those with hereditary cancer, at least one of the mutations necessary for cancer development was present at birth.

The BRCA1 and BRCA2 genes were discovered by examining families with very high incidence of early-onset breast cancer. The BRCA1 gene was mapped to a position on chromosome 17 and BRCA2 to a position on chromosome 13. Interestingly, even though BRCA1 was discovered in 1994 and BRCA2 was discovered in 1995, we are still not sure of the exact function of the proteins coded for by these two genes or how they specifically contribute to the development of breast cancer. BRCA1 is believed to be a tumor suppressor gene. Recent work on BRCA1 has suggested that it is involved in the damage control process, and may help recognize broken DNA molecules. If this is the case, it may explain why inheriting a mutation in this gene has such a strong effect on the likelihood of cancer development. If the defect from BRCA1 mutations reduces the detection of DNA damage, it would reduce the chance that it would be repaired. In these individuals, DNA damage would accumulate more rapidly and accelerate cancer formation.

The characterization of these genes points out another important aspect of cancer research. In families with inherited cancer, it is now possible to do genetic testing to determine just which individuals carry mutations in genes such as BRCA1 and BRCA2 that are known to increase the likelihood of cancer. These tests allow people with high levels of cancer risk to be identified. They can then go for checkups more frequently and improve the chances of detecting early any cancer that does arise.

Smoking and Cancer

Just as we all have a sense that a predisposition to some cancers seems to be inherited, we also all have a sense that environmental factors can be involved in the onset of cancer. A great example of this is the relationship between smoking and lung cancer. For a very long time, epidemiological evidence has been accumulating that links cigarette smoking to lung cancer. (Epidemiological evidence is simply data that draw a correlation between the occurrence of a disease and other factors.) As the prevalence of smoking in a population increases, the prevalence of lung cancer also increases. In the United States this was true when men began to smoke in large numbers and much later when women began to smoke in large numbers. There is also a relationship between the number of cigarettes smoked and the likelihood of developing cancer. The more cigarettes one smokes the more likely one is to develop cancer. Finally, stopping smoking can be demonstrated to decrease the likelihood of developing lung cancer. This is all strong evidence but none of it demonstrates a direct cause-and-effect relationship.

Just showing a correlation, or coincidence in the occurrence of two events, is not always completely convincing. For years the tobacco companies obscured the dangers of smoking by attacking the fact that it was "just" correlations between smoking and lung cancer that were used to argue that smoking actually causes cancer. It would be better to show cause and effect directly to demonstrate that smoking cigarettes can cause lung cancer. The first evidence for a direct cause-and-effect relationship came in 2001 when researchers were able to demonstrate that a chemical in cigarette smoke causes mutations in the tumor suppressor gene that codes for the p53 protein. The chemical, benzopyrene, is found in the tars of cigarette smoke. Ironically, in an attempt to rid the body of this insoluble chemical, the liver converts benzopyrene into the more chemically reactive benzopyrene diol epoxide. It is this chemical that interacts with DNA and cause mutations in specific sites in the p53 gene. As we have already learned, the p53 protein plays an important role in arresting cell division, activating repair enzymes, and if necessary, triggering cell death. The loss of these tumor-suppressor functions is an important step in the development of lung cancer.

The idea that cigarette smoke causes lung cancer by producing mutations also helps to explain another phenomenon. The link between cigarette smoking and lung cancer is not an immediate one. The prevalence of lung cancer in a population does not go up as soon as the rate of cigarette smoking begins to increase. There is a lag of between 20 and 30 years. We know that cancers develop through the accumulation of a series of mutations. It takes time for the entire series of mutations to build up, even if they are being produced in part by chemicals in smoke. Even if one or more of the mutations is inherited, the remainder of mutations must occur to ultimately lead to the category of disease we know as cancer.

Randall Phillis
Department of Biology
University of Massachusetts
Amherst, MA 01002
rphillis@bio.umass.edu

Steve Goodwin
Department of Microbiology
University of Massachusetts
Amherst, MA 01002
sgoodwin@microbio.umass.edu

▷ Web Resources

Cancer Cell Cam
http://www.cellsalive.com/cam1.htm
This site presents images of human melanoma cells growing in cell culture. The sequence presents a number of cell divisions over a 24-hour period. A fresh image is loaded every 10 minutes. It is maintained on the cellsalive.com website authored by James A. Sullivan of Charlottesville, VA.

Cancer.gov
http://www.cancer.gov/cancer_information/
This site created by the National Cancer Institute (NCI) of the National Institutes of Health (NIH), contains straightforward information about cancer intended for patients, healthcare providers and the public. Of particular interest might be the section on clinical trials.

NCI
http://www.nci.nih.gov/
This is the official site of the National Cancer Institute, the primary U.S. government agency that oversees cancer research and treatment.

http://www.infobiogen.fr/services/chromcancer/
Atlas of Genetics and Cytogenetics in Oncology and Haematology
This site has resources for understanding chromosome rearrangements that occur in certain kinds of cancer, particularly leukemias. In addition, there are several links to other cancer related sites.

http://www.cancercare.org/
CANCERcare
This site has several resources related to cancer diagnosis, treatement and care of cancer patients.

http://www.nabco.org/
National Alliance of Breast Cancer Organizations
This site contains a comprehensive set of links and information about breast cancer.

http://www.fhcrc.org/
Fred Hutchinson Cancer Research Center
This is a world renowned cancer research center. There are a wide range or resources on this site including information for students about undergraduate and graduate opportunities to participate in projects and reseach underway at the center.

http://oncolink.upenn.edu/
OncoLink
This is the web site of the University of Pennsylvania Cancer Center. This has important links to information about clinical trials underway to test new cancer treatments.

http://www.cshl.org/public/overviews/cancer.html
Cold Spring Harbor Laboratory Cancer Research
This is the home page for cancer researchers at the Cold Spring Harbor Laboratory, a world leading institution for molecular biology research. Information from several labs working on current problems in cancer research are featured.

http://www.cancersource.com/
CancerSource
A rich array of resources about cancer types, and treatements.

http://www.academicpress.com/semcancer
Seminars in Cancer Biology—Academic Press
For cancer professionals, this journal has topical issues about specific cancer topics.

▷ Books and Articles

Cooper, G. M. (1993). *The Cancer Book.* Jones and Bartlett Publishers, Boston.

Hanahan, D., and R. A. Weinberg (2000). "The Hallmarks of Cancer." *Cell, 100*:57–70.

Varmus, H., and R. A. Weinberg (1993). *Genes and the Biology of Cancer.* Scientific American Library (distributed by W. H. Freeman).

Weinberg, R. A. (1996). "How Cancer Arises." *Scientific American, 275*(3):62–70. (http://www.sciam.com/0996issue/0996weinberg.html)

Weinberg, R. A. (1996). *Racing to the Beginning of the Road: The Search for the Origin of Cancer.* Harmony Books.

Welsch, P., and M. C. King (2001). "BRCA1, BRCA2 and the genetics of breast and ovarian cancer." *Human Molecular Genetics, 10*:705–713.

21 Stem Cells and Cloning

▷ Introduction

A woman with Parkinson's disease shuffles along a hallway with awkward, rigid movements and tremors. A man sits by a window in a wheelchair, ten years after an accident left him paralyzed from his neck down. Another man lies in a hospital bed after a heart attack has damaged part of his heart. What do these three individuals have in common? They have hope that stem cells may be able to help them to regenerate tissues in their bodies. **Regenerative medicine**, growing cells and tissues that can be used to replace or repair defective tissues and organs, is undergoing exciting changes as a result of recent advances in stem cell technology. Conditions such as these are just a few examples in which the treatment may drastically change in the future as our understanding of stem cells continues to improve. Some of the diseases that scientists believe stem cell technologies may one day play an important role in treating are listed in **Table 21.1**.

You are likely familiar with some of the controversy surrounding stem cells today, but did you know that some stem cell therapies have been around for decades? For example, bone marrow transplantation is a form of stem cell therapy. Bone marrow contains one kind of **adult-derived stem cells (ASCs)**, the stem cells that regenerate tissues similar to those various, specialized tissues of the body in which they are found. During a bone marrow transplant, stem cells are transferred from a healthy donor to a needy recipient, where they then regenerate various blood cell types as needed. Obviously, then, some stem cells are already successfully being used in regenerative medicine today, and it looks like they continue to hold much hope for the future.

Scientists believe that another type of stem cell may have an even greater potential. The **embryonic stem cell (ESC)** is a type of stem cell retrieved from an early stage embryo. Unlike an ASC, which is limited in the type of tissue it can regenerate (e.g., a bone marrow cell only forms blood cells); an ESC can form all tissues of the body. Nevertheless, there are many hurdles yet to be overcome to make ESCs a viable treatment in regenerative medicine.

TABLE 21.1   STEM CELL–BASED THERAPIES MAY POTENTIALLY BENEFIT MILLIONS OF PEOPLE

Disease condition	Number of patients in the United States
Cardiovascular disease	58 million
Autoimmune diseases	30 million
Diabetes	16 million
Osteoporosis	10 million
Cancers (urinary bladder, prostate, ovarian, breast, brain, lung, and colorectal cancers; brain tumors)	8.2 million
Degenerative retinal disease	5.5 million
Phenylketonuria (PKU)	5.5 million
Severe combined immunodeficiency (SCID)	0.3 million
Sickle-cell disease	0.25 million
Neurodegenerative diseases (Alzheimer's and Parkinson's diseases)	0.15 million

Source: Table adapted from Stem Cells and the Future of Regenerative Medicine, www.nap.edu/catalog/10195.html.

While scientists can make many different cell types from ESCs, they still have much to learn about how these cells might behave if transplanted into a person. Additionally, much of the research needed to answer these questions has been slowed by political and ethical opposition to working with these cells. Traditionally, human ESCs have been retrieved from 5- to 7-day-old embryos, and retrieval of these cells destroys the embryos. Many people believe that ESC research should not be carried out if embryos are destroyed in the process.

While there is substantial political and ethical debate surrounding stem cells, scientists continue to make advances. Some scientists may avoid the moral debate by continuing the important search for new types of ASCs and new therapies utilizing them. Other scientists work within the framework of the current tense political climate. They continue to explore the possibilities of ESCs, including cells derived from controversial cloning techniques. In this booklet, we will examine what important discoveries scientists have made with stem cells and cloning, while concurrently being subjected to intense scrutiny.

▷ Stem Cell Basics

What is a Stem Cell?

What makes stem cells such attractive candidates for repairing failing tissues and organs? A **stem cell** has two basic characteristics that make it unique from other cell types (**Figure 21.1**). The first is that it continues to grow and proliferate, maintaining a pool of cells just like itself for possible future use (termed **self-renewal**). The second characteristic of a stem cell is that, given the correct signals, it can **differentiate** into a particular specialized cell type, such as a muscle or blood cell. When a stem cell divides, each of the daughter cells can either remain a stem cell or become a specialized cell. Let's further consider the concept of differentiation. Aside from gametes (egg and sperm cells), all the cells in an individual's body have the same DNA content and the same genes. What makes one of your muscle cells different from one of your blood cells? These cells are

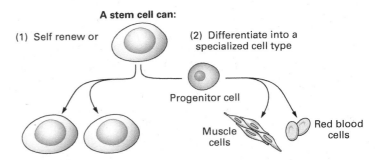

A stem cell can:
(1) Self renew or
(2) Differentiate into a specialized cell type
Progenitor cell
Muscle cells
Red blood cells

▲ **Figure 21.1** Characteristics of a stem cell. Differentiation often occurs in various steps. Partly differentiated precursors, also known as progenitor cells, give rise to fully differentiated cells such as red blood cells or muscle cells.

Source: Figure adapted from "Understanding Stem Cells," National Academies.

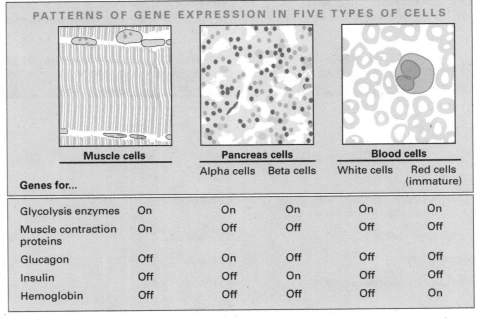

PATTERNS OF GENE EXPRESSION IN FIVE TYPES OF CELLS

Genes for...	Muscle cells	Pancreas cells		Blood cells	
		Alpha cells	Beta cells	White cells	Red cells (immature)
Glycolysis enzymes	On	On	On	On	On
Muscle contraction proteins	On	Off	Off	Off	Off
Glucagon	Off	On	Off	Off	Off
Insulin	Off	Off	On	Off	Off
Hemoglobin	Off	Off	Off	Off	On

▲ **Figure 21.2** Unique "protein profiles" of five differentiated cell types. These differentiated cells have identical genes, but not all of the same genes are expressed in each cell type. If a particular gene is expressed in a specific cell type it is labeled as "on." Note that some genes are expressed in all cells (e.g., glycolysis enzymes involved in storing energy for a cell), while others are unique to one cell type (e.g., an oxygen transport protein, hemoglobin, is specific to red blood cells).

Source: Figure adapted from Campbell, Reece, Mitchell, and Taylor, *Biology: Concepts and Connections*, Fourth Edition, p. 212.

differentiated, or specialized to carry out a particular task (e.g., contraction in muscle cells or oxygen transport in red blood cells). While these two cell types contain the same genes, the specific set of genes that are being turned "on" or expressed are *not* identical. Since gene expression ultimately leads to protein expression, the "profiles" of proteins in specialized cells are different from each other (**Figure 21.2**). In fact, we all began life unspecialized. As our cells divided and began expressing a unique set of genes necessary for specific tasks, we each became a complex adult with over 200 differentiated cell types.

Some stem cells seem to have more abilities, or possibilities, than other stem cells; this flexibility is termed the **potency** of the stem cell. A stem cell that is **unipotent** can form only one differentiated cell type. A **multipotent** stem cell can form multiple different cells and tissue types. A **pluripotent** stem cell can form most or all of the 200 or more differentiated cell types in the adult body. A **totipotent** stem cell can form not only all adult body cell types, but also the specialized tissues needed for development of the embryo, such as the placenta.

Where do Stem Cells Come From?

At one time, it was thought that stem cells were only present in an embryo. Now we know that there are actually a lot of sources of stem cells, ranging from cells of the early embryo to the adult body. We can follow human development and examine the stages from which scientists have found stem cells (**Figure 21.3**). Traditionally, each of these stem cells has been categorized as either an embryonic stem cell (ESC) or adult-derived stem cell (ASC); but, as the research continues, the categories become less clear.

When a sperm cell fertilizes an egg cell, a single-celled embryo (**zygote**) forms. The zygote contains a complete set of genetic material (both the sperm and egg contribute half). This cell divides to become two cells, which divide to form four cells, and each of these cells divide to form an 8-celled embryo (three days after fertilization). Recently, scientists have demonstrated that cells of the 8-celled embryo can be removed from the embryo and grown in a laboratory dish to become ESCs.

Around five to seven days into development, the human embryo consists of approximately 100 to 150 cells and resembles a hollow ball with some cells inside; this is termed a **blastocyst.** Since 1981, when two independent groups first established pluripotent stem cell lines from mouse blastocysts, scientists have focused on this stage in embryonic development as the key stage in development for human ESC retrieval. The outer layer of the blastocyst, called the **trophoblast** cells, consists of cells which develop to form parts of the placenta that are derived from the embryo. The cells inside the blastocyst are called the **inner cell mass**—these form all the cells of the baby. However, if these inner cells are removed and grown in a laboratory dish, these are now termed ESCs. Human ESCs were first retrieved from blastocysts in 1998 by Dr. James Thomson and his colleagues at the University of Wisconsin in Madison. Removal of the inner cells destroys the embryo. We will examine ESCs in much more detail later.

The largest potential source of ESCs is from the excess embryos produced by assisted reproductive technologies. Fertilization of an egg by sperm can occur either *in vivo* (inside a woman's body) or *in vitro* (outside of the body; e.g., in a test

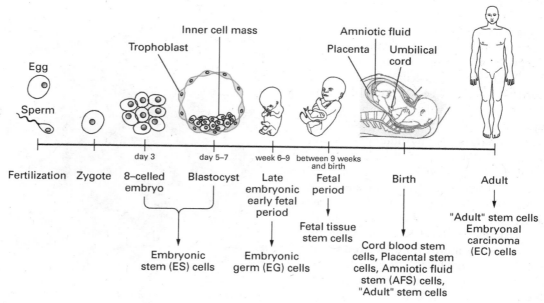

▲ **Figure 21.3** The continuum of human development and sources of stem cells at various stages.

Source: Figure adapted from Prentice and Palladino, *Stem Cells and Cloning*, p. 5, Figure 2.

tube). *In vitro* **fertilization (IVF)** is a type of assisted reproductive technology that involves the removal of multiple eggs from a woman and fertilization *in vitro*. Resulting embryos are then implanted into the woman's uterus. Usually only a few of the embryos produced by the technique will be implanted, thus creating an excess of embryos in freezers around the country. These "leftover" embryos may be donated (with the couple's consent) for research. It is estimated that approximately 400,000 embryos are stored in clinics around the United States, although there is controversy about how many of these would actually be available for research purposes.

About the same time that human ESCs were isolated, Dr. John Gearhart and his team at Johns Hopkins University reported that they had isolated what they called **human embryonic germ (hEG) cells.** These cells are derived from the precursor cells that will become germ cells (egg or sperm) and were removed from early embryos that are developing into fetuses (around 6 to 9 weeks of development). When grown *in vitro,* the cells show many of the same characteristics as ESCs. That is, they seem to be pluripotent and able to form most or all of the tissues of the adult body.

As human development proceeds and various tissues start to form, the ESCs form **progenitor cells,** the partially specialized precursor cells that go on to form the specific differentiated tissues of the body. This is a gradual process, and the fetus continues to contain many multipotent stem cells (now termed **fetal tissue stem cells**) that form several different cell types.

The stem cells that are found in differentiated tissues of the body at *any* stage of development are commonly known as adult-derived stem cells (ASCs). The term "adult-derived" stem cell is actually not completely correct and can be confusing. What scientists often define as an ASC can be present before birth, at birth, or much later in life. Some other terms for ASCs that might be more inclusive and could be used interchangeably are: **somatic stem cell**, **tissue-specific stem cells** or **nonembryonic stem cells**. Nevertheless, we will use the term "adult-derived stem cell" to be consistent with the current nomenclature.

As we follow human development further, we find that the prenatal tissues necessary for supporting human development, such as the placenta and umbilical cord, are rich sources of stem cells. Multipotent stem cells derived from the umbilical cord—**cord blood–derived embryonic-like stem cells (CBEs)**—appear to be less versatile than embryonic stem cells, but may have greater potential than the stem cells found in adult tissues. In early 2007, Dr. Anthony Atala from the Institute for Regenerative Medicine at Wake Forest University School of Medicine announced that he and colleagues had carefully characterized a group of pluripotent stem cells that seemed to behave halfway between embryonic stem cells and adult-derived stem cells. These cells can be found in the placenta and the amniotic fluid that surrounds the fetus in the womb and are termed **amniotic fluid–derived stem (AFS) cells.** As research continues with these prenatal tissues and the potential of their stem cells are realized, many experts believe they will become their own "category" of stem cells.

In thinking about the human body after birth, scientists have known for years that some tissues, such as bone marrow, contain ASCs, and they have been used in many successful clinical treatments. In recent years, ASCs have been identified in most differentiated tissues of the human body and have demonstrated variant potency. Although they are sparse and difficult to locate, they have been successfully isolated from tissues such as the brain, muscle, skin, pancreas, bone marrow, blood, and liver.

One last type of stem cell that is also part of the broad category of adult-derived stem cells actually comes from a tumor called a **teratoma** (if benign) or a **teratocarcinoma** (if malignant). (Scientists noticed that occasionally such tumors contained not just a disorganized mass of growing cells, as in most tumors, but also some differentiated tissues, such as a bit of bone, hair, or teeth! [**Figure 21.4**]). These types of tumors form when a germ cell (sperm or egg) spontaneously starts to grow and divide. The cells retrieved from these tumors, **embryonal carcinoma (EC) cells,** have the properties of stem cells. This led to research in which the EC cells were grown over a period of years and "tamed," so that they would not grow as disorganized tumor masses but instead form specific differentiated cell types such as nerves.

As you can see, there are various sources of stem cells. Keep in mind that each type has its advantages and disadvantages, and scientists continue to examine all possibilities. In general, the controversy that exists is summed up using the terms "embryonic" and "adult-derived" stem cells. Some scientists believe that pluripotent embryonic stem cells, which can form all tissues in the body, hold the greatest hope for treating degenerative diseases. However, there are many ethical issues to consider when using cells from early embryos (we will discuss this later). Adult-derived stem cells create less of an ethical dilemma but may not have the capabilities for treating disease such as is thought possible with embryonic stem cells. Both options present technical challenges that still must be overcome. Let's consider these two groups of cells in more detail.

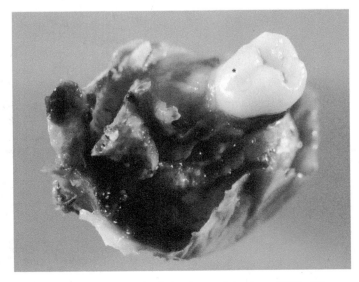

▲ **Figure 21.4**   An example of a benign cystic teratoma. Within this disorganized mass of tissue, teeth that have developed are obvious (*).

Source: © CNRI/Photo Researchers

▷ Embryonic Stem Cells (ESCs)

Human ESCs have been touted as a "virtual fountain of youth" because of their potential to repair and rejuvenate any damaged tissue in the body. In theory, this should be possible because these are the cells that initially form all body tissues during development. As mentioned before, human ESCs were first isolated from the blastocyst stage of development. The procedure involves removing the inner cell mass of about 30 cells from inside the blastocyst (**Figure 21.5**). Once scientists isolate these cells, maintain them in a laboratory dish, and show that they have the properties of embryonic stem cells, we call this an **embryonic stem cell line.** These cell lines are continually growing, dividing, and crowding the laboratory dish. To keep them in a pluripotent, undifferentiated state, the cell line needs to be carefully cared for and replated to new dishes as they continue to proliferate. Millions of ESCs are derived from the original 30 cells after several months of replating.

Removing the inner cells destroys the embryo, and this is the main reason that research on human ESCs is so controversial. Scientists continue to search for ways to derive ESCs without damaging the embryo. Independent of how these cells are derived, some embryos have been, and will be destroyed during the scientific discovery process. However, if ESCs can perform all the wonders claimed for them in tissue regeneration, might it be acceptable that some human embryos are destroyed so that millions of lives can be spared? We'll first examine the scientific facts, and then we'll come back to this ethical question later.

Characteristics of Embryonic Stem Cells

Embryonic stem cells are pluripotent, meaning they can potentially form all tissues of the human body. This is what they do during normal embryological development; their "job description" is the initial formation of all the body tissues. Remember the characteristics of all stem cells: 1) continued growth and self-renewal, and 2) the ability to form differentiated tissues when given the correct signals.

We know that ESCs have an amazing ability for prolonged growth and self renewal, but why is this so? The ends of linear chromosomes are called **telomeres** and have been compared to the plastic caps on the end of shoelaces that prevent them from unraveling. With each cell division, the telomere progressively shortens. Once some critical amount of the DNA at the telomere has been lost, a cell stops dividing and undergoes

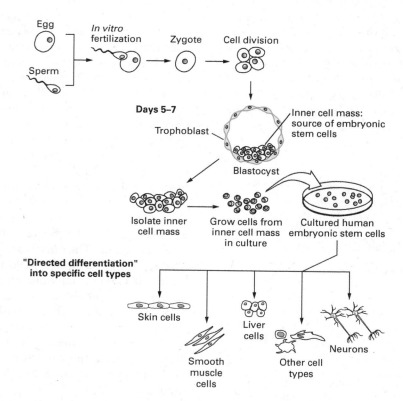

▲ **Figure 21.5**   Isolating and culturing human embryonic stem cells (ESCs). Cells isolated from blastocysts can be grown in culture as a source of ECSs. Under the proper conditions, ESCs can be stimulated to differentiate into virtually all cell types in the body.

Source: Figure adapted from Thieman and Palladino, *Introduction to Biotechnology*, p. 257, Figure 11.18.

senescence (cell aging). Telomerase is an enzyme that counteracts this process. **Telomerase** repairs telomere length at the ends of chromosomes by adding DNA nucleotides to cap the telomere after each round of cell division. Telomerase is not active in typical differentiated cells, but scientists have observed that human ESCs express high levels of this enzyme. For example, after approximately 50 to 80 population doublings *in vitro,* typical differentiated cells will senesce. In contrast, several groups have shown that after 600 population doublings (more than three years in culture), human ESCs still continue to proliferate without apparent problems. Scientists believe that human ESCs can be grown in the laboratory in a pluripotent state indefinitely. In fact, some mouse cell lines have been growing for 30 years! However, these mouse ESCs and some human ESC lines have demonstrated that the longer a cell line is maintained in culture, the more genetic mutations it acquires. Eventually a buildup of small mutations "tip the

scales," and the line is no longer useful. In sum, by preventing telomere shortening, telomerase activity is a major reason why ESCs can divide indefinitely.

As for the ability of ESCs to differentiate, scientists have been able to directly differentiate these cells into many unique cell types (see **Figure 21.5**). A few of the cell types into which ESCs have already been made are: heart, nerve, cartilage-forming, immune, skin, bone, adipocyte (fat), pancreatic, skeletal muscle, smooth muscle, and blood vessel cells. Research continues in this area of "**directed differentiation**" to discover the correct signals needed to produce the various cell types of the human body (think of this as tweaking a recipe so that it is just perfect). The signals that stimulate differentiation of stem cells include hormones, molecules called growth factors, and small proteins. Additionally, once a specific cell type is obtained, the cells need to undergo testing to be sure they actually function as expected.

Tests for Pluripotency, the Ability to Form any Body Tissue

What is the basis for the claim that an ESC can form any adult tissue? It is based on several different types of scientific studies. First is the simple fact that, under normal developmental conditions in an intact embryo and when left alone to do their job, ESCs will form all the tissues of our bodies.

Scientists have devised several tests for pluripotency. For ethical reasons, not all of these have been performed with human ESCs, but rigorous experimentation with mouse ESCs have demonstrated the pluripotency of these cells. In all tests, scientists look to see if the ESCs differentiate into cells that represent each of the three major layers of an early embryo (**Figure 21.6**). During embryological development, the inner cells first form three semi-specialized layers, the three **primary germ layers,** which then form the specific tissues in the body. These tissues are committed to a developmental pathway at this point. The outer layer, **ectoderm,** gives rise to skin, brain, and nerves.

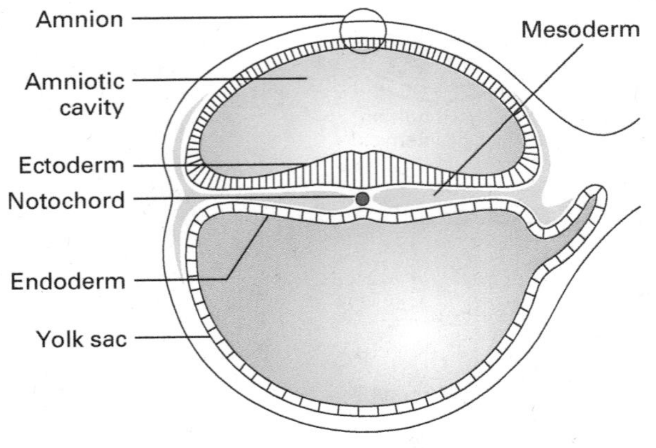

The middle layer, or **mesoderm,** forms blood, heart, bone, kidney, muscle, and cartilage. The innermost layer, the **endoderm,** develops into the lung, liver, and digestive system. It has been well demonstrated *in vitro* that human ESCs can differentiate into numerous cells types that represent all three germ layers. It is necessary, of course, to also demonstrate their abilities in a living system (*in vivo*), where they are exposed to the normal signals that cells experience.

In vivo tests to demonstrate pluripotency with human ESCs are limited. One that has been performed with several human cell lines tests their ability to form all three germ layers upon injection into mice. Injecting foreign cells into a normal mouse would cause a major immune system response, and these cells would be rejected by the host mouse. For this reason, these tests are performed with **immunodeficient** mice—that is, mice lacking a functional immune system. Such mice need to be kept in special sterile environments so that they do not get an infection; even a common cold might be deadly. Their lack of an immune system means that they will not reject the transplanted human cells. When embryonic stem cells are placed in these immunodeficient mice, tumors form. These tumors are similar to teratomas, with some of the ESCs differentiating into specialized cell types and tissues. The tumors are examined closely to see what types of specialized cells grow. For example, if ESCs that are injected into the immunodeficient mice form nerve cells, heart cells, and intestinal cells, this indicates that they should be pluripotent. Why? These three cell types each originate from a different primary germ layer. Although they may not form every single tissue type, experiments such as these have demonstrated that human ESCs have the ability.

Most scientists agree that the "gold standard" for demonstrating pluripotency *in vivo* would be to inject human ESCs into a developing embryo at the blastocyst stage (the same stage used to isolate embryonic stem cells). The resulting developing fetus would then be examined to determine if the

▲ **Figure 21.6**   The gastrula stage of human development. The three primary germ layers are formed (i.e., the ectoderm, the mesoderm, and the endoderm).

Source: Figure adapted from http://www.britannica.com/eb/art-2921/Development-of-the-human-embryo?articleTypeId=1.

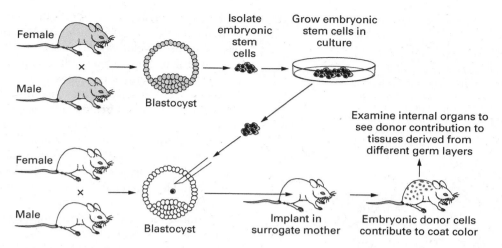

▲ Figure 21.7 Evidence that an embryonic stem cell is pluripotent and can contribute to all tissues. Mouse ESCs from one mouse (black) can be transferred to a blastocyst (produced from white mice). The resulting mouse will be a chimeric mouse. Various tissues, representing the three germ layers, will have formed from both the white and black stem cells.

Source: Figure adapted from Prentice and Palladino, *Stem Cells and Cloning*, p. 8, Figure 5.

injected ESCs contributed to development of all three germ layers. Experiments such as these have been performed with mouse cells—putting ESCs from one type of mouse into the embryo of another type of mouse (Figure 21.7). For example, if embryonic stem cells from a black mouse were put into an embryo for a white mouse, then the coat color of the mouse once born should be both white and black. (Other genetic markers can be tracked to see what tissues the injected stem cells helped to form internally, too.) Using these types of experiments, mouse ESCs have been able to help construct most or all of the body tissues of the mouse born.

Rather than using human embryos as hosts, which has major ethical implications, some scientists would like to perform similar experiments to test the pluripotency of human ESCs in which the human embryonic cells are injected into *mouse* blastocysts. The resulting fetus would similarly be examined for human cell contribution to various mouse tissues. However, the creation of embryos which are part human and part mouse, termed **human-mouse chimeras,** also has been strongly opposed on ethical grounds. Many people worry that this type of research is a "slippery slope" and that these experiments might lead to allowing adult mice, with human tissues, to be born. As eloquently stated by Nancy L. Jones, from the Center for Bioethics and Human Dignity:

> *Until such an experiment is actually conducted, there is no way of knowing if human stem cells could even produce tissue in a mouse, if such tissue would grow normally and function, or if all types of animal tissue could be converted to human tissue (the intriguing question emerges here of whether we would feel differently about human stem cells that contributed to the liver, rather than, say, to the brain). In the face of such ambiguity, the overarching ethical question is: Should we even begin these types of experiments?*

For now, scientists rely on the experiments that have been performed with human ESCs to demonstrate pluripotency and infer much from the numerous *in vivo* studies that have been performed with mouse ESCs. Interestingly, the nature of pluripotency remains a mystery. For example, what controls pluripotency? A hot area of stem cell research is to find a gene expression "profile" of a pluripotent stem cell in order to better understand the signals that control it.

What are the Possible Uses for Embryonic Stem Cells?

Many of the hopes for ESCs are based upon the past two decades of basic research with mouse ESCs. Medical research was transformed when scientists learned how to delete, add, or change genes in mouse ESCs. In fact, the 2007 Nobel Prize in Medicine was awarded to three scientists for their pioneering work in this area. By genetically engineering mouse ESCs, scientists learned to model many different human genetic diseases in mice, such as hemophilia and cystic fibrosis. Embryonic stem cells from many other mammals, such as cows and monkeys, have also provided valuable information about how these cells behave. The knowledge gained by working with various ESCs has led to important animal models for most major genetic diseases, and many useful therapies have followed. Research in the area of human ESCs is relatively new because these cells were not isolated until 1998. Let's explore some of the possible uses for human ESCs.

The hopes for human ESCs are enormous (Figure 21.8); and, despite what is most publicized in the media, not all of these hopes focus on direct use in patients. For example, many scientists see these types of cells as a basic science research tool to learn more about normal embryonic development. That is, what differentiation factors trigger development of progenitor cells into specialized tissues? How is pluripotency defined by a cell? What genes are specifically

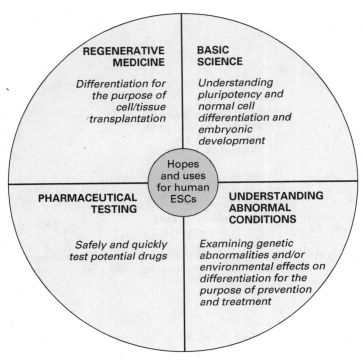

REGENERATIVE MEDICINE

Differentiation for the purpose of cell/tissue transplantation

BASIC SCIENCE

Understanding pluripotency and normal cell differentiation and embryonic development

Hopes and uses for human ESCs

PHARMACEUTICAL TESTING

Safely and quickly test potential drugs

UNDERSTANDING ABNORMAL CONDITIONS

Examining genetic abnormalities and/or environmental effects on differentiation for the purpose of prevention and treatment

▲ **Figure 21.8** A summary of the hopes and uses for human embryonic stem cells.

turned "on" or "off" in a pluripotent cell compared to a differentiated cell? Although scientists have learned much about human development using various animal models, there are significant differences between animals and humans. In fact, researchers are already finding that the signals that keep mouse ESCs and human ESCS in an undifferentiated state *in vitro* differ.

Another less obvious use for human ESCs is the ability to closely study specific genetic abnormalities. For diseases in which we know the genetic basis, scientists have the ability to add, delete, or alter genes in human ESC lines to model the human disorder at the cellular level. However, for more complex genetic diseases that require unknown causes for onset, scientists could use the genetic material from a person with that complex disease to make a new, unique ESC line (this is called therapeutic cloning, and we will discuss it later). What types of questions could be answered with these "diseased" ESCs? For example, when and why does a pancreatic cell stop producing insulin in a diabetic individual? Scientists could examine the process of pancreatic differentiation in ESCs that are normal and diabetic and compare them under different environmental conditions. In this way, scientists will learn much about how and why cells become "sick."

An important application of studies of human ESCs would be in the field of pharmaceutical testing. Consider this example: a scientist develops a drug for heart cells and needs to test the drug on human heart cells before going into human clinical trials. Because it is not possible to maintain human heart cell lines, the scientist must use animal models. Because animals and humans differ, the information gained about the drug's effectiveness or toxicity may not necessarily apply to humans. However, with the ability to differentiate human ESCs into heart cells, scientists can make an appropriate cell line at the time a drug is ready for testing. This type of application could lead to the faster development of safer and more effective drugs.

Of course, the most publicized hope for human ESCs is their possible use in regenerative medicine, in which failing body parts would be replaced with ESC-derived tissue. Unlike many therapies that exist today, this could, in theory, provide an unlimited supply of tissue. Some diseases are caused by the loss or dysfunction of only one or a few cell types. For example, insulin-producing pancreatic cells do not function in diabetes, and dopamine producing neurons are lost in Parkinson's disease. Scientists envision injecting a few ESC-derived pancreatic cells or neurons into the area in which they are needed and allowing the body to direct the regeneration. Others envision growing more patterned tissues and even whole organs that could repair larger failing parts. Additionally, with a process called therapeutic cloning, which we will discuss in detail later, these cells could theoretically be customized to an individual to avoid immune rejection. For example, if you had a heart attack, physicians could take some of your DNA from, say, a skin cell and make new ESCs that contain your genetic material. Once these cells were differentiated into heart cells, they could be used to repair your damaged heart!

So, human ESCs hold much promise for regenerative medicine, but they are not ready for use in humans. However, various experiments with ESCs demonstrate their potential. For example, mouse ESCs that were differentiated to endoderm-like precursor cells and injected into mouse livers were able to cure these mice of hemophilia. Human ESCs that were differentiated into heart cells and injected into pig hearts lacking normal electrical signals were able to reestablish heart function. Human ESCs that were differentiated into dopamine-producing neurons were able to significantly reduce symptoms in a rat model of Parkinson's disease when injected into rat brains. There are many more examples of promising uses for ESCs, so why are these applications so slow to reach human clinical trials?

What are Some of the Problems with Embryonic Stem Cells?

Although they are relatively easy to identify, expand, and grow, there are many reasons why human ESCs are not likely to be used in the immediate future in regenerative

medicine. In addition to ethical and political barriers that we will discuss later, safety is a major concern. Controlling which cell types ESCs will differentiate into when injected into the body is a major barrier. For example, when the rats with Parkinson's disease were injected with human ESC derived neurons, many of the rats developed tumors. Why? When pluripotent ESCs are injected into animals, they form tumors called teratomas. Although these human ESCs were differentiated into neurons, it is likely that not all were fully differentiated. For these reasons, many scientists believe it will be best to differentiate ESCs into maturing cell types that would be injected into the body instead of injecting ESCs that could potentially differentiate into unwanted cell types.

Another hurdle to overcome for clinical therapy is the immune system of the host. Generally, when foreign cells are injected into a host, the immune system of the host attacks and destroys these cells. It is not yet clear from animal studies if this would be a major problem for humans, although many scientists think it is likely to be. As with other transplants, a patient could take immunosuppressive drugs to minimize this immune response. Imagining much further into the future of medicine, we could envision ESC lines that are genetically altered to avoid detection by any patient's immune system or ESC lines that are customized for each person. If we can overcome the issues of safety and immune rejection, what will be the long-term fate of these injected cells in a person? Once introduced into the body at a specific location, there is no guarantee that the cells would remain at that location. There is still much to be learned from animal studies that will affect our ability to safely use human ESCs in humans. Nonetheless, Geron, a company working to cure spinal cord injuries, surprised many when they announced that they were seeking FDA approval to begin injecting ESC-derived cells into humans. Geron was the first company to make such an announcement and, as of March 2008, still awaits FDA approval.

▷ Adult-Derived Stem Cells (ASCs)

As mentioned earlier, the label of "adult-derived" stem cells is a bit of a misnomer in that these cells can be found in any differentiated tissues at any stage of development. So, what we call "adult-derived stem cells" is a broad category of cells, each with unique potential. For now, we can think of ASCs as nonembryonic stem cells. Many differentiated tissues have been found to have ASCs. They have been identified in the skin, bone marrow, fat, and muscle, to name just a few!

Characteristics of Adult-Derived Stem Cells

Traditionally, we think about ASCs being different from ESCs for two major reasons: 1) they can not grow indefinitely, and 2) they are limited in their ability to differentiate. Adult-derived stem cells can be very challenging to grow in the lab because they do not divide often or easily. For example, they may only double one time *in vitro* before dying. Compounding this issue, they are often present in tissues in small quantities and can be difficult to identify, purify, and isolate. For instance, in mouse bone marrow, only 1 in approximately 10,000 cells is a stem cell. Even if a few ASCs are isolated, being able to grow large numbers of them in the lab can be difficult. The reason ASCs are often labeled as "limited" is because of their potential to regenerate a narrow range of damaged tissues. That is, skin stem cells only give rise to skin. Blood stem cells only give rise to various blood cells. Right? But what if a blood stem cell from the bone marrow were put into a different environment, such as a liver? Would environmental cues from the liver affect what that blood stem cell became? Think about it as analogy with yourself...would you be the same person you are today if at birth you were raised in a different location with a different family? Probably not! Your environment (culture and experiences) play a major role in your development. If you grew up in a completely different place, you might speak a different language, have a different hairstyle, have different hobbies, and a different career goal. Similarly, scientists have placed blood stem cells (that normally make blood cells) into host mouse livers and observed that some of the blood stem cells became liver cells.

Observations such as these support the hypothesis that some ASCs may be **plastic,** or changeable, in response to regenerative signals. (Plasticity is sometimes referred to as **transdifferentiation** if the differentiation event causes the cell to cross the germ layer barrier, such as from mesoderm to endoderm; Figure 21.9). Examining bone marrow transplants between people of different genders was one of the initial observations that suggested that plasticity might be possible. For example, when bone marrow from a male (in which all the cells contained a Y chromosome) were transplanted into a female host (in which all the cells contain only X chromosomes and no Y chromosomes), some cells containing Y chromosomes were found in the liver; this result was unexpected because it was thought that bone marrow cells only gave rise to blood cells. The Y-containing cells could only have been derived from the bone marrow transplant. Similar observations showed that Y-containing cells were found in other unexpected tissues, such as the heart and brain. These experiments generated much hope for ASCs and suggested that they might have as much potential as ESCs. However, alternative explanations exist for these results. For instance, one group of

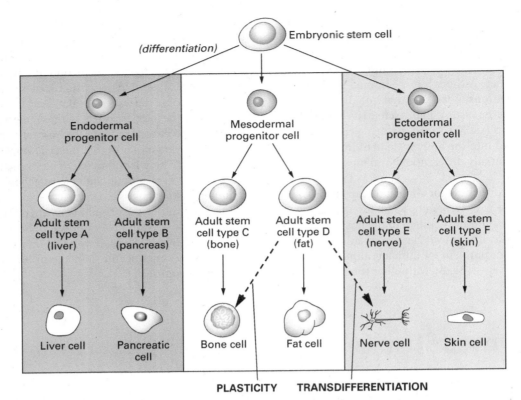

▲ **Figure 21.9** The concept of plasticity overlaid upon a more traditional approach to thinking about adult stem cell (ASC) differentiation. The ability of ASCs to become other cell types is referred to as plasticity. If the change crosses a germ line barrier, this is a specific type of plasticity known as transdifferentiation.

scientists demonstrated with mouse experiments that transplanted bone marrow cells that appeared in various host tissues were actually due to cell-to-cell fusion (i.e., two cells fuse to become one large cell with two sets of genetic material).

There is now much debate as to whether plasticity is a real phenomenon *in vivo*. Many scientists think that if this type of event can occur with bone marrow cells *in vivo*, it happens so rarely that it is not likely to be useful in terms of treating various organ failures with bone marrow transplants.

Interestingly, we are seeing many new reports now that various adult stem cells grown *in vitro* demonstrate plasticity. For example, skin stem cells can become bone, muscle, or fat, and fat stem cells can become bone, cartilage, and nerve. Can you imagine the potential of the stem cells in the thousands of pounds of skin and fat being discarded from procedures such as liposuction every year in the United States? We are likely to see many new therapies being developed based upon the *in vitro* plasticity of these cells in the future.

Adult-Derived Stem Cells are Already in Use in Regenerative Medicine

So while there is still a lot unknown, many scientists think that most of the body's own tissue repair mechanisms *in vivo* come from ASCs that reside in *each* tissue. That is, if your liver needs repair, liver stem cells—not circulating multipotent stem cells or ASCs from other tissues with high plasticity—repair it. While individual ASCs may be limited in their potency, clinicians have made amazing progress in the area of regenerative medicine by utilizing these cells. Scientist can take one of two approaches when thinking about the regenerative potential of ASCs in each tissue. The first approach would be to expand a patient's own tissue-specific stem cells in the lab and then transplant numerous derived cells or organized tissues into the patient. The second approach would be to get the resident stem cells

to become more active after injury by stimulation with a pharmaceutical.

To consider both approaches, let's look at the heart as an example (**Figure 21.10**). Because the heart is not very good at regenerating heart muscle after injury, it was assumed for a long time that the heart did not have ASCs. A normal repair mechanism after a heart attack is the replacement of dead muscle cells with noncontractile scar tissue. However, in 2004 and 2005, various research groups identified these elusive cardiac stem cells. Let's first consider the transplant approach to repair the heart. Physicians initially would isolate a small amount of heart tissue (about the size of a grain of rice) through a thin tube from a patient undergoing a cardiac biopsy. Some of the cells in this tissue would be heart

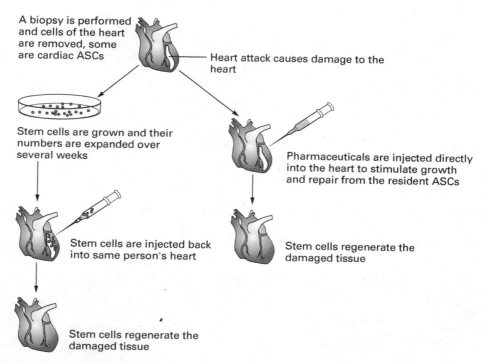

▲ Figure 21.10 Two possible approaches utilizing adult-derived stem cells (ASCs) of the heart to regenerate damage after a heart attack.

Source: Figure adapted from Thieman and Palladino, *Introduction to Biotechnology*, p. 259, Figure 11.19.

ASCs. After approximately three weeks of growth in the lab, there would be enough stem cells to transplant the cells into an injured heart. If the cells went back to the same patient from which they were originally isolated, this is termed an **autologous transplant.** A benefit to this type of transplant is that there will not be immune rejection because the cells are from the same person. (This is in contrast to **allogenic transplants,** in which cells are transplanted from one person to another.) While this type of cardiac stem cell transplant therapy is not being done with humans yet, studies in mice and pigs show promising results; the injected cells migrate to the damaged zones of the heart and repair damaged tissue.

Transplantation may be a solution for some patients, but it also has its drawbacks. For example, a patient in critical condition who has just had a heart attack may not be able to wait three weeks for treatment. Thus, a pharmaceutical approach to treating heart attacks may be the preferred treatment for other patients. With this approach, researchers try to develop chemicals that might cause the few residing ASCs to become more active or recruit other stem cells from different places in the body. For example, in one study designed to activate the resident stem cells of the heart, scientists injected various drugs directly into the hearts of dogs with a heart injury. The dead tissue was significantly repaired with new heart cells that contracted and improved overall function. Other scientists are searching for chemicals that cause the process of **dedifferentiation,** when a body cell (such as the injured heart cell or a cell nearby) might lose its specialized, differentiated characteristics and become a stem cell (**Figure 21.11**). While this is a new area of research for therapeutic purposes, dedifferentiation has been well studied in the tail regeneration of

some amphibians, such as salamanders. When the tail is cut or pulled off, scientists have observed that various mature cells, such as muscle cells, dedifferentiate and eventually give rise to a new limb, including spinal cord, muscle, bone, and skin.

Transplanting ASCs holds much promise in the future... but wouldn't it be amazing if entire organs could be grown from few stem cells? This has already been done! As you likely know, there is quite a shortage of organs available for transplants; in 2007, the U.S. government estimated that 94,000 people were waiting for organs, and that number will continue to increase. Whereas allogenic transplants save lives every day, there are serious complications with immune rejection. What if your *own* cells could be used to grow a new organ that could then be transplanted back into you? This was once the material of science fiction novels but now is reality. In 2006, Dr. Anthony Atala and colleagues at Wake Forest University School of Medicine announced that they had done just this for seven patients who were born with defective bladders (**Figure 21.12**). Whereas most cells of the bladder will only grow and divide for a few days, the team removed from each patient a small amount (dime sized) of the bladder that was present and that included ASCs. They grew the cells on a hollow, biodegradable scaffold, and, after many weeks of growth, transplanted the artificial bladder back into the patient. After seven years, the patients still have much improved or normal bladder function without ill effects. These artificial bladders marked the beginning of an era for growing artificial organs for autologous transplant using ASCs. Dr. Atala's group is working on more than 20 different organs using a similar technique.

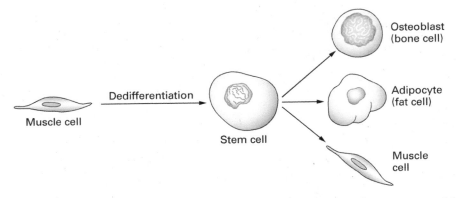

▲ Figure 21.11 Dedifferentiation of a specialized body cell (such as a heart muscle cell) might cause it to become a stem cell that can give rise to new heart muscle cells or other cell types.

Source: Figure adapted from "Future of Stem Cells," SCIAM, 2005.

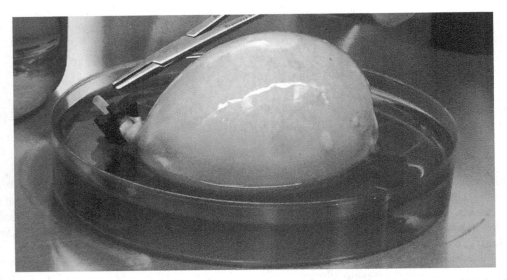

▲ Figure 21.12 A real application of adult-derived stem cells—growing human organs. A biodegradable scaffold that is molded to the shape of a bladder is seeded with a patient's own bladder stem cells. After weeks of growth, these artificial bladders are transplanted into the patient.

Source: Brian Walker/AP Photo, http://news.nationalgeographic.com/news/2006/04/0404_060404_bladders_2.html.

What scientists are learning about these many different kinds of ASCs and how this knowledge is being utilized in medicine is changing daily. Sometimes, scientists learn the basic science behind stem cells in the lab and hope to translate this to a clinical use. Scientists at Duke University Medical Center and Pratt School of Engineering have found that fat stem cells isolated from human liposuction procedures could be efficiently coaxed to become cartilage cells *in vitro*. Cartilage injury is very difficult for the body to repair on its own, and current methods with cartilage transplants don't work well. Knowing how to convert fat cells into cartilage cells puts

scientists in a good place to develop clinical stem cell therapies based upon their findings. Yet sometimes a reverse approach is used. For example, there is some improvement in cardiac function when a person's own bone marrow stem cells are infused into his/her heart after a heart attack. So how does it work? Scientists don't completely understand how the stem cells may cause improvement; it is possible that they produce signals that cause other cells to respond and repair the heart. So whether scientists move toward a stem cell therapy from the basic science or develop the therapy first, this is certainly an exciting time in regenerative medicine.

▷ A Multipronged Approach to Curing Diseases

In general, scientists want to pick the most efficient, safest, and quickest way to cure a disease. For this reason, we see each disease being approached from many angles (e.g.,

pharmaceuticals, gene therapy, surgery)—not just with stem cells. Scientists work together in curing a disease with a multipronged approach. Not surprisingly, when we examine how stem cells are affecting basic research on diseases, we can find researchers using ESCs, fetal stem cells, and various types of ASCs. To make an example of the many approaches within the stem cell field that are being used to solve a common problem, let's examine the neurodegenerative disease, Parkinson's disease. You are likely somewhat familiar with this disease, since Michael J. Fox has made his disease and foundation public.

Parkinson's disease (PD) is a debilitating disease affecting approximately 1.5 million older Americans (the age of onset is usually around 65 years). The disease is caused by a loss of specific neurons, or nerve cells, in the brain. These neurons normally produce a chemical messenger called dopamine that is responsible for the smooth, coordinated movement of muscles. When approximately 80% of the dopamine- producing (DA) neurons are lost, symptoms appear; these include slowness of movement, stiffness, shaking, and difficulty balancing. Currently there is no cure, but pharmaceuticals can help lessen the symptoms. A common pharmaceutical that is used for treatment, called levodopa or L-dopa, has been in use for decades. While levodopa helps to elevate levels of dopamine in the brain, patients respond less to it over time. Other pharmaceuticals are difficult to develop due to the blood-brain barrier that prevents many substances, including drugs, from entering the brain. Stem cells are now offering hope for new treatments and maybe even a cure for PD. However, predicting what type of stem cell will prove most useful years from now would require a crystal ball. We are at the cutting edge with stem cells, so let's just examine some of the fascinating studies to date that relate to stem cells and PD (Table 21.2)

Some studies have utilized ESCs as the starting cell type for trying to ameliorate PD in animal models. For instance, monkey ESCs have been used to generate neurons. With the addition of a particular growth promoting factor, DA neurons were effectively produced. When transplanted into the brains of monkey models of PD, the DA neurons functioned and diminished symptoms of the disease. However, only 1 to 3% of the transplanted cells survived, indicating that there is room for much improvement before this type of technique can be thought of as a therapy for PD. Better survival and incorporation of the DA neurons would be necessary. Similar experiments have been done in which human ESCs generated DA neurons. When transplanted into the brains of rat models of PD, the treatment improved muscle coordination such that the rats were almost normal. A pitfall to these, and other similar experiments with mice, was highlighted by the multiple tumors found in the brains of these animals. Better control over differentiation to lessen the odds of tumor development needs to be possible before trials with humans can take place. (Recall from the previous discussion that undifferentiated ESCs injected into an animal cause tumors.) In line with this, new methods have been developed with mouse cells to define and identify a pure population of completely differentiated neural cells (derived from ESCs). Applied to transplant studies, the methods are proving useful in removing the unwanted side effect of tumor formation.

Other studies similarly designed to improve PD in animal models have used fetal stem cells rather than ESCs as the initial cell type. Specifically, **human neural progenitor cells (hNPCs)** obtained from fetal tissues at 10 to 15 weeks' gestation have been examined. In one study, these cells were genetically modified to produce a survival factor for DA neurons and were then transplanted into the brains of rat or monkey models of PD. These cells continued to produce the survival factor, which led to DA neuron generation and subsequent dopamine production. Physical improvements that lasted for several months were seen in the animals. Nonetheless, these promising studies indicate that this is not a long-lasting cure and that controlling the levels of the survival factor must still be refined.

Adult brain tissue has also been used in studies designed to correct PD. For example, when brain cells from patients

TABLE 21.2   A SUMMARY OF SOME STEM CELL EXPERIMENTS RELATED TO THE NEURODEGENERATIVE PARKINSON'S DISEASE (PD).

Source cells	Differentiated cell type	Host animal receiving brain transplant	Results
Monkey ESCs	Dopamine-producing neurons	Monkey model of PD	Diminished PD symptoms Low survival rate of the transplanted cells
Human ESC	Dopamine-producing neurons	Rat model of PD	Significantly improved muscle coordination Tumor formation in brains
Human neural progenitor cells (hNPCs) from fetal tissue engineered to express a "survival factor"	N/A	Rat and monkey models of PD	Improved symptoms of PD New dopamine-producing neurons generated Effects were not long lasting
Adult human brain biopsy cells	Neural progenitor cells	Mouse	New neurons generated
Mouse or human neural ASCs	N/A	Mouse model of the related disease, Sandhoff's disease	Increased life span
Human ESCs	Neural progenitor cells		Delayed loss of motor function No tumors

N/A = not applicable.

undergoing surgery were grown in the lab in the presence of a specific growth-promoting factor, scientists noticed that neural progenitor cells developed. (Remember, progenitor cells are a bit further down the pathway of differentiation compared to stem cells.) When these progenitor cells were transplanted into mouse brains, scientists observed development of new neurons and incorporation of these cells into various regions of the brain. If these strategies can be applied to correct PD in humans, there are advantages to beginning with adult cells as the starting material (e.g., less chance of tumor development, a person's own cells could be used for autologous transplantation, and fewer ethical and political issues compared with using embryonic and fetal tissue).

A recent study with **Sandhoff's disease,** a neurodegenerative disease related to PD, has offered new hope for PD patients. Scientists transplanted adult neural stem cells from mice or humans or fully differentiated human

neurons derived from ESCs into the brain of a mouse model of Sandhoff's disease. All types of stem cells prolonged the lifespan, delayed the loss of motor function, and, importantly, did not invoke immune rejection or tumor formation. An important first discovery was also made—the mouse neural cells replaced damaged neurons and were able to transmit impulses. Lastly, these studies clearly illustrate the multipronged approach that will eventually include stem cells. When these mice were given a specific pharmaceutical, in addition to the stem cells, their lifespan doubled. In fact, the two treatments together demonstrate *more* than an additive result (i.e., the results were better than the sum of the individual effects of each treatment), and this is termed a **synergistic effect.** In sum, while stem cells are certainly a new frontier in the battle against diseases like PD, they will not be the only frontier. Without doubt, stem cell treatments will be routinely combined with other important therapies.

▷ Cloning

When people think about cloning, images are conjured up of Elvis returning from the past or armies of identical soldiers in science fiction movies. However, cloning does not simply apply to an entire organism. Molecules, such as DNA, or individual cells can be cloned—cloning processes make multiple copies of the original DNA molecule or cell. These processes have been done in the lab for decades, and many of the modern medical breakthroughs have been based on cloning DNA

and cells. When an entire organism is cloned, the complete adult animal is not immediately produced. The clone starts as a one-celled embryo and must still go through an embryonic stage, grow, and develop. Frogs were first cloned in the 1960s, but it was not until 1996 that the first mammal, Dolly the sheep, was cloned using an adult sheep cell nucleus. Dolly was born in 1997.

What is Cloning?

To understand cloning, let's first begin by thinking about sexual reproduction—the union of a sperm and an egg. During sexual reproduction, the sperm and the egg each bring half of the chromosomes for the new individual, so that the one-celled embryo contains a full set of chromosomes (half from mom and half from dad). This process can happen *in vivo,* inside a female's reproductive tract or *in vitro.* The latter would be termed *in vitro* fertilization, and the embryo would be placed into the uterus after several days to go on to form a normal baby. (As we discussed previously, if the *in vitro* embryo was grown to the blastocyst stage and then dissociated instead of being implanted into a uterus, an ESC line could be generated.) In the end, sexual reproduction produces offspring that are *not* identical to either parent.

So how does cloning differ from sexual reproduction? Unlike sexual reproduction, a sperm cell is not needed. The process of cloning requires two main ingredients: 1) the genetic material from a **somatic cell** (a body cell other than a sperm or egg) of the organism to be cloned, and 2) an egg (**Figure 21.13**). *In vitro,* the nucleus (containing the genetic

material) is first removed from the egg, a process termed **enucleation.** Next, the nucleus containing a complete set of genetic material is taken from a somatic cell and inserted into the enucleated egg. This cloning process creates a one-celled embryo. Contrary to sexual reproduction, in which the sperm and egg each donate half the chromosomes, the somatic cell donates all of the chromosomes needed to make an individual. Terms used to describe this process are **somatic cell nuclear transfer (SCNT)** or **nuclear transplantation.** At this stage, the embryo is then stimulated to divide and grow with the help of electric shock or chemicals. Once the embryo has developed for several days *in vitro,* the embryo must be placed in the uterus of a surrogate mother to complete development and undergo normal gestation until birth. The organism produced by this method, a **reproductive clone,** will be genetically identical to the somatic donor. In contrast, if the embryo is never placed into a uterus, it can be dissociated and an ESC line can be generated. These stem cells can be differentiated into various tissues for the purpose of treating patients. This is termed **therapeutic cloning.**

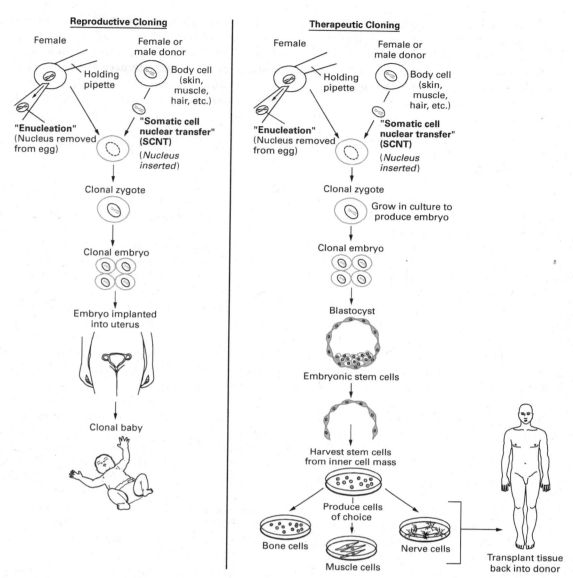

▲ Figure 21.13 Reproductive and therapeutic cloning use many of the same procedural steps.

Source: Figure adapted from Thieman and Palladino, *Introduction to Biotechnology*, p. 261, Figure 11.20.

Purposes of Cloning—Why do We Want to Clone?

So why would we want to make a clone? For agricultural uses, there are many reasons why having cloned animals could be an advantage. Selectively breeding the best livestock—for example, crossing the best bull with the best cow—can produce champion animals, such as good milk or wool producers; but, when the champion animal is bred, there is no guarantee that its offspring will have all of the same characteristics because only half of the genetic makeup of the offspring will be from that champion animal. However, if we could produce a clone of that animal, then the cloned offspring would have the same genetic makeup of the champion. It is even possible to genetically engineer animals so that their milk contains medically valuable human proteins, such as insulin, or so that their organs can be used for transplantation and not be

rejected by humans transplant patients (transplanting animal organs into humans is termed **xenotransplantation**). For these types of animals, cloning could ensure that there are many identical animals available. Cloning could also be useful in producing **animal models of disease**—animals that have a specific disease—so that the medical condition can be studied in attempts to find treatments and cures. Interestingly, another use that was not commercially successful was attempted by a company in California. For $50,000 this company would clone your pet cat. Apparently there was not enough of a demand, and the company closed its doors!

For human cloning there are two purposes proposed. One is **reproductive cloning,** sometimes called **live-birth cloning.** After the SCNT process, the cloned human embryo would be implanted into the uterus and would develop until birth. Proponents of this purpose for human cloning talk about using it to reproduce a child who has died or to help infertile couples to have a child. The other purpose for human cloning has been called **therapeutic cloning** or **research cloning**. The idea here is to use SCNT to produce a cloned embryo that is identical to a patient who has a degenerative disease. Yet instead of implanting the embryo in a uterus, the embryo is dissociated and ESCs are retrieved, in hopes of treating the patient. In theory, the cells derived from the ESCs, such as liver or pancreatic cells *etc.*, would be a genetic match for the patient and would not cause transplant rejection.

Reproductive Cloning

Reproductive cloning—cloning to produce a live birth—has been accomplished with several other mammals thus far. Since Dolly was cloned, other mammals that have been cloned and brought to birth are mice, goats, pigs, cattle, rabbits, dogs, and cats. Cloning primates (e.g., monkeys and humans) has been more challenging. The embryos produced by SCNT in primates have not developed past an early stage. This points out one of the biggest problems in cloning—most clones do *not* survive.

Cloning, as it turns out, is a very inefficient process. It took 277 tries to get *one* Dolly. Each attempt involved creating a cloned embryo by SCNT. Mammary gland cells from the udder of a 6-year-old sheep were used as the somatic donor nuclei, fusing these cells with an enucleated egg to produce the one-cell clones. Only about 10% of these single-celled cloned embryos typically develop to the blastocyst stage (in Dolly's case, only 29 of the 277 cloned embryos). Those that reach the blastocyst stage can be implanted in the uterus of a **surrogate mother** for gestation. Most of the implanted embryos don't develop or survive to birth; of the 29 implanted embryos, only Dolly was born.

Similar problems have occurred with other animal species that have been cloned. The process is simply inefficient and generally the success rate ranges from 0.1% up to 5.4% (the 5.4% was reported from a SCNT using mouse adult skin cell nuclei). That means that, for every 1000 nuclear transfers into eggs, at best, 54 clones might be born, depending on the species and donor cell type. Why are the numbers so low? There are several steps that often don't work: if the egg with the new nucleus does not begin to divide or develop normally, if the embryo does not implant correctly into the uterus of the surrogate, or if the fetus dies before it has reached full term.

What about reproductive cloning in primates? Unlike other mammals, primates are far more challenging to clone using SCNT. In 2001, Advanced Cell Technology announced that it had performed SCNT with human cells. The embryos only developed to a 6-celled stage. SCNT has not worked in monkeys either. Upon further investigation of the early stage embryos produced with SCNT using monkey or human cells, it was found that the primate cells had major problems with the number of chromosomes in each cell. Some cells had normal chromosome numbers, but some had too many, too few, or none at all. Researchers now know that essential proteins in primate eggs are lost during the SCNT process. Without these proteins, chromosomes are not equally distributed to daughter cells during cell division. In June of 2007, advances in the SCNT procedure gave rise to healthier monkey embryos. What was new to this study was that the scientists performed the nuclear transfer using a light source to visualize the eggs; they believe this modification was less damaging than the earlier technique used with primate cells. Rather than implanting the embryos for live births, the embryos were dissociated and two ESC lines were established. Additionally, news in January 2008 from Stemagen, a company based in La Jolla, California, suggests that SCNT is looking more promising with humans, too. They announced that they had successfully cloned a human to the blastocyst stage using SCNT. These recent experiments demonstrate that some of the early technical barriers to reproductively cloning primates have been overcome.

Somatic cell nuclear transfer is not the only way to make clones. Scientists have shown in animals such as mice and monkeys that if the nucleus from an embryonic cell (rather than from a fully differentiated somatic cell) is injected into the enucleated egg (termed **embryonic cell nuclear transfer, or ECNT**) that the cloning efficiency is significantly greater. The reason for this is likely because embryonic cells are already capable of giving rise to many different cell types. Using cells from the same embryo for each nuclear transfer, this process can produce many identical clones of the embryo (**Figure 21.14A**). Note that, unlike SCNT, you cannot clone an adult this way. This process is more like a "multiples" birth, in which the offspring are clones of each other (such as identical triplets are identical to each other). So while SCNT has not been very successful with primates, in 1997, two monkeys were born via the ECNT process performed by Dr. Gerald P. Schatten and colleagues at the Oregon Regional Primate Research Center.

A second alternative to SCNT to clone an animal is the way in which Tetra, a female rhesus monkey, was cloned in 2000, also by Dr. Gerald P. Schatten and colleagues through a process known as **embryo splitting** (**Figure 21.14B**). The process involves normal fertilization by a sperm and egg and allowing initial development. When the embryo reaches the 8-cell stage, the embryo is split into four 2-celled embryos that can give rise to four genetically identical clones. This technique can be thought of as a way to produce "artificial quadruplets." Embryo splitting is similar to ECNT in that an adult cannot be cloned by this technique but several identical clones could be made. Tetra was the only one of the four clones to survive until birth and is the first primate produced by this cloning technique. Scientists trying to clone monkeys suggest that having identical monkeys is useful for medical tests because they represent the closest animal model for

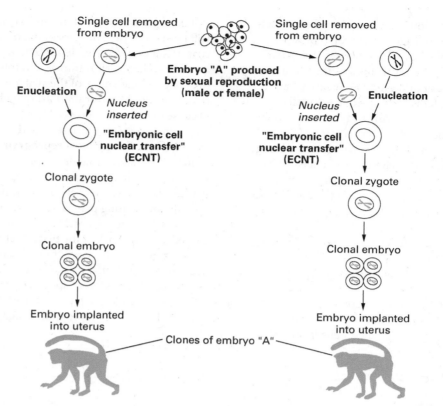

▲ **Figure 21.14A** The process of embryonic cell nuclear transfer (ECNT) can make several identical clones if several cells from the same embryo are used.

Source: Figure adapted from Thieman and Palladino, *Introduction to Biotechnology*, p. 261, Figure 11.20.

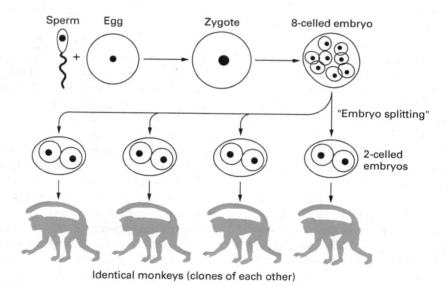

▲ **Figure 21.14B** The process of embryo splitting produces (at best) four identical clones.

human diseases and reduce the variability of using nonclones. For example, several animals with the identical immune systems would be useful in testing vaccines for HIV because it would rule out genetic diversity as a variable.

The Health of Reproductive Clones

We have discussed how very few clones survive and grow to adulthood. Are any of the clones that survive normal? Although there is not enough evidence to make a concrete conclusion about Dolly the sheep, many scientists believe that she aged prematurely. When scientists studied her telomeres ("caps" at the ends of her chromosomes) they found that they were slightly shorter than would be expected in a sheep of her age. Her telomeres suggested that her "genetic age" was greater than her true birth age, fitting with the reality that she was cloned from a 6-year-old sheep. And yet, shortened telomeres have not been consistently observed with other cloned animals. Other circumstantial evidence supports the idea of premature aging in Dolly—she developed early onset arthritis and died at the young age of 6 (sheep typically live 11 to 12 years) from a progressive lung disease. When we consider other cloned animals of various species, it is evident that making it to birth does not necessarily mean the animal is normal. Other problems seen in cloned animals are weak immune systems, tumor growth, and death at a young age. Additionally, reproductive clones and their placentas sometimes grow faster and larger than normal, termed **large offspring syndrome.** These large clones would need to be delivered by caesarian (C-) section. It is not known exactly why this overgrowth occurs, but it might have something to do with the way different genes are expressed during embryological development.

Normal development is an intricate dance of genes being expressed at the right time in the right cells. The difficulty in getting normal clones has a lot to do with gene reprogramming when the nucleus is transferred to the enucleated egg. In sexual reproduction, the egg and the sperm each have their genes programmed to start normal development. The way that genes are set to be expressed is called **gene imprinting.**

Think of genes as a set of on/off switches; different switches will be set "on" or "off," depending on the particular cell type, tissues, or stage of development. When the nucleus of an adult somatic cell is transferred into the enucleated egg to create a clone, many of the switches are set differently than they would be for the start of embryonic development because by then the body cell has its programming set to do its job in a particular differentiated tissue (e.g., skin). The cytoplasm in the egg must **reprogram** the genes, resetting the switches so that normal development can occur. The failure of most reproductive cloning attempts is likely a result of not getting all the switches set correctly. In fact, one study examined the imprinting patterns for five specific genes in mouse embryos generated by SCNT. They found that only 4% of the cloned mice mimicked the blastocyst mode of expression for all five genes. These types of reprogramming errors also likely account for large offspring syndrome and other problems seen with many different species of clones. The reason that ECNT may be more efficient than SCNT is that embryonic cells likely need less reprogramming.

Therapuetic Cloning

Therapeutic cloning (research cloning) involves cloning to produce embryonic stem cells (ESCs) for medical therapies. The idea is to provide therapies for patients with diseases such as Parkinson's disease, diabetes, and so on, using ESCs. By performing SCNT with an enucleated egg, a cloned embryo of the patient (see **Figure 21.13**) is produced. Instead of implanting the embryo, ESCs would be derived from the blastocyst stage and grown *in vitro*. Theoretically, these cells would be a perfect tissue match, getting around the problem of transplant rejection. The ESCs would be stimulated in the laboratory to differentiate into healthy tissues. A person with Parkinson's disease might receive nerve cells to cure the disease, and an individual who has suffered a heart attack might receive heart muscle cells to repair his/her damaged heart. It should be noted that even if the cloned ESCs are never used in patients, the technique is still a powerful one for basic research. For example, the molecular mechanisms that cause many inherited diseases are unknown. Scientists could derive various ESC lines from individuals with genetic diseases and watch exactly how these cloned cells differentiate and function compared to normal cells. Pharmaceuticals could also be screened on these cloned cells to test their ability to slow or reverse the disease process.

The idea of therapeutic cloning is still somewhat theoretical and poses many problems. From a technical standpoint, it is still not possible because it would require SCNT to work successfully with human cells to consistently produce healthy cloned blastocysts for ESC retrieval. The first successful production of *some* such blastocysts was done with primates in June of 2007, and it required 278 eggs to obtain just two stem cell lines from cloned rhesus monkey embryos. News in January 2008 from Stemagen suggests that therapeutic cloning may be closer to reality in humans. They announced that they had successfully cloned a human to the blastocyst stage.

Many Eggs Are Needed for Cloning

Eggs are necessary to make clones. Not just any cell will do, since the egg's cytoplasm contains materials that activate the various genes to send the embryo through development properly. However, it takes more than one egg to make a clone. As we discussed previously, cloning is an inefficient process, even just to get the clone to the blastocyst stage where stem cells can be harvested. At best, the current success rate to clone a human embryo to the blastocyst stage from a pool of eggs is approximately 10%. This rate is based upon Stemagen's announcement regarding SCNT to produce cloned human blastocysts. With the current technology, many human eggs will be needed. Who will donate the eggs? To get numerous eggs (more than one per month), a woman must receive high doses of hormones to cause multiple eggs to mature, and surgery is then required to retrieve the eggs. The hormones can have serious side effects, and surgery poses risks to the egg donor, as well. In addition, if women are willing to donate eggs, what would the cost of this be? In 2003, a study was published that reported it would cost up to $200,000 per patient just to pay for the human eggs needed to derive one usable ESC line that could be used for therapeutic cloning. The high cost of developing a procedure that will undoubtedly remain costly for each patient has made some venture capitalists hesitant about investing in this field of biotechnology. Hence, it may not be possible or practical to get enough human eggs for cloning attempts.

One proposal is to use cow or rabbit eggs, instead of human eggs. These are readily available and can be harvested in greater numbers. Naturally, there is some concern about mixing species, even though the hybrid embryo will not be brought to birth. There is still some uncertainty if this would work for the patient receiving the resulting cells, since there would be a slight genetic contribution from the cow or rabbit egg.

A clone produced by nuclear transfer is *virtually* genetically identical to the donor genetic material. The "virtually" part arises because there is some contribution from the egg. The genetic contribution comes not from the egg's chromosomes, which are removed during enucleation, but from the mitochondria, the little energy-generating factories in the cytoplasm of each cell. These are still present in the egg when the donor nucleus is transferred in. Even though mitochondria do not contain much DNA, there are lots of them to make energy for the cell. As much as 1% of the DNA in the clone may be derived from the egg in this way. Some of the proteins made from these genes do wind up on the surface of the cell, where there is the possibility that they could trigger an immune response. While the chance of this may be low using human eggs, it could cause a significant problem if cow or rabbit eggs are used.

Before we move away from this topic of therapeutic cloning, it is worthy to note a news story that made international headlines in 2005. A South Korean researcher, Hwang Woo Suk, published a report in a world-renowned science journal in which he claimed that he had derived 11 human ESC lines from cloned human embryos. Many scientists were excited by the news that, not only was he able to perform SCNT on human eggs, but he had derived ESC lines from them. At the time, it appeared that therapeutic cloning was a reality and it was just a matter of time before it proved useful as a clinical therapy. Not long after his publication appeared, however, he was exposed for falsifying the data presented. After much investigation into his studies, it became clear that he had not successfully created cloned human ESCs nor had he even been successful at SCNT to produce blastocysts. This publicity caused much skepticism about stem cell research among the public. When Stemagen announced that they had successfully cloned a human to the blastocyst stage using SCNT, they validated their results with accompanying evidence that it had worked. Yet because of the previous Hwang scandal, many scientists remain skeptical about the news. It remains to be seen if Stemagen can produce blastocysts that are healthy enough to produce cloned human ESCs.

▷ Bioethics of Stem Cells and Cloning

Bioethics of Stem Cell Research

The real root of the debates regarding stem cells is the question of moral status of the human embryo. Scientifically, the embryo is a human being, just starting out on its developmental journey, but the science has no answers for the deeper questions regarding how we view this tiny entity. Instead these are moral, philosophical, and theological questions. Does it have a soul? Is it conscious? Is it a person or a piece of property? When does human life begin? On the one hand, a human blastocyst is a mere dot (it fits into Roosevelt's eye on the face of a U.S. dime). It does not possess a beating heart or brain waves; it is without arms and legs. Of course those things develop later; but, at the very early stages, the embryo lacks these things that we usually associate with our idea of a person. There are various views but no consensus of the status of the early human embryo. Some say it is simply a clump of cells, just like a chunk of skin. Others believe that it is a form of human life, deserving of profound respect yet only a *potential* person. Still others maintain that an embryo has the same moral value as any other member of the human species. How individuals answer these questions may be based on religious views. Interestingly, defining when life begins is different for various faiths, and so some religions are more tolerant than others of aspects of this research. For example, the Jewish faith believes that humanhood begins at a later stage of development than the blastocyst, and it does

not grant legal status to an embryo. As a result, groups such as Hadassah, the Women's Zionist Organization of America, and the Union of Orthodox Jewish Congregations of America are outspoken supporters of ESC research for the purpose of curing disease. In contrast, the Catholic Church believes that at the time of conception (either *in vitro* or *in vivo*) the embryo is a human being with full rights. The Catholic Church opposes the direct destruction of blastocysts for any purpose, including research. Faith is just one of the many factors that might shape a person's opinion on these moral questions. The news, education, personal nonreligious beliefs, and personal experiences are other major factors shaping people's views about stem cells.

The concept of using human embryos for research and potential stem cell cures started with the so-called "excess" embryos, left in the freezers at fertility clinics. For *in vitro* fertilization (IVF), a woman is given high dose of hormones to mature many eggs at once—ten, twenty, even thirty. These eggs are then surgically harvested and fertilized in a laboratory dish. The purpose of IVF is to help a couple conceive a baby. After fertilization and growth in a dish for a few days, anywhere from one to six of the embryos are implanted in the woman's uterus, and the rest of the embryos are frozen. If the couple is not successful with the first round, the frozen embryos may be thawed and used for a second attempt. Or, after the initial birth, the couple may want to use the frozen embryos to produce more children. Nevertheless, there are inevitably some embryos that are not used and are left in the freezer. They can survive for extremely long periods of time.

Inevitably, some of the frozen embryos are discarded. Fertility clinics obtain a signed consent form from the couple, and one option allows the clinic to discard embryos after several years if they are not used. However, most are not discarded. What to do with all the frozen embryos? One option for frozen embryos is relatively new—embryo adoption. The Snowflakes Embryo Adoption program sets up adoptions for embryos whose genetic parents have achieved their family. However, it is estimated that there are 400,000 excess embryos in freezers around the country, so embryo adoption may not make a big impact on this number. Newer techniques often don't create as many embryos in the past. For example, it is possible to only create as many embryos at one time as will actually be implanted or to freeze just the eggs, which can be thawed, fertilized, and the embryos implanted as needed.

Nonetheless, there *is* an excess of embryos from IVF. Another option for parents: their embryos may be donated for research. This was the bone of contention in the stem cell debate. Should human embryos be used for research, given their original purpose was to be implanted for a birth? Why not use them for research if they would be discarded (with the parent's permission) anyway?

When considered in the context of using human embryos for their ESCs, the necessary destruction of the embryo is a contentious one. Should human embryos be destroyed if, from that destruction, it might be possible to treat many patients suffering from disease? Are embryonic stem cells as good for potential treatments as claimed, or are there still viable alternatives that are just as good? Or is the research still necessary so that science can explore all possible avenues for medical breakthroughs? Do the ends justify the means?

Alternatives to Destroying Embryos for Stem Cell Retrieval

"...although adult stem cells may not provoke much political rancour today, they have become more scientifically controversial than their embryonic counterparts" –Christine Soars (SCIAM, July 2005).

The quote above states the dilemma clearly. The view of many scientists at this point is that adult stem cells alone just won't do. For example, finding and characterizing these cells has been difficult and not everyone is in agreement about their abilities to differentiate and even transdifferentiate. For this reason, the push goes on for work with ESCs. However, some scientists are trying to find ways around destroying an embryo; they are attempting to find alternative sources for ESCs in order to skirt ethical issues. How scientists have approached this dilemma demonstrates just how creative they can be as a group—when presented with a problem, scientists will attempt to find many ways to solve it. One way around the ethical dilemma of destroying embryos for their unique pluripotent cells would be to find another cell type that behaves like or can be coaxed into behaving just like embryonic stem cells. Let's examine some of these alternatives.

Amniotic fluid–derived **stem (AFS) cells** have recently been well characterized and demonstrate similarities to ESCs. Amniotic fluid–derived stem cells show pluripotentiality and, similar to ESCs, have been differentiated into cells representing all three germ layers, such as muscle, brain, and liver cells. A unique aspect of AFS cells is that they grow fast like ESCs but do not show signs of aging or developing into tumors, even after two years of *in vitro* growth. While they may not provide an alternative for all types of research, they may prove to be a suitable choice for many uses. These cells can be easily collected from amniotic fluid, as early as 10 weeks after conception, and from the placenta, which is often discarded at birth. Similar to umbilical cord blood, these cells could be saved at birth for an individual's potential use later in life. Of course, privately banking stem cells is costly on a per individual basis. However, a bill has passed in the Senate and awaits a House committee that would provide funds to establish national banks to maintain amniotic fluid and placental stem cells. One-hundred thousand samples has been suggested as the approximate number of samples needed to account for the genetic diversity needed to provide enough immunologically compatible tissues for everyone in the United States. However, a bill has been introduced in the U.S. Congress that would provide funds to establish national banks to maintain 100,000 amniotic fluid and placental stem cell units. This many samples has been suggested as the approximate number of samples needed to account for the genetic diversity needed to provide enough immunologically compatible tissues for everyone in the United States.

What if other cells could be coaxed into behaving like ESCs? There is evidence that this is possible scientifically and support for it ethically. A stem cell may turn out to be not an entity so much as a "state"—one that any cell could enter under the right conditions. Along these lines, some groups are trying to determine what genes must be expressed to make a cell behave like a pluripotent ESC. In 2006, scientists from Japan, Kazutoshi Takahashi and Shinya Yamanaka, first described **induced pluripotent stem (iPS) cells**—differentiated cells that are reprogrammed to become pluripotent *in vitro*. Using a virus to introduce just four genes (*c-Myc, Oct3/4, Sox2, Klf4*) into mouse skin cells, they showed that their iPS cells were similar to ESCs; they could differentiate into all three germ layers *in vivo* and *in vitro* (**Figure 21.15**). In late 2007, the Japanese scientists and an independent group at the University of Wisconsin–Madison announced that they had used the same method to produce human iPS cells from differentiated skin cells. Significant technical challenges may

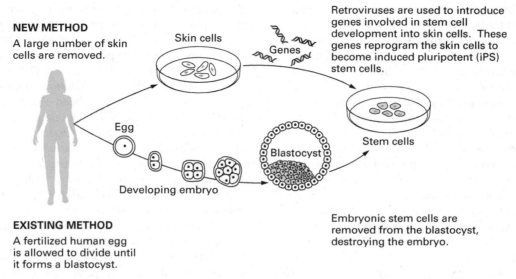

▲ **Figure 21.15** Reprogramming human skin cells. Researchers have developed a technique for creating stem cells (induced pluripotent stem [iPS] cells) without the controversial use of human eggs or embryos. If the method can be perfected, it could quell the ethical debate troubling this field.

Source: Figure adapted from New York Times Website http://www.nytimes.com/2007/11/21/science/21stem.html?_r=1&sq=embryonic+stem+cells&st=nyt&oref=slogin.

still need to be overcome to apply this technology, but this type of experiment demonstrates that it may one day be possible to avoid destroying embryos for their unique pluripotent cells. Even outspoken opponents to ESC work find this new technique ethically acceptable. For example, Richard Doerflinger, the U.S. Conference of Catholic Bishops' spokesman on stem cell issues states it *"raises no serious moral problem because it creates embryonic-like stem cells without creating, harming, or destroying human lives at any stage."* So while scientists creatively develop techniques to avoid ethical issues, they additionally gain a better understanding for the cellular "state" of pluripotency.

Recently, a promising innovative treatment using iPS cells to correct sickle cell anemia in mice was reported. iPS cells were produced from skin cells of mice that express a mutated version of the human sickle cell hemoglobin gene and display sickle cell disease. The iPS were genetically engineered to correct the hemoglobin gene mutation. Blood stem cells were then made from the corrected iPS cells and transferred into donor sickle cell mice which produced functional red blood cells that corrected the disease condition. This is an incredibly exciting result combining aspects of both stem cell technologies and gene therapy to treat a genetic disorder.

Another method designed to avoid the ethical dilemma of destroying an embryo for ESCs is to "pluck" one cell, termed a **blastomere,** from an 8-celled embryo. The single cell would be developed into an ESC line while the now 7-celled embryo would go on to develop into a healthy baby. In 2006, scientists at Advanced Cell Technology demonstrated that it is possible to derive ESCs from this one cell, although these "proof of principle" experiments demonstrated how technically challenging this could be. They have since improved the process and established five more cell lines. But how do we know the 7-celled embryo can go on to produce a healthy baby? A process called preimplantation genetic diagnosis provides

evidence. **Preimplantation genetic diagnosis (PGD)** is a technique sometimes used to determine if an embryo generated by *in vitro* fertilization has a genetic defect. During PGD, one of the eight cells is used for genetic testing (which destroys the cell), but the 7-celled embryo successfully develops into a viable human. This has been successfully done for many years. The significance of the experiments by Advanced Cell Technology is to demonstrate that ESCs can be derived from an embryo without destroying it. Nonetheless, opponents to this method for deriving ESCs state that it is still unethical because the procedure still poses a needless risk of death to the embryo.

Would the ethical dilemma be avoided if ESCs were removed from embryos that are not inherently capable of developing past a particular stage of development? A method such as this was introduced in 2005 at the Massachusetts Institute of Technology. In these studies, they produced a mouse that has a gene defect such that the embryo cannot attach to the uterus wall. Without attachment, they are not considered to be viable. These same ideas could then be applied to defective human embryos. The human embryos would develop normally for the first few days but would not have the ability to continue development without attachment. Would removing cells from these types of embryos be considered ethically acceptable? It appears there is little support for this method as an ethical alternative. As stated by a representative from the U.S. Conference of Bishops, *"Creating these human lives just to destroy them is wrong,"* he said. *"Engineering them so they will self-destruct after a certain point in development is wrong."*

Another source of embryonic stem cells that may prove to be ethically acceptable was reported in June 2007 by scientists at Lifeline Cell Technology of Walkersville, Maryland, and from Moscow, Russia. In these experiments, unfertilized human eggs were stimulated to begin dividing, a process known as **parthenogenesis,** and were grown to the blastocyst stage (scientists don't believe these embryos have the potential to develop long enough to produce babies). Embryonic stem cell lines were then derived from these parthenogenic blastocysts. You are probably wondering how an embryo can be made if there is no fertilization. It turns out that normally before fertilization, the egg actually still has a full number of chromosomes—half will be used to merge with the half brought in by the sperm, and, upon fertilization, the other half of the egg's chromosomes will be shot out of the egg in what is called a **polar body.** For parthenogenesis to occur, the egg is induced by chemicals to keep both sets of chromosomes, resulting in a full number of chromosomes inside the egg. Some animals can reproduce this way in nature, such as salamanders, some reptiles, birds such as chickens, and some insects. When used in humans, this technique can produce ESCs that are not true clones of but are genetically matched for the woman who donates the egg. With drugs to suppress the immune system, patients other than the female donor might be able to use these cells as well. Technical issues still need to be resolved, such as determining if these cells are genetically flawed and if they can be safely used for treatments. Since some people see these as only "activated" eggs, they are not morally conflicted. Others may see these embryos as defective but human nonetheless.

Another proposal that has been discussed for avoiding the destruction of embryos to obtain ESCs is to remove living stem cells from surplus IVF embryos that are not healthy enough to develop further (i.e., are developmentally arrested). Two scientists at Columbia University, Donald Landry and Howard Zucker, propose that some embryos with severe genetic defects that are arrested in development have individual cells that are healthy. These cells could be harvested from the embryos analogously to a situation in which organs are removed for transplantation from brain-dead individuals. Current technical methods still need to be developed to distinguish embryos that are healthy versus those arrested in development versus those that are dead.

Bioethics of Cloning

Human cloning raises even more questions about what it means to be human. Cloning involves the specific creation of human embryos with certain ends in mind. For reproductive cloning, there are worries beyond the safety factors. For a couple who create a cloned child, a clone of the wife will not be the genetic daughter but instead will be the sister, a late-born twin, and will not be related to the husband. How will this change the kinship and family relationships? What will be the expectations put on a clone once born? And what if—and this is possible—a previously existing person, now deceased, is cloned? The genetic makeup of a clone will already be known, already dictated because the process of reproductive cloning reproduces a previously existing individual. Will the clone be expected to live up to that genetic legacy? Will there be heightened expectations by the parents and others based on what was achieved by the donor of the genetic material that has made the clone?

However, keep in mind that even though the genetic makeup of the clone is predetermined, there are many other factors that go into our overall composition. Our genes determine many of our physical characteristics and even predispose us to various diseases or behaviors, but we are also products of our own environment and experience. A good example is the first cloned cat, "cc" (short for "carbon copy"). Even though she looks very similar to the cat who donated her genetic material, her coat pattern is slightly different (**Figure 21.16**). This is because even the environment in the womb can affect development (in this case, coat pattern). Even identical twins have different fingerprints. Of course after we are born, there are many experiences that make us who we are. Those experiences can't be duplicated, so the clone will grow up differently than the one who was cloned and may behave quite differently. A clone of Einstein might become an artist instead of a scientist. We are so much more than just our genes!

Creating cloned embryos for experimental or medical use raises the questions previously posed regarding moral status. Should humans (realized or potential) be created and destroyed for the potential benefit of others? Again, there is a range of viewpoints regarding the status of the embryo. If the embryo at this early stage does not have as high a value, or any value, compared to other human life, then **utilitarian logic** (the idea that something is only good if it is useful and that actions should promote the greatest good for the greatest number of people) would dictate that it should by all means be used. Others argue that it should be protected, not because of its inherent value but because creation of human embryos for such purposes can lead to human commercialization, making any human life a commodity to be bought, sold, and used, thereby cheapening the value of life. Still others would say that we should not create human embryos for purposes other than reproduction and not in a manner that manufactures human life, so-called "designer embryos." The question still goes back to what it means to be human and what value is placed on human life.

Have you considered your own thoughts on cloning? Do your thoughts differ when considering humans versus animals? According to Gallup's 2007 Values and Beliefs Survey, conducted in May of 2007, when asked about reproductively cloning animals, 36% thought this was morally acceptable. Yet, the view is different when the life is a human one. Most scientists and the general public oppose attempts to clone a human to produce a child. Only 11% of the American public believes reproductive cloning of humans is morally acceptable. The National Academies of Sciences has recommended that cloning humans should not be done at present, simply because it is "unsafe."

There is far more support for therapeutic cloning than reproductive cloning in the American public. Another poll

▲ **Figure 21.16** "CC" the cloned cat (*left*) and her genetic donor, Rainbow (*right*). Although they have the same DNA, they have slightly different coat patterns.

Source: http://www.cbc.ca/news/story/2002/02/14/copycat020214.html.

asked by the Coalition for the Advancement of Medical Research (CAMR) found that, as people learned more about what therapeutic cloning was, they became more accepting. For example, when a group was asked about their opinion

of cloning to develop stem cells, 60% strongly or somewhat favored the research. However, after reading a more detailed description of what therapeutic cloning research involves, 72% of the respondents favored the research.

▷ Stem Cell and Cloning Policies

In such contentious and divisive issues, with prestige and money at stake, politics and policymaking are in play as well. The issues of stem cells and cloning have generated a great

deal of debate, Congressional hearings, speeches, and rhetoric. The ongoing debate is helping everyone learn the issues and make their voices heard.

The Debate in the United States

In the United States, the main focus has been on federal funding. In 1996 under the Clinton administration, a legislative ban stated that federally appropriated funds could not be used for the creation of a human embryo for research purposes. The ban clearly defined "human embryo." However, once human ESC lines had been well established two years later in 1998, the legal definition of ESCs had to be considered; were these cells defined as "embryos"? In 1999, Harriet S. Rabb, then general counsel of the Department of Health and Human Services, provided her legal opinion to the National Institutes of Health (NIH). She stated that the ban did not apply to *isolated* pluripotent stem cells because they were not capable of developing into a human, even if placed in a uterus. Guidelines were established by the NIH that stated that pluripotent stem cells (ESCs) could be used in NIH-funded studies, provided that some other (nonfederal) entity paid for removal of the cells from human embryos. The NIH initiated the applications process, but ultimately funding

was not granted to the applications because of the new president's policy. On August 9, 2001, President George W. Bush announced that only human ESC lines that had already been established *before* this date would be eligible for federally-funded research. At this time, it was believed that 78 lines met the qualifications set by President Bush. Subsequently, it became clear that many of these lines were either duplicates, failed to grow, or were held by labs that either withdrew them or refused to send them to U.S. researchers. As of March 2007, the NIH was reporting that 21 lines were available to researchers performing research with federal funds.

The limited number of cell lines has frustrated scientists who perform human ESC research for several reasons. Why? First, the limited number of lines means there is limited genetic diversity. To learn how "normal" ESCs behave would require many more cell lines, as would predicting how cells from various ethnic groups would respond to the same drug treatment. Second, cell lines can acquire genetic mutations over time, and this can render them useless for various applications. As these 21 lines age, this genetic instability becomes an increasing concern to scientists working with them. Third, the original cell lines were isolated and cocultured with mouse "feeder" cells and bovine serum. Contamination with nonhuman products makes these lines risky for future use in human therapies because they may incite serious immune system responses. (Since 2001, technology has significantly improved such that it is now possible to derive new ESC lines in defined conditions that completely lack animal products.) Last, not only do scientists want to study normal cells from "normal" embryos, but they want to study cells that contain genes for specific diseases. Being able to observe cells as they develop abnormalities may allow researchers to see exactly where development goes wrong and provide insight in correcting it. For all the reasons described, many scientists would like to see the ban lifted so that new ESC lines could be derived from surplus IVF embryos.

As of 2008, researchers in the United States using federal funds were still subject to the ban set by President Bush in 2001. However, several bills had been in Congress in attempts to overturn the ban. In May 2005, the House of Representatives passed H.R. 810, the **Stem Cell Research Enhancement Act,** which would expand federal funding to lines created *after* August 9, 2001, from excess embryos stored in fertility clinics. In July of 2006, the Senate also passed the bill, but it immediately fell to a presidential veto, President Bush's first veto in six years! (Neither the Senate nor the House could gather enough votes for the 2/3 majority required to override the veto). The Stem Cell Research Enhancement Act (renamed H.R.3) was reintroduced after mid-term Congressional elections. In late spring of 2007, both the Senate and House of Representatives approved the bill, once again. Despite even more support than for H.R. 810 there was still not enough support to override President George W. Bush's second veto of his presidency. This issue will certainly be raised again for the president-elect of 2008.

The U.S. public opinion reflects the votes in Congress. While some groups may loudly protest the use of medical research using stem cells obtained from human embryos, as a whole, it seems that Americans have grown more accepting. National polls attempt to take a "snapshot" view of current opinion across the country. According to one group, The Gallup Organization, which followed the public's views from 2002 to 2007, the percentage of Americans considering the use of ESCs obtained from embryos morally acceptable has gradually increased from 52% to 64% (Figure 21.17).

Although the development of stem cell lines with federal funds remains stalled at the time this text was written, it is legal—in most states—to produce new ESC lines, provided that the funding is from state or private sources. Many people believe that without the NIH, the largest supporter of biomedical science in the United States, the field is hampered and American scientists are at a disadvantage. Although private companies fund this research, too, these companies may closely protect their results for proprietary reasons to gain exclusive commercialization rights (patents) to the cell lines and technologies they have invented.

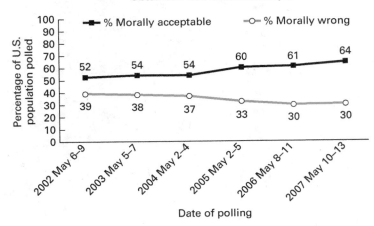

Medical Research Using Stem Cells Obtained From Human Embryos

▲ **Figure 21.17** Since 2002, Americans have grown more accepting of medical research using stem cells obtained from human embryos. The percentage considering this morally acceptable has gradually increased from 52% to 64%.

Source: Gallup Poll, http://www.galluppoll.com/content/default.aspx?ci=27757.

Patents are another controversial area within the field of stem cell research because some people argue that patents impede the ability of some research to move forward. Three patents specifically have been central in the news. These three key patents are held by the Wisconsin Alumni Research Foundation (WARF), which manages the intellectual property of University of Wisconsin–Madison. (Remember, it was James Thomson at Wisconsin who first derived human ESCs in 1998.) The patents protect Wisconsin's ESC lines and the methods used to grow them. The result is that WARF has charged biotechnology firms license fees up to $400,000 for permission to use the ESCs and/or methods. Academic labs even have to pay a small fee. However, the patents were challenged in July 2006 by the U.S. Foundation for Taxpayer and Consumer Rights (FTCR) and the Public Patent Foundation (PUBPAT) because much of the money used to support academic and institutional research comes from taxpayers. They state that these patents, "purport to cover stem cells that are looting taxpayer funds and forcing research overseas." As of 2008, only one of the three patents was upheld by the U.S. Patent and Trademark Office (PTO). The two others were revoked but are under appeals.

Despite the lack of NIH funds to public institutions, private donations to universities and institutions and initiatives in various states continue to push the field forward in the United States. California leads other states with the most dollars committed by taxpayers with a measure passed in November 2004. **Proposition 71, the California Stem Cell Research and Cures Act,** provides $3 billion for research and facilities and created the California Institute for Regenerative Medicine to regulate stem cell research. Other states that have committed to funding embryonic stem cell research are: New Jersey, Connecticut, Illinois, Maryland, Massachusetts, Indiana, and Wisconsin. Interestingly, while some states are encouraging stem cell research, others (such as South

Dakota) prohibit research specifically on cells or tissues derived from an embryo outside a woman's body.

Until now, we have only discussed the politics of ESC research, but what about cloning? You might be surprised to find out that there are no federal laws against reproductive or therapeutic (research) cloning. In 2003, the House of Representatives passed a bill (Human Cloning Prohibition Act, H.R. 534) to ban both reproductive and therapeutic cloning, which President Bush indicated he would sign. The Senate tabled the legislation, and a vote was never taken. The Human Cloning Prohibition Act of 2007 (H.R. 2560) was introduced in the House by Representative Diana DeGette (Democrat–Colorado) and was voted down. The Act would have made it unlawful for "any person, including a governmental entity, to perform or attempt to perform human cloning." A Representative opposed to the bill (Joseph Pitts, Republican–Pennsylvania) stated that the bill, "*allows for unlimited cloning of human embryos but prevents women and doctors from trying to implant one of these embryos to initiate a pregnancy. In practice, this means that embryos will be cloned, used for experimentation, harvesting, research, then assigned a death sentence. So cloned embryos would be required by law to die. Not only does this bill allow the practice of cloning to move forward, it also mandates the killing of those human embryos.*"

There is discussion in the Senate as well. In 2007, Sam Brownback (Republican, Kansas) reintroduced legislation in Congress that would make all human cloning, including therapeutic cloning, illegal in the United States. The legislation would also ban importation of any medical products created using the technology in other countries. Punishment would be up to 10 years in prison and a $1 million fine. An alternative act, introduced by U.S. Senators Orrin G. Hatch (Republican–Utah) would make reproductive cloning illegal, too, but permits SCNT for therapeutic cloning. Neither Senate bills had been voted on by mid-2008.

In the absence of federal legislation, various states have made laws pertaining to human cloning. Although some states have banned both reproductive and therapeutic cloning, others have banned only reproductive cloning. For example, New Jersey and California have both passed laws that specifically permit SCNT for the purpose of making ESC lines. So, as long as scientists are not using federal money, it is legal to derive ESCs from cloned embryos in these states. Almost all states are currently debating stem cell and cloning issues and have bills under consideration. The individual states may be the ones that move faster in terms of the legislation, which may affect the debate at the federal level.

What are Other Countries Doing?

Not surprisingly, stem cells and cloning are issues for debate not just in the United States but around the world. Many countries are establishing stem cell research centers, including the United Kingdom, France, Germany, Switzerland, Belgium, Sweden, China, Taiwan, South Korea, Japan, India, Australia, Turkey, and Israel. As you might expect, there is no consensus about policies regarding existing ESC lines or establishing new cell lines. Some countries don't allow any work with human ESCs, some only allow work with human ESCs if they are imported from another country, and others have vague or very relaxed laws about the sources of human ESCs. Much is at stake in terms of possibilities for scientific advances, economic and biotechnology development, and national prestige. In September of 2003, the InterAcademy Panel on International Affairs (IAP) published a statement that called "on all countries worldwide to ban reproductive cloning of human beings" yet requested that cloning for research and therapeutic purposes be excluded from the ban. More than 60 science academies from across the world signed the statement. Although there is international agreement that reproductive cloning should be banned, therapeutic cloning continues to be controversial.

In early 2005, the United Nations (UN) General Assembly passed a nonbinding declaration banning all human cloning, including therapeutic cloning. The vote was 84 to 34 (with 37 abstentions), reflecting the partition over the issue worldwide. The United States was an outspoken supporter of the UN ban. Some countries already have laws reflecting this sentiment. For example, our next-door neighbor, Canada,

passed legislation in 2004 that specifically prohibited both types of human cloning. Nonetheless, there are many stem cell advocates. The United Kingdom (UK) legalized SCNT in 2001 and, despite the UN's declaration, continues to support this type of research. Several other countries, such as South Korea, Australia, Belgium, Israel, India, and Singapore, also allow SCNT, and scientists from these countries are attempting to establish ESC lines from cloned embryos.

Permitting therapeutic cloning necessitates further policy, as outlined by the first international guidelines issued by the International Society for Stem Cell Research (ISSCR) in February of 2007. Two key issues are highlighted in these nonbinding guidelines: 1) payment for women donating eggs, and 2) control on animal-human chimeras. As you now know, the inefficiency of therapeutic cloning requires a large source of human eggs for nuclear transfer. The UK leads on this issue with a law prohibiting the use of cash payments to induce women to donate eggs for research. One research institute in the UK now offers an "egg-sharing" scheme: in return for donating spare eggs, women will be offered contributions towards expensive IVF treatment. Another area of policy that "cloning permissive" countries must face involves controls on projects involving animal-human chimeras. In lieu of human eggs for nuclear transfer, animal eggs might be a more readily abundant source. The resulting embryos would then be almost entirely human, with only animal DNA outside of the nucleus. Policymakers in the UK are currently debating these issues, as a cow-human hybrid proposal was submitted in late 2006 for the purpose of creating ESC cell lines.

The Future

If you follow the media related to stem cells, it appears at times that there is a war in which adult-derived stem cells are against embryonic stem cells. Which will win? Are adult or embryonic stem cells the future of this field? The simple answer is that it depends on the scientific application. For example, if the purpose of using stem cells is to regenerate tissues in a patient, the "best" cells might be those least likely to cause immune complications, that is, the patient's own adult-derived stem cells. However, if the intent of use for stem cells is to better understand the basic science of pluripotency, the "best" cells might be embryonic stem cells. As we view this exciting time in stem cell biology, we should consider each type of stem cell for its own unique characteristics. And remember, while it has been traditional to think about stem cells as adult or embryonic, the cells that we have discussed will not fit so neatly into two categories. In actuality, there is a continuum of stem cells (e.g., embryonic, fetal, amniotic, adult tissue) with different characteristics that are best suited for different applications.

What makes the future of stem cell science (and cloning) so unique compared to other biological advances is that the ethical and political issues are so closely tied to each experiment. It is precisely these political and ethical "limitations" that have pushed scientists to explore acceptable "alternatives" to embryonic stem cells. We have seen demonstrations of inventiveness and creativity in the scientists seeking alternative sources of pluripotent cells. For example, scientists are now learning how to induce pluripotency in adult cells. In the future, might a patient be able to give a few skin cells, have them induced to a pluripotent state, and then have these cells differentiated into any tissue that needs repairing? If so, it would avoid the destruction of embryos as a source of ESCs and would obliterate the need for the inefficient SCNT process for the purpose of "customizing" cells. The alternatives (already discovered or soon to be) may hold the key to the future of regenerative medicine; they may provide an abundant source of pluripotent cells that are easily obtained, cost-effective, and morally acceptable to all.

Because the moral and political issues may guide the science, it is difficult to predict where this nascent field of stem cell biology is going. We are left with a lot of questions at this time. For example, will the United States be a leader in the field of stem cell science, or will regulations hinder advances? Will ESCs even be necessary or practical in regenerative medicine if a pluripotent adult cell can be identified or induced? Will therapeutic cloning change the face of medicine, or will some other technology serve the same purpose? Will humans eventually be reproductively cloned? In the current climate, it seems important to many, but certainly not all, scientists that there be exploration of all types of stem cells for various research and therapeutic applications. (Even if U.S. policy doesn't permit this, other countries will support it.) Nevertheless, the science will eventually align with what works best technically, morally, and financially. It is safe to say that stem cells will change regenerative medicine immensely in the next few decades. However, the nature of these stem cells and the methods that will be used are not obvious yet. I anxiously await the new advances and hope you will continue to follow this ever-changing field that is so carefully scrutinized by all.

Kelly A. Hogan
Department of Biology
University of North Carolina at Chapel Hill
Chapel Hill, NC 27599-3280
Email: Kelly_Hogan@unc.edu

Resources

Websites

(*Note:* Because the information of these resources is relatively new and changing rapidly, websites provide some of the best up-to-the-minute information regarding background as well as current knowledge. The following are some of the best across a wide spectrum of view points.)

Tutorials/Educational Information

National Institutes of Health Stem Cell Information (http://stemcells.nih.gov/index. asp) Basic information on stem cells, research guidelines, approved stem cell lines, and other information. Two useful reports: Stem Cell Basics (http://stemcells.nih.gov/info/basics/) and Regenerative Medicine 2006 (http://stemcells.nih.gov/info/scireport/2006report.htm).

The National Academies (http://dels.nas.edu/bls/stemcells/booklet.shtml) Understanding Stem Cells: An Overview of the Science and Issues

National Center for Case Study Teaching in Science (http://ublib.buffalo.edu/libraries/projects/cases/case.html) The Center provides a site to search for educational case studies related to various topics in science including many related to regenerative medicine, cloning, stem cells, and genetics.

Animations/Videos

University of Michigan's Interactive Tutorial: Stem Cells Explained (http://www.lifesciences.umich.edu/research/featured/tutorial.html)

Howard Hughes Medical Institute: Biointeractive (http://www.hhmi.org/biointeractive/stemcells) Many videos, lectures, animations related to stem cells and cloning.

University of Utah Genetics Learning Science Center (http://learn.genetics.utah.edu). Lessons, quizzes, and animations related to stem cells and cloning.

Riken Center for Developmental Biology (http://www.cdb.riken.jp/jp/stemcells/) A Japanese Research Foundation with excellent animations related to basic characteristics of stem cells.

Sumanas, Inc. (www.sumanasinc.com/webcontent/anisamples/nonmajorsbiology/stemcells.html) A basic animation related to isolating embryonic stem cells.

PBS Nova: Science Now (http://www.pbs.org/wgbh/nova/sciencenow/3209/04.html) Video clip explaining therapeutic cloning, and various interviews, photographs, issues are highlighted at the site.

News

Yahoo News Full Coverage: Stem Cell Research (http://news.yahoo.com/fc/Science/Stem_Cell_Research) Provides links to news, editorials relate to stem cell research.

Stem Cell Research News (http://www.stemcellresearchnews.com/) Independent reporting organization providing current objective headline news on all facets of stem cell research.

New Scientist **Special Report on Stem Cells** (http://www.newscientist.com/channel/sex/stem-cells) Website for *New Scientist* magazine with current news and information related to stem cells and cloning.

Scientific American's **Science News** (http://www.sciam.com/news_directory.cfm) Updated daily with science news stories. Search for news related to stem cells and cloning.

National Public Radio (http://www.npr.org/) Search for short news stories and audio interviews related to stem cells and cloning.

Policy

National Institute of Health (http://stemcells.nih.gov/policy/guidelines.asp) See a listing of current and older official documents related to U.S. policy relating to stem cells.

StemGen (http://www.stemgen.org/) A website providing a world map and searchable database about laws and policies relating to stem cell research.

National Conference of State Legislatures: State Embryonic and Fetal Research Laws (http://www.ncsl.org/programs/health/genetics/embfet.htm) This website is updated often and provides text and a table comparing the laws relating to stem cells and cloning for various states.

Interest Groups

(*Note:* These groups have an agenda and the information provided by them is not always objective!)

The Coalition for the Advancement of Medical Research (http://www.camradvocacy.org/) Consists of patient organizations, universities, scientific societies, and foundations advocating the advancement of breakthrough research and technologies in regenerative medicine.

The Royal Society (http://www.royalsoc.ac.uk/landing.asp?id=1202) The Royal Society is the national academy of science of the UK and the Commonwealth. They endorse research for adult-derived stem cells and therapeutic cloning and support a ban of reproductive cloning.

Americans to Ban Cloning (http://cloninginformation.org) A group of concerned Americans and U.S.-based organizations that promote a global ban on human cloning.

Do No Harm: The Coalition of Americans for Research Ethics (http://www.stemcellresearch.org/) A national coalition of researchers, health care professionals, bioethicists, legal professionals, and others dedicated to the promotion of scientific research and health care that does no harm to human life.

Juvenile Diabetes Research Foundation International (http://www.jdrf.org/index.cfm?page_id=103932) A charitable funder and advocate for type I diabetes research worldwide. The foundation supports and expansion of embryonic stem cell research.

Genetics Policy Institute (http://www.genpol.org/) A nonprofit organization dedicated to establishing a positive legal framework to advance stem cell research

Catholic Church (http://www.americancatholic.org/ and http://www.catholicnewsagency.com/) The Catholic Church is against embryonic stem cell research because it involves the destruction of human embryos. Search for articles on topics relating to stem cells and cloning.

Bioethics

Bioethics.net. The American Journal of Bioethics Online (http://bioethics.net/) Contains lots of articles and basic discussion on bioethics issues relating to stem cells and cloning.

The Council for Responsible Genetics (http://www.gene-watch .org) A nonprofit, nongovernmental organization that fosters public debate about the social, ethical, and environmental implications of genetic technologies. Search for articles related to stem cells and cloning in their bimonthly magazine, *GeneWatch*.

Bioethics.com (http://www.bioethicsnews.com/) A global information source on bioethics news and issues. You can vote on polls and see current results too.

The President's Council on Bioethics (http://www.bioethics.gov/) Established in 2001, the Council contains members appointed by the President for the purpose of advising on bioethical issues that may emerge as a consequence of advances in biomedical science and technology.

▷ Articles

Cookson, C., et al. (July 2005). The future of stem cells. *Scientific American and Financial Times* Special Report. July 2005 (pages A1–A35).

Gilbert, D. (2004). The future of human embryonic stem cell research: Addressing ethical conflict with responsible scientific research. *Medical Science Monitor*, 10, RA99–103.

Hanna, J., Wernig, M., Markoulaki, S., et al. (2007). Treatment of sickle cell anemia mouse model with iPS cells generated from autologous skin. *Science*, *318*:1920–1923.

Lanza, R. and N. Rosenthal (June, 2004). The stem cell challenge. *Scientific American*. 290(6):92-9. (See also sidebar by Christine Soares.)

Yu, J., Vodyanik, M.A., Smuga-Otto, K., et al. (2007). Induced pluripotent stem cell lines from human somatic cells. *Science*, *318*:1917–1920.

▷ Books

Bailey, R. (2005) *Liberation biology: The scientific and moral case for the biotech revolution*. New York: Prometheus Books.

Fox, C. (2007). *Cell of cells: The global race to capture and control the stem cell*. New York: W.W. Norton and Company.

Herold, E. (2006). *Stem cell wars: Inside stories from the frontlines*. New York: Palgrave Macmillan.

Scott. C. T. (2005). *Stem cell now: From the experiment that shook the world to the new politics of life*. Upper Saddle River, New Jersey: Pi Press.

▷ Questions for Further Discussion or Research

1. National polls often examine stem cell and cloning issues. By searching on the Internet, examine a few questions asked within the past few years to the American public. Poll your class or school, and see if the opinions are similar. Think about making up some of your polling questions. (Be aware that the choice of words used in your question can be very important!) Websites to get you started: http://www.pollingreport.com/science.htm#Stem and http://www.galluppoll.com/.

2. Compare and contrast ESCs and ASCs. Include an explanation of where each cell type comes from and how each type can be isolated. Give examples of how stem cells may be used to help human genetic disease conditions.

3. When first introduced, there was much controversy about *in vitro* fertilization (IVF). Think well into the future when reproductive cloning will presumably be better understood. Consider a time when humans could be successfully cloned and the procedure is safe enough to produce healthy individuals. Is this unethical? Can you compare it ethically to *in vitro* fertilization?

4. In this text, we considered a multipronged approach to using stem cells in treating Parkinson's disease. See if you can find out how scientists are using various types of stem cells for battling some other disease, such as diabetes.

5. If you were about to have a baby, would you consider banking the umbilical cord blood in a private bank, why or why not? See if you can find out the typical costs associated with it. If you decided not to save it for your own personal use, what else could you do with the cord blood?

6. Examine the laws in place for embryonic stem cell research and cloning in the state in which you live. Do you agree with these laws? Why or why not?

7. At the time this booklet was printed, President George W. Bush was still in office. Has a new president had any impact on stem cell and cloning policies? If so, explain.

8. One use for cloning is to make clones of animals, such as pigs, that would be used as a supply for human organ transplants. This area of biology is called xenotransplantation. What are the advantages and disadvantages of xenotransplantation?

9. In the text, we briefly mentioned preimplantation genetic diagnosis (PGD). While this technique can be used to avoid implanting embryos with devastating abnormalities, it can also be used to make "designer babies." Research examples of how PGD has been used and how there may be a fine line between its use in research and in making designer babies. As a side note: *My Sister's Keeper* is an interesting top-selling, fictional novel by Jodi Picoult that examines aspects of the life of a girl who has been chosen by PGD to be a perfect tissue match for her sister with leukemia (based upon a true situation).

10. What is currently being done in stem cell therapies with spinal cord injury?

11. What are some antirejection drugs currently used by tissue and organ transplant patients? What are some side effects of these drugs, and how long can they prevent rejection? Can stem cell therapies avoid these problems with tissue rejection? Explain your answer.

22 Understanding the Human Genome Project

▷ Introduction

It is indeed an exciting time to be studying biology. Over the next decade and beyond, you will witness some of the most significant biological discoveries in our history. The wealth of knowledge to be gained from the Human Genome Project will have tremendous impact in basic science and medicine in the near future. In many ways, the human genome is considered one of the great unsolved mysteries of biology—a treasure chest of genetic information. The Human Genome Project was a biological research project of unprecedented magnitude, and the challenge of identifying all the genes contained in human cells is now complete. Whether you are a biology major or nonmajor, this booklet will provide you with a basic overview of important goals and outcomes of the Human Genome Project; stimulate thought and discussion on the potential future impact of the project; and introduce some of the ethical, legal, and social implications of unraveling the keys to our genetic material. Throughout this booklet, key terms appear in bold to help you learn important concepts related to the Human Genome Project.

▷ Defining the Human Genome Project

Genome Basics

A human embryo is formed shortly after fertilization—the joining of a human egg and a sperm cell. Eggs and sperm are types of cells known as sex cells or **gametes**. Contained within each gamete is nearly 6 feet of highly coiled **deoxyribonucleic acid (DNA)** packaged and condensed into a single set of 23 **chromosomes**. All the other cells in your body, such as skin cells, muscle cells, and liver cells, are known as **somatic cells** (derived from the Greek word *soma*, "body"). Over 100 trillion somatic cells are found in the human body. Each human somatic cell contains 46 chromosomes— 23 chromosomes inherited from your mother and 23 chromosomes inherited from your father.

The number of chromosomes in a cell can be revealed by a **karyotype** (Figure 22.1). In karyotype analysis, cells (such as human white blood cells) are spread on a microscope slide, then treated with chemicals to release and stain the chromosomes. Stained chromosomes show an alternating series of light and dark bands. Although these bands are not visible in Figure 22.1, chromosomes can be aligned and paired based on their banding pattern and their size. The largest chromosome is chromosome 1. Chromosome pairs 1 through 22 are known as the **autosomes**, while the X and Y chromosomes are called the **sex chromosomes** because they are involved in sex determination. Karyotypes are frequently used to determine the sex of a fetus, and they can also be used to detect genetic abnormalities such as Down syndrome, a condition in which individuals have three copies of chromosome 21. Was the karyotype in Figure 22.1 produced from a somatic cell of a male or a female human? How do you know? If you have studied chromosomes before, you may already know that human female somatic cells have two X chromosomes, while somatic cells from males have one X and one Y chromosome. Notice that this karyotype is from a human male.

DNA consists of a double-stranded helix of chemical structures called **nucleotides** (Figure 22.2). Nucleotides are the building blocks of DNA structure. Each nucleotide consists of a phosphate group, a sugar molecule (deoxyribose sugar), and a base chemically bonded together. Four bases are found in a DNA molecule: adenine (A), guanine (G), cytosine (C), and thymine (T). The bases of DNA in two opposing strands join together by hydrogen bonding, creating **base pairs (bp)** that attach both strands of the double helix. Adenine always forms base pairs with thymine, while guanine always forms base pairs with cytosine. There are approximately 3 billion base pairs in the DNA contained within every human cell.

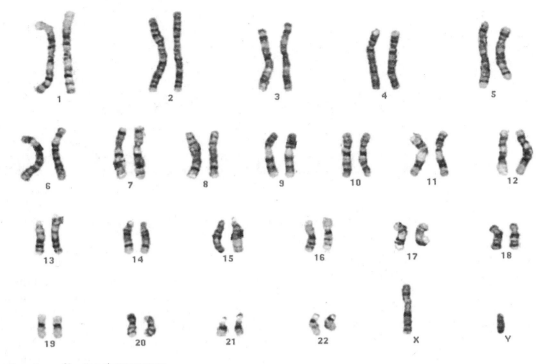

▲ **Figure 22.1**   Karyotype of human chromosomes

Source: Thieman and Palladino, *Introduction to Biotechnology*, p. 33, Figure 2.7.

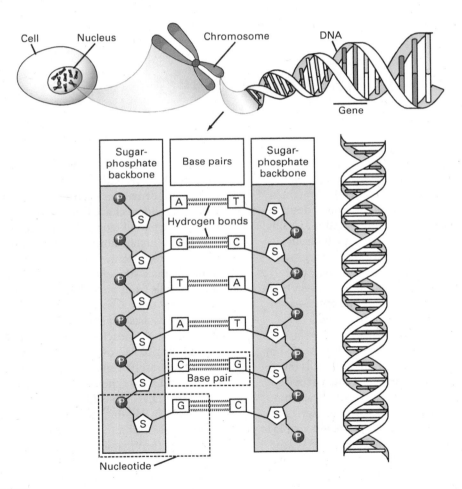

▲ **Figure 22.2**   DNA structure

Source: Figures adapted from http://www.accessexcellence.org/AB/GG/dna2.html and http://www.accessexcellence.org/AB/GG/basePair2.html

Contained within DNA are the instructions for life—**genes**. Most genes contain a specific sequence of nucleotides that provide cells with the instructions for the synthesis of a protein, but there are also many genes that do not encode proteins. Genes are approximately 2,000 to 4,000 nucleotides long, although many smaller and larger genes have been identified. The entire set of genes in an organism's DNA is called the **genome**. For a long time it was estimated that the human genome consisted of approximately 100,000 genes; however, as you will soon learn, this estimate has been reevaluated based on recent information from the Human Genome Project. Visit NOVA Online for "Journey into DNA," a great animation that takes you through layers of the body into the DNA contained within cells (http://www.pbs.org/wgbh/nova/genome/media/journeyintodna.swf).

By controlling the proteins produced by a cell, genes influence how cells, tissues, and organs appear, both through the microscope and with the naked eye. These inherited appearances are called **traits**. You have inherited traits from your parents by virtue of the DNA contained in your cells. Perhaps you have studied the inheritance of human traits such as eye color and skin color. Some traits are controlled by a single gene, others by multiple genes that must interact in complex ways to produce a trait. In general, traits are governed by our genes. But there is more to any trait than just genetics. Environmental conditions strongly influence gene behavior, which in turn can influence visible traits. For example, people of the same ethnic background living in warmer climates exhibit darker skin colors than people from colder climates, even though the genetics of these individuals may be very similar. Many traits go far beyond characteristics that are visible to the naked eye. Traits also include events at the molecular level, such as the metabolism of a cell—the cell's ability to manufacture molecules and utilize nutrients for energy.

As shown in **Figure 22.3**, making proteins requires that genes are copied into single-stranded molecules called messenger RNA (**mRNA**) in a complex process called **transcription**. Scientists also refer to transcription as **gene expression**. The mRNA molecules literally act as "messengers" of the genetic code by carrying information, in the form of nucleotide sequence, from the nucleus to the cytoplasm of a cell, where protein synthesis, or **translation,** occurs. **Proteins** are created by the joining together of long chains of building blocks called amino acids. The nucleotide sequence of a gene—the specific order of As, Gs, Ts, and Cs—determines which amino acids, and the amino acid composition of a protein is largely responsible for the three-dimensional shape (structure) and the function of a protein.

Because a large majority of the molecules in a cell are proteins, proteins ultimately affect the traits displayed by cells in a variety of ways. Proteins are considered the major structural and functional molecules in a cell because of the range of important roles they play. For example, some proteins function as pigments responsible for eye color, hair color, and skin color. Many proteins function as **enzymes**, proteins responsible for carrying out and accelerating chemical reactions in cells. Other proteins function as transport molecules that serve to move vitamins, minerals, hormones, and body gases throughout the body. You may be familiar with an important oxygen-transporting protein in red blood cells called hemoglobin. Large classes of proteins, such as antibodies, play significant roles in our immune system and our ability to recognize and destroy foreign materials such as bacteria and viruses.

Genes can undergo genetic change. A **mutation** is a nucleotide change in the sequence of a gene. Mutations can involve large changes in genetic information or single nucleotide changes within a gene, such as changing an A to a C or a G to a T. Some mutations are due to spontaneous errors during DNA replication in cells, while others are "induced" by environmental causes, such as exposure to X-rays or ultraviolet light from the sun (that glowing tan you have is not as healthy as you might think!) and exposure to chemicals called **mutagens** that can change DNA structure. Regardless of how mutations arise, they can result in changes in protein production in cells. In some cases, mutations completely block the synthesis of a protein from a gene. In other types of mutations, a gene can still synthesize a protein, but the protein doesn't function as well as the normal protein. By affecting the proteins made by a cell, mutations can alter traits (**Figure 22.4**).

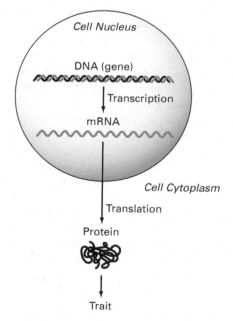

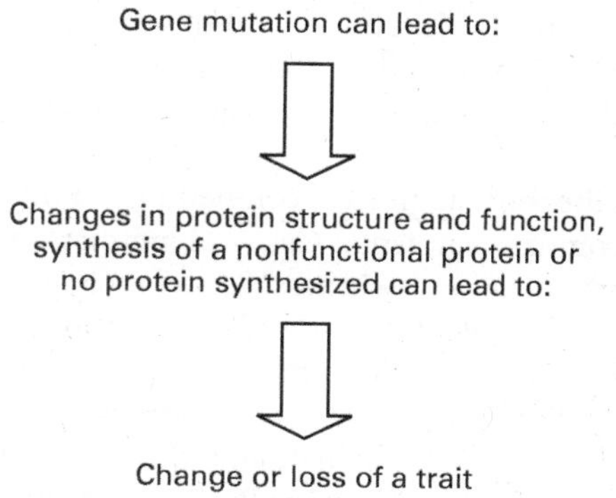

▲ **Figure 22.3** The flow of genetic information in human cells

Gene mutation can lead to:

Changes in protein structure and function, synthesis of a nonfunctional protein or no protein synthesized can lead to:

Change or loss of a trait

▲ **Figure 22.4** How mutations change protein structure and influence traits

Nucleotide changes in a gene affect proteins because the nucleotide sequence of a gene provides a cell with the information required to synthesize a protein. Change the DNA sequence of a gene, and the amino acid sequence of a protein can change. Altering the amino acid sequence of a protein often changes the overall shape of a protein, which in turn affects how the protein functions.

It might surprise you that a single nucleotide change in the genetic code of a gene can cause such a problem. A striking example of how this can happen is illustrated by the human genetic condition called **sickle-cell disease**. Sickle-cell disease results from a single mutation in the gene used to synthesize protein chains that assemble to form hemoglobin, the oxygen-binding protein contained in human red blood cells. A single nucleotide change in this gene (out of several hundred nucleotides) creates a single amino acid change in hemoglobin (out of 146 amino acids) that produces an altered hemoglobin molecule with an abnormal three-dimensional shape. While you might be thrilled to score 145 correct answers out of 146 on a biology exam, this level of accuracy in a protein can be devastating. In this case, the abnormal hemoglobin molecules bind oxygen poorly. In addition, abnormal hemoglobin changes the shape of red blood cells from disklike cells to irregularly shaped cells that take on a "sickled" look. Sickled red blood cells do not travel well through blood vessels, resulting in poor oxygenation of body tissues and other painful symptoms.

A number of conditions arise from genetic changes similar to those described for sickle-cell disease. It is likely that you have heard of cystic fibrosis, albinism, phenylketonuria, and Tay-Sachs disease. Similarly, certain behavioral and psychological illnesses result from genetic changes and can be inherited. For some genetic disease conditions to be expressed—sickle-cell disease included—a person must have inherited two chromosomes carrying the same defective gene. If only one chromosome contains a mutation for a given gene, a person is likely to be normal for that trait, because one chromosome with a "good," nonmutated copy of the gene can often produce enough protein to override the effects of the defective gene. Individuals with one defective and one normal copy of a gene are commonly called **carriers** because they can pass ("carry") a defective gene to offspring but will typically never show the diseased trait themselves. Remember this concept for our later discussion concerning genetic testing and genetic privacy. Now that we have considered some of the basics of human genetics, let's explore the purpose of the Human Genome Project.

Goals of the HUMAN Genome Project

In 1990, the Office of Health and Environmental Research of the U.S. Department of Energy (DOE) proposed the Human Genome Project as a joint venture between the National Institutes of Health (NIH) and DOE, with a 15-year time frame for completion. You might wonder why DOE was involved. DOE had long been interested in studying genetics, in part because of their research on the effects of nuclear radiation on human genetics. The project funded seven major sequencing centers in the United States. Over time the project grew to become an international effort with contributions from scientists in 18 countries, but the work was primarily carried out by the International Human Genome Sequence Consortium, which involved nearly 3,000 scientists working at 20 centers in six countries: China, France, Germany, Great Britain, Japan, and the United States. The estimated budget for completing the genome was $3 billion, a cost of $1 per nucleotide. Driven in part by competition from private companies, the Human Genome Project turned out to be a rare government project that completed all of its initial goals, and several addition goals, more than 2 years ahead of schedule and under budget!

One of the most aggressive competitors on the project was a private company known as Celera Genomics—aptly named from a word meaning "swiftness." The company was swift indeed when in 1998 it announced its intention to use novel technologies to sequence the entire human genome in three years! Fearful of how private corporations might control the release of genome information, U.S. government groups involved in the Human Genome Project were effectively forced to keep pace with private groups to stay competitive in the race to complete the genome. Interestingly, in July 2005, Celera Genomics released its formerly proprietary human, mouse, and rat genome sequences to the public domain.

In 1998, as a result of accelerated progress, a revised target date of 2003 was set for completion of the project. On June 26, 2000, leaders of the Human Genome Project and Celera Genomics participated in a press conference with President Clinton to announce that a rough "working draft" of approximately 95% of the human genome had been assembled (nearly 4 years ahead of the initially projected timetable). At a joint press conference on February 12, 2001, Dr. Francis Collins, director of the NIH National Human Genome Research Institute and director of the Human Genome Project, and Dr. J. Craig Venter, director of Celera Genomics, announced that a series of papers describing the initial analysis of the genome working draft sequence were to be published by their research groups in the prestigious journals *Nature* and *Science* respectively.

Scientists spent the next two years working to fill in thousands of gaps in the genome by completing the sequencing of pieces not yet finished, correcting misaligned pieces, and comparing sequences to ensure the accuracy of the genome. Finally, on April 14, 2003, the International Human Genome Sequencing Consortium announced that its work was done. A "map" of the human genome was essentially complete with virtually all bases identified and placed in their proper order with the exception of about 300 relatively small gaps of DNA that remain problematic but will be completed shortly.

What were the goals and objectives of the Human Genome Project? Specifically, the project was designed to do the following:

- Create genetic and physical maps of the 24 human chromosomes (22 autosomes, X and Y chromosomes).

- Identify the entire set of genes in the DNA of human cells. This included mapping each gene to its chromosome and determining the sequence of each gene. Originally thought to be around 100,000 genes when the project started, the total number of human genes is much less than this, as you'll soon learn.

- Determine the nucleotide sequence of the estimated 3 billion base pairs of DNA that comprise the human genome.

- Analyze genetic variations among humans. This included the identification of single-nucleotide polymorphisms (SNPs).

- Map and sequence the genomes of **model organisms,** including bacteria, yeast, roundworms, fruit flies, and mice.

- Develop new laboratory and computing technologies (including databases of genome information) that can be used to advance our analysis and understanding of gene structure and function.

- Disseminate genome information among scientists and the general public.

- Consider ethical, legal, and social issues that accompany the Human Genome Project and genetic research.

Although many scientists were skeptical that the project would succeed and critical of the large amounts of money allocated for the project, the Human Genome Project has been described by others as a research effort guaranteed to succeed, because so many scientists believed it was eventually possible to determine the sequence for all 3 billion base pairs in the human genome. What has surprised nearly everyone has been the speed with which many of the project's goals were achieved.

With completion of the Human Genome Project, scientists now have access to the "book of life." Yet, as you will learn in this booklet, completion of the Human Genome Project is just the tip of the iceberg in our understanding of genes and human genetics. How can information from the genome project be used? Gaining a better understanding of normal gene structure and function is one great benefit of the project. However, one of the most exciting outcomes will be a greater ability to identify and treat genetic disorders. For instance, new knowledge from the Human Genome Project will lead to the development of advanced screening techniques for diseased genes, early warning, and even prevention and treatment of human genetic diseases through development of genetics-based therapies, including gene therapy—topics we will discuss shortly.

▷ How is the Genome Studied? The Tools

Studying the genome of any organism is possible because of a range of sophisticated and elegant laboratory techniques in molecular biology. Most genome studies begin with isolating DNA from a tissue sample of interest. In the Human Genome Project, DNA was primarily isolated from human blood samples. Adult human red blood cells cannot be used as a source of DNA because they lack a nucleus and therefore do not contain DNA. Instead, white blood cells—important cells in the immune system that do contain a nucleus— can be removed from a blood sample and used to isolate DNA.

Isolating chromosomal DNA from blood cells is relatively simple. You may have the opportunity to isolate DNA in one of your biology courses. Once DNA is obtained, however, it is not possible to sequence an entire chromosome at once. Whole chromosomes are simply too large. Most chromosomes average around 150 million base pairs in size! The largest human chromosome, chromosome 1, is ~260 million base pairs. Even the smallest human chromosome, the Y chromosome, is ~60 million base pairs in size. A chromosome must be broken into small pieces that can be easily manipulated to identify genes and ultimately to determine the nucleotide sequence of the entire chromosome.

Cutting a chromosome down to size is accomplished using DNA-cutting enzymes called **restriction enzymes**. Restriction enzymes are essentially "scissors" for molecular biologists. A quick look in the freezer of any molecular biology lab will reveal dozens of restriction enzymes. These enzymes are

isolated from bacteria and given abbreviated names based on the bacteria they come from. For example, one of the first enzymes identified and most widely used is called *Eco*RI. *Eco*RI is isolated from *Escherichia coli*, the bacterium naturally found in the intestines of animals, including humans. Restriction enzymes have the ability to cut DNA strands at specific sequences of base pairs (**Figure 22.5**).

Restriction enzymes allow scientists to cut DNA into small pieces that can be copied—a technique called **gene cloning**. A wide range of gene cloning techniques exist.

In gene cloning, the DNA pieces of interest can be spliced into other pieces of DNA, called **vectors** that are used to carry and replicate the DNA piece of interest. Scientists cut and splice human DNA pieces into a variety of different vectors depending on the size of the DNA piece to be cloned. This must be done because human chromosomes are generally too

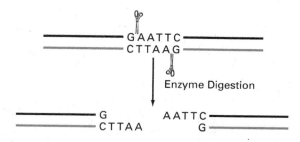

▲ **Figure 22.5**   The action of restriction enzymes

large to manipulate and clone without breaking them up into smaller fragments of a more manageable size. Yeast artificial chromosomes (YACs), bacterial artificial chromosomes (BACs), cosmids, and plasmids (small circular pieces of DNA found in bacteria) all serve as vectors that can be used to clone pieces of human DNA. Each vector is limited by the size of DNA fragments that can be inserted into the vector. Details of these vectors are not important, but you are likely to encounter these terms as you review some of the websites described in this booklet.

Once a human DNA piece has been inserted into a vector, the vector can be used to make more copies (or clones) of the human DNA piece. To accomplish this, vectors are usually placed into bacteria or yeast for DNA cloning. These microorganisms are used because they are easy and cheap to grow in the lab, and they are pretty good at replicating DNA, even if the DNA is from a human source. An illustration of cloning a piece of a human chromosome is shown in **Figure 22.6**. As shown in this figure, one strategy for cloning human chromosomes involves using restriction enzymes to cut DNA fragments into fragments of varying sizes, from larger to smaller, which are subsequently cloned into small vectors (plasmids) that allow the DNA to be sequenced.

DNA sequencing involves determining the exact arrangement of DNA nucleotides—the specific order of As, Gs, Ts, and Cs—in a piece of DNA. A variety of sequencing techniques exist, but most use DNA nucleotides that have been tagged with different-colored dyes that fluoresce when exposed to a laser. Reactions are carried out to copy a DNA sequence in the presence of these modified nucleotides, and then the sequence can be read based on the fluorescence pattern resulting from illumination of DNA samples with a laser beam. Progress of the Human Genome Project was greatly accelerated by the development of fast-paced computer-automated sequencing machines that work around the clock to generate large amounts of sequence data. As sequencing technology has continued to improve, there have been some scientists who have suggested that in the future it may be possible for a person to have his or her genome sequenced for as little as $1,000! Once DNA has been sequenced, computer programs are used to catalog the sequence information; interpret the sequence to determine if it contains protein-coding instructions; and compare it to databases of known sequences to find out if this sequence has already been determined, if it represents a novel piece of chromosome sequence, or if it shares similar sequences with other DNA pieces. The use of computer hardware and software for sequence analysis, along with many other applications such as archiving sequences in databases to store, share, and compare DNA and protein data, is part of a relatively new discipline called **bioinformatics,** an integrated field involving biology and information technology.

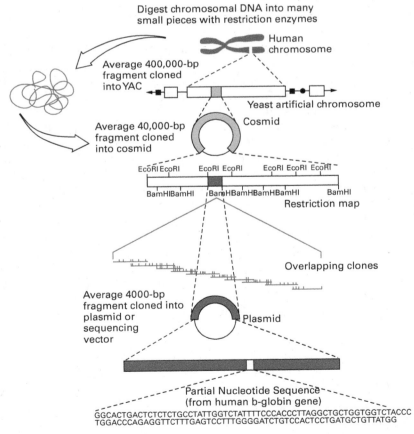

▲ **Figure 22.6** Cloning and sequencing pieces of a human chromosome

Source: Thieman and Palladino, *Introduction to Biotechnology,* p. 265, Figure 11.21.

The approach we have just discussed is a very basic overview of one of the primary methods used to clone and sequence human DNA. But if a single chromosome contains millions of base pairs, how can all this sequence data be assembled to construct a sequence of an *entire* chromosome? A challenging task indeed!

One way to sequence an entire chromosome involves a random cloning process called "shotgun" cloning and sequencing. In this process, chromosomal DNA is cut into smaller pieces with several different restriction enzymes. For example, *Eco*RI and another enzyme called *Bam*HI can be used. The different pieces generated are cloned and sequenced as we just discussed. The idea behind this approach is to randomly generate and sequence short pieces of DNA fragments with the hope of sequencing short overlapping pieces. High-powered computer programs are then put to work to look for and align overlapping sections of DNA sequences from individual pieces cut with the two restriction enzymes. By completing this genetic puzzle, it is possible to literally reconstruct a chromosome by walking along these overlapping fragments and assembling a stretch of continuously overlapping sequences (**Figure 22.7**). Data that result from this type of study produce a map of overlapping pieces and restriction-enzyme cutting sites on a chromosome called a **physical map**.

Before cloning and sequencing technologies were available to identify and map genes, scientists often studied large numbers of families with a history of a particular genetic disorder and created genetic maps based on intricate patterns of inheritance and other genetic data. Genetic maps are still used when studying disease genes to provide supporting data for physical mapping studies. Physical maps provide the molecular details of a gene and its location.

Visit the NOVA Online "Sequence for Yourself" site at http://www.pbs.org/wgbh/nova/genome/media/sequence.swf for informative animations on DNA cloning and sequencing and assembling cloned DNA fragments to create a physical map of a chromosome.

In 1995, a shotgun-cloning strategy was used by scientists at The Institute for Genomic Research to sequence the 1.8 million base pairs in the genome of a strain of bacteria called *Haemophilus influenza*. This was the first time an entire genome for any organism had been sequenced. Many doubted that shotgun-cloning strategies could be effectively used to sequence larger genomes, but development of this technique and novel sequencing strategies rapidly accelerated progress of the Human Genome Project.

While shotgun approaches are very effective for sequencing and mapping segments of a chromosome, such approaches are not practical for identifying expressed genes because, as you will learn shortly, only a very small percentage of human DNA consists of genes used to make proteins. Much of our genome contains non-protein-coding DNA. In some ways, using a shotgun approach to identify gene sequences in the genome is like searching for a needle in a haystack. A better approach for identifying genes involves techniques using mRNA. Recall that mRNA is a copy of a gene that is used to make a protein. By working with mRNA, scientists are studying expressed genes in a tissue and not looking at non-protein-coding DNA. The mRNA can be copied into DNA. This DNA is now called **complementary DNA,** or **cDNA,** because it is identical to a sequence of mRNA. Pieces of cDNA can be sequenced to produce fragments called **expressed-sequence tags,** or **ESTs.** ESTs represent small pieces of DNA sequenced from genes that are expressed in a cell. Rarely do ESTs span an entire gene, but these small pieces can be used as "tags" to ultimately determine the sequence of an entire gene. ESTs have played an important role in the identification of human genes.

Figure 22.8 shows a "big picture" representation of how DNA sequence can be determined from restriction fragments of DNA and how overlapping restriction fragments can be assembled to create a physical map of a chromosome. Notice that partial maps of chromosome 19 are shown, including the location of human disease genes for a type of diabetes (insulin-resistant diabetes) and an inherited condition in fat metabolism that results in high blood cholesterol and increased risk of heart disease (familial hypercholesterolemia).

As you will learn when we discuss how the Internet can be used to help us find out more about the genome, scientists

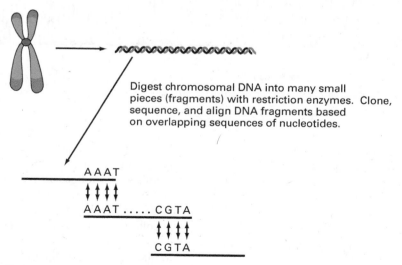

Digest chromosomal DNA into many small pieces (fragments) with restriction enzymes. Clone, sequence, and align DNA fragments based on overlapping sequences of nucleotides.

AAAT

AAAT . . . . . CGTA

CGTA

▲ **Figure 22.7** Aligning pieces of human chromosomal DNA to create a chromosome map

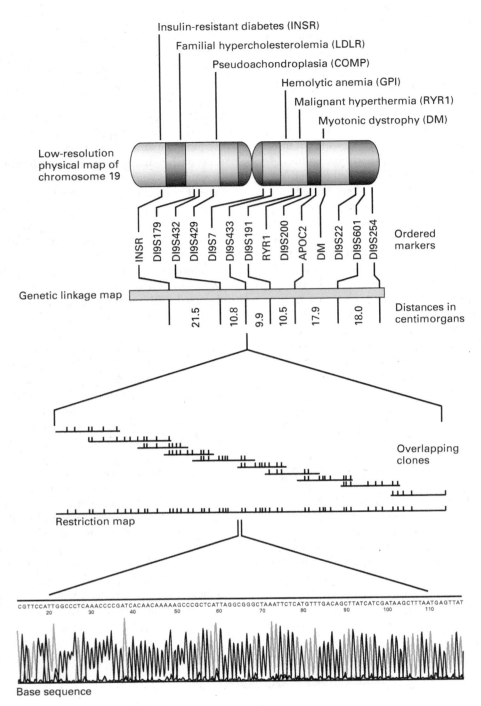

▲ Figure 22.8 Partial gene maps and DNA sequence for human chromosome 19

Source: Printed with the permission of the U.S. Department of Energy Human Genome Program. Adapted from Figure 3, p. 11 from "To Know Ourselves." Human Genome Program, U.S. Department of Energy, To Know Ourselves, 1996.

have assembled maps of human chromosomes with the locations of all known normal and disease genes.

Manipulating DNA to map genes involves some very powerful and sophisticated science. I expect that you may have more than a few questions about how the genome is studied. Shortly, you'll be introduced to websites that may provide answers to many of your questions. Meanwhile, here are a few questions to consider.

Whose genome is being sequenced, and how do we know it is representative of all humans?

Obviously, it is not possible to collect and sequence DNA from every living human. So how can we say the human genome has been determined? In some genome centers, DNA was collected from many different individuals. Scientists at Celera Genomics worked with DNA from five individuals: two males and three females self-identified as Caucasian, African American, Hispanic, or Asian.

What is a truly normal genome? With the exception of identical twins, the genome of each person is unique. All humans share a basic set of genes that control human development and normal body functions. It is not possible to determine a sequence that is an exact match for any one person's genome. Because there are thousands of variations in the range of different human traits, there is no one "normal" genome sequence.

Rather, you should think of the Human Genome Project as an effort to produce an initial sequence as a typical "reference" sequence of our genome. This reference sequence will be a resource for evaluation and comparison to help scientists understand human genetic similarities and, perhaps more importantly, the range of genetic variation between individuals. The reference sequence will tell us what genes are in the human genome and what some of the most common variations are, but it will not be possible to identify all variations of all genes in humans without sequencing the genome of every human.

By sequencing the genome from individuals of different races, scientists are assembling a picture of what a representative (reference) genome is, and over time this reference genome will be expanded as we learn more about genetic variations among humans. But without question, we now know that virtually all of DNA in humans of all backgrounds is exactly the same. The Human Genome Project has revealed that 99.9% of the nucleotide sequence of the human genome is exactly the same in all humans.

If all cells have the same DNA, then what makes a skin cell different from a muscle cell or a neuron different from a liver cell?
After fertilization, each individual begins life as a single cell. During development of the embryo, how do some cells know they should become skin, while other cells form the tissues of the kidneys or muscle or brain? These are questions with complex answers. Part of the answer lies in understanding the genes that control cell and tissue development and how they interact with one another. There are a number of genes that are tissue specific, meaning they are expressed by certain tissues but not others. Tissue-specific genes are part of the genetic "programming" that tells some cells to develop into skin and some cells to become muscle. One of the real challenges following the Human Genome Project will be to learn how tissue-specific genes function and interact with each other to trigger organ development. A better understanding of the cellular events and genes involved in tissue development may lead to a greater ability to produce tissues and organs for wound healing and transplantation in humans.

A major goal of the Human Genome Project was to sequence the genomes of "model" organisms, such as flies, yeast and worms. Why do scientists care about the genomes of these other organisms?
Model organisms are critically important to scientists because we can't do many of our sophisticated genetic studies on humans. It is unethical and illegal to force humans to breed or to insert or remove genes into humans to learn how human genes function! However, these approaches are widely used to study genes in model organisms. Mice, yeast, fruit flies, worms, and even the zebrafish (a common fish in home aquariums) have all played important roles in our understanding of human genetics. *Arabidopsis thaliana*, a small, flowering plant related to cabbage, is also widely used as a model organism in plant biology. Although not of major agricultural value, *Arabidopsis* also offers many advantages for basic research in genetics and molecular biology.

Important genes are highly conserved from species to species. This is one reason why model organisms are so valuable. If we can identify and learn about important genes in model organisms, we can form hypotheses and make predictions about how these genes may function in humans. Comparing segments of DNA between different species as a way to compare similarities and differences in DNA and to identify genes and gene regulatory sequences is a field of genetics known as **comparative genomics**. See Table 22.1 to compare the genome size of humans and several model organisms.

Many genes in different model species have been shown to be related to human genes based on DNA sequence similarity (see Figure 22.9). Genes with sequence similarity are called **homologs**. For instance, the **obese *(ob)* gene**, which produces a protein hormone called leptin, was first discovered in mice. Eating stimulates fat cells to produce leptin, which affects cells in the brain to suppress appetite and stimulate metabolism of food. Other studies have shown that mice deficient in the leptin gene grow dramatically overweight. Although the genetics of weight control involves much more than just one gene, subsequent discovery of a human homolog for leptin has led to a new area of research with great promise for providing insight on fat metabolism in humans and the genetics that may influence weight disorders.

Historically, significant scientific discoveries in almost all fields of biology, including anatomy and physiology, biochemistry, cell biology, developmental biology, genetics, and molecular biology, were first made in model organisms and then related to humans. For instance, in most developing embryos, some cells have to die to make room for others. How does the body know where to develop certain organs and determine which cells must die to make room for others?

Answering these important developmental questions has been greatly advanced by the roundworm *Caenorhabditis elegans*. The adult *C. elegans* has 959 cells. Maps of *C. elegans* have been created that allow scientists to determine the fate (lineage) of all 959 cells to form the nervous system, intestine, and other tissues of the worm. Of these cells, 131 are destined to die in a form of cell suicide known as programmed cell death, or apoptosis. During development of a human embryo, sheets of skin cells create webs between the fingers and toes; apoptosis is responsible for the degeneration of these webs prior to birth. But apoptosis is significant in other ways. We now know, for example, that apoptosis is involved in neurodegenerative diseases such as Alzheimer's disease, Huntington's disease, amyotrophic lateral sclerosis (Lou Gehrig's disease), and Parkinson's disease, as well as other conditions such as arthritis and forms of infertility. How might we better understand the genes involved and slow or stop these degenerative processes? Model organisms will help us answer these questions.

How do cells know if they are to become heart or liver, and how do they know how to move and where to move to settle and form an organ? How does an embryo know where and

TABLE 22.1   COMPARISON OF SELECTED GENOMES

Organism (scientific name)	Approximate size of genome (date completed)	Number of genes	Approximate percentage of genes shared with humans	Web access to genome databases
Bacterium (*Escherichia coli*)	4.1 million bp (1997)	4,403	Not determined	www.genome.wisc.edu/
Chicken (*Gallus gallus*)	1 billion bp (2004)	~20,000– 23,000	60%	http://genomeold.wustl.edu/projects/chicken
Dog (*Canis familiaris*)	6.2 million bp (2003)	~18,400	75%	http://www.ncbi.gov/genome/guide/dog
Chimpanzee (*Pan troglodytes*)	~3 billion bp (initial draft, 2005)	~20,000– 24,000	96%	http://www.nature.com/nature/focus/chimpgenome/index.html
Fruit fly (*Drosophila melanogaster*)	165 million bp (2000)	~13,600	50%	www.fruitfly.org
Humans (*Homo sapiens*)	~2.9 billion bp (2004)	~20,000– 25,000	100%	www.doegenomes.org
Mouse (*Mus musculus*)	~2.5 billion bp (2002)	~30,000	~80%	www.informatics.jax.org
Plant (*Arabidopsis thaliana*)	119 million bp (2000)	~26,000	Not determined	www.arabidopsis.org
Rat (*Rattus norvegicus*)	~2.75 billion bp (2004)	~22,000	80%	www.hgsc.bcm.tmc.edu/projects/rat
Roundworm (*Caenorhabditis elegans*)	97 million bp (1998)	19,099	40%	genomeold.wustl.edu/projects/celegans
Yeast (*Saccharomyces cerevisiae*)	12 million bp (1996)	~5,700	30%	genomeold.wustl.edu/projects/yeast.index.php

Source: Nature Genome Gateway Web site www.nature.com/genomics/papers/.

▲ **Figure 22.9**   Comparison of the human and mouse ob genes Partial sequences for these homologs are shown with the human gene on top and the mouse gene sequence below it. Notice how the nucleotide sequence for these two genes is very similar as indicated by the vertical lines between identical sequences.

Source: Sequence comparison conducted by BLAST analysis at: http://www.ncbi.nlm.nih.gov/BLAST/

how to form limbs? Model organisms were also used to identify another important set of human developmental genes called the homeobox genes. This cluster of genes provides instructions that tell the developing embryo where to position cells to form limbs. Mutations in human homeobox genes can result in infants being born with missing fingers or extra fingers.

Recently researchers at the University of Utah have initiated a project to determine the genome of planaria (*Schmidtea mediterranea*), small translucent aquatic flatworms that are commonly studied in high school and college biology labs. One reason why the planaria genome is of interest is that cells from these organisms show little signs of cell aging, cells that do age are continually replaced, and planaria have incredible abilities to regenerate tissues when damaged.

It is possible to learn a great deal about gene function in model organisms in ways that are not possible to study in humans. For instance, gene **knockout mice** can be created in which a particular gene is disrupted to make it nonfunctional, and the effect of losing the function of that gene is studied. For example, as shown in Figure 22.10, knocking out the *ob* gene in mice provided researchers with compelling evidence that the *ob* gene is clearly involved in obesity.

As another example, disrupting a gene involved in fat metabolism in the *C. elegans* has been shown to dramatically alter the life span of these worms, and we now know that a similar gene is found in humans. Extra copies of a gene can also be inserted in mice to study the effects of overexpression of a gene. Gene addition has been used in mice and flies to reverse the effects of damaged genes that cause altered traits. As you will learn later in this booklet, model organisms are being used to develop gene therapy strategies that will be applied to humans to treat genetic diseases.

As you can see, model organisms offer much to help us learn about human genetics. In the next section, we will

▲ **Figure 22.10** Knocking out the ob gene creates obese mice

Source: Thieman and Palladino, *Introduction to Biotechnology,* Figure 11.1, p. 235.

continue to see the importance of model organisms when we consider what genes have been identified in the genomes of both humans and model organisms.

▷ What Have We Learned So Far?

In 2004, the completed sequence published by the International Human Genome Sequencing Consortium reported a genome of 2.85 billion nucleotides. Eventually when all of the small gaps are fixed it is likely that the "final" size of the genome will be around 3.1 billion nucleotides. The genome was sequenced with an accuracy of ~99.999%. This equates to one mistake every 100,000 base pairs. About 10 times more accurate than initially expected!

A great deal about the human genome has been revealed in a relatively short period of time, although many of the greatest challenges and discoveries lie ahead. This section briefly highlights some of the major discoveries of the Human Genome Project.

Where are All the Genes?

On February 12, 2001, the International Human Genome Sequencing Consortium and Celera Genomics held a joint press conference to announce that nearly 95% of the human genome had been sequenced. One of the most surprising aspects of this press conference was a new estimation that the genome consists of only 30,000 to 40,000 genes and not 100,000 genes, as previously predicted.

By 2004 this number had been revised to approximately 20,000 to 25,000 protein-coding genes. The prediction of 100,000 genes was based primarily on estimates that human cells make approximately 100,000 to 150,000 proteins. One reason why the actual number of genes is so much lower than the predicted number is the discovery of large numbers of gene families with related functions. In addition, it has been found that many genes can code for multiple proteins through a complex process of mRNA processing known as **alternative splicing**.

Analysis of human genes by functional categories has provided genome scientists with a snapshot of the numbers of genes involved in different molecular functions. Figure 22.11 shows one proposed interpretation of assigned functions to human genes based on gene sequence similarity to genes of known function. Not surprisingly, many genes encode enyzmes, while other large categories of genes encode proteins involved in signaling and communication within and between cells and DNA and RNA binding proteins. Notice that this estimate also shows that approximately 42% of human genes have no known function, although recent evidence suggests that functions for over half of our genes remains unknown! Keep this in mind if you are interested in a career in genetics research, because understanding what these genes do will provide exciting career opportunities for many years into the future.

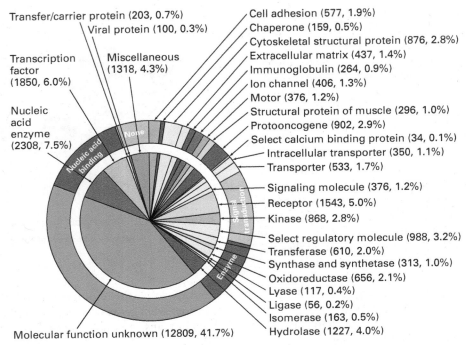

Transfer/carrier protein (203, 0.7%)
Viral protein (100, 0.3%)
Transcription factor (1850, 6.0%)
Miscellaneous (1318, 4.3%)
Nucleic acid enzyme (2308, 7.5%)
None
Nucleic acid binding

Cell adhesion (577, 1.9%)
Chaperone (159, 0.5%)
Cytoskeletal structural protein (876, 2.8%)
Extracellular matrix (437, 1.4%)
Immunoglobulin (264, 0.9%)
Ion channel (406, 1.3%)
Motor (376, 1.2%)
Structural protein of muscle (296, 1.0%)
Protooncogene (902, 2.9%)
Select calcium binding protein (34, 0.1%)
Intracellular transporter (350, 1.1%)
Transporter (533, 1.7%)
Signaling molecule (376, 1.2%)
Receptor (1543, 5.0%)
Kinase (868, 2.8%)
Select regulatory molecule (988, 3.2%)
Transferase (610, 2.0%)
Synthase and synthetase (313, 1.0%)
Oxidoreductase (656, 2.1%)
Lyase (117, 0.4%)
Ligase (56, 0.2%)
Isomerase (163, 0.5%)
Hydrolase (1227, 4.0%)
Molecular function unknown (12809, 41.7%)
Signal transduction
Enzyme

▲ **Figure 22.11**   Proposed functions for human genes Proposed functions for the numbers of human genes assigned to different functional categories. Parentheses show percentages based on the 2001 published data by Venter et al. for 26,383 genes.

Source: From Venter, J. C., et al. (2001). The sequence of the human genome. *Science*, 291, 1304–1351, Figure 15.

Most human genes average around 3,000 base pairs in size, and the largest gene, called the dystrophin gene, is ~2.4 million base pairs in size. Mutations in this gene are responsible for the muscle disorder muscular dystrophy. Not surprisingly, the largest chromosome, chromosome 1, has the most genes, approximately 3,000 genes. The smallest chromosome, the Y, has the fewest genes, ~250 genes.

What is this "junk"?

As a result of the Human Genome Project, it is now known that over 95% of our DNA consists of non-protein-coding DNA—DNA that does not contain genes. Because this DNA does not contribute directly to our traits, it has often been referred to as "junk DNA." Does it surprise you to learn that most of the DNA in your cells is junk? Actually, this DNA is not junk at all. This tongue-in-cheek expression was coined because of our lack of understanding of what non-protein-coding DNA does, not because this DNA is unimportant.

Over 50% of the non-protein-coding DNA consists of a variety of repeat sequences—sequences of repeating base pairs (such as GCGCGC) that have been duplicated in large numbers and randomly scattered throughout the genome. Many of these sequences are ancient sequences of DNA that have existed in the human genome for well over 400 million years. Repeat sequences truly represent fossil records of our genetic past. By learning about other species that contain similar sequences, we can begin to better understand where these sequences came from and how they became part of the human genome through evolution.

For example, a short sequence (approximately 300 base pairs) of junk DNA called *Alu* appears almost a million times in our genome. Recent estimates suggest that *Alu* sequences may comprise nearly 7% of our entire genome. Why do we have these sequences? In some cases, junk DNA appears to be remnants of older genes that are no longer used, and perhaps there is no good reason to eliminate it from the genome. Some scientists have suggested that certain junk DNA sequences act in a "selfish" manner because in fact they may be difficult to remove from the genome through evolution. In other cases, junk DNA probably plays a number of structural roles by connecting adjacent genes, allowing for spacing between genes, and creating the folding and overall structure of chromosomes.

Some segments of junk DNA also contain regulatory sequences that are important for controlling the expression of many genes. Recent studies also suggest that some junk DNA is used to make regulatory RNA molecules that may play a role in controlling gene expression. So even if geneticists sometimes refer to the majority of your DNA as junk, that doesn't mean you don't need it! Genome scientists are likely to change their perspective on this noncoding DNA as they begin to understand what it really does.

Are Humans Really Unique?

We think of ourselves as unmatched by other species for our ability to communicate through speech and writing as well as many other attributes, including walking upright, creating music, making a good pizza, and exploring distant planets. Humans take pride as a unique, superior species. But are we really so unique? At the genetic level, the answer to this question may surprise you. Genetically, we are not so different from many other species—species often considered inferior to humans.

From yeast and bacteria to mice, we share large numbers of genes with these species. As we have discussed, one of the goals of the Human Genome Project was to develop a better understanding of genetic similarities and differences between humans and other species, particularly other mammals. This understanding has been fostered in part by studying model organisms.

The Human Genome Project has shown us that we share a large number of genes with other organisms—proof that there is great unity of life even between seemingly very different organisms and providing solid evidence for the evolution of genes from species to species. Can you believe that you share approximately 50% of your genes with the pesky fruit flies that you bring home on fruit from the grocery store? We share nearly 40% of our genes with roundworms and 30% of our genes with yeast—the same yeast we use to help make bread rise and ferment alcoholic beverages. We share even more genes with mice; approximately 80% of our genes are similar in structure and function.

Recently, the genome for "man's best friend" was completed, which revealed that we share about 75% of our genes with dogs. Human DNA even contains around 100 genes that are also present in many bacteria. However, humans do make many more proteins than most model organisms. Refer again to Table 22.1 for a comparison of the genomes from model organisms and humans. The websites presented in the table are excellent resources for learning about the genomes of model organisms.

Our genetic relatedness to model organisms is evidence of our evolutionary past. What can we learn from our inappropriately called "lower" relatives? If genes found in bacteria, fruit flies, yeast, mice, and other organisms are also found in humans, doesn't this suggest that these genes must be pretty important? Many genes that determine our body plan, organ development, and eventually our aging and death are virtually identical to genes in fruit flies. Mutated genes that are known to give rise to disease in humans also cause disease in fruit flies. According to a report from the Howard Hughes Medical Institute (*The Genes We Share with Yeast, Flies, Worms, and Mice: New Clues to Human Health and Disease*), approximately 61% of genes mutated in 289 human disease conditions are found in the fruit fly. This group includes the genes involved in prostate cancer, pancreatic cancer, cardiac disease, cystic fibrosis, leukemia, and a host of other human genetic disorders.

It may seem hard to believe that it takes only about twice as many genes to make a human as it does a fruit fly (~25,000 versus 13,600). And plants, such as rice, have even more genes than we do! Who would argue that a rice plant is more complex than a human? But in fact plants possess many complex aspects of metabolism that humans lack such as using photosynthesis to convert energy from the sun into chemical energy. What and who we are is clearly much more than the total number of genes we have. Being human is far more complicated that simply possessing a human genome—we are infinitely more complex than just the sum of our genes and body parts. What defines us genetically is the complexity of how our genes are used and how these genes interact with one another to provide the myriad functions and unique characteristics of the creatures we call humans. This is what distinguishes us from other species.

Gene Discovery

As expected, the Human Genome Project has led to the discovery of new genes involved in a wide range of activities in human cells. The total number of human genes is smaller than expected in part because of duplicate genes and gene families—genes with related functions. By grouping genes into families, it becomes easier to determine how related genes work and identify important functions they may have. Not surprisingly, many of the newly discovered genes are involved in complex reactions that control body metabolism. Another large group of genes control the expression of other genes. Still others are responsible for maintaining the shape, structure, and function of body tissues.

As genome scientists evaluate the functions of newly discovered genes, they begin to identify genes that not only control normal functions but also may be connected to human disease conditions. These discoyeries are especially significant. For many diseases, particularly those that occur rarely and are poorly understood, identifying genes involved in the disease process is the first step toward improved detection and treatment strategies. Now that a reference set of genes has been identified, scientists can begin to better understand how gene variations are responsible for genetic disease. One type of variation in DNA sequence between individuals is called a single-nucleotide polymorphism, or SNP. We will talk about the role of SNPs in diagnosing genetic diseases later in this booklet.

Although the approximate number of human genes is now known, it will be many years before some of the greatest secrets in the genome will be revealed. As we have already discussed, understanding how genes function will be an enormous challenge. Long after the Human Genome Project, scientists will be challenged to understand how our all of our genes work and how genes interact.

"Take Home" Message

The past few pages have provided a basic overview of some of the major findings of the genome project. Below is a top-ten list as a summary of important highlights to remember about what we have learned from the Human Genome Project:

1. The human genome consists of ~3.1 billion base pairs; 2.85 billion base pairs have been fully sequenced.

2. The genome is approximately 99.9% the same between individuals of all nationalities and backgrounds.

3. Less than 2% of the genome codes for genes.

4. The vast majority of our DNA is non-protein-coding, and repetitive DNA sequences account for at least 50% of the noncoding DNA.

5. The genome contains approximately 20,000–25,000 protein-coding genes.

6. Many human genes are capable of making more than one protein, allowing human cells to make perhaps 80,000–100,000 from only 20,000–25,000 genes.

7. Functions for over half of all human genes are unknown.

8. Chromosome 1 contains the highest number of genes. The Y chromosome contains the fewest genes.

9. Over 50% of the human genome shows a high degree of sequence similarity to genes in other organisms.

10. Thousands of human disease genes have been identified and mapped to their chromosomal locations.

▷ Learning About the Human Genome Project via the Internet

With emergence of the Internet as an information and communication tool and the almost simultaneous expansion of genetic knowledge from the Human Genome Project, both scientists and laypersons now have easy access to detailed and very current information on the progress being made by the Human Genome Project. There are a number of genome-related sites available on the Web. In this section, I'll describe a few of my favorites. I recommend these student-friendly and easy-to-navigate sites as outstanding resources that provide a wealth of up-to-date information. Use these sites for your own knowledge and enjoyment, as credible resources when writing papers and reports, and for reference when asked by a friend or family member about a genetic disease.

Sites to Visit and Internet Exercises

I recommend that you begin your Internet search of the genome by visiting the **DOEgenomes** site of the U.S. Department of Energy (DOE) at http://www.doegenomes.org/. This site is an excellent resource that serves as an informative introduction to the Human Genome Project. The "Human Genome Project Information" link (http://www.ornl.gov/sci/techresources/Human_Genome/home.shtml) is *the best* place to start for general information about the history of the project; its goals; answers to frequently asked questions (FAQs),; ethical, legal, and social issues; and sequencing and mapping technologies. Quite simply, you will be hard pressed to find a more accurate and informative site on the Web. **Figure 22.12** shows a screen shot of the Human Genome Project Information page indicating major headings and subtopics to a variety of genome links. Can't-miss links include:

■ *What is the Human Genome Project?* Takes you to a series of pages that describe the primary goals and objectives of the Human Genome Project with a number of important links to related topics. Provides the history of why DOE became interested in the project, a basic introduction—especially helpful for nonscience majors—on DNA structure and the genetic code, primary goals of the project, a basic explanation of different types of chromosome maps and their importance and applications, a discussion of the role that model organisms have in genetics, a basic overview of DNA sequencing technologies, and discussions on ethical issues surrounding the genome project.

■ *Primer: Genomics and Its Impact on Science and Society.* Links to pages that provide a good basic overview on the organization of genetic material in human cells.

■ *Science Behind the Human Genome Project: Understanding the Basics.* Presents some of the basic facts about DNA structure, chromosomes, and genes for the newcomer and discusses implementation and goals of the Human Genome Project.

■ *Ethical, Legal, and Social Issues.* Exactly what the title says—an excellent resource.

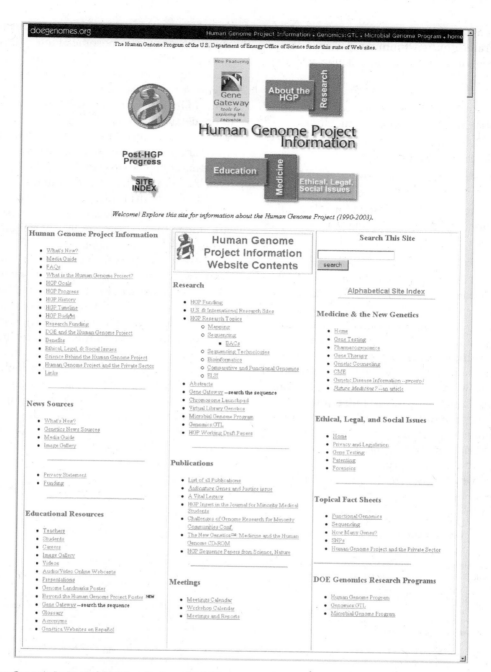

▲ **Figure 22.12**   Human Genome Project information site from the DOE genomes web

Source: Screen shot provided by U.S. Department of Energy Human Genome Program. http://www.ornl.gov/sci/techresources/Human_Genome/home.shtml.

■ *Frequently Asked Questions (FAQs).* A great place to begin seeking answers to some of the questions you may have.

■ *Facts About Genomic Sequencing.* Student-friendly pages of text, figures, and video clips describe common and new methodologies for DNA sequencing. This site also presents a glossary of genetic terms and discusses sequencing the genomes of model organisms as part of the project.

■ *HGP Progress.* Many informative links to project updates, milestones, individual chromosome data, and much more.

■ *HGP Timeline.* Provides an informative timeline with links to relevant articles.

■ *Human Chromosome Launchpad.* Links to detailed information on identified genes, gene maps, sequence data, genetic disorders, and research efforts for each human chromosome. Be sure to visit this link!

■ *Medicine and the New Genetics.* Links on gene therapy, pharmacogenomics, and topics related to how medical practice in the future will be changed by genetic information.

■ *Student Guide to the Human Genome.* These pages incorporate many of the links designed for students that were described above. Another link that shouldn't be missed!

The Howard Hughes Medical Institute has a great site called **Blazing a Genetic Trail** (http://www.hhmi.org/GeneticTrail). There are over a dozen excellent links. In particular, visit the following links:

- *Why So Many Errors in Our DNA?* A nice discussion on how mutations arise and consequences of mutations.
- *Stalking a Lethal Gene.* An informative overview of how the gene for cystic fibrosis was mapped.
- *Reading the Human Blueprint.* A basic overview of genetic technologies.
- *Of Mice and Men.* Excellent discussion on the role of mice as model organisms for studying and curing genetic diseases.

Finding a Gene and Viewing Chromosome Maps

As of 1989, less than 12 disease genes had been mapped by traditional genetic approaches. Now, thousands of disease genes have been discovered through the Human Genome Project and organized into chromosome maps. An excellent way to learn about what the Human Genome Project has revealed is to review some of the chromosome maps available on the Web. For instance, suppose you were interested in the Y chromosome. How could you find out what genes are located on this chromosome? One way to find out why this chromosome is partially responsible for making the strange creatures we call human males is to review maps of the Y chromosome and descriptions of the genes found on this sex chromosome. If you are a male, you can whet your curiosity for genetic clues as to why females are the way they are by learning about genes on the X chromosome!

I encourage you to use the sites presented here to learn about a gene or chromosome of interest. Also, these sites are great resources for finding information on a gene you may have heard or read about but want more information on. If a friend or family member asks you about a gene or a chromosome of interest, you can take them to these sites and uncover more details about that gene than you may ever want to know. I often suggest that students go to these sites to learn more about a rare disease gene related to a disease condition affecting someone close to them. These sites present up-to-date information that can't be found in even the most recent books. If you can't find a gene of interest in these sites, it probably hasn't been identified yet. The sites described here are among the best sites for learning about human disease genes and chromosome maps.

Online Mendelian Inheritance in Man (OMIM) at http://www.ncbi.nlm.nih.gov/entrez/query.fcgi?db=OMIM is a great database of human genes and genetic disorders. In the keyword box, type in the name of a gene or disease you may be interested in. For example, type in "breast cancer," then click the search button. When the next page appears, you will see a list of genes implicated in breast cancer along with corresponding access numbers highlighted in blue as links. Click on one of the links for a gene from this list that you are interested in, and you will be taken to a wealth of information about that gene including background information, links to scientific papers about the gene, genes maps, and even nucleotide and protein sequence data (when available). You might also want to search this site to see if a gene has been found for a particular behavioral condition (for example, alcoholism or depression). OMIM is perhaps the

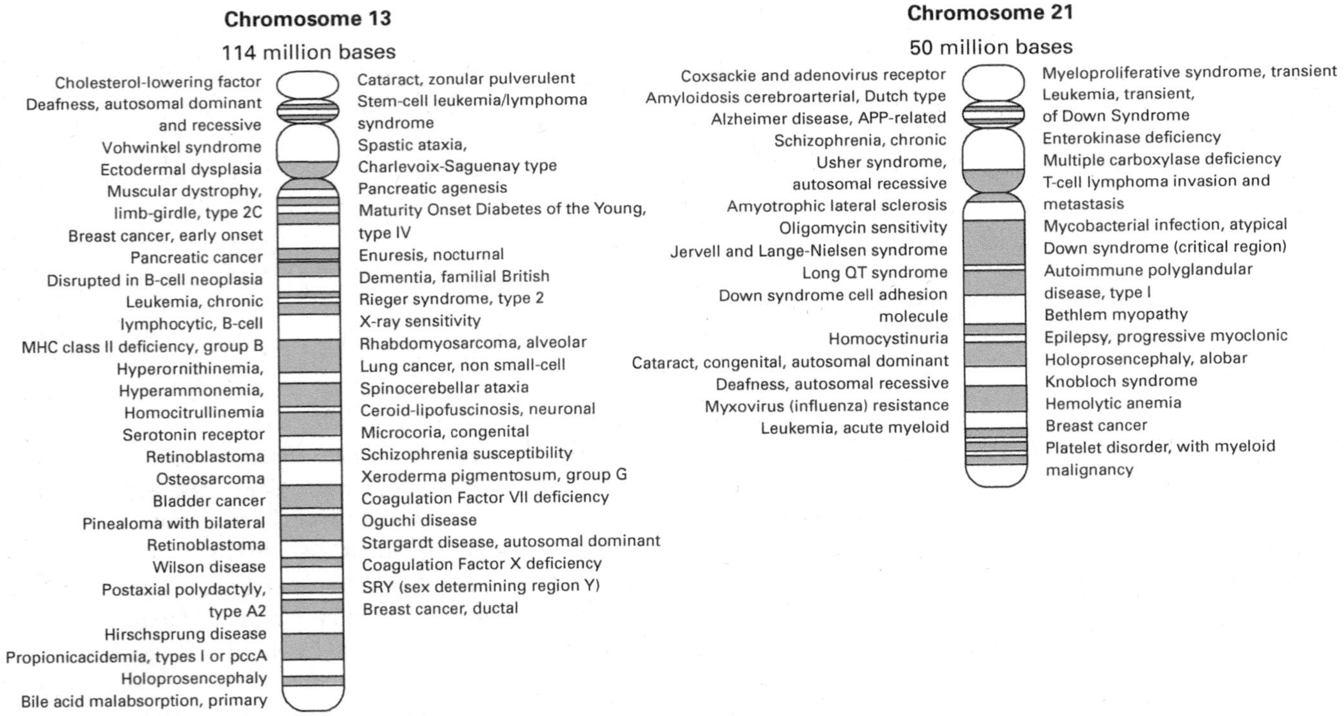

Chromosome 13
114 million bases

Cholesterol-lowering factor
Deafness, autosomal dominant and recessive
Vohwinkel syndrome
Ectodermal dysplasia
Muscular dystrophy, limb-girdle, type 2C
Breast cancer, early onset
Pancreatic cancer
Disrupted in B-cell neoplasia
Leukemia, chronic lymphocytic, B-cell
MHC class II deficiency, group B
Hyperornithinemia,
Hyperammonemia,
Homocitrullinemia
Serotonin receptor
Retinoblastoma
Osteosarcoma
Bladder cancer
Pinealoma with bilateral
Retinoblastoma
Wilson disease
Postaxial polydactyly, type A2
Hirschsprung disease
Propionicacidemia, types I or pccA
Holoprosencephaly
Bile acid malabsorption, primary

Cataract, zonular pulverulent
Stem-cell leukemia/lymphoma syndrome
Spastic ataxia,
Charlevoix-Saguenay type
Pancreatic agenesis
Maturity Onset Diabetes of the Young, type IV
Enuresis, nocturnal
Dementia, familial British
Rieger syndrome, type 2
X-ray sensitivity
Rhabdomyosarcoma, alveolar
Lung cancer, non small-cell
Spinocerebellar ataxia
Ceroid-lipofuscinosis, neuronal
Microcoria, congenital
Schizophrenia susceptibility
Xeroderma pigmentosum, group G
Coagulation Factor VII deficiency
Oguchi disease
Stargardt disease, autosomal dominant
Coagulation Factor X deficiency
SRY (sex determining region Y)
Breast cancer, ductal

Chromosome 21
50 million bases

Coxsackie and adenovirus receptor
Amyloidosis cerebroarterial, Dutch type
Alzheimer disease, APP-related
Schizophrenia, chronic
Usher syndrome, autosomal recessive
Amyotrophic lateral sclerosis
Oligomycin sensitivity
Jervell and Lange-Nielsen syndrome
Long QT syndrome
Down syndrome cell adhesion molecule
Homocystinuria
Cataract, congenital, autosomal dominant
Deafness, autosomal recessive
Myxovirus (influenza) resistance
Leukemia, acute myeloid

Myeloproliferative syndrome, transient
Leukemia, transient, of Down Syndrome
Enterokinase deficiency
Multiple carboxylase deficiency
T-cell lymphoma invasion and metastasis
Mycobacterial infection, atypical
Down syndrome (critical region)
Autoimmune polyglandular disease, type I
Bethlem myopathy
Epilepsy, progressive myoclonic
Holoprosencephaly, alobar
Knobloch syndrome
Hemolytic anemia
Breast cancer
Platelet disorder, with myeloid malignancy

▲ **Figure 22.13** Partial maps for disease genes on chromosomes 13 and 21

Source: From: Thieman and Palladino, *Introduction to Biotechnology*, p. 4 Figure 1.2.

best site to use when searching for information on a gene of interest.

Similarly, the **Weizmann Institute of Science** in Israel (http://bioinfo.weizmann.ac.il/cards/index.shtml) has an excellent site of "gene cards" that provide summaries of information about known genes.

The National Center for Biotechnology Information (NCBI) sponsors **The HumanGenome** Web site (http://www.ncbi.nlm.nih.gov/genome/guide/human/). This site is a nice way to access many of the sites mentioned previously. Click on "Genes & Disease (GD)" or go directly to http://www.ncbi.nlm.nih.gov/disease/ for a student-friendly set of pages on selected disease genes that have been mapped to chromosomes. Clicking on each gene takes you to detailed information about the gene.

Some of the **DOEgenomes** links also provide excellent pages with chromosome maps of identified genes. Visit http://www.ornl.gov/hgmis/posters/chromosome and http://www.ornl.gov/hgmis/launchpad. See Figure 22.13 for an example of mapped disease genes on chromosomes 13 and 21 adapted from this site. Notice how genes for several types of cancers are shown on these chromosomes.

▷ Genome Issues

Mike, a physically fit and intelligent college student, walks into the campus pub to order a nonalcoholic drink. Mike is approached by Lauren, an attractive student in his genetics class. Lauren finds Mike interesting. Mike and Lauren exchange small talk, and Mike asks Lauren for a date. While Mike pictures the perfect date, Lauren wonders if she and Mike are genetically compatible. Before giving Mike an answer, Lauren asks to see Mike's "carrier card." Lauren wants to see what genes Mike might be a carrier for before deciding if it's worth her time to go on a date with him. Why waste time dating someone if that person is genetically inferior to you or if there is a chance that your mating in the future would lead to children with genetic defects? Rejected by Lauren, Mike quickly focuses his attention across the room to Elizabeth, a student in his sociology class who he hopes is less informed about genome issues than Lauren!

While I hope the preceding scene never becomes a reality, is it really so farfetched? As we learn more about human disease genes and develop strategies for the screening and detection of these genes, we will have the ability to visit a physician and gain insight into what genes we have—for better or worse.

From the beginning of the Human Genome Project, the Department of Energy and the National Institutes of Health recognized the importance of informing the general public about genome issues in a practical context to help nonscientists make informed decisions. Significant resources have been committed to examine the ethical, legal, and social issues of genome research.

There are many issues related to the Human Genome Project that will impact all of us in the future. Some of these concerns can be addressed more easily than others. Some will involve personal choices and decisions that individuals will have to make—hopefully with a knowledgeable and informed opinion. Many genome issues will be ballot-box issues in the future.

The range of genome issues is far too great to be completely addressed in this booklet. A few of the most controversial issues are the privacy of genetic information; the moral, ethical, and legal dilemmas posed by genetic technology; and the patenting of genetic information.

How can genetic information be used beyond personal and private decisions? Consider some of these issues:

- As a result of the Human Genome Project, we will have a greater ability to screen, diagnose, prevent, and treat disease conditions. But should we test for genetic conditions for which there is currently no cure? For example, if one of your parents suffered from a debilitating disease, such as Huntington's disease (a disabling disorder of the nervous system that presents few obvious symptoms until after 30 years of age or so), you have a 50% chance of inheriting the defective gene. Currently there is no cure for Huntington's disease, although a test is available to detect the defective Huntington gene. This raises the question, would you want to be tested for the defective gene even if there is no treatment or cure for the disease?

- Should we test unborn children for a gene defect for which there is no medical remedy or adequate treatment?

- What are acceptable consequences if parents learn that their unborn child has a genetic defect?

- Privacy of genetic information is of considerable concern. Who should have access to your genetic information? Could your genetic background be used to discriminate against you? Should a potential or current employer know about your genetic tests? If so, how might this information affect your job success or ability to obtain and retain a job? Should your insurance company gain access to your genetic information? What if your health or life insurance company learned that you or a family member had a gene that increased your incidence of developing a particular type of cancer? Could they raise your premiums based on "genetic" risk (in the same way that premiums are raised based on other risks, such as how old you are and the car you drive) or deny you coverage?

- We have no control over the genetic lottery we inherit from our parents. In fact, we may all be carriers for some genetic condition. If you were a carrier for a genetic condition, even though you weren't at risk for developing the disease, how might employers and insurance companies view this information, given that you could potentially have a child with the disease (if your spouse were a carrier too)? Days spent at home caring for your child might make you less desirable as an employee.

- How do we ensure privacy and confidentiality of genetic information? What are your obligations to inform others (a potential spouse, employer, or insurance provider) of your knowledge about a potential genetic disorder?

- If genes are discovered for undesirable human behaviors, how will these genes be perceived in legal courts if accused criminals use genetics as their basis for a not-guilty, by reason of genetics, plea?

- If you were an employer or director of an insurance company, what access to genetic information would you want, and what would you want to do with this information?

- How would information derived from testing for a genetic mutation affect your life? For many genetic conditions, there is a high likelihood that an individual with a defective gene will enjoy a long, normal, and relatively healthy life span. Think about the dilemmas and stress that would ensue if a genetic test was performed incorrectly, or if inaccurately interpreted or incorrect results leading to a misdiagnosis, for or against a disease, were given to the patient.

- Would society implement mechanisms to prevent or dissuade individuals with genetic defects from having children?

Visit the DOE "Your Genes, Your Choices" website (http://www.ornl.gov/hgmis/publicat/genechoice/contents.html) for a thought-provoking series of ethical dilemmas created by genetic testing and genetic technology. What would you do if you had to face the scenarios presented at this site? How would you decide what to do?

Go to Bioethics.net (http://www.bioethics.net) for links on ethical issues related to human genetics and human cloning. Also visit the website for The President's Council on Bioethics (http://bioethics.gov). A similar group was originally appointed in 1996 by President Clinton in response to concerns about the potential for human cloning after the cloning of Dolly the sheep was announced. We'll save the pros and cons of organism cloning for another booklet!

Another hot area of debate concerns products of the Human Genome Project. Does a researcher have the right to patent a gene sequence because he or she discovered it first (and wants to claim his or her "property") even if we don't know what it does and there are no clear uses for the DNA sequence? Should scientists be allowed to patent pieces of human DNA? Would patenting slow progress to clone genes if groups hoarded data and didn't share information? Should a group be permitted to stake a claim to a gene, thereby preventing others from working on it or developing a product from it?

Given that in many large labs computers do most of the routine work of genome sequencing, who should get the patent for a sequenced piece of DNA? What about the individuals who figure out *what* to do with the gene? What about patenting a genetically engineered living organism? Bioengineered bacteria (for example, those used to clean up environmental pollution) and genetically altered model organisms have been patented. Can a group claim rights to speculative, anticipated future use of a gene, even if there is no data to substantiate such claims? What if a gene sequence may be involved in a disease process for which a genetic therapy may be developed? What is the best way to use this information to advance medicine and cure disease?

Many scientists believe that it is more appropriate to patent novel technology used to discover and study genes, as well as applications of genetic technology, such as gene therapy approaches, rather than patent gene sequences themselves. What do you think? It is impossible to predict all of the long-term ramifications associated with the Human Genome Project. There are no easy answers to many of these questions. However, knowledge is key to helping us navigate through these issues. Regardless of your major, I encourage you to stay well informed about the power and pitfalls of genetic technology. More than likely, you will encounter some of these issues in your future.

▷ Where Do We Go From Here?

Now that the Human Genome Project is complete, what's next? The legacy of this project will be the wealth of information to be gained from studying the genome in detail. As mentioned earlier, one significant priority of genome scientists will be to learn more about the functions of each human gene—a very challenging task that will take many years of research. Remember, at present the functions for over 50% of human genes remain largely unknown. Many researchers will be working on elucidating the functions of human genes, how genes are regulated, and how different genes affect one another.

Identifying the chromosomal location and sequencing of genes in the human genome will undoubtedly increase our understanding of the complexity of human genetics and the proteins made by human cells. But the substantial task of understanding the functions of all human genes and proteins lies ahead as a major challenge for researchers. Discussion has begun on a possible **Human Proteome Project**, which would focus on the structure and functions of the entire complement of human proteins—a task that will be helped substantially by the identification of the genes that code for all human proteins. Already underway is a 10-year project sponsored by the NIH called the **Protein Structure Initiative (PSI)**. The PSI is designed to examine the three-dimensional structure of human proteins and analyze functions of human protein families based on structural predictions.

Data from the PSI will shed light on how proteins functions and provide valuable information that can be used to develop new medicines.

An advanced understanding of human genetic disease will transform medicine as it is currently practiced. However, for this to happen basic research on the functions of human genes and the controlling factors that *regulate* gene expression will provide immeasurable insight into normal gene function and the molecular basis of many human disease conditions. Recently a project called **ENCODE (ENCyclopedia of DNA Elements)** was initiated with the purpose of identifying gene regulatory sequences (many of which reside in noncoding "junk" DNA) that control how genes are turned on or off during transcription.

A whole range of genome studies have been initiated as a direct result of technology advances created by the Human Genome Project. As mentioned earlier, genome projects for many model organisms have been completed and many more are underway. The DOE has established a **Microbial Genome Program** which involves sequencing genomes for a wide range of bacteria, fungi, parasites, protozoa and yeast, including human disease causing microbes such as the Trypanosome *T. brucei* which causes African Sleeping Sickness, the malaria parasite *P. falciparum*, and a wide range of disease causing bacteria. The DOE has also developed a **Genomes to Life Program** which has a number of research goals related to microbial genomes including characterizing microbial genes and proteins and understanding their roles in a wide range of microbial functions, and to exploring novel ways in which microbes can be used to provide energy, clean the environment and carry out other applications.

Human genome pioneer J. Craig Venter left Celera in 2003 to form the J. Craig Venter Institute. One of the Institute's major initiatives is a global expedition to sample marine and terrestrial microorganisms from around the world and to sequence their genomes. Called the **Sorcerer II Expedition**, Venter and his researchers will travel the globe by yacht in a sailing voyage that has been described as a modern day version of Charles Darwin's famous treks on the HMS *Beagle*. A pilot study the Institute conducted on Sargasso Sea off Bermuda yielded around 1,800 new species of microorganisms and over 1.2 million new genes! To date, Venter's research team has detected over 100,000 microbes and sequenced in excess of 4 million genes. This Expedition has great potential for identifying new microbes and genes with novel functions, including commercially valuable genes. For example, the Sargasso Sea project identified thousands of photoreceptor genes. Some microorganisms rely on photoreceptors for capturing light energy to power photosynthesis. Scientists are interested in learning more about photoreceptors to help develop ways in which photosynthesis may be used to produce hydrogen as a fuel source. Medical researchers are also very interested in photoreceptors because in humans and many other species, photoreceptors in the eye are responsible for vision.

Let's consider just a few ways that the Human Genome Project will impact medicine. Genome information has and will continue to result in the rapid, sensitive, and early detection and diagnosis of genetic disease conditions in humans of all ages, from unborn children to the elderly. Increased knowledge about genetic disease conditions will lead to preventive approaches designed to foster healthier lifestyles. Once a disease condition has been identified, new, safer, and more effective approaches for drug therapy and gene therapy will be available.

Every day, new information is helping scientists decipher genetic diseases such as sickle-cell disease, Tay-Sachs disease, cystic fibrosis, cancer, forms of blindness, and certain forms of infertility, to name just a few. Increased knowledge of genes involved in organ development and growth is leading to novel strategies for tissue transplantation and tissue regeneration, including the potential future treatment of spinal cord injuries and neurodegenerative conditions.

From its inception, the Human Genome Project yielded immediate dividends in our ability to identify and diagnose disease conditions. The identification of disease genes has enabled scientists and physicians to screen for a wide range of genetic diseases. This screening ability will continue to grow in the future. Aiding in the diagnosis of genetic disease will be applications involving **single-nucleotide polymorphisms** (**SNPs**, pronounced "snips"). SNPs are single- nucleotide changes in DNA sequences that vary from individual to individual (see **Figure 22.14**). These subtle changes represent one of the most common examples of genetic variation in humans and are largely responsible for the 0.1% differences in DNA sequence between individuals (remember, 99.9% of DNA sequence is the same between all humans).

Most SNPs have no effect on a cell because they occur in non-protein-coding (junk DNA) regions of the genome. But when an SNP occurs in a gene sequence, it can influence traits in a variety of ways, including conferring susceptibility for some types of disease conditions. It has been estimated that SNPs occur every 100 to 300 bases in the human genome. Over 1.4 million SNPs have been identified to date.

SNPs represent variations in DNA sequence that ultimately influence how we respond to stress and disease. Most scientists believe that SNPs will help them identify some of the genes involved in stroke, cancer, heart disease, diabetes, behavioral and emotional illnesses, and a host of other disorders. In 2001, one of the revised goals of the Human Genome Project was to identify SNPs and develop SNP maps of the human genome.

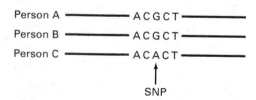

▲ **Figure 22.14** Single-nucleotide polymorphisms (SNPs) A small piece of a gene sequence for three different individuals is represented. For simplicity only one strand of a DNA molecule is shown. Notice how person C contains an SNP in this gene. This subtle genetic change may affect how person C responds to a medical drug or influence the likelihood of person C to develop a genetic disease.

Another relatively new technique for studying genomes will also play an important role in the detection of genetic disease. **Gene microarrays**, also called **gene chips**, are glass microscope slides spotted with genes. Computer-automated instruments are used to create tiny spots of DNA on the slide. Each spot contains DNA for one gene. A single microarray can contain thousands of genes. Researchers can use microarrays to screen a patient for a pattern of genes that might be expressed in a particular disease condition. Microarray data can then be used to figure out the patient's risk of developing that disease based on the number of expressed genes for the disease the patient shows.

Researchers are using microarrays in a range of different projects designed to evaluate gene expression in normal cells compared to diseased cells, such as cancer cells, in studies designed to better understand genetic difference that occur in disease states.

Many pharmaceutical and biotechnology companies are heavily involved in the search for SNPs and the development of gene microarrays—good indication of the tremendous potential both approaches may provide for detecting disease in the near future. The discovery of SNPs is partially responsible for the emergence of a field called **pharmacogenomics**. Pharmacogenomics is customized medicine (**Figure 22.15**). It involves designing the most effective drug therapy and treatment strategies based on the specific genetic profile of a patient instead of using a "one drug fits all" approach to treating illness.

Consider the following example of pharmacogenomics in action. Breast cancer is a disease that shows familial inheritance for some women. Women with defective copies of the genes called *BRCA1* or *BRCA2* may have an increased risk of developing breast cancer, but there are many other cases of breast cancer in which a clear mode of inheritance is not seen. Perhaps there may be additional genes or nongenetic factors at work in these cases. If a woman has a breast tumor thought to be cancerous, a small piece of cancerous tissue could be used to prepare DNA for SNP and microarray analysis. SNP and microarray data could be used to determine which genes are involved in the form of breast cancer that this particular woman has. Armed with this genetic information, a physician could design a drug treatment strategy—based on the genes involved—that would be *specific* and *most effective* against this woman's type of cancer. A second woman with a different genetic profile for her type of breast cancer might undergo a different treatment.

Many drugs currently used to treat cancer (drug treatment of cancer is known as chemotherapy) may be effective against cancerous cells but also affect normal cells. Hair loss, dry skin, changes in blood cell counts, and nausea are all related to the effects of chemotherapy on normal cells. Wouldn't it be great if drugs could be designed that are effective against cancer cells with no effect on normal cells in other tissues? This may be possible as the genetic basis of cancer is understood and drugs can be designed based on the genetics of different types of cancer. These same principles of pharmacogenomics will also be applied to a wide range of other human diseases.

Based on the pharmacogenomics concepts, some scientists have speculated that **nutrigenomics** will be an emerging field in the future. Nutrigenomics involves developing a personalized diet and exercise plan based on a person's genetic profile. For example, if a person is known to lack genes required for synthesizing vitamin A, that individual would be told to follow a diet plan to supplement vitamin A. Limited applications of nutrigenomics are already being used to screen individuals for genes involved in diabetes and then limiting dietary sugar for these patients, and to screen for genes that elevate blood cholesterol levels to in turn control fat intake.

In addition to advances in drug treatment, **gene therapy** represents one of the ultimate strategies for combating genetic disease. Gene therapy technologies involve replacing or augmenting defective genes with normal copies of a gene. Think about the power of this approach! Currently, there are many barriers that must be overcome before gene therapy becomes a safe, practical, effective, and well-established approach to treating disease. Scientists are working on a variety of ways to deliver healthy genes into humans, but many significant obstacles prevent gene therapy from being widely used in humans. For example, how can normal genes be delivered to virtually all the cells in the body? What are the long-term effects of introducing extra genes into humans? What must be done to be sure the normal protein is properly made once genes are delivered into the body? Great strides toward answering these and other questions are being made using gene therapy in model organisms.

In the future, **stem cells** may be another tool for treating and curing disease. Stem cells are immature cells that can grow and divide to produce different types of cells, such as skin, muscle, liver, kidney, or blood cells. In a laboratory environment, stem cells can be coaxed to form almost any tissue of interest, depending on how they are treated. Imagine growing skin and other organs in the lab for tissue and organ transplantation. In the future, it may be possible to collect stem cells from patients with genetic disorders, genetically manipulate these cells by gene therapy, and reinsert them into the patients they were collected from to help treat their genetic disease. Some of this work is already possible, and researchers are working to optimitze these technologies.

▲ **Figure 22.15** Pharmacogenomics is customized medicine based on a person's genetic profile

Source: Thieman and Palladino, *Introduction To Biotechnology,* opening figure p. 233.

Disease conditions that result from mutations in a single gene (as in sickle-cell disease) will be the easiest conditions to develop therapies for. Genetic conditions with a multigene basis and multifactorial influences (such as diet, environment, exercise, and stress) will be more difficult to understand and treat because of the complexity of multiple gene interactions. Pharmacogenomics, gene therapy, and stem cell technologies are not the answers to all of our genetic problems, but with continued rapid advances in genetic technology, many seemingly impossible problems may not be so insurmountable in the future.

In some ways, a complete understanding of the human genome may redefine who we are or at least how we perceive who we are with respect to other organisms. The Human Genome Project has confirmed that many human genes share common ancestral origins with genes in other species. Will understanding the genome be the key to unlocking the mysteries of normal biological processes and disease processes, human development, behavior, aging, mental illness, and addictions? In some cases, the answer is likely to be *yes*. But there will be few quick fixes, and only time will tell how great an effect the Human Genome Project will have in these areas.

Completion of the Human Genome Project is not the end of our understanding human genetics but a historic and revealing step that will provide critically important insight about our genome. Current students will become the future generations of scientists and physicians who will advance this work in the years to come. Perhaps as a future biologist, you, too, may contribute to our understanding of the genome and its secrets.

As a biology professor and scientist, I am very excited to see the genome story unfold, and I eagerly anticipate watching powerful applications of the project begin to be realized. I hope you have enjoyed our brief tour of the Human Genome Project and that you have learned something new about this landmark scientific endeavor. I welcome hearing from you about your thoughts about this booklet and the Human Genome Project. Please feel free to contact me at the following address. Good luck with your studies.

Michael A. Palladino, Ph.D.
Associate Professor
Monmouth University
Biology Department
400 Cedar Avenue
West Long Branch, NJ 07764
E-mail: mpalladi@monmouth.edu.
Web: http://bluehawk.monmouth.edu/mpalladi

▷ Resources for Students and Educators

For Students

The following websites are among the most informative and student-friendly genomics resources freely available on the Internet. Visit these sites to discover a wealth of information on the Human Genome Project and related topics.

AAAS Functional Genomics Site
(http://www.sciencemag.org/feature/plus.sfg)
Science magazine site provides up-to-date links to a variety of genome topics.

Bioethics.net
(http://www.bioethics.net/)
Site for learning about bioethical issues related to human genetics and cloning.

The Biology Project
(http://www.biology.arizona.edu/molecular_bio/molecular_bio.html)
University of Arizona site provides problem sets and tutorial on DNA structure and gene expression.

Biopharmaceutical Glossaries and Taxonomies
(http://www.genomicglossaries.com)
A good resource with a wide range of links to genome pages and sites that describe some of the language of genomics.

Case Studies in Science
(http://www.ublib.buffalo.edu/libraries/projects/cases/ubcase.htm)
Molecular biology/genetics section presents interesting ethical issues as prenatal genetic diagnosis, sickle-cell anemia, fetal tissue research, and other topics.

Cold Spring Harbor DNA Learning Center
(http://www.dnalc.org)
A student-friendly resource with links to current topics in gene cloning and excellent animations of recombinant DNA techniques.

DNA From the Beginning
(www.dnaftb.org/dnaftb)
Informative overview of the history of DNA and animated primers on the basics of DNA, genes, and heredity.

DOEgenomes.org
(http://doegenomes.org/)
Comprehensive site covering genome programs of the U.S. Department of Energy Office of Science.

DOE Joint Genome Institute
(http://www-hgc.lbl.gov/GenomeHome.html)
Human Genome Sequencing Department home page.

European Bioinformatics Institute (EBI)
(http://www.ensembl.org/)
Provides datasets on eukaryotic genomes, access to chromosome maps, SNP data, and a range of other features.

Federation of American Societies for Experimental Biology Career Opportunity Site
(http://ns1.faseb.org/genetics/gsa/careers/bro-menu.htm)
Tips for careers in genetics and genomics.

Functional Genomics
(http://www.sciencemag.org/feature/plus/sfg/)
Science magazine site provides current headlines in genetics.

GenBank
(http://www.ncbi.nlm.nih.gov/entrez/query.
fcgi?db=Nucleotide)
One of the sites most frequently visited by scientists and educators. GenBank is the gene sequence database maintained by the National Institutes of Health. GenBank is the premier resource as a public collection of DNA sequences.

Geneforum.org
(http://www.geneforum.org/)
Designed to inform citizens about advances in genetic research and biotechnology and issues surrounding these sciences.

Genetic Science Learning Center
(http://gslc.genetics.utah.edu)
Interactive, student-friendly animations of DNA structure and replication, transcription, translation, and more.

The Genome Database
(http://gdbwww.gdb.org/gdbreports/
CountGeneByChromosome.html)
A current count of mapped genes by chromosome.

Genomics Glossary
(http://www.genomicglossaries.com/)
Good resource for keeping up with the vocabulary of genetics.

GenomicsGTL
(http://doegenomestolife.org/)
DOE Genomes to Life website..

Howard Hughes Medical Institute: Blazing a Genetic Trail
(http://www.hhmi.org/genetictrail)
Excellent web site that provides actual stories of gene discovery (such as the search for the cystic fibrosis gene) and dilemmas presented by genetic testing and gene therapy.

Human Chromosome Maps
(http://www.ornl.gov/sci/techresources/Human_Genome/
posters/chromosome and http://www.ornl.gov/sci/
techresources/Human_Genome/launchpad)
DOE sites with current updates on human chromosome maps and gene loci.

Human Genome Program Information Career Page
(http://www.ornl.gov/hgmis/education/careers)
An outstanding site on career possibilities in genetics and genomics, which also includes links to many other valuable resources.

Human Genome Project Information Site
(http://www.ornl.gov/sci/techresources/Human_Genome/
home.shtml)
The definitive site for learning about the history, goals, technologies, future directions, and ethical, legal, and social issues of the Human Genome Project. This site also has a wealth of information for educators regarding genome meetings, teaching materials, publications, and medical applications of the Genome Project.

Microbial Genome Program
(http://microbialgenome.org/)
U.S. Department of Energy Microbial Genome Project site. http://microbialgenome.org/

Model Organisms for Biomedical Research
(http://www.nih.gov/science/models/)
Excellent site for current information on biomedical research using model organisms.

National Center for Biotechnology Information: Human Genome Resources
(NCBI; http://www.ncbi.nlm.nih.gov/genome/guide/human/)
An excellent resource for chromosome maps and disease gene information.

National Center for Genome Resources
(http://www.ncgr.org/)
Good resources for information on genomics and bioinformatics.

National Human Genome Research Institute—National Institutes of Health
(http://www.nhgri.nih.gov)
Informative NIH site on goals and accomplishments of the Human Genome Project. Visit http://www.nhgri.nih.gov/DIR/VIP/Glossary/pub_glossary.cgi for a glossary of genetic terms.

NOVA Online: "Sequence for Yourself"
(http://www.pbs.org/wgbh/nova/genome/media/
sequence.swf)
Outstanding animations on DNA cloning and assembling cloned DNA fragments to sequence segments of a chromosome.

Online Mendelian Inheritance in Man
(http://www.ncbi.nlm.nih.gov/entrez/query.
fcgi?db=OMIM)
An outstanding way to search for information on human disease genes.

The President's Council on Bioethics
(http://www.bioethics.gov)
Presidential appointed council charged with reviewing and establishing policy on research involving human subjects.

Rosalind Franklin Centre for Genomics Research Project Resource Centre
(http://www.hgmp.mrc.ac.uk/)
Genome website maintained by the Medical Research Council of the United Kingdom.

Science.bio.org
(http://science.bio.org)
Science news website provided by the Biotechnology Industry Organization.

Science Odyssey: DNA Workshops
(http://www.pbs.org/wgbh/aso/tryit/dna)
This site provides animations of DNA replication, transcription, and translation.

The SNP Consortium LTD
(http://snp.cshl.org/)
Website providing a wealth of information on SNPs.

UCSC Genome Bioinformatics
(http://genome.ucsc.edu)
Contains links to an assembly of the current draft of oriented DNA fragments of the human genome.

Understanding Gene Testing
(http://newscenter.cancer.gov/sciencebehind/genetesting/
genetesting26.htm)
Student-friendly, illustrated guide to gene testing.

University of Pennsylvania Center for Bioethics
(http://bioethics.upenn.edu/)
Home page for the UPenn Center for Bioethics, providing a range of useful and thought-provoking links to topics related to human genetics.

Weizmann Institute of Science
(http://bioinfo.weizmann.ac.il/cards/index.shtml)
Good site for information on human genes presented as gene (index) "cards."

Your Genes, Your Choices
(http://www.ornl.gov/hgmis/publicat/genechoice/contents.html)
U.S. Department of Energy-funded site explores issues raised by genetic research. Contains excellent case situations and ethical dilemmas for student discussion.

For Educators

Education Resources: Human Genome Program of the U.S. Department of Energy (http://www.ornl.gov/hgmis/ education/education.html and http://www.genome.org.gov/ Education/)
Outstanding sites with a wealth of print and media resources available to educators such as PowerPoint slides (http://www. ornl.gov/sci/techresources/Human_Genome/education/ education.shtml)and other materials.

"The Genes We Share with Yeast, Flies, Worms, and Mice: New Clues to Human Health and Disease" (2001).
An outsanding report from the Howard Hughes Medical Institute. A limited number of free copies are available to educators. Send a letter on official stationary describing how the publication will be used to: Howard Hughes Medical Institute, Office of Communications; 4000 Jones Bridge Road; Chevy Chase, MD 20815-9864.

The Human Genome Project: Exploring Our Molecular Selves.
Limited Edition Multimedia Education Kit produced by the National Human Genome Research Institute of the National Institutes of Health. Designed as an educational tool for high school and college students, the kit contains a commemorative wall poster, a brochure ("Genetics—The Future of Medicine"), a video, and a CD-ROM that contains three-dimensional animations of cells and molecules, timelines in genetics, activities on genome sequencing, a talking glossary, and a discussion of ethical and social issues among other topics. http://www.genome.gov/Pages/EducationKit/.

Nature's Genome Gateway (www.nature.com/genomics/papers):
Free access to published genome research categorized according to organisms. A great collection of genome papers.

Palladino, M. A. (2002). Learning about the Human Genome Project via the Web: Internet resources for biology students. *The American Biology Teacher,* 64, 110–116. Paper describing sites and exercises for teaching majors and nonmajors about the Human Genome Project via the Internet.

Primary Research Papers: The following publications are available free online through the journals *Nature* (www. nature.com/genomics) and *Science* (www.scienceonline. org), respectively. These are landmark papers on the Human Genome Project.

IHGS Consortium. (2004). Finishing the euchromatic sequence of the human genome. *Nature,* 431, 931–945.

IHGS Consortium. (2001). Initial sequencing and analysis of the human genome. *Nature,* 409, 860–891.

Venter, J. C., et al. (2001). The sequence of the human genome. *Science,* 291, 1304–1351.

Journal Articles

Bamshad, M. J., & Olson, S. E. (2003). Does race exist?" *Scientific American,* 289, 78–85.

Collins, F. S., Morgan, M., & Patrinos, A. (2004). The Human Genome Project: Lessons from large-scale biology. *Science,* 300, 286–290.

Popular Books

Cook-Deegan, R. (2004). *The gene wars: Science, politics, and the human genome.* New York: W. W. Norton & Company. Engaging story about controversies, politics, economics, and the personalities involved in the genome project.

Davies, K. (2001). *Cracking the genome: Inside the race to unlock human DNA.* New York: Free Press. An account of goals, problems, issues and competition surrouding the Human Genome Project.

Dennis, C., & Gallagher, R. (Eds.). (2001). *The human genome.* New York: Nature Publishing Group/Palgrave.

Hamer, D. (1998). *Living with our genes: Why they matter more than you think.* New York: Anchor Books. Great reading on the nature-nurture controversy and the role of genes in many aspects of human biology.

Ridley, M. (2000). *Genome: The autobiography of a species in 23 chapters.* New York: HarperCollins Publishers. A clever and engaging tour of the 23 human chromosomes.

Shreeve, J. (2004). *The genome war: How Craig Venter tried to capture the code of life and save the world.* New York: Knopf. A compelling chronicle of the race to finish the genome project.

Silver, J. M. (1997). *Remaking Eden: How genetic engineering and cloning will transform the American family.* New York: Avon Books. A thought-provoking book that address future possibilities and consequences of genetic technologies.

Zweiger, G. (2001). *Transducing the genome: Information, anarchy, and revolution in the biomedical sciences.* New York: McGraw-Hill. A well-written overview of historical aspects of the genome project and the genomics industry, genome technologies, and future prospects of genome information.

Note: All of the websites and links presented in this booklet were last accessed and verified for accuracy on January 12, 2005.

Taken from:

Genetic Testimony: A Guide to Forensic DNA Profiling
by Charlotte A.Spencer

23 Genetic Testimony: A Guide to Forensic DNA Profiling

▷ Preface

Modern forensic DNA profiling is rapidly changing all facets of the criminal justice system. The extreme sensitivity and high levels of discrimination inherent in these methods now make it possible to identify a person who dropped a bloodspot the size of a pinhead or who licked the back of a postage stamp. Crime scene samples that are decades old or ravaged by fire and decay are now yielding profiles that answer questions about identity or guilt.

Forensic DNA profiling names suspects, exonerates the innocent, and identifies the remains of disaster victims. It also challenges traditional forensic methods and pinpoints weaknesses in police techniques and the criminal justice system. As police and governments expand the uses of DNA profiling and compile DNA databanks, questions arise about who should be profiled and how DNA databanks should be regulated.

Over the next decade, it will be increasingly important for all of us to understand the workings of these technologies, why they hold such power, and what shortcomings exist.

In this guide, we explain how current DNA profiling methods work. We also answer questions about the uses of this new technology and how forensic DNA profiling is changing both criminal investigations and the criminal justice system.

The information presented is as current and accurate as possible, and it is derived from scientific literature, the media, and government sources. Because forensic DNA profiling methods are changing rapidly, readers are encouraged to refer to the publication and Internet sources listed in the References and Resources section for the latest developments.

▷ Introduction

"DNA evidence offers prosecutors important new tools for the identification and apprehension of some of the most violent perpetrators, particularly in cases of sexual assault. At the same time, DNA aids the search for truth by exonerating the innocent. The criminal justice system is not infallible."

Former Attorney General Janet Reno

At 5 P.M. on April 8, 2002, Ray Krone took off his orange jumpsuit, pulled on a T-shirt and a pair of blue jeans, and walked out of the Arizona State Prison into the late afternoon sunshine. After two convictions for a murder he did not commit, after 10 years in prison—three of them on death row—he was a free citizen (**Figure 23.1**). "There's tears in my eyes," he said. "Your heart's beating. You can't hardly talk."[1]

Ray Krone and his family never gave up hope that one day the truth would come out—the truth that he did not sexually assault and kill Kim Ancona in 1991. But he had to wait in prison for a decade until new DNA profiling techniques could prove his innocence.

▲ **Figure 23.1** Ray Krone (right) with his lawyer, after release from prison.

Source: AP/World Wide Photos

---

[1] *Arizona Republic*, April 9, 2002, page A1.

On the morning of December 29, 1991, Kim Ancona, a 36-year-old cocktail waitress, was found naked and stabbed to death in the men's washroom of the Phoenix, Arizona, bar where she worked. There was little forensic evidence at the crime scene. No fingerprints were found and no semen was detected. Blood found at the crime scene matched Kim's blood type, and saliva on her body and clothes was of the most common type. The only useful pieces of physical evidence were bite-marks on Kim's breast and neck. When police learned that Ray Krone had offered to help Kim close up the bar on the night of the murder, they asked him to make a Styrofoam impression of his teeth for comparison with the crime scene bite-marks. They then arrested him and charged him with first-degree murder, kidnapping, and sexual assault. Krone was assigned an attorney. Prior to his arrest, Krone had no criminal record, had been honorably discharged from the military, and had been a postal worker for seven years.

At his trial, Krone maintained his innocence, saying that he was asleep in bed at the time of the murder. The prosecution's expert witness testified that the bite-marks found on Kim's body matched those on Krone's Styrofoam impression. The prosecution called 19 witnesses, but the defense called only five, including Krone. The jury deliberated for two hours and found him guilty of first-degree murder and kidnapping. The judge sentenced him to death and a consecutive 21-year term of imprisonment.

Ray Krone appealed his sentence and won a new trial in 1996. However, the jury convicted him a second time of first-degree murder and kidnapping, based primarily on the forensic expert's bite-mark testimony. He was sentenced to life in prison rather than death, as the judge admitted having doubts about the identity of the killer.

In 2002, his new defense attorney obtained a court order to test the saliva on Kim Ancona's tank top, using new DNA technology. The results clearly excluded Krone as the source of the saliva, but matched a DNA profile found in the FBI's databank of convicted felons—that of Kenneth Phillips, an inmate serving time for an unrelated sex crime. Although Phillips had lived close to Kim Ancona's bar in 1991, he was not a suspect in her murder.

On April 8, 2002, Ray Krone was released from prison and subsequently exonerated of all convictions. Kenneth Phillips has since been charged with the murder and sexual assault of Kim Ancona.

Krone was the hundredth inmate sentenced to death and subsequently proven innocent and released from prison since 1976, when the U.S. Supreme Court reinstated capital punishment. He was the 12th death row inmate to have his innocence proven by forensic DNA profiling.

A month after his release from prison, Ray Krone stood before a crowd of supporters in his home state of Pennsylvania, vowing to "offer any support I can, anytime, anywhere" to those who seek laws permitting the testing and introduction of DNA evidence to exonerate inmates who are wrongfully convicted.

"I'm thankful to be able to be out here to talk to you all," he said. "DNA made the difference, and I hope that people start realizing the scientific value of DNA and the need for us to update our justice system. And to use this valuable tool, not only to free the innocent, but also to prosecute those that are guilty."[2]

In the last decade, forensic DNA profiling has emerged as a powerful method to identify the guilty and exonerate the innocent. What makes it such a powerful technique? How does DNA profiling work? What are the advantages and drawbacks to the technology, and how is DNA profiling changing the way the criminal justice system functions?

In this guide, we will answer these questions, outlining the basic methods used in forensic DNA profiling and explaining how DNA evidence has the power to convict or exonerate. We will also relate some of the extraordinary stories that have come to light as this new technology expands and transforms criminal justice systems throughout the world.

▷ Questions About DNA Profiling Methods

What Is the Biological Basis for Forensic DNA Profiling?

The Same DNA is Found in Virtually All Cells in Our Bodies
Each of us is made up of hundreds of billions of cells, each one of which is derived by cell division from a single fertilized egg. Our cells contain two main compartments—the cytoplasm and the nucleus (**Figure 23.2**). An exception is the red blood cell, which contains no nucleus. Within the nucleus are the chromosomes—threadlike structures that carry the genetic material. Human cells contain 23 pairs of chromosomes, one of each pair inherited from the mother via the egg cell and one of each pair inherited from the father via the sperm cell. Males inherit a Y chromosome from the father's sperm, whereas females inherit an X chromosome. Therefore, each person is either an XY male or an XX female (**Figure 23.3**).

Genetic Information is Contained Within the Base Pair Sequence of DNA
Each chromosome is made up of a single linear molecule of DNA (deoxyribonucleic acid). Each DNA molecule is comprised of two strands coiled around each other in a double helix. Each single strand is made up of a repetitive sugar-phosphate backbone to which are linked four *bases*, arranged in various orders (**Figure23.4**). The bases are known as A,

---

[2] *York Daily Record*, May 8, 2002, page 1A.

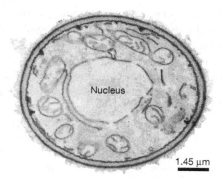

Nucleus

1.45 μm

Figure 23.2 Microscopic view of a single cell. Cells are comprised of a nucleus which contains the chromosomes, and the cytoplasm which contains structures called mitochondria. Both mitochondria and nuclear chromosomes contain DNA.

Source: Scott Freeman, *Biological Sciences*, Prentice Hall

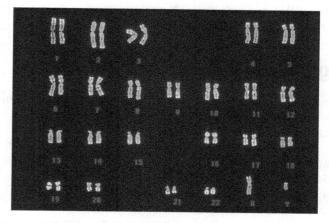

Figure 23.3 Human chromosomes, seen at high magnification. The nucleus of each human cell contains 23 pairs of chromosomes—22 autosomal chromosomes and one pair of sex chromosomes. This set of chromosomes was derived from a male (XY).

Source: William S. Klug and Michael R. Cummings, *Concepts of Genetics*, Prentice Hall

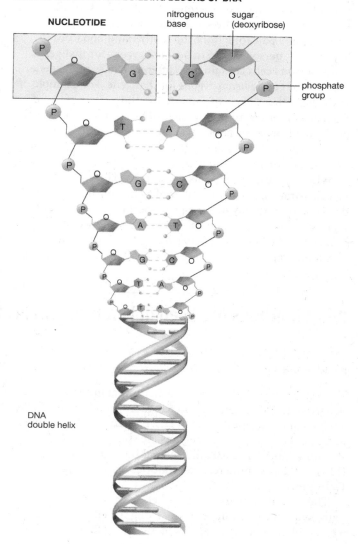

NUCLEOTIDES ARE THE BUILDING BLOCKS OF DNA

NUCLEOTIDE — nitrogenous base — sugar (deoxyribose) — phosphate group

DNA double helix

Figure 23.4 Diagram of DNA molecule, showing double helix, sugar-phosphate backbone and bases A, T, G, and C. Hydrogen bonds between the bases of the two single strands hold the double helix together. These bonds can be broken by heat, chemicals or enzymes. The DNA sequence of this molecule would be **G T G A G T T** on one strand, and **C A C T C A A** on the complementary strand.

Source: David Krogh, *Biology: A Guide to the Natural World*, Prentice Hall

T, C, and G (abbreviations for adenine, thymine, cytosine, and guanine). These chemical bases pair with each other by hydrogen bonding and hold the two strands of the double helix together. The T base always pairs with A, and the G base always pairs with C. The base pairs on each DNA molecule are arranged in a specific order, like a four-letter Morse code. This is known as the DNA *sequence*. Because A always pairs with T, and G always pairs with C, the DNA sequences on each strand are *complementary* to each other. There are about 6 billion base pairs of DNA in a human cell. The entire complement of DNA in a cell's nucleus is known as the *genome*.

A *gene* is a portion of DNA of about 1,000 to 100,000 base pairs in length. There are approximately 30,000 genes in the entire human genome. Each gene occupies a specific region on a specific chromosome. Specific regions of a chromosome, whether occupied by genes or not, are known as *loci*. Each is a *locus*. The cell reads the linear sequence of base pairs within a gene and converts that information into the linear sequence of amino acids in a particular protein. In this way, each gene specifies the synthesis of one specific protein.

DNA Sequences Differ Between Individuals

Although humans are fundamentally similar, enough genetic difference exists between individuals to make each of us detectably unique. Most of our DNA sequences are identical, but approximately one base pair in 1,000 differs between individuals. As there are 6 billion base pairs in the human genome, this means that about 6 million base pairs differ between individuals. This small amount of genetic diversity accounts for slight differences in the proteins found in cells and hence the range of physical differences seen in humans. These DNA sequence differences are also the basis for forensic DNA profiling. If we could compare the complete DNA sequences from two people, we could be certain that the DNA came from two distinct individuals.

Alternative forms of a gene or locus, due to the presence of DNA sequence differences, are known as *alleles*. If a person's cells contain the same allele of a gene on each of a chromosome pair (one from the mother and one from the father), that person is said to be *homozygous* for that gene. If the person's cells contain two different alleles of the gene, they are said to be *heterozygous* for that gene. For example, if you inherit the A allele of Gene A and the b allele of Gene B from your mother, and the *a* allele of Gene A and the *b* allele of Gene B from your father, you are an *Aa* heterozygote for Gene A and a *bb* homozygote for Gene B. Another way this is expressed is that your *genotype* is *Aa/bb*.

When egg and sperm cells develop, the chromosome pairs separate, and each member of a chromosome pair is distributed randomly to the egg or sperm. This independent segregation of chromosomes, combined with recombination events during egg and sperm development, creates an enormous variety of genetic allele combinations in eggs and sperm. This means that even siblings are genetically different, although less different than two people chosen at random from a population. The only individuals with an identical genetic makeup are identical twins, who develop from a single fertilized egg. In a population, there are usually numerous different alleles for any gene or locus. This is known as gene *polymorphism*.

Surprisingly, coding regions of genes make up only about 5% of the human genome. The remaining 95% of human DNA is sometimes called "junk DNA," as it is unclear what functions are performed by much of this material. These noncoding regions are particularly useful for forensic DNA analysis, as they are rich in tandomly repeated DNA sequences. These repeats can vary from two base units (e.g., AT) repeated from two to dozens of times (ATAT to ATATATATAT etc.), up to 80 base units repeated from two to dozens of times. These repeat regions are the basis for many of the DNA profiling methods used in forensics.

What Methods Are Used in Forensic DNA Profiling and How Do They Work?

Variable Number of Tandem Repeat (VNTR) Methods

Background

The first use of DNA profiling in a criminal investigation occurred in 1986 in the United Kingdom, and it involved the analysis of large repeat areas of DNA called variable number of tandem repeat (VNTR) regions (see box: The Colin Pitchfork Story). In 1988, the Federal Bureau of Investigation (FBI) and U.S. commercial laboratories began using VNTR DNA profile methods.

The VNTRs contain DNA sequence units eight to 80 base pairs long repeated consecutively along the chromosome. The number of tandem repeats in each VNTR locus differs from person to person. A VNTR may contain anywhere from a thousand to several thousand base pairs of DNA. Each of these tandem repeat lengths is considered to be an allele.

One of the reasons that VNTRs are useful for DNA profiling is the large number of alleles (30 or more) at each VNTR locus that are present in a population. The large number of alleles means that the number of possible genotypes is immense. For example, if there are 20 alleles at VNTR locus A (A1, A2, A3, etc.), the total number of possible genotypes for locus A would be 210. If one analyzed a person's DNA at four different VNTR loci, and each VNTR locus had 20 possible al-leles, the number of possible genotypes in this four locus profile would be 210^4 (about 2 billion).

The Colin Pitchfork Story

Between 1983 and 1986, police were unable to solve two murders in the village of Narborough in Leicestershire, England. Two 15-year-old schoolgirls, Lynda Mann and Dawn Ashworth, had been raped, strangled, and thrown into the bushes next to secluded pathways near the town. The perpetrator left no clues at the crime scene except for his semen. Initially, police focused their investigation on a 17-year-old mentally retarded kitchen porter from a nearby mental hospital, as he had a previous history of sexual offences. When questioned, the porter made a full confession to the murder of Dawn Ashworth. Police accepted his confession, but they were interested to know whether the porter might also be responsible for Lynda Mann's death.

Police asked Dr. Alec Jeffreys of the University of Leicester to help them identify the perpetrator of the Mann murder. Dr. Jeffreys had been studying variable number of tandem repeat (VNTR) regions in human populations and had developed methods for measuring the sizes of VNTR loci. Police provided Dr. Jeffreys with semen samples from the girls' bodies, as well as a blood sample from the porter. Dr. Jeffreys' VNTR analysis clearly showed that the DNA profiles of semen from both crime scenes matched, suggesting that the same person had committed the rapes. However, neither DNA profile matched that of the porter. The porter had become the first person in history to be exonerated by DNA profiling.

Police now turned their attention to the entire male population of Narborough and surrounding villages. They requested that every adult male in the area provide them with a blood sample to compare with those from the crime

Method for VNTR Profiling

A VNTR DNA profile is created by measuring the lengths of a number of different VNTR loci in a person's DNA. Originally, this method of generating a VNTR profile was called *DNA fingerprinting*. This terminology has now been replaced by *DNA profiling* to differentiate it from classic dermal ridge pattern fingerprinting methods.

The method entails the following (**Figure 23.5**):

1. DNA is extracted from the sample using a series of chemical treatments.

2. The DNA is cut into millions of small pieces using a *restriction enzyme*, which recognizes specific sequences in the DNA and makes double-stranded cuts through the DNA at those positions. For example, the restriction enzyme *Hae*III recognizes the DNA sequence GGCC. It then cuts the DNA between the G and C. For example (showing a short region of double-stranded DNA):

---ATCGTTAGGCCTCAAG--- → ---ATCGTTAGG--- ---CCTCAAG---

---TAGCAATCCGGAGTTC--- ---TAGCAATCC--- ---GGAGTTC---

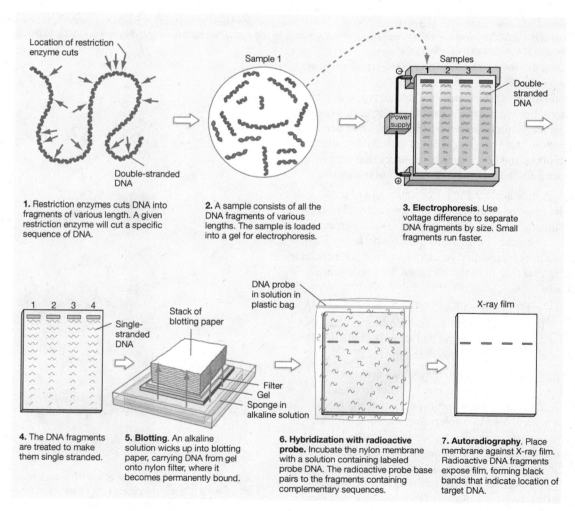

1. Restriction enzymes cuts DNA into fragments of various length. A given restriction enzyme will cut a specific sequence of DNA.

2. A sample consists of all the DNA fragments of various lengths. The sample is loaded into a gel for electrophoresis.

3. Electrophoresis. Use voltage difference to separate DNA fragments by size. Small fragments run faster.

4. The DNA fragments are treated to make them single stranded.

5. Blotting. An alkaline solution wicks up into blotting paper, carrying DNA from gel onto nylon filter, where it becomes permanently bound.

6. Hybridization with radioactive probe. Incubate the nylon membrane with a solution containing labeled probe DNA. The radioactive probe base pairs to the fragments containing complementary sequences.

7. Autoradiography. Place membrane against X-ray film. Radioactive DNA fragments expose film, forming black bands that indicate location of target DNA.

Figure 23.5 Method of creating a VNTR profile

Source: Scott Freeman, *Biological Science*, Prentice Hall

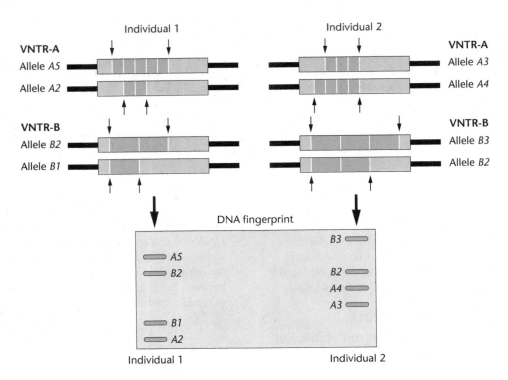

▲ Figure 23.6 Two VNTR loci in two individuals and their analysis by VNTR profiling. Arrows indicate the sites of cutting by restriction enzymes. The DNA fragments are separated by gel electrophoresis and detected as bands after probing the membrane with a labelled probe and exposing the membrane to X-ray film. Because the sizes of the VNTR fragments differ between individuals, the bands on the autoradiograph appear at different positions. In these profiles, one band (the B2 allele band) is shared by the two individuals.

Source: William S. Klug and Michael R. Cummings, *Concepts of Genetics*, Prentice Hall

Restriction enzymes are chosen that do not cut within the VNTR locus, but cut the DNA on either side of it. Because the recognition sequences for restriction enzymes occur throughout the DNA molecule, but at various distances from each other, the DNA is cut into pieces that vary in length from a few base pairs to thousands of base pairs.

3. The DNA sample is placed in a well at the end of a slab of jelly-like material (called a *gel*) and an electrical charge is passed through the gel. Smaller-sized DNA fragments migrate more quickly through the gel than do larger fragments. This process is called *gel electrophoresis*. The distance that a particular fragment travels down the gel depends upon its size.

4. Because the gel is fragile and difficult to handle, the DNA in the gel is transferred onto a nylon membrane. The DNA is treated with alkali, so that the two strands of the double helix denature (come apart), exposing the bases.

5. Up until now, the DNA fragments are not detectable on either the gel or on the membrane. In order to detect the VNTR fragments, the membrane bearing the DNA fragments is incubated in a solution containing a *probe*. The probe consists of single-stranded DNA, which is complementary in its DNA sequence to the VNTR region that is of interest. The probe also contains a tag—either radioactivity or a chemical that emits light. The probe *hybridizes* (binds) to any piece of DNA on the membrane that bears the complementary DNA sequence (following the A-T, G-C base-pairing rules).

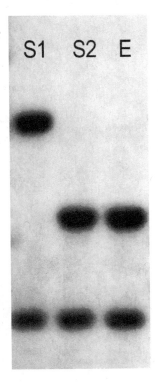

▲ Figure 23.7 An example of a VNTR autoradiograph. The DNA profile of Suspect 2 (S2) matches that of the crime scene evidence (E). Suspect 1 (S1) is excluded as the source of the crime scene evidence. Both suspects share one allele at this VNTR locus.

Source: William S. Klug and Michael R. Cummings, *Concepts of Genetics*, Prentice Hall

6. The excess probe that does not hybridize to the VNTR DNA fragments is washed off.

7. The membrane with its hybridized probe is exposed to X-ray film. Positions on the membrane that contain the probe (and hence the VNTR of interest) create an image on the film and show up as bands. The resulting photographic image is known as an autoradiograph. The position of the bands within the lane of DNA fragments, when compared to standard size markers in adjacent lanes, indicates the size of the fragment in each band. A typical VNTR analysis is shown in Figure 23.6, and an example of a VNTR *autoradiograph* is shown in Figure 23.7.

Usually, the DNA samples to be compared are placed in adjacent lanes on the same gel. If the two VNTR bands from one DNA sample run at different positions on the gel from the two VNTR bands from another DNA sample, they are considered a nonmatch, and the two samples must have come from different people. However, if the two samples show the same-sized VNTR bands, the profiles are considered a match. A match means that either the two DNA samples came from

Polymerase Chain Reaction

The polymerase chain reaction (PCR) is a method for generating multiple copies of specific regions of DNA. The PCR technique is based on the principles of DNA base pairing and DNA replication, and it consists of four steps:

1. DNA is extracted from the sample. This is the template DNA. It is mixed with:
   - A solution of four dNTPs (building blocks of the DNA molecule, containing a sugar, phosphate, and one of the bases A, T, G, or C).
   - A heat-resistant DNA polymerase enzyme called Taq polymerase.
   - A solution containing millions of copies of specific PCR primers. The PCR primers are very short (about 20 bases long) single-stranded DNA molecules that have been synthesized in the laboratory and have defined DNA sequences. The primer sequences are chosen to flank the region that is to be amplified.

2. The reaction mixture is heated to 95°C for 5 minutes, which causes the two strands of the DNA double helix to denature, exposing the bases.

3. The temperature is lowered to between 50° and 70°C for several minutes. The primers hybridize to their complementary base pair sequences present in the template DNA.

4. Taq polymerase extends the primers by adding dNTPs to the ends of the primers, filling in the gaps between the primers and creating double-stranded DNA in the region between the primers.

Steps two to four are repeated 20 to 30 times. At each cycle, the number of double-stranded DNA molecules doubles. Two single strands of the target DNA yield two double-stranded copies. The two copies now act as templates for the creation of four copies, and so on, up to a million-fold increase in the amount of DNA of the target sequence. The PCR reaction is carried out in a single test tube, and the entire process is automated in machines called *thermocyclers*.

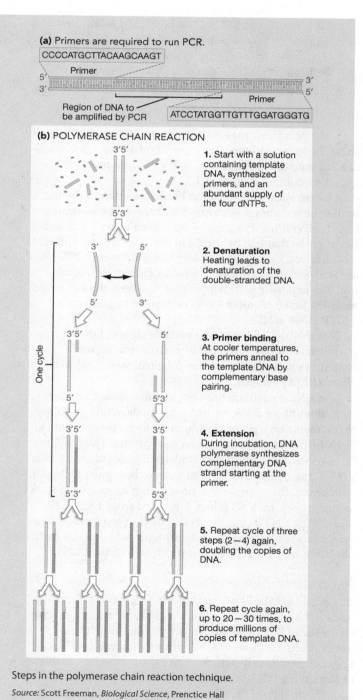

(a) Primers are required to run PCR.

CCCCATGCTTACAAGCAAGT

Primer

Region of DNA to be amplified by PCR

Primer

ATCCTATGGTTGTTTGGATGGGTG

(b) POLYMERASE CHAIN REACTION

One cycle

1. Start with a solution containing template DNA, synthesized primers, and an abundant supply of the four dNTPs.

2. Denaturation
Heating leads to denaturation of the double-stranded DNA.

3. Primer binding
At cooler temperatures, the primers anneal to the template DNA by complementary base pairing.

4. Extension
During incubation, DNA polymerase synthesizes complementary DNA strand starting at the primer.

5. Repeat cycle of three steps (2—4) again, doubling the copies of DNA.

6. Repeat cycle again, up to 20—30 times, to produce millions of copies of template DNA.

Steps in the polymerase chain reaction technique.

Source: Scott Freeman, Biological Science, Prentice Hall

Because the PCR method selectively amplifies a specific short region of a DNA molecule, the template DNA for the first PCR cycle can be impure, present in minuscule amounts (theoretically one molecule), and can be partially degraded, as long as one DNA molecule in the sample has an intact amplification region. These features make PCR particularly useful for forensic DNA analysis, which can be performed on single hairs, a small number of cells in saliva on the back of a postage stamp, or decayed samples from old crime scenes.

Once the relevant regions of DNA have been amplified by PCR, they can be analyzed using a number of different methods, such as STR, SNP, mtDNA, and Y chromosome DNA profiling—as described in this guide.

The great sensitivity and power of PCR—amplifying a single copy of a DNA molecule into millions of copies—also creates a potential problem. Any contamination of the DNA sample with DNA from another source could potentially result in amplification of the wrong DNA, or amplification of a mixture of two types. This is a particular problem when trace amounts of material must be amplified for forensic DNA profiling. If the contaminating DNA is present in small amounts compared with the primary DNA, the PCR products from the contaminant will be present in lower concentrations than will those from the primary DNA. However, if only a few cells of both primary and contaminant samples are present, a mixed DNA profile or an incorrect one may be generated. These limitations must be kept in mind when analyzing PCR-based DNA profiles.

the same person, or they came from two different people who share the same genotype by chance. Probability calculations can estimate the likelihood of such a random match at any locus or a combination of loci.

After an autoradiograph has been created from the membrane, the membrane is stripped of its probe by washing at high temperature. The membrane is then treated with a different probe that will hybridize to the DNA from a different VNTR locus. Usually, at least five or six different VNTR loci are analyzed to create a DNA profile. Each cycle of probing, film exposure and stripping takes several days or weeks, meaning that it requires weeks or months to generate a VNTR DNA profile.

This method of measuring variable sizes of DNA fragments that have been cut by restriction enzymes is sometimes known as *restriction fragment length polymorphism (RFLP)* analysis.

The VNTR profiling has several limitations. Relatively large amounts of DNA are necessary to detect the presence of fragments on a gel or membrane—about the amount of DNA from a blood stain the size of a quarter. The DNA must be in good condition (not degraded) in order to create intact VNTR fragments of up to thousands of base pairs in length. In addition, the procedure is slow, taking up to several weeks to analyze several VNTR loci. First used from 1985 to the mid-1990s, VNTR profiling is still used in some cases; however, it has been almost completely replaced by newer methods based on PCR technology, which is described next.

Polymerase Chain Reaction (PCR)–Based Methods

To circumvent the limitations of VNTR profiling, forensic scientists have developed a number of new techniques based on the use of PCR, a method for amplifying small quantities of specific regions of DNA prior to analysis (see box: Polymerase Chain Reaction). The PCR method is capable of amplifying DNA in a single cell, and it typically requires about 50-fold less DNA than that required for VNTR

analysis. The following is a brief summary of the current DNA profiling methods based on PCR technology.

Short Tandem Repeats (STRs)

Background

Analysis of STRs has essentially replaced VNTR analysis as the method of choice for forensic DNA profiling. Like VNTRs, STRs are regions within a person's DNA that contain specific DNA sequences tandomly repeated a number of times. However, STRs consist of smaller repeat units (two to seven base pairs long) repeated fewer times (seven to 40 repeats per STR region). The short lengths of STR regions allow them to be amplified using the PCR technique, which cannot efficiently amplify the longer VNTR regions.

Although hundreds of STR loci are contained within a person's genome, only a subset of these is used for DNA profiling. At present, the FBI specifies 13 STR loci as a core set to be used in forensic analysis. The core STR loci are listed in Table 23.1. For example, one STR locus (D8S1179) has 10 alleles (10 different repeat lengths) and has a four base pair repeat unit (TCTA). When all 13 core STR loci are used to generate a DNA profile, the probability that two randomly chosen profiles will match is approximately one in 6×10^{14} (one in 600 trillion) in a Caucasian American population or one in 9×10^{14} (one in 900 trillion) in an African American population.

Method for STR Profiling

1. DNA is extracted from the sample.
2. The DNA undergoes PCR amplification of the selected STR locus.
3. The sizes of the amplified fragments are measured.

After PCR amplification, the DNA sample will contain a small quantity of the original DNA (the template for the PCR reaction) and a large quantity of amplified DNA of the locus

TABLE 23.1 CHARACTERISTICS OF THE FBI'S 13 CORE STR LOCI

Locus	Repeat	# Alleles	Population Match Probabilities	
			Caucasian American	African American
CSF1PO	AGAT	11	0.112	0.081
TPOX	AATG	7	0.195	0.090
TH01	AATG	7	0.081	0.109
vWA	TCTA	10	0.062	0.063
D16S539	GATA	8	0.089	0.070
D7S820	GATA	11	0.065	0.080
D13S317	TATC	8	0.085	0.136
D5S818	AGAT	10	0.158	0.112
FGA	TTTC	19	0.036	0.033
D3S1358	TCTA	10	0.075	0.094
D8S1179	TCTA	10	0.067	0.082
D18S51	AGAA	15	0.028	0.029
D21S11	TCTA	20	0.039	0.034
Product			1.738×10^{-15}	1.092×10^{-15}
One in			5.753×10^{14}	9.161×10^{14}

Source: The Future of Forensic DNA Testing: Predictions of the Research and Development Working Group, by the National Institute of Justice, November 2000.

selected for amplification. Because each person has two copies of each STR locus (one on the maternal chromosome, one on the paternal chromosome), there will usually be two STR amplification products of slightly different sizes present in the reaction. At this point, the two products are separated as to size, by one of several methods.

First, the amplified fragments may be analyzed by slab gel electrophoresis—the same method used to analyze VNTR fragments (Figure 23.5). Following gel electrophoresis, the gel is stained with silver so as to visualize the two amplified STR bands. By comparing the STR bands to the standard DNA size markers on the gel, the size of each band can be computed.

A second method requires that the primers in the PCR reaction bear fluorescent tags. When the primers become incorporated into the amplified DNA fragments, they make those fragments fluorescent. After the PCR amplification step, the amplified DNA fragments are separated by a form of gel electrophoresis called *capillary electrophoresis*. This method uses fine-bore glass capillaries filled with gel material similar to that used in slab gel electrophoresis. The DNA sample is placed at the top of the capillary tube and an electric current is passed through the gel in the capillary. The DNA fragments are separated as to size as they pass down the capillary toward the positive electrode. A laser detector at the bottom of the tube detects fluorescent DNA as it passes the end of the capillary. The data are collected and analyzed by software that calculates the DNA fragment sizes as well as the relative amount of DNA in each band. Data are visualized as graphs showing the position and size of the DNA fragments. Capillary electrophoresis is faster than slab gel electrophoresis, requires less DNA, and is amenable to automation.

Automated capillary gel instruments can analyze up to 96 samples over a period of a few hours. An example of an STR DNA profile using this method is shown in **Figure 23.8.**

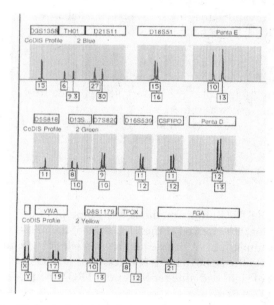

▲ **Figure 23.8** An STR profile, created using the PowerPlex® Kit (Promega Corp.) This kit amplifies all 13 core STR loci, as well as two extra loci (Penta E and D) and a locus (Amelogenin) that indicates the presence of either an X or a Y chromosome in the DNA sample. Most loci in this profile are heterozygous; however, three loci (D3S1358, D5S818 and FGA) appear to be homozygous. Primers in this reaction were labelled with blue, green or yellow fluorescent dyes, allowing simultaneous amplification of all 16 loci and simultaneous capillary electrophoresis of all loci. The numbers in boxes below each peak indicate the allele (15 repeats, 6 repeats, etc).

Source: H. Edward Grothan

Forensic DNA Databases

The United States, Canada, Australia, China, the United Kingdom and many European countries have established national forensic DNA databases. The first of these databases containing STR profiles was created in the United Kingdom in 1995. In the United Kingdom, all suspects and arrestees are compelled to submit samples for DNA testing. The U.K. database now consists of over 1.5 million DNA profiles and will contain 3 million profiles by 2004. Government figures indicate that about 1,600 DNA matches are obtained each week by searching the database. These either link a suspect to a crime scene or reveal links between different crime scenes.

In 1998, the FBI established a national DNA database, called the Combined DNA Index System (CODIS). All 50 states have laws requiring convicted offenders of certain crimes to submit DNA samples for profiling. At present, all but three states (Hawaii, Rhode Island, and Mississippi) submit these profiles to CODIS. States vary considerably in the types of crimes that qualify for database entry. Some states collect DNA samples from all arrested people, but others collect samples only from offenders convicted of specific violent crimes such as rape and murder.

The CODIS system contains two main criminal DNA databases—the Convicted Offender database and the Forensic Evidence database—as well as one missing persons index. In addition, CODIS contains computer software that allows investigators to search for matches within and across the DNA profile databases, as well as STR allele frequency data from major population groups. The Convicted Offender database contains DNA profiles of individuals convicted of certain violent crimes. The Forensic Evidence database contains DNA profiles from biological evidence samples collected from crime scenes, such as semen, saliva, or bloodstains. The missing persons database contains mtDNA and STR DNA profiles from remains such as bones, teeth, or hair. It also contains DNA profiles from relatives of missing persons, so that comparisons can be made between known and unknown samples.

The FBI has chosen 13 core STR loci as standards for CODIS profiles (Table 23.1). All 13 loci are used by Canada's Royal Canadian Mounted Police (RCMP) and eight core STR loci are used in the U.K. database, which could facilitate international cross-referencing of DNA profiles.

The DNA profile databases have helped investigations into murders, rapes, burglaries, and even forgeries. These databases are particularly useful in solving *cold cases*—unsolved cases in which there is no suspect. In Virginia, 178 cold hits were obtained in 2000 and about 300 in 2001. By May 2002, CODIS had contributed to 5,000 forensic investigations and had produced over 4,000 DNA profile matches.

Prime Minister Tony Blair, supporting U.K. DNA legislation by donating a mouth swab for DNA profiling and entry into Britain's national DNA database.

Source: AP/World Wide Photos

In all STR profiling methods, the genotype of the individual is expressed as the allele sizes of the STR fragments. For example, a DNA profile may show alleles of 11 and 12 repeats at the D5S818 locus (expressed as D5S818 11,12) and alleles of eight and nine repeats at the TPOX locus (expressed as TPOX 8,9).

Commercial kits are now available for generating STR-based DNA profiles. In some cases, these kits amplify all 13 core STR loci (as well as other loci) simultaneously in a single reaction, a feature that speeds the analysis and preserves limited amounts of forensic evidence. This type of DNA profiling is termed *multiplexing*.

After a DNA profile is generated, it is compared to another profile from another person or from a crime scene sample. Also, DNA profiles can be compared with profiles stored in national or regional DNA databanks (see box: Forensic DNA Databases).

Single Nucleotide Polymorphisms (SNPs)

A new and emerging method of DNA profiling involves analysis of single nucleotide polymorphisms (SNPs). The SNPs are differences in the DNA sequence at single positions in the genome. An SNP may be due to a single base pair change or to a small insertion or deletion at that position. An example of a single base pair SNP is shown in Figure 23.9.

Single nucleotide polymorphisms are present about once every 1,000 bases throughout the entire genome, making the number of potential profiling loci enormous (about 6 million). Most SNPs have only two alleles; hence, analysis of a single SNP is not very discriminating for identification

```
5'-----A T C C G A G C T T C A A-----3'
3'-----T A G G C T C G A A G T T-----5'
                  ↓
5'-----A T C C G A G C C T C A A-----3'
3'-----T A G G C T C G G A G T T-----5'
```

▲ **Figure 23.9** Example of a Single Nucleotide Polymorphism (SNP) creating a single base pair change in a short region of a double-stranded DNA molecule.

purposes. However, when combined with analysis of a large number of other SNP loci, SNP profiling can be as informative as STR or VNTR profiling. At present, SNP loci are being catalogued and characterized for future DNA profiling purposes.

In order to detect SNPs, the DNA is first amplified by PCR. The amplified DNA is then subjected to DNA sequencing. As DNA sequencing is fairly cumbersome, alternate methods for detecting single base pair differences in amplified DNA are currently being developed.

One of the early applications of SNP analysis was known as HLA-DQA1 and Polymarker profiling. In this method, six SNP loci are PCR-amplified and hybridized to filters that contain probe DNA that is specific for each polymorphism. Hybridization is detected by staining. Although simple and accurate, the discriminating power of this method is only about one in 4,000. The method has now been replaced by standard STR analysis.

There are several major advantages to SNP DNA profiling. The human genome contains vast numbers of these loci, their analysis may become automated in the future, and the regions of interest are so small that highly degraded DNA samples are still amenable to PCR amplification and SNP detection. Currently, SNP profiling is being used to identify the remains

DNA Profiling Identifies September 11 Victims

Identifying the remains of victims from the September 11, 2001, terrorist attacks on the World Trade Center in New York has been the largest and most difficult forensic DNA investigation in American history.

By the end of 2002, the official death toll stood at 2,795. About 1.6 million tons of debris has been removed from the site, as well as 293 whole bodies and about 20,000 pieces of bone and tissue—some pieces as small as a fingertip. The trauma of the collapsing skyscrapers pulverized most of the victims' bodies to dust, and much of the remaining fragments were damaged by fire, water, and bacterial degradation.

Bodies and body parts were brought to the Medical Examiner's Office in New York City, where they were stored in 16 refrigerated trailers. From there, they were examined by pathologists, fingerprint experts, and forensic dentists. The initial identifications were made using traditional forensic identification methods, such as fingerprinting and dental records. Only 10 of the victims could be identified visually. In order to identify the partial remains, authorities turned to DNA profiling. The profiling was carried out by the N.Y. Medical Examiner's Office, which assembled the data, and by private DNA analysis laboratories in Utah, Texas, Maryland, and Virginia. In order to match DNA profiles to victims, laboratories collected personal items from the victims' homes—about 7,000 razor blades, combs, toothbrushes, and other items, as well as about 7,000 cheek swabs from the victims' relatives.

The method of choice for the initial DNA profiling was STR (short tandem repeat) analysis—profiling the 13 core STR loci and comparing the profiles with those generated from DNA extracted from the victim's personal property. Half the tissue and bone samples yielded sufficient STR profiles to identify the remains. However, the other half either provided no STR DNA profile or only a partial one.

By September 2002, about half of the World Trade Center victims had been identified. To complete the identification of remains, DNA laboratories are turning to more sensitive profiling methods—mtDNA and SNP (single nucleotide polymorphism) analysis. These profiling methods are capable of generating DNA profiles from highly degraded DNA, even as little as 60 base pairs of intact DNA per locus. The hope is that samples that did not generate a usable STR profile will give sufficient mtDNA or SNP profiles to identify the victim. New mtDNA and SNP profile technologies and new database analysis methods are being developed specifically to deal with the volume and condition of material from the World Trade Center attacks. The new technologies will undoubtedly have an impact on forensic DNA profiling in the future.

The goal is to complete identification of all victims by the middle of 2003.

Remains of the World Trade Center, New York, after the September 11 terrorist attacks.

Source: REUTERS/CORBIS BETTMANN

of victims of the September 11, 2001, terrorist attacks on the World Trade Center in New York (see box: DNA Profiling Identifies September 11 Victims).

Mitochondrial DNA (mtDNA)

Analysis of mtDNA is a recent addition to the repertoire of forensic DNA profiling. Mitochondria are organelles present in thousands of copies within the cytoplasm of cells, and they are responsible for generating energy via oxidative respiration (**Figure 23.2**).

Mitochondria contain their own small (approximately 16,000 base pairs) circular DNA genomes, and they replicate independently of the cell's nuclear chromosomes. When a cell divides, the mitochondria are distributed to the two new daughter cells. Human egg cells contain mitochondria in their cytoplasm and pass these mitochondria on to the zygote. However, sperm cells contain few mitochondria and do not pass these to the zygote on fertilization. Hence, offspring contain only maternally derived mitochondria. Because of these features, all mtDNA is identical in each cell of the body, and is passed from grandmother to mother to child.

The DNA profiles of mtDNA are generated by PCR amplification of regions of mtDNA that exhibit DNA sequence polymorphisms within populations. Amplification is followed by determination of the DNA sequence in that region. The DNA sequence is then compared with that from a reference sample to determine a match or nonmatch.

Although direct sequencing of mtDNA is still relatively slow and expensive, technical advances may soon make it a standard procedure in forensic science. Databases of mtDNA polymorphisms and allele frequencies are being compiled.

DNA Identifies Victims of Srebrenica Massacre

In July 1995, Serbian troops seized the Bosnian town of Srebrenica. About 25,000 Muslim inhabitants fled—some to the woods and some to the United Nation's (U.N.) compound outside the town. Unfortunately, the compound was full and the gates were locked. The Muslim refugees camped outside the gates, hoping to be protected by U.N. soldiers; however, the Serbian forces arrived unopposed. Over 7,500 men and boys from outside the U.N. compound were shipped to execution sites, killed, and buried in mass graves. Later, the bodies from these graves were dug up and reburied throughout the region in an attempt to conceal evidence. The massacre was the largest mass murder of European civilians since World War II.

In 1996, U.S. President Bill Clinton established the International Commission on Missing Persons (ICMP) to return massacre victims to their families. The goal of ICMP is to identify the approximately 30,000 persons missing in the former Yugoslavia—an effort that will be the world's largest DNA profiling project to identify human remains. By the end of 2002, about 6,000 bodies from the Srebrenica massacre had been exhumed from a number of grave sites and stored in plastic bags in a warehouse near Tuzla. Standard postmortem procedures determine the age, gender, injuries, and general stature of the victims. Clothing is removed, laundered, and displayed for families to identify. However, as identification papers are missing and bodies are severely disfigured and decayed, visual identification is virtually impossible. Only a handful of remains have been identified by standard forensic methods.

The ICMP's DNA profiling will cost approximately $25 million. Outreach programs are collecting thousands of blood samples from relatives of the missing people. In addition, the bones of massacre victims are being cleaned and prepared for analysis. Samples will be sent to four DNA analysis laboratories situated in the former Yugoslavia. The DNA will be extracted from these samples, and relevant regions of nuclear and mitochondrial DNA (mtDNA) will be amplified by PCR. As mitochondrial genomes are often more resistant to degradation than nuclear DNA, mtDNA profiling is expected to provide the most efficient way to identify many of the victims. In addition, there are often surviving maternal relatives who can provide blood samples in order to match the DNA profiles to those of the missing persons. As it will not be possible to distinguish siblings simply by mitochondrial profiles, additional DNA profiling of STR loci, and Y chromosome markers will be necessary to ascribe names to the thousands of anonymous victims of the Srebrenica massacre.

Identifications are proceeding at a rate of two or three per day. By the end of 2002, over 100 bodies had been identified. However, some remains will never be identified. The names of the missing will be listed at a memorial center in the cemetery outside of Srebrenica.

Mass grave, near Srebrenica.

Source: AP/World Wide Photos

There are several advantages to mtDNA profiling. Because mtDNA is present in thousands of copies per cell, extremely small amounts of biological material can often be analyzed successfully. Also, severely degraded material such as charred remains and old bones can sometimes be analyzed, even when chromosomal DNA is too severely degraded to yield STR profiles. In addition, mtDNA can be analyzed in samples such as hair shafts, which contain no nuclear DNA. The DNA profiling of mtDNA has been used to identify victims of disasters, assassinations, and mass murders (see boxes: DNA Profiling Identifies September 11 Victims and DNA Identifies Victims of Srebrenica Massacre).

One disadvantage of mtDNA typing is that it cannot distinguish between mtDNA from siblings or maternal relatives. It is even possible for two people who are apparently unrelated to share the same mtDNA profile, if they shared a maternal ancestor in the distant past. Also, mtDNA profiles do not provide the same discriminating power as do STR profiles.

Y Chromosome Analysis

Profiling of Y chromosome DNA is used to distinguish multiple male contributors to biological samples. It is useful in sexual assault cases, as most vaginal swabs from rape cases contain a large number of female victim cells and a smaller number of sperm cells. The DNA in X chromosomes does not amplify by Y chromosome-specific PCR, and therefore does not interfere with analysis of Y chromosome loci. Over 100 loci on the Y chromosome are useful as DNA profile loci, including STRs and SNPs.

The Y chromosome is inherited from father to son as a single unpaired chromosome, and it is not present in females. Similar to mtDNA, all the loci on the Y chromosome behave as a single locus that is inherited as a unit. As all males in the paternal line carry the same Y chromosome, this method can also be used to trace family relationships between males, and has been used in human evolution studies.

A complication of Y chromosome profiling is that it cannot distinguish between siblings or other males in the paternal line. In addition, a Y chromosome profile can be shared by those who unknowingly shared a distant male ancestor.

An interesting case in Poland involved Y chromosome analysis to help screen hundreds of men during a police dragnet for a serial rapist-murderer (see box: Polish Dragnet Apprehends Serial Rapist).

▷ Questions About Interpreting DNA Profiles

Why are DNA Profiles Interpreted in Terms of Probabilities?

A typical DNA forensics case involves comparing the DNA profile from an evidence sample (such as a bloodstain from a murder or a semen sample from a rape) to a profile derived from a suspect (usually from a mouth swab or blood sample).

There are three possible outcomes of this comparison: the profiles match, the profiles do not match, or the data are inconclusive. If the suspect and evidence samples do not match, it can be concluded that the suspect was not the

Polish Dragnet Apprehends Serial Rapist

Over a six-year period, 14 young women between the ages of nine and 26 years were brutally raped near the town of Swinoujscie in northwest Poland. In 2000, one of the rape victims was also murdered. Although the victims described the rapist as tall, athletic, and carrying a handgun, they were unable to identify him because he wore a mask.

Vaginal swabs were obtained from the rape victims, and DNA was analyzed by STR and

Y chromosome profiling. The Y chromosome DNA profiles confirmed that all the rapes had been committed by the same man. In one case, a mixture of two profiles was obtained. The victim of this rape reported that she had sexual intercourse with her boyfriend four days prior to the rape. The peak heights of the two superimposed profiles showed that the largest of the peaks for each allele corresponded to the same allele as that of the rapist in the other cases. The STR profiles of 10 autosomal loci also showed mixed alleles, due to a predominance of female cells in the vaginal swabs. By comparing the mixed profiles with the profiles of samples from each of the victims, the profile of the serial rapist was deduced.

In an effort to apprehend the perpetrator of these crimes, the police decided to investigate all young men between the ages of 22 and 38 who lived in the area. Of the 12,000 potential suspects, 714 were interrogated and 421 submitted mouth swabs or blood samples for DNA profiling. Police decided to use Y chromosome profiling in the initial screening to eliminate suspects. One of the 421 Y chromosome profiles (from suspect KW) was identical to the Y chromosome profile obtained from the victims' vaginal swabs. However, when KW's DNA was further analyzed at 10 autosomal STR loci, it did not match perfectly. One of the 10 alleles differed between KW's DNA and the rapist's DNA. This suggested that the rapist was likely to

source of the crime scene sample—therefore, an exclusion. If the DNA profiles from the suspect and evidence samples are indistinguishable, the profiles are said to match. In this case, the samples either came from the same person or came from two different people who simply share the same DNA profiles by chance. In order to present the DNA evidence in such a way as to convey its significance, it is necessary to estimate the probability that the two profiles are a random match.

How are DNA Profile Probabilities Calculated and Presented?

There are several different ways in which match probabilities are calculated. However, the simplest is termed the *profile probability* method. The profile probability is the probability that a person chosen at random from a population would have the same DNA profile as the evidence or suspect samples.

The following is an example of how to calculate a profile probability. This example involves calculating the profile probability at five STR loci as set out in Table 23.2.

The CSF1PO Locus

In this profile of five STR loci, the person exhibited two different-sized alleles at the CSF1PO locus (alleles of 10 and 11 repeats). In the Caucasian American database of 430 alleles (that is, two alleles from each of 215 people sampled),

these alleles were observed 108 and 133 times, respectively. Therefore, the frequency of observing these alleles at random in the Caucasian American population would be 0.25 (the p frequency) and 0.31 (the q frequency), respectively. The person who contributed this DNA profile can be assumed to have received each of his or her CSF1PO alleles at random from each parent. In other words, the probability of receiving allele 10 from the mother and allele 11 from the father is pq. Similarly, the probability of receiving allele 11 from the mother and allele 10 from the father is also pq. Therefore, the total probability of receiving a 10,11 genotype by chance is $2pq$. In this case, $2pq$ is about 16%. One can see from this example that DNA profiling at one locus is not very discriminating, as about 16% of the population would share

TABLE 23.2

DNA Profile		Allele Frequencies from Caucasian American Database			Genotype Frequency in Population	
Locus	Alleles Observed	Times allele observed	Size of Database	Frequency	Formula	Frequency
CSF1PO	10	108	430	p = 0.25	2 pq	0.16
	11	133		q = 0.31		
TPOX	8	227	430	p = 0.53	p^2	0.28
	8	227		p = 0.53		
TH01	6	101	426	p = 0.24	2pq	0.07
	7	63		q = 0.15		
vWA	16	90	426	p = 0.21	p^2	0.04
	16	90		p = 0.21		
D5S818	13	80	420	p = 0.19	2pq	0.14
	11	155		q = 0.37		
				Profile Frequency = 0.00002 (1 in 50,000)		

Adapted from: Brenner, C.H., **Forensic Mathematics of DNA Matching**. **http://dna-view.com/profile.htm** and Promega Corporation, Population Data Allele Frequencies.

this 10,11 DNA profile just by chance. The strength of a profile match, however, increases as one adds more loci to the analysis.

The TPOX Locus

This person exhibited two identical TPOX alleles (of 8 repeats) and is therefore homozygous at the TPOX locus. The combined probability of inheriting the eight allele from each parent is $pp = p^2$ and the frequency that one would observe the p^2 genotype in a Caucasian American population would be about 28%. The probability that a person would have a combined TPOX 8,8/CSF1PO 10,11 genotype would be 28% of 16% = about 4%.

The TH01, vWA, and D5S818 Loci

The probability calculations for these loci are the same for the remaining loci. By multiplying all the genotype probabilities at the five loci, one obtains an overall profile probability of 0.00002—or a one in 50,000 chance that a person chosen at random from that population would show the same DNA profile.

The method of multiplying all the frequencies of genotypes at each locus is sometimes called the *product rule*. It is the most frequently used method of DNA profile interpretation, and is widely accepted in U.S. courts.

Is a Person's DNA Profile Unique?

At present, the FBI uses 13 core STR loci in its profiles. The expected genotype frequency of the most common 13-locus profile would be less than one in 10 billion, and depends slightly upon allele frequencies in different populations. Although these numbers would strongly suggest that two matching profiles came from the same person, they cannot rule out the possibility of a random match.

As one increases the number of loci analyzed in a DNA profile, the probability of a random match in the population becomes smaller. If enough loci were analyzed, one might be certain that the DNA profile is unique. The FBI's policy is that if the match probability is much lower than one in 290 million (U.S. population) then it can be said with reasonable certainty that the DNA profile is unique to one individual.

Several situations exist that modify the profile probability calculations and the interpretation of matching profiles:

▪ Because they developed from a single fertilized egg, identical twins have identical DNA. Therefore, their DNA profiles will be identical. The frequency of identical twins is about one in every 250 births.

▪ Because they share parents, siblings often share alleles at any locus. About a quarter of the time, siblings will share both alleles at a particular locus. About half the time, they will share one allele at a locus. Using a DNA profile of 13 core STR loci, the profile probability is about 100,000 times greater if the DNA samples come from siblings than if they come from two unrelated persons. For an example of siblings that matched at a large number of loci, see box: Polish Dragnet Apprehends Serial Rapist.

▪ A parent and a child will always share one allele at a locus, but they will not usually share two alleles. Other relatives may share a single allele at a locus, but rarely will they share both alleles at a locus.

▪ The allele frequencies and probability calculations described above are based on the assumption that the population in question is large, with little interrelatedness or inbreeding. For populations that do not meet these assumptions, profile probabilities must be adjusted to reflect certain degrees of interrelatedness.

If a Defendant's Profile Matches that of the Crime Scene Sample, Does that Prove the Defendant's Guilt?

It is important to remember that a match between a crime scene DNA profile and a suspect's profile does not necessarily prove guilt, in the absence of other evidence. As explained in a later section (What Are the Main Problems With Forensic DNA Profiling?), human error or contamination may contribute to a match between a profile from a crime scene sample and a profile from an innocent person. In addition, a suspect's DNA may be introduced to a crime scene before, during, or after the crime for reasons unrelated to

the suspect's involvement in the crime. Also, DNA may be introduced to a crime scene by inadvertent or deliberate tampering.

Conversely, a DNA profile exclusion does not necessarily mean innocence. In a rape case, for example, a suspect may not contribute the semen sample, but may have been involved in the crime by restraining the victim. Once again, DNA profiles must always be interpreted in the context of all available evidence.

What Sort of Crime Evidence is Suitable for DNA Analysis?

The sensitivity of PCR-based DNA profiling methods means that any biological material—in theory, even a single cell—can generate a DNA profile. Types of samples include semen from rape cases, bloodspots from murder or assault cases, hairs left behind during robberies, and fingernail scrapings from assaults or murders. Dandruff on hat bands, saliva on cigarette butts, envelopes, stamps, or chewing gum, skin cells on eyeglasses, or even cells from a fingerprint can all generate DNA profiles, as can ear wax, bones, teeth, urine, and feces.

The amounts of biological material necessary to generate a DNA profile can be tiny—as small as the head of a pin or even invisible to the naked eye.

Forensic DNA samples can also be useful when they are decades old and in a partially degraded state. Molecules of DNA are relatively stable to drying, heat, and degradation compared with other types of biological evidence such as enzymes from blood or saliva. In addition, STR and mtDNA loci are small enough that they can be PCR-amplified even if most of the DNA has been degraded into small fragments. Samples of DNA have yielded profiles from the 70-year-old remains of the assassinated Romanov family in Russia, as well as from the prehistoric bones of Kennewick Man in the Pacific Northwest. In theory, DNA profiles can be obtained from samples that are hundreds to thousands of years old.

What are the Uses of Forensic DNA Profiling?

In the United States, the most common forensic use of DNA profiles is in sexual assault cases, as DNA profiles generated from semen on vaginal swabs can provide convincing evidence of a perpetrator. In the United Kingdom, DNA profiles from a wider range of crime scenes, including burglaries, are commonly used. The following list outlines the types of forensic cases that have involved DNA profiling:

- *Convicting the guilty.*
  DNA profiles from rape, murder, burglary, and other crime scenes have been matched with a suspect. Also, DNA profiles from multiple crime scenes have been compared in order to identify common perpetrators.

- *Exonerating the innocent.*
  In the United States, 123 innocent people have been exonerated of their convictions using DNA evidence. Twelve of these were death row inmates, some only days or hours away from execution.

- *Excluding suspects.*
  FBI data show that in sexual assault cases, DNA evidence excludes about 25% of primary suspects prior to trial. This not only allows police forces to redirect investigations at an early stage but also saves resources and the injustice of bringing innocent people to trial.

- *Identifying missing persons.*
  DNA profiles obtained from the remains of missing persons have been compared with profiles from relatives in order to establish the identity of body or skeletal remains.

- *Establishing paternity.*
  DNA evidence can help establish parentage. A recent example of DNA profiling in a paternity case is that of Thomas Jefferson, the third president of the United States. The DNA profiling of Y chromosome loci revealed that Jefferson could have fathered children by Sally Hemings, one of his slaves.

- *Identifying military personnel.*
  The military obtains DNA samples from its personnel so as to identify soldiers who may be killed in the line of duty. The bodies of over 500 servicemen and women who died in the Vietnam War have been identified using DNA profiling.

- *Identifying disaster victims.*
  DNA profiling has been employed to identify victims of air crashes such as Swissair Flight 111, which crashed off the coast of Nova Scotia in 1998, and other catastrophes such as the September 11, 2001, terrorist attacks.

- *Identifying victims of mass murders and assassinations.*
  DNA profiling identified the remains of Tsar Nicholas II and members of his family, who were assassinated in Russia in 1918, and also the remains of individuals murdered in Bosnia and Argentina.

- *Identifying protected species (wildlife forensics).*
  DNA samples have been used to determine whether the remains of a particular animal came from an endangered or protected species. Also, DNA profiles have linked an animal's remains with a crime scene or with a suspect.

What are the Advantages of DNA Evidence Over Other Types of Biological Forensic Evidence?

Forensic DNA evidence has essentially replaced traditional blood typing and saliva testing methods, as it is more sensitive, more informative, and more resilient than older serological methods. Prior to the advent of DNA profiling, combinations of blood types and serum markers could provide match probabilities of about one in several hundred to several thousand. Other biological forensic assays such as microscopic hair analysis have been challenged and will likely be replaced by mtDNA typing in the near future.

The O.J. Simpson Story

Nicole Brown Simpson and Ronald Goldman were stabbed to death on June 12, 1994, outside Mrs. Simpson's home in Brentwood, California. Actor and ex-football star O.J. Simpson was charged with the murders, and the succeeding trial was one of the most highly publicized trials in American history.

At first it appeared that the forensic DNA evidence against Simpson was overwhelming. The DNA profile from drops of blood leading away from the crime scene were consistent with O.J. Simpson's DNA profile at 5 VNTR loci and 7 PCR DQA1 loci. Also, the DNA profile from blood on a glove found at O.J. Simpson's home was consistent with Mrs. Simpson's profile at 5 VNTR loci and 2 PCR loci, and with Ronald Goldman's profile at 8 VNTR loci and 2 PCR loci. Mrs. Simpson's DNA profile was detected in blood from socks found at the O.J. Simpson home (14 VNTR loci and 7 PCR loci). Expert witnesses testified that such a profile would occur at random in only one of 9.7 billion Caucasians.

Much was made of the DNA profile evidence in this trial. However, in the end, it was the way that the forensic samples had been collected and stored that cast doubt on much of the DNA evidence. Police admitted that they did not wear protective clothing at the crime scene. Photographs showed detectives walking through bloodstains, leaving bloody shoe prints throughout the crime scene as well as outside. This became particularly problematic when it was revealed that detectives who used no protective clothing traveled from the crime scene to O.J. Simpson's residence and potentially could have transferred forensic evidence from one location to another. Defense lawyers showed that a scientist with the Los Angeles Police Department who processed much of the forensic evidence did not change gloves between handling different samples, did not adequately document his blood testing, and failed to follow rules that would ensure against contaminating blood samples. At one point, blood that had been collected from O.J. Simpson was spilled onto plastic gloves and may have contaminated evidence material.

Unimpressed by the prosecution's mountain of DNA evidence and appalled by the apparent sloppiness of police techniques, the jury acquitted O.J. Simpson on two counts of first-degree murder on October 3, 1995.

The O.J. Simpson case was significant in the history of forensic DNA profiling, as it triggered reassessment of police and laboratory procedures for processing crime scene evidence. It also stimulated research on DNA profiling methods and DNA database analysis. The importance of this trial to the development of modern DNA forensics is reflected in the recent donation of the DNA evidence from the O.J. Simpson trial to the Smithsonian Institution.

O.J. Simpson
Source: AP/World Wide Photos

How Reliable is DNA Profile Technology?

In general, the techniques used to generate a DNA profile are highly reliable. Nonetheless, the reliability of DNA profiling can be significantly affected by the methods used to collect, store, and analyze the crime samples, as well as by the interpretation of a profile. For example, during the O.J. Simpson trial, there was relatively little argument with the results of the DNA tests themselves; however, the methods used to collect, store, and handle the crime scene samples shed doubt upon the integrity and origin of the samples used to generate the profiles (see box: The O.J. Simpson Story).

The most persistent problems with PCR-based DNA profiles derive from the presence of contaminants or mixtures in the evidence samples. Contaminants can mix with the evidence samples before, during, or after their collection, and can come from persons unrelated to the crime, from the investigating officers, or from co-perpetrators of the crime. Current STR technology can often discern the presence of contaminants in a forensic sample, even when these contaminants comprise only 10% of the sample. Contaminants are particularly problematic when there is only a trace amount of evidence material. If the evidence sample contains biological material from two or more people, there will be three or more bands at each STR locus. If the mixture contains STR loci with some identical alleles, the peaks for these alleles will be twice as high. By examining more than one sample from the crime scene, it is often possible to discriminate between alleles in a mixture. Nonetheless, the presence of contaminants and mixtures must be taken into account during presentation of DNA evidence, and may affect the interpretations of profiles.

The National Research Council (NRC) recommends that forensic laboratories in the United States be accredited for doing DNA testing so as to standardize methods and quality. To date, not all private laboratories or police department forensic laboratories are accredited. The NRC also recommends that laboratories routinely use positive and negative controls and take periodic proficiency tests. Another recommendation is that forensic samples be divided into two or more portions so that samples can be retested at a later date. As yet, these recommendations have not been made mandatory for all DNA analysis facilities.

What are the Main Problems With Forensic DNA Profiling?

Although DNA profiling methods are highly sensitive and accurate, limitations exist. Most forensic cases do not involve biological evidence, and in those that do, the evidence may not be informative. Evidence may be degraded and yield no profile or may give partial profiles that are not informative.

Not all cases that could benefit by DNA evidence are able to do so. In the United States, about 20% of all rape samples that are collected are not processed. In New York City, the backlog of untested rape samples numbers about 16,000. Nationwide, more than 500,000 DNA samples from convicted prisoners are backlogged and untested, and about 1 million violent offenders who are on supervised release remain untested.

As described in the answer to the previous question, contamination can be a serious complication in the interpretation of a DNA profile. Over the last decade, police have become better trained in collecting crime scene evidence and in documenting the chain of custody of evidence samples. However, the possibility of contamination, either

The Sotolusson Story

In 2001, Lazaro Sotolusson was arrested for a technical immigration violation in Las Vegas, Nevada. While in prison, his cellmate accused him of rape. Samples of DNA were taken from both inmates, and the forensics laboratory ran the profiles through the Nevada State DNA database. Sotolusson's DNA profile matched profiles from two unsolved rapes in 1998 and 1999, and he was arrested for sexual assault and first-degree kidnaping. Experts stated that the chance of a random match to Sotolusson's profile was about 1 in 600 billion—convincing evidence that could convict him of these rapes. In addition, during a preliminary hearing, one of the rape victims identified Sotolusson as the perpetrator.

A year later, just before the trial, Sotolusson's lawyer hired an independent DNA expert who discovered that Sotolusson's name had been accidentally switched with the name of his cellmate prior to entering the DNA data into the database. The forensics laboratory admitted its mistake, and all sexual assault charges against Sotolusson were dismissed. Sotolusson had spent a year in prison for two crimes that he did not commit. Police are now investigating Sotolusson's former prison cellmate as a suspect in the two rapes.

This case demonstrates how easily human error, in combination with the persuasiveness of DNA profiling, can lead to the arrest of an innocent person.

inadvertently or planted, needs to be considered. It might be necessary to obtain profiles from family members or crime scene officers in order to eliminate contaminating bands in a DNA profile. In rape cases, it might be necessary to obtain a DNA sample from anyone having consensual intercourse with the victim within four days prior to the assault, as DNA profiles may be mixed.

One of the most serious complications is human error, either innocent or intentional. An example of human error is illustrated by the Sotolusson case (see box: The Sotolusson Story). Although human error is impossible to eliminate, consideration of all the evidence in a case may pinpoint those instances where accidental or intentional errors have occurred.

▷ Questions About the Use, Collection, and Storage of DNA Profiles

How Many Profiles are in the CODIS Databanks?

At the end of 2002, there were over 1 million profiles entered into the Convicted Offender database and over 44,000 profiles in the Forensic Evidence database. Over 5 million DNA profiles will be entered into CODIS within the next five years.

All but three U.S. states have submitted profiles to the CODIS national database. The CODIS system has contributed to about 6,400 criminal investigations and has yielded over 6,000 matches between submitted profiles.

Whose DNA ProfileS Should be Included in DNA Profile Databases?

Although DNA profile databases are rapidly proving to be valuable aids in criminal investigations, their use raises some serious ethical and legal questions concerning the collection and storage of DNA evidence as well as the intended uses of the databases.

Laws and standards for DNA profile collection vary dramatically both within the United States and internationally. In the United Kingdom, everyone arrested for any offense that carries a prison term is obliged to provide a DNA sample. These samples and the profiles generated from them can be retained by police and entered into the U.K.'s national DNA databank. In addition, the United Kingdom permits police to conduct mass screenings (dragnets) to gather profiles from large numbers of people in a given area in attempts to find a suspect. There have been 120 such dragnets in England and Wales. In the United States, rules governing DNA sample collection and database entry form a state-by-state patchwork. The CODIS rules limit DNA profiles to those from convicted offenders. However, state-based databases do not necessarily follow these same rules. For example, some states permit the taking of a suspect's DNA sample at the time of arrest. One state (Ohio) is reported to retain all profiles regardless of whether the suspect is convicted. Other states restrict sample collection to convicted offenders only, or to offenders convicted of specific violent crimes. Some states allow juveniles to be DNA profiled and others do not. There have even been cases where DNA dragnets were carried out, and the profiles and samples retained.

The intended uses of DNA profile databanks also vary. Some states allow databanks to be used for any criminal investigation, but others limit searches to sex-related or violent crimes. The CODIS rules allow searching the databases for any criminal investigation.

In the United States, considerable interest exists in expanding DNA database entries to all arrestees. Although there are clear advantages, such as the ability of police to exclude suspects early in an investigation and to find perpetrators through database searches, many people are alarmed at this prospect and demand that safeguards be in place. Most believe that profiles and samples must be expunged from the system if the suspect is not charged, or if a suspect is found not guilty. Many critics question the expansion of DNA databases, based on the Fourth Amendment, which protects citizens against unreasonable search and seizure. So far, legal challenges to DNA sample collection and database entry have been unsuccessful. Some people question DNA databanks on the basis of social inequality. Because some groups, such as African Americans, are overrepresented in convictions, they may also be overrepresented in DNA databanks. Some critics of the present system of DNA databanking argue that universal DNA profiling of all citizens would be a fairer policy than profiling only certain individuals. Such an idea raises even more questions about how personal privacy would be safeguarded for profiles held by police and governments.

After DNA Profiling and Electronic Storage of the Profile, Should the Tissue Sample be Retained or Destroyed?

Another contentious question is that of tissue sample retention. Forensic experts have argued that tissue samples should be retained in case the currently used 13-core STR loci system becomes superseded by a newer and more efficient system, such as the emerging SNP and mtDNA technologies. Also, retention of the original samples would allow retesting in the event of a suspected technical error. Others argue that the original samples should be destroyed after DNA profiles are generated so as to protect citizens from present and future unauthorized use of the samples. Currently, state laws vary as to the retention of samples and DNA profiles from people found innocent or those who have been wrongly convicted.

Can Personal or Medical Information be Obtained from DNA Profiles?

One of the concerns about DNA databases is that they may allow authorities to violate a person's genetic privacy and obtain information about a person's disease susceptibility, race, physical features, or parentage. Another concern is that databases could be used for genetic research without the consent of those in the database. At present, the loci used for DNA profiling are not known to be associated with any physical or behavioral traits. However, in the future it may be possible to link DNA profile information with physical characteristics that would help police identify a suspect.

Also, DNA databases have the potential to point toward close relatives of a suspect. For example, a crime scene DNA profile may partially match that of a convicted offender whose profile is located in the offender database. A partial match, although excluding the offender, might suggest that a sibling or other close relative of that offender may match the profile (see box: Polish Dragnet Apprehends Serial Rapist). It is a matter of debate whether police should have the right to obtain profiles from relatives under these circumstances, without any other probable cause for obtaining the information. States differ in their rules about the admissibility of pursuing offender's relatives based on partial DNA matches.

▷ Questions About DNA Profiling and the Criminal Justice System

How Can DNA Evidence Exonerate Those Who are Wrongly Convicted?

Since 1992, over 120 convicted prisoners, including 12 on death row, have been exonerated based on DNA evidence. Most of these exonerations were for cases tried prior to 1994, when DNA profiling was either not available or required large amounts of DNA for VNTR analysis. Now that modern DNA profiling methods can generate information on small quantities of DNA that are degraded and even decades old, convictions are being challenged and some are being overturned. In over a dozen cases, DNA evidence not only exonerated an innocent inmate, but also led to the identification of the perpetrator through DNA database searches.

Some people find the rising number of post-conviction exonerations disturbing, not only because of the injustice of incarcerating and perhaps executing innocent people, but also because the perpetrator of these crimes may remain free to commit more offences. In January 2003, Illinois Governor George Ryan commuted all death sentences to life in prison without parole, after learning that the state had executed 12 death row prisoners, but exonerated 13, some based on DNA evidence. Governor Ryan was concerned that innocent people could have been executed in the absence of post-conviction evidence disproving their guilt.

It is difficult to estimate how many inmates could be exonerated if DNA testing was available to illuminate their cases. The majority of criminal cases do not involve biological evidence, and of those that do, the evidence may be destroyed or lost over the years. The Innocence Project, a nonprofit legal clinic at the Benjamin N. Cardozo School of Law in New York, has taken on 123 cases in which DNA evidence led to post-conviction exonerations. Thousands more have requested assistance, but in about 75% of cases, the biological evidence cannot be located. Presumably the number of exonerations would increase if DNA samples were available. For examples of post-conviction exonerations based upon DNA profiling, see boxes: The Marvin Anderson Story, and The Earl Washington Story.

Despite the power of post-conviction DNA testing to exonerate the innocent and identify the guilty, obstacles prevent its routine use or effectiveness. For example, current U.S. laws limit the time during which convicted people can introduce new evidence, usually less than two or three years

In July 1982, a young white woman in Ashland, Virginia, was raped by a black man who had approached her on a bicycle. The rapist threatened her with a gun, then beat, raped, and sodomized her. He then bragged to her that he "had a white girl."

After the victim reported the crime, the police focused on Marvin Anderson as a suspect, as he was the only black man in the area that the police knew who had a white girl friend. Anderson had no criminal record, so police obtained a photo from Anderson's employer, using it in a photo lineup. From the photo lineup, the victim picked Anderson as the rapist. In the subsequent suspect lineup, the victim also picked out Anderson. He was the only person in the suspect lineup whose photo was also in the photo lineup. Serological analyses of rape samples were not informative.

Although Anderson was charged with the crime, members of the community suspected that the real rapist was probably another man named John Otis Lincoln. Lincoln had stolen a bicycle less than an hour before the rape, and the bicycle was identified by the owner. Anderson requested that both the bicycle's owner and Lincoln himself testify at the trial, however, his legal counsel refused. On December 14, 1982, an all-white jury convicted Marvin Anderson of robbery, forcible sodomy, abduction, and two counts of rape. He was sentenced to 210 years in the Virginia State Penitentiary.

Six years later, John Otis Lincoln admitted that he had committed the crime. However, the judge that had presided over Anderson's trial refused to accept Lincoln's confession. Anderson's case was taken up by civil rights groups, church leaders, and Virginia politicians. However, Governor Wilder denied their request for clemency in 1993. Anderson attempted to prove his innocence by demanding DNA analysis of the rape samples. Authorities informed his lawyers that the rape samples had been destroyed.

In 1994, Marvin Anderson's case was accepted by the Innocence Project. In 2001, Virginia's Division of Forensic Science informed the Innocence Project that the rape samples had been found—taped into the laboratory notebook of the forensic scientist who had done the conventional serology tests in 1982. This mistake by the forensics lab had saved the vaginal swabs from being destroyed.

On December 6, 2001, partial DNA profiles generated from the old rape evidence excluded Marvin Anderson as the perpetrator of the crimes. The DNA profile was run through Virginia's offender DNA database, and it matched the profiles of two inmates. One of these profiles is reported to be from John Otis Lincoln.

Marvin Anderson had spent 15 years in prison and four years on parole for a crime he did not commit. He became the 99th person in the United States to be exonerated based on postconviction DNA profiling.

Marvin Anderson, with his son, after his exoneration in December 2001.

Source: New York Times Pictures

following conviction. In some instances, exonerations have been delayed or prevented when the prosecution introduced a new theory about the case that was not part of the original trial. In addition, many suspects and convicts are indigent and cannot afford the costs of DNA testing or adequate legal counsel to challenge their arrests or convictions.

Why are Innocent People Convicted of Violent Crimes and then Exonerated?

The Innocence Project and the U.S. Department of Justice have studied DNA-based exonerations and have identified a number of common features. The most common cause of wrongful conviction is mistaken eyewitness testimony. It has been shown that eyewitness testimony is the least dependable, but most persuasive, evidence in a court case. Memory is extremely plastic and unreliable even when the victim attempts to carefully remember the perpetrator. Time, stress,

The Earl Washington Story

In June 1982, a 19-year-old white woman, Rebecca Williams, was raped and murdered in her Culpeper, Virginia, apartment. Before she died, she told police that she had been assaulted by a black man.

A year later, Earl Washington, a 22-year-old farmhand with an IQ of 69, was arrested for an alleged burglary and malicious wounding. Police questioned Washington for two days, during which time he confessed to five different crimes, including the rape and murder of Rebecca Williams. Four of the confessions were dismissed when witnesses stated that Washington was not the perpetrator. However, the murder confession remained and he was charged. Washington's murder confession was taken by a Virginia state trooper who asked, "Did you kill the woman in Culpeper?" and "Did you stab the woman in Culpeper?" Washington replied, "Yes, sir." However, when asked for details of the murder, he was not able to supply them. He did not know the race or height of the victim, how the crime was committed, or the location of the apartment.

The confession was the only evidence linking Earl Washington to the rape and murder of Rebecca Williams. Serological tests on blood and semen stains were inconclusive. Psychological tests showed that Washington politely agreed with any authority figure in order to gain approval and to compensate for his mental disabilities. Washington's legal defense did not bring out the results of the psychological tests, the inconsistencies in his confession, the weaknesses in the prosecution's case, or even argue against the sentence.

Earl Washington's trial lasted three days. On January 20, 1984, he was convicted of murder and sentenced to death.

Nine days before he was to be executed, lawyers from a New York firm obtained a stay of execution and later appealed Washington's conviction. Although the court agreed that Washington had been denied his constitutional right to effective counsel, his confession was still accepted and his conviction upheld.

In 1993, Earl Washington's lawyers asked Virginia Governor Wilder to grant Washington a pardon. The governor requested DNA tests before making a decision. Results showed that semen on the vaginal swab could not have come from Washington. At this point, a new prosecution theory emerged: Earl Washington, along with someone else who contributed the DNA in the semen stain, was responsible for the crime. Although there was no evidence that two people were involved in the crime, the theory gained credence. On the last day of Governor Wilder's term, Washington and his counsel were given two hours to accept commutation of the death sentence to life imprisonment without parole. They accepted.

Earl Washington remained in prison for another six years before his lawyers were able to persuade Governor Gilmore to do more DNA testing. On October 2, 2000, the governor announced that the STR (short tandem repeat) DNA profiles from the crime scene evidence excluded Earl Washington and granted his absolute pardon. Finally, on February 12, 2001, Earl Washington was released from prison into parole supervision, 17 years after his wrongful murder conviction.

Earl Washington with his lawyers, Marie Deans and Robert T. Hall, after his exoneration from rape charges on February 12, 2001, in Virginia Beach, Virginia.

Source: AP/World Wide Photos

---

and confusion can lead to a false identification. In addition, eyewitnesses can be influenced by the composition of police lineups. If the perpetrator is not present in the lineup, victims tend to pick the person who best fits their memory, and this identification becomes fixed in their minds. Also, police can sometimes unwittingly lead the victim to choose the suspect that they favor.

Another surprising cause of wrongful convictions is false confession. About 20% of DNA exonerations have occurred in cases where defendants confessed to a crime they did not commit. Police interrogation techniques and the mental incapacity of the suspect are important factors in false confessions. The cases of Earl Washington (see box: The Earl Washington Story) and Colin Pitchfork (see box: The Colin Pitchfork Story) illustrate how a false confession can lead to a wrongful conviction.

About half of DNA-based exonerations involve misconduct of prosecutors or police—for example, by using forced confessions or manufactured evidence. About one-third involve incompetent or inadequate defense counsel, usually when the defendant was indigent and relied on public defenders with inadequate resources or training. In 25 of the first 82 exonerations based on DNA evidence, the court was swayed by fraudulent or "junk" science. Expert witnesses lied about, misinterpreted, exaggerated, or suppressed scientific test results (see Ray Krone's story in the Introduction). For further information about the causes and remedies of wrongful convictions, see the Innocence Project's Web site: (www.innocenceproject.org).

Is it Possible for an Innocent Person to be Convicted Based on DNA Evidence?

So far, there appear to be no cases in which a PCR-based DNA profile led to a wrongful conviction; however, it is feasible that it could happen. Current techniques in DNA profiling are extremely sensitive, with the capacity to generate a profile from only a few cells. It is possible for an innocent person's DNA to be found at a crime scene, either from directly depositing cells at the scene, or from having the cells introduced indirectly by a third person or object. If the innocent person's DNA masks or substitutes for the DNA of the real perpetrator in one or more crime scene samples, it is possible that his or her profile could contribute to a conviction. It is standard practice to obtain elimination samples from family members and investigators who have access to a crime scene, or from consensual sexual partners in a rape case; however, innocent people may contribute material to a crime scene and not be eliminated in this way. It would be relatively simple to plant DNA evidence at a crime scene, as very little material would be required to generate an incriminating profile. Crime scene evidence is not always in good condition, leading to partial profiles that detect only a few loci. It is possible for the profile of an innocent person whose DNA is in a DNA databank to match a partial profile from the crime scene. Close relatives of perpetrators, conceivably even identical twins, could also be incriminated based on partial profiles. Given the fallibility of other types of evidence such as eyewitness identification, and the possibility of false confessions and inadequate defense counsel, it is not impossible for modern DNA profiling to contribute to a wrongful conviction. In light of these possibilities, it is important to remember that the relevance of DNA profiling must be assessed in the context of all evidence in a case.

How is DNA Evidence Changing the U.S. Criminal Justice System?

Over the last decade, forensic DNA profiling has significantly altered the operation of the criminal justice system. Old cases are being reexamined, leading to exonerations of innocent prisoners and identification of perpetrators from searches of databases. By using DNA profiling early in an investigation, police are able to exclude innocent suspects, saving both time and effort in locating the real perpetrator. In the future, DNA profiling will undoubtedly reduce the number of wrongful convictions, particularly in sexual assault cases where DNA evidence has the power to convincingly identify a perpetrator.

The ever increasing number of exonerations of wrongfully convicted prisoners, based on re-examination of DNA evidence, has pointed out significant problems with many aspects of the criminal justice system. Police techniques that lead to false confessions and faulty eyewitness identifications have been seriously examined and reforms outlined. Police are being trained in the collection, storage, and chain of custody of forensic evidence, to avoid the types of challenges that arose in cases such as the O.J. Simpson trial. There is now pressure to accredit and review the operations of forensic laboratories, as well as to ensure that such facilities are independent of law enforcement agencies, as is the case in the United Kingdom and Canada. Evidence from DNA samples also challenges many traditional and controversial forensic methods. For example, methods such as microscopic hair examination will likely be replaced by more accurate STR and mtDNA testing.

Perhaps the most profound effect of DNA forensics has been its convincing proof that the system sends innocent people to death row. This revelation has triggered legislative efforts to remedy the situation. In 2002, the Innocence Protection Act was introduced in the U.S. House of Representatives. This legislation would grant convicted prisoners the right to have DNA testing done if the test has the potential to establish innocence. It also outlines measures to ensure that evidence is preserved, and that testing will be paid for by the state in cases of indigence. The legislation would also establish standards for legal representation in capital cases, would set minimum levels of compensation for years of wrongful incarceration, and would ensure that prisoners are not executed while their cases are being heard by the U.S. Supreme Court. The Innocence Protection Act is expected to be passed in 2003.

In the future, DNA profiling will continue to alter criminal justice systems around the world. In order to protect society and individuals from potential abuses, the power of this technology must be tempered by safeguards. Governments must devise rules dealing with DNA databanking, the taking and storing of DNA samples, and the accreditation of DNA analysis laboratories. Police, lawyers, judges, and the public must be informed about the pros and cons of forensic DNA profiling so as to evaluate it and question it intelligently. In addition, sufficient funding must be allocated to ensure that all suspects and convicted persons have full and impartial access to this powerful new technology.

▷ References and Resources

Publications

National Institute of Justice. 2000. *The Future of Forensic DNA Testing: Predictions of the Research and Development Working Group.* (**http://www.ncjrs.org/pdffiles1/nij/183697.pdf**)

National Institute of Justice, National Commission on the Future of DNA Evidence. 2002. *Using DNA to Solve Cold Cases.* (**http://www.ncjrs.org/pdffiles1/nij/194197.pdf**)

National Research Council, Commission of DNA Forensic Science: An Update. 1996. *The Evaluation of Forensic DNA Evidence.* National Academy Press. (**http://search.nap.edu/readingroom/books/DNA/**)

Weedn, V.W. and Hicks, J.W. 1998. *The Unrealized Potential of DNA Testing.* National Institute of Justice, U.S. Department of Justice. (**http://www.ncjrs.org/pdffiles/170596.pdf**)

Connors, E. et al. 1996. *Convicted by Juries, Exonerated by Science: Case Studies in the Use of DNA Evidence to Establish Innocence After Trial.* National Institute of Justice, U.S. Department of Justice. (**http://www.ncjrs.org/pdffiles/dnaevid.pdf**)

Reilly, P. 2001. *Legal and Public Policy Issues in DNA Forensics. Nature Reviews Genetics* 2:313–317.

Gill, P. 2002. *Role of Short Tandem Repeat DNA in Forensic Casework in the UK—Past, Present and Future Perspectives. BioTechniques* 32:366–385.

Hand, L. 2002. *SNP Technology Focuses on Terror Victims' IDs. The Scientist* 16:20.

Ruitberg, C.M. et al. 2001. *STRBase: A Short Tandem Repeat DNA Database for the Human Identity Testing Community. Nucleic Acids Res* 29:320–322.

Bunk, S. 2000. *Forensics Fights Crimes Against Wildlife: DNA Technologies Can Nab a Killer, Even When the Victim Is a Moose or Bear. The Scientist* 14:24.

Robb, N. 1999. *229 People, 15,000 Body Parts: Pathologists Help Solve Swissair 111's Grisly Puzzles. Can Med Assoc J* 160:241–243.

Miller, K.A. 2002. *Identifying Those Remembered: New Technologies Promise to Speed DNA Identification at Disaster Sites and in Criminal Investigations. The Scientist* 16:40.

Lipton, E. and Glanz, J. 2002. *A Nation Challenged: Forensics; DNA Science Pushed to the Limit in Identifying the Dead of Sept. 11. The New York Times,* April 22, 2002.

Puit, G. *DNA Evidence: Officials Admit Error, Dismiss Case. Las Vegas Review–Journal,* April 18, 2002. (**http://www.forensicdna.com/DNAerror.htm**)

Carey, L. and Mitnik, L. 2002. *Trends in DNA Forensic Analysis. Electrophoresis* 23:1386–1397.

Williamson, R. and Duncan, R. 2002. *DNA Testing for All. Nature* 418:585–586.

Web Sites

The Innocence Project **http://www.innocenceproject.org**

Forensic mathematics of DNA matching, by Charles H. Brenner, Ph.D. **http://dna-view.com/profile.htm**

DNA Technology links **http://www.law-forensic.com/dnalinks.htm**

True Crimes Criminal Investigations—DNA & Forensic Science **http://www.karisable.com/crdna1.htm**

STRBase: short tandem repeat DNA internet database **http://www.cstl.nist.gov/biotech/strbase/**

"The Case for Innocence: Why do inmates remain in prison despite DNA evidence which exonerates them with near certainty?" PBS Frontline program, 2000. **http://www.pbs.org/wgbh/pages/frontline/shows/case/**

"What Jennifer Saw: Ronald Cotton's wrongful conviction" PBS Frontline program, 1998. **http://www.pbs.org/wgbh/pages/frontline/shows/dna/cotton**

Kennewick Man DNA testing **http://www.cr.nps.gov/aad/kennewick/**

Romanovs find closure in DNA **http://users.rcn.com/web-czar/dna.htm**

The Innocence Protection Act of 2001 (Introduced in the U.S. House of Representatives) **http://thomas.loc.gov/cgi-bin/query/z?c107:H.R.912:**

How DNA technology is reshaping judicial process and outcome Co-sponsored by CSIS and the Whitehead Institute for Biomedical Research, May 2001. **http://www.csis.org/tech/Biotech/nbpp/Seminar2Brief.htm**

DNA Forensics. Human Genome Project Information **http://www.ornl.gov/hgmis/elsi/forensics.html**

Forensic Bioinformatics, Inc., a private company that provides independent reviews of forensic DNA evidence. **http://www.bioforensics.com**